Autodata®

Pin Data

For Engine Management Systems

2006

Pin voltages - input and output
Duty cycles
Wave forms
Oscilloscope settings
ECM pin connections
Pin configuration illustrations
ECM locations

Petrol and Diesel Cars, MPVs, 4x4s and LCVs 1998-2006

Autodata Limited, Priors Way, Maidenhead, Berkshire SL6 2HP, England
Tel: 01628 634321   Fax: 01628 770385   email: sales@autodata.ltd.uk   technical@autodata.ltd.uk

Argentina
Condistelec S.A, Carlos Pellegrini 1785 (1602), Florida, Pcia de Buenos Aires
Tel: 0054-11-4730 3533
Fax: 0054-11-4760 0596   email: condistelec@condistelec.com.ar

Australia
Autodata Australia Pty Ltd., Unit 5, 25 Veronica Street, Capalaba, Queensland 4157
Tel: +61 (7) 3245 3282   Fax: +61 (7) 3245 3422   email: info@autodata.com.au

Bookworks Pty. Ltd., 56 Bonds Road, Punchbowl, NSW 2196
Tel: (02) 9740 6766   Fax: (02) 9740 6591   email: sales@bookworks.com.au

Bookworks Pty. Ltd., 46 Isabella Street, Moorabbin, Vic 3189
Tel: (03) 9555 6555   Fax: (03) 9553 3897   email: sales@bookworks.com.au

Austria
AUTODATA AUSTRIA prachner & godai, Mariahilferstr. 169, 1150 Wien
Tel: 01 - 892 91 60 / 25 DW
Fax: 01 - 892 91 60 / 26 DW   email: autocd@godai.at

Belgium
Autodata, Thillostraat 3, 2920 Kalmthout
Tel: 03 666 45 36   Fax: 03 666 58 99   email: autodata@scarlet.be

Canada
Autodata Publications Inc., 19 Bonazzoli Avenue, Hudson, MA 01749 , U.S.A.
Tel: 978 562-9511   Fax: 978 562-9533   email: sales@autodatapubs.com

Croatia
Autoelektrika Novak d.o.o., T. Ujevića 29, HR - 40323 Prelog
Tel: (00385-40) 645 861   Fax: (00385-40) 645 861

Cyprus
Pergamon Bookhouse, 12-12A King Paul Street, PO Box 25062, Nicosia
Tel: (02) 676 343   Fax: (02) 676 773

Czech Republic
AUTOservis akademie s.r.o., Přepeřská 1809, 511 01 Turnov
Tel: (+420) 481 323 931/481 382 173
Fax: (+420) 481 323 712   email: info@autoservisakademie.cz

Denmark
Robert Bosch A/S, Telegrafvej 1, 2750 Ballerup
Tel: 44 89 83 80   Fax: 44 89 86 87

Autodata Skandinavien ApS, Box 96, Trehøjevej 2, 7200 Grindsted
Tel: 75 32 55 57   Fax: 75 31 02 41

Estonia
AS Megastar, Kanali tee 1, 10112 Tallinn
Tel: +372 601 6026   Fax: +372 601 6027   email: megastar@megastar.ee

Finland
Autodata Oy, PL 29, Onkkaalantie 71, 36601 PÄLKÄNE
Tel: (03) 53 43 980   Fax: (03) 53 43 983   email: myynti@autodata.fi

France
S.F.T.A. Autodata, 13 rue Paul Sabatier, Z.A. de Faveyrolles nº1, 26700 Pierrelatte
Tel: 04.75.96.96.96   Fax: 04.75.96.96.95   email: contact@autodata-sfta.fr

Germany
Fust, Wever & Co. GmbH, Maxstr. 9, 45127 Essen
Tel: 0201 82774-0 / 22 79 12
Fax: 0201 82774-39 / 23 25 56   email: info@fust-wever.de

Hungary
Maróti Könyvkereskedés Kft. 1205 Budapest, Nagykőrösi út 91.
Tel: 285-6608   Fax: 285-0116   email: maroti.konyvker@enternet.hu

Iceland
Bilgreinasambandid, Hus Verslunarinnar, 103 Reykjavik
Tel: (01) 68 15 50   Fax: (01) 68 98 82   email: bgs@centrum.is

Ireland
Hella Ireland Ltd., Unit 6.1, Woodford Business Park, Santry, Dublin 17
Tel: (01) 862 0000   Fax: (01) 862 1133   email: sales@hella.ie

Snap-on Tools, Unit 8, Block 6, Fullwood Ind. Est., Hamilton, Scotland ML3 9AZ.
Tel: 01698-422622   Fax: 01698-422114   email: hamilton.branch.uk@snapon.com

Israel
Esco Engineering Supplies Ltd., 22 Harakevet Street, PO Box 45, Tel Aviv 61000
Tel: (03) 560 3472   Fax: (03) 560 2153

Italy
Tecnodata, Via le Petrene, 53017 Radda in Chianti (Si)
Tel: (0577) 738 239   Fax: (0577) 738 790   email: tecnodata@albaclick.com

Latvia
Autodati, 6 - 216 Ezermalas Street, Riga, LV-1006
Tel: 371 7089 741   Fax: 371 7089 744   email: autodati@rtu.lv

Robert Bosch SIA, A. Deglava Str. 60, Riga, LV-1035,
Tel: 371 7802 080   Fax: 371 7548 441   email: rigaoffice@bosch.lv

Netherlands
Autodata, Postbus 581, 4645 ZX Putte
Tel: 00 32 3 666 45 36   Fax: 00 32 3 666 58 99   email: autodata@scarlet.be

New Zealand
Autodata Australia Pty Ltd.,
Unit 5, 25 Veronica St, Capabala, Queensland 4157, Australia
Tel: +61 (7) 3821 4271 Fax: +61 (7) 3245 3422   email: sales@autodata.com.au

Autodata (NZ) Ltd., 59 Roberts Road, Whangaparaoa 1463
Tel: (09) 424 8990   Fax: (09) 424 8990   email: marilyn@ihug.co.nz

Norway
Autodata Skandinavien A/S, Kongensgate 6, Postboks 2047, 3202 Sandefjord
Tel: 33 46 73 70   Fax: 33 46 45 40

Poland
Precyzja-Service Sp. zo.o., ul. Gdańska 99, 85 022 Bydgoszcz
Tel: (052) 325 1026   Fax: (052) 321 0571   email: sales@precyzja-service.pl

Portugal
Autodata, Thillostraat 3, B-2920 Kalmthout, Belgium
Tel: 0032 3 666 45 36   Fax: 0032 3 666 58 99   email: autodata@scarlet.be

Russia
Legion-Autodata, Trofimova Str. 13, 115432, Moscow
Tel: (095) 679-96-12, 679-96-07, 679-96-78, 679-96-63
Fax: (095) 679-97-36   email: legion@autodata.ru

South Africa
The Phoenix Exchange, PO Box 273, Edenvale 1610,
Tel: (011) 452 0875   Fax: (011) 452 8372   email: ty@phoenixchange.co.za

Spain
Autodata, Thillostraat 3, B-2920 Kalmthout, Belgium
Tel: 0032 3 666 45 36   Fax: 0032 3 666 58 99   email: autodata@scarlet.be

Sweden
Autometric AB, Tillverkarvägen 16, 187 66 Täby
Tel: (08) 630 00 77   Fax: (08) 756 11 51   email: sales@autometric.se

Switzerland
Autodata GmbH, Bahnhofstrasse 28, 8153 Rümlang
Tel: (044) 880 7400   Fax: (044) 880 7434   email: autodata@swissonline.ch

U.S.A.
Autodata Publications Inc., 6301 Bandel Road NW, Suite 403, Rochester, MN 55901
Tel: (507) 285-4803   Toll Free: (800) 305-0338
Fax: (507) 285-3131   email: sales@autodatapubs.com

Yugoslavia
GIIR d.o.o., Gabrovacki put II deo 32a, 18000 Nis
Tel: +381 18 531 528/18 327 617
Fax: +381 18 338 832   email: giir@bankerinter.net

Compiled and published by:

Autodata Limited
Priors Way,
Maidenhead,
Berkshire,
SL6 2HP, England

Printed in England by: Page Bros

| Product No.: 06-4100 | ISBN: 1-904473-86-5 | 010406 |

Contents

This manual is a comprehensive single source of information on pin data for petrol and diesel engine management system control modules for European and Asian cars introduced or revised during the period 1998 to 2006.

The manual, is part of a series from Autodata, and deals specifically with fuel and ignition systems under the control of the engine management system. It has been written and presented in a way to enable any professional automotive technician with appropriate skills and competence to make accurate tests and diagnoses, on the fuel and ignition related components and circuits.

Detailed knowledge of fuel injection or ignition systems is not required in order to make full use of this manual. With a basic understanding of fuel and electrical systems and cross-reference to Autodata's Fuel Injection, Electronic Ignition and Engine Management Manuals, tests and diagnoses can be made using the minimum of specialised test equipment. However, whenever possible, the use of a breakoutbox is recommended. A digital oscilloscope is recommended for checking certain signals.

Index	**4**
Abbreviations, terminology and signal symbols	18
About this manual	**19**
General notes and test procedures	19
How to use the model specific pin data tables	20
Safety precautions	**22**
Tools and equipment	23
General recommendations	**23**
Using multi-meters	**23**
Oscilloscope testing	27
Oscilloscope wave forms	
Petrol	38
Diesel	55
ECM locations	**66**
Pin data tables	
Alfa Romeo - Volvo	88

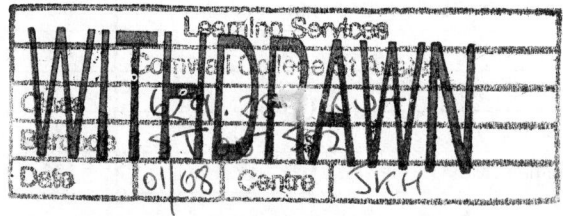

Index

Model	Year	Engine code	System	Page
ALFA ROMEO				
145/146 1,4/1,6/1,8/2,0	1995-99	335/671/672/676	Bosch Motronic M2.10.4	**88**
145/146 1,4/1,6/1,8/2,0	1998-02	335/676/322/323	Bosch Motronic M1.5.5	**91**
155 1,6/1,8/2,0	1995-98	671/672/676	Bosch Motronic M2.10.4	**88**
156 1,6	1997-00	676	Bosch Motronic M2.10.4	**88**
156 1,8/2,0	1998-02	322/323	Bosch Motronic M1.5.5	**91**
166 2,0	1998-02	341	Bosch Motronic M1.5.5	**91**
GTV/Spider 1,8/2,0	1998-02	322/323/162	Bosch Motronic M1.5.5	**91**
GTV/Spider 2,0	1997-01	162.01	Bosch Motronic M2.10.4	**88**
AUDI				
A3 1,6	1996-03	AEH/AKL	Siemens Simos 2	**94**
A3 1,8/Turbo	1996-03	AGN/AGU	Bosch Motronic M3.8.2/4/5	**97**
A3 1,9 TDI	1996-07/99	AGR/AHF/ALH	Bosch EDC 15V	**100**
A3 1,9 TDI	08/99-03	AGR/AHF/ALH/ASV	Bosch EDC 15V	**103**
A3 1,9 TDI PD	2001-03	ASZ/ATD/AXR	Bosch EDC 15P/16	**106**
A4 1,6	1996-02	AHL/ARM	Siemens Simos 2	**94**
A4 1,8/Turbo	07/96-01	AEB/ADR/AJL	Bosch Motronic M3.8.2/4/5	**97**
A4 1,9 TDI PD	1999-01	AJM/ATJ	Bosch EDC 15P/16	**106**
A4 2,4/2,8	1995-01	AGA/AJG/ACK/ALG	Bosch Motronic M3.8.2	**110**
A4 2,5 TDI	1997-01	AFB, AKN	Bosch EDC 15M-4	**113**
A6 1,8/Turbo	1997-05	AEB/AJP	Bosch Motronic M3.8.2/4/5	**97**
A6 1,9 TDI PD	2001-05	AJM/AVF/AWX	Bosch EDC 15P/16	**106**
A6 2,4	1997-05	ALF/ALN	Bosch Motronic M3.8.2	**110**
A6 2,4/2,8	1997-05	AGA/AJG/ACK/ALG/ALF	Bosch Motronic M3.8.2	**110**
A6 2,5 TDI	1997-05	AFB/AKN	Bosch EDC 15M-4	**113**
TT 1,8 Turbo	1998-06	AJQ/APP/APX/ARY/AUM/AUQ/BAM	Bosch Motronic ME7.5	**116**
BMW				
316i/318i (E36)	1995-00	16 4E 2/18 4E 2	Bosch Motronic M1.7.3	**120**
316i/318i (E46)	1998-04	19 4E 1	Bosch BMS 46	**123**
316i Compact (E36)	1998-02	19 4E 1	Bosch BMS 46	**123**
316i/316i Compact (E46)	2001-05	N42 B18A	Bosch ME9.2	**126**
318iS/Coupe/Compact (E36)	1996-99	19 4S 1	Bosch Motronic 5.2	**130**
318ti Compact (E36)	1996-01	19 4S 1	Bosch Motronic 5.2	**130**
318d (E46)	2000-05	20 4D 1	Bosch DDE3	**133**
320i 24V Vanos (E36)	1994-99	20 6S 3	Siemens MS 41	**136**
320i 24V Vanos (E46)	1998-02	20 6S 4	Siemens MS 42	**139**
320d (E46)	1998-02	20 4D 1 (M47 D20)	Bosch EDC 15M 6.1 (DDE 3.0)	**143**
320d (E46) - AT	2001-06	20 4D 4	Bosch DDE7	**146**
323i/Compact (E36)	1995-01	25 6S 3	Siemens MS 41	**136**
323i 24V Vanos (E46)	1998-02	25 6S 4	Siemens MS 42	**139**
328i (E36)	1995-99	28 6S 1	Siemens MS 41	**136**

Autodata

Model	Year	Engine code	System	Page
328i 24V Vanos (E46)	1998-02	28 6S 2	Siemens MS 42	139
520i 24V Vanos (E39)	1996-00	25 6S 3	Siemens MS 41	136
520i 24V Vanos (E39)	1998-02	20 6S 4	Siemens MS 42	139
520d (E39)	2000-03	20 4D 1	Bosch DDE3	149
523i 24V Vanos (E39)	1996-00	25 6S 3	Siemens MS 41	136
523i 24V Vanos (E39)	1998-02	25 6S 4	Siemens MS 42	139
525d (E60/61)	2003-06	25 6D 2	Bosch DDE7	152
528i (E39)	1996-00	28 6S 1	Siemens MS 41	136
528i 24V Vanos (E39)	1998-02	28 6S 2	Siemens MS 42	139
728i 24V Vanos (E38)	1998-02	28 6S 2	Siemens MS 42	139
Z3 2,0	1998-02	20 6S 4	Siemens MS 42	139
Z3 2,8	1998-02	28 6S 2	Siemens MS 42	139

CITROEN

Model	Year	Engine code	System	Page
Berlingo 1,1	1996-02	HDY/Z (TU1M/L3)	Bosch Mono-Motronic MA3.1	155
Berlingo 1,4	1997-02	KFX (TU3JP/L3)	Magneti-Marelli 1AP.20/40/41	157
Berlingo 1,4	1998-02	KFX (TU3JP/IFL4)	Bosch Motronic MP7.2/3	161
Berlingo 1,4	2001-02	KFW (TU3JP/L4)	Sagem S2000	191
Berlingo 1,8	1997-02	LFX (XU7JB/L3)	Magneti-Marelli 1AP.20/40/41	157
Berlingo 2,0 HDi	1999-06	DW10TD (RHY)	Bosch EDC 15C2 HDi	178
Berlingo 2,0 HDi	2002-06	RHY (DW10TD)	Siemens SID 801	194
C5 2,0 HDi	2000-04	RHZ (DW10ATED)	Bosch EDC 15C2	182
C5 2,0 HDi	2001-04	RHY (DW10TD)	Siemens SID 801	171
Saxo 1,0	1996-03	CDY/Z (TU9M/L3)	Bosch Mono-Motronic MA3.1	155
Saxo 1,1	1996-03	HDY/Z (TU1M/L3)	Bosch Mono-Motronic MA3.1	155
Saxo 1,4	1997-02	KFX (TU3JP/L3)	Magneti-Marelli 1AP.20/40/41	157
Saxo 1,6 MT	1996-02	NFZ (TU5JP/L3)	Bosch Motronic MP5.1	159
Saxo 1,6 MT	1998-01	NFZ (TU5JP/L3)	Bosch Motronic MP7.2/3	161
Saxo 1,6 16V	1997-03	NFX (TU5JP4/L3)	Magneti-Marelli 1AP.20/40/41	157
Synergie 1,8	1998-02	LFW (XU7JP/L3)	Magnetti Marelli 8P.15/8P.22	185
Synergie 2,0	1998-02	RFU (XU10J2C/Z)	Magnetti Marelli 8P.15/8P.22	185
Synergie 2,0 16V	1998-02	RFV (XU10J4R)	Bosch Motronic MP7.2/3	161
Synergie 2,0 Turbo	1994-00	RGX (XU10J2TE)	Bosch Motronic MP3.2	176
Synergie 2,0 HDi	1999-02	RHZ (DW10ATED)	Bosch EDC 15C2	187
XM 2,0 16V	1993-00	RFV (XU10J4R)	Bosch Motronic MP5.1/2	169
XM 2,0 Turbo	1994-00	RGX (XU10J2TE)	Bosch Motronic MP3.2	176
Xantia 1,8	1993-97	LFZ (XU7JP/Z)	Bosch Motronic MP5.1	159
Xantia 1,8 16V	1995-01	LFY (XU7JP4)	Bosch Motronic MP5.1.1	174
Xantia 1,8 16V	1997-01	LFY (XU7JP4/L3)	Sagem SL96	164
Xantia 2,0 16V	1995-01	RFV (XU10J4R)	Bosch Motronic MP5.1/2	169
Xantia 2,0 16V/Turbo	1993-01	RFY/RGX	Bosch Motronic MP3.2	176
Xantia 2,0 HDi	1998-01	DW10ATED (RHZ)	Bosch EDC 15C2 HDi	178
Xantia 2,0 HDi	1998-01	DW10TD (RHY)	Bosch EDC 15C2 HDi	178
Xsara 1,4	1997-02	KFX (TU3JP)	Magneti-Marelli 1AP.20/40/41	157
Xsara 1,4	1998-02	KFX (TU3JP/L3)	Sagem SL96	164
Xsara 1,4	07/01-04	KFW (TU3JP/L4)	Sagem S2000	166

Index

Model	Year	Engine code	System	Page
Xsara 1,6	1998-01	NFZ (TU5JP/L3)	Bosch Motronic MP7.2/3	161
Xsara 1,8 MT	1997-02	LFX (TXU7JB)	Magneti-Marelli 1AP.20/40/41	157
Xsara 1,8 16V	1997-02	LFY (XU7JP4/L3)	Sagem SL96	164
Xsara 2,0	1998-02	RFV (XU10JP4R)	Bosch Motronic MP5.1/2	169
Xsara 2,0 HDi	2001-06	RHY (DW10TD)	Siemens SID 801	171
Xsara Picasso 1,6 MT	1999-01	NFZ (TU5JP/L3)	Bosch Motronic MP7.2/3	161
ZX 1,8	1992-98	LFZ (XU7JP/LZ)	Bosch Motronic MP5.1	159

DAEWOO

Model	Year	Engine code	System	Page
Lanos	1997-01	A1DM	Daewoo EIFI-6	200
Matiz	1998-05	F8CV	Siemens Fenix 5M	197
Nubira 1,6/2,0	1997-03	A16DM/C20SE	GM ITMS-6F	202

FIAT

Model	Year	Engine code	System	Page
Barchetta 1,8 16V	1998-01	183 A1 000	Hitachi	227
Brava/Bravo 1,2	1998-02	182 B2 000	Bosch Motronic M1.5.5	230
Brava/Bravo 1,6	1995-98	182 A4/6 000	Weber-Marelli IAW 1AF	233
Brava/Bravo 1,8 16V	1999-02	183 A2 000	Hitachi	227
Brava/Bravo 1,9 JTD	1998-02	182B4.000	Bosch EDC 15C	235
Bravo 2,0 20V	1995-99	182 A1 000	Bosch Motronic M2.10.4	238
Cinquecento	1991-98	170/1170 A1 046	Weber-Marelli IAW 06F/16F	205
Cinquecento Sporting	1994-98	176 B2 000	Weber-Marelli IAW 06F/16F	205
Coupe 1,8 16V	1998-02	183 A1 000	Hitachi	227
Doblo 1,9 JTD	2004-06	223A7.000	Bosch EDC 15C	243
Doblo Cargo 1,9 JTD	2004-06	223A7.000	Bosch EDC 15C	243
Marea 1,6	1996-99	182 A4 000	Weber-Marelli IAW 1AF	233
Marea/Weekend 1,8 16V	1999-03	183 A1 000	Hitachi	227
Marea 1,9 JTD	1998-03	182B4.000	Bosch EDC 15C	235
Marea 2,0 20V	1996-99	182 A1 000	Bosch Motronic M2.10.4	238
Multipla 1,9 JTD	1999-02	182B4.000	Bosch EDC 15C	235
Panda 1,2 Dual Logic	2003-06	188A4.000	Weber-Marelli 1AW 5NF	209
Punto 1,2 8V	1999-06	188 A4 000	Weber-Marelli IAW 59F	216
Punto 1,2 16V	1999-06	188 A5 000	Bosch ME 7.3H4	219
Punto 1,4	2003-06	843A1.000	Bosch ME 7.3H4	224
Punto 1,8	1999-03	183 A1 000	Hitachi	227
Punto 55	1993-99	176 A6/B2 000	Weber-Marelli IAW 06F/16F	205
Punto 60	1994-99	176 A7/B4 000	Weber-Marelli IAW 06F/16F	205
Punto 75	1993-99	176 A8 000	Weber-Marelli IAW 08F/18F	212
Punto 85	1997-99	176 B9 000	Weber-Marelli IAW 18FD	214
Punto GT	1994-99	176 A4 000	Bosch Motronic M2.7	222
Seicento 900	1998-02	1170 A1 046	Weber-Marelli IAW 06F/16F	207
Seicento Sporting	1998-02	176 B2 000	Weber-Marelli IAW 06F/16F	207
Stilo 1,9 JTD	2001-06	192A1.000/192A3.000	Bosch EDC 15C	240
Ulysse 2,0	1994-00	RFU	Weber-Marelli IAW 8P.22	246

Model	Year	Engine code	System	Page
FORD				
Cougar 2,0	1998-02	EDBA/C	Ford EEC V	302
Cougar 2,5	1998-02	LCBA/C	Ford EEC V	326
Escort 1,3	1994-98	J4B	Ford EEC V	248
Escort 1,4	1994-99	F4B	Ford EEC IV	261
Escort 1,6 16V/1,8 16V	1994-99	L1K/RKC	Ford EEC V	248
Fiesta 1,25	10/97-02	DHA/B/C/D	Ford EEC V	251
Fiesta 1,25	2000-02	DHE/DHF/DHG	Siemens SIM 19	255
Fiesta 1,25	2002-06	FUJA/FUJB/M7JA/M7JB	Siemens SIM 22/210	258
Fiesta 1,25/1,3/1,4	1995-10/97	DHA/J4C/FHA	Ford EEC V	248
Fiesta 1,3	10/97-02	J4C/L/J/JJC/E	Ford EEC V	251
Fiesta 1,4	10/97-02	FHA/E	Ford EEC V	251
Fiesta 1,4	1994-95	F4A	Ford EEC IV	261
Fiesta 1,4	2002-06	FXJA/FXJB	Siemens SIM 22/210	258
Fiesta 1,4D TDCi	2002-06	F6JA	Siemens SID 802	264
Fiesta 1,6	2000-02	L1T	Ford EEC V	251
Fiesta 1,6	2002-06	FYJA/FYJB	Siemens SIM 22/210	258
Fiesta 1,6/1,8	1994-95	L1G/RDB	Ford EEC IV	261
Focus 1,4 MT	1998-02	FXDA/C	Ford EEC V	267
Focus 1,4 MT	2000-05	FXDB/D	Ford EEC V	270
Focus 1,4	2004-06	FXJA	Siemens SIM 28	273
Focus 1,6	2004-06	HWDA	Siemens SIM 28	273
Focus 1,6 AT	1998-02	FYDA/C	Ford EEC V	276
Focus 1,6 MT	1998-02	FYDA/C	Ford EEC V	267
Focus 1,6 MT	2000-05	FYDB/D	Ford EEC V	270
Focus 1,8 MT	2002-05	EYDG/EYDI/EYDJ/EYDL	Ford EEC V	280
Focus 1,8 TDdi	1998-01	C9DA/B/C	Bosch EDC/EEC V	283
Focus 1,8 TDCi	08/02-05	F9DA/B	Delphi	291
Focus 1,8 TDCi	2001-07/02	F9DA/B	Delphi/EEC V (engine control module)	286
Focus 1,8 TDCi	2001-07/02	F9DA/B	Delphi/EEC V (injector control module)	289
Focus 1,8/2,0 MT	1998-02	EYDC/EDDC	Ford EEC V	267
Focus C-MAX 1,8	2003-06	CSDA	Visteon System 7	295
Focus C-MAX 2,0 TDCi	2003-06	G6DA	Siemens SID 803	298
Fusion 1,4D TDCi	2002-06	F6JA	Siemens SID 802	264
Galaxy 1,9 TD	1995-01	1Z/AHU/AFN	Bosch EDC 1.3/1.4	331
Galaxy 1,9 TDI	1999-02	ANU/AUY	Bosch EDC 15P/16	334
Galaxy 2,0/2,3	1995-02	NSD/E/Y5B	Ford EEC V	276
Galaxy 2,8	1995-01	AAA	Bosch Motronic M3.8.1	337
Ka 1,3	1996-98	J4D	Ford EEC V	248
Ka 1,3	1999-02	J4D/K/M/JJD/F	Ford EEC V	251
Mondeo 1,6	1996-01	L1J/L/N/Q	Ford EEC V	302
Mondeo 1,8	1996-01	RKB/F/J/H	Ford EEC V	302
Mondeo 1,8	2000-06	CDBB/CGBA/B/CHBA/B/CHBB	Visteon Black Oak	305
Mondeo 2,0	1996-01	NGA/B/C	Ford EEC V	302
Mondeo 2,0	2000-06	CJBA/B	Visteon Black Oak	305

Index

Model	Year	Engine code	System	Page
Mondeo 2,0 TDCi 115 hp MT	2002-01/03	HJBA/B	Delphi/EEC V (engine control module)	314
Mondeo 2,0 TDCi 115 hp MT	2002-01/03	HJBA/B	Delphi/EEC V (injector control module)	324
Mondeo 2,0 TDCi 115 hp MT	02/03-04	HJBA/B/C	Delphi/EEC V (engine control module)	317
Mondeo 2,0 TDCi 115 hp AT	2002-04	HJBA/B/C	Delphi/EEC V (engine control module)	321
Mondeo 2,0 TDCi 115 hp AT	2002-04	HJBA/B/C	Delphi/EEC V (injector control module)	324
Mondeo 2,0 TDCi 130 hp MT	2001-01/02	FMBA/B	Delphi/EEC V (engine control module)	308
Mondeo 2,0 TDCi 130 hp MT	02/02-03	FMBA/B	Delphi/EEC V (engine control module)	311
Mondeo 2,0 TDCi 130 hp MT	2001-03	FMBA/B	Delphi/EEC V (injector control module)	324
Mondeo 2,0 TDCi 130 hp AT	2002-04	FMBA/B	Delphi/EEC V (engine control module)	321
Mondeo 2,0 TDCi 130 hp AT	2002-04	FMBA/B	Delphi/EEC V (injector control module)	324
Mondeo 2,0 TDCi 130 hp MT	2003-04	N7BA	Delphi/EEC V (engine control module)	317
Mondeo 2,0 TDCi 130 hp AT	2003-04	N7BA	Delphi/EEC V (engine control module)	321
Mondeo 2,0 TDCi 130 hp AT	2003-04	N7BA	Delphi/EEC V (injector control module)	324
Mondeo 2,5	1996-01	SEA/B/SGA	Ford EEC V	326
Puma 1,4	1997-02	FHD/F	Ford EEC V	251
Puma 1,7	1997-02	MHA	Ford EEC V	302
Scorpio 2,9	1994-98	BOB	Ford EEC V	326
Transit 2,0	1994-00	NSG/NSF	Ford EEC V	276
Transit 2,0 TDCi	2000-07/03	FIFA	Delphi/EEC V (engine control module)	342
Transit 2,0 TDCi	2000-07/03	FIFA	Delphi/EEC V (injector control module)	345
Transit 2,0 TDCi	08/03-06	FIFA	Delphi/EEC V	347
Transit 2,0D Di	2000-06	ABFA/D3FA/F3FA	Bosch EDC/EEC V	339
Transit 2,4 TDCi	2003-06	FXFA/H9FA	Delphi/EEC V	347

HONDA

Model	Year	Engine code	System	Page
Accord 1,8/2,0/2,2	1998-03	F18B2/F20B6/H22A7	Honda PGM-FI	360
Accord 2,2	1996-99	F20Z1/F22Z2	Honda PGM-FI	364
Civic 1,4	1996-00	D14A3/4	Honda PGM-FI	352
Civic 1,4	1999-01	D14Z1/D14Z2	Honda PGM-FI	354
Civic 1,4/1,6/VTEC	1996-99	D14A2/D16Y2/3	Honda PGM-FI	350
Civic 1,5	1999-01	D15Z6	Honda PGM-FI	354
Civic 1,6 VTEC	1996-99	D16Y5	Honda PGM-FI	357
Civic 1,6	1999-01	B16A2/D16Y5	Honda PGM-FI	354
CR-V 2,0	1999-02	B20Z1	Honda PGM-FI	367

HYUNDAI

Model	Year	Engine code	System	Page
Accent 1,5	1995-00	G4K	Hyundai ECFI (55-pin)	370

JAGUAR (DAIMLER)

Model	Year	Engine code	System	Page
X-Type 2,0	2001-02/04	YB	Denso	372
XJ8/Sovereign 3,2/Sport	1999-03	AC/KC	Denso	376
XJ8/Sovereign 4,0	1999-03	BC/LC/DC/MA	Denso	376
XK8 4,0	1999-02	CE/CC/NC	Denso	376
XKR 4,0	2000-02	EC/PA	Denso	376

Model	Year	Engine code	System	Page
LAND ROVER				
Defender 2,5D TD5	1999-06	VIN No. digit 8 = 8	Lucas	387
Discovery 2,5D TD5	1998-02	VIN No. digit 8 = 8 or 9	Lucas	387
Discovery 4,0	1998-02	–	Bosch Motronic M5.2.1	390
Freelander 2,0D Turbo	1997-01	20T	Bosch MSA 11	382
Freelander 2,5	2000-06	KV6	Siemens EMS 2000	384
Range Rover 4,0	1994-01	42D	Sagem/Lucas GEMS 8.2	393
Range Rover 4,6	1994-01	46D	Sagem/Lucas GEMS 8.2	393
MAZDA				
6 1,8	2002-06	L8	Mazda EGI	396
6 2,0	2002-06	LF	Mazda EGI	396
6 2,3 (2WD)	2002-06	L3	Mazda EGI	396
MERCEDES-BENZ				
A140/A160/A180	1998-08/01	166.940	Siemens MSM 1.4	400
200E/CE/TE (124)	1992-93	111.940	Mercedes-Benz PMS	403
C180 (202)	1993-01	111.920	Mercedes-Benz PMS	403
C180K (203)	2002-06	271.946	Siemens ME-SIM4	405
C200 (202)	1993-01	111.941	Mercedes-Benz PMS	403
C200K (203)	2002-06	271.940	Siemens ME-SIM4	405
C200 CDI (203)	2003-06	646.962/646.963	Bosch EDC 15C	411
C200/C220 (202) CDI	1998-01	611.96	Bosch EDC 15C0	408
C220 CDI (203)	2003-06	646.962/646.963	Bosch EDC 15C	411
C230K (202)	1997-01	111.975	Bosch ME 2.1	414
C230K (203)	2002-06	271.948	Siemens ME-SIM4	405
C240 (202)	1997-01	112.910	Bosch ME 2.0	417
C280 (202)	1997-01	112.920	Bosch ME 2.0	417
CLK 220 CDI (209)	2005-06	646.963	Bosch EDC 15C	411
CLK 200K (209)	2002-06	271.940	Siemens ME-SIM4	405
CLK 230K (208)	1997-03	111.975	Bosch ME 2.1	414
CLK 320 (208)	1997-03	112.940	Bosch ME 2.0	417
E200 (124)	1992-95	111.940	Mercedes-Benz PMS	403
E200K (211)	2002-06	271.941	Siemens ME-SIM4	420
E200 (211) CDI	2002-06	646.951	Bosch EDC	423
E200/E220 (210) CDI	1998-03	611.961	Bosch EDC 15C0	408
E220 (211) CDI	2002-06	646.951/961	Bosch EDC	423
E240 (210)	1997-03	112.911	Bosch ME 2.0	417
E270 (211) CDI	2002-05	647.961	Bosch EDC	426
E280/E320 (210)	1997-03	112.921/941	Bosch ME 2.0	417
S280 (220)	1996-98	104.944	Bosch ME 2.1	414
S320 (220)	1996-98	104.994	Bosch ME 2.1	414
Sprinter 2,2 CDI	1999-06	611.981/611.987	Bosch EDC 15C	429

Index

Model	Year	Engine code	System	Page
MITSUBISHI				
Carisma 1,8 GDI	1997-99	4G93	Mitsubishi MFI (engine control module)	438
Carisma 1,8 GDI	1997-99	4G93	Mitsubishi MFI (injector control module)	441
Colt/Lancer 1,3 12V	1996-03	4G13	Mitsubishi MFI	432
Colt/Lancer 1,6 16V	1996-03	4G92 – SOHC	Mitsubishi MFI	435
Space Wagon 2,0	1994-99	4G63	Mitsubishi MFI	442
NISSAN				
Almera 1,4/1,6	1995-00	GA14DE/GA16DE	Nissan ECCS	451
Almera 1,5/1,8	2000-06	QG15DE/QG18DE	Nissan ECCS	454
Almera Tino 1,8	2000-06	QG18DE	Nissan ECCS	454
Almera Tino 2,0	2000-03	SR20DE	Nissan ECCS	457
Micra 1,0/1,3	1996-05/00	CG10DE/CG13DE	Nissan ECCS	445
Micra 1,2	2003-06	CR12DE	Nissan ECCS	448
Primera 1,6	1996-99	GA16DE	Nissan ECCS	451
Primera 1,6	2000-02	QG16DE	Nissan ECCS	454
Primera 1,8	2000-02	QG18DE	Nissan ECCS	454
Primera 2,0	2000-02	SR20DE	Nissan ECCS	457
PEUGEOT				
106 1,0/1,1	1996-03	TU9M/TU1M (HDY/Z/CDY/Z)	Bosch Mono-Motronic MA3.1	460
106 1,3 Rallye	1994-97	TU2J2L/Z (MFZ)	Magneti-Marelli 8P	462
106 1,4	1997-03	TU3JP (KFX)	Magneti-Marelli 1AP	464
106 1,4	1998-03	KFX (TU3JP/IFL4)	Bosch Motronic MP 7.2/7.3	466
106 1,6	1997-02	TU5JP (NFZ)	Bosch Motronic MP5.2	469
106 1,6 GTi	1997-03	TU5J4/L3 (NFX)	Magneti-Marelli 1AP	464
206 1,1/1,4	1998-06	TU3JP/L3	Magneti-Marelli 1AP	464
206 1,4	1998-06	KFX (TU3JP)	Bosch Motronic MP 7.2/7.3	466
206 1,6	1998-02	NFZ (TU5JP/L3/D3)	Bosch Motronic MP 7.2/7.3	466
206 2,0	1998-06	RFR (EW10J4)	Magnetti-Marelli 4.8P	471
306 1,4	1997-02	TU3JP/L3	Magneti-Marelli 1AP	464
306 1,4	1998-02	KFX (TU3JP/L3)	Sagem SL96	475
306 1,4	2000-02	TU3JP (KFW)	Sagem S2000	477
306 1,6	1997-02	TU5JP/L3	Bosch Motronic MP5.2	469
306 1,6	1998-03	NFZ (TU5JP/L3/D3)	Bosch Motronic MP 7.2/7.3	466
306 1,8	1993-03	XU7JP/Z/L3 (LFZ)	Magneti-Marelli 8P	462
306 1,8 16V	1998-03	LFY (XU7JP4/Z/L/3)	Sagem SL96	475
306 2,0	1993-01	XU10J2CL/Z (RFX)	Magneti-Marelli 8P	462
306 2,0 16V	1997-01	XU10J4RS/L3	Magneti-Marelli 1AP.10	480
306 2,0 16V	1997-03	RFV (XU10J4R/L3)	Bosch Motronic MP5.2	469
307 2,0 HDi	2001-06	RHY (DW10TD)	Bosch EDC 15C2	482
307 2,0 HDi	2001-06	RHY (DW10TD)	Siemens SID 801	485
405 1,8	1992-97	XU7JP/Z (LFZ)	Magneti-Marelli 8P	462
405 2,0	1992-97	XU10J2C (RFX)	Magneti-Marelli 8P	462
406 1,6	1995-97	XU5JP (BFZ)	Magneti-Marelli 8P	462

Autodata

Model	Year	Engine code	System	Page
406 1,8	1997-02	LFX (XU7JB)	Magnetti-Marelli 1AP.20	488
406 1,8 16V	1995-02	XU7JP4 (LFY)	Bosch Motronic MP5.1.1	490
406 1,8 16V	1998-02	LFY (XU7JP4/Z/L/3)	Sagem SL96	475
406 1,9D Turbo	1995-00	XUD9BTF/L3 (DHX)	Bosch AS3	492
406 2,0	1998-04	RFR (EW10J4)	Magnetti-Marelli 4.8P	471
406 2,0 16V	1995-02	XU10J4R (RFV)	Bosch Motronic MP5.1.1	490
406 2,0 HDi	1998-01	DW10ATED (RHZ)	Bosch EDC 15C2	494
406 2,0 HDi	1999-01	DW10TD (RHY)	Bosch EDC 15C2	494
406 2,0 HDi	2001-04	DW10ATED (RHS)	Bosch EDC 15C2	498
406 2,2 HDi	2000-05	DW12ATED (4HX)	Bosch EDC 15C2	494
406 Coupe 2,2 HDi	2000-06	DW12ATED (4HX)	Bosch EDC 15C2	494
605 2,0 16V	1995-99	XU10J4R/L/Z (RFX)	Bosch Motronic MP5.1.1	490
806 1,9D Turbo	1995-00	XUD9BTF/L3 (DHX)	Bosch AS3	492
806 2,0	1994-02	XU10J2C/Z (RFU)	Magneti-Marelli 8P	462
806 2,0 16V	1998-02	RFV (XU10J4R)	Bosch Motronic MP 7.2/7.3	466
806 2,0 HDi	1999-02	DW10ATED (RHZ)	Bosch EDC 15C2	502
806 2,0 Turbo	1994-02	XU10J2U/X3 (RFW)	Magneti-Marelli 8P	462
Partner 1,1	1996-02	TU1M (HDZ)	Bosch Mono-Motronic MA3.1	460
Partner 1,4	1996-02	TU3JP/L3	Magneti-Marelli 1AP	464
Partner 1,8	1996-02	LFX (XU7JB)	Magnetti-Marelli 1AP.20	488
Partner 1,9D	1999-06	WJY (DW8B)	Delphi DCN2.2	506
Partner 2,0 HDi	2002-06	RHY (DW10TD)	Siemens SID 801	508

RENAULT

Model	Year	Engine code	System	Page
Clio 1,2	1995-98	D7F 730	Sagem/Magnetti Marelli	511
Clio 1,2	1998-06	D7F 720	Sagem/Magnetti Marelli	511
Clio 1,2 AC	1998-06	D7F 720	Sagem/Magnetti Marelli	513
Clio 1,2 16V	2001-06	D4F 712	Magneti-Marelli 5NR	516
Clio 1,4	1998-05	E7J 780	Siemens Fenix	519
Clio 1,4 16V	1998-06	K4J	Siemens Sirius 32	521
Clio 1,5 dCi	2001-06	K9K 702/704/710	Delphi	524
Clio 1,6	1998-03	K7M 744/5	Siemens Fenix	519
Espace 1,9 dTi	1999-01	F9Q 720/722	Bosch MSA 15.5	542
Kangoo 1,2	1998-06	D7F 710	Sagem/Magnetti Marelli	511
Kangoo 1,2 AC	1998-05	D7F 720	Sagem/Magnetti Marelli	513
Kangoo 1,4	1998-05	E7J 780	Siemens Fenix	519
Kangoo 1,5 dCi	2001-03	K9K 700/702/704/710	Delphi	551
Laguna 1,6	1998-01	F4P 760	Siemens Sirius 32	521
Laguna 1,8	1996-99	F3P 670	Fenix 5	536
Laguna 1,8	1999-01	K4M 720/724	Siemens Sirius 32	521
Laguna 1,9 dCi	1999-01	F9Q 718	Bosch EDC 15C3	545
Laguna 1,9 dCi	2001-10/02	F9Q 750	Bosch EDC 15C3	548
Laguna 1,9 dTi	1998-01	F9Q 710/716	Bosch MSA 15.5	542
Laguna 2,0	1996-01	F3R 728/729	Fenix 5	536
Laguna 2,0 16V	1996-99	N7Q 700	Fenix 5	536
Laguna 2,0 16V	1999-01	F4R 780	Siemens Sirius 32	521

Index

Model	Year	Engine code	System	Page
Mégane 1,4	1999-03	K4J 750	Siemens Sirius 32	**521**
Mégane 1,6	1995-99	K7M 702/703	Fenix 5	**513**
Mégane 1,6	1999-03	K4M 700	Siemens Sirius 32	**521**
Mégane 1,6	2002-06	K4M 760/761	Sagem S3000	**527**
Mégane 1,9 dCi	1999-03	F9Q 732/733	Bosch EDC 15C3	**533**
Mégane 1,9 dTi	1999-03	F9Q 731/736/744	Bosch MSA 15.5	**530**
Mégane 1,9D Turbo	1997-99	F9Q 730/734	Bosch MSA 15.5	**530**
Mégane 2,0	1995-99	F3R 750/751	Fenix 5	**536**
Mégane 2,0	1999-03	F4R 740/741/744	Siemens Sirius 32	**521**
Mégane 2,0 16V	1995-99	F7R 710	Fenix 5	**536**
Mégane Scénic 1,9D Turbo	1997-99	F9Q 730/734	Bosch MSA 15.5	**530**
Scénic 1,4	1999-03	K4J 750	Siemens Sirius 32	**521**
Scénic 1,6	1999-03	K4M 700	Siemens Sirius 32	**521**
Scénic 1,6	2003-06	K4M 760/761	Sagem S3000	**527**
Scénic 1,9 dCi	1999-03	F9Q 732	Bosch EDC 15C3	**533**
Scénic 1,9 dTi	1999-03	F9Q 731	Bosch MSA 15.5	**539**
Scénic RX4 1,9 dCi	2000-03	F9Q 740/746/748	Bosch EDC 15C3	**533**
Scénic 2,0	1999-02	F4R 740/741/744	Siemens Sirius 32	**521**
Scénic RX4 2,0	1999-03	F4R 740/741/744	Siemens Sirius 32	**521**
Safrane 2,0 16V	1996-01	N7Q 710/711	Fenix 5	**536**

ROVER

Model	Year	Engine code	System	Page
25 1,4/1,6	1999-05	14K4/16K4	Rover MEMS 3	**567**
25 1,8/VVC	1999-05	18K4	Rover MEMS 3	**567**
25 2,0D Turbo	1999-05	20T	Bosch EDC15M	**570**
45 1,4	1999-05	14K4	Rover MEMS 3	**572**
45 1,6/1,8	1999-05	16K4/18K4	Rover MEMS 3	**572**
45 2,0D Turbo	1999-05	20T	Bosch EDC15M	**575**
75 1,8	1999-05	18K4	Rover MEMS 3	**572**
75 2,0 CDT/CDTi	1999-05	M47R	Bosch DDE 4.0	**577**
111i/114i	1996-98	K8	Rover MEMS MPI	**557**
200 Vi	1995-99	18K16	Rover MEMS 2J MPI	**559**
214i/414i	1995-98	14K8/16	Rover MEMS MPI	**557**
216i Cabrio/Coupe/416i	1995-99	K16	Rover MEMS MPI	**557**
218i Coupe VVC	1996-99	18K16	Rover MEMS 2J MPI	**559**
220 2,0D Turbo	1995-99	20T2N	Bosch MSA 11 EDC	**562**
220 2,0D Turbo	1995-99	20T2R	Rover EDC	**565**
420 2,0D Turbo	1995-00	20T2R	Rover EDC	**565**
420 2,0D Turbo	1995-99	20T2N	Bosch MSA 11 EDC	**562**
420i	1995-98	T16	Rover MEMS MPI	**557**
825i	1996-99	KV6	Rover MEMS 2J MPI	**580**
MG ZR 2,0D 101	2001-05	20T	Bosch EDC15M	**570**
MG ZS 2,0D 101	2001-05	20T	Bosch EDC15M	**575**
MG ZT 2,0 CDT/CDTi	1999-05	M47R	Bosch DDE 4.0	**577**

Model	Year	Engine code	System	Page
MGF 1,8i	1995-02	K16	Rover MEMS MPI	557
MGF 1,8i VVC	1995-99	K16-1,8	Rover MEMS 2J MPI	559
Mini 1,3i	1996-01	12AZK70	Rover MEMS Dual Point	554

SAAB

Model	Year	Engine code	System	Page
9-3 2,0 Turbo	1999-03	B205L	Saab Trionic T7	583
9-3 2,0 Turbo	1999-03	B205R	Saab Trionic T7	583
9-3 2,0 Turbo	2000-03	B205E	Saab Trionic T7	583
9-3 2,2 TiD	1998-02	D223L	Bosch EDC15M	586
9-3 2,3 Turbo	1999-01	B235R	Saab Trionic T7	583
9-5 2,0 Turbo	1997-06	B205E/F	Saab Trionic T7	583
9-5 2,3 Turbo	1997-06	B235E	Saab Trionic T7	583
9-5 2,3 Turbo	1999-06	B235R/TK	Saab Trionic T7	583
9000 2,0/ Turbo	1994-98	B204S/E/L	SAAB Trionic	588
9000 2,3/ Turbo	1994-98	B234/L	SAAB Trionic	588

SEAT

Model	Year	Engine code	System	Page
Alhambra 1,9 TDI	1996-00	1Z/AHU/AFN/AVG	Bosch EDC 1.3.3/1.4 (MSA 12/15)	628
Alhambra 1,9 TDI PD	1999-06	ANU/AUY/ASZ	Bosch EDC 15P	631
Alhambra 2,0	1996-98	ADY	Siemens Simos	612
Arosa 1,0	1999-03	ANV/AUC	Bosch Motronic ME7.5.10	591
Arosa 1,0/1,4	1997-05	AER/AEX/ALL	Bosch Motronic MP 9.0	594
Arosa 1,0/1,4	1999-03	ALD/ALK	Bosch Motronic ME7.5.10	617
Arosa 1,4	1999-03	ANW/AUD	Bosch Motronic ME7.5.10	591
Cordoba 1,0/1,4	1999-02	ANV/ANW/AUC/AUD	Bosch Motronic ME7.5.10	591
Cordoba 1,2 12V	2002-06	AZQ	Siemens Simos 3PE	601
Cordoba 1,4	1999-02	APE/AQQ/AUA/AUB	Magneti Marelli 4LV	606
Cordoba 1,4	2002-06	BBY/BBZ	Magneti Marelli 4MV	609
Ibiza 1,0/1,4	1999-02	ANV/ANW/AUC/AUD	Bosch Motronic ME7.5.10	591
Ibiza 1,2 12V	2002-06	AZQ	Siemens Simos 3PE	601
Ibiza 1,4	1999-02	APE/AQQ/AUA/AUB	Magneti Marelli 4LV	606
Ibiza 1,4	2002-06	BBY/BBZ	Magneti Marelli 4MV	609
Ibiza/Cordoba 1,05/1,4	1993-99	AAU/ABD	Bosch Mono-Motronic	599
Ibiza/Cordoba 1,4	1996-99	AEX/APQ	Bosch Motronic MP 9.0	594
Ibiza/Cordoba 1,4	1997-99	AFH	Magnetti-Marelli 1AV	604
Ibiza/Cordoba 1,0/1,4	1999-02	ALD/AKK	Bosch Motronic ME7.5.10	617
Ibiza/Cordoba 1,6	1996-99	AEE/ALM	Magnetti-Marelli 1AV	604
Ibiza/Cordoba 1,6	1996-99	AFT	Siemens Simos	612
Ibiza/Cordoba 1,6	1999-02	AEH/AKL	Siemens Simos 2	614
Ibiza/Cordoba 1,6/1,8	1993-99	ABU/1F/ADZ	Bosch Mono-Motronic	599
Ibiza/Cordoba 1,9 TDI PD	2002-06	ASZ/ATD	Bosch EDC 15P	619
Ibiza/Cordoba 2,0	1995-99	ADY	Siemens Simos	612
Ibiza/Cordoba 2,0 16V	1996-99	ABF	VAG Digifant	620
Inca 1,6	1995-00	1F	Bosch Mono-Motronic	599
Inca 1,6	1998-00	AEE/ALM	Magnetti-Marelli 1AV	604
Leon 1,4	2000-05	APE/AXP	Bosch Motronic ME7.5.10	591

Index

Model	Year	Engine code	System	Page
Leon 1,6	1999-02	AEH/AKL	Siemens Simos 2	614
Leon 1,6 16V	2000-05	AUS	Magneti Marelli 4LV	622
Leon 1,6 16V	2001-05	AZD/BCB	Magneti Marelli 4MV	625
Toledo 1,4	2000-05	APE/AXP	Bosch Motronic ME7.5.10	591
Toledo 1,6	1996-99	AFT	Siemens Simos	612
Toledo 1,6	1999-02	AEH/AKL	Siemens Simos 2	614
Toledo 1,6 16V	2000-05	AUS	Magneti Marelli 4LV	622
Toledo 1,6 16V	2001-05	AZD/BCB	Magneti Marelli 4MV	625
Toledo 1,6/1,8	1994-97	1F/ABS/ADZ	Bosch Mono-Motronic	599
Toledo 2,0	1994-99	AGG	Siemens Simos	612
Toledo 2,0 16V	1994-99	ABF	VAG Digifant	620

SKODA

Model	Year	Engine code	System	Page
Fabia 1,2	2002-04	AWY	Siemens Simos 3PD	634
Fabia 1,2	2002-06	AZQ	Siemens Simos 3PE	637
Fabia 1,9 TDI PD	2000-06	ATD	Bosch EDC 15P	640
Fabia 1,9 TDI PD vRS	2003-06	ASZ	Bosch EDC 15P	640
Octavia 1,6	1997-05	AEH/AKL	Siemens Simos 2	644
Octavia 1,8/Turbo	1996-05	AGN/AGU	Bosch Motronic M3.8.2/3.5	647
Octavia 1,9 TDI PD	2000-05	ATD	Bosch EDC 15P	640
Octavia 1,9 TDI PD	2003-05	ASZ	Bosch EDC 15P	640
Octavia 2,0	1999-02	AEG/AQY/APK	Bosch Motronic M5.9.2	651

TOYOTA

Model	Year	Engine code	System	Page
Avensis 1,6i	1997-01	4A-FE	Toyota TCCS	653
Avensis 1,8i	1997-01	7A-FE	Toyota TCCS	656
Avensis 2,0i	1997-01	3S-FE	Toyota TCCS	659
Carina E 1,6i MT	1992-95	4A-FE	Toyota TCCS	653
Corolla 1,6i	1992-97	4A-FE	Toyota TCCS	653
Landcruiser Colorado 3,0D Turbo	1996-02	1KZ-TE	Toyota ECD	670
MR2 2,0 GT	1990-00	3S-GE	Toyota TCCS	662
RAV4 2,0 AT	1994-00	3S-FE	Toyota TCCS	667
RAV4 2,0 MT	1994-00	3S-FE	Toyota TCCS	665

VAUXHALL-OPEL

Model	Year	Engine code	System	Page
Astra-F 1,4/1,6 16V	1995-99	X14XE/X16XEL	GM Multec S	676
Astra-F 1,6	1996-98	X16SZR	GM Multec Central	678
Astra-G 1,2	1998-02	X12XE	Bosch Motronic M1.5.5	673
Astra-G 1,4	2000-06	Z14XE	GM Multec S (F)	710
Astra-G 1,4/1,6 16V	1998-02	X14XE/X16XEL	GM Multec S	707
Astra-G 1,6	1998-02	X16SZR	GM Multec F	715
Astra-G 1,6	2000-06	Z16XE	GM Multec S (F)	710
Astra-G 1,6	2000-06	Z16SE	GM Multec S (F)	717
Astra-G 1,6	2004-06	Z16XEP	GM Multec S	721

Model	Year	Engine code	System	Page
Astra-G 1,7 DTi	2000-04	Y17DT	Denso V5	728
Astra-G 1,7 TD	1998-01	X17DTL	Bosch EDC 15M	725
Astra-G 1,8	2001-06	Z18XE	Siemens Simtec 71	731
Astra-G 1,8/2,0 16V	1998-02	X18XE1/X20XEV	Siemens Simtec 70	735
Astra-G 2,0 TD	1998-01	X20DTL	Bosch EDC 15M	725
Astra-H 1,8	2004-06	Z18XE	Siemens Simtec 71	739
Combo-C 1,3 CDTi	2003-06	Z13DT	Magneti Marelli 6JF	695
Combo-C 1,7 Di	2001-05	Y17DTL	Denso V5	704
Combo-C 1,7 DTi	2001-05	Y17DT	Denso V5	704
Corsa-B 1,0/1,2	1997-02	X10XE/X12XE	Bosch Motronic M1.5.5	673
Corsa-B 1,4/1,6	1994-00	X14XE/X16XE	GM Multec S	676
Corsa-C 1,0	2000-06	Z10XE	Bosch Motronic ME1.5.5	680
Corsa-C 1,0	2003-06	Z10XEP	Bosch Motronic ME7.6.1/2	683
Corsa-C 1,2	2000-06	Z12XE	Bosch Motronic ME1.5.5	687
Corsa-C 1,2	2004-06	Z12XEP	Bosch Motronic ME7.6.1/2	691
Corsa-C 1,3 CDTi	2003-06	Z13DT	Magneti Marelli 6JF	695
Corsa-C 1,4	2000-06	Z14XE	GM Multec S (F)	699
Corsa-C 1,4	2003-06	Z14XEP	Bosch Motronic ME7.6.1/2	691
Corsa-C 1,7 Di	2000-05	Y17DTL	Denso V5	704
Corsa-C 1,7 DTi	2000-05	Y17DT	Denso V5	704
Frontera 2,0	1995-99	X20SE	Bosch Motronic M1.5.4	743
Frontera 2,2 16V	1995-99	X22XE	Bosch Motronic M1.5.4	743
Omega-B 2,0 16V	1994-96	X20SE	Bosch Motronic M1.5.4	743
Omega-B 2,0 TD	1998-01	X20DTH	Bosch EDC 15M	746
Omega-B 2,5/3,0	1994-01	X25XE/X30XE	Bosch Motronic M2.8.1	751
Sintra 2,2 16V	1996-99	X22XE	Bosch Motronic M1.5.4	743
Sintra 3,0	1996-99	X30XE	Bosch Motronic M2.8.3	748
Tigra 1,4/1,6	1995-99	X14XE/X16XE	GM Multec S	676
Vectra-B 1,6	1995-99	X16SZR	GM Multec Central	678
Vectra-B 1,6/16V	1996-02	X16SEJ/X16XEL	GM Multec S	676
Vectra-B 1,8 16V	1998-02	X18XE1	Siemens Simtec 70	735
Vectra-B 2,0 16V	1995-02	20NEJ	Bosch Motronic M1.5.4	743
Vectra-B 2,0 DTi	1998-01	X20DTH	Bosch EDC 15M	746
Vectra-B 2,5	1995-00	X25XE	Bosch Motronic M2.8.3	748
Zafira 1,6	2000-05	Z16XE	GM Multec S (F)	754
Zafira 1,6 16V	1999-02	X16XEL	GM Multec S	707
Zafira 1,8 16V	1999-02	X18XE1	Siemens Simtec 70	735

VOLKSWAGEN

Model	Year	Engine code	System	Page
Beetle 1,9 TDI	05/99-04	ALH	Bosch EDC 15V	789
Beetle 1,9 TDI PD	2000-06	ATD	Bosch EDC 15P	792
Beetle Convertible 1,9 TDI PD	2003-06	AXR	Bosch EDC 15P	792
Caddy 1,4	1995-99	AEX/AKV/APQ/ANX	Bosch Motronic MP9.0	759
Caddy 1,6	1995-00	AFT	Siemens Simos	779

Index

Model	Year	Engine code	System	Page
Caddy 1,7/1,9 SDI	12/97-01	AEY/AKW	Bosch EDC 15V	784
Corrado 2,0	1994-95	ADY	Siemens Simos	779
Golf 1,4 FSI	2003-06	BKG	Bosch Motronic MED9.5.10	796
Golf 1,6 FSI	2003-06	BAG	Bosch Motronic MED9.5.10	796
Golf/Bora 1,4	1998-05	AHW/AKQ	Magneti Marelli 4AV/4CV	768
Golf/Bora 1,4	1999-03	APE/AXP	Bosch Motronic ME7.5.10	763
Golf/Bora 1,6	1997-02	AEH/AKL	Siemens Simos 2	781
Golf/Bora 1,6	1999-02	ATN	Magneti Marelli 4LV	802
Golf/Bora 1,6	2000-02	AUS	Magneti Marelli 4LV	802
Golf/Bora 1,6	2000-05	AZD/BCB	Magneti Marelli 4MV	805
Golf/Bora 1,8	1997-03	AGN	Bosch Motronic M3.8.3/5	808
Golf/Bora 1,8 Turbo	1997-04	AGU	Bosch Motronic M3.8.3/5	808
Golf/Bora 1,8 Turbo	1998-03	AQA/ARZ	Bosch Motronic ME7.5	812
Golf/Bora 1,8 Turbo	2000-04	AUM/AUQ	Bosch Motronic ME7.5	816
Golf/Bora 1,9 TDI	1997-04/99	AGR/AHF/ALH	Bosch EDC 15V	820
Golf/Bora 1,9 TDI PD	1999-05	AJM/ARL/ASZ/ATD/AUY	Bosch EDC 15P/16	823
Golf/Bora 2,0	1998-02	AQY/APK/ATU	Bosch Motronic M5.9.2	827
Golf/Vento 1,4	1991-95	ABD	Bosch Mono-Motronic MA1.2.2/1.2.3/1.3	800
Golf/Vento 1,4	1995-98	AEX/APQ	Bosch Motronic MP9.0	759
Golf/Vento 1,6	1992-95	ABU/AEA	Bosch Mono-Motronic MA1.2.2/1.2.3/1.3	800
Golf/Vento 1,6	1995-98	AFT/AKS	Siemens Simos	779
Golf/Vento 1,8	1991-98	AAM	Bosch Mono-Motronic MA1.2.2/1.2.3/1.3 (45-pin)	800
Golf/Vento 1,8	1991-98	ABS/ADZ	Bosch Mono-Motronic MA1.2.2/1.2.3/1.3 (45-pin)	800
Golf/Vento 1,8	1998	ANN/ANP	Bosch Mono-Motronic MA1.2.2/1.2.3/1.3 (45-pin)	800
Golf/Vento 2,0	1995-98	ADY/AGG/AKR	Siemens Simos	779
Golf Cabrio 1,6	1995-02	AFT/AKS	Siemens Simos	779
Golf Cabrio 1,8	1991-00	AAM	Bosch Mono-Motronic MA1.2.2/1.2.3/1.3 (45-pin)	800
Golf Cabrio 1,8	1991-00	ABS/ADZ	Bosch Mono-Motronic MA1.2.2/1.2.3/1.3 (45-pin)	800
Golf Cabrio 1,8	1998-00	ANN/ANP	Bosch Mono-Motronic MA1.2.2/1.2.3/1.3 (45-pin)	800
Golf Cabrio 2,0	1995-02	ADY/AGG/AKR	Siemens Simos	779
Golf Cabrio 2,0	1998-02	AQY/APK/ATU	Bosch Motronic M5.9.2	827
Lupo 1,0	1998-05	AHT	Siemens Simos 2P	766
Lupo 1,0	1998-05	AER/ALL	Bosch Motronic MP9.0	759
Lupo 1,0	1998-05	ALD	Bosch Motronic ME7.5.10	761
Lupo 1,0/1,4	1998-05	ANV/AUC/AUD	Bosch Motronic ME7.5.10	763
Lupo 1,4	1998-05	AHW/AKQ	Magneti Marelli 4AV/4CV	768
Lupo 1,4	2000-05	AUD	Bosch Motronic ME7.5.10	763
Passat 1,6	1995-97	AFT/AKS	Siemens Simos	779
Passat 1,6	1996-99	ADP	Bosch Motronic M3.2	830
Passat 1,6	1996-00	AHL/ARM	Siemens Simos 2	781
Passat 1,8/Turbo	1996-99	ADR/AEB	Bosch Motronic M3.8.2	832
Passat 1,9 TDI	08/97-01	AFN/AHH/AHU/AVG	Bosch EDC 15V	834
Passat 1,9 TDI PD	1998-05	AJM/ATJ/AVB/AVF/AWX	Bosch EDC 15P/16	823
Passat/Syncro 2,0	1995-97	AKR/ADY/AGG	Siemens Simos	779

Model	Year	Engine code	System	Page
Polo 1,0	1996-05	AER/ALL	Bosch Motronic MP9.0	759
Polo 1,0	1999-02	ALD	Bosch Motronic ME7.5.10	761
Polo 1,0	1999-02	AUC	Bosch Motronic ME7.5.10	763
Polo 1,2	2002-06	AWY	Siemens Simos 3PD	770
Polo 1,4	1998-02	AKK	Bosch Motronic ME7.5.10	761
Polo 1,4	1999-02	AKP/ANW/AUD	Bosch Motronic ME7.5.10	763
Polo 1,4	1999-02	APE/AUA/AUB	Magneti Marelli 4LV	773
Polo 1,4	2001-02	AQQ	Magneti Marelli 4LV	773
Polo 1,4	2002-06	BBY/BBZ	Magneti Marelli 4MV	776
Polo 1,7/1,9 SDI	1997-09/99	AGD/AHG/AKU	Bosch EDC 15V	784
Polo 1,9 TDI PD	2002-06	ATD/AXR/ASZ	Bosch EDC 15P	786
Polo Classic/Estate 1,4	1995-02	AEX/AKV/APQ/ANX	Bosch Motronic MP9.0	759
Polo Classic/Estate 1,4	1999-02	AKK	Bosch Motronic ME7.5.10	761
Polo Classic/Estate 1,4	1999-02	ANW/AUD	Bosch Motronic ME7.5.10	763
Polo Classic/Estate 1,6	1995-99	AFT/AKS	Siemens Simos	779
Polo Classic/Estate 1,6	1999-02	AEH/AKL	Siemens Simos 2	781
Polo Classic/Estate 1,7/1,9 SDI	12/97-01	AEY/AKW	Bosch EDC 15V	784
Sharan 1,8 Turbo	1997-00	AGU	Bosch Motronic M3.8.3/5	808
Sharan 1,9 TDI PD	1999-06	ANU/AUY	Bosch EDC 15P/16	823
Sharan 2,0	1995-00	ADY	Siemens Simos	837
Transporter 2,5	1996-98	AET	Siemens Simos	779

VOLVO

Model	Year	Engine code	System	Page
850 2,0 Turbo	1995-97	B5204T/T2/T3	Bosch Motronic 4.3/4.4	860
850 2,3i Turbo	1993-97	B5234T	Bosch Motronic 4.3/4.4	860
850 2,5i/Turbo	1995-97	B5254S/T	Bosch Motronic 4.3/4.4	860
850 R/T-5R	1994-97	B5234T4/T5	Bosch Motronic 4.3/4.4	860
S40/V40 1,6/1,8	2000-04	B4164S2/B4184S2/3	Siemens EMS 2000	842
S40/V40 1,6i/1,8i	1996-00	B4164S/B4184S	Bendix Fenix 5.1	839
S40/V40 1,8 Bi-fuel	2000-02	B4184S9/10	Siemens EMS 2000	842
S40/V40 1,8 GDI	1998-02	B4184SM	Melco 1 (engine control module)	845
S40/V40 1,8 GDI	1998-02	B4184SM	Melco 1 (injector control module)	848
S40/V40 1,9 Turbo	1998-02	B41194T/T2	Siemens EMS 2000	842
S40/V40 2,0i	1996-01	B4204S	Bendix Fenix 5.1	839
S40/V40 2,0/Turbo	1998-04	B4204S2/B4204T/T2	Siemens EMS 2000	842
S40/V40 2,0 Turbo	2000-04	B4204T3/T5	Siemens EMS 2000	849
S60 2,4i	2000-06	B5244S/S2	Denso	852
S60 2,4D D5	2001-06	D5244T/T2	Bosch EDC 15C11	856
S70/V70 2,3i Turbo	1997-01	B5234T/T3/T4/T6/T7/FS	Bosch Motronic 4.3/4.4	860
S70/V70/C70 2,0i Turbo	1997-99	B5204T/T2/T3	Bosch Motronic 4.3/4.4	860
S70/V70/C70 2,3i/2,4i	1999-06	B5234FS/B5244S/S2	Denso	852
S70/V70/C70 2,5i	1999	B5254S	Denso	852
S70/V70/C70 2,5i 20V/Turbo	1997-98	B5254S/T	Bosch Motronic 4.3/4.4	860
S80 2,4i	1998-06	B5244S/S2	Denso	852
S80 2,4D D5	2000-06	D5244T/T2	Bosch EDC 15C11	856
V70 2,4D D5	2001-06	D5244T/T2	Bosch EDC 15C11	856

Abbreviations, terminology and signal symbols

AC	Air conditioning
ac	Alternating current
AAV	Auxiliary air valve
AIR	Air injection
APP	Accelerator pedal position
ARF	Exhaust gas recirculation
ASR	Acceleration skid control
AT	Automatic transmission
AWD	All wheel drive
BARO	Barometric pressure
BPP	Brake pedal position
CAN	Controller area network (data bus)
Cat	Catalytic converter
CDI	Capacitor discharge ignition
CFi	Central fuel injection
CHT	Cylinder head temperature
CKP	Crankshaft position
CO	Carbon monoxide
CO2	Carbon dioxide
CPP	Clutch pedal position
CPU	Central processing unit
CVT	Continuously variable transmission
DOHC	Double overhead camshaft
DVM	Digital volt meter
ECi	Electronically controlled injection
ECM	Engine control module
ECT	Engine coolant temperature (sensor)
EDIS	Electronic distributorless ignition system
EFi	Electronic fuel injection
EFP	Electronic accelerator pedal
EGR	Exhaust gas recirculation
EGRT	Exhaust gas recirculation temperature
EOT	Engine oil temperature
EPROM	Electronically programmable read only memory
EPT	Exhaust pressure transducer
ETS	Electronic throttle system
ETV	Electronic throttle valve
EVAP	Evaporative emission
FWD	Front wheel drive
HEGO	Heated exhaust gas oxygen (sensor)
HFM	Hot film management
HO2S	Heated oxygen sensor
HRW	Heated rear window
HT	High tension
Hz	Hertz – frequency (cycles per second)
I/O	Input-output
IAC	Idle air control
IAT	Intake air temperature
IC	Integrated circuit
ICM	Ignition control module
IFS	Inertia fuel shut-off
ISC	Idle speed control
K	Kilo (ohms)
KAM	Keep alive memory
LED	Light emitting diode
LH	Left-hand
LHD	Left-hand drive
MAF	Mass air flow (sensor)

MAP	Manifold absolute pressure
MFI	Multi-port fuel injection
MIL	Malfunction indicator lamp
MPI	Multi-port injection
ms	Milliseconds
MT	Manual transmission
MY	Model year
N	Neutral position (automatic transmission)
NP	Neutral position
NTC	Negative temperature coefficient
OHC	Overhead camshaft
P	Park position (automatic transmission)
PAIR	Pulsed secondary air injection
PATS	Passive anti-theft system
PC	Personal computer
PCV	Positive crankcase ventilation
PGM-FI	Programmed fuel injection
PMS	Pressure management system
PNP	Park neutral position
PS	Power steering
PSP	Power steering pressure
PTC	Positive temperature coefficient
quattro	All wheel drive
RAM	Random access memory
RH	Right-hand
RHD	Right-hand drive
ROM	Read only memory
RPM	Revolutions per minute
SC	Supercharged
SEFI	Sequential electronic fuel injection
SFI	Sequential fuel injection
SPI	Single point injection
STO	Self test output
TBI	Throttle body injection
TC	Turbocharged
TCCS	Toyota computer control system
TCM	Transmission control module
TP	Throttle position
TPS	Throttle position switch/sensor
TR	Transmission range
V	Volt
VAF	Volume air flow (sensor)
VIS	Variable intake system
VSS	Vehicle speed sensor
VSV	Vacuum switching valve
WOT	Wide open throttle
8V	Eight valve
10V	Ten valve
16V	Sixteen valve
20V	Twenty valve
24V	Twenty four valve
%	Duty cycle – ON time

 input/output signal

 **input signal**

output signal

 ECM switched earth

ECM earth circuit

Autodata

About this manual

General notes

- All pin data in this manual refers to a closed circuit with all components connected.
- Typical values are an approximate guide only and should not be regarded as specific.
- Typical values should be measured with the engine at normal operating temperature, unless otherwise stated.
- All test voltages are measured by connecting the positive meter probe to the engine control module (ECM) pin and the negative probe to earth or a second ECM pin.
- Only ECM pins connected to a circuit are listed in pin data tables. Pins not listed may have a wire connected and even a measurable voltage output, but are not used.
- If available, connect a breakout box between harness multi-plug and ECM.
- Refer to Safety Precautions section of this manual before proceeding with any tests.

Test procedure – without breakout box

- Find the model related chapter from vehicle manufacturer, model name, year of manufacture, engine code and fuel system type.
- If required locate ECM position within vehicle by referring to ECM locations section.
- Turn to appropriate pin data table.
- Ensure ignition switched OFF.
- Connect fine test probes to multi-meter.
- Pull out ECM for easy access to multi-plug(s).
- Access wire side of harness multi-plug(s) by removing cover or dust boot.
- Ensure ECM multi-plug(s) are securely connected.
- Identify location of pin(s) to be tested from multi-plug diagram at beginning of appropriate pin data table.
- Connect test probe between ECM terminal and a good earth or second ECM terminal (shown in brackets), from the wire side of the harness plug.
- CAUTION: Avoid shorting a live connector terminal to earth with the test probe as this could damage the ECM, wiring and sensor.
- Note conditions (e.g. Ignition ON, engine cranking, 3000 rpm etc.).
- Measure signals at selected pins and compare results with data provided.
- If the test involves a wave form pattern, refer to the Oscilloscope testing section of this manual.
- If any test reading is incorrect, reference should be made to wiring diagrams and component test procedures as published in our Fuel Injection, Electronic Ignition and Engine Management manuals which are also available on CD.
- Verify any repairs by rechecking pin data.

Test procedure – with breakout box

- Find the model related chapter from vehicle manufacturer, model name, year of manufacture, engine code and fuel system type.
- If required locate ECM position within vehicle by referring to ECM locations section.
- Turn to appropriate pin data table.
- Ensure ignition switched OFF.
- If required, pull out ECM for easy access to multi-plug(s).
- Disconnect ECM harness multi-plug(s).
- Connect T-harness between ECM, breakout box and vehicle harness.
- Fit appropriate overlay card to breakout box (refer to equipment manufacturer's instructions).
- Connect suitable test probes to multi-meter.
- Ensure ECM and breakout box multi-plugs are securely connected.
- Connect test probe between breakout box terminal and a good earth or second breakout box terminal.
- CAUTION: Avoid shorting a live breakout box terminal to earth with the test probe as this could damage the ECM, wiring and sensor.
- Note conditions (e.g. Ignition ON, engine cranking, 3000 rpm etc.).
- Measure signals at selected pins and compare results with data provided.
- If the test involves a wave form pattern, refer to the Oscilloscope testing section of this manual.
- If any test reading is incorrect, reference should be made to wiring diagrams and component test procedures as published in our Fuel Injection, Electronic Ignition and Engine Management manuals which are also available on CD.
- Verify any repairs by rechecking pin data.

About this manual

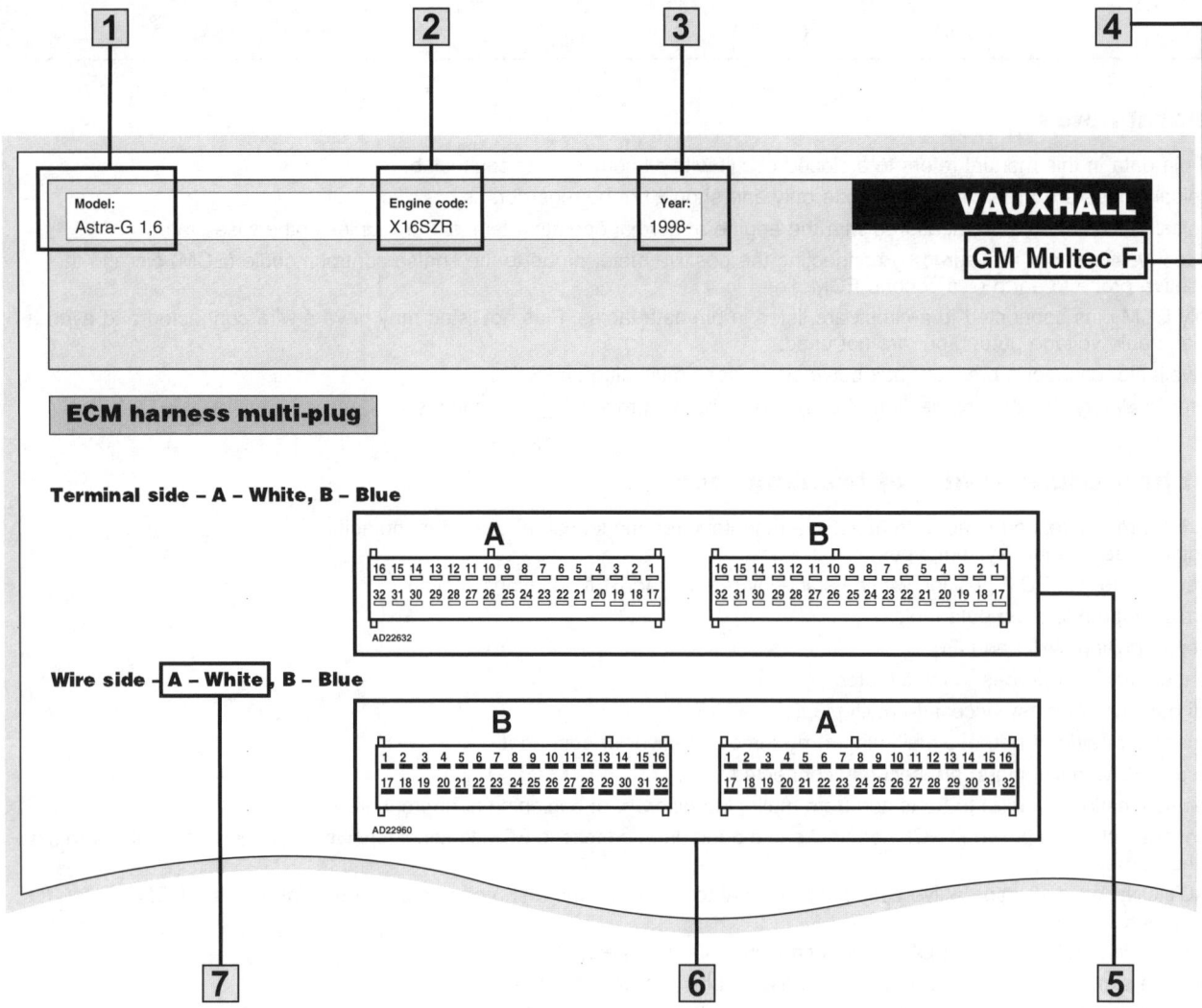

ECM harness multi-plug

Terminal side – A – White, B – Blue

Wire side – A – White, B – Blue

[1] Model range and engine capacity

[2] Engine code

[3] Year range

[4] Fuel injection/engine management system identification

[5] Schematic diagram of ECM harness multi-plug pin locations – viewed from terminal side

[6] Schematic diagram of ECM harness multi-plug pin locations – viewed from wire side

[7] ECM harness multi-plug colour – assists correct harness multi-plug identification

[8] Component/circuit description

[9] ECM pin number

[10] Additional ECM pin number – used instead of earth for some tests

[11] Signal input – battery voltage supply or signal voltage from sensor

[12] Signal output – signal or reference voltage sent to component

[13] Switched earth – transistor controlled earth within ECM

[14] Permanent earth – external earth connection to vehicle ground

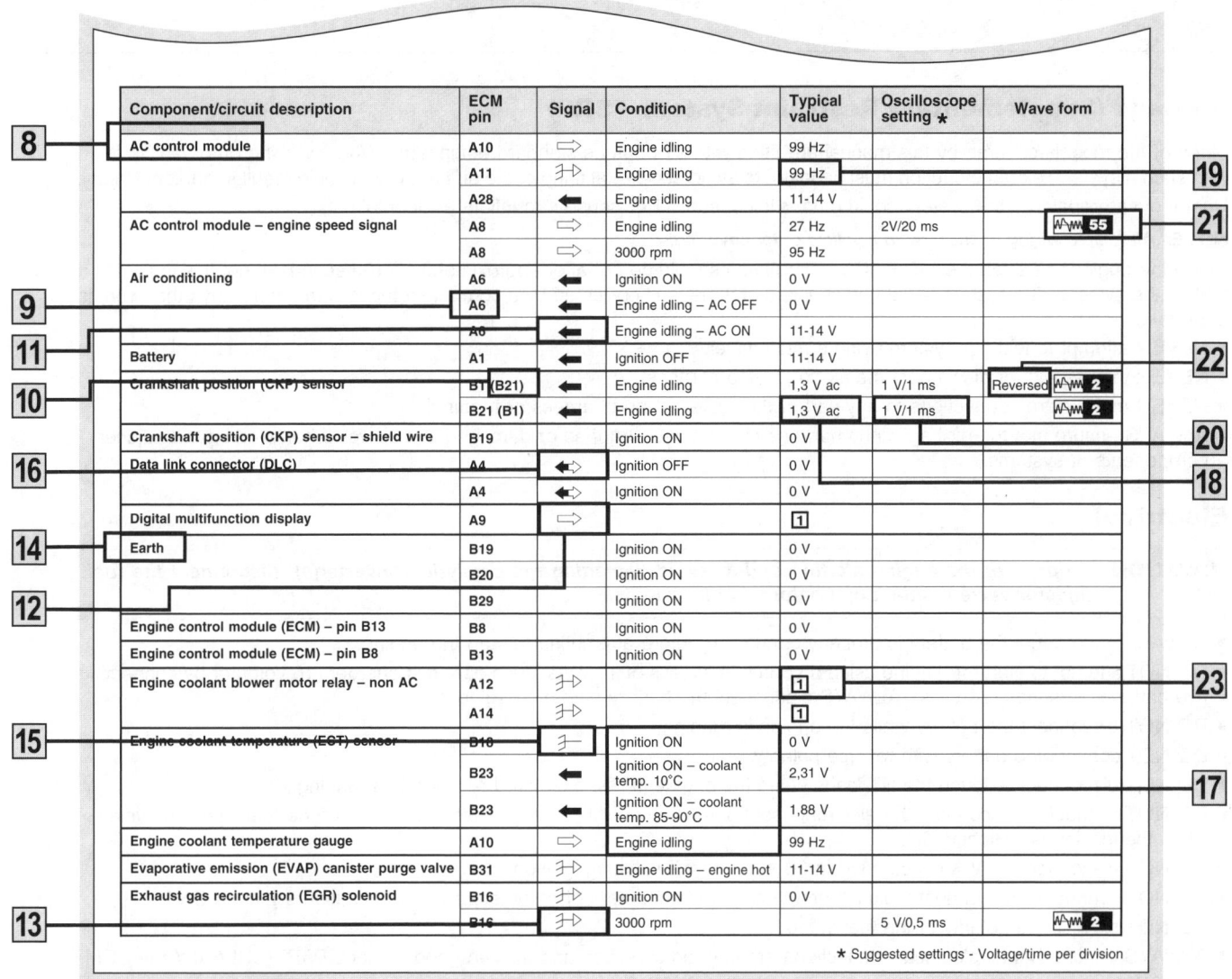

Component/circuit description	ECM pin	Signal	Condition	Typical value	Oscilloscope setting ★	Wave form
AC control module	A10	⇒	Engine idling	99 Hz		
	A11	⇥	Engine idling	99 Hz		
	A28	⇐	Engine idling	11-14 V		
AC control module – engine speed signal	A8	⇒	Engine idling	27 Hz	2V/20 ms	ᴡᴡ 55
	A8	⇒	3000 rpm	95 Hz		
Air conditioning	A6	⇐	Ignition ON	0 V		
	A6	⇐	Engine idling – AC OFF	0 V		
	A6	⇐	Engine idling – AC ON	11-14 V		
Battery	A1	⇐	Ignition OFF	11-14 V		
Crankshaft position (CKP) sensor	B1 (B21)	⇐	Engine idling	1,3 V ac	1 V/1 ms	Reversed ᴡᴡ 2
	B21 (B1)	⇐	Engine idling	1,3 V ac	1 V/1 ms	ᴡᴡ 2
Crankshaft position (CKP) sensor – shield wire	B19		Ignition ON	0 V		
Data link connector (DLC)	A4	⇔	Ignition OFF	0 V		
	A4	⇔	Ignition ON	0 V		
Digital multifunction display	A9	⇒		1		
Earth	B19		Ignition ON	0 V		
	B20		Ignition ON	0 V		
	B29		Ignition ON	0 V		
Engine control module (ECM) – pin B13	B8		Ignition ON	0 V		
Engine control module (ECM) – pin B8	B13		Ignition ON	0 V		
Engine coolant blower motor relay – non AC	A12	⇥		1		
	A14	⇥		1		
Engine coolant temperature (ECT) sensor	B18	⇤	Ignition ON	0 V		
	B23	⇐	Ignition ON – coolant temp. 10°C	2,31 V		
	B23	⇐	Ignition ON – coolant temp. 85-90°C	1,88 V		
Engine coolant temperature gauge	A10	⇒	Engine idling	99 Hz		
Evaporative emission (EVAP) canister purge valve	B31	⇥	Engine idling – engine hot	11-14 V		
Exhaust gas recirculation (EGR) solenoid	B16	⇥	Ignition ON	0 V		
	B16	⇥	3000 rpm		5 V/0,5 ms	ᴡᴡ 2

★ Suggested settings - Voltage/time per division

[15] Permanent (sensor) earth – internal earth connection through ECM

[16] Two-way signal – input/output communication between ECM and component or diagnostic equipment

[17] Operating conditions relevant to each typical value

[18] Typical value obtained – ac voltages shown use the root mean square (RMS) system as obtained from a voltmeter

[19] Signal frequency – Hertz (Hz)

[20] Suggested oscilloscope settings for voltage and time per division to obtain the typical wave form

[21] Oscilloscope wave form

[22] 'Reversed' or 'Intermittent' – some components which display analogue ac waveforms e.g. inductive type crankshaft position (CKP) sensors are shown with a reversed image under some test conditions. Certain components are controlled by an intermittent signal e.g. idle speed control (IAC) actuators

[23] Connected pin without test data or a random digital signal which is of limited diagnostic value

Safety precautions

Air bags (Supplementary Restraint System – SRS)

Many of the models covered by this manual are fitted with air bags as standard equipment. When working on a vehicle fitted with such a system, extreme caution must be taken to avoid accidental firing of the air bag, which could result in personal injury. Unauthorised repairs to the system could render it inoperative, or cause it to inflate accidentally.

NOTE: *All related wiring is encased in a yellow outer covering.*

When the engine is started the AIR BAG warning lamp should go out after approximately 5-10 seconds, if not this indicates a fault in the system. The system should be checked and the fault corrected by a competent technician before any other work is undertaken.

- NEVER attempt to test the system using a multi-meter.
- NEVER tamper with or disconnect the air bag wiring harness.
- NEVER make extra connections to any part of the system wiring harness or terminals.
- ALWAYS ensure that the air bag wiring harness has not been trapped or damaged in any way when working on adjacent components or systems.

Electrical

> **CAUTION:** *To prevent the engine starting and to avoid damaging the catalytic converter(s), disconnect the fuel injector valve multi-plug(s) before cranking tests.*

- ALWAYS ensure that the battery is properly connected before attempting to start the engine.
- DO NOT attempt to start the engine using a source in excess of 12 volts, such as a fast charger (16 volts) or by connecting two batteries in series (24 volts). ALWAYS disconnect the battery before charging it.
- DO NOT disconnect the battery while the engine is running.
- DO NOT connect the battery with reverse polarity.
- DO NOT disconnect or touch the HT leads when the engine is being cranked or when it is running.
- DO NOT connect or disconnect the electronic control module (ECM), or any other component of the fuel injection system while the ignition is switched ON.
- DO NOT disconnect ECM Multi-plug within 30 seconds of switching ignition OFF.
- DO NOT connect or disconnect multi-meters, voltmeters, ammeters or ohmmeters with the ignition switched ON.
- DO NOT reverse the polarity of the fuel pump.
- ALWAYS ensure that all electrical connections are in good condition and making good contact, PARTICULARLY the ECM connector.
- ALWAYS disconnect the ignition coil, ECM, fuel pump relay/fuse before carrying out a compression test.
- DO NOT flash a wire or circuit to ground to check that continuity exists.
- Modern ignition systems operate at very high voltages and these high voltages can severely damage transistorised components such as a wrist-watch if electrical contact is made. Wearers of heart pacemaker devices, therefore, should not at any time carry out work involving ignition systems. In addition to the danger from electric shock, further hazards can arise through sudden uncontrolled body movement causing involuntary contact with moving parts of the engine, i.e. fan blades, pulleys and drive belts.
- ALWAYS ensure that any replacement fuel or ignition system parts are correct for the application in question. Many units share common external features, but differ internally.

Mechanical

> **CAUTION:** *To minimise fire risk, fuel system must be depressurised before disconnecting any fuel lines or fuel system components. DO NOT connect pressure testing equipment to the fuel rail or other high pressure fuel system components of a common rail diesel injection system.*

- ALWAYS disconnect the distributor before carrying out a fuel pump pressure or delivery check.
- DO NOT attempt to slacken any high pressure fuel pipe connections with the ignition on or the engine running.
- AVOID the risk of fire – ALWAYS disconnect the ignition coil supply and earth the coil HT lead, so that NO HT spark can be emitted, before checking the fuel injector valves, or any other component of the fuel injection system likely to result in the presence of fuel in or around the engine bay.
- AVOID the risk of fire – NEVER work on the fuel injection system when SMOKING or close to a NAKED FLAME.
- ALWAYS keep a fire extinguisher close at hand when working on the fuel injection system.
- ALWAYS ensure that test equipment, leads, tools and especially items of clothing, are clear of moving parts and are not liable to fall into the engine bay, due to vibration, when the engine is running.
- ALWAYS ensure that any replacement fuel system parts are correct for the application in question. Many units share common external features, but differ internally.

Tools & equipment

General recommendations

- Electronic control modules such as the engine control module (ECM) need special care during engine management system fault diagnosis. They are easily damaged by excess voltage or reversed polarity. Whenever possible disconnect them before testing wiring continuity.
- Some ECMs have an adaptive memory which may have to be re-learned (during driving) if the power supply is interrupted, for instance to erase fault codes.
- Electrical wiring can be repaired where practicable but ensure that all repairs are properly insulated, preferably with heat shrink tubing and protected by a fuse of the correct amperage.

NOTE: *Many other electronic control modules fitted to the vehicle could have fault memories which may be erased if the power supply is interrupted.*

- Check condition of ALL fuses in the system prior to circuit testing.

Test equipment

Multi-meter types

- The majority of electrical tests described in this manual require the use of a digital multi-meter.
  Many suitable instruments are available, with a wide range of prices and specifications, as described below.
- Certain other tools, such as a breakout box, digital oscilloscope (see separate section), vacuum pump, and memory saver will be necessary, or desirable to make best use of this manual.
- A high impedance (10 K ohms/volt minimum) multi-meter that includes a 0-20 V voltage scale and a low (0-200) and high (0-20 K) range ohm scale is recommended for measuring the voltage and resistance of the system components.
- Analogue meters (with a needle sweeping across a numerical scale), due to their continuous readout are useful for certain applications, such as counting needle deflections to identify fault codes on certain models and the identification of intermittent faults, but for general workshop use a digital meter is easier to use and is more resistant to rough handling and less likely to be damaged by incorrect use.
- Digital meters (with an LED or LCD display), are available in many different types. In addition to the basic, general purpose meters with voltage, resistance and amperage scales additional features such as temperature, duty cycle and engine RPM etc. are often incorporated in dedicated test meters for automobile applications.

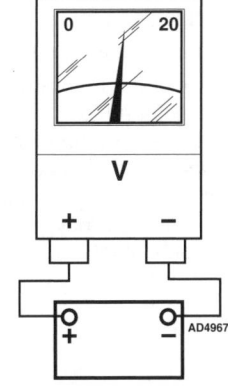

Fig. 1

Checking voltage with multi-meter

Using multi-meters

Voltage checking – Fig. 1, Fig. 2, Fig. 3 & Fig. 4

- Set the meter to VOLTAGE.
- If applicable, set the meter to the correct scale e.g. ac/DC, V/mV etc. (most modern meters are self-ranging).
- Connect the black test lead to a good earth or the negative battery terminal.
- Observe the conditions of the test, e.g. ignition OFF, ignition ON etc.
- Connect the red test lead to the positive terminal being tested.
- If the meter does not automatically select the appropriate voltage range, ensure correct meter scale selected, e.g. 0-12 volts.
- Read and record the value displayed.
  - □ Measurement of voltage drop through cables and components can be a useful diagnostic tool, as any abnormal condition will have an effect on the operation of the circuit(s) and components involved.
  - □ The multi-meter should be set to measure milli-volts and the circuit should be in its normal operating mode e.g. all multi-plugs connected and current flowing.
  - □ Maximum voltage drop should not exceed the following values:
    - Control module harness wire – 200 mV
    - Switch – 300 mV
    - Earth connection – 100 mV
    - Sensor connection – 50 mV

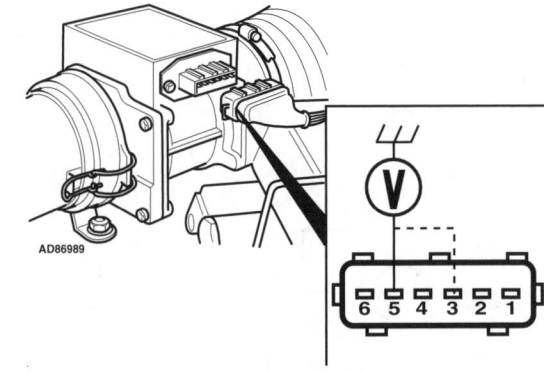

Fig. 2

Checking supply voltage – harness multi-plug disconnected

Fig. 3

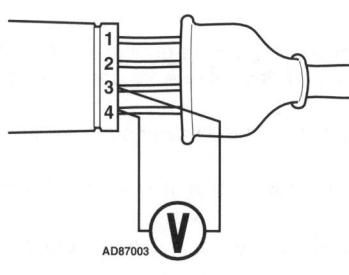

Checking signal voltage between wires – harness
multi-plug connected

Fig. 4

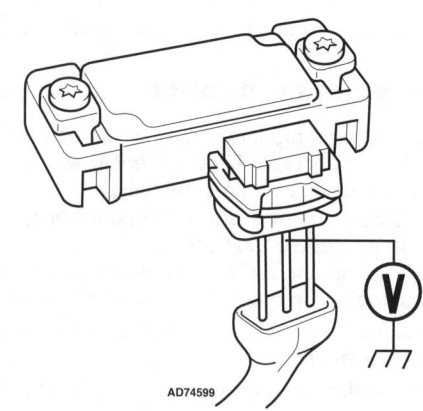

Checking signal voltage between wire and earth –
component multi-plug connected

Resistance and continuity checking – Fig. 5 , Fig. 6 , Fig. 7 & Fig. 8

- ☐ High resistance in earth connections can cause unusual (and apparently illogical) symptoms that are seemingly unconnected with the components involved.
- ☐ Earth connections should be thoroughly cleaned and treated with a proprietary contact cleaner before assembly.
- ☐ Connections in the vicinity of the battery are particularly vulnerable to corrosion.
- ☐ Earth wires should be checked along their whole length for chafing, corrosion and mechanical damage. A typical earth wire may have 20-30 strands and although there will still be a connection if only a few of these are intact, the resulting high resistance will cause problems.
- ☐ Suspect multi-plugs should be 'dismantled' (if possible) and the terminals thoroughly inspected and cleaned.
- Set the meter to RESISTANCE.
- If applicable, set the meter to the correct scale (most modern meters are self-ranging).
- Connect the black test lead to the red test lead and check that the meter displays ZERO Ω.

NOTE: *If ZERO Ω is not displayed, refer to the meter operating instructions.*

- Disconnect the component from any wiring.
- Connect the black test lead to one terminal being tested.
- Connect the red test lead to the other terminal being tested.
- Read and record the value displayed.
- If the meter displays ZERO, **Fig. 5** this indicates continuity.
- If the meter displays INF (infinity) **Fig. 6** , this indicates NO continuity (open circuit).

Fig. 7

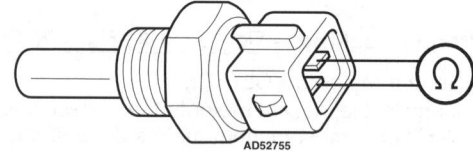

Checking component resistance

Fig. 5

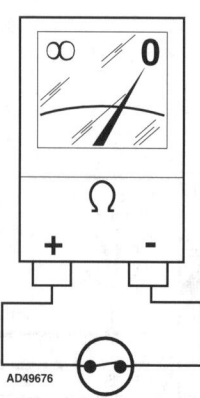

Circuit continuity

Fig. 6

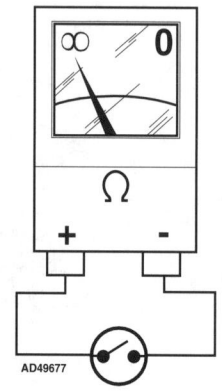

Open circuit

Fig. 8

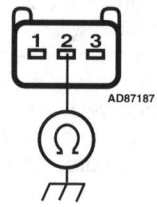

Checking earth connection at harness
multi-plug

Diode checking – Fig. 9 & Fig. 10

- Set the meter to RESISTANCE or DIODE.
- Connect the red test lead to positive terminal of the diode.
- Connect the black test lead to the negative terminal of the diode.
- The meter should display continuity **Fig. 9**.
- Reverse the test leads, the meter should display NO continuity **Fig. 10**.

NOTE: *If the meter displays continuity in both tests the diode is faulty.*

Fig. 9

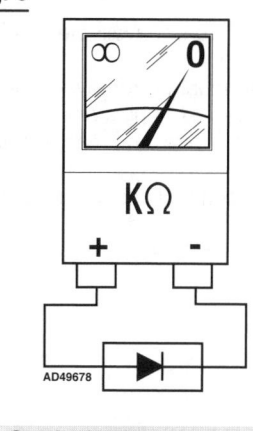

Fig. 10

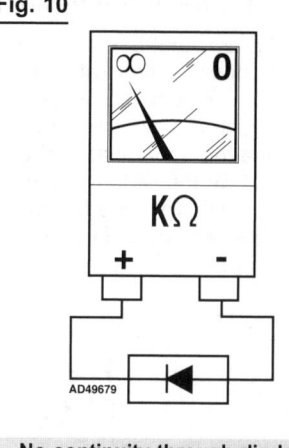

Continuity through diode   **No continuity through diode**

Signal checking with LED tester – Fig. 11

CAUTION: *Circuit testers incorporating a bulb should not be used on electronic circuits as the high current involved could damage sensitive components.*

- LED testers can be used safely on electronic circuits as their low current consumption cannot damage electronic components.
- They are particularly useful where a pulse or intermittent signal is being checked.
- Most LED testers are in the form of a probe attached to the tester body, with a test lead and clip for the other terminal. The more sophisticated testers have different coloured LEDs to indicate polarity.

Breakout box – Fig. 12

- Whenever possible a breakout box should be used for circuit testing at the control module multi-plug and when checking pin data.
- A breakout box [1] is a means of connecting test equipment to the control module harness without the need to probe into the back of the harness multi-plug. For checking pin data it is connected by an adaptor lead [2] between the ECM [3] and the car's wiring harness [4].
- For circuit testing the harness multi-plug is disconnected from the control module and connected to the breakout box.
- The pin connections are laid out in rows in numerical order and have large connecting sockets, enabling test leads to be securely plugged into a circuit, and avoiding the possibility of connecting to the incorrect pin, due to miscounting.
- The possibility of damaging components or wiring, due to shorting live pins to ground or to other components, is also much reduced.
- The limiting factor is the range of adaptor leads. Several equipment manufacturers produce breakout boxes, but none are able to supply a complete range of leads to cover all the models included in this manual.

Fig. 11

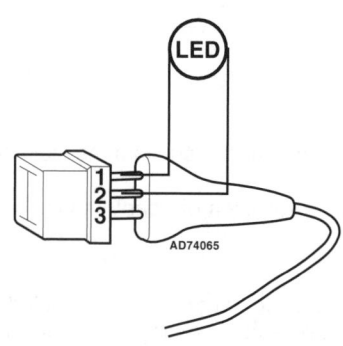

Checking sensor signal with LED tester – multi-plug connected

Fig. 12

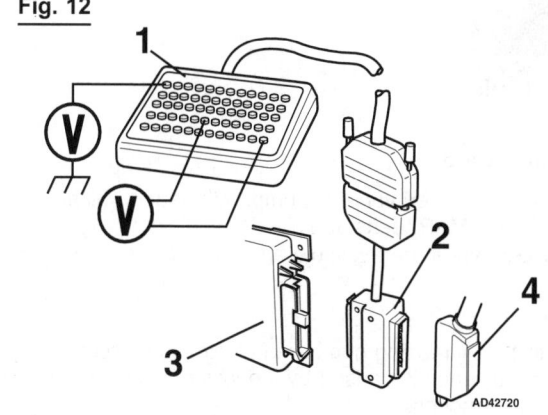

Breakout box connections

Tools & equipment

ECM harness multi-plug testing – Fig. 13 , Fig. 14 & Fig. 15.

- If a breakout box and suitable adaptor leads are not available, testing must be carried out at the wire side of the ECM harness multi-plug **Fig. 13**.
- To access the terminals the protective cover must be removed from the plug. Many different types of plug are used for engine management wiring harnesses and two examples are shown in **Fig. 14** and **Fig. 15**.
- Use the appropriate ECM harness multi-plug – wire side diagram and identify the pin(s) to be tested – refer to Autodata CD2 or Pin Data manual.
- Use only very fine test probes to access the connections and measure the signal between the pin and earth **Fig. 13** [1], or between two ECM pins **Fig. 13** [2].

Fig. 13

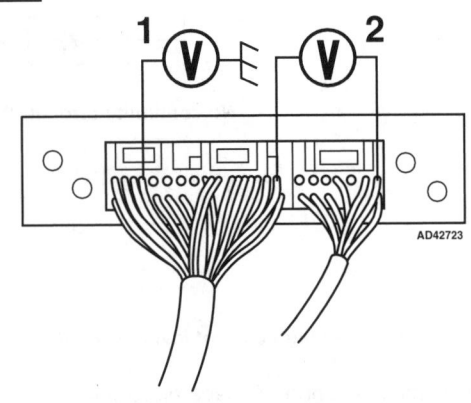

Testing at wire side of harness multi-plug

Fig. 14

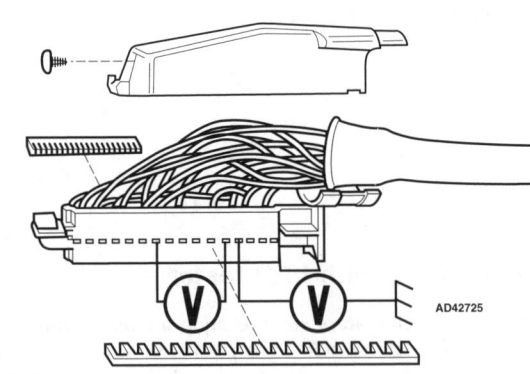

Testing at harness multi-plug

Fig. 15

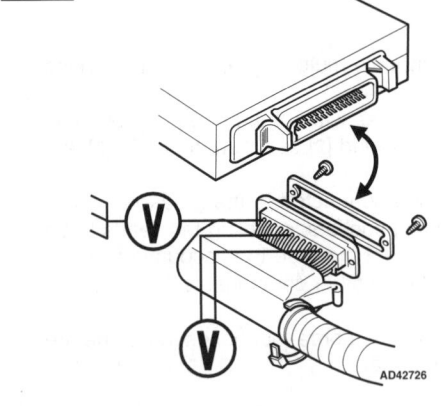

Testing at harness multi-plug

Fig. 16

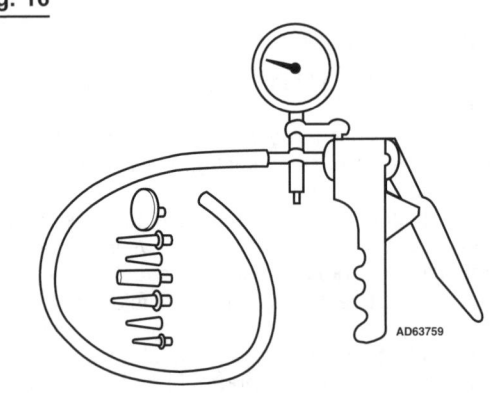

Typical vacuum pump

Other tools

Vacuum pump

- A hand operated vacuum pump, with gauge, will be necessary for testing certain components, such as manifold absolute pressure (MAP) sensors.
- Several types are available and are usually supplied with a connecting hose and a selection of adaptors **Fig. 16**.

Memory savers

- With the increasing number of electronic devices incorporating a memory, whenever the battery is disconnected inconvenience is caused by the loss of such information as radio security codes and station settings, clock settings and ECM memories.
- This situation can be avoided by the use of an alternative power source such as the memory savers marketed by several of the leading test equipment manufacturers.

Oscilloscope testing

Oscilloscopes

- Digital multi-meters are entirely satisfactory for checking circuits in a static condition and for instances where any change in reading is a gradual one, but for dynamic checking and the diagnosis of intermittent faults, the oscilloscope is a very powerful workshop tool.
- Unlike older analogue oscilloscopes dedicated to HT ignition testing, a modern digital oscilloscope has a variable voltage scale, enabling low voltages (typically 0-5 V or 0-12 V) to be displayed and also an adjustable time scale, enabling any wave form to be displayed in the ideal manner.
- Most oscilloscopes designed for automotive use can be hand-held and are therefore ideal for use in the workshop. They can also be used inside the car, while the vehicle is driven, to capture dynamic data.
- Usually it is possible to store wave forms and associated data in an internal memory and then print out or download the information onto a PC, enabling the scope patterns to be studied in detail.
- The oscilloscope display can show the amplitude, frequency, pulse width, shape and pattern of the signal received, by effectively drawing a graph of voltage (vertically) and time (horizontally).
- It is easy to connect (normally just two leads) and the speed of sampling can be far in excess of even the best of digital multi-meters.
- This fast response time enables diagnosis of intermittent problems and also enables the effect of disturbing parts of the system to be observed. When necessary, the response time can be slow enough to display signals such as the throttle position sensor.
- Once the cause of a problem has been diagnosed and rectified, the repair can be verified by retesting with the oscilloscope.
- The oscilloscope can also be used to check the overall condition of an engine management system equipped with a catalytic converter, by monitoring the activity of the oxygen sensor.
- The complex electronic engine management systems fitted to catalyst equipped vehicles are designed to maintain the mixture level between quite close tolerances so that the oxygen sensor is able react to small changes in the exhaust oxygen level and feed this information back to the ECM in the form of a voltage signal. By watching the oxygen sensor signal with an oscilloscope any irregularity in the overall system performance can be detected. If the wave form displayed is satisfactory this is a reliable indication that the whole system is operating correctly.
- Currently available oscilloscopes are easy to connect and use, enabling a trace to be displayed on the screen without any specialist knowledge or experience. The interpretation of this trace can be greatly assisted by reference to the typical wave forms illustrated in this chapter.

Wave forms – Fig. 1

- Each oscilloscope wave form has one or more of the following parameters:
- Amplitude – voltage (V)
  □ The signal voltage at a certain moment in time
- Frequency – cycles per second (Hz)
  □ The time between points of the signal
- Pulse width – duty cycle (%)
  □ The period during which the signal is ON – expressed as a percentage (%) of the total
- Shape – spike, curve, saw-tooth etc.
  □ The overall 'picture' of the signal
- Pattern – repeated shapes
  □ The pattern of repetition of the overall shape of the signal
- The oscilloscope will show all these parameters in one display and by comparing the scope traces from the vehicle under test with those illustrated, a judgement can be made about the condition of each circuit and its components.
- The scope trace for a faulty circuit or component will usually appear very different to that for a satisfactory one, thus simplifying fault identification.
- The five parameters listed above can be categorised as follows:

Fig. 1

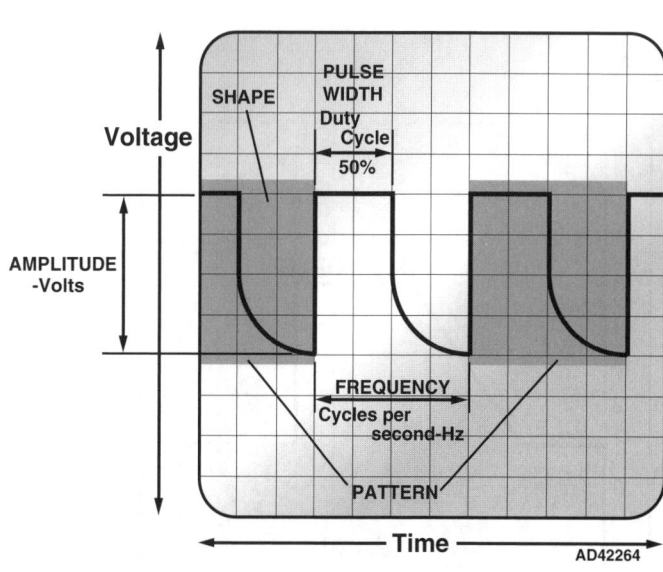

Wave form parameters

Direct current (DC) voltage signals – amplitude only

- Analogue signal voltages from components such as:

Fig. 2

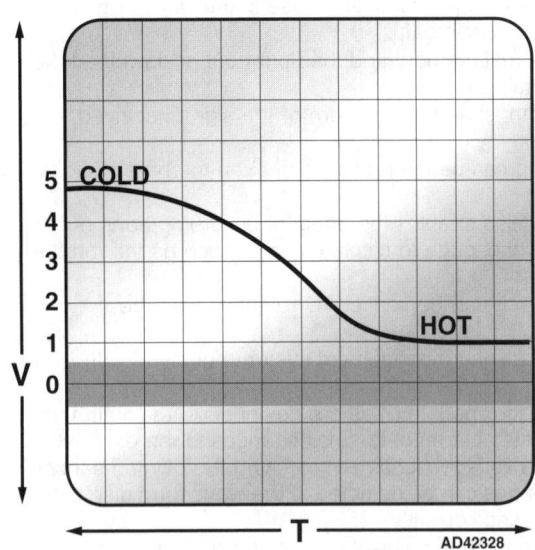

Engine coolant temperature (ECT) sensor

Fig. 3

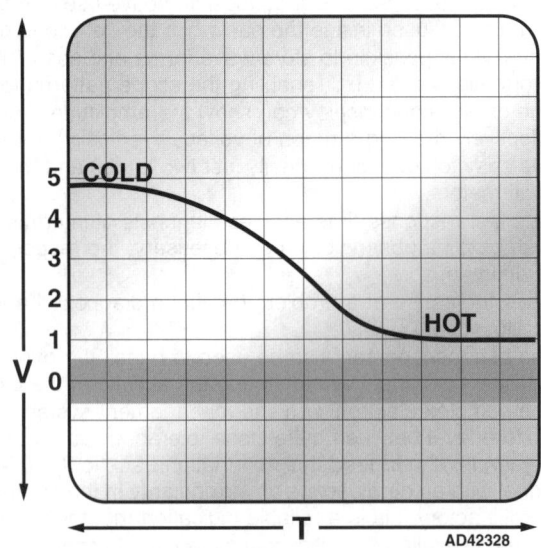

Intake air temperature (IAT) sensor

Fig. 4

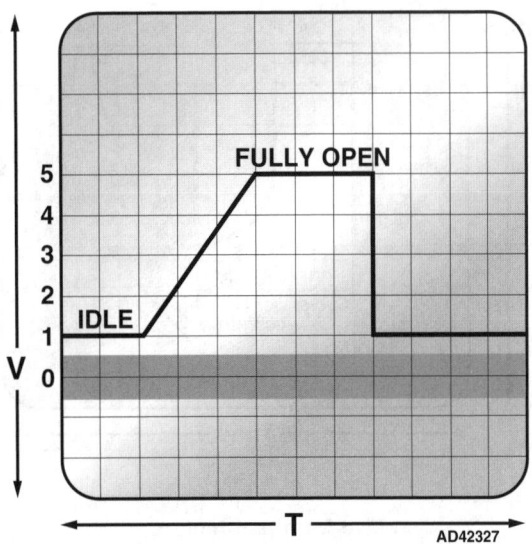

Throttle position (TP) sensor

Fig. 5

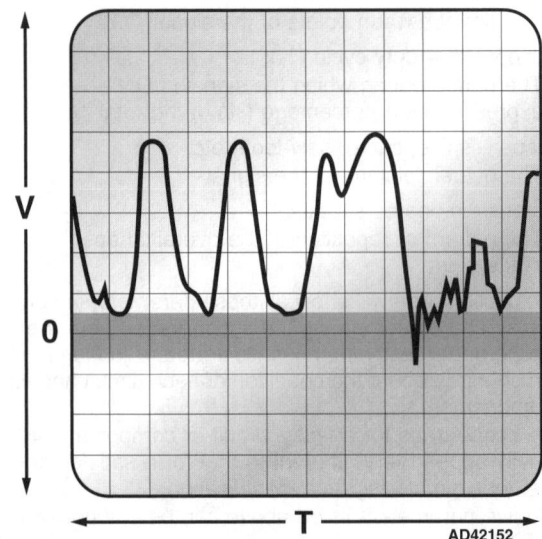

Heated oxygen sensor (HO2S)

Fig. 6

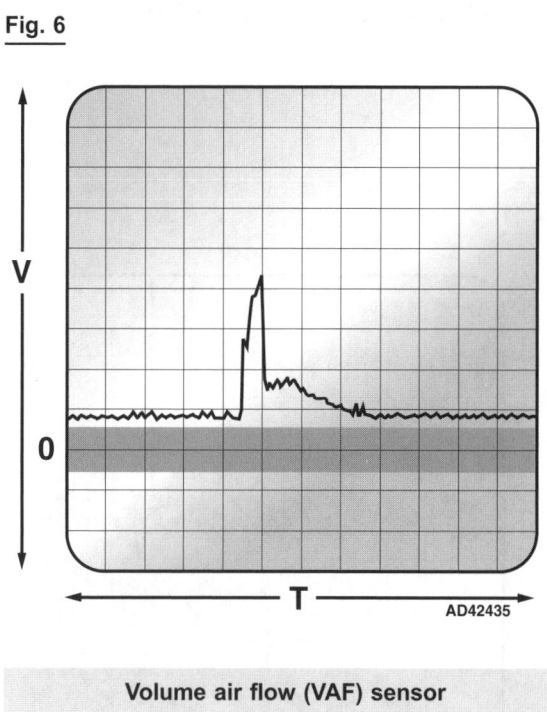

Volume air flow (VAF) sensor

Fig. 7

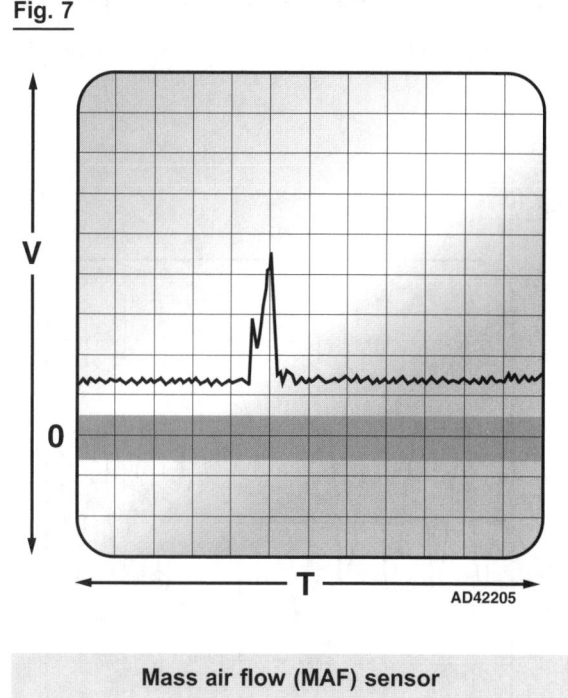

Mass air flow (MAF) sensor

Alternating current (ac) voltage signals – amplitude, frequency and shape

- ac voltage signals are generated by components such as:

Fig. 8

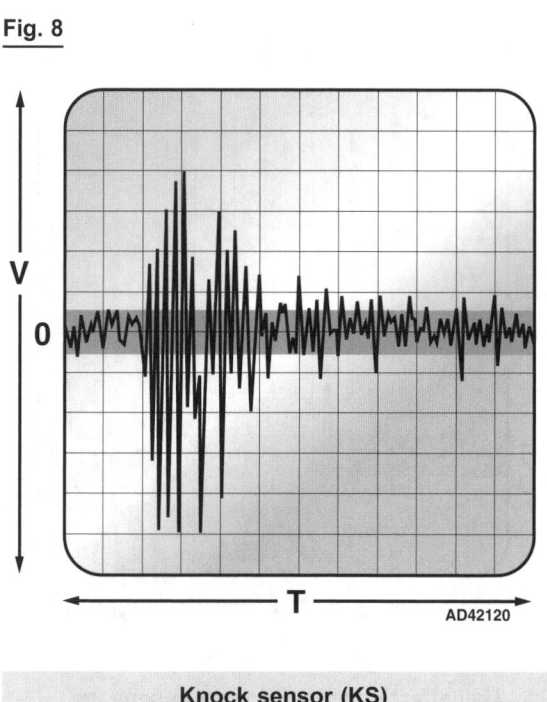

Knock sensor (KS)

Fig. 9

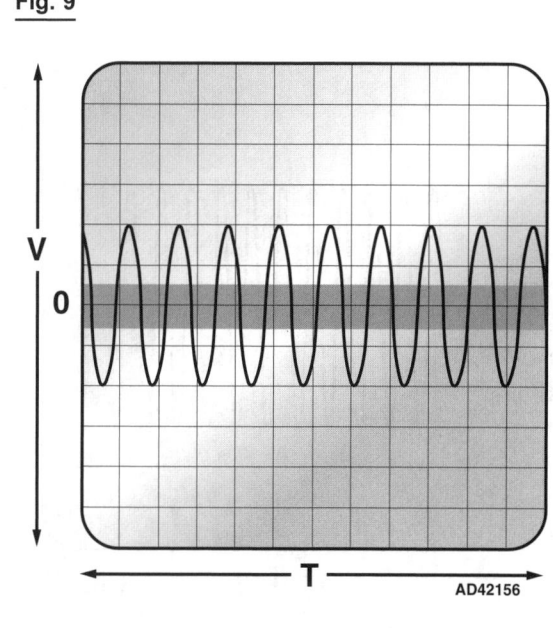

Engine speed (RPM) sensor – inductive type

Oscilloscope testing

Frequency modulated signals – amplitude, frequency, shape and pulse width

- Frequency modulated signals are generated by components such as:

Fig. 10

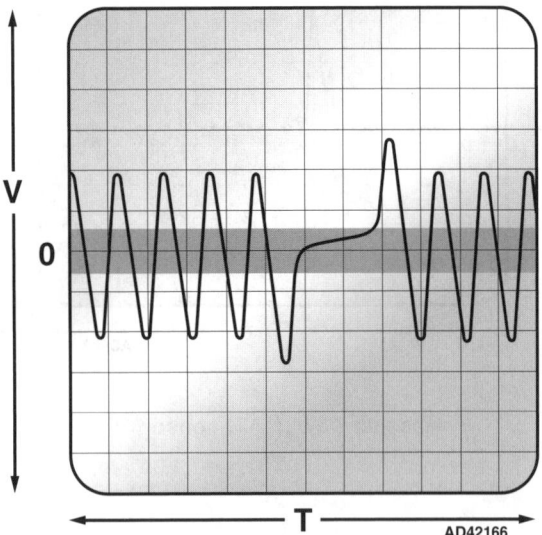

Crankshaft position (CKP) sensor – inductive type

Fig. 11

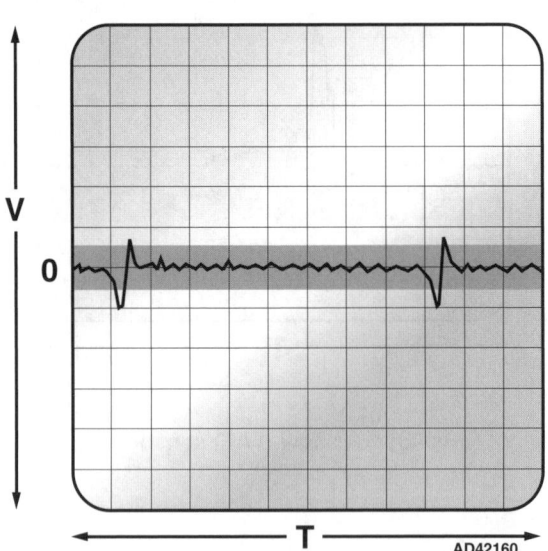

Camshaft position (CMP) sensor – inductive type

Fig. 12

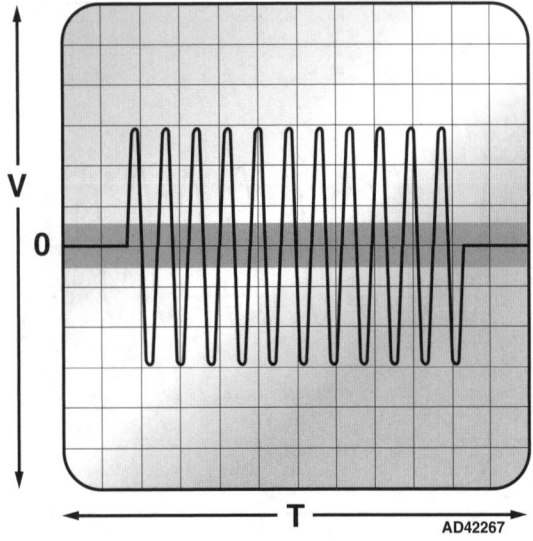

Vehicle speed (VSS) sensor – inductive type

Fig. 13

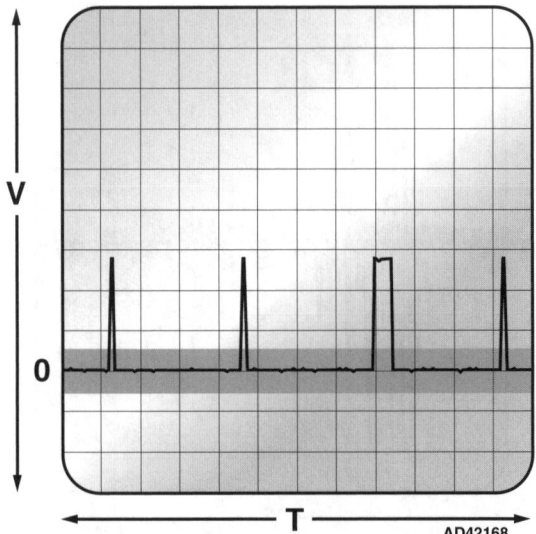

Hall effect speed and position sensors

Fig. 14

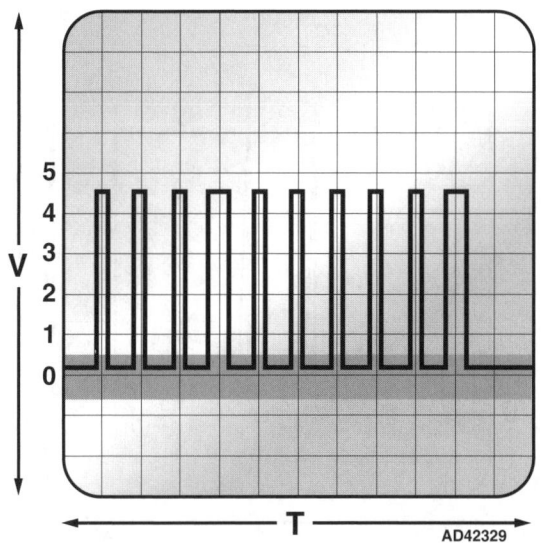

Optical speed and position sensors

Fig. 15

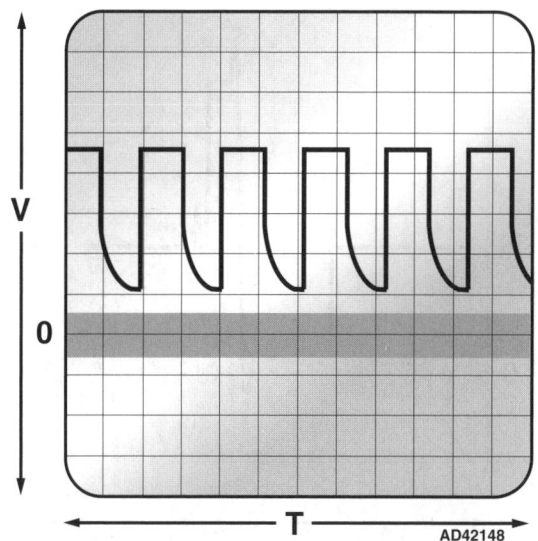

Mass air flow (MAF) and manifold absolute
pressure (MAP) sensors – digital type

Pulse width modulated signals – amplitude, frequency, shape, pulse width

● Pulse width modulated signals from components such as:

Fig. 16

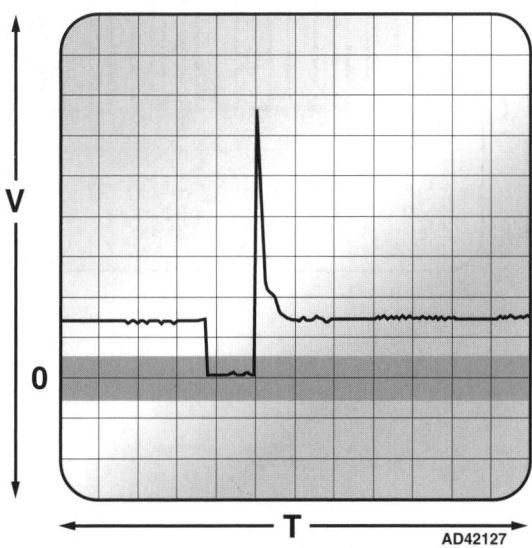

Injectors

Fig. 17

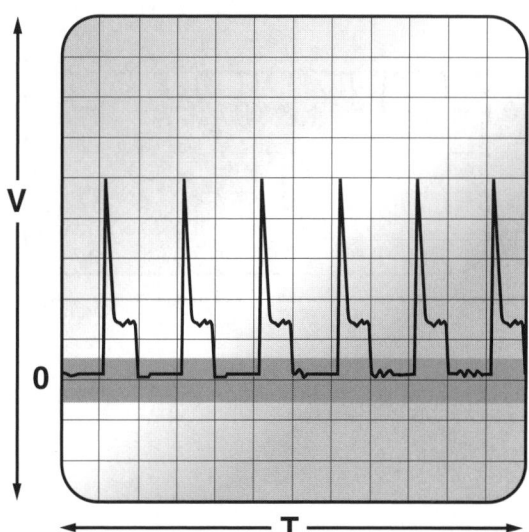

Idle air control (IAC) devices

Fig. 18

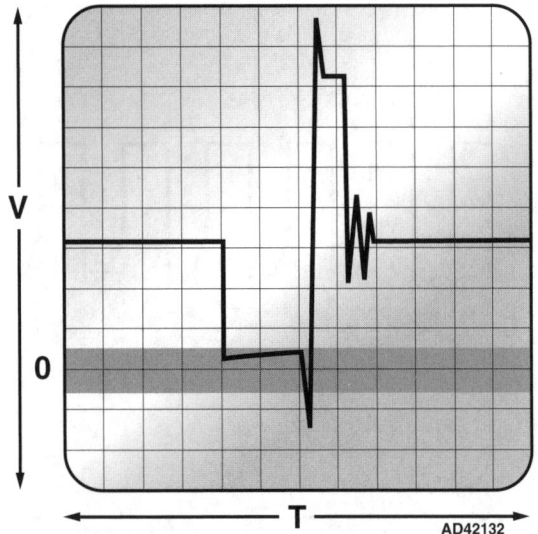

AD42132

Ignition coil primary circuits

Fig. 19

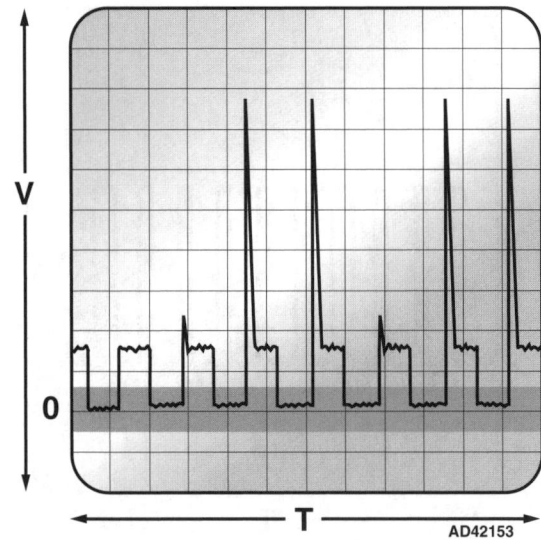

AD42153

Evaporative emission (EVAP) canister purge valve

Fig. 20

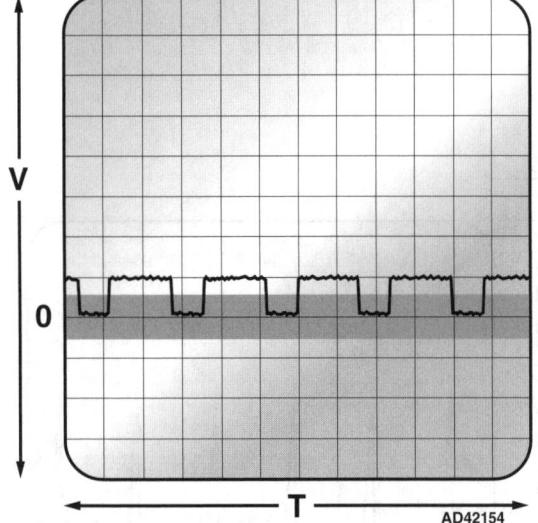

AD42154

Exhaust gas recirculation (EGR) valves

Fig. 21

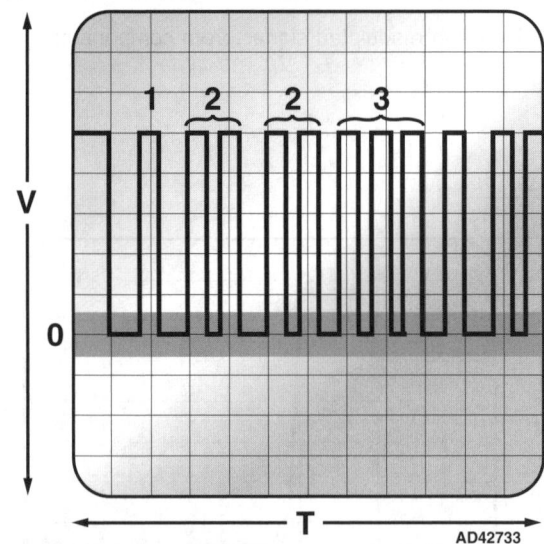

AD42733

Trouble code wave form

Serial data – amplitude, frequency, shape, pulse width and pattern

- Serial data signals will be generated by the engine control module (ECM), if it has a self-diagnosis facility – **Fig. 21**.
- By noting the pulse width, pattern and frequency, the short pulses can be counted in groups and interpreted as a trouble code, in this case 1223.
- The amplitude and shape remain constant and the pattern will be repeated until the trouble code has been erased.

Interpreting wave forms

Typical wave forms – Fig. 22 & Fig. 23

- Oscilloscope wave form patterns can vary greatly and are dependent on many factors. Therefore prior to making a diagnosis or changing components the following points should be considered when the wave form obtained does not appear to be correct when compared with the 'typical' wave form.

Fig. 22

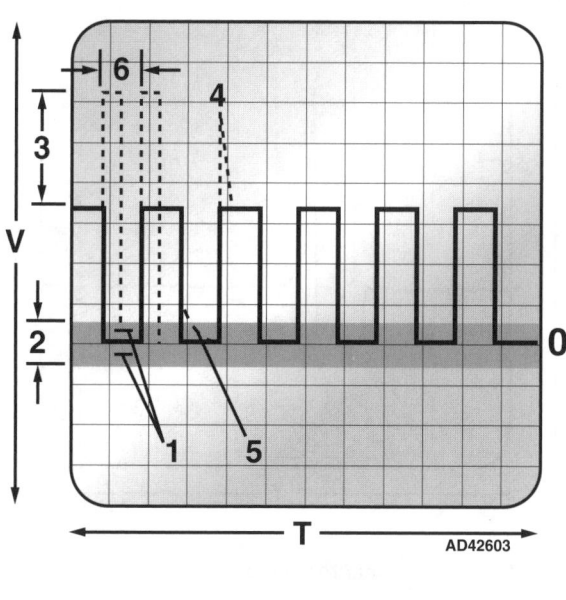

Digital wave form

Fig. 23

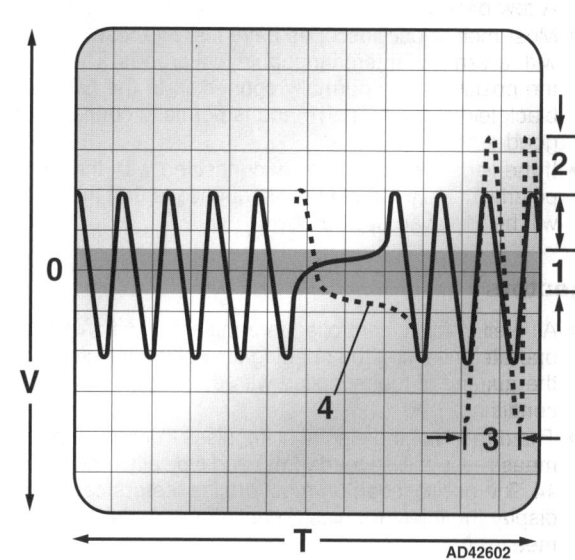

Analogue wave form

Voltage

- Typical wave forms indicate the approximate position of the wave form in relationship to the 'zero grid', but this may vary **Fig. 22** [1], dependent on the system being tested and may be positioned anywhere within the approximate 'zero range' **Fig. 22** [2] & **Fig. 23** [1].
- The amplitude or overall height of the pattern (the voltage) **Fig. 22** [3] & **Fig. 23** [2], will depend on the circuit's operating voltage.
- For direct current (DC) circuits this will depend on the voltage being switched, for example, idle speed control device voltage will be constant and will not vary with engine speed.
- For alternating current (ac) circuits this will depend on the speed of the signal generator, for example, an inductive crankshaft position (CKP) sensor's output voltage will increase with engine speed.
- Therefore if the oscilloscope pattern is too high (or the upper part is missing) increase the voltage scale to obtain the view required. If the pattern is too low decrease the voltage scale.
- Some circuits operating solenoid components, for example idle speed control devices, may display voltage spikes **Fig. 22** [4], when the circuit is switched off. This voltage is generated by the component and can normally be ignored.
- Some circuits that have a square wave type of typical wave form may display the voltage decaying at the end of the switching period **Fig. 22** [5]. This is a characteristic of some systems and can normally be ignored, as it does not by itself indicate a fault.

Frequency

- The overall width of the pattern (the frequency), will depend on the circuit's operating speed.
- The typical wave forms illustrated show the wave form viewed with the oscilloscope's time scale set to enable detailed observation.
- In direct current (DC) circuits the time scale will be dependant on the speed at which the circuit is switched **Fig. 22** [6], for example, the frequency of an idle speed control device will vary with engine load.

Oscilloscope testing

- In alternating current (ac) circuits the time scale will depend on the speed of the signal generator **Fig. 23** [3], for example, an inductive crankshaft position (CKP) sensor's frequency will increase with engine speed.
- If the oscilloscope pattern is too compressed, decrease the time scale to obtain the view required. If the pattern is too expanded, increase the time scale.
- If the pattern is reversed **Fig. 23** [4], this indicates that the system being tested has its component connected in the opposite polarity to the typical wave form shown and can normally be ignored as it does not by itself indicate a fault.

Component testing

- Wave forms for a variety of components can be displayed. A few of the more common examples are described below.
- Most modern oscilloscopes have just two test leads, used with a variety of interchangeable test probes. The red lead is the positive and is normally connected to the ECM pin. The black lead is the negative and is normally connected to a good earth.
- If the leads are inadvertently connected with the wrong polarity, usually the only consequence is that the wave form will be displayed upside down.

Injectors

- All electronically controlled intermittent injection systems operate by varying the opening time of the injectors to match the quantity of fuel supplied with the engine operating conditions.
- The duration of the electrical impulses from the control unit is measured in milliseconds (ms) and typically ranges from 1 to 14. The oscilloscope on most engine testers can be used to display the injector pulse, enabling the duration to be measured.
- A typical oscilloscope trace is shown in **Fig. 24**.
- A series of smaller pulses, which hold the injector open after the initial negative pulse and a sharp positive voltage spike may be displayed as the injector closes.
- It is therefore possible to check that the control unit is operating correctly by observing the changes in injector opening times during various engine operating conditions.
- Pulse duration during cranking and at cold idle will be higher than at hot idle, and will increase as engine load increases.
- This effect will be particularly evident if the throttle is 'blipped'.

Fig. 24

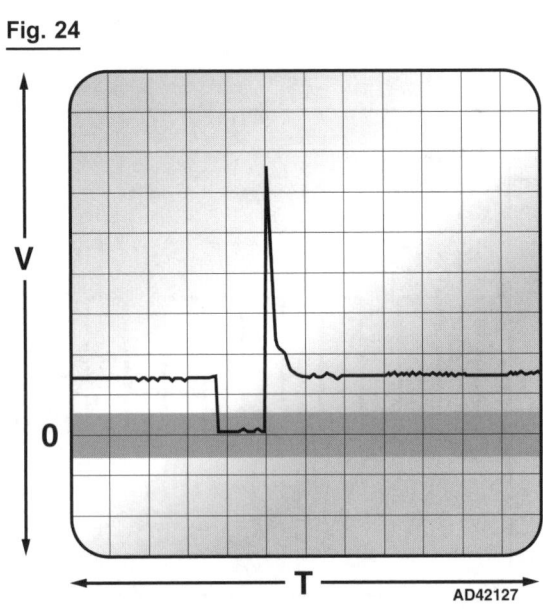

Injector wave form

Injector pulse

- Using a thin probe, connect the oscilloscope test probe to the ECM injector terminal and the second test probe to earth.
- Crank the engine and check the wave form.
- Start engine and observe the wave form at idle speed.
- Open the throttle rapidly to increase engine speed to around 3000 rpm.
- The measured pulse duration should increase during acceleration and then stabilise at a reading equal to or slightly below the idle speed value.
- Close the throttle rapidly and the trace should become a straight line with no pulse indicating that injection has been cut-off (for systems fitted with overrun injection cut-off).
- When the engine is started from cold the quantity of fuel required is increased and therefore the pulse duration or dwell will be greater.
- During warm-up the injection period should progressively decrease until the engine reaches normal operating temperature.
- Systems without a cold start injector usually give additional injector pulses during the cold start, which may be seen as long and short pulses on the scope.

Typical injector duration periods

CONDITION	DURATION
Idle speed	1-6 ms
2000-3000 rpm	1-6 ms
Full throttle	6-35 ms

Inductive sensors Fig. 25

- The general procedure is as follows:
- Select sensor pin from pin data list with wave form reference.
- Connect oscilloscope probe to ECM pin and second probe to earth.
- Start engine and observe test conditions.
- Compare scope trace with wave form reference.
- Raise the engine speed and watch for the voltage (amplitude) display to increase.

Idle air control (IAC) valve

- Idle air control (IAC) valves come in many different types, each with a different wave form.
- In each case the duty cycle (or ON time) of the valve should increase when any additional engine load starts to reduce the idle speed.
- If the duty cycle varies but the idle speed is not maintained under load, this indicates a faulty valve.
- If the wave form shows a straight line around the zero mark, or the line is constant at the 5 V or 12 V level, this indicates a fault in the IAC valve circuit or ECM signal output.
- The commonly used 4 pin stepper motor type is described below. Two and three pin IAC valves can be tested in a similar way, but will of course generate very different wave forms.
- The stepper motor responds to an oscillating signal from the ECM, enabling small adjustments to be made to the engine idle speed, in reaction to variations of operating temperature and load.
- This voltage signal can be checked by connecting the oscilloscope test probe to each of the four stepper motor ECM pins in turn.
- Ensure engine is at normal operating temperature.
- Start the engine and allow idle speed to stabilise.
- Increase the load on the engine by switching on the headlights, air conditioning or by turning the steering (power steering only).
- The idle speed should momentarily drop, but then be stabilised by the action of the IAC valve.
- Compare scope trace with wave form reference Fig. 26.

Fig. 25

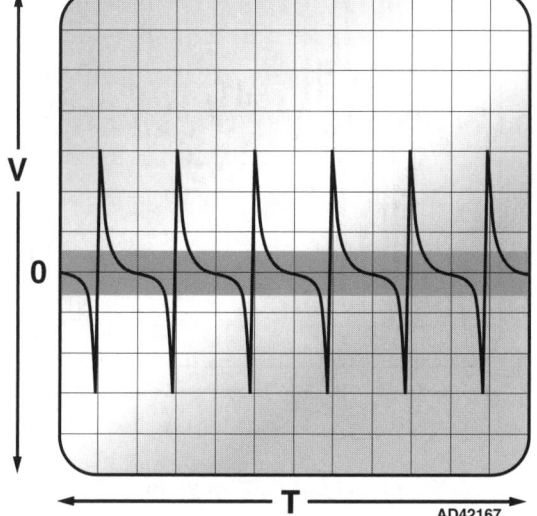

Inductive sensor wave form

Fig. 26

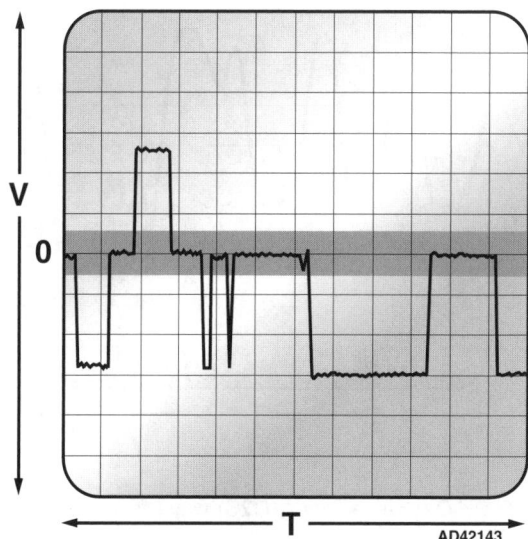

Idle air control (IAC) valve wave form

Oxygen sensor (O2S)

NOTE: *The following voltage figures refer to the almost universally used Zirconium type O2S, without a 0,5 V control reference. A few recent models are fitted with a Titanium sensor which has an operating range of 0-5 volts and shows a high voltage signal with a weak mixture and a low voltage signal with a rich mixture.*

- Connect oscilloscope test probes between oxygen sensor ECM pin and earth.
- Ensure engine is at normal operating temperature.
- Compare scope trace with wave form reference **Fig. 27**.
- If the trace shows no wave form but instead is a straight line, this usually indicates a weak mixture if the voltage is approximately 0-0,15, or a rich mixture if the voltage is approximately 0,6-1 – refer to Autodata fuel injection/engine management manuals or CD2 for possible causes of this condition.
- If the wave form is satisfactory at idle, open the throttle briefly several times in succession.
- The wave form should show the signal voltage 'cycling' between approximately 0-1 Volt.
- The increasing voltage corresponds to the engine speed rising and the decreasing voltage corresponds to the engine speed falling.

Knock sensor (KS)

- Connect oscilloscope test probes between knock sensor ECM pin and earth.
- Ensure engine is at normal operating temperature.
- Briefly snap throttle open.
- Wave form should display an ac signal showing a considerable increase in amplitude **Fig. 28**.
- If this signal is not distinctly displayed, tap the cylinder block lightly in the region of the sensor.
- If the signal is still not satisfactory this indicates a faulty sensor or associated circuit.

Fig. 27

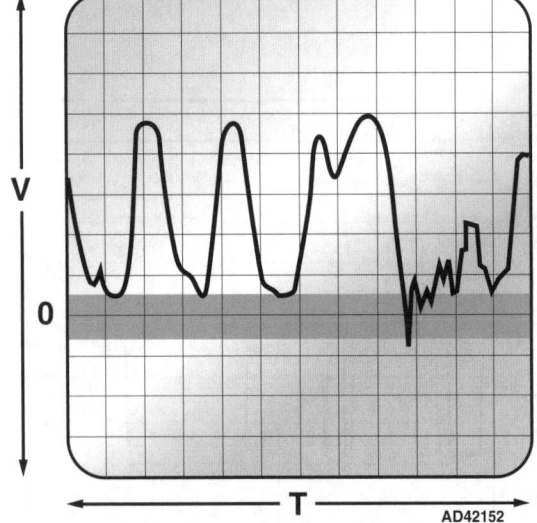

AD42152

Oxygen sensor (O2S) wave form

Fig. 28

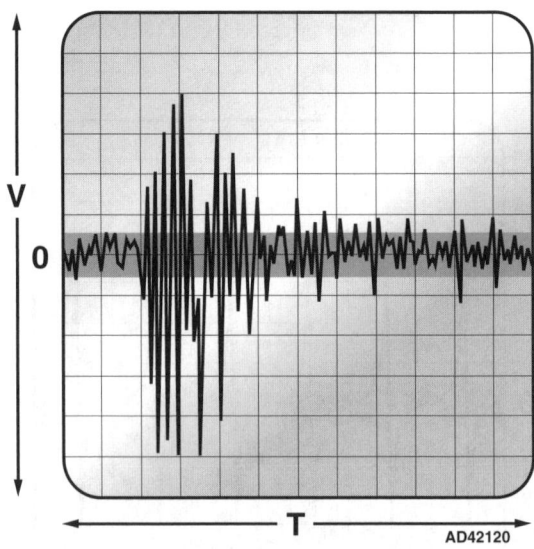

AD42120

Knock sensor (KS) wave form

Ignition amplifier

- Connect oscilloscope test probes between ignition amplifier ECM pin and earth.
- Ensure engine is at normal operating temperature.
- Start the engine and allow to idle.
- The signal should show a digital DC voltage pulse.
- Compare scope trace with wave form reference **Fig. 29**.
- If the signal is satisfactory the amplitude, frequency and shape of each pulse should be closely matched.
- Increase the engine speed and check that the signal frequency increases in proportion to the engine rpm.

Ignition coil – primary

- Connect oscilloscope test probes between ignition coil ECM pin and earth.
- Ensure engine is at normal operating temperature.
- Start the engine and allow to idle.
- Compare scope trace with wave form reference **Fig. 30**.
- Positive voltage spikes should be of even amplitude.
- Major differences of amplitude could indicate either a high resistance in the secondary circuit or a faulty spark plug or HT lead (where applicable).

Electronic control modules

- Without specialist equipment and data no testing of control modules is possible, except by self-diagnosis (if applicable) or substitution.
- Several companies operate a repair or exchange service for control modules and some offer a diagnosis service via a modem link to an appointed agent.

Fig. 29

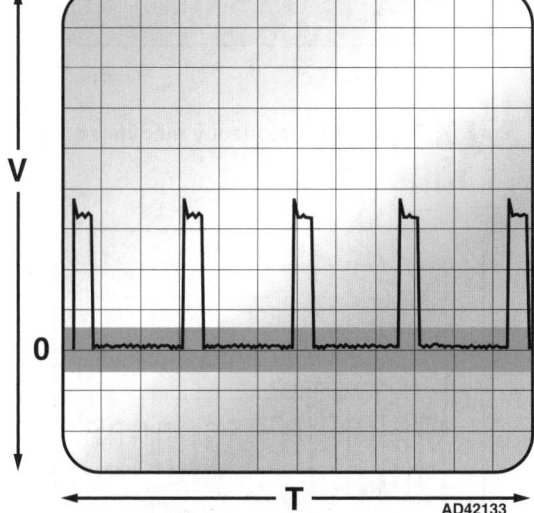

Ignition amplifier wave form

Fig. 30

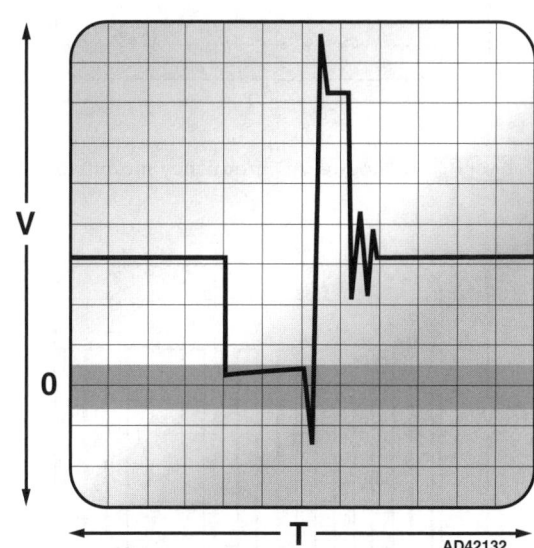

Ignition coil wave form

Typical oscilloscope wave forms – petrol

NOTE: *The following illustrations show typical representations of the wave forms that can be expected from the ECM pins referred to in the pin data tables. These wave forms are not unique to a particular circuit or component and may be cross-referenced to various components, in different pin data tables.*

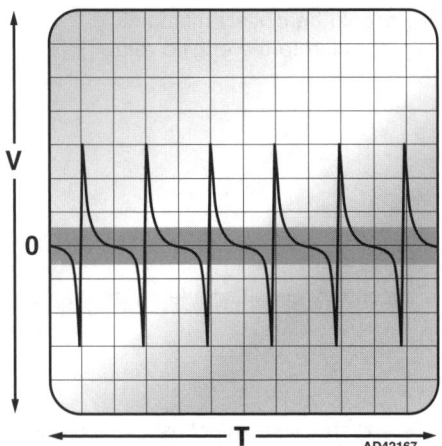

AD42167

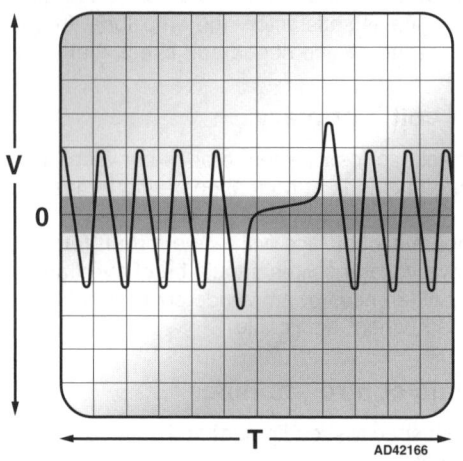

AD42166

1 Analogue, AC, frequency modulated

2 Analogue, AC, frequency modulated

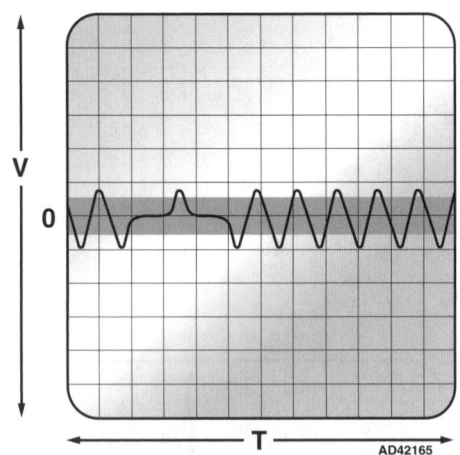

AD42165

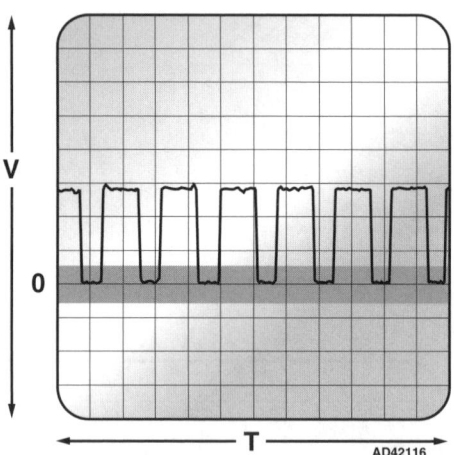

AD42116

3 Analogue, AC, frequency modulated

4 Digital, DC, frequency modulated

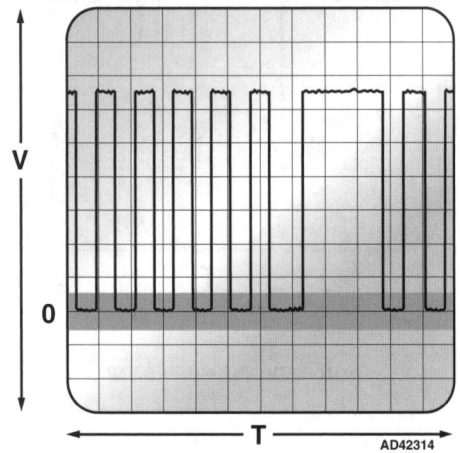

AD42314

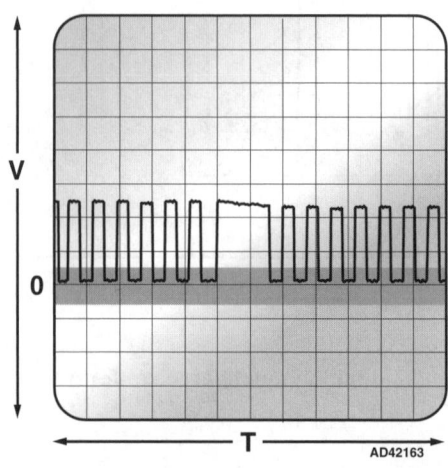

AD42163

5 Digital, DC, frequency modulated

6 Digital, DC, frequency modulated

NOTE: *The following illustrations show typical representations of the wave forms that can be expected from the ECM pins referred to in the pin data tables. These wave forms are not unique to a particular circuit or component and may be cross-referenced to various components, in different pin data tables.*

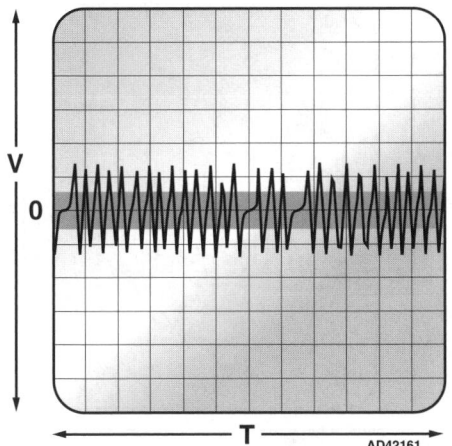

AD42161

7 Analogue, AC, frequency modulated

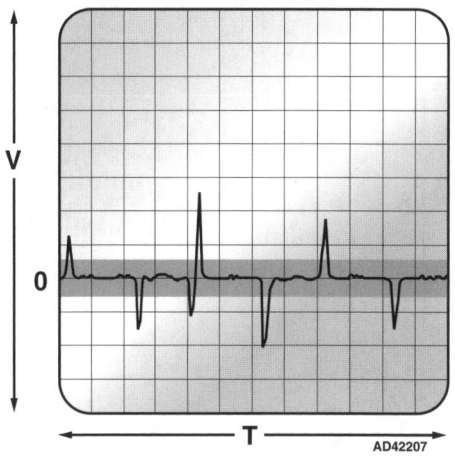

AD42207

8 Analogue, AC, frequency modulated

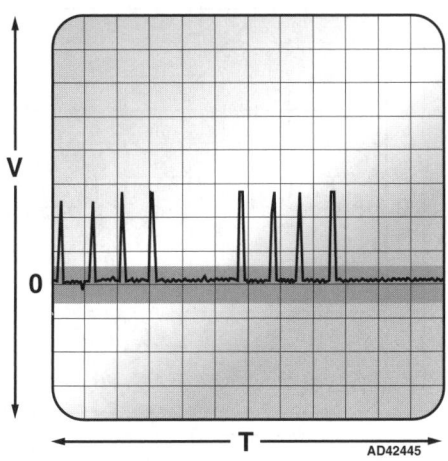

AD42445

9 Digital, DC, frequency modulated

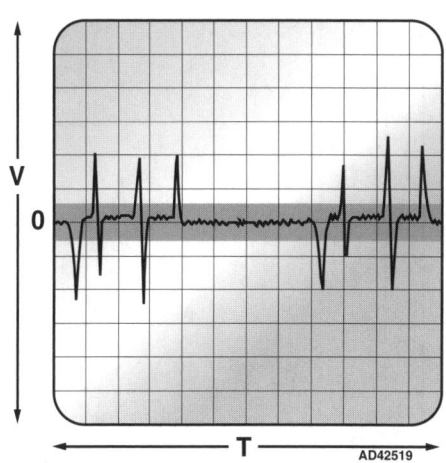

AD42519

10 Analogue, AC, frequency modulated

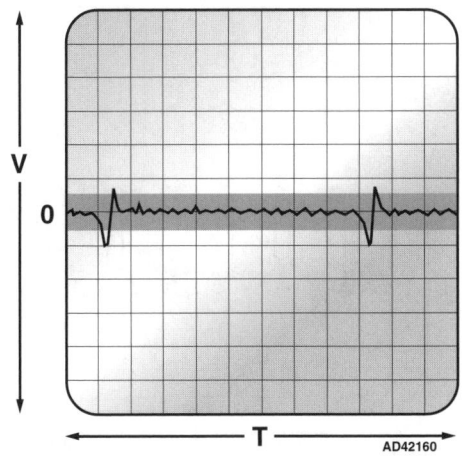

AD42160

11 Analogue, AC, frequency modulated

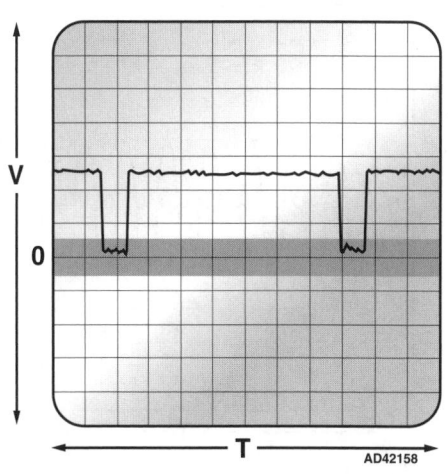

AD42158

12 Digital, DC, frequency modulated

Typical oscilloscope wave forms – petrol

NOTE: *The following illustrations show typical representations of the wave forms that can be expected from the ECM pins referred to in the pin data tables. These wave forms are not unique to a particular circuit or component and may be cross-referenced to various components, in different pin data tables.*

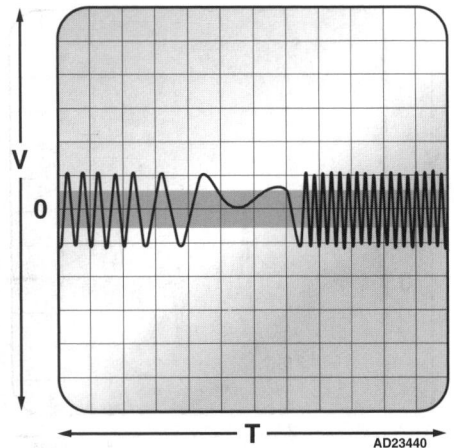

AD23440

13 Analogue, AC, frequency modulated

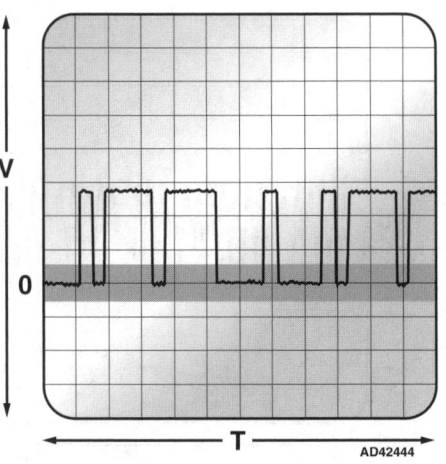

AD42444

14 Digital, DC, frequency modulated

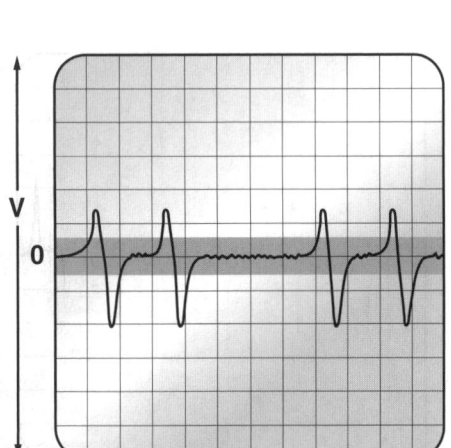

AD42442

15 Analogue, AC, frequency modulated

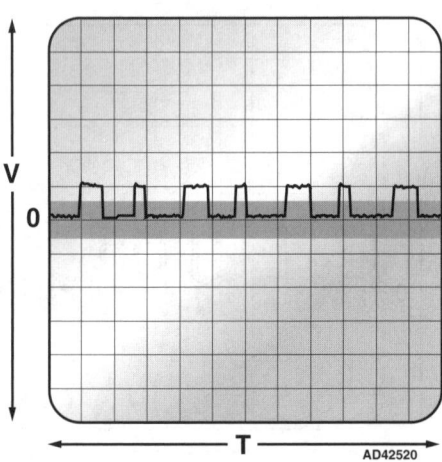

AD42520

16 Digital, DC, frequency modulated

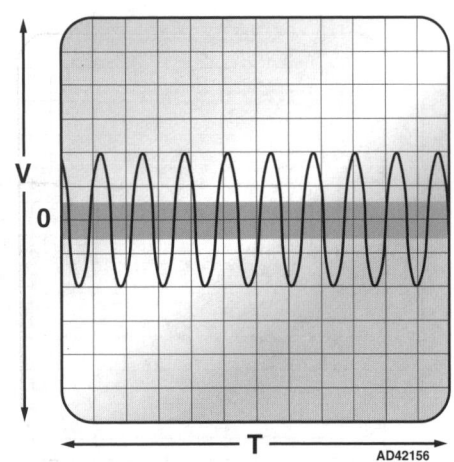

AD42156

17 Analogue, AC, frequency modulated

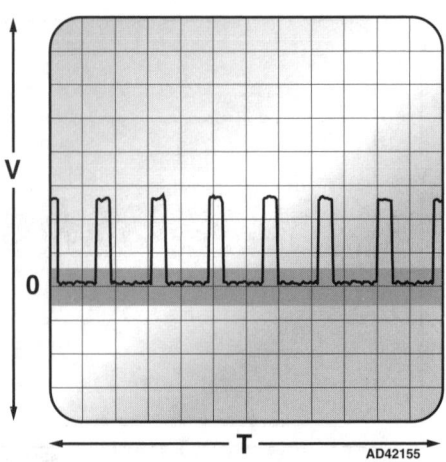

AD42155

18 Digital, DC, frequency modulated

NOTE: *The following illustrations show typical representations of the wave forms that can be expected from the ECM pins referred to in the pin data tables. These wave forms are not unique to a particular circuit or component and may be cross-referenced to various components, in different pin data tables.*

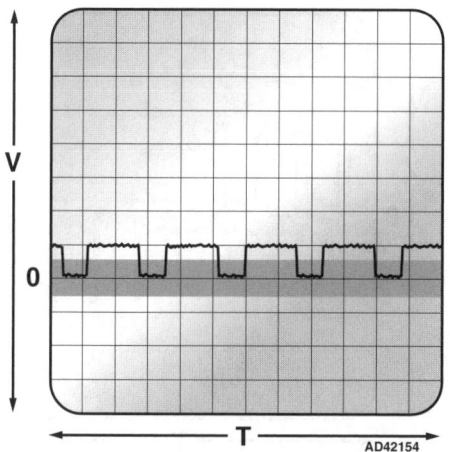

AD42154

19 Digital, DC, pulse width modulated or digital, DC, frequency modulated

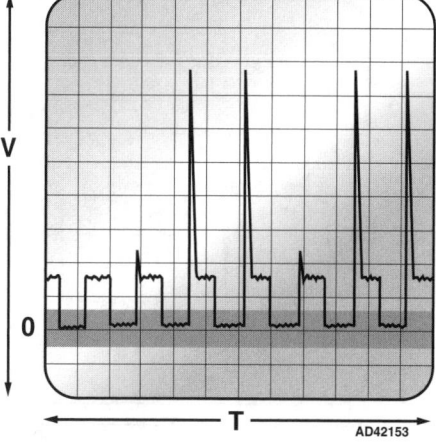

AD42153

20 Digital, DC, pulse width modulated or digital, DC, frequency modulated

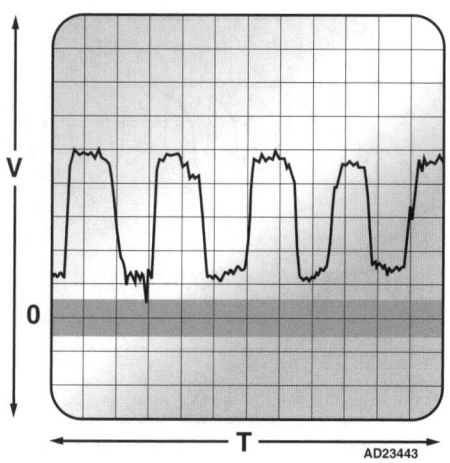

AD23443

21 Analogue, DC

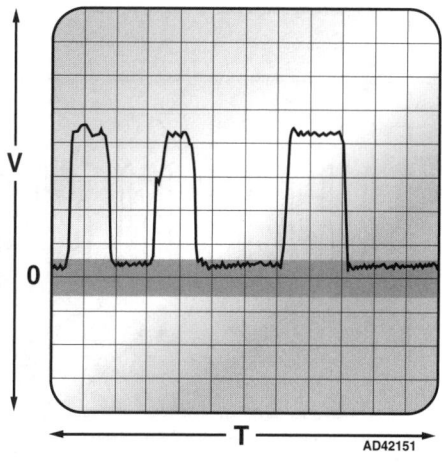

AD42151

22 Digital, DC

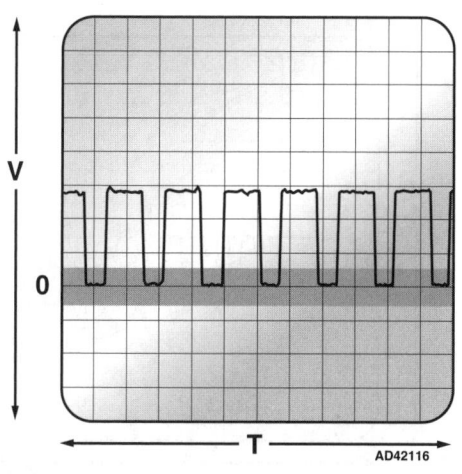

AD42116

24 Digital, DC, pulse width modulated or digital, DC, frequency modulated

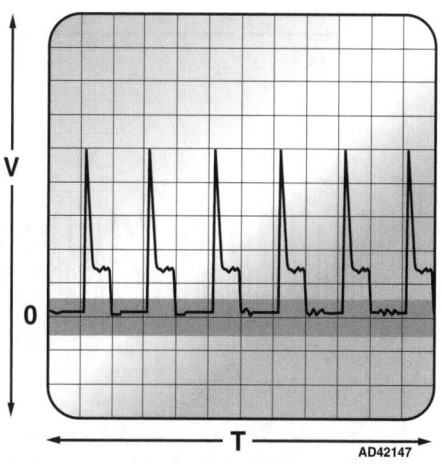

AD42147

25 Digital, DC, pulse width modulated or digital, DC, frequency modulated

Typical oscilloscope wave forms – petrol

NOTE: *The following illustrations show typical representations of the wave forms that can be expected from the ECM pins referred to in the pin data tables. These wave forms are not unique to a particular circuit or component and may be cross-referenced to various components, in different pin data tables.*

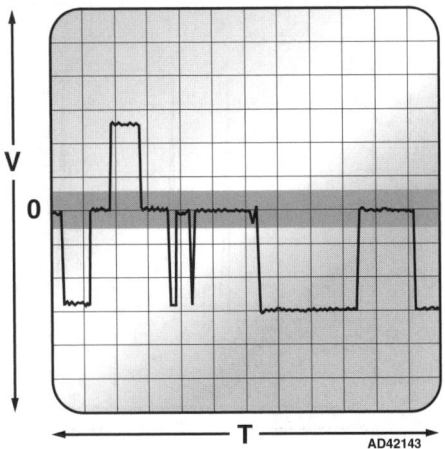

AD42143

26 Digital, DC, pulse width modulated or digital, DC, frequency modulated

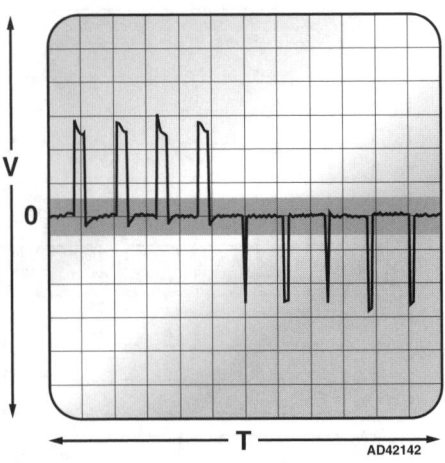

AD42142

27 Digital, DC, pulse width modulated or digital, DC, frequency modulated

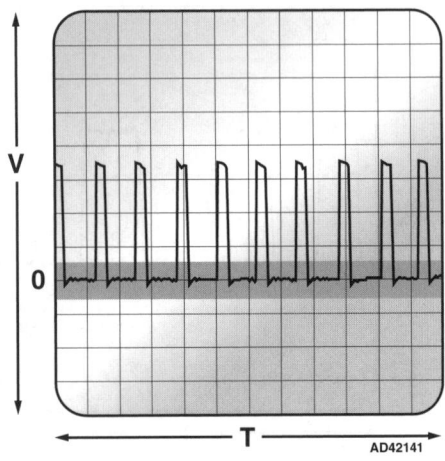

AD42141

28 Digital, DC, pulse width modulated or digital, DC, frequency modulated

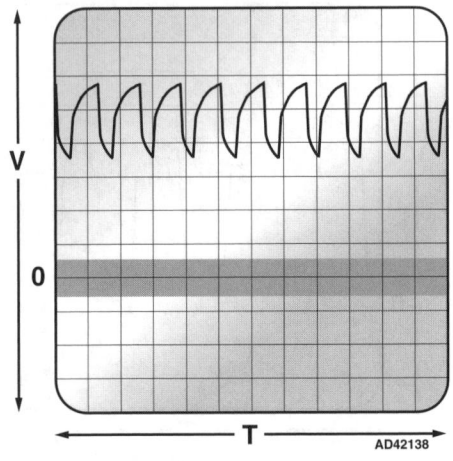

AD42138

29 Digital, DC, pulse width modulated or digital, DC, frequency modulated

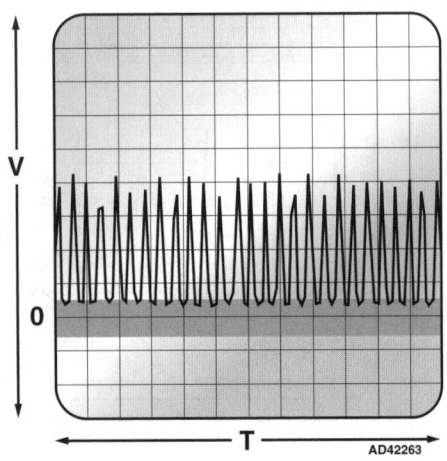

AD42263

30 Digital, DC, pulse width modulated or digital, DC, frequency modulated

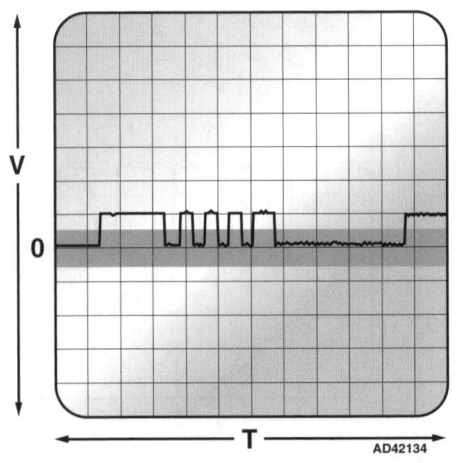

AD42134

31 Digital, DC, pulse width modulated

NOTE: *The following illustrations show typical representations of the wave forms that can be expected from the ECM pins referred to in the pin data tables. These wave forms are not unique to a particular circuit or component and may be cross-referenced to various components, in different pin data tables.*

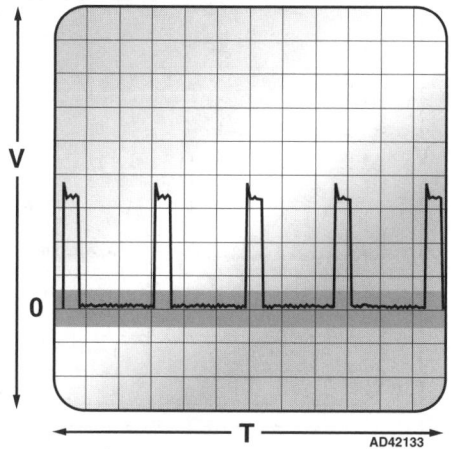

AD42133

32 Digital, DC, frequency modulated

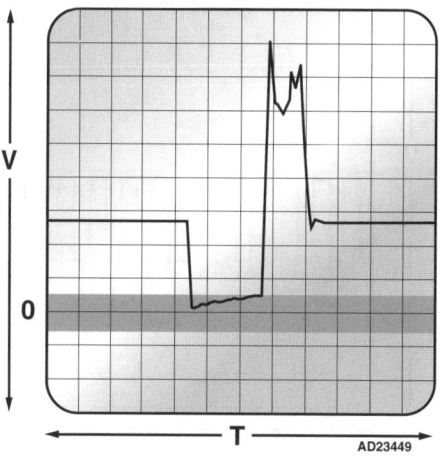

AD23449

33 Digital, DC, frequency modulated

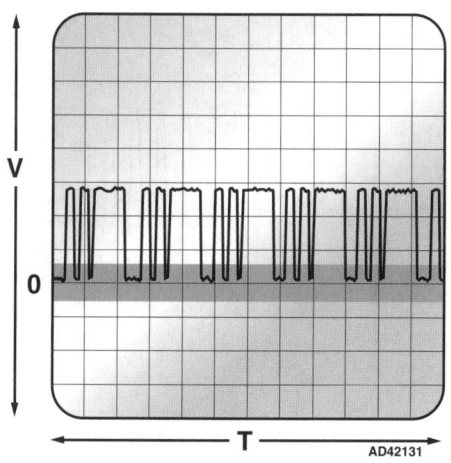

AD42131

34 Digital, DC

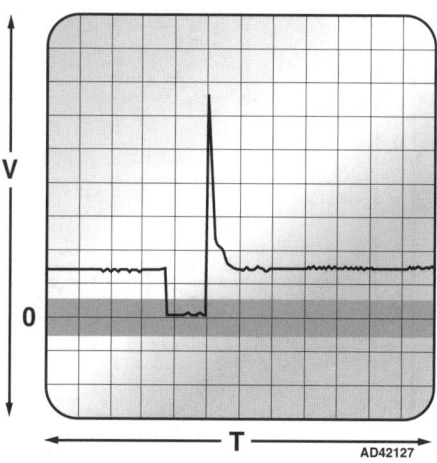

AD42127

35 Digital, DC, pulse width modulated

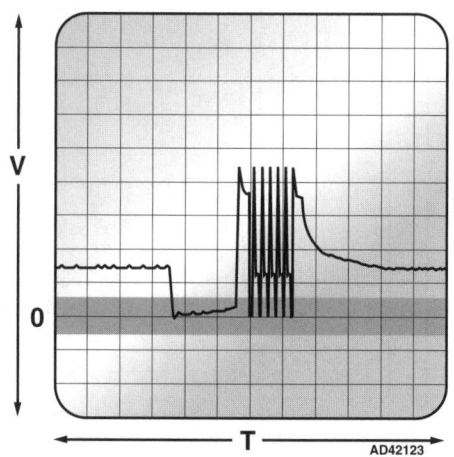

AD42123

36 Digital, DC, pulse width modulated

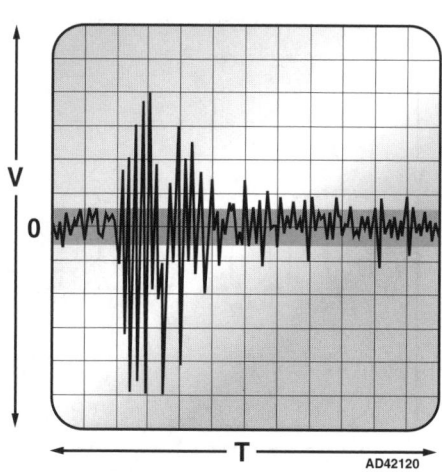

AD42120

38 Analogue, AC

Typical oscilloscope wave forms – petrol

NOTE: *The following illustrations show typical representations of the wave forms that can be expected from the ECM pins referred to in the pin data tables. These wave forms are not unique to a particular circuit or component and may be cross-referenced to various components, in different pin data tables.*

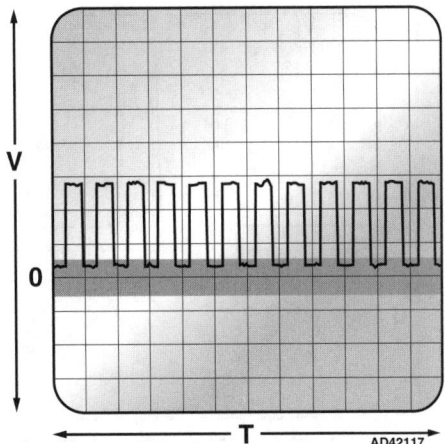

AD42117

39 Digital, DC, frequency modulated

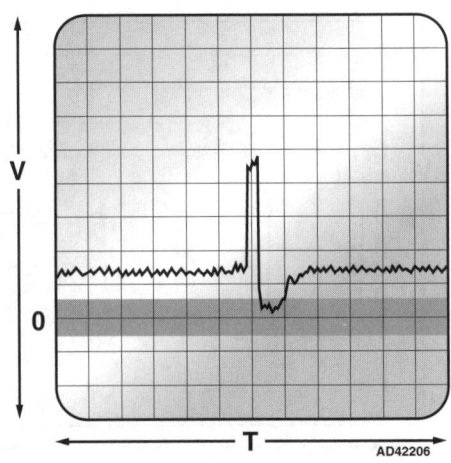

AD42206

40 Analogue, DC

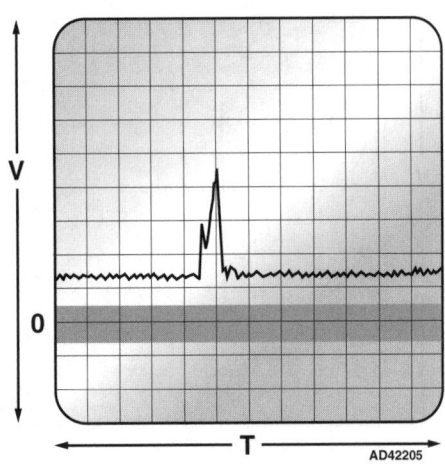

AD42205

41 Analogue, DC

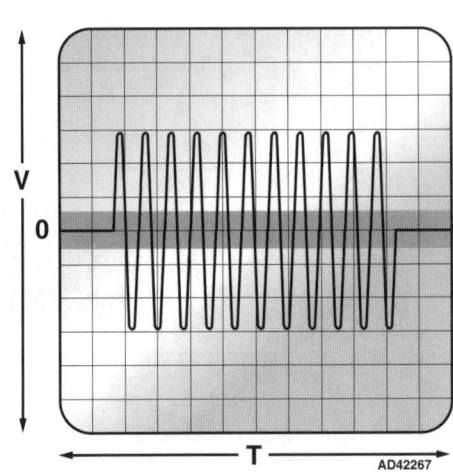

AD42267

42 Analogue, AC, frequency modulated

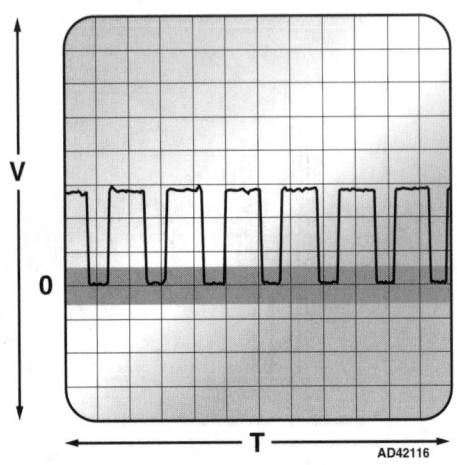

AD42116

43 Digital, DC, frequency modulated

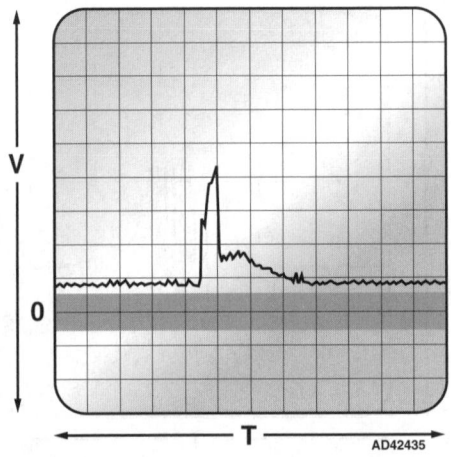

AD42435

44 Analogue, DC

NOTE: *The following illustrations show typical representations of the wave forms that can be expected from the ECM pins referred to in the pin data tables. These wave forms are not unique to a particular circuit or component and may be cross-referenced to various components, in different pin data tables.*

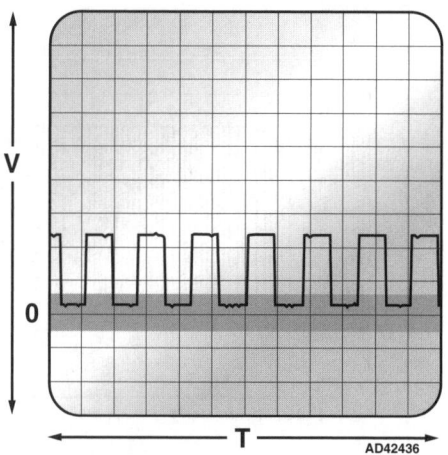

AD42436

45 Digital, DC, frequency & pulse width modulated

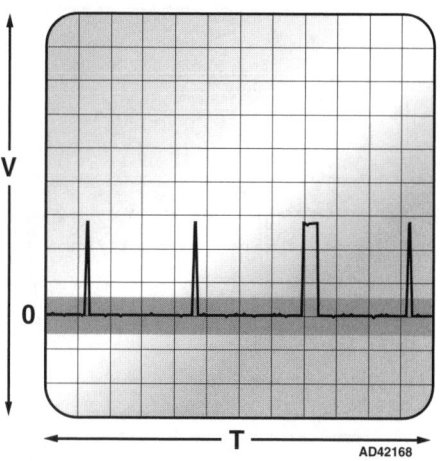

AD42168

46 Digital, DC, frequency modulated

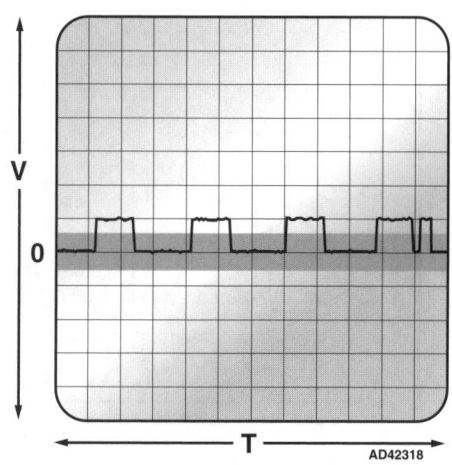

AD42318

47 Digital, DC, frequency modulated

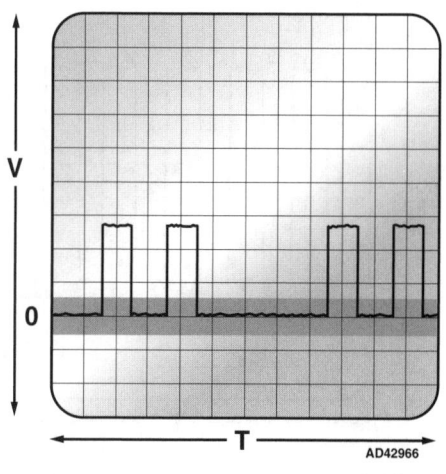

AD42966

49 Digital, DC, frequency modulated

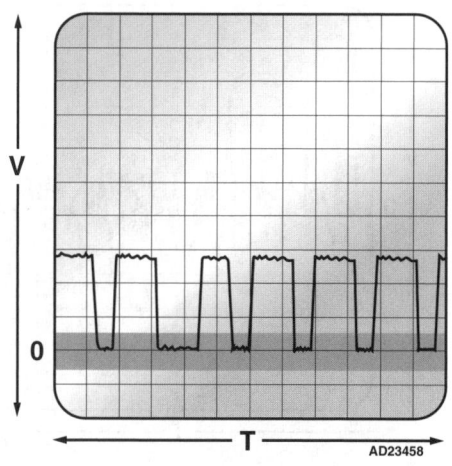

AD23458

51 Digital, DC, frequency modulated

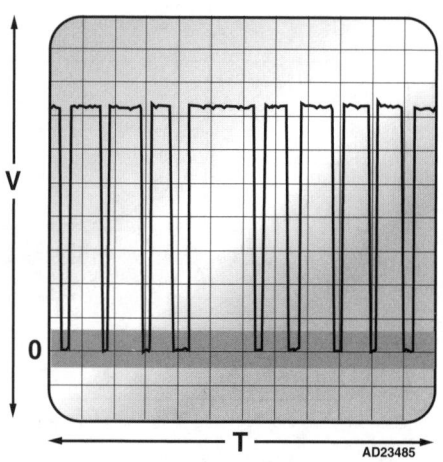

AD23485

52 Digital, DC, pulse width modulated or digital, DC, frequency modulated

Typical oscilloscope wave forms – petrol

NOTE: *The following illustrations show typical representations of the wave forms that can be expected from the ECM pins referred to in the pin data tables. These wave forms are not unique to a particular circuit or component and may be cross-referenced to various components, in different pin data tables.*

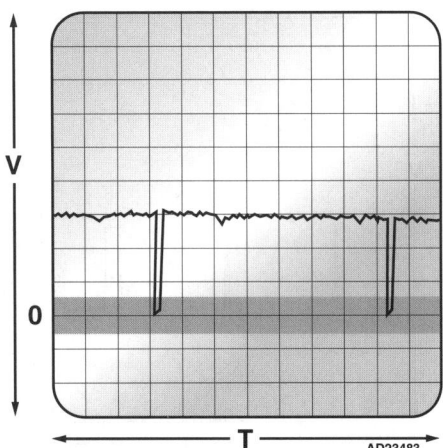

AD23483

53 Digital, DC, frequency modulated

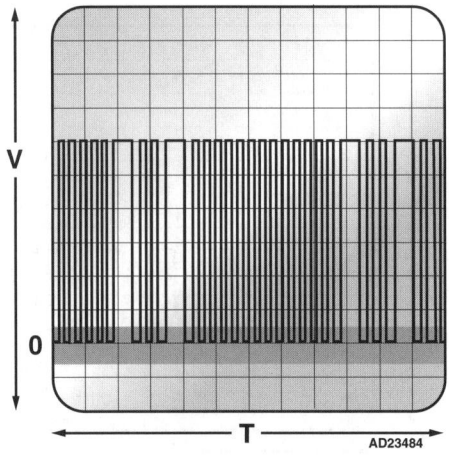

AD23484

54 Digital, DC, frequency modulated

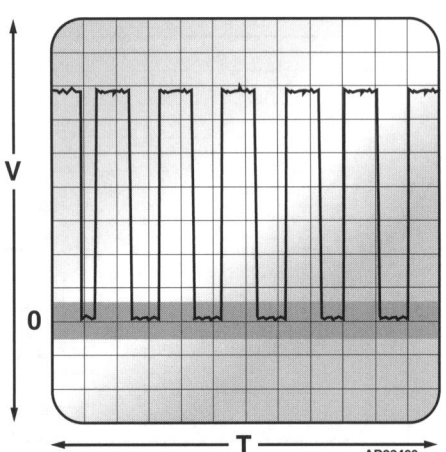

AD23488

55 Digital, DC, frequency modulated

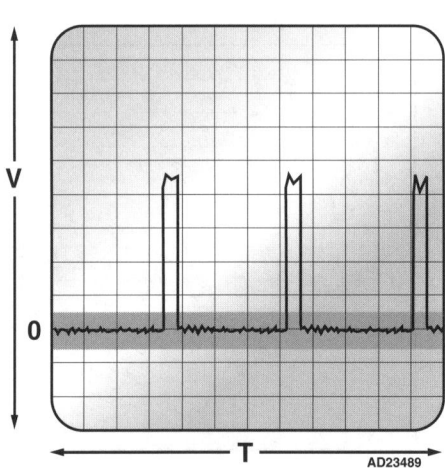

AD23489

56 Digital, DC, frequency modulated

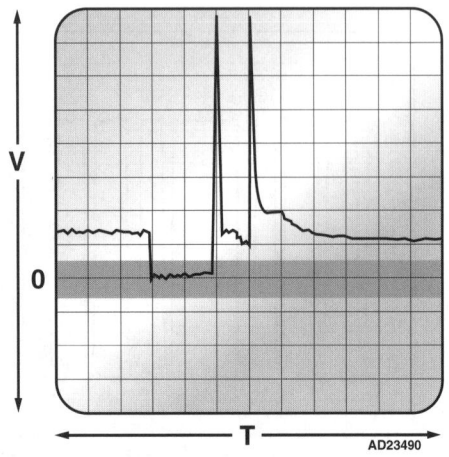

AD23490

57 Digital, DC, pulse width modulated

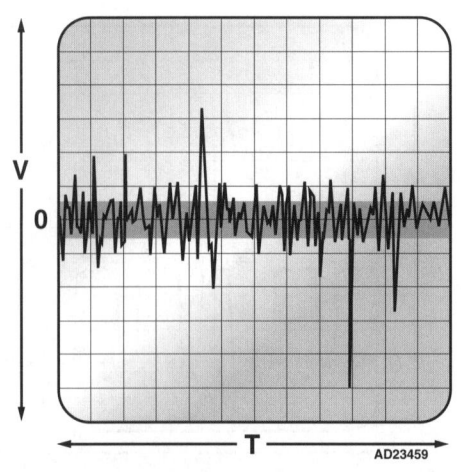

AD23459

58 Analogue, AC

NOTE: *The following illustrations show typical representations of the wave forms that can be expected from the ECM pins referred to in the pin data tables. These wave forms are not unique to a particular circuit or component and may be cross-referenced to various components, in different pin data tables.*

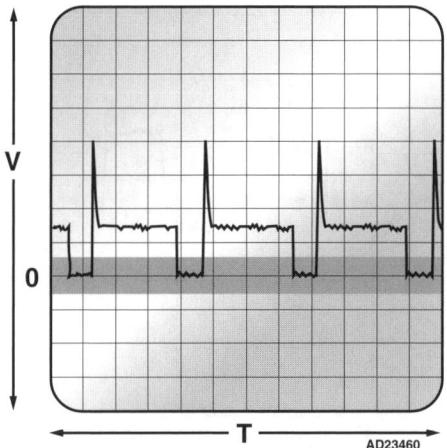

AD23460

59 Digital, DC, pulse width modulated or digital, DC, frequency modulated

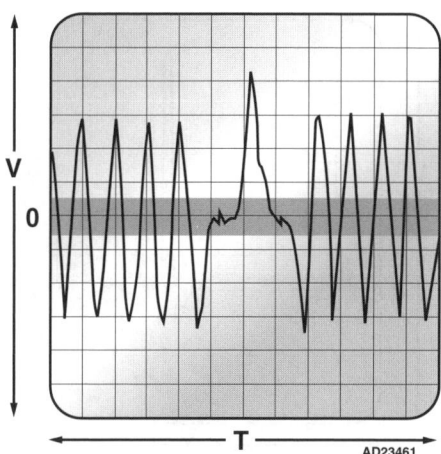

AD23461

60 Analogue, AC, frequency modulated

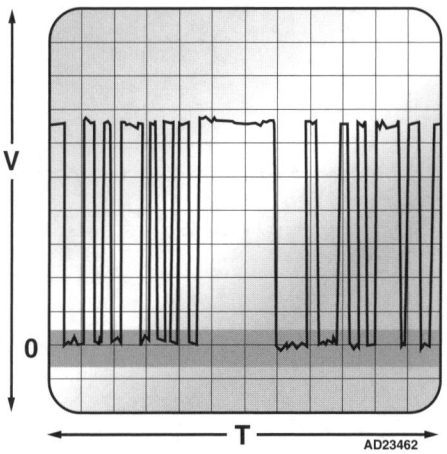

AD23462

61 Digital, DC

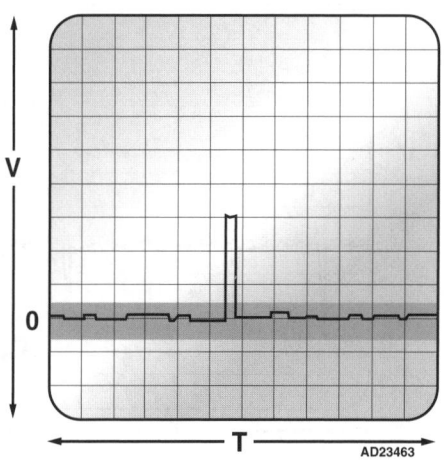

AD23463

62 Digital, DC

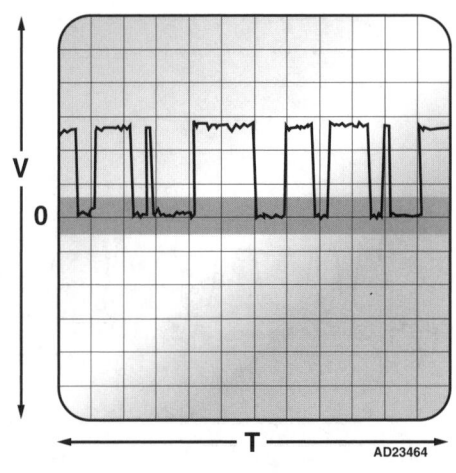

AD23464

63 Digital, DC, frequency modulated

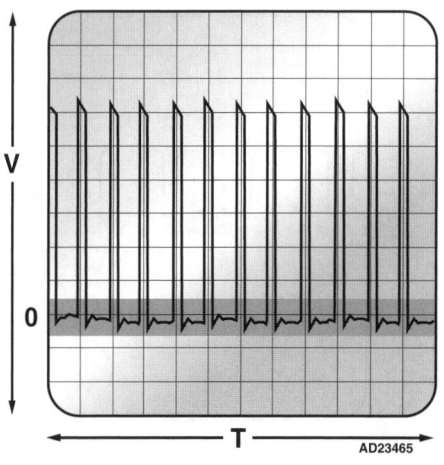

AD23465

64 Digital, DC, frequency modulated

Typical oscilloscope wave forms – petrol

NOTE: *The following illustrations show typical representations of the wave forms that can be expected from the ECM pins referred to in the pin data tables. These wave forms are not unique to a particular circuit or component and may be cross-referenced to various components, in different pin data tables.*

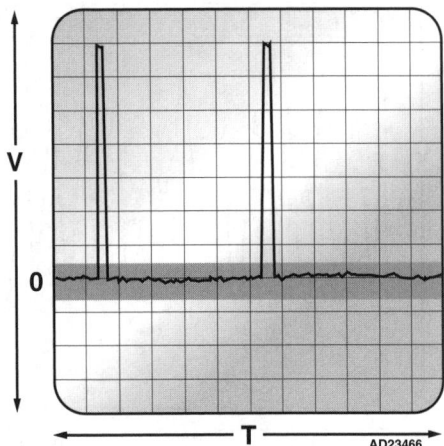

65 Digital, DC

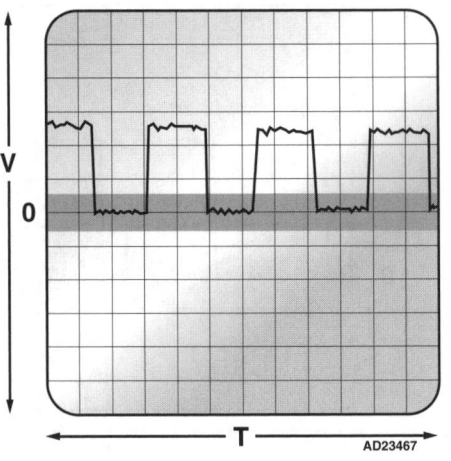

66 Digital, DC, frequency modulated

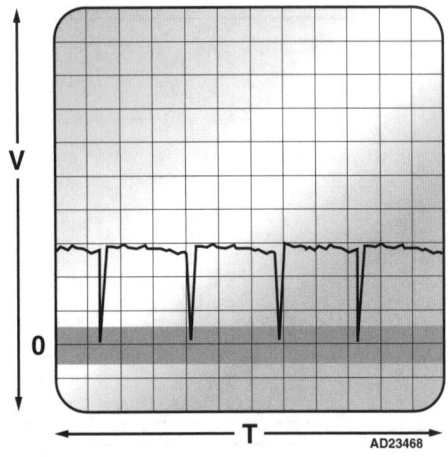

67 Digital, DC, pulse width modulated or digital, DC, frequency modulated

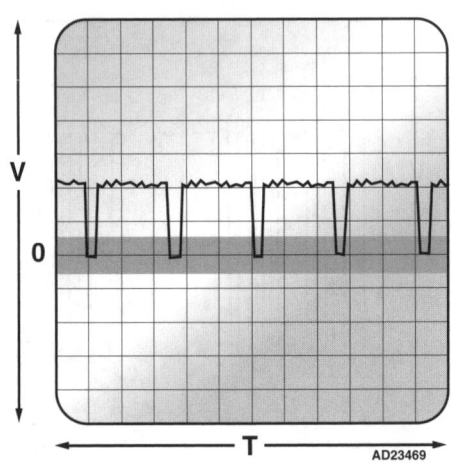

68 Digital, DC, pulse width modulated or digital, DC, frequency modulated

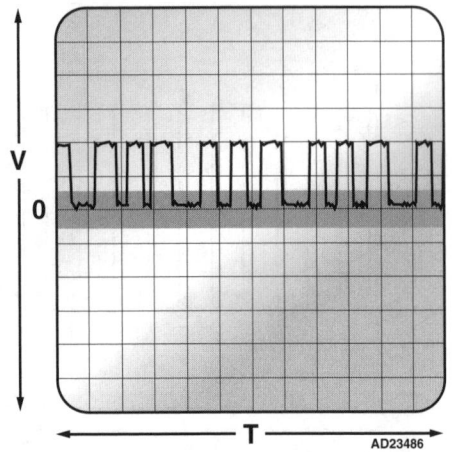

69 Digital, DC, frequency modulated

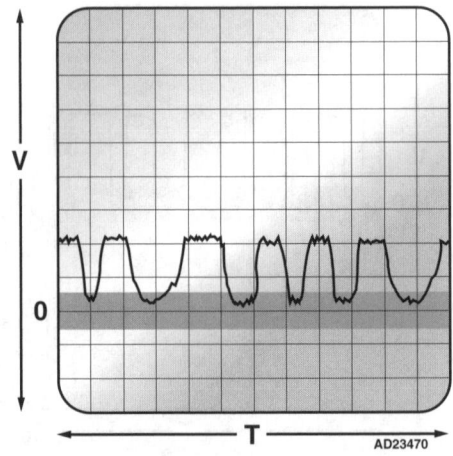

70 Analogue, DC

NOTE: *The following illustrations show typical representations of the wave forms that can be expected from the ECM pins referred to in the pin data tables. These wave forms are not unique to a particular circuit or component and may be cross-referenced to various components, in different pin data tables.*

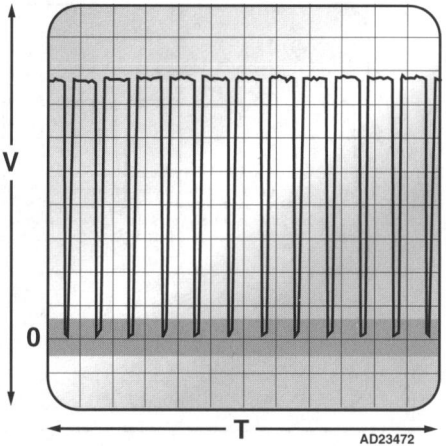

71 Digital, DC, pulse width modulated

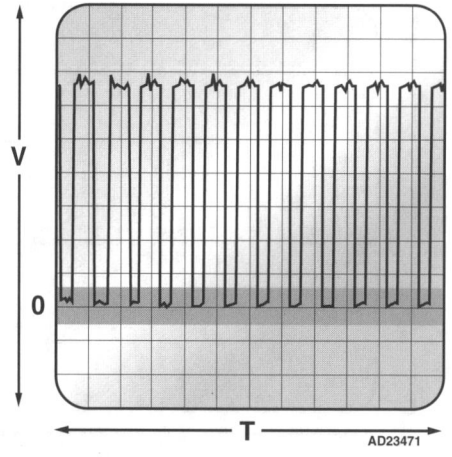

72 Digital, DC

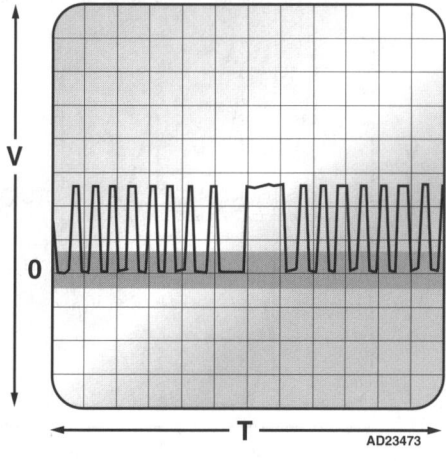

73 Digital, DC, frequency modulated

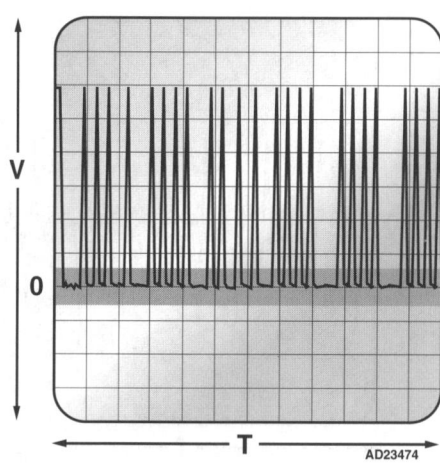

74 Analogue, DC, frequency modulated

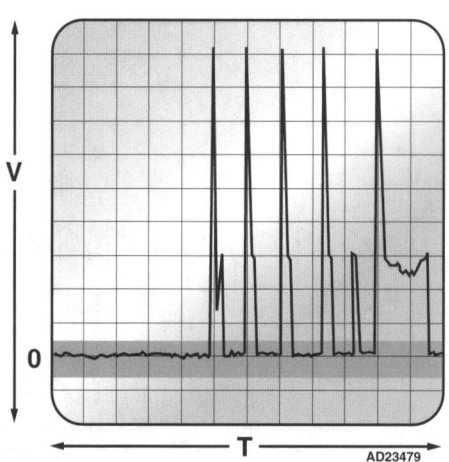

75 Digital, DC, frequency modulated

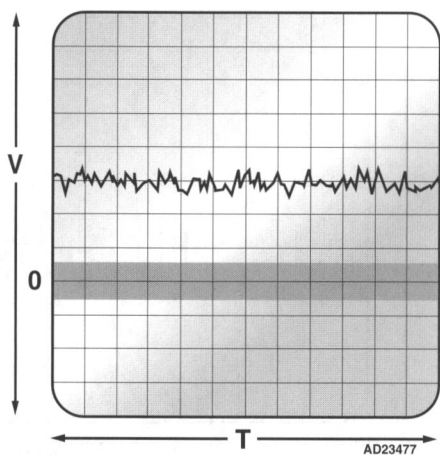

76 Analogue, DC

Typical oscilloscope wave forms – petrol

NOTE: *The following illustrations show typical representations of the wave forms that can be expected from the ECM pins referred to in the pin data tables. These wave forms are not unique to a particular circuit or component and may be cross-referenced to various components, in different pin data tables.*

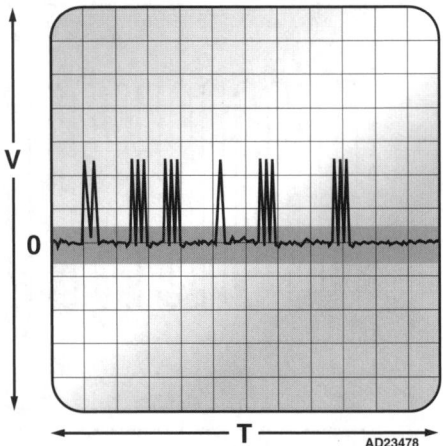

77 Analogue, DC, frequency modulated

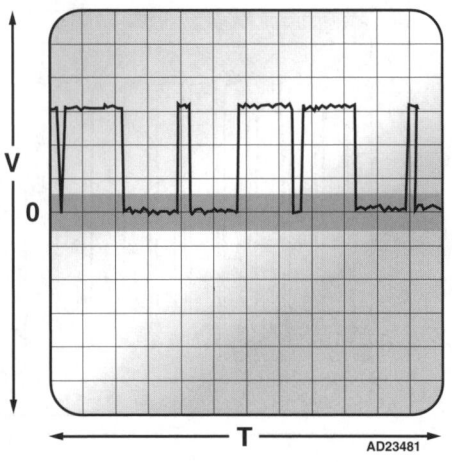

78 Digital, DC, frequency modulated

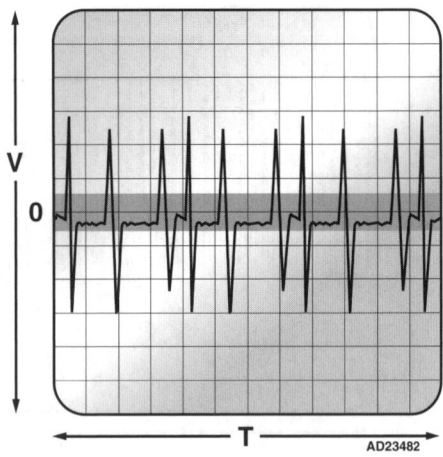

79 Analogue, AC, frequency modulated

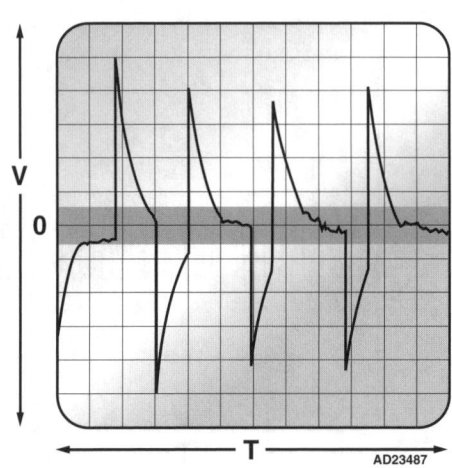

80 Digital, DC

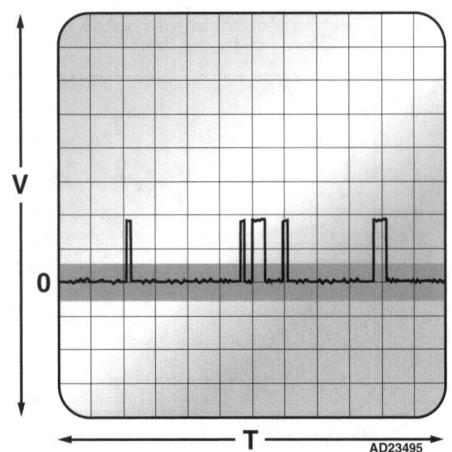

81 Digital, DC

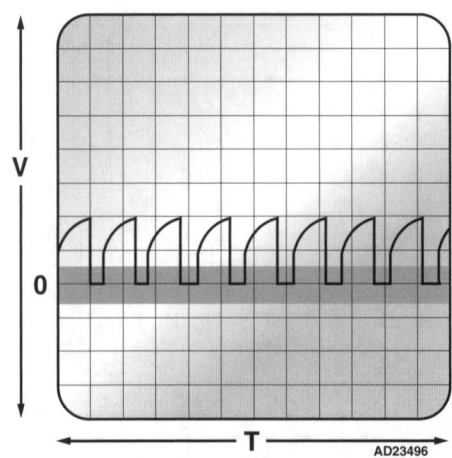

82 Digital, DC, pulse width modulated or digital, DC, frequency modulated

Autodata

NOTE: *The following illustrations show typical representations of the wave forms that can be expected from the ECM pins referred to in the pin data tables. These wave forms are not unique to a particular circuit or component and may be cross-referenced to various components, in different pin data tables.*

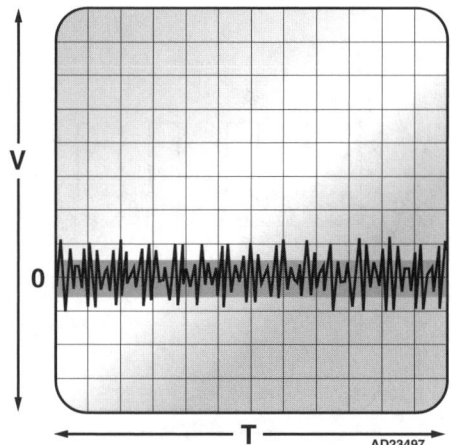

AD23497

83 Analogue, AC, frequency modulated

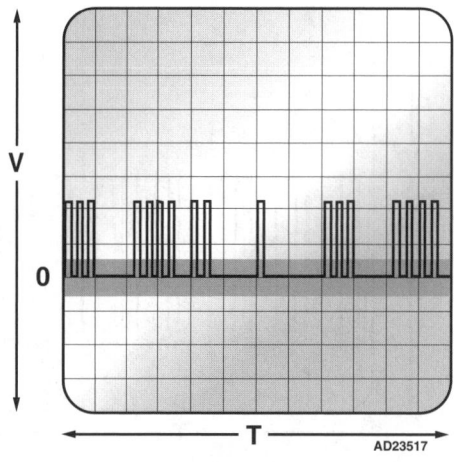

AD23517

84 Digital, DC, frequency modulated

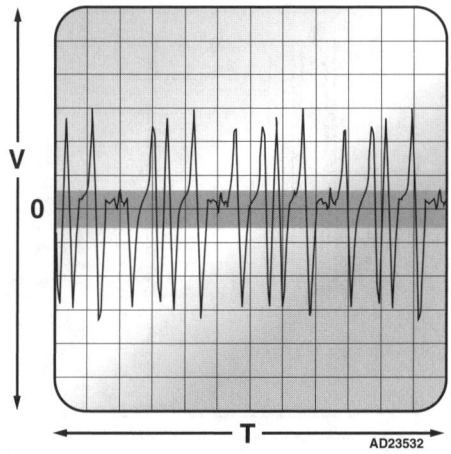

AD23532

85 Analogue, AC, frequency modulated

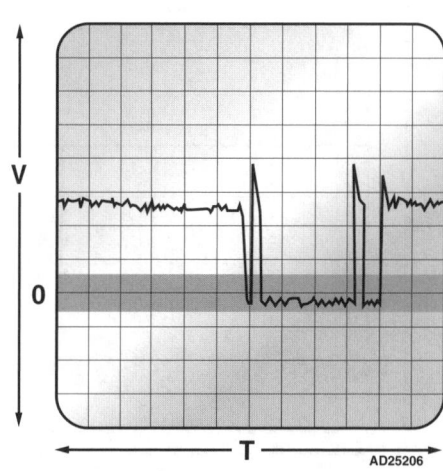

AD25206

86 Digital, DC, pulse width modulated

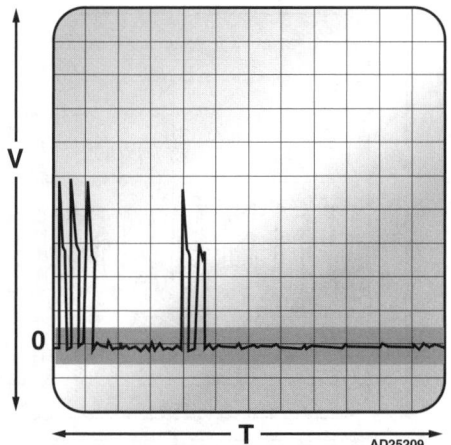

AD25209

87 Digital, DC, pulse width modulated

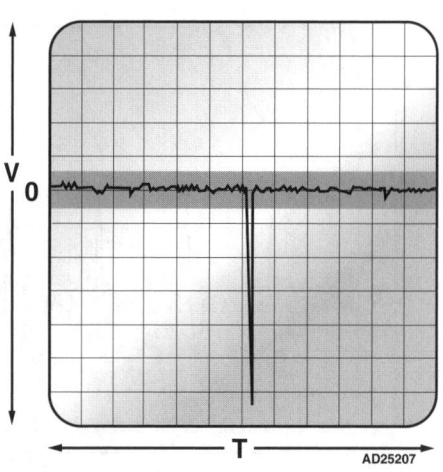

AD25207

88 Digital, DC, frequency modulated

Typical oscilloscope wave forms – petrol

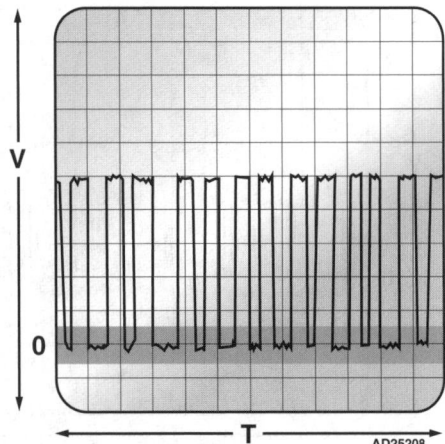

▆▆ **89** Digital, DC, frequency modulated

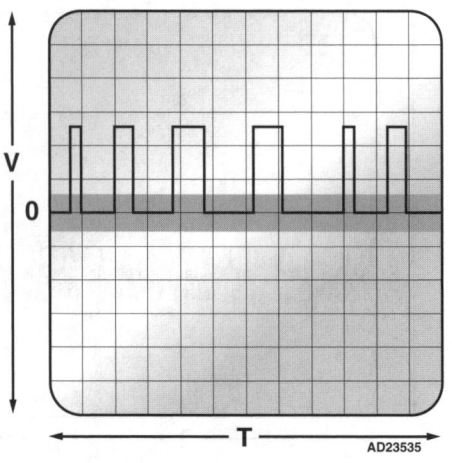

▆▆ **90** Digital, DC, frequency modulated

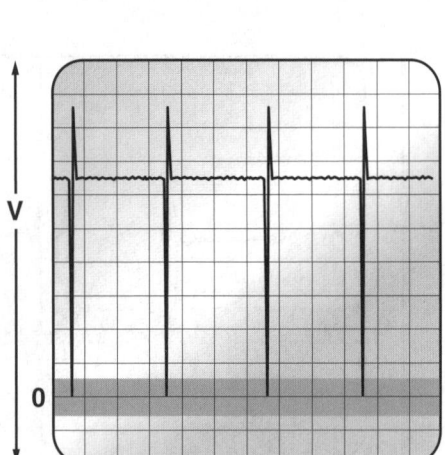

▆▆ **91** Digital, DC, frequency modulated

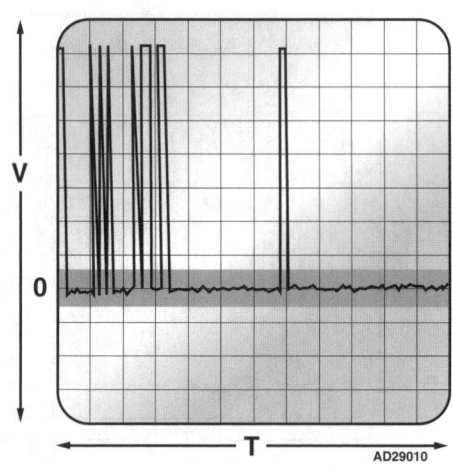

▆▆ **92** Digital, DC, pulse width modulated

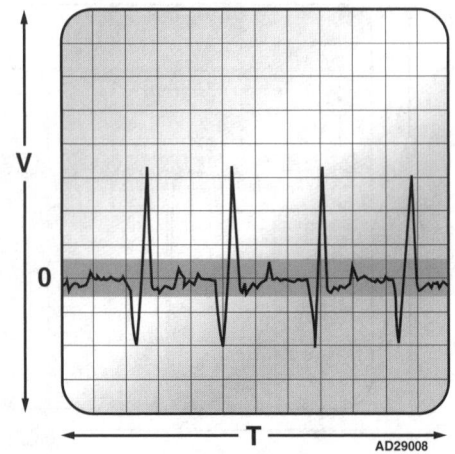

▆▆ **93** Analogue, AC, frequency modulated

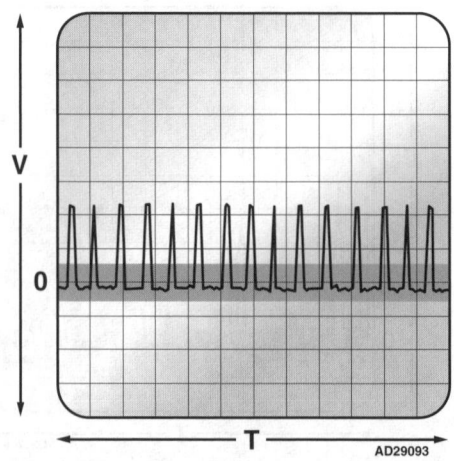

▆▆ **94** Digital, DC, frequency modulated

NOTE: *The following illustrations show typical representations of the wave forms that can be expected from the ECM pins referred to in the pin data tables. These wave forms are not unique to a particular circuit or component and may be cross-referenced to various components, in different pin data tables.*

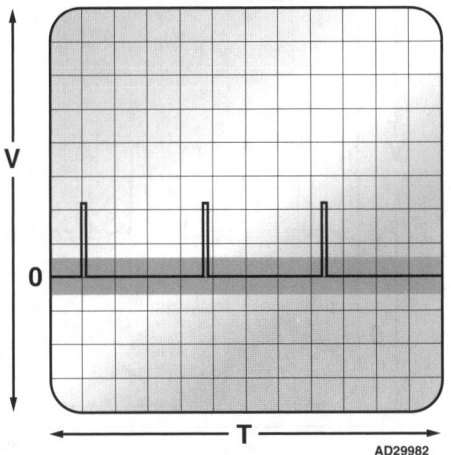

AD29982

99 Digital, DC, frequency modulated

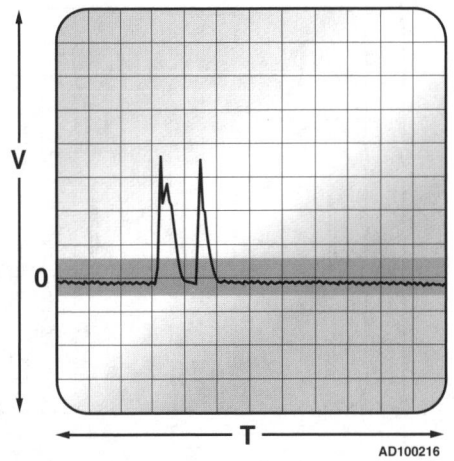

AD100216

100 Analogue, DC

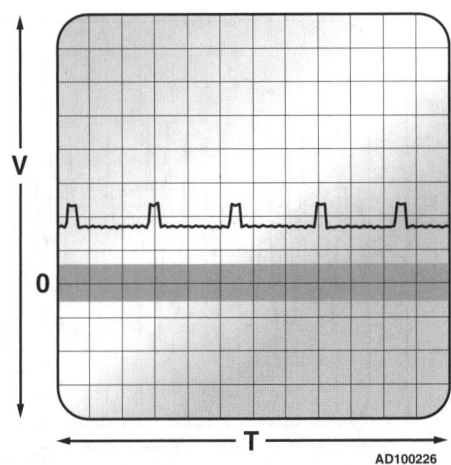

AD100226

101 Digital, DC, frequency modulated

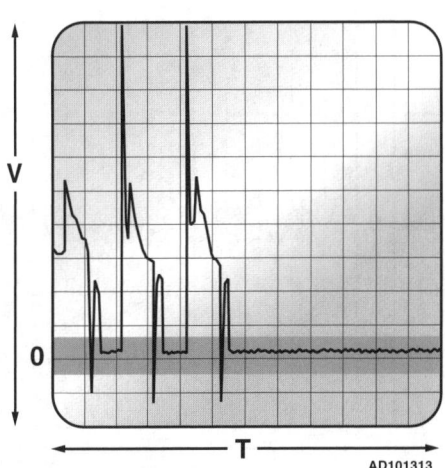

AD101313

102 Digital, DC, frequency modulated

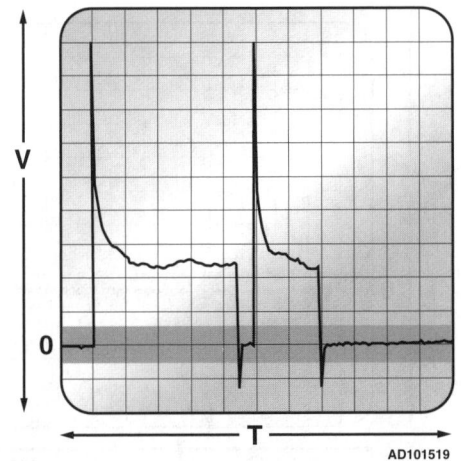

AD101519

103 Digital, DC, pulse width modulated

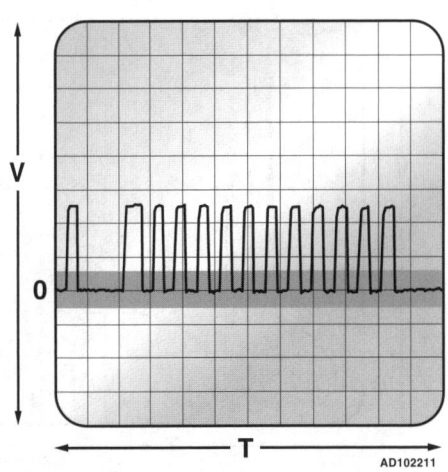

AD102211

104 Digital, DC, frequency modulated

Typical oscilloscope wave forms – petrol

NOTE: *The following illustrations show typical representations of the wave forms that can be expected from the ECM pins referred to in the pin data tables. These wave forms are not unique to a particular circuit or component and may be cross-referenced to various components, in different pin data tables.*

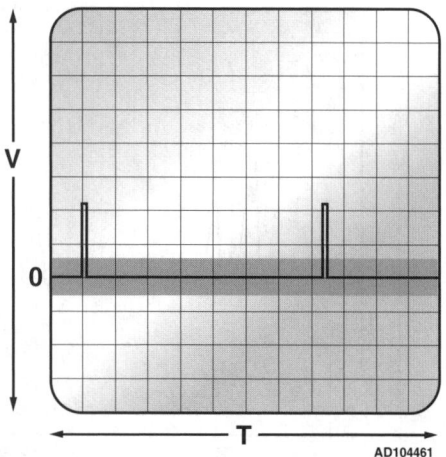

AD104461

106 Digital, DC, frequency modulated

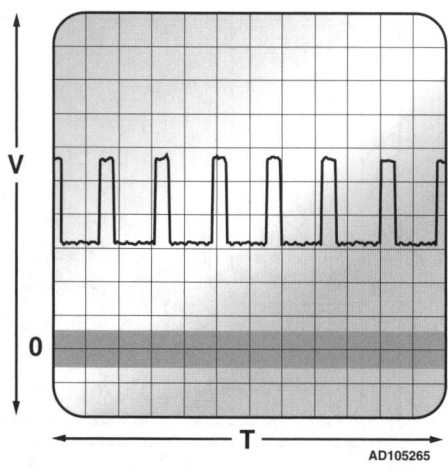

AD105265

107 Digital, DC, frequency modulated or digital, DC, pulse width modulated

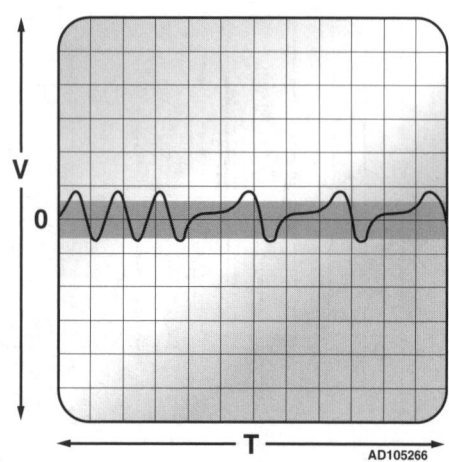

AD105266

108 Analogue, AC, frequency modulated

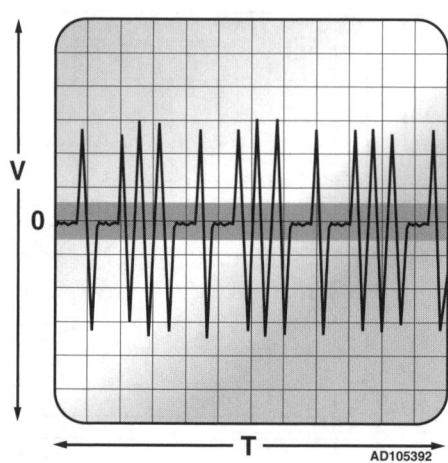

AD105392

109 Analogue, AC, frequency modulated

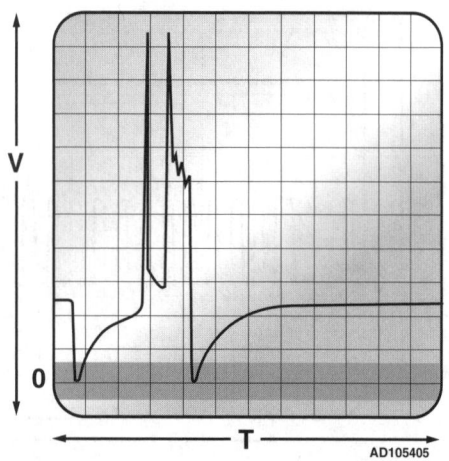

AD105405

110 Digital, DC, frequency modulated

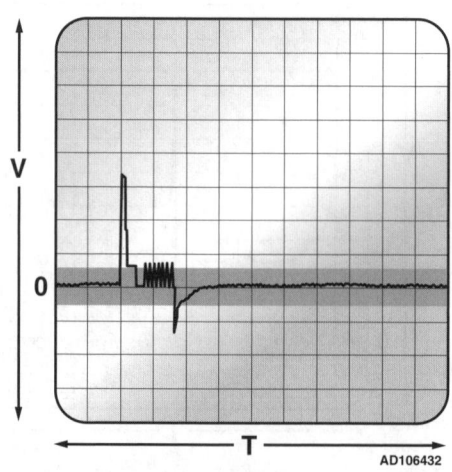

AD106432

111 Digital, DC, pulse width modulated

Autodata

Typical oscilloscope wave forms – diesel

NOTE: *The following illustrations show typical representations of the wave forms that can be expected from the ECM pins referred to in the pin data tables. These wave forms are not unique to a particular circuit or component and may be cross-referenced to various components, in different pin data tables.*

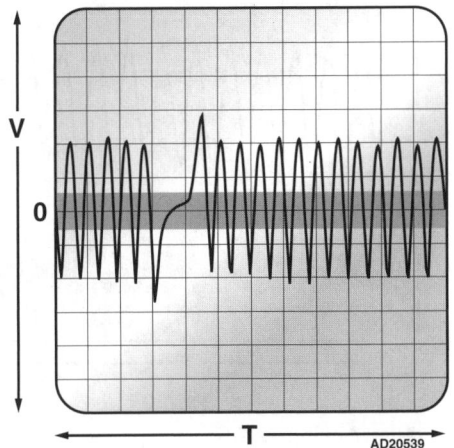

AD20539

1 Analogue, AC

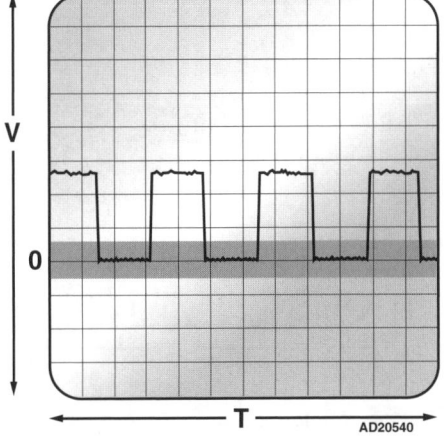

AD20540

2 Digital, DC

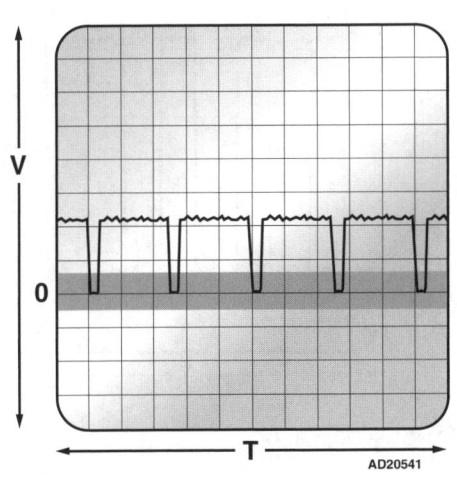

AD20541

3 Digital, DC

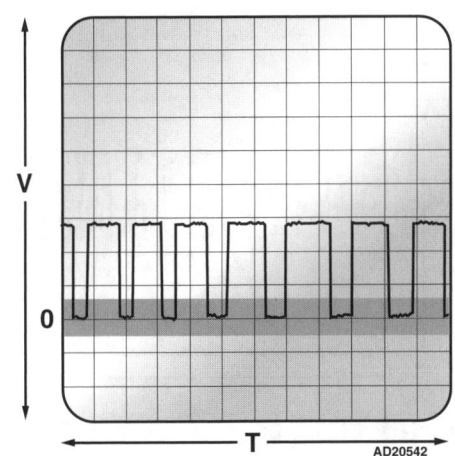

AD20542

4 Digital, DC

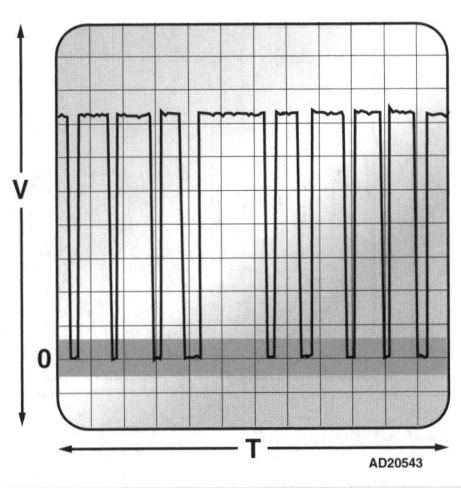

AD20543

5 Digital, DC

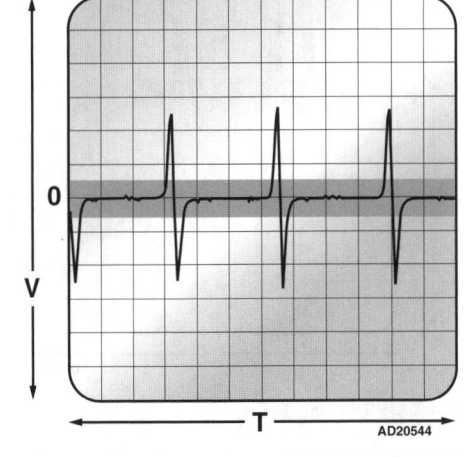

AD20544

6 Analogue, AC

Typical oscilloscope wave forms – diesel

NOTE: *The following illustrations show typical representations of the wave forms that can be expected from the ECM pins referred to in the pin data tables. These wave forms are not unique to a particular circuit or component and may be cross-referenced to various components, in different pin data tables.*

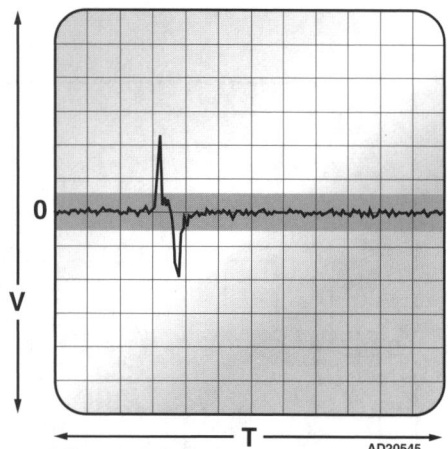

AD20545

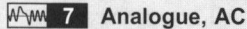 **7** Analogue, AC

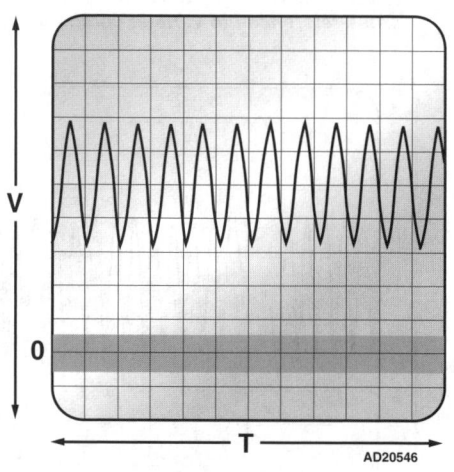

AD20546

8 Analogue, DC

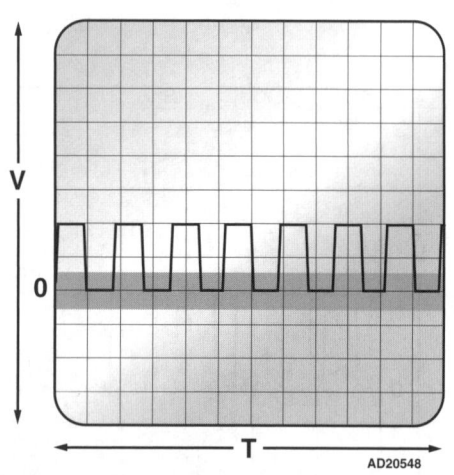

AD20548

9 Digital, DC

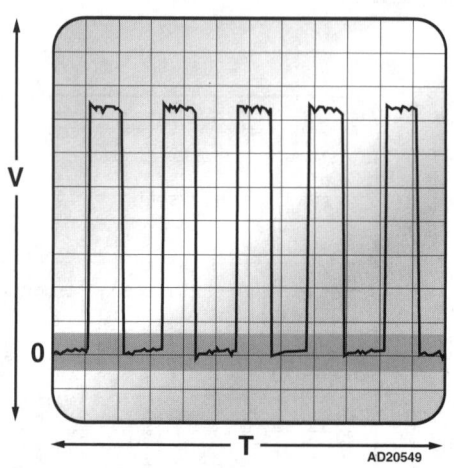

AD20549

10 Digital, DC

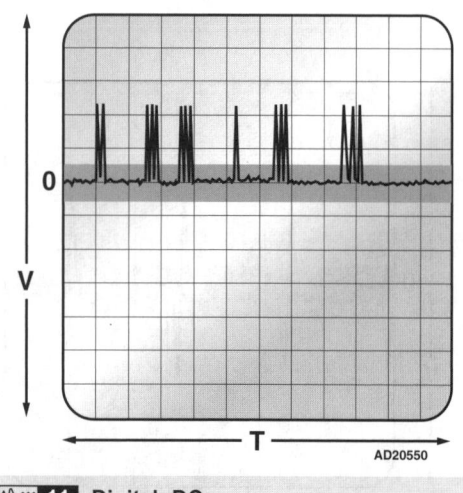

AD20550

11 Digital, DC

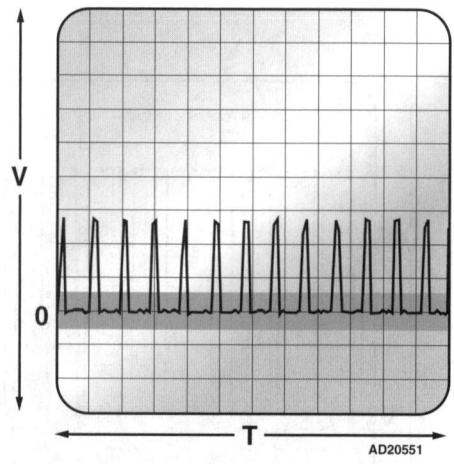

AD20551

12 Digital, DC

NOTE: *The following illustrations show typical representations of the wave forms that can be expected from the ECM pins referred to in the pin data tables. These wave forms are not unique to a particular circuit or component and may be cross-referenced to various components, in different pin data tables.*

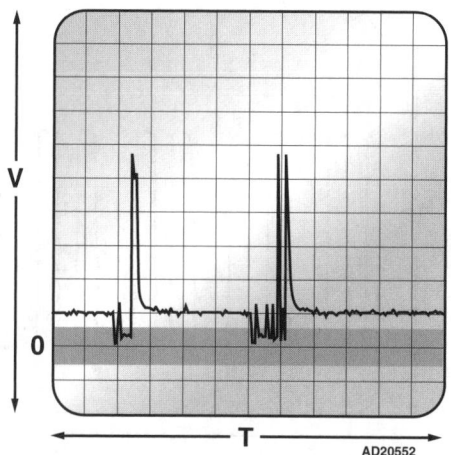

AD20552

🗠 **13** Digital, DC

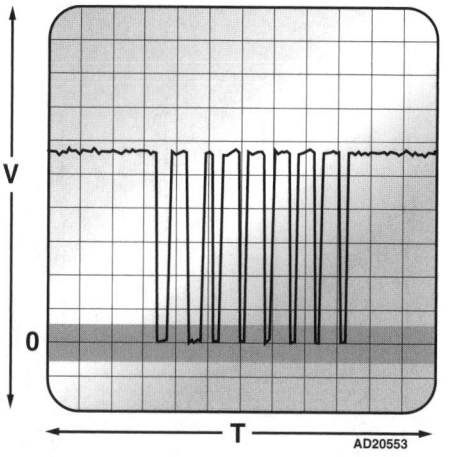

AD20553

🗠 **14** Digital, DC

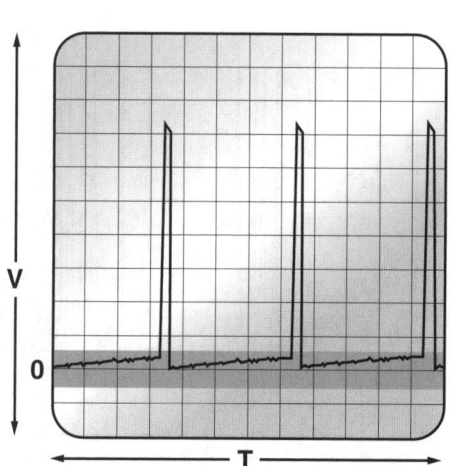

AD20355

🗠 **15** Digital, DC

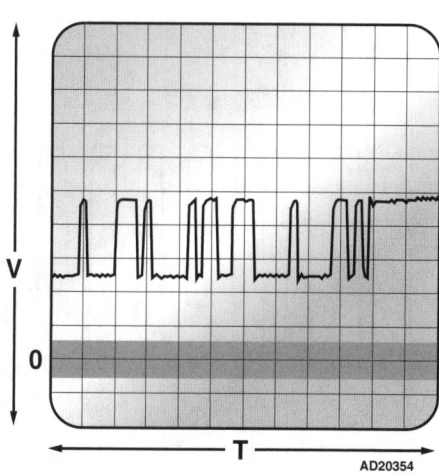

AD20354

🗠 **16** Digital, DC

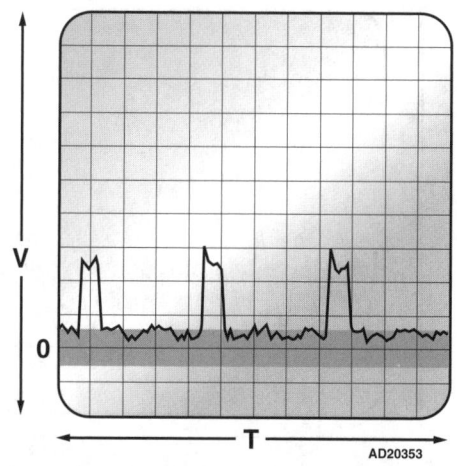

AD20353

🗠 **17** Digital, DC

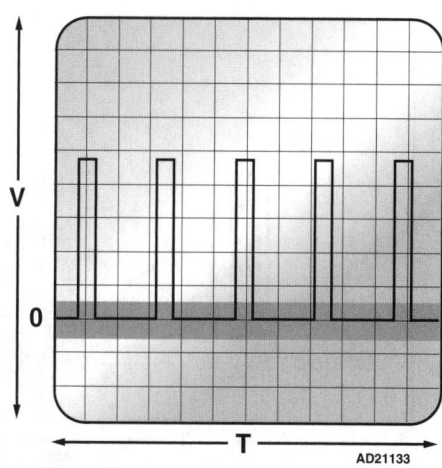

AD21133

🗠 **19** Digital, DC

Typical oscilloscope wave forms – diesel

NOTE: *The following illustrations show typical representations of the wave forms that can be expected from the ECM pins referred to in the pin data tables. These wave forms are not unique to a particular circuit or component and may be cross-referenced to various components, in different pin data tables.*

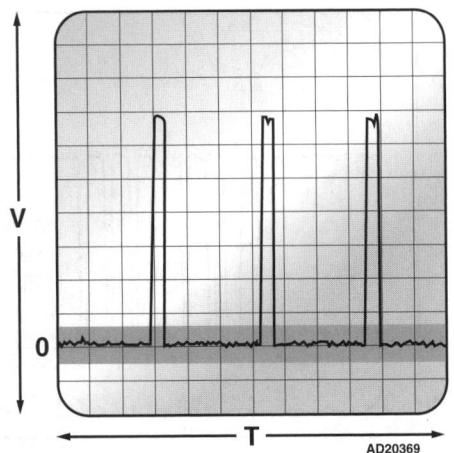

AD20369

20 Digital, DC

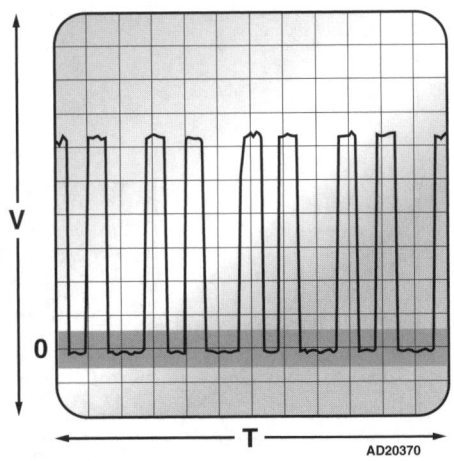

AD20370

21 Digital, DC

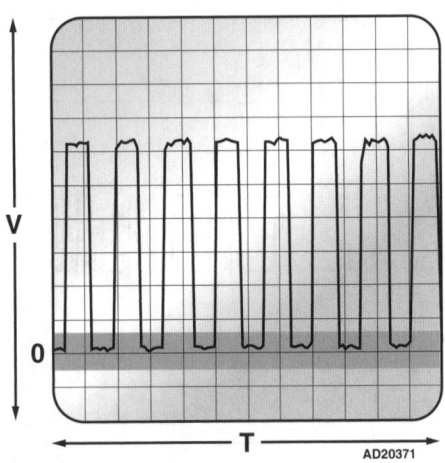

AD20371

22 Digital, DC

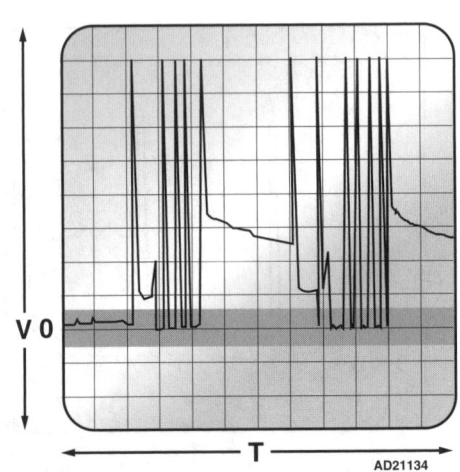

AD21134

23 Digital, DC

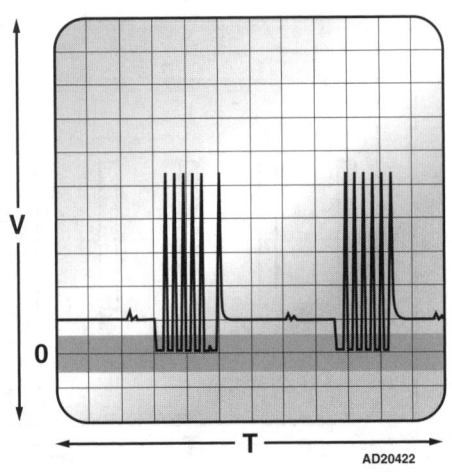

AD20422

24 Digital, DC

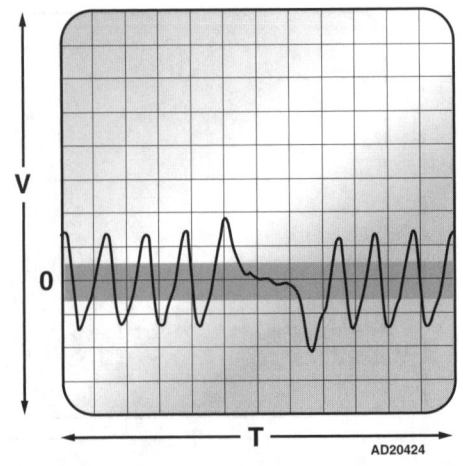

AD20424

25 Analogue, AC

NOTE: *The following illustrations show typical representations of the wave forms that can be expected from the ECM pins referred to in the pin data tables. These wave forms are not unique to a particular circuit or component and may be cross-referenced to various components, in different pin data tables.*

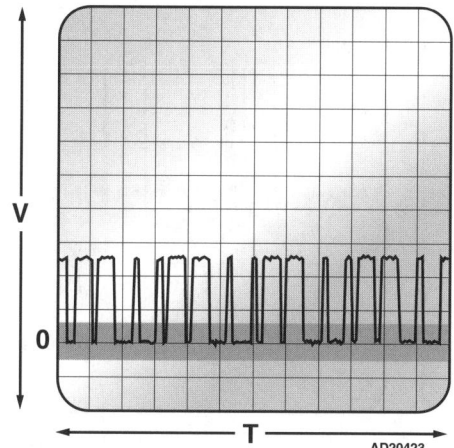

AD20423

⌁⌁ **26** Digital, DC

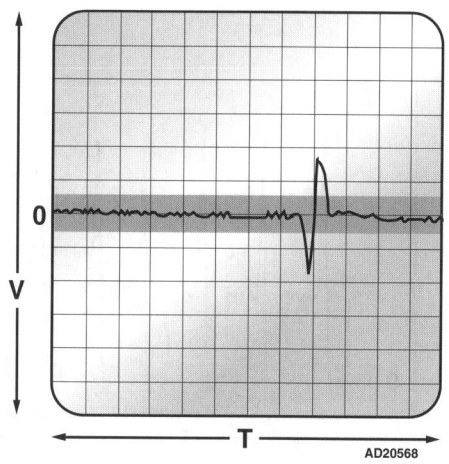

AD20568

⌁⌁ **27** Analogue, AC

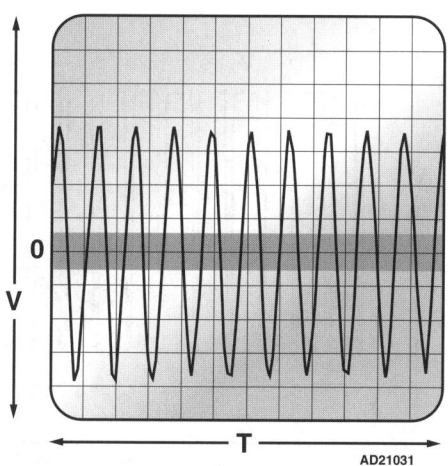

AD21031

⌁⌁ **28** Analogue, AC

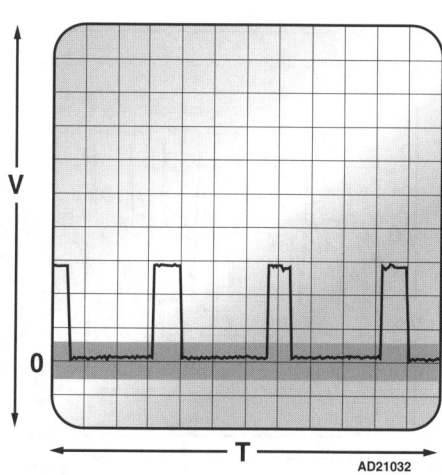

AD21032

⌁⌁ **29** Digital, DC

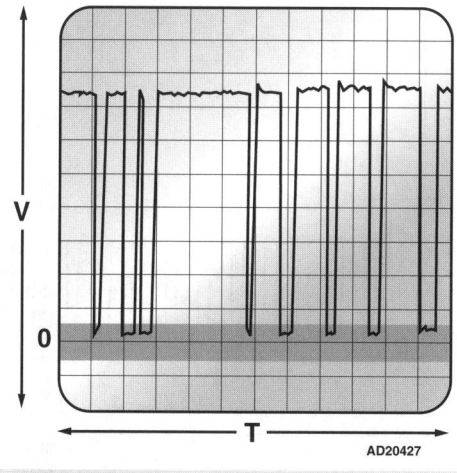

AD20427

⌁⌁ **30** Digital, DC

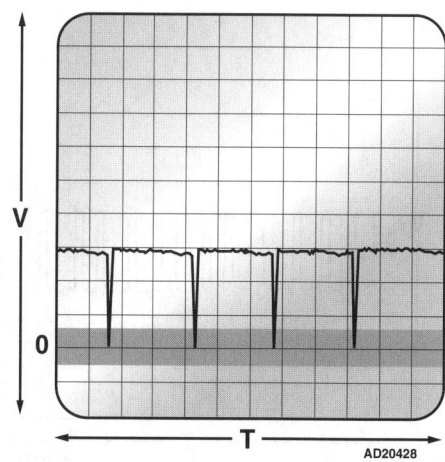

AD20428

⌁⌁ **31** Digital, DC

Typical oscilloscope wave forms – diesel

NOTE: *The following illustrations show typical representations of the wave forms that can be expected from the ECM pins referred to in the pin data tables. These wave forms are not unique to a particular circuit or component and may be cross-referenced to various components, in different pin data tables.*

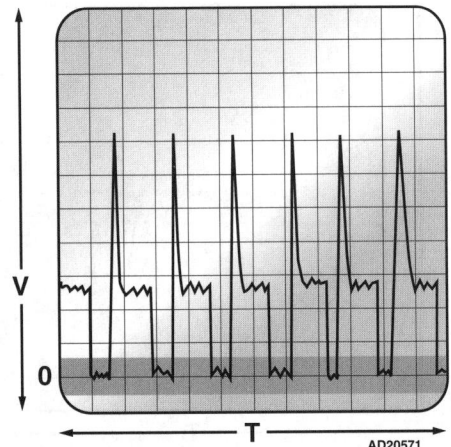

AD20571

 **33** Digital, DC

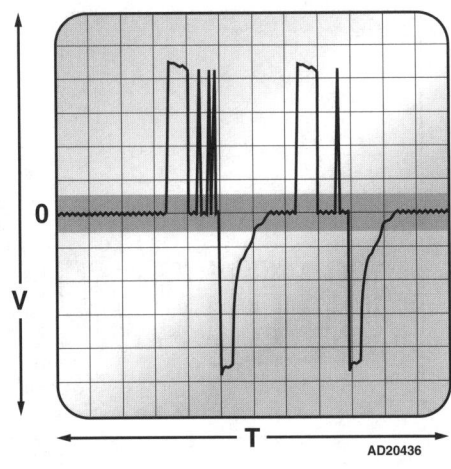

AD20436

35 Digital, DC

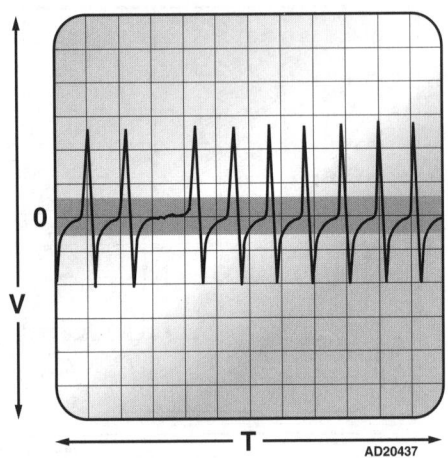

AD20437

36 Analogue, AC

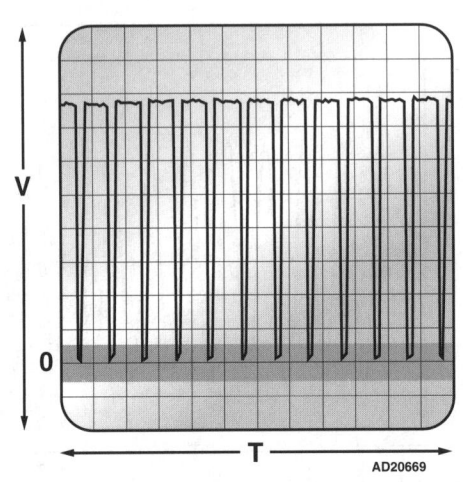

AD20669

37 Digital, DC

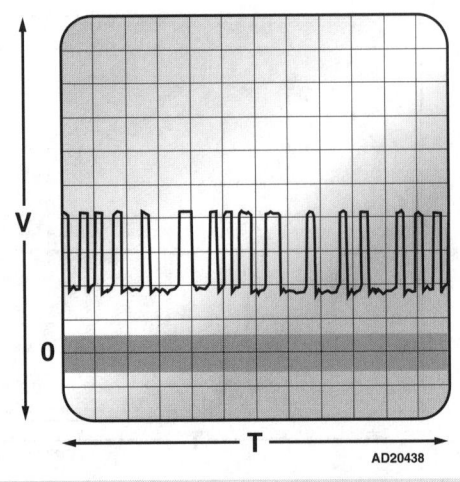

AD20438

38 Digital, DC

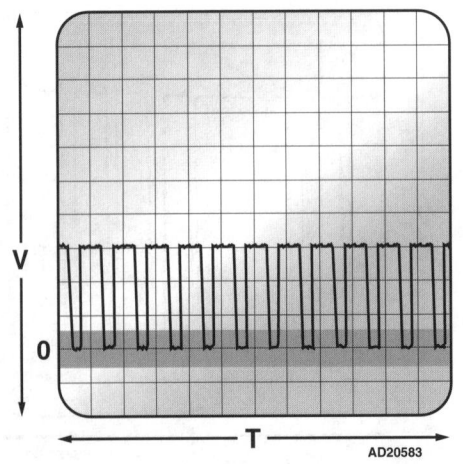

AD20583

39 Digital, DC

NOTE: *The following illustrations show typical representations of the wave forms that can be expected from the ECM pins referred to in the pin data tables. These wave forms are not unique to a particular circuit or component and may be cross-referenced to various components, in different pin data tables.*

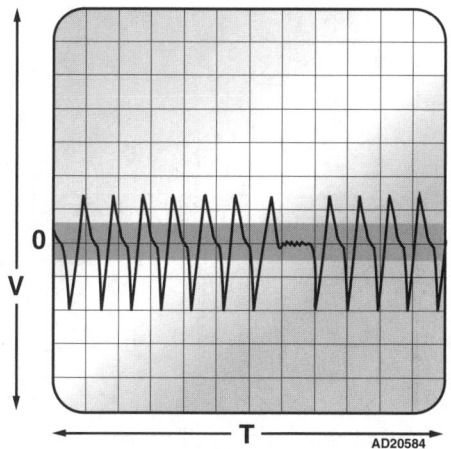

AD20584

40 Analogue, AC

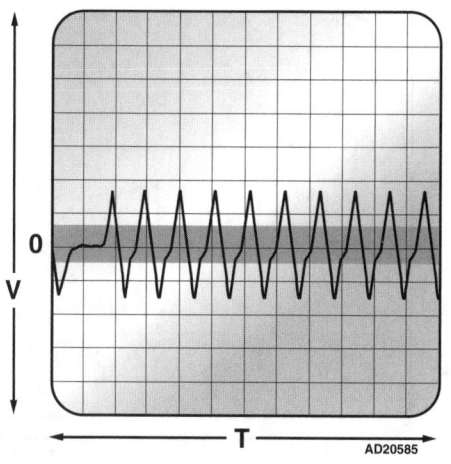

AD20585

41 Analogue, AC

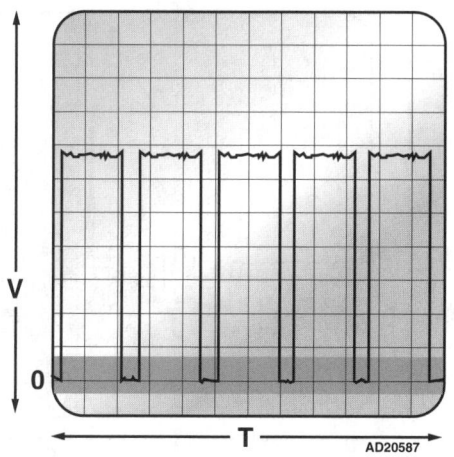

AD20587

43 Digital, DC

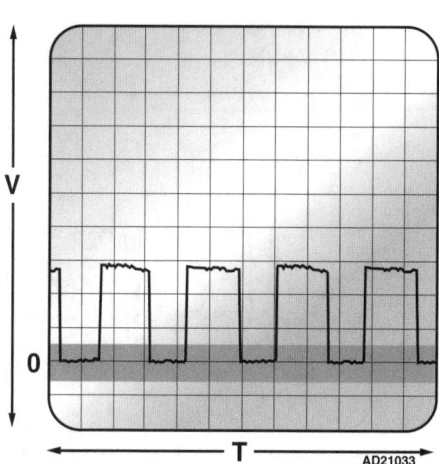

AD21033

48 Digital, DC

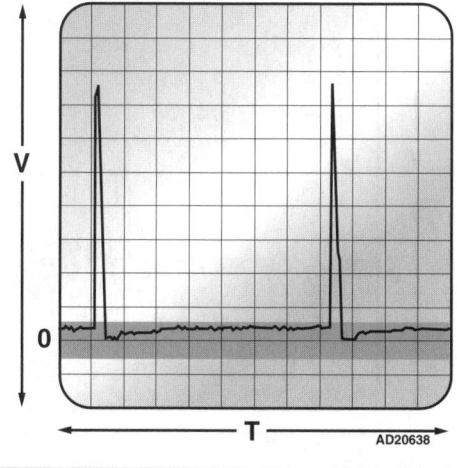

AD20638

49 Digital, DC

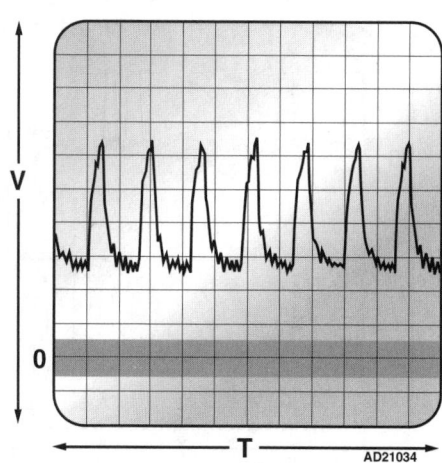

AD21034

53 Digital, DC

Typical oscilloscope wave forms – diesel

NOTE: *The following illustrations show typical representations of the wave forms that can be expected from the ECM pins referred to in the pin data tables. These wave forms are not unique to a particular circuit or component and may be cross-referenced to various components, in different pin data tables.*

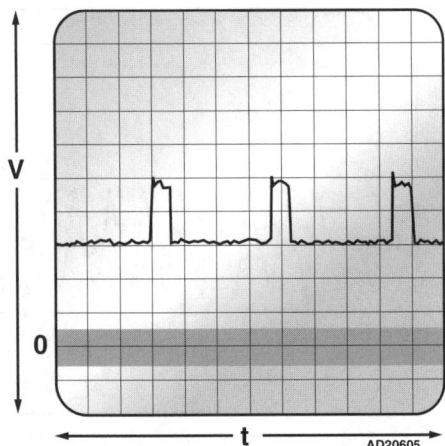

AD20605

54 Digital, DC

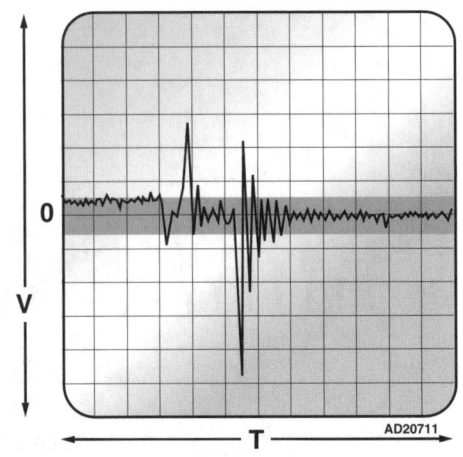

AD20711

55 Analogue, AC

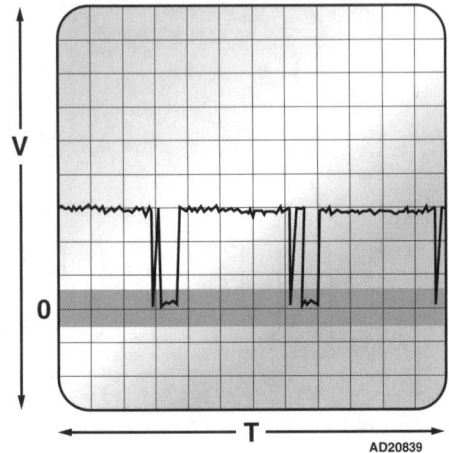

AD20839

56 Digital, DC

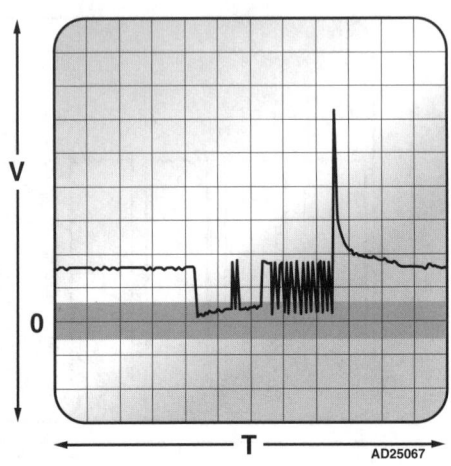

AD25067

57 Digital, DC

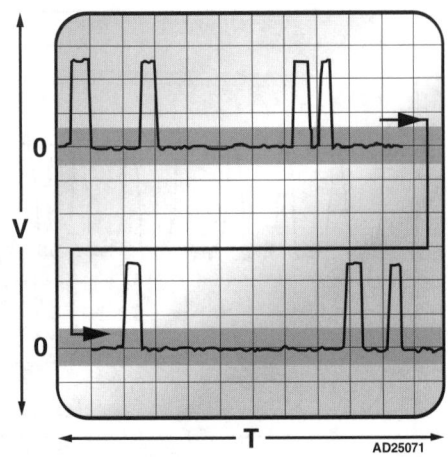

AD25071

58 Digital, DC

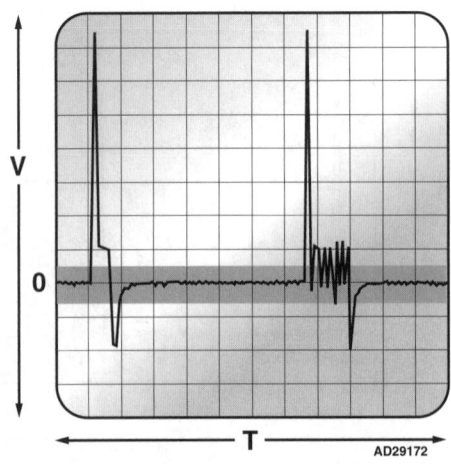

AD29172

59 Digital, DC

NOTE: *The following illustrations show typical representations of the wave forms that can be expected from the ECM pins referred to in the pin data tables. These wave forms are not unique to a particular circuit or component and may be cross-referenced to various components, in different pin data tables.*

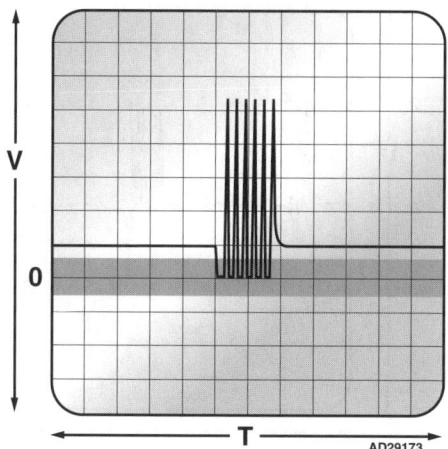

AD29173

〰〰 **60** Digital, DC

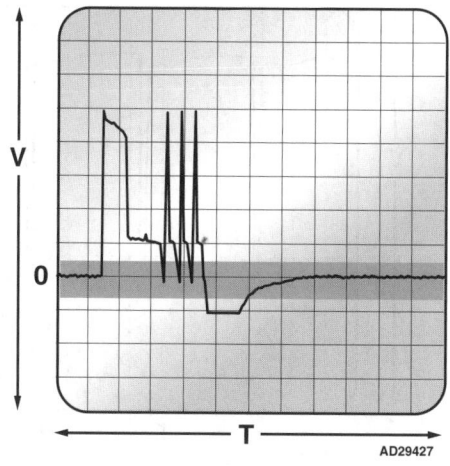

AD29427

〰〰 **61** Digital, DC

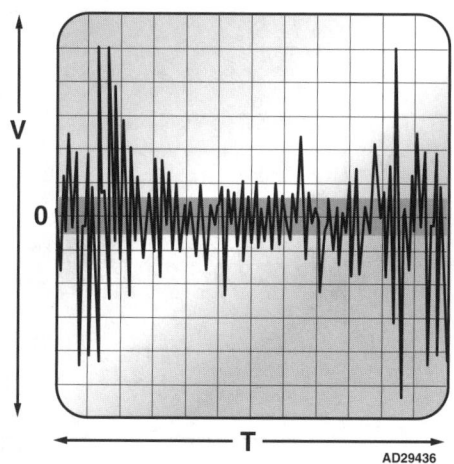

AD29436

〰〰 **62** Analogue, AC

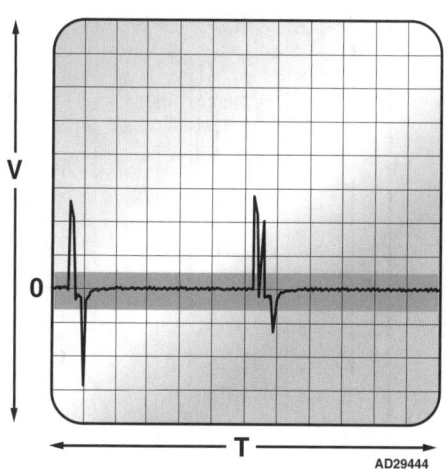

AD29444

〰〰 **63** Digital, DC

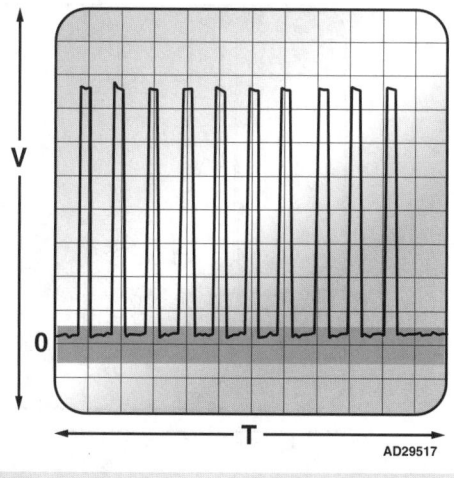

AD29517

〰〰 **64** Digital, DC

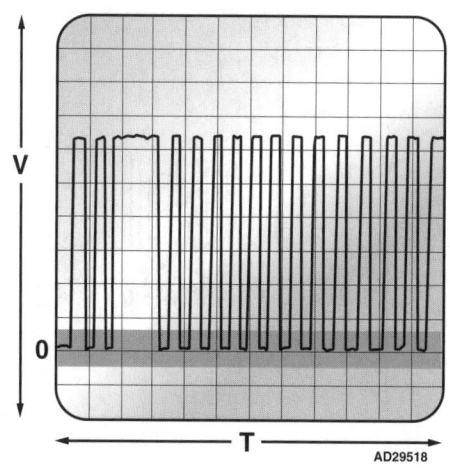

AD29518

〰〰 **65** Digital, DC

Typical oscilloscope wave forms – diesel

NOTE: *The following illustrations show typical representations of the wave forms that can be expected from the ECM pins referred to in the pin data tables. These wave forms are not unique to a particular circuit or component and may be cross-referenced to various components, in different pin data tables.*

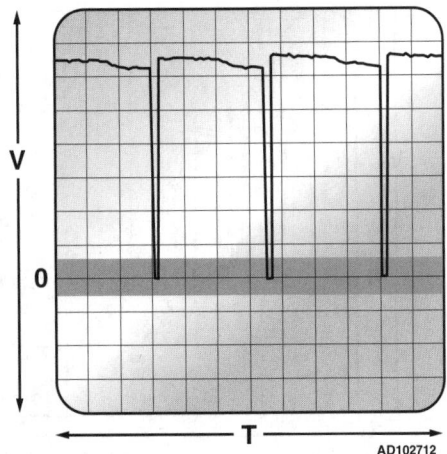

AD102712

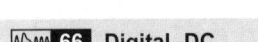 **66** Digital, DC

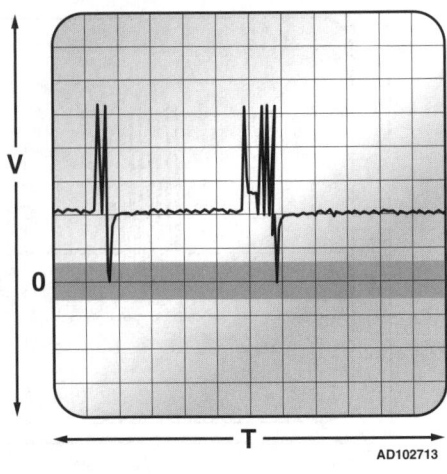

AD102713

〰〰 **67** Digital, DC

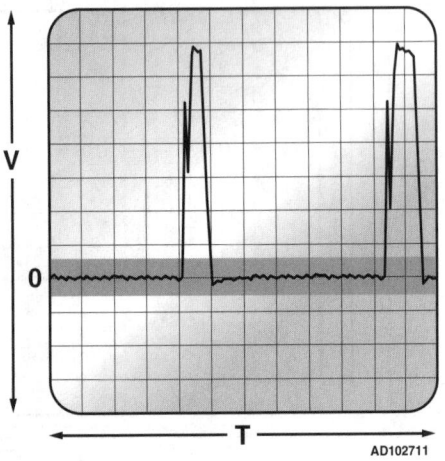

AD102711

〰〰 **68** Digital, DC

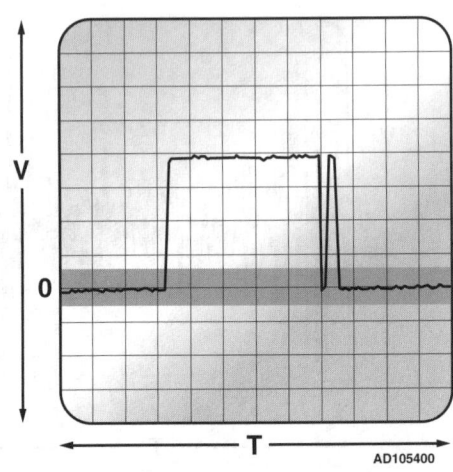

AD105400

〰〰 **69** Digital, DC

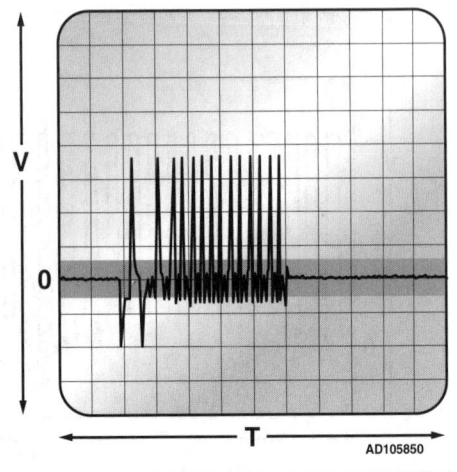

AD105850

〰〰 **70** Digital, DC

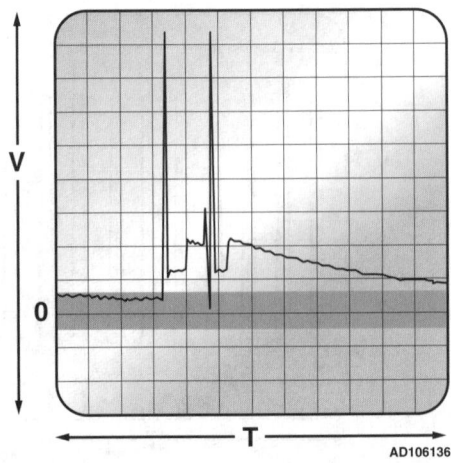

AD106136

〰〰 **71** Digital, DC

Autodata

64

/Autodata

NOTE: *The following illustrations show typical representations of the wave forms that can be expected from the ECM pins referred to in the pin data tables. These wave forms are not unique to a particular circuit or component and may be cross-referenced to various components, in different pin data tables.*

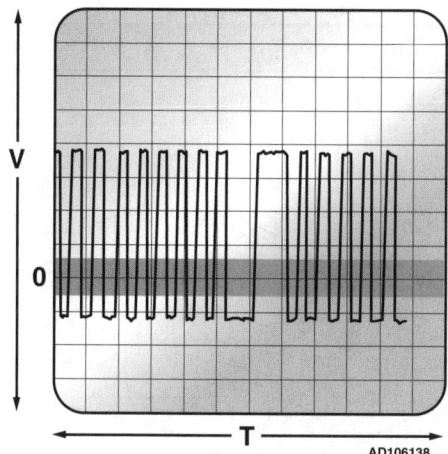

AD106138

72 Digital, DC

ECM locations

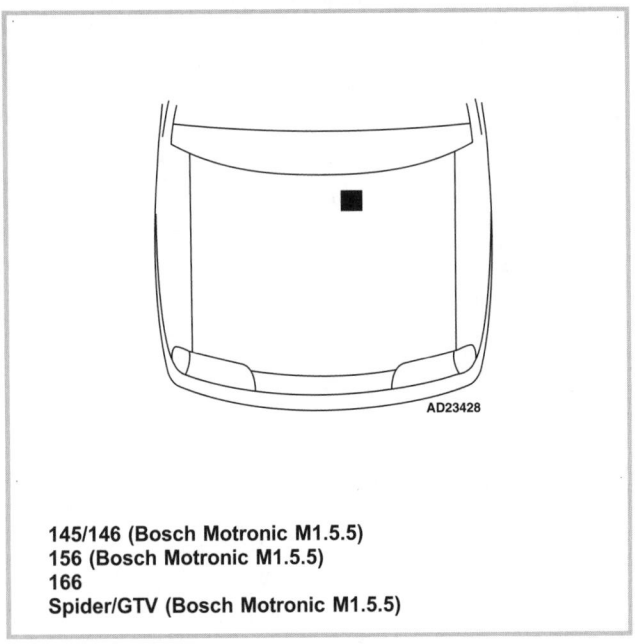

AD23428

145/146 (Bosch Motronic M1.5.5)
156 (Bosch Motronic M1.5.5)
166
Spider/GTV (Bosch Motronic M1.5.5)

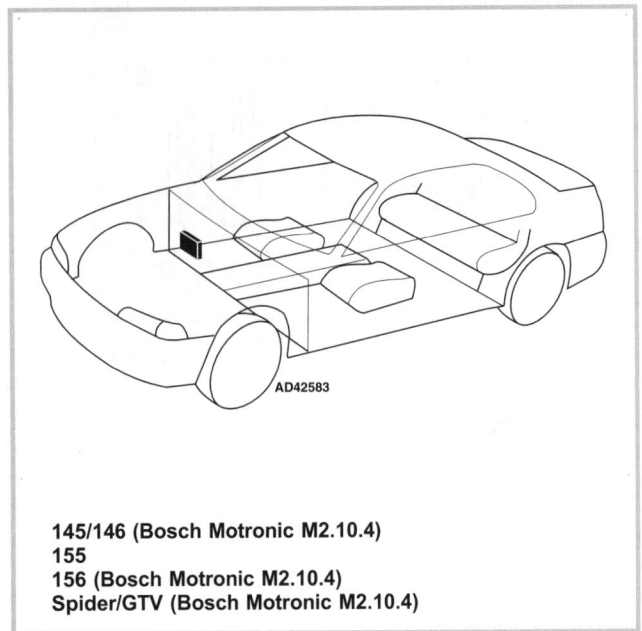

AD42583

145/146 (Bosch Motronic M2.10.4)
155
156 (Bosch Motronic M2.10.4)
Spider/GTV (Bosch Motronic M2.10.4)

AUDI

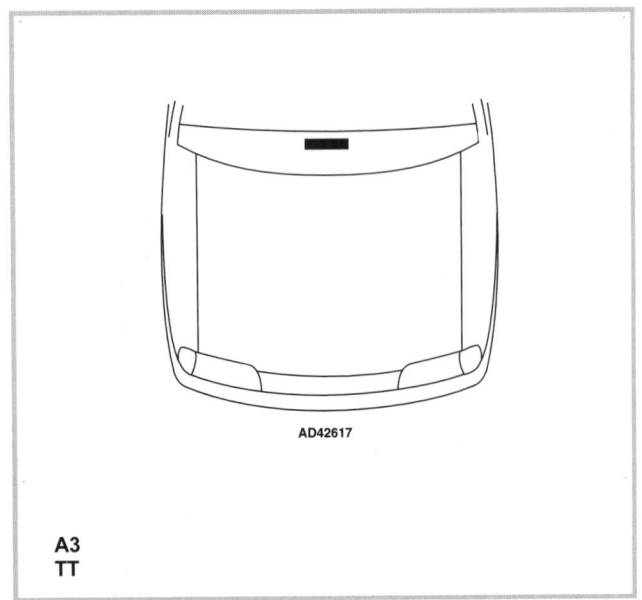

AD42617

A3
TT

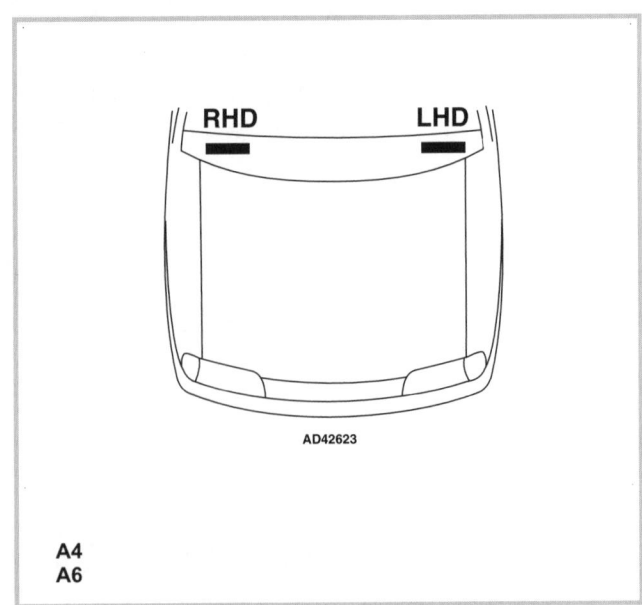

RHD   LHD

AD42623

A4
A6

BMW

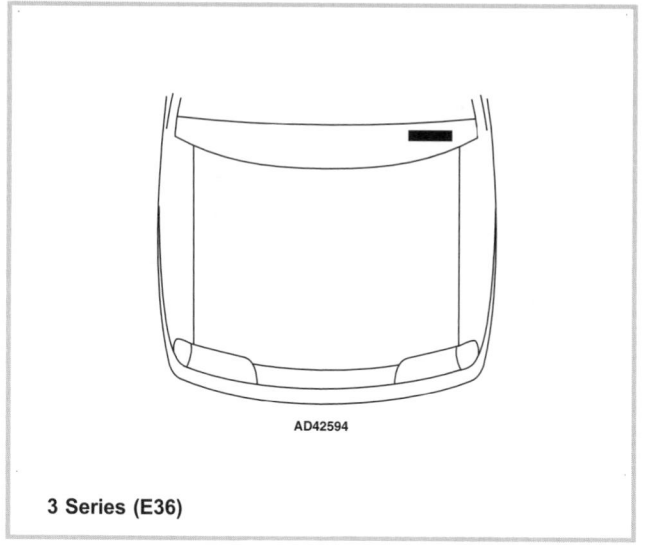

AD42594

3 Series (E36)

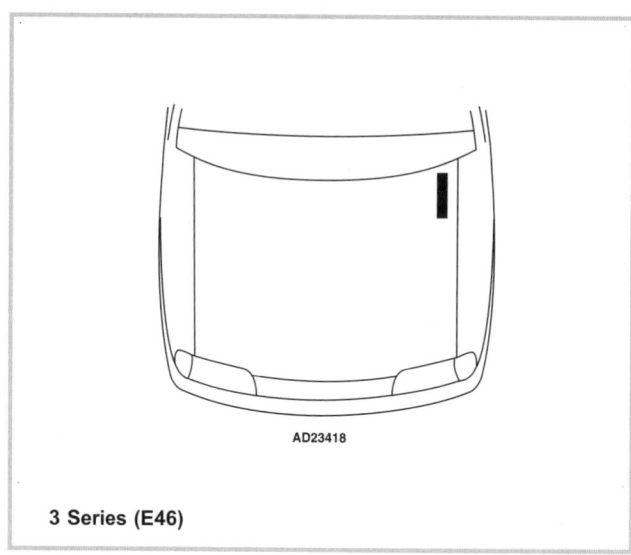

AD23418

3 Series (E46)

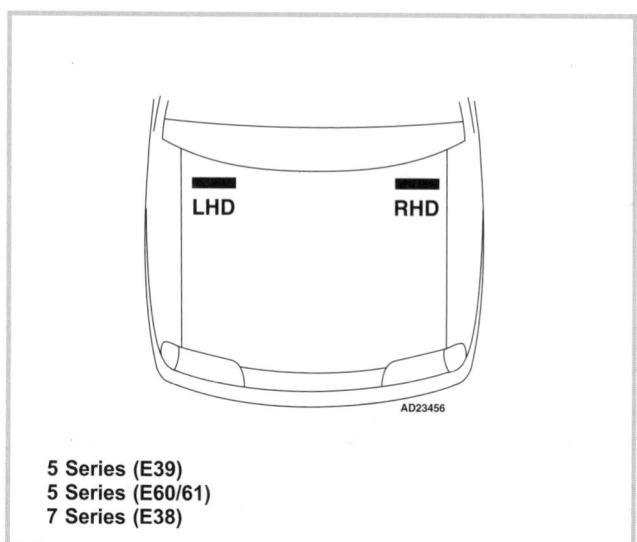

LHD   RHD

AD23456

5 Series (E39)
5 Series (E60/61)
7 Series (E38)

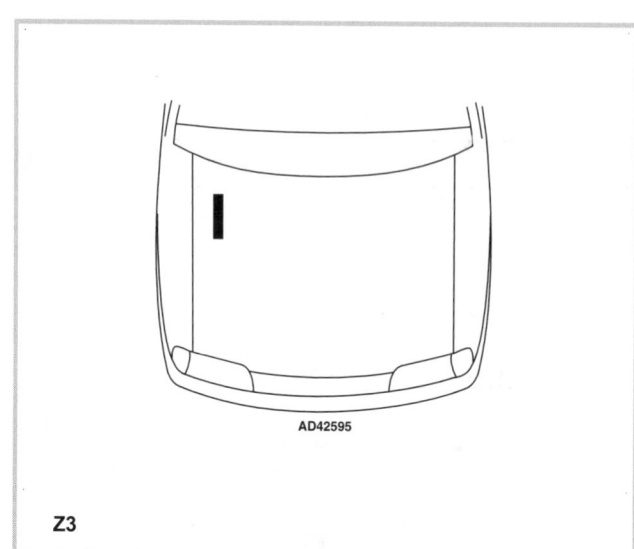

AD42595

Z3

CHRYSLER

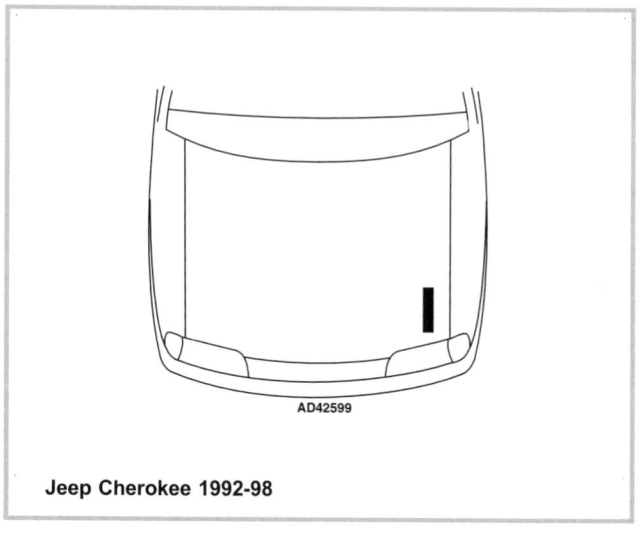

AD42599

Jeep Cherokee 1992-98

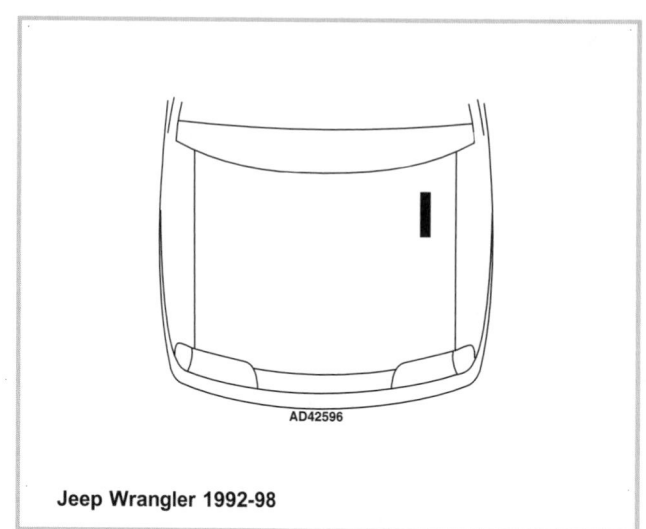

AD42596

Jeep Wrangler 1992-98

CITROEN

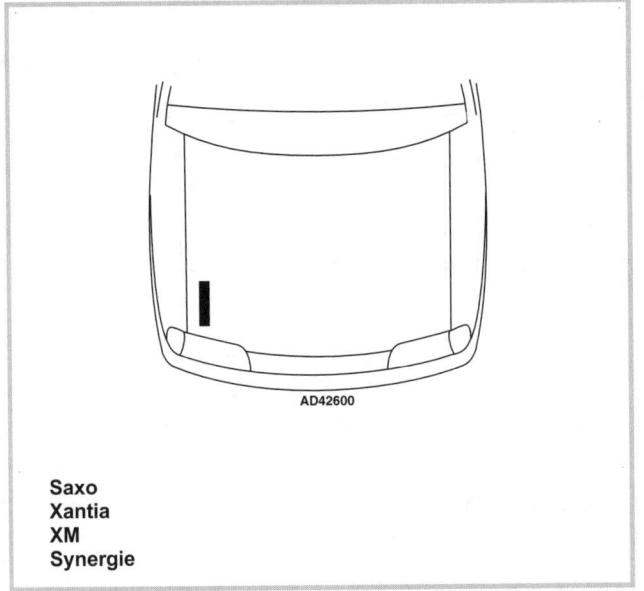

AD42600

Saxo
Xantia
XM
Synergie

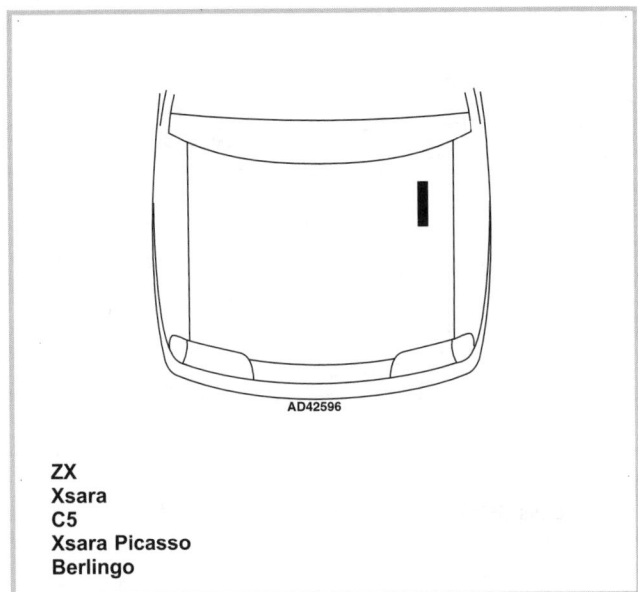

AD42596

ZX
Xsara
C5
Xsara Picasso
Berlingo

DAEWOO

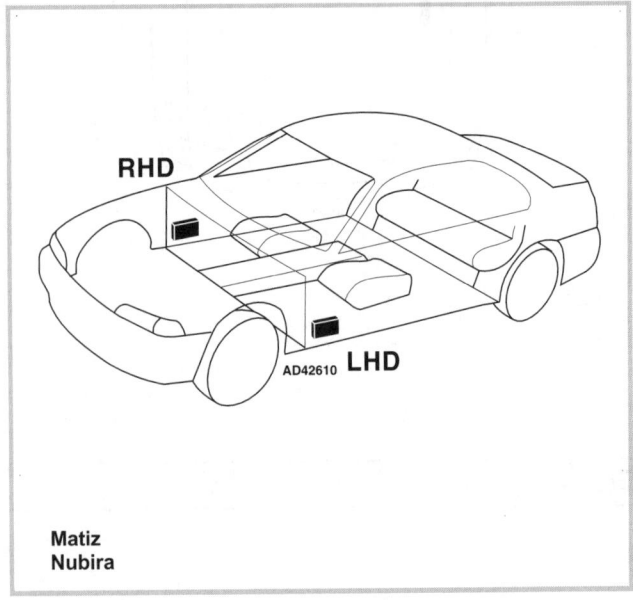

RHD

LHD
AD42610

Matiz
Nubira

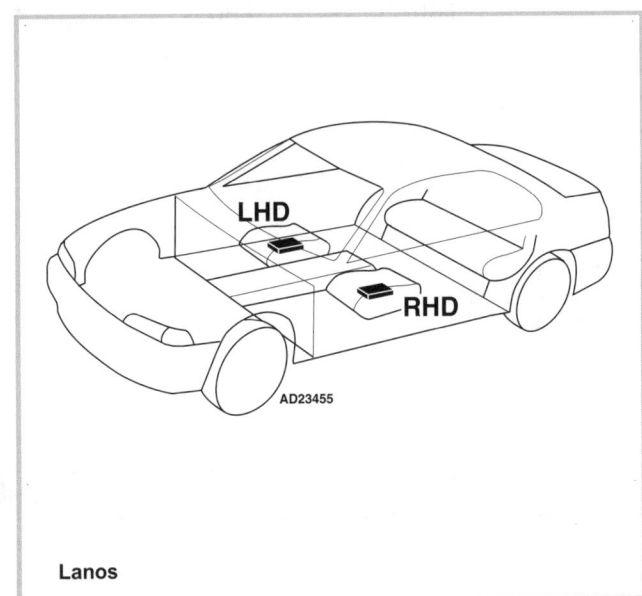

LHD

RHD
AD23455

Lanos

FIAT

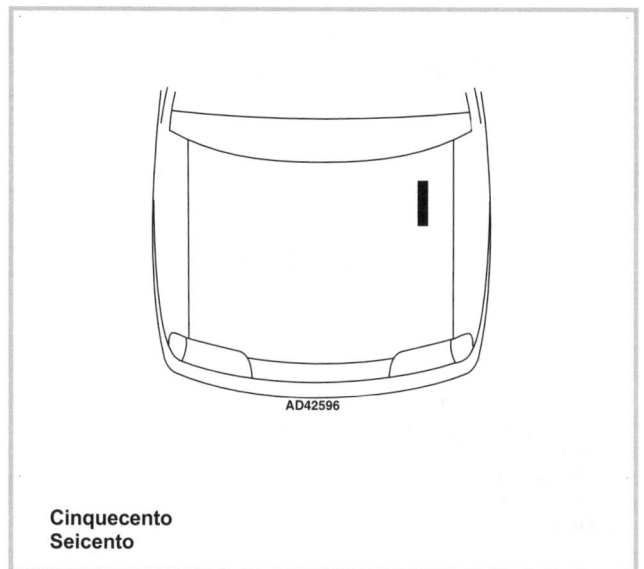

AD42596

Cinquecento
Seicento

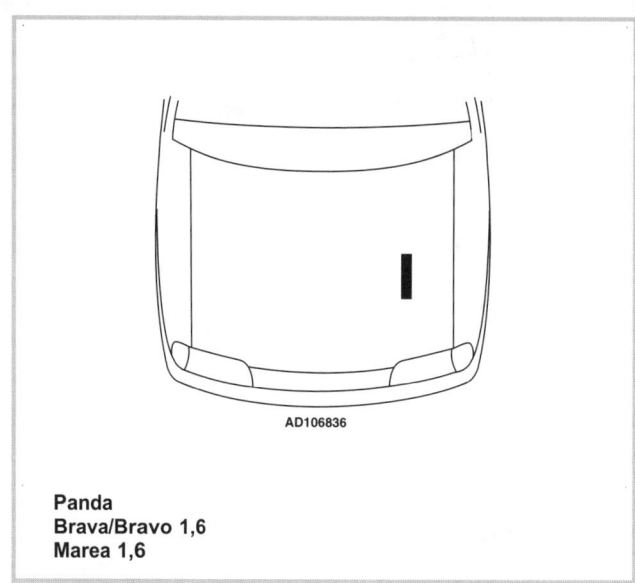

AD106836

Panda
Brava/Bravo 1,6
Marea 1,6

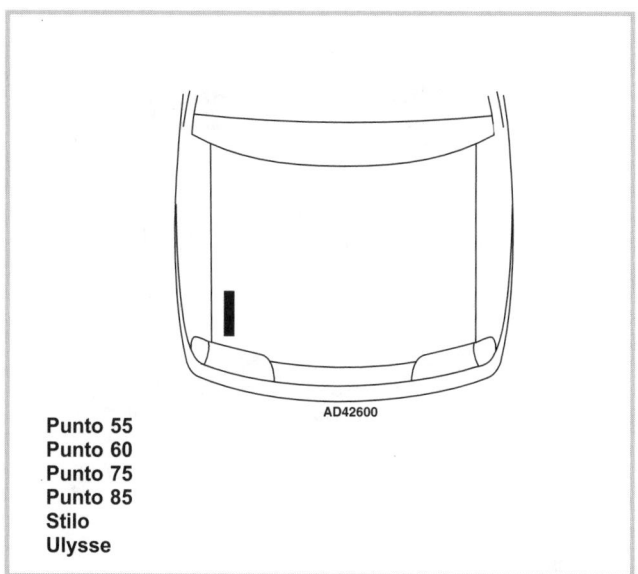

AD42600

Punto 55
Punto 60
Punto 75
Punto 85
Stilo
Ulysse

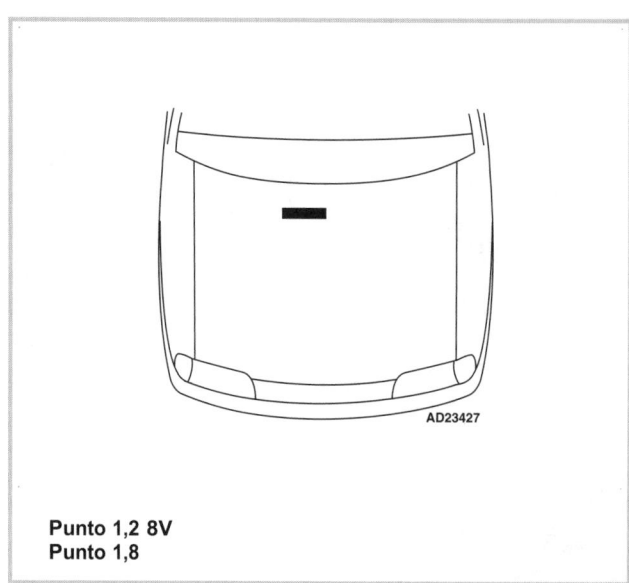

AD23427

Punto 1,2 8V
Punto 1,8

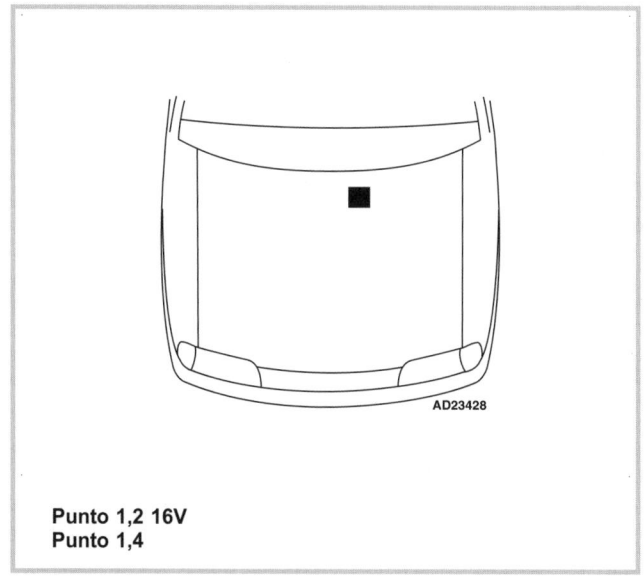

AD23428

Punto 1,2 16V
Punto 1,4

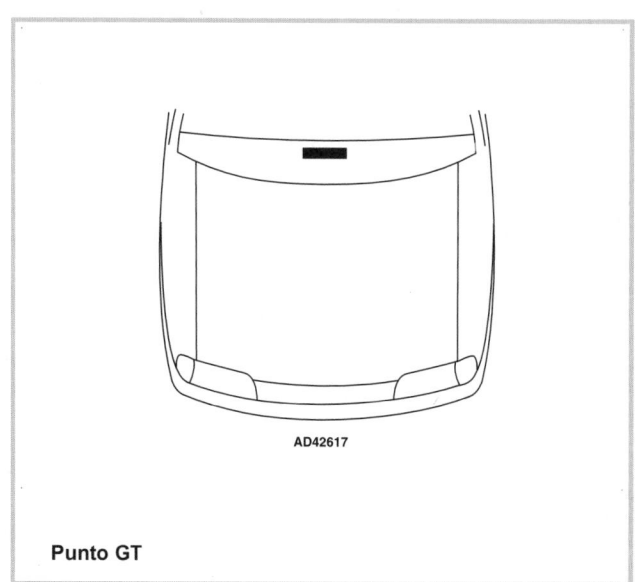

AD42617

Punto GT

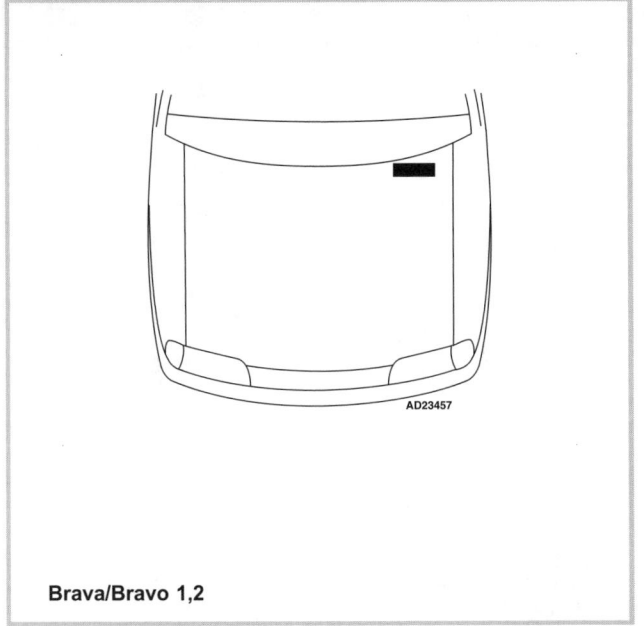

Brava/Bravo 1,2

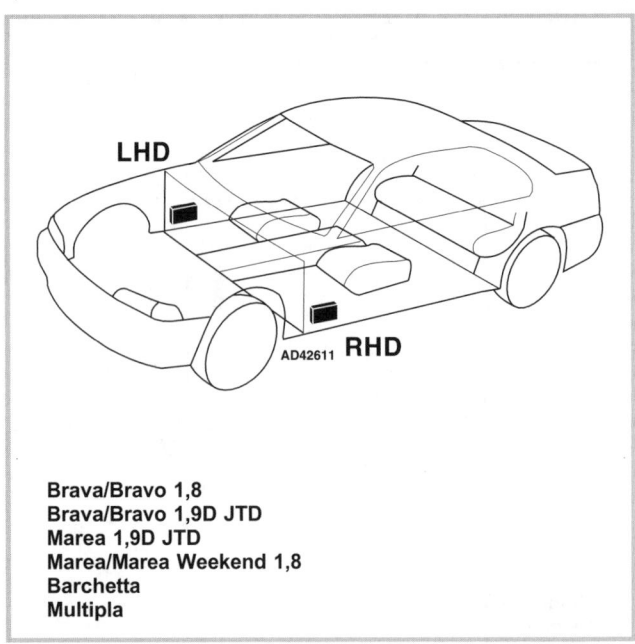

Brava/Bravo 1,8
Brava/Bravo 1,9D JTD
Marea 1,9D JTD
Marea/Marea Weekend 1,8
Barchetta
Multipla

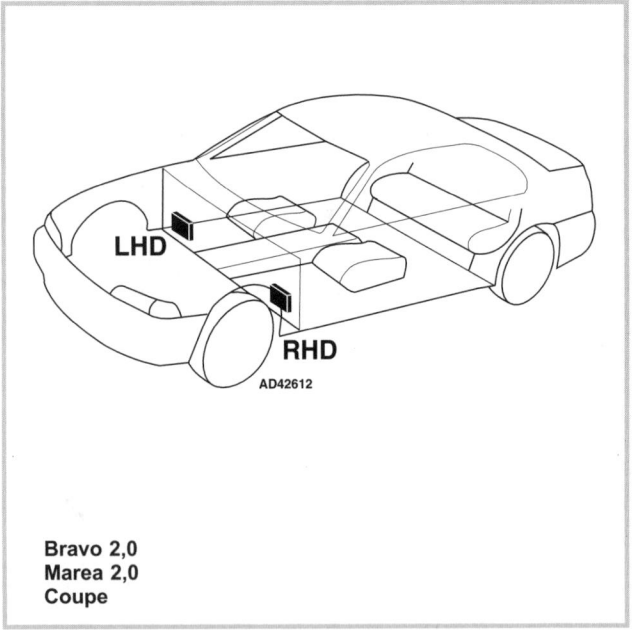

Bravo 2,0
Marea 2,0
Coupe

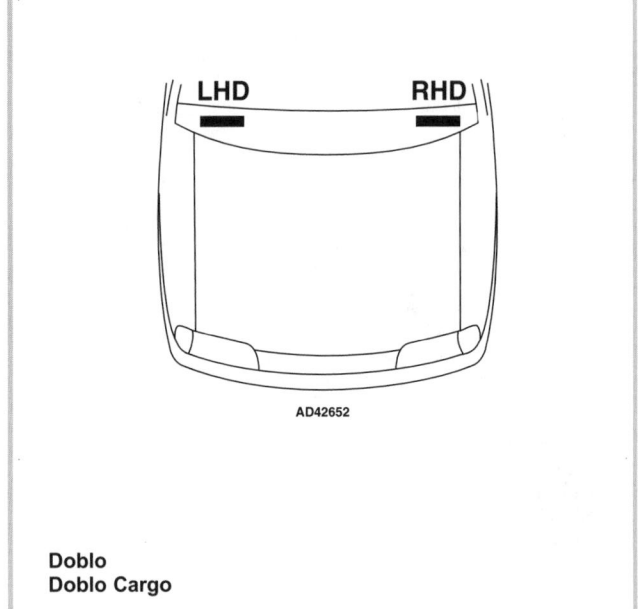

Doblo
Doblo Cargo

FORD

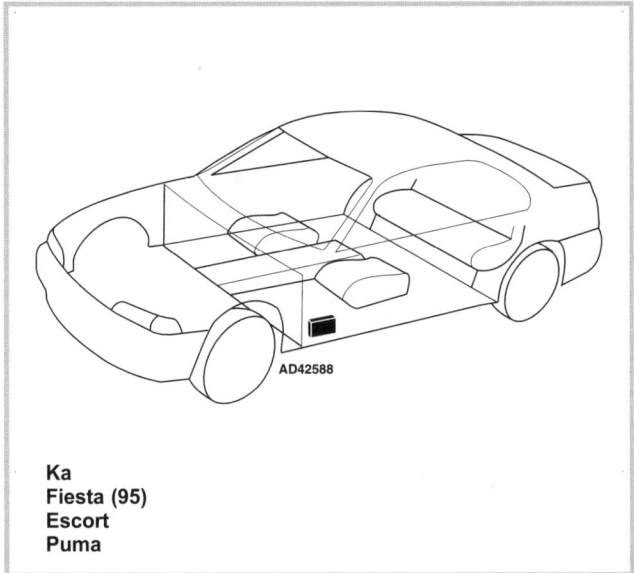

AD42588

Ka
Fiesta (95)
Escort
Puma

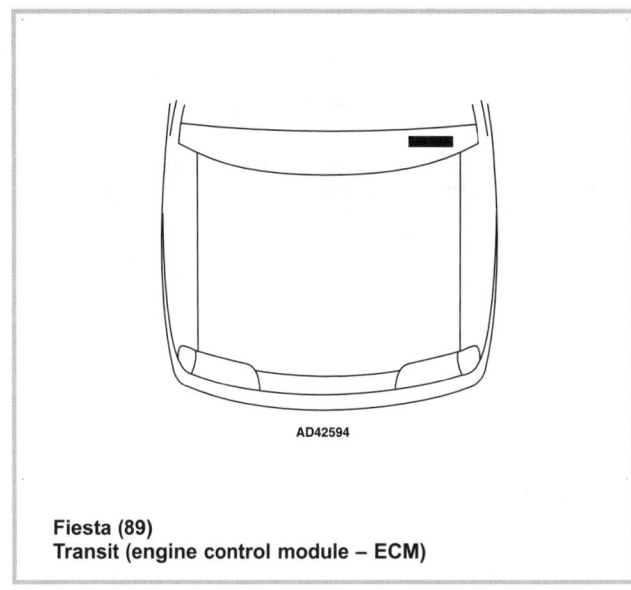

AD42594

Fiesta (89)
Transit (engine control module – ECM)

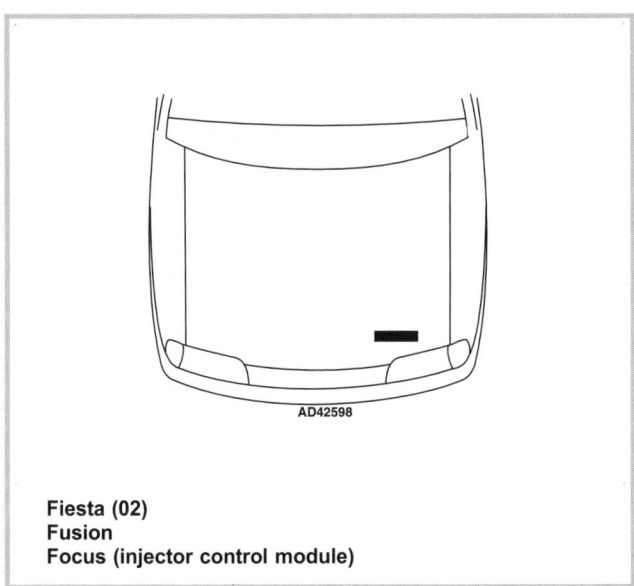

AD42598

Fiesta (02)
Fusion
Focus (injector control module)

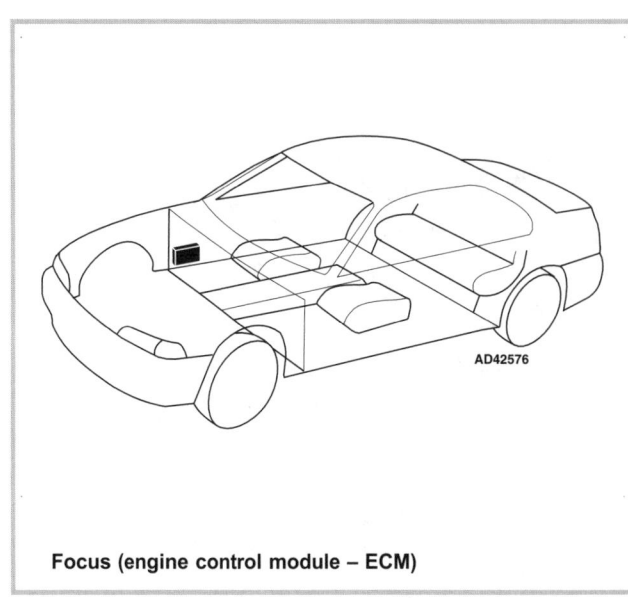

AD42576

Focus (engine control module – ECM)

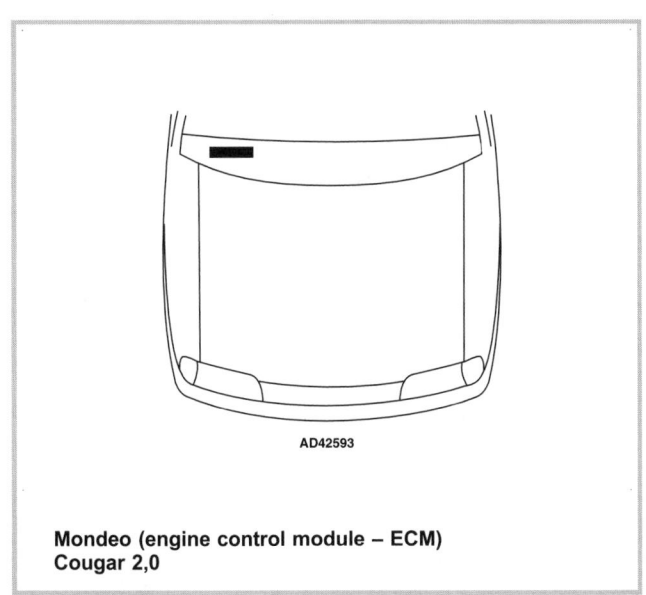

AD42593

Mondeo (engine control module – ECM)
Cougar 2,0

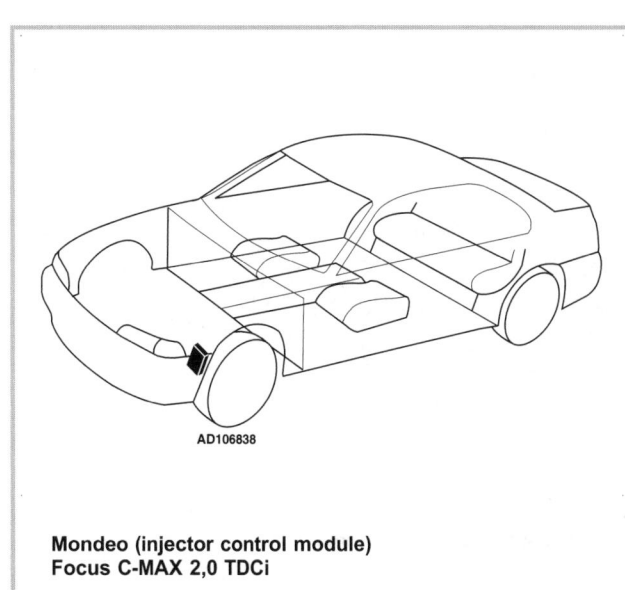

AD106838

Mondeo (injector control module)
Focus C-MAX 2,0 TDCi

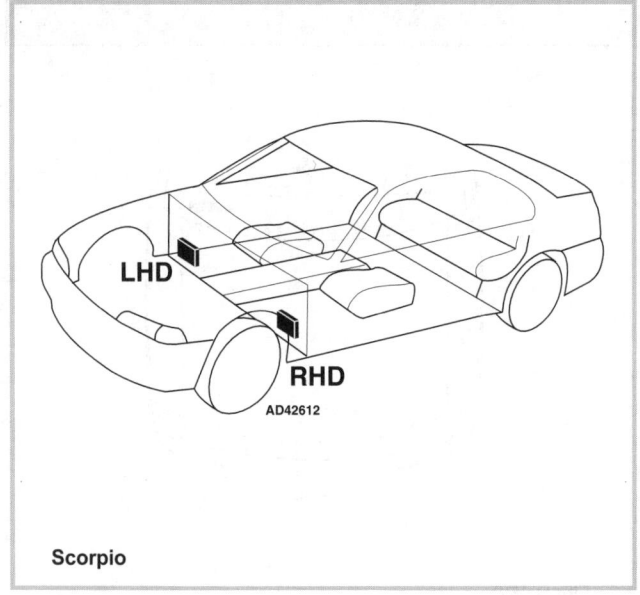

Scorpio

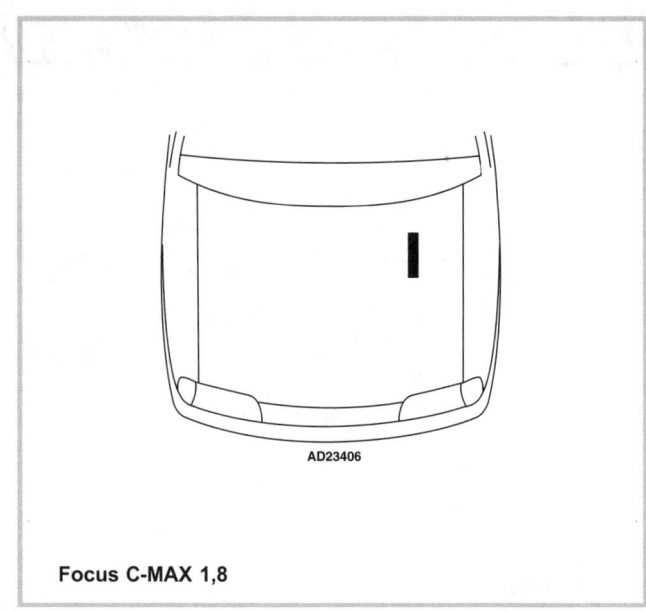

Focus C-MAX 1,8

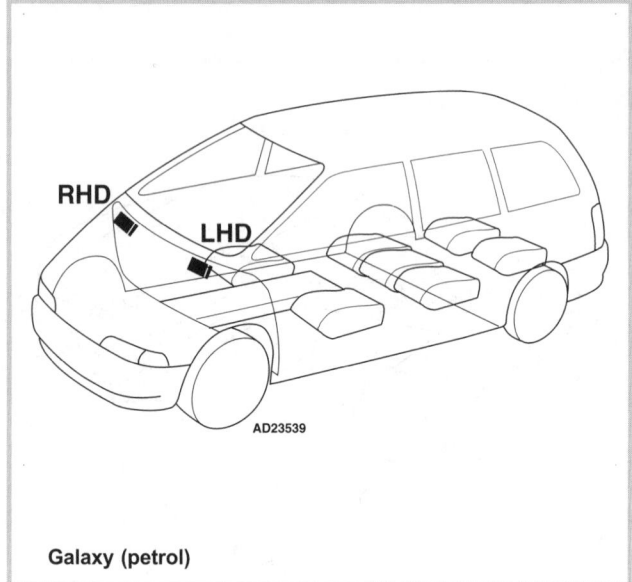

Galaxy (petrol)

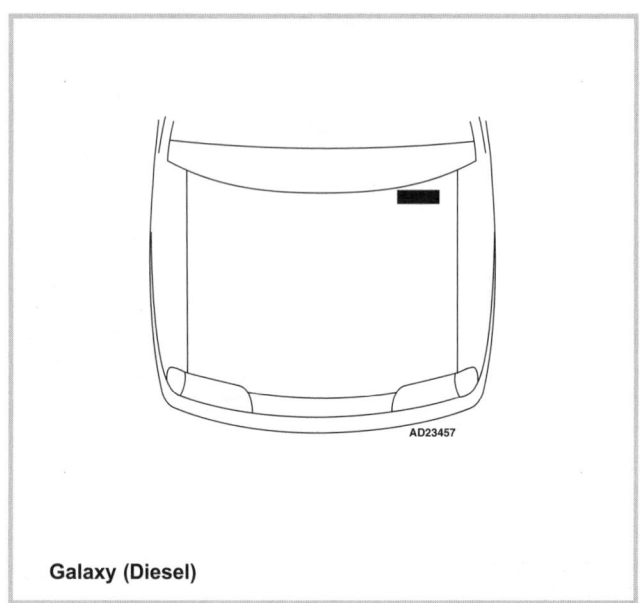

Galaxy (Diesel)

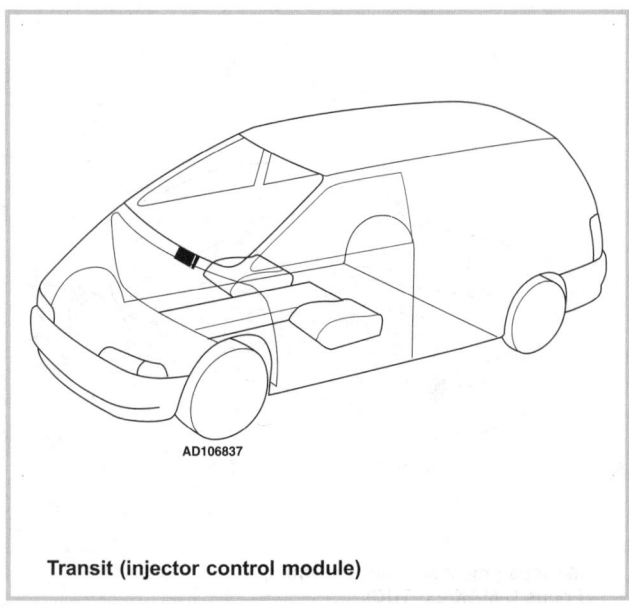

Transit (injector control module)

HONDA

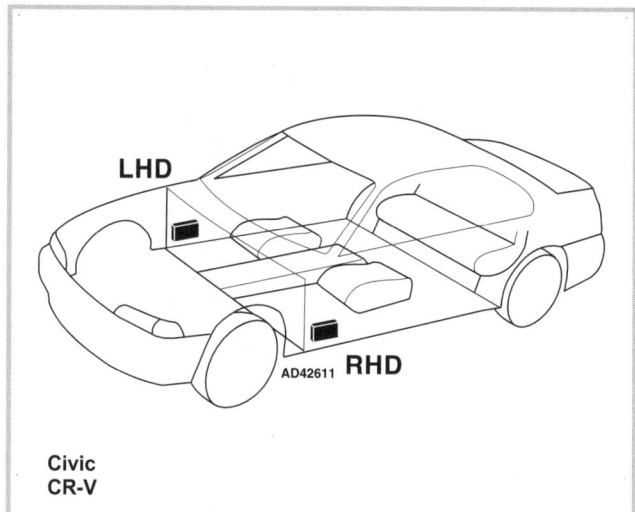

Civic
CR-V

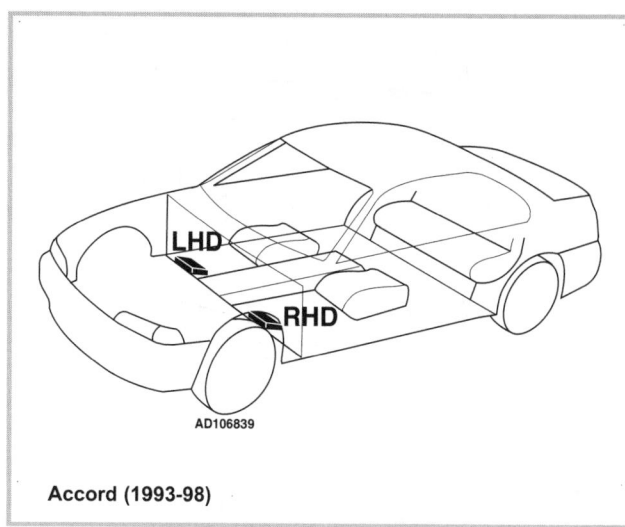

Accord (1993-98)

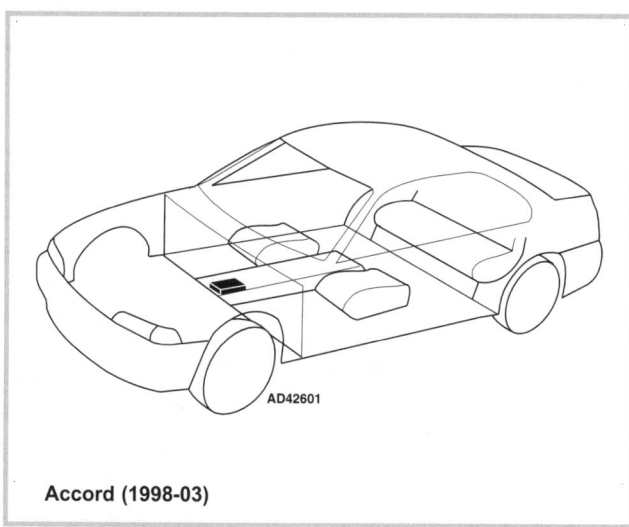

Accord (1998-03)

HYUNDAI

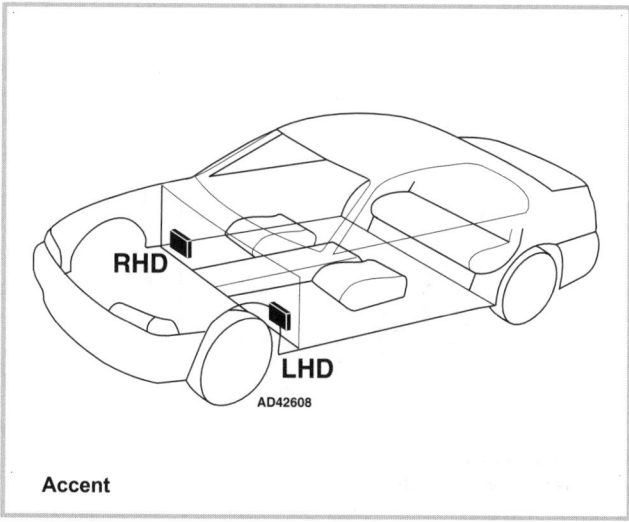

Accent

ECM locations

JAGUAR (DAIMLER)

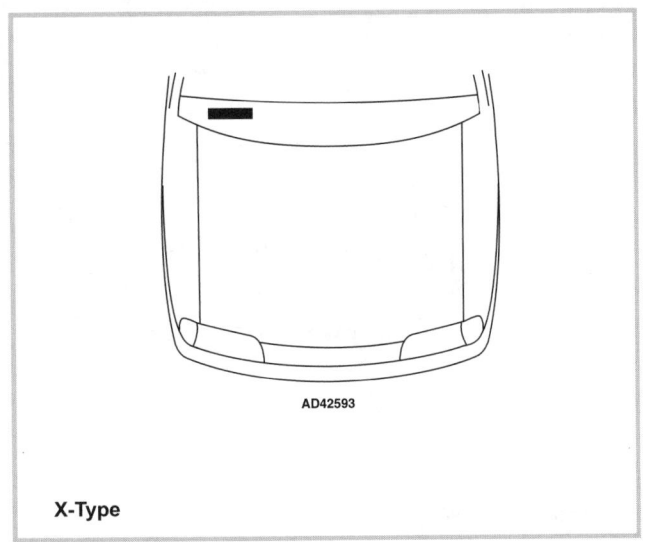

AD42593

X-Type

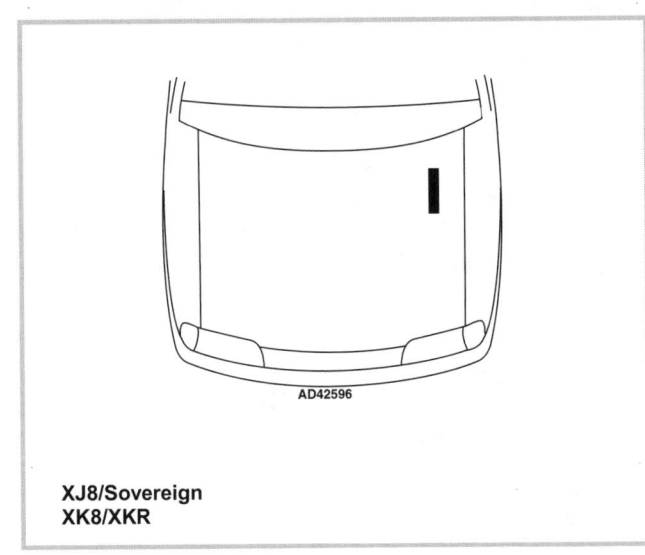

AD42596

XJ8/Sovereign
XK8/XKR

LAND ROVER

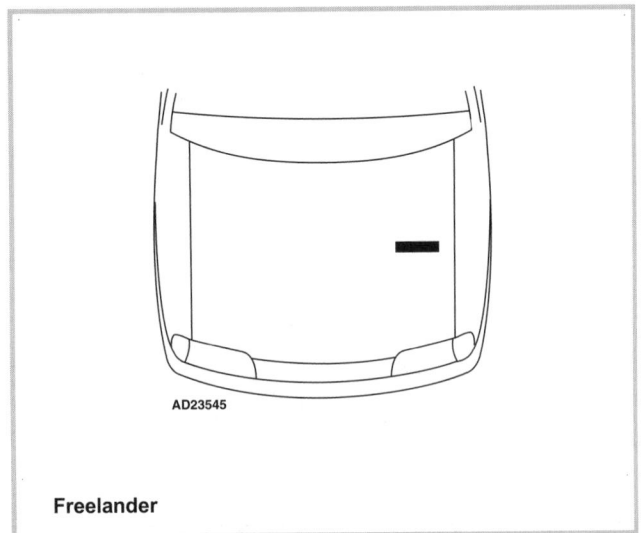

AD23545

Freelander

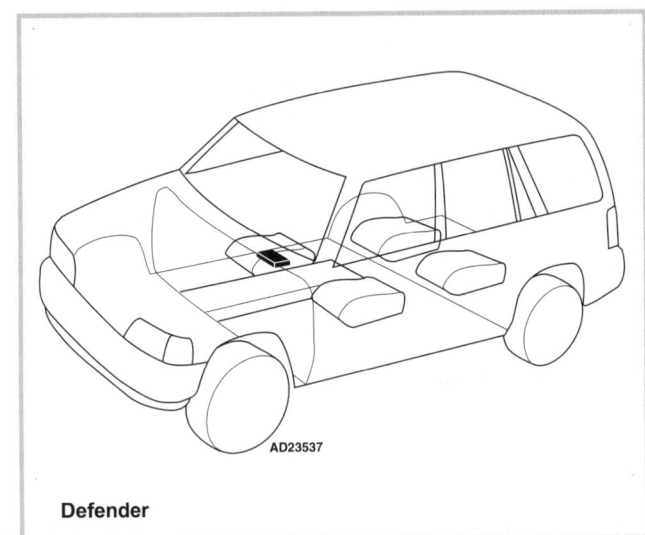

AD23537

Defender

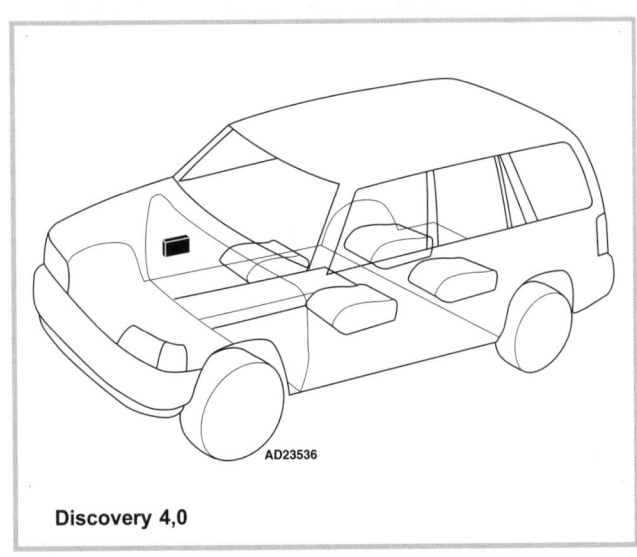

AD23536

Discovery 4,0

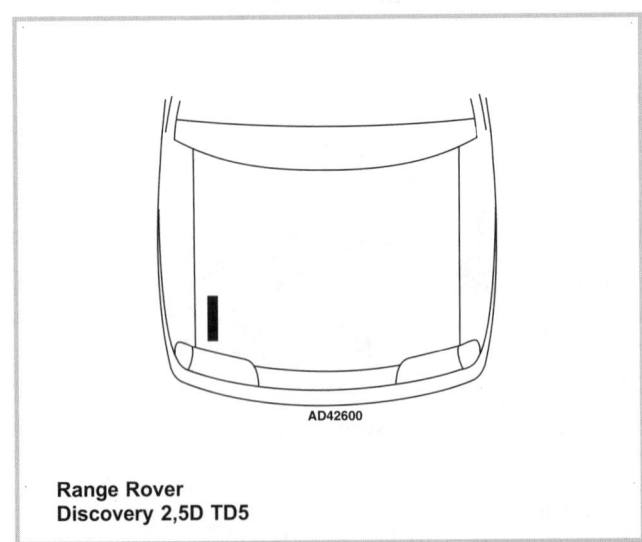

AD42600

Range Rover
Discovery 2,5D TD5

MAZDA

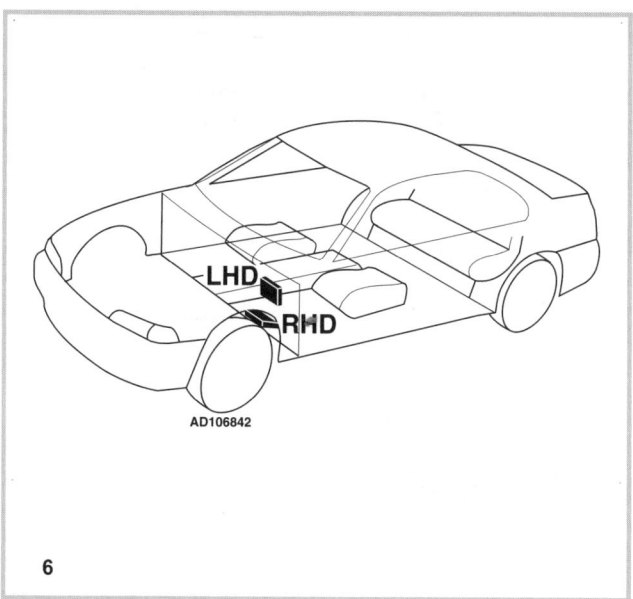

AD106842

6

MERCEDES-BENZ

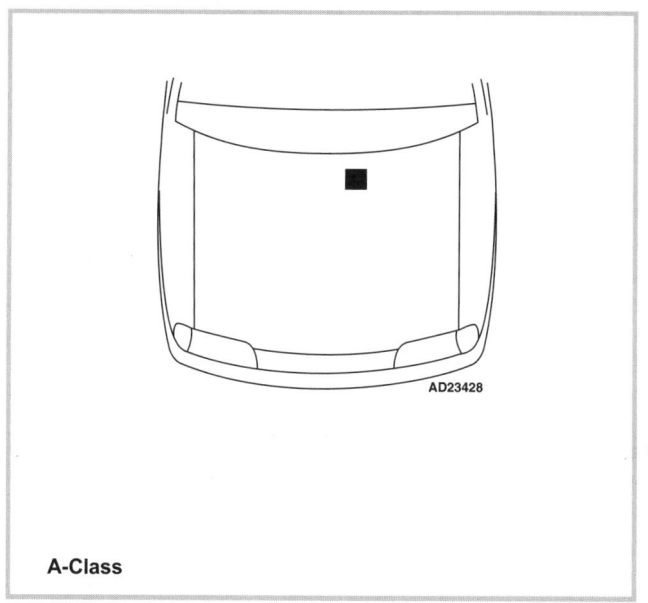

AD23428

A-Class

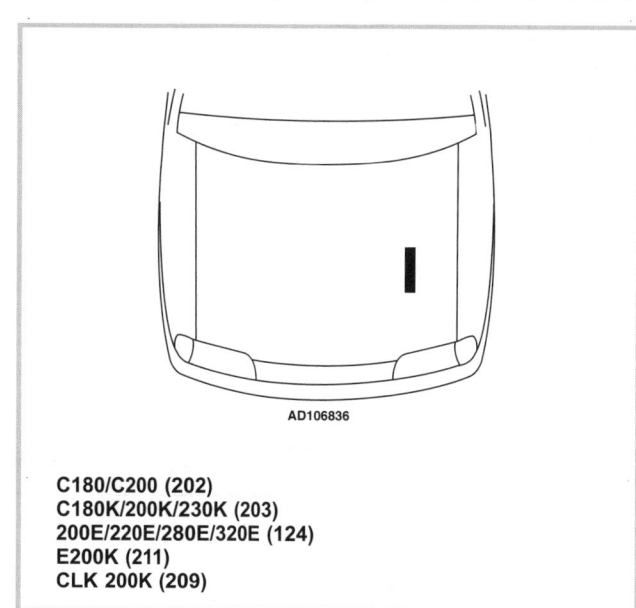

AD106836

C180/C200 (202)
C180K/200K/230K (203)
200E/220E/280E/320E (124)
E200K (211)
CLK 200K (209)

ECM locations

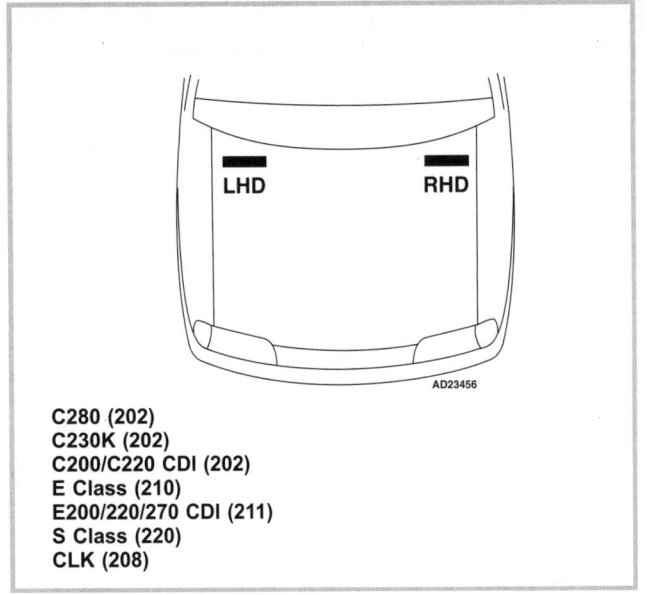

C280 (202)
C230K (202)
C200/C220 CDI (202)
E Class (210)
E200/220/270 CDI (211)
S Class (220)
CLK (208)

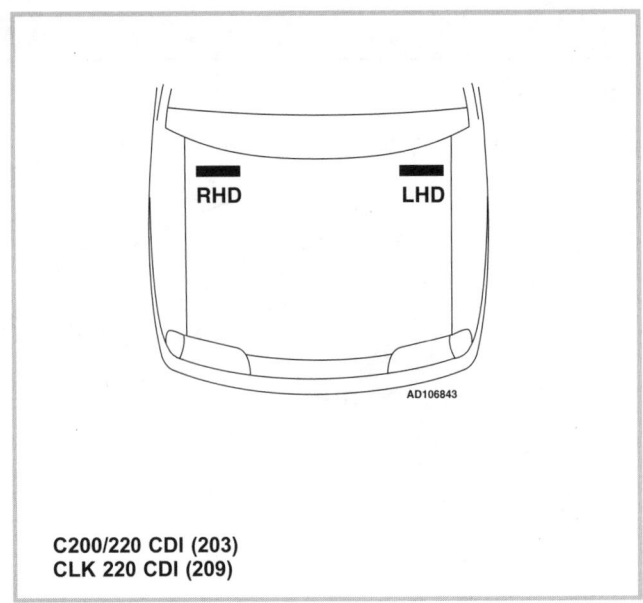

C200/220 CDI (203)
CLK 220 CDI (209)

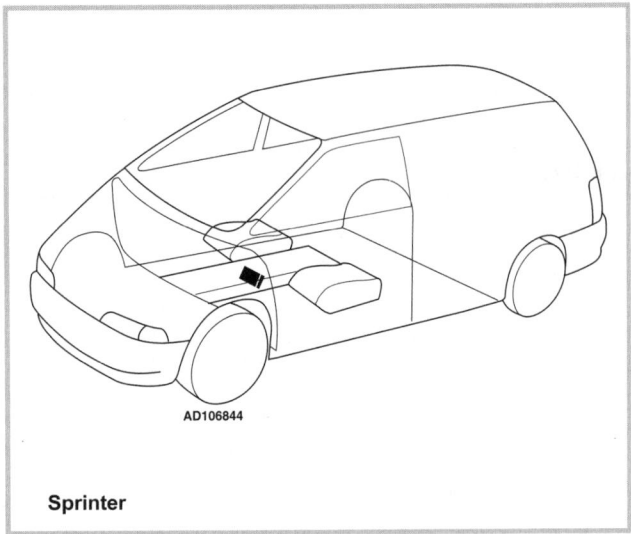

Sprinter

MITSUBISHI

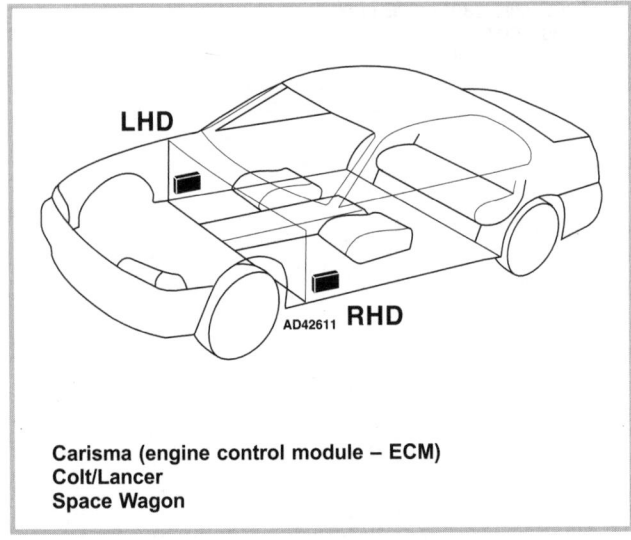

Carisma (engine control module – ECM)
Colt/Lancer
Space Wagon

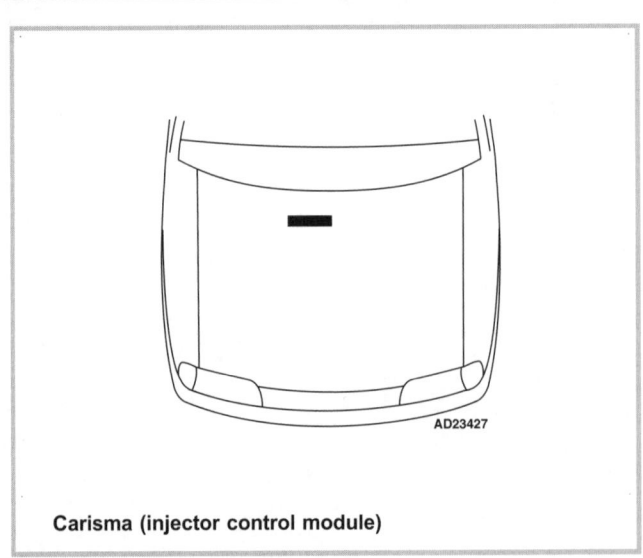

Carisma (injector control module)

Autodata

NISSAN

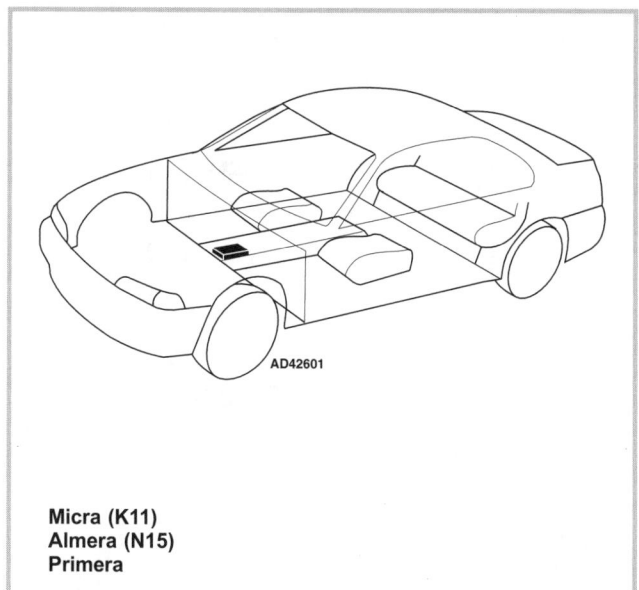

AD42601

Micra (K11)
Almera (N15)
Primera

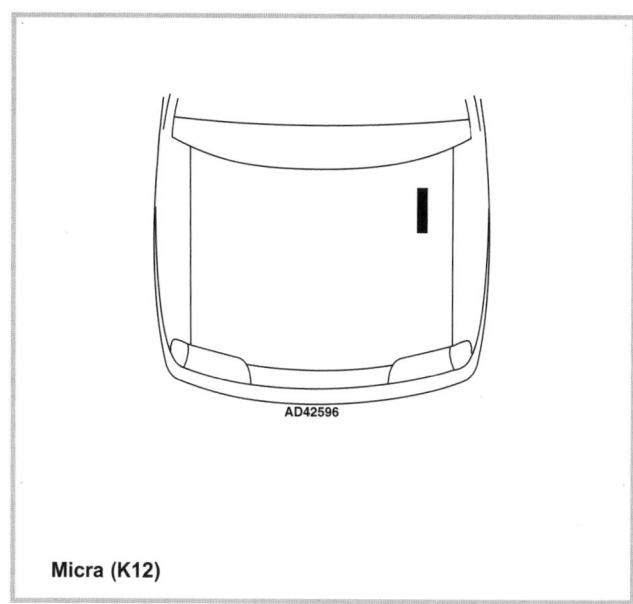

AD42596

Micra (K12)

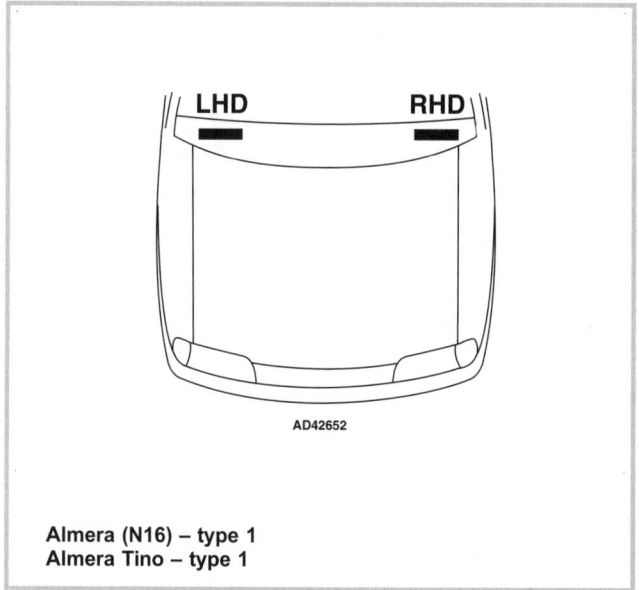

LHD　　　RHD

AD42652

Almera (N16) – type 1
Almera Tino – type 1

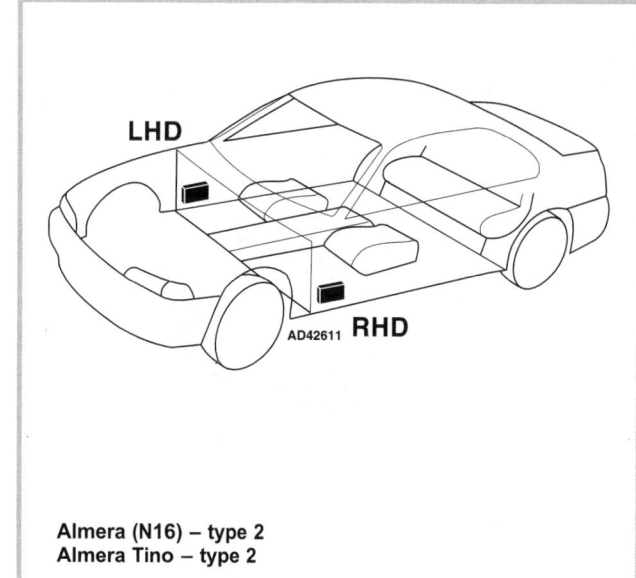

LHD

AD42611　RHD

Almera (N16) – type 2
Almera Tino – type 2

PEUGEOT

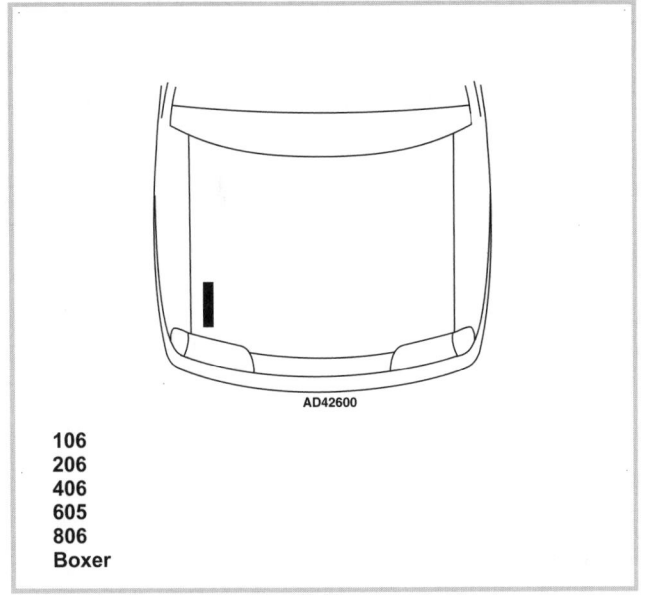

AD42600

106
206
406
605
806
Boxer

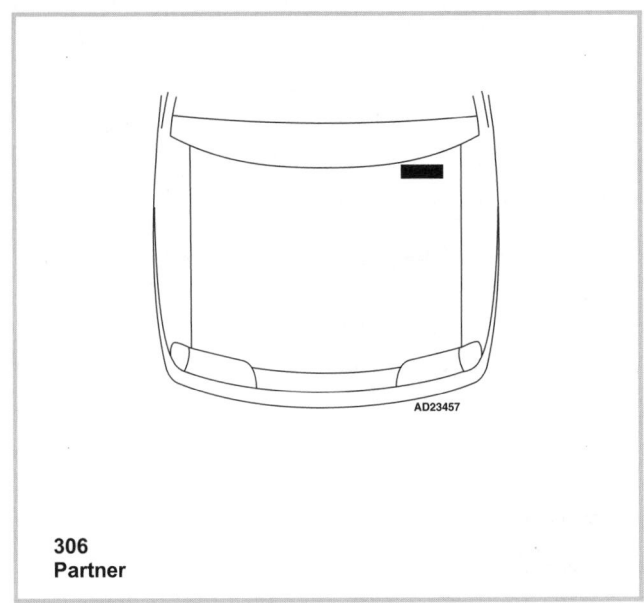

AD23457

306
Partner

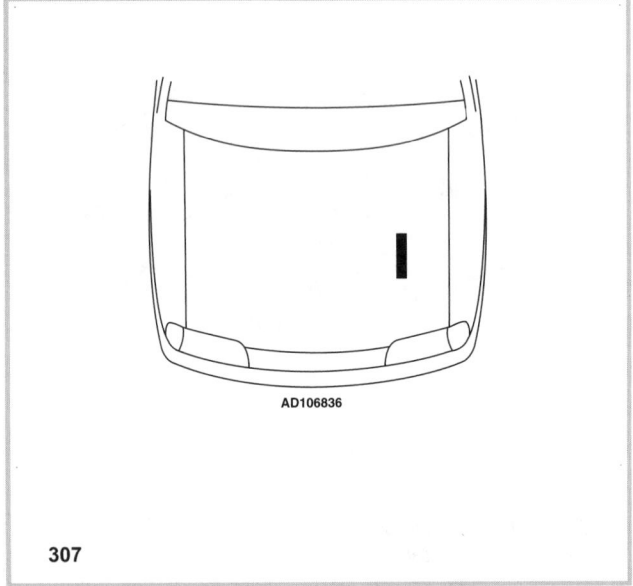

AD106836

307

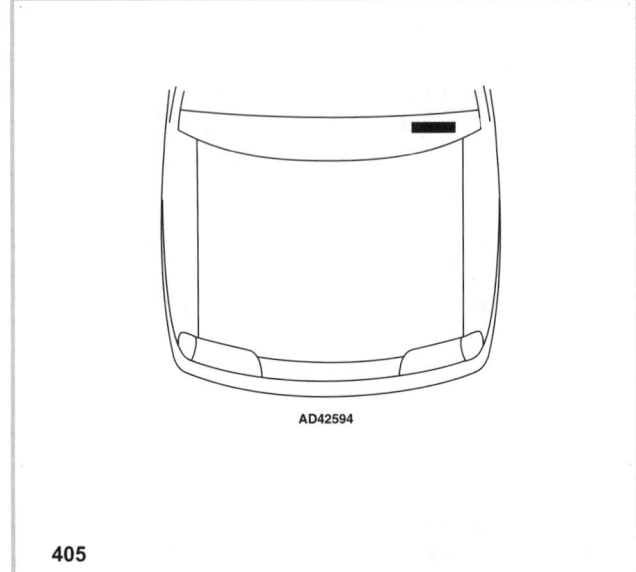

AD42594

405

RENAULT

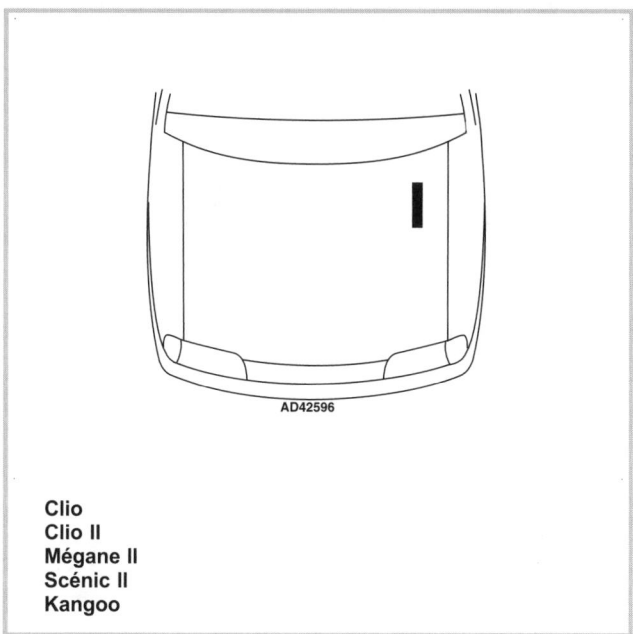

AD42596

Clio
Clio II
Mégane II
Scénic II
Kangoo

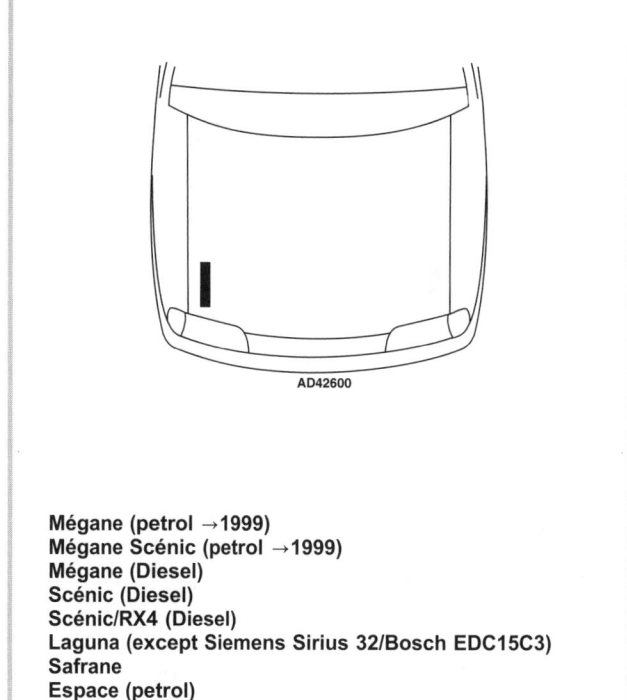

AD42600

Mégane (petrol →1999)
Mégane Scénic (petrol →1999)
Mégane (Diesel)
Scénic (Diesel)
Scénic/RX4 (Diesel)
Laguna (except Siemens Sirius 32/Bosch EDC15C3)
Safrane
Espace (petrol)

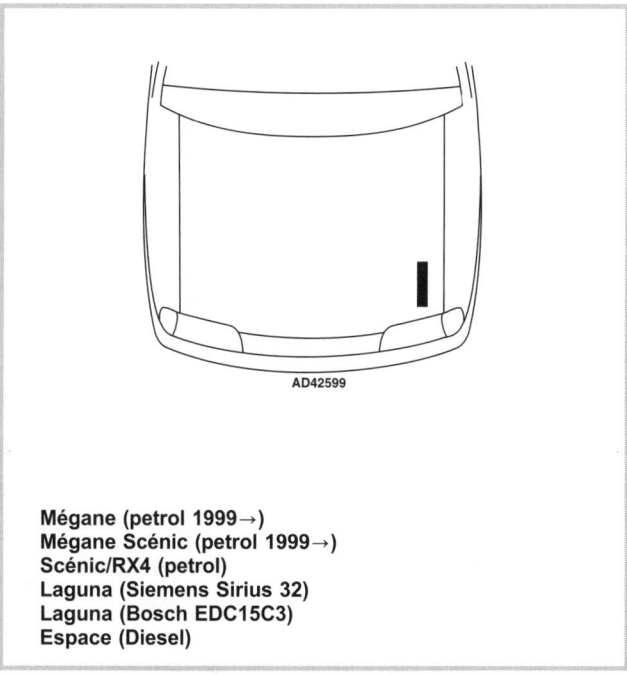

AD42599

Mégane (petrol 1999→)
Mégane Scénic (petrol 1999→)
Scénic/RX4 (petrol)
Laguna (Siemens Sirius 32)
Laguna (Bosch EDC15C3)
Espace (Diesel)

ROVER

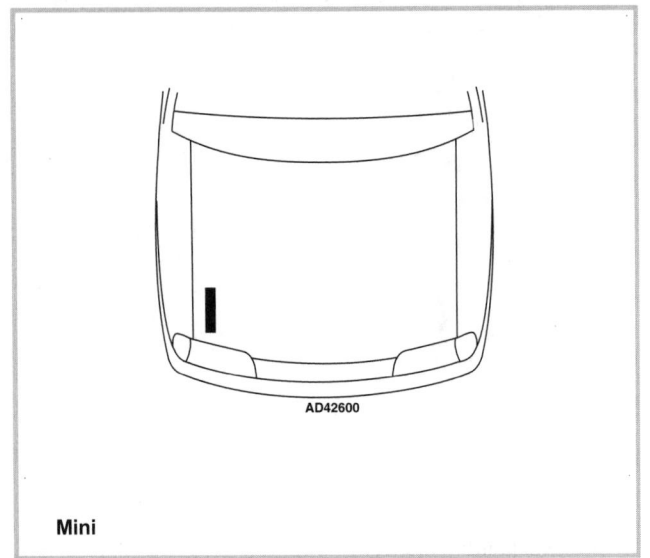

AD42600

Mini

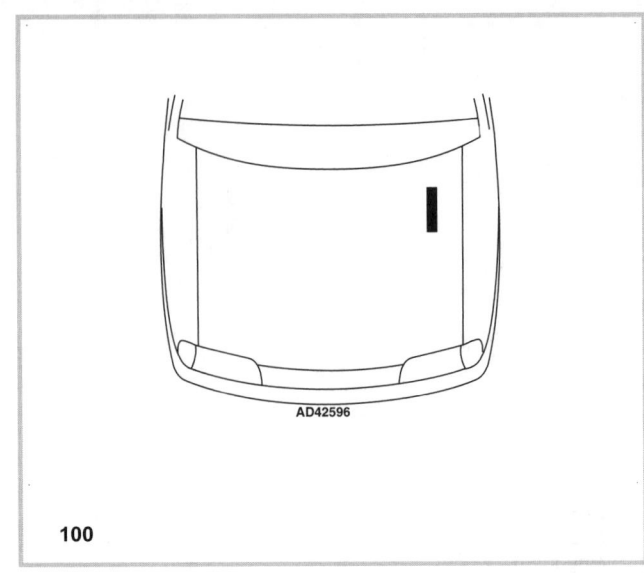

AD42596

100

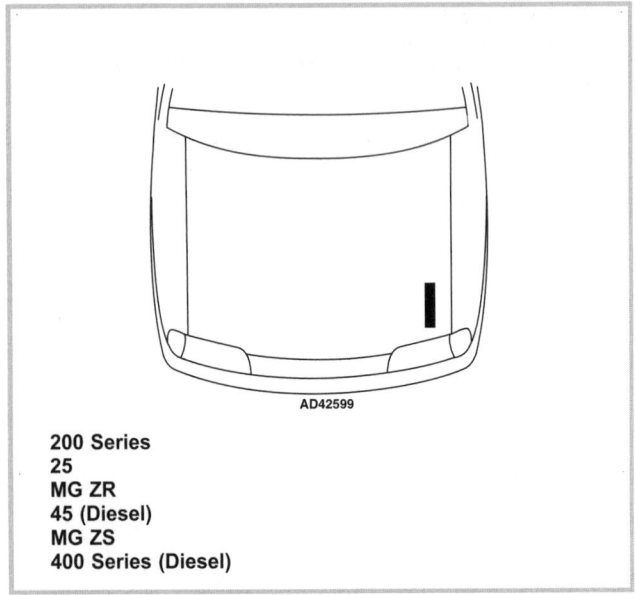

AD42599

200 Series
25
MG ZR
45 (Diesel)
MG ZS
400 Series (Diesel)

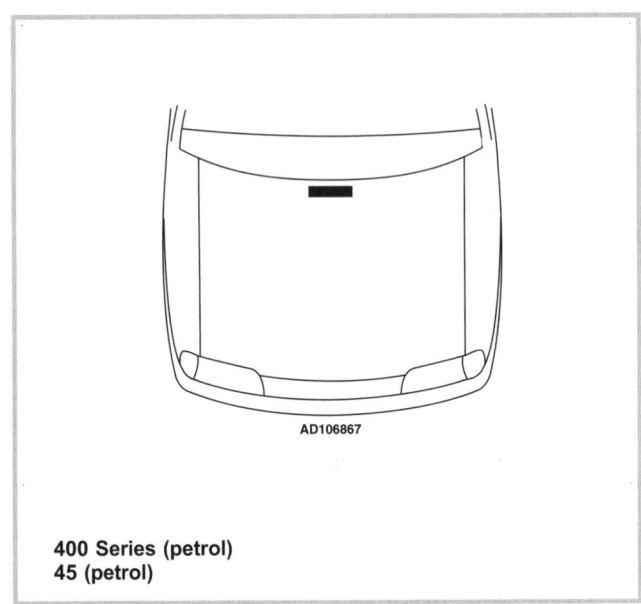

AD106867

400 Series (petrol)
45 (petrol)

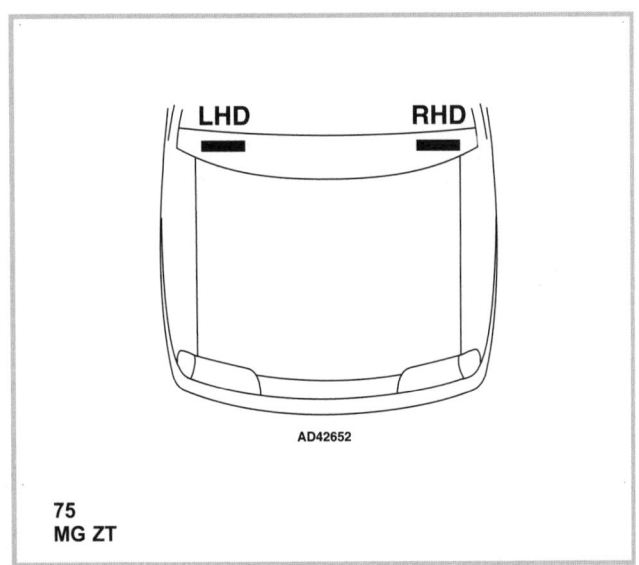

LHD   RHD

AD42652

75
MG ZT

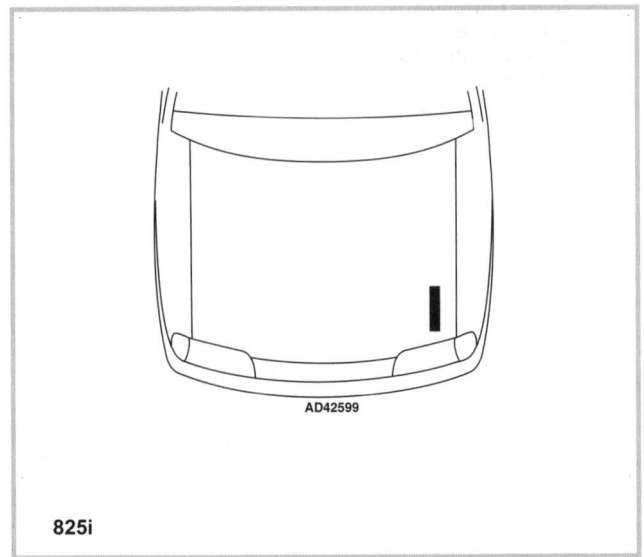

AD42599

825i

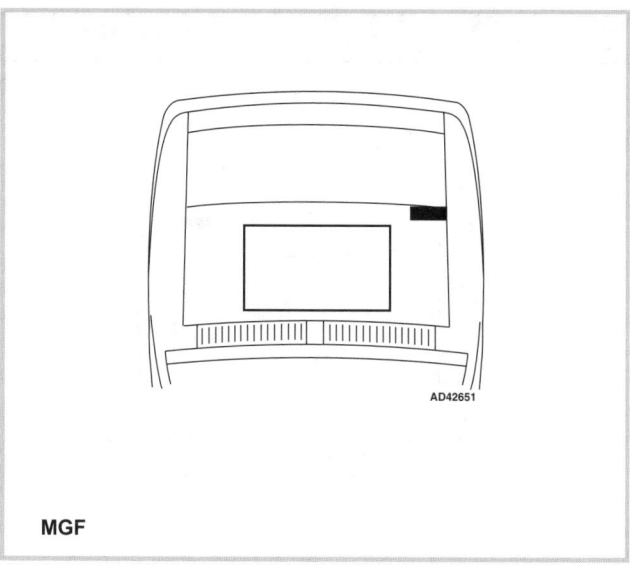

AD42651

MGF

SAAB

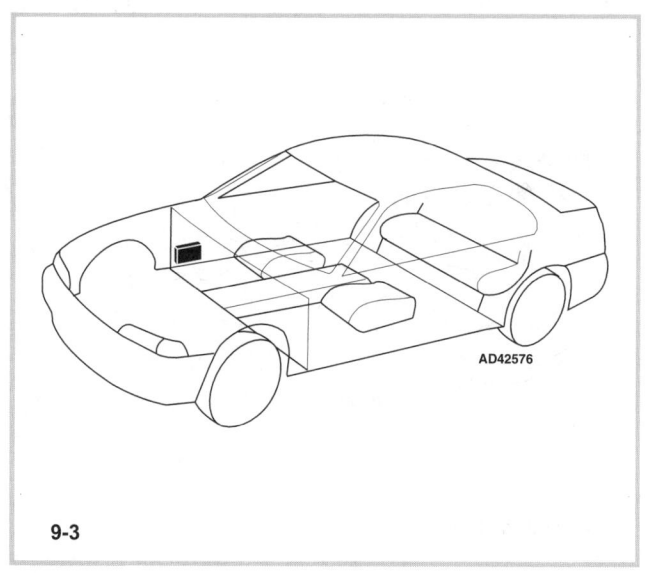

AD42576

9-3

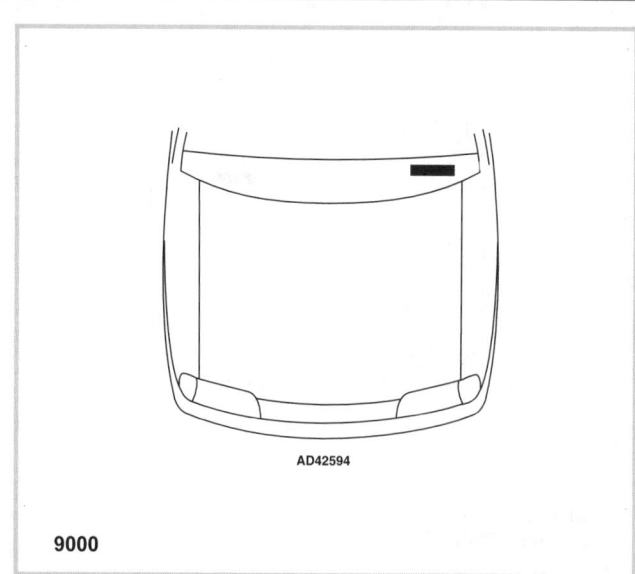

AD42594

9000

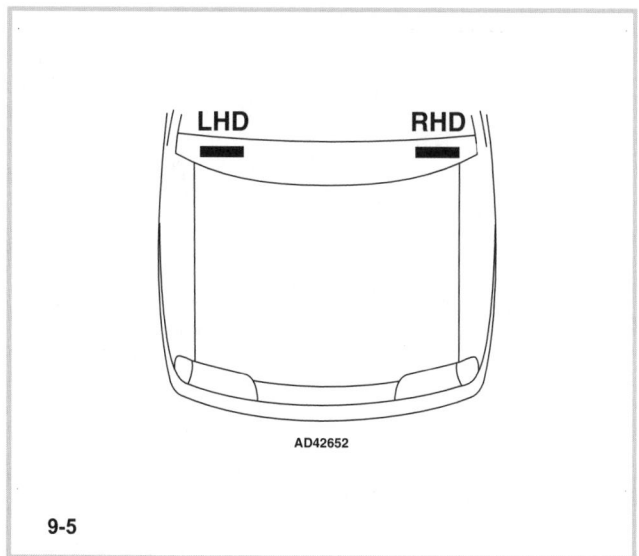

LHD   RHD

AD42652

9-5

SEAT

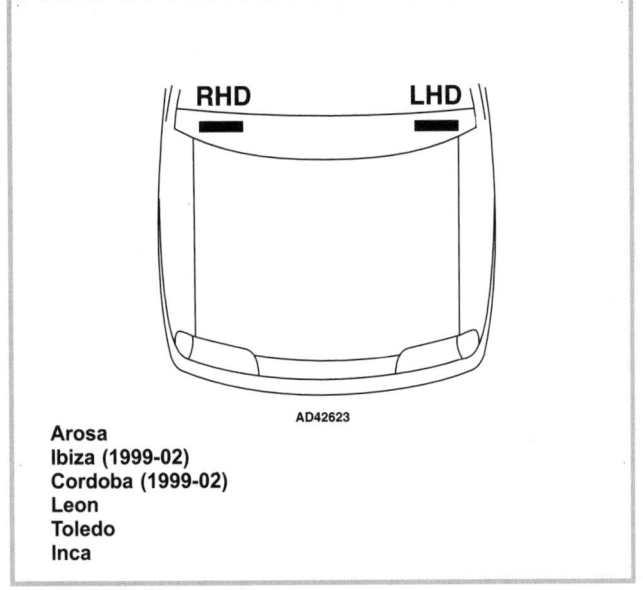

AD42623

Arosa
Ibiza (1999-02)
Cordoba (1999-02)
Leon
Toledo
Inca

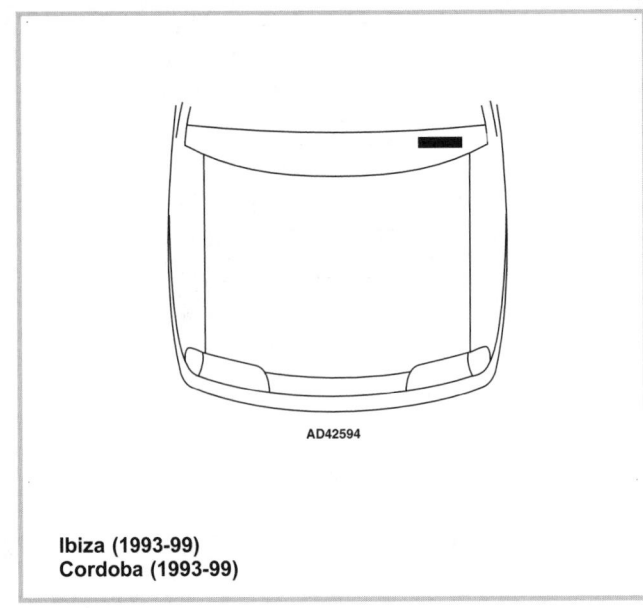

AD42594

Ibiza (1993-99)
Cordoba (1993-99)

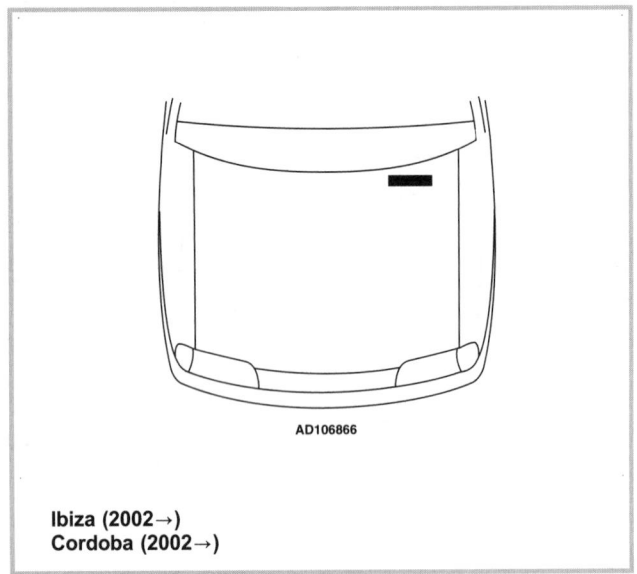

AD106866

Ibiza (2002→)
Cordoba (2002→)

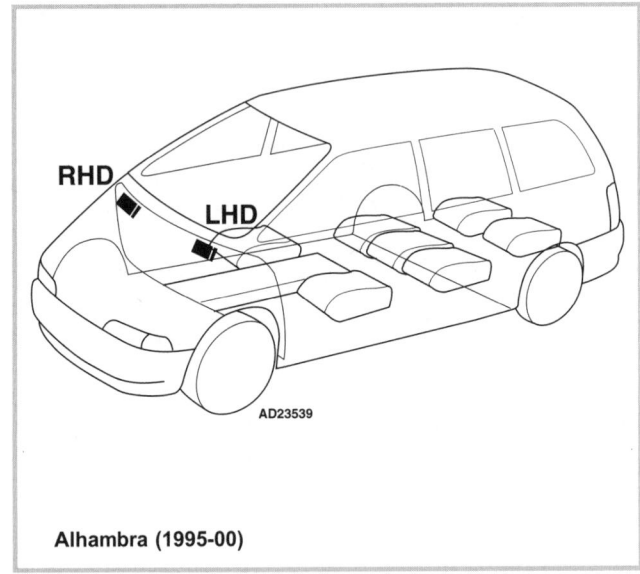

AD23539

Alhambra (1995-00)

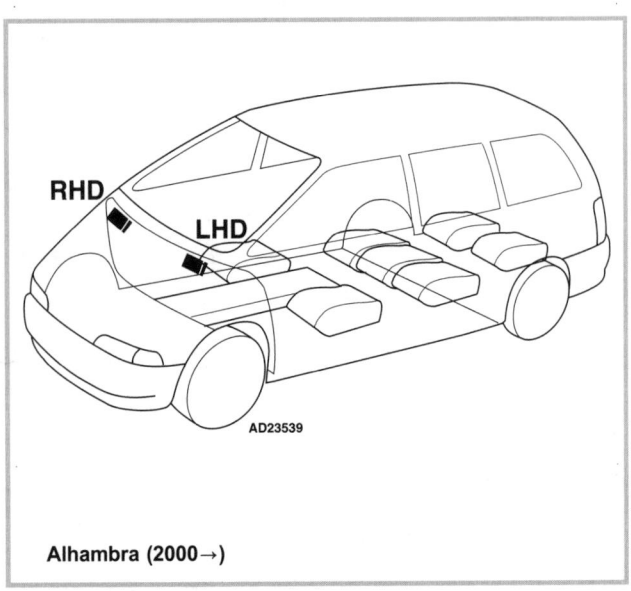

AD23539

Alhambra (2000→)

SKODA

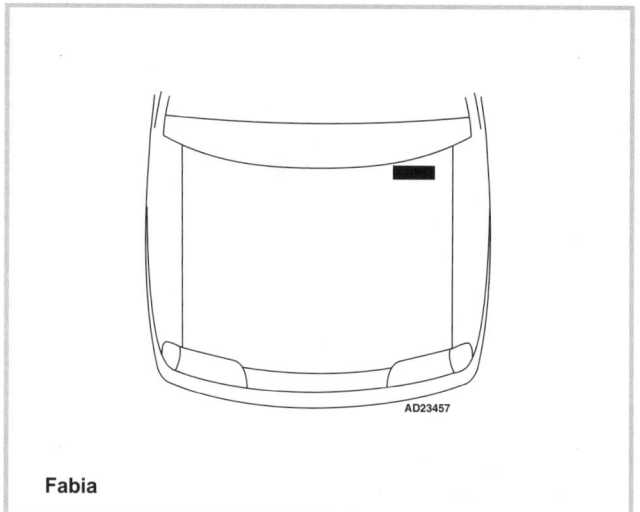

Fabia

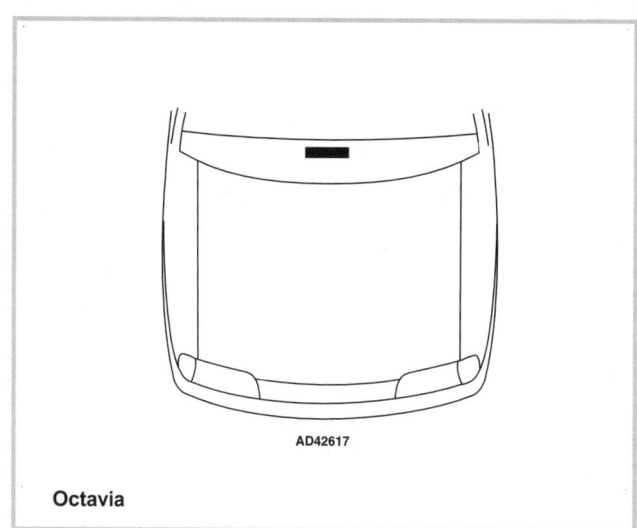

Octavia

TOYOTA

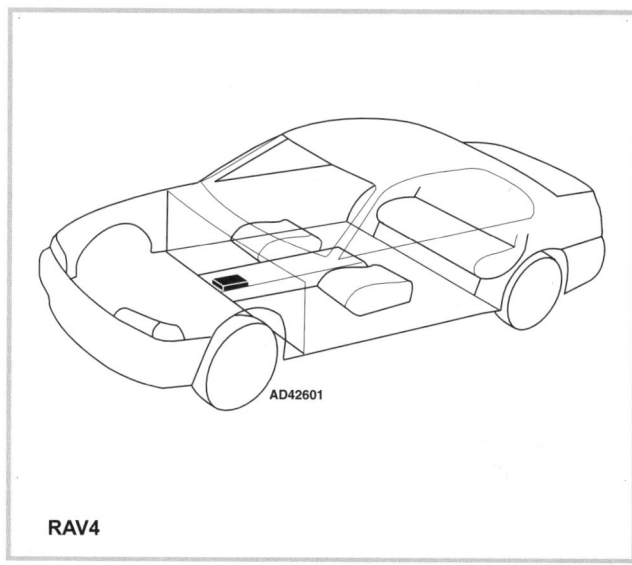

RAV4

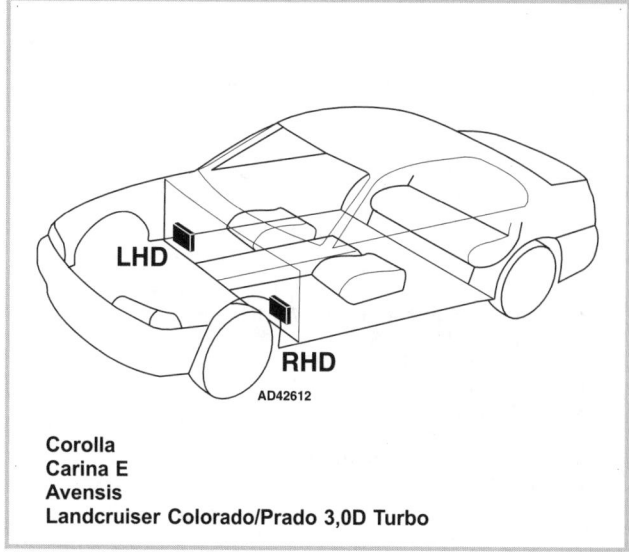

Corolla
Carina E
Avensis
Landcruiser Colorado/Prado 3,0D Turbo

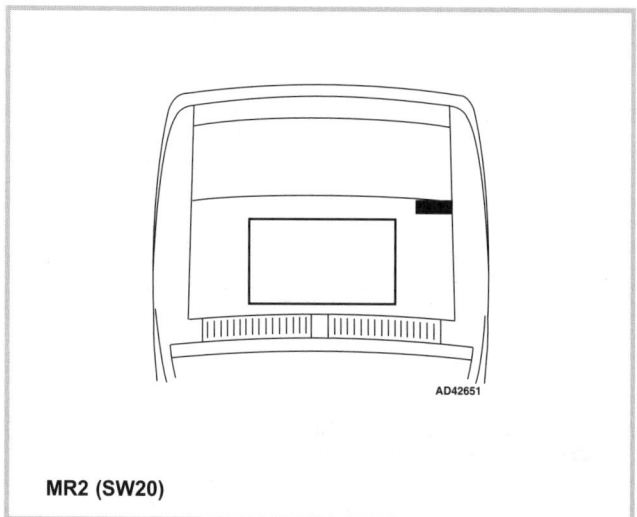

MR2 (SW20)

ECM locations

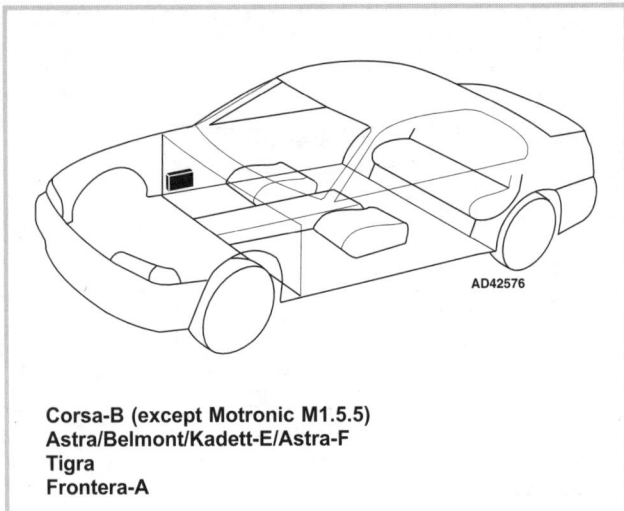

Corsa-B (except Motronic M1.5.5)
Astra/Belmont/Kadett-E/Astra-F
Tigra
Frontera-A

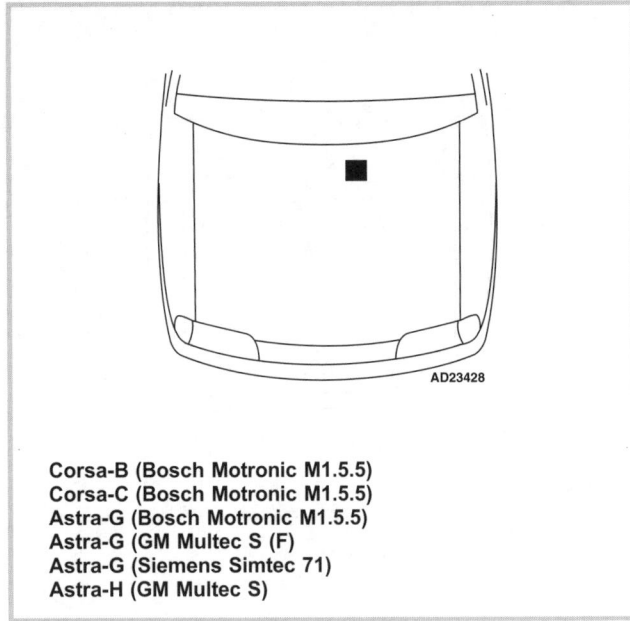

Corsa-B (Bosch Motronic M1.5.5)
Corsa-C (Bosch Motronic M1.5.5)
Astra-G (Bosch Motronic M1.5.5)
Astra-G (GM Multec S (F))
Astra-G (Siemens Simtec 71)
Astra-H (GM Multec S)

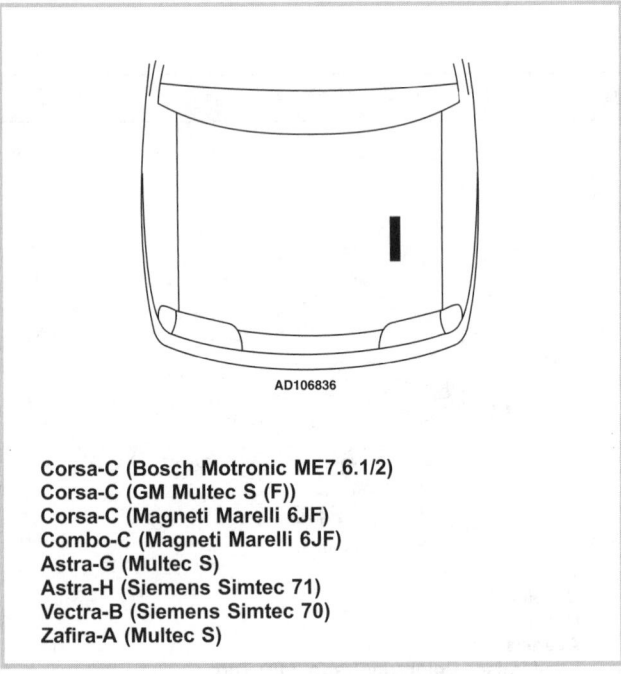

Corsa-C (Bosch Motronic ME7.6.1/2)
Corsa-C (GM Multec S (F))
Corsa-C (Magneti Marelli 6JF)
Combo-C (Magneti Marelli 6JF)
Astra-G (Multec S)
Astra-H (Siemens Simtec 71)
Vectra-B (Siemens Simtec 70)
Zafira-A (Multec S)

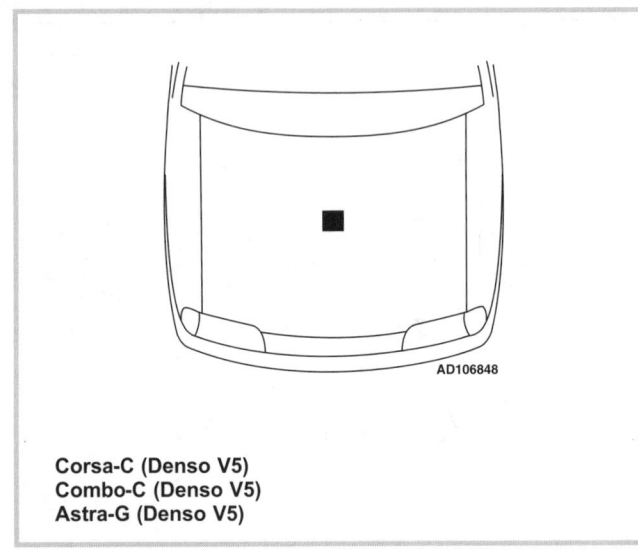

Corsa-C (Denso V5)
Combo-C (Denso V5)
Astra-G (Denso V5)

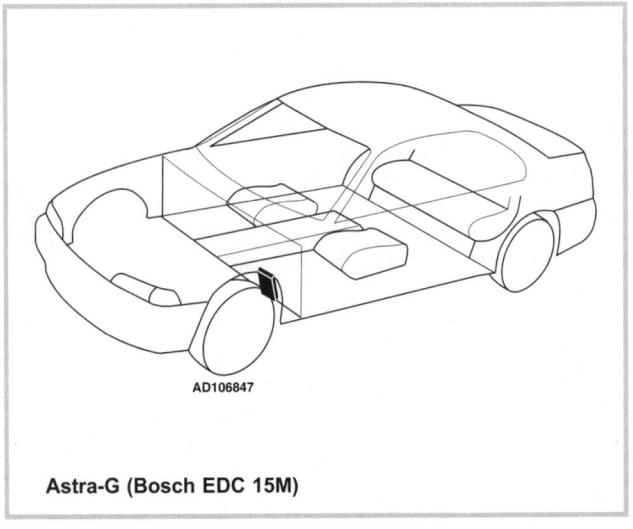

Astra-G (Bosch EDC 15M)

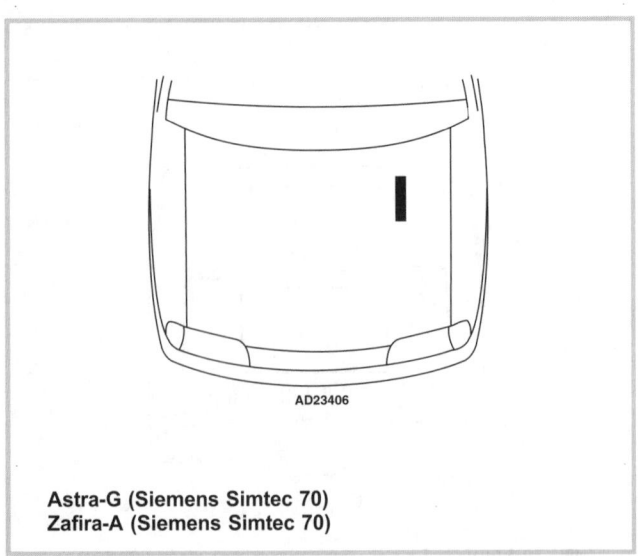

Astra-G (Siemens Simtec 70)
Zafira-A (Siemens Simtec 70)

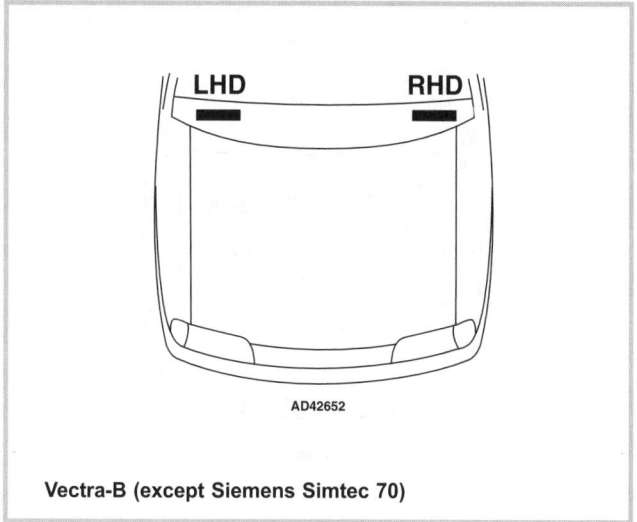

Vectra-B (except Siemens Simtec 70)

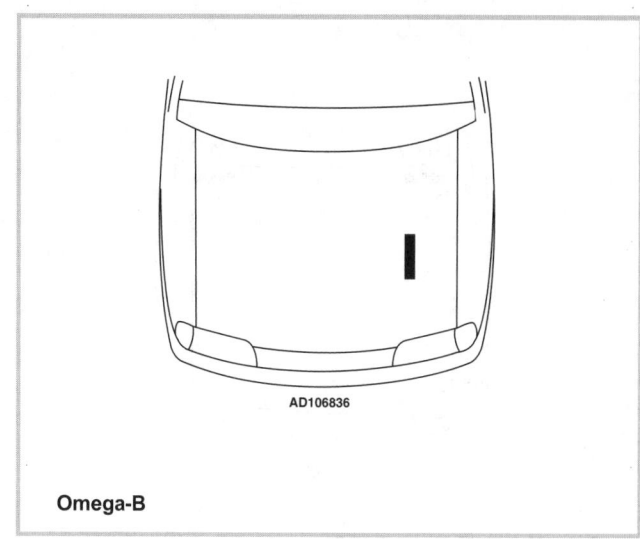

Omega-B

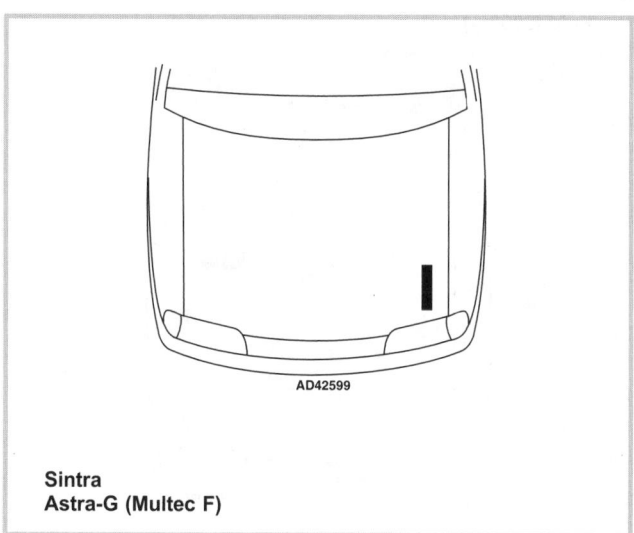

Sintra
Astra-G (Multec F)

VOLKSWAGEN

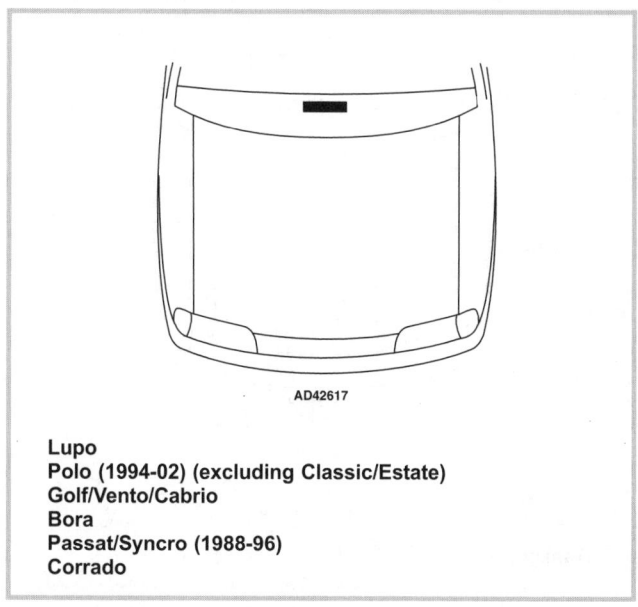

Lupo
Polo (1994-02) (excluding Classic/Estate)
Golf/Vento/Cabrio
Bora
Passat/Syncro (1988-96)
Corrado

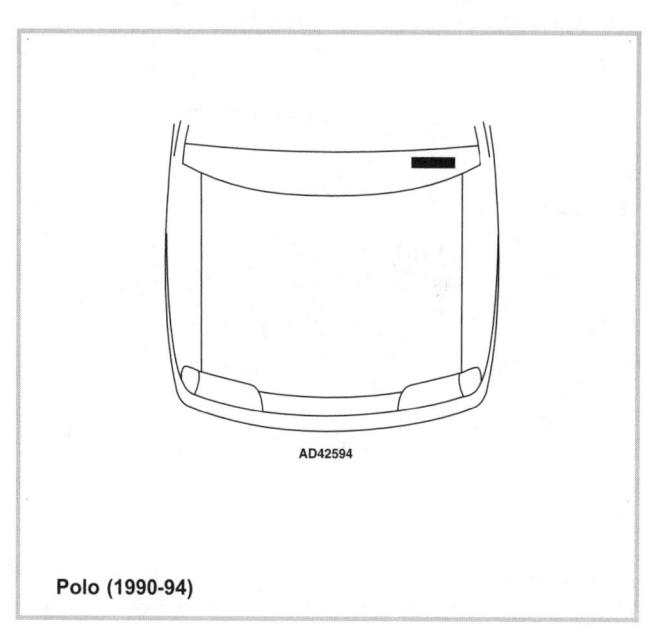

Polo (1990-94)

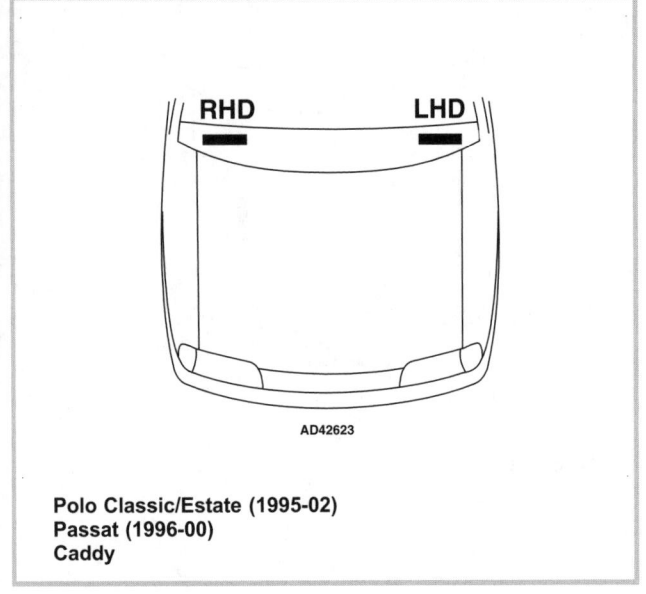

AD42623

Polo Classic/Estate (1995-02)
Passat (1996-00)
Caddy

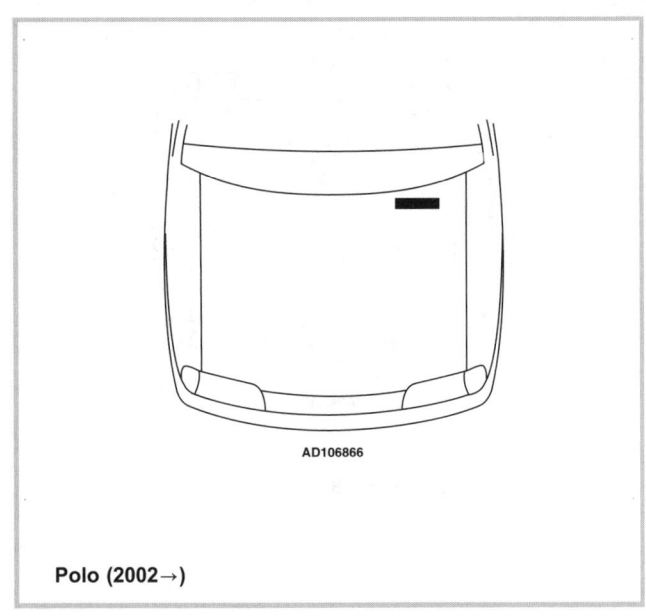

AD106866

Polo (2002→)

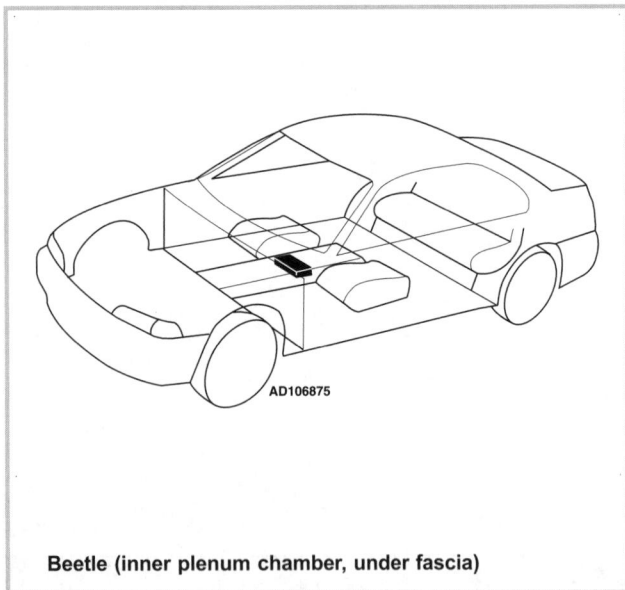

AD106875

Beetle (inner plenum chamber, under fascia)

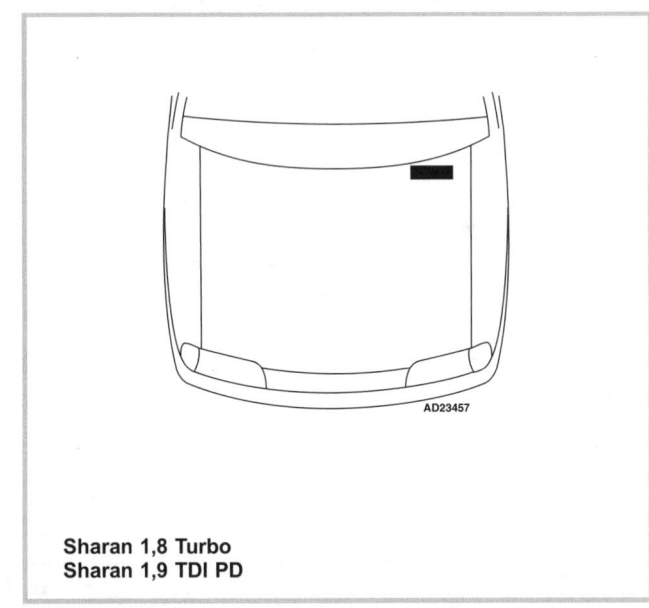

AD23457

Sharan 1,8 Turbo
Sharan 1,9 TDI PD

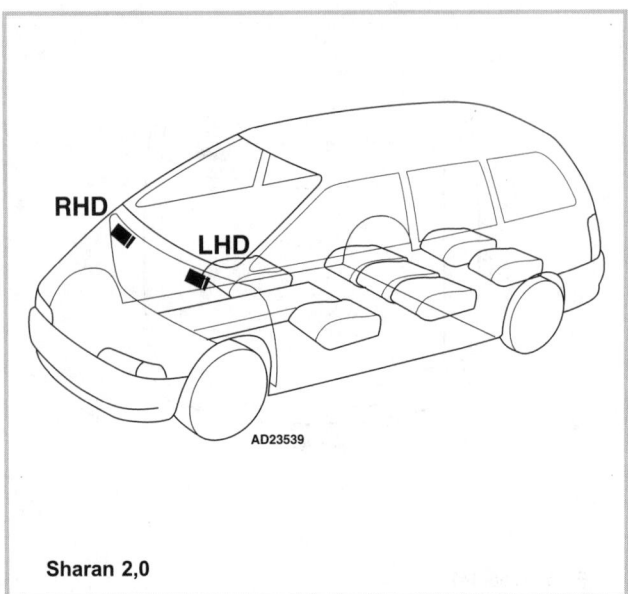

AD23539

Sharan 2,0

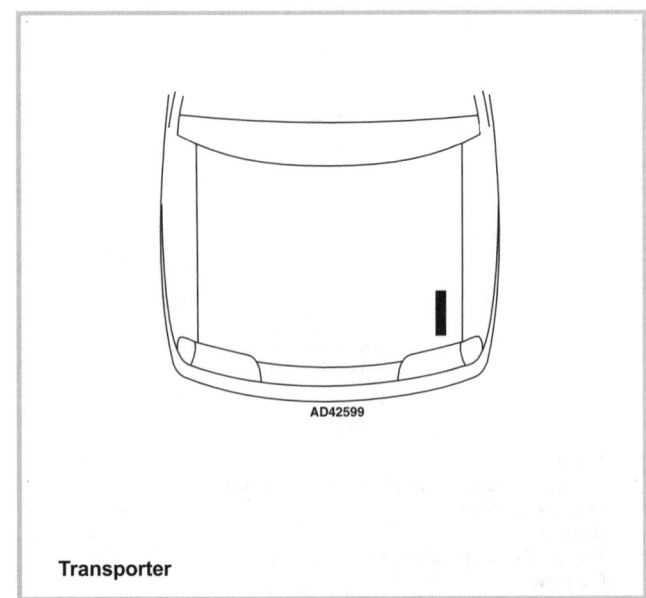

AD42599

Transporter

VOLVO

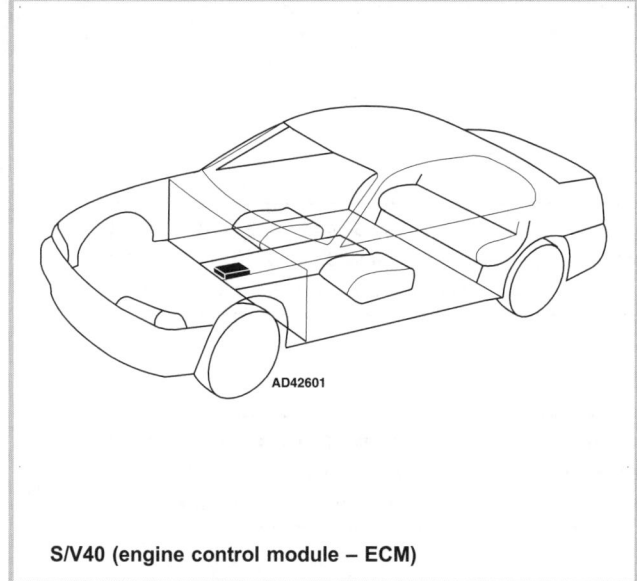

S/V40 (engine control module – ECM)

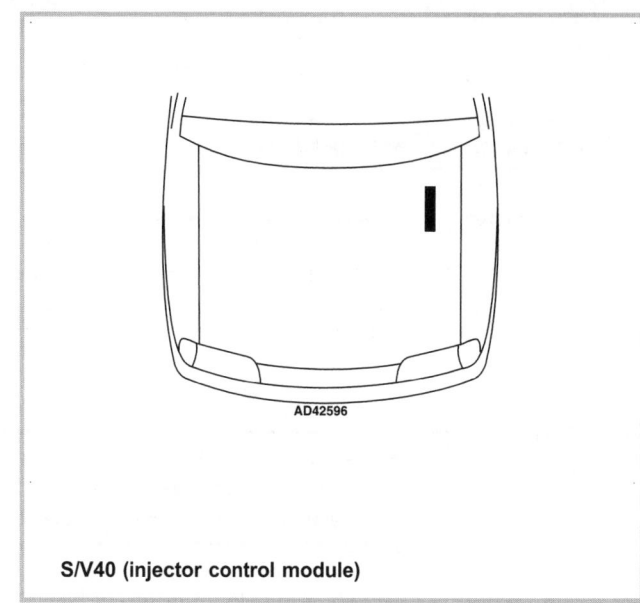

S/V40 (injector control module)

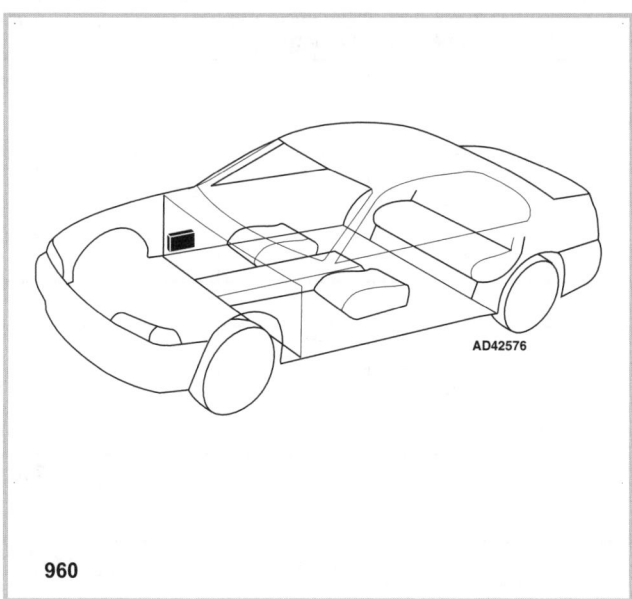

960

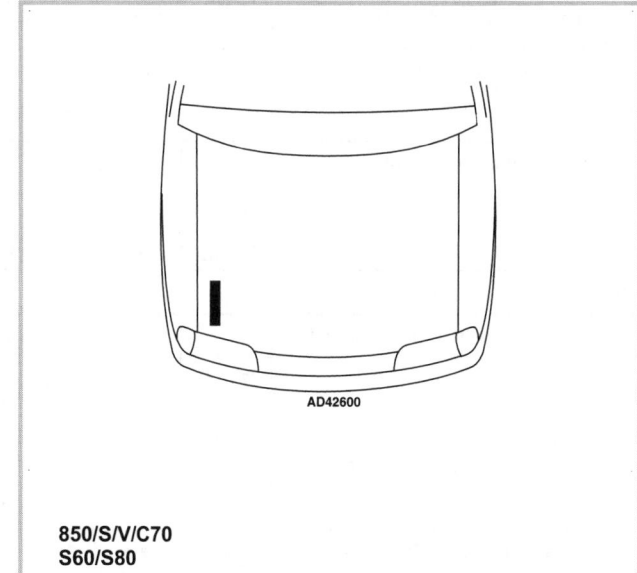

850/S/V/C70
S60/S80

Model:	Engine code:	Year:
145/146 1,4/1,6 Twin Spark	335.03/676.01	1995-99
145/146 1,8/2,0 Twin Spark	671.06	1996-98
155 1,6/1,8/2,0 Twin Spark	676.01/671.06/672.04	1995-98
156 1,6 Twin Spark	676.01	1997-00
Spider/GTV 2,0 (VIN 6023907-)	162.01	1996-01

ECM harness multi-plug

Terminal side

19 18 17 16 15 14 13 12 11 10 9 8 7 6 5 4 3 2 1
37 36 35 34 33 32 31 30 29 28 27 26 25 24 23 22 21 20
55 54 53 52 51 50 49 48 47 46 45 44 43 42 41 40 39 38

AD72618

Wire side

1 2 3 4 5 6 7 8 9 10 11 12 13 14 15 16 17 18 19
20 21 22 23 24 25 26 27 28 29 30 31 32 33 34 35 36 37
38 39 40 41 42 43 44 45 46 47 48 49 50 51 52 53 54 55

AD42077

Component/circuit description	ECM pin	Signal	Condition	Typical value	Oscilloscope setting★	Wave form
AC compressor clutch relay	32	⅂→	Engine idling – AC OFF	11-14 V		
	32	⅂→	Engine idling – AC ON – AC compressor ON	0-1 V		
AC refrigerant pressure switch	40	←		[1]		
	43	←	Ignition ON	5 V		
	44	←	Ignition ON	5 V		
Battery	18	←	Ignition OFF	11-14 V		
Camshaft position (CMP) actuator relay	52	⅂→	Ignition ON	11-14 V		
	52	⅂→	Engine idling	11-14 V		
	52	⅂→	Engine idling – accelerate briefly	0-1 V briefly		
Camshaft position (CMP) sensor	8	←	Engine idling		2 V/50 ms	⋀⋁⋀ 12
	12	⇒	Ignition ON	5 V		
Crankshaft position (CKP) sensor	48 (49)	←	Engine idling	9 V ac	5 V/2 ms	⋀⋁⋀ 2
	48 (49)	←	3000 rpm	22 V ac		
	49 (48)	←	Engine idling	9 V ac	5 V/2 ms	Reversed ⋀⋁⋀ 2
	49 (48)	←	3000 rpm	22 V ac		
Data link connector (DLC)	55		Ignition OFF	0 V		
	55		Ignition ON	11-14 V		
Earth	2		Ignition ON	0 V		
	14		Ignition ON	0 V		
	19		Ignition ON	0 V		
	24		Ignition ON	0 V		
Engine control relay	36	⅂→	Ignition OFF	11-14 V		
	36	⅂→	Ignition ON	0-1 V		
	37	←	Ignition ON	11-14 V		
Engine coolant blower motor relay	26	⅂→	Ignition ON	11-14 V		
	26	⅂→	Coolant blower motor OFF	11-14 V		

★ Suggested settings - Voltage/time per division

/Autodata

Component/circuit description	ECM pin	Signal	Condition	Typical value	Oscilloscope setting*	Wave form
Engine coolant blower motor relay – with AC (Spider/GTV)	25	⊐▷	Ignition ON	11-14 V		
	25	⊐▷	Coolant blower motor OFF	11-14 V		
	25	⊐▷	Coolant blower motor ON – low speed	11-14 V		
	25	⊐▷	Coolant blower motor ON – high speed	0-1 V		
	26	⊐▷	Coolant blower motor ON – high speed	11-14 V		
	26	⊐▷	Coolant blower motor ON – low speed	0-1 V		
Engine coolant blower motor relay – without AC (except Spider/GTV)	26	⊐▷	Coolant blower motor ON	0-1 V		
Engine coolant temperature (ECT) sensor	30	⊐—	Ignition ON	0 V		
	45	◀—	Ignition ON – coolant temp. 10°C	3,7 V		
	45	◀—	Ignition ON – coolant temp. 80°C	0,9 V		
Evaporative emission (EVAP) canister purge valve	5	⊐▷	Ignition ON	11-14 V		
	5	⊐▷	Engine running – valve not operating	0%		
	5	⊐▷	Engine running – valve operating	1-99%	10 V/20 ms	20
Fuel pump relay	3	⊐▷	Ignition ON	0-1 V briefly then 11-14 V		
	3	⊐▷	Engine cranking	0-1 V		
	3	⊐▷	Engine idling	0-1 V		
Heated oxygen sensor (HO2S)	10 (28)	◀—	Engine idling – accelerate briefly	0-1 V fluctuating	0,2 V/1 sec.	21
	28 (10)	◀—	Engine idling – accelerate briefly	0-1 V fluctuating	0,2 V/1 sec.	21
Idle air control (IAC) valve	4	⊐▷	Ignition ON	9,3 V		
	4	⊐▷	Engine idling	35%	5 V/5 ms	Intermittent 25
	22	⊐▷	Ignition ON	3,3 V		
	22	⊐▷	Engine idling	65%	5 V/5 ms	Intermittent 25
Ignition coil – cylinders 1 & 4	1	⊐▷	Ignition ON	11-14 V		
	1	⊐▷	Engine idling		5 V/2 ms	33
	21	⊐▷	Ignition ON	11-14 V		
	21	⊐▷	Engine idling		5 V/2 ms	33
Ignition coil – cylinders 2 & 3	20	⊐▷	Ignition ON	11-14 V		
	20	⊐▷	Engine idling		5 V/2 ms	33
	38	⊐▷	Ignition ON	11-14 V		
	38	⊐▷	Engine idling		5 V/2 ms	33
Ignition switch	27	◀—	Ignition ON	11-14 V		
Immobilizer control module	47	◀▷	Ignition ON	11-14 V		
Injector 1	17	⊐▷	Ignition ON	11-14 V		
	17	⊐▷	Engine idling	3,6 ms		
	17	⊐▷	Engine idling		10 V/2 ms	35
Injector 2	34	⊐▷	Ignition ON	11-14 V		
	34	⊐▷	Engine idling	3,6 ms		
	34	⊐▷	Engine idling		10 V/2 ms	35
Injector 3	16	⊐▷	Ignition ON	11-14 V		
	16	⊐▷	Engine idling	3,6 ms		
	16	⊐▷	Engine idling		10 V/2 ms	35

* Suggested settings - Voltage/time per division

Component/circuit description	ECM pin	Signal	Condition	Typical value	Oscilloscope setting*	Wave form
Injector 4	35	⊐▷	Ignition ON	11-14 V		
	35	⊐▷	Engine idling	3,6 ms		
	35	⊐▷	Engine idling		10 V/2 ms	〰〰 35
Intake air temperature (IAT) sensor	30	⊐—	Ignition ON	0 V		
	54	◄—	Ignition ON – air temp. 10°C	3,7 V		
Knock sensor (KS)	11	◄—	Engine idling – accelerate briefly		50 mV/1 ms	〰〰 38
	30	⊐—	Engine running	0 V		
Malfunction indicator lamp (MIL)	51	⊐▷	Ignition ON – MIL ON	0-1 V		
	51	⊐▷	Ignition ON – MIL OFF	11-14 V		
Mass air flow (MAF) sensor	7	◄—	Ignition ON	0,15 V		
	7	◄—	Engine idling	0,9 V		
	7	◄—	Engine idling – accelerate briefly	3,7 V briefly		
	30	⊐—	Ignition ON	0 V		
Tachometer	6	⇒	Ignition ON	11-14 V		
	6	⇒	Engine idling	30 Hz	2 V/20 ms	〰〰 55
	6	⇒	3000 rpm	100 Hz		
Throttle position (TP) sensor	12	⇒	Ignition ON	5 V		
	30	⊐—	Ignition ON	0 V		
	53	◄—	Ignition ON – throttle closed	0,5 V		
	53	◄—	Ignition ON – throttle fully open	4,4 V		
Vehicle speed sensor (VSS)	9	◄—	Ignition ON – vehicle pushed	0 V or 6 V fluctuating		

*Suggested settings - Voltage/time per division

1 Connected pin - no test data available or random digital signal

Model:	Engine code:	Year:
145/146 1,4/1,6/1,8/2,0	AR 335.03/676.01/322.01/323.01	1998-02
156 1,8/2,0	AR 32201/32301	1998-02
166 2,0 Twin Spark	AR 341.03	1998-02
Spider/GTV 1,8/2,0 Twin Spark	322.01/162.01/323.01	1998-01

ALFA ROMEO

Bosch Motronic M1.5.5

ECM harness multi-plug

Terminal side

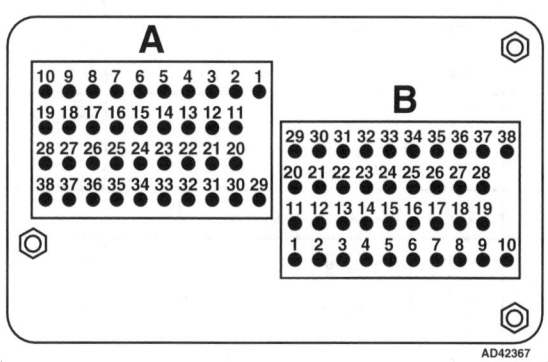

Wire side

Component/circuit description	ECM pin	Signal	Condition	Typical value	Oscilloscope setting*	Wave form
AC compressor clutch relay	A19	⊐⊳	Engine idling – AC OFF	11-14 V		
	A19	⊐⊳	Engine idling – AC ON – AC compressor ON	0-1 V		
AC refrigerant pressure switch	A31	←		1		
	A34	←		1		
	A35	←		1		
Battery	A18	←	Ignition OFF	11-14 V		
Camshaft position (CMP) actuator	B24	⊐⊳	Engine idling	11-14 V		
	B24	⊐⊳	Above 1800 rpm	0-1 V		
Camshaft position (CMP) sensor	B23	←	Engine idling		2 V/20 ms	〰 14
	B29	⊳	Ignition ON	5 V		
Crankshaft position (CKP) sensor	B22	←	Engine idling		2 V/2 ms	〰 2
	B32	←	Engine idling		2 V/2 ms	Reversed 〰 2
Data link connector (DLC)	A11	←⊳	Engine idling	11-14 V		
Engine control module (ECM) – case		⊐	Ignition ON	0 V		

* Suggested settings - Voltage/time per division

Component/circuit description	ECM pin	Signal	Condition	Typical value	Oscilloscope setting*	Wave form
Engine control relay	A7	←	Ignition OFF	0 V after 5 seconds		
	A7	←	Ignition ON	11-14 V		
	A9	⊐▷	Ignition OFF	11-14 V		
	A9	⊐▷	Ignition ON	0-1 V		
	A17	←	Ignition OFF	0 V after 5 seconds		
	A17	←	Ignition ON	11-14 V		
Engine coolant blower motor relay 1	A13	⊐▷	Engine idling – coolant blower motor OFF	11-14 V		
	A13	⊐▷	Engine idling – coolant blower motor ON – low speed	0-1 V		
Engine coolant blower motor relay 2 – with AC	A4	⊐▷	Engine idling – coolant blower motor OFF	11-14 V		
	A4	⊐▷	Engine idling – coolant blower motor ON – high speed	0-1 V		
Engine coolant temperature (ECT) sensor	B1	⊐—	Ignition ON	0 V		
	B5	←	Ignition ON – coolant temp. 10°C	3,5 V		
	B5	←	Ignition ON – coolant temp. 80°C	0,8 V		
Evaporative emission (EVAP) canister purge valve	B34	⊐▷	Ignition ON	11-14 V		
	B34	⊐▷	Engine hot – valve operating		10 V/20 ms	20
Fuel pump relay	A3	⊐▷	Engine cranking	0-1 V		
Heated oxygen sensor (HO2S)	B8	⊐▷	Engine idling	0-1 V		
	B21	⊐—	Engine idling	0 V		
	B30	←	Engine idling – engine hot	0-1 V fluctuating	0,2 V/1 sec.	21
Idle speed control (ISC) actuator	B26	⇨	Engine idling		2 V/20 ms	28
	B35	⇨	Engine idling		2 V/20 ms	28
Idle speed control (ISC) actuator position sensor	B1	⊐—	Ignition ON	0 V		
	B4	←	Engine idling	3,3 V		
Ignition coil – cylinder 1	B38	⊐▷	Engine idling		5 V/2 ms	33
Ignition coil – cylinder 2	B37	⊐▷	Engine idling		5 V/2 ms	33
Ignition coil – cylinder 3	B9 – some models	⊐▷	Engine idling		5 V/2 ms	33
Ignition coil – cylinder 3	B18 – some models	⊐▷	Engine idling		5 V/2 ms	33
Ignition coil – cylinder 4	B10	⊐▷	Engine idling		5 V/2 ms	33
Ignition switch	A8	←	Ignition OFF	0 V after 5 seconds		
	A8	←	Ignition ON	11-14 V		
Immobilizer control module	A16	←	Ignition ON	11-14 V		
Injector 1	B6	⊐▷	Ignition ON	11-14 V		
	B6	⊐▷	Engine idling – engine hot	2,8 ms	10 V/2 ms	35
Injector 2	B17	⊐▷	Ignition ON	11-14 V		
	B17	⊐▷	Engine idling – engine hot	2,8 ms	10 V/2 ms	35
Injector 3	B16	⊐▷	Ignition ON	11-14 V		
	B16	⊐▷	Engine idling – engine hot	2,8 ms	10 V/2 ms	35

* Suggested settings - Voltage/time per division

Component/circuit description	ECM pin	Signal	Condition	Typical value	Oscilloscope setting*	Wave form
Injector 4	B7	⊐▷	Ignition ON	11-14 V		
	B7	⊐▷	Engine idling – engine hot	2,8 ms	10 V/2 ms	〜 35
Instrument panel	A6 – some models			1		
Intake air temperature (IAT) sensor	A29	⊐–	Ignition ON	0 V		
	A30	⬅	Ignition ON – air temp. 10°C	3,5 V		
Intake manifold air control solenoid	B33	⊐▷	Ignition ON	11-14 V		
	B33	⊐▷	Engine running – throttle fully open briefly	0-1 V		
Knock sensor (KS)	B2	⬅	Engine idling – accelerate briefly		50 mV/1 ms	〜 38
	B11	⬅	Engine idling – accelerate briefly		50 mV/1 ms	〜 38
Malfunction indicator lamp (MIL)	A12	⊐▷	Ignition ON – MIL ON	0-1 V		
	A12	⊐▷	Engine idling – MIL OFF	11-14 V		
Mass air flow (MAF) sensor	A1	⟹	Ignition ON	5 V		
	A20	⬅	Engine idling	1,4 V		
	A20	⬅	3000 rpm	2 V		
	A29	⊐–	Ignition ON	0 V		
Spare cable	B25			1		
Speedometer	A27	⬅	Ignition ON	11-14 V		
Tachometer	A2	⟹	Ignition ON	11-14 V		
	A2	⟹	Engine idling	28 Hz	2 V/20 ms	〜 55
Throttle position (TP) sensor	B1	⊐–	Ignition ON	0 V		
	B13	⬅	Ignition ON – throttle closed	1,4 V		
	B13	⬅	Ignition ON – throttle fully open	4,5 V		
	B29	⟹	Ignition ON	5 V		

*Suggested settings - Voltage/time per division

1 Connected pin - no test data available or random digital signal

AUDI

Siemens Simos 2

Model:	Engine code:	Year:
A3 1,6	AEH/AKL	1996-03
A4 1,6	AHL/ARM	1996-02

ECM harness multi-plug

Terminal side

```
80 79 78 77 76 75 74        52 51 50 49 48 47 46 45 44 43 42 41
 73 72 71 70 69 68 67         40 39 38 37 36 35 34 33 32 31 30 29      28 27
66 65 64 63 62 61 60        26 25 24 23 22 21 20 19 18 17 16 15
 59 58 57 56 55 54 53         14 13 12 11 10  9  8  7  6  5  4  3        2  1
AD42344
```

Wire side

```
           41 42 43 44 45 46 47 48 49 50 51 52      74 75 76 77 78 79 80
          29 30 31 32 33 34 35 36 37 38 39 40       67 68 69 70 71 72 73
27 28      15 16 17 18 19 20 21 22 23 24 25 26        60 61 62 63 64 65 66
 1  2      3  4  5  6  7  8  9 10 11 12 13 14         53 54 55 56 57 58 59
AD42345
```

Component/circuit description	ECM pin	Signal	Condition	Typical value	Oscilloscope setting*	Wave form
Air conditioning – A3 08/98→	11			1		
Air conditioning, AC ON signal	10	←		1		
Air conditioning, compressor ON/shut-off signal	8	←▷		1		
Battery	3	←	Ignition OFF	11-14 V		
Camshaft position (CMP) sensor	62	▷	Ignition ON	5 V		
	76	←	Ignition ON – engine turned	0 V or 5 V switching		
	76	←	Engine idling	2 V/50 ms		45
Camshaft position (CMP) sensor – A3 08/97→	70	⊣	Engine idling	0 V		
Camshaft position (CMP) sensor – except A3 08/97→	67	⊣	Engine idling	0 V		
CAN data bus – 08/97→, AEH/AKL/ARM	29	←▷		1		
	31	←▷		1		
Closed throttle position (CTP) switch	69	←	Ignition ON – throttle closed	0 V		
	69	←	Ignition ON – throttle open	9 V min.		
Closed throttle position (CTP) switch – A3 08/97→	70	⊣	Engine idling	0 V		
Closed throttle position (CTP) switch – except A3 08/97→	67	⊣	Engine idling	0 V		
Clutch pedal position (CPP) switch – A3 08/97-07/98	21	←	Ignition ON	11-14 V briefly then 0 V		
	21	←	Engine idling – clutch pedal released	11-14 V		
	21	←	Engine idling – clutch pedal depressed	0 V		
Clutch pedal position (CPP) switch – A3 08/98→, if fitted	21	←	Ignition ON – clutch pedal released	11-14 V		
	21	←	Ignition ON – clutch pedal depressed	0 V		
Crankshaft position (CKP) sensor	56	←	Engine idling	13,7 V ac	10 V/1 ms	2
	63	←	Engine idling	0 V		
Crankshaft position (CKP) sensor – shield wire – A3 →07/97	67	⊣	Engine idling	0 V		
	70	⊣	Engine idling	0 V		
Diagnostic module – A4	18	▷		1		
Earth	2		Ignition ON	0 V		

★ Suggested settings - Voltage/time per division

Component/circuit description	ECM pin	Signal	Condition	Typical value	Oscilloscope setting*	Wave form
Engine coolant temperature (ECT) sensor	53	←	Ignition ON – coolant temp. 15°C	2,1 V		
	53	←	Ignition ON – coolant temp. 80°C	0,4 V		
Engine coolant temperature (ECT) sensor – A3 08/97→	70	⊐–	Engine idling	0 V		
Engine coolant temperature (ECT) sensor – except A3 08/97→	67	⊐–	Engine idling	0 V		
Evaporative emission (EVAP) canister purge valve	15	⊐▷	Ignition ON	11-14 V briefly then 0 V		
	15	⊐▷	Engine idling – engine hot	10%	10 V/20 ms	⟋⟍ 59
Exhaust gas recirculation (EGR) valve – A3 08/98→, if fitted	72	⊐▷	Ignition ON	11-14 V		
	72	⊐▷	Engine hot – valve operating		10 V/50 ms	⟋⟍ 59
Exhaust gas recirculation (EGR) valve position sensor – A3 08/98→, if fitted	61	⊐▷		☐1		
Fuel pump relay	4	⊐▷	Ignition ON	0-1 V briefly then 11-14 V		
	4	⊐▷	Engine idling	0-1 V		
Heated oxygen sensor (HO2S)	25	⊐–	Engine idling	0 V		
	26	←	Engine idling – engine hot	0,1-1 V fluctuating	0,2 V/1 sec.	⟋⟍ 21
	27	⊐▷	Ignition ON	11-14 V briefly then 0 V		
	27	⊐▷	Engine idling	0-1 V		
Heated rear window (HRW) switch – non-AC	10	←		☐1		
Idle speed control (ISC) actuator	59	⇨	Ignition ON	11-14 V		
	66	⇨	Ignition ON	11-14 V		
	66	⇨	Engine idling	10-20%	2 V/2 ms	⟋⟍ 71
Idle speed control (ISC) actuator position sensor	62	⇨	Ignition ON	5 V		
	74	←	Ignition ON	3,8 V		
	74	←	Engine idling	3,8 V		
Idle speed control (ISC) actuator position sensor – A3 08/97→	70	⊐–	Engine idling	0 V		
Idle speed control (ISC) actuator position sensor – except A3 08/97→	67	⊐–	Engine idling	0 V		
Ignition amplifier	71	⇨	Engine idling		2 V/10 ms	⟋⟍ 32
	78	⇨	Engine idling		2 V/10 ms	⟋⟍ 32
Ignition switch	1	←	Ignition OFF	0 V		
	1	←	Ignition ON	11-14 V		
Ignition switch, start signal – A3	22	←	Engine cranking	8 V min.		
Immobilizer control module, immobilization/diagnosis signal – A4 →07/97	19	⬌		☐1		
Injector 1	73	⊐▷	Ignition ON	11-14 V briefly then 0 V		
Injector 1 – A3	73	⊐▷	Engine idling – engine hot	2-4,1 ms	10 V/2 ms	⟋⟍ 35
Injector 1 – A4	73	⊐▷	Engine idling – engine hot	2-5 ms	10 V/2 ms	⟋⟍ 35
Injector 2	80	⊐▷	Ignition ON	11-14 V briefly then 0 V		
Injector 2 – A3	80	⊐▷	Engine idling – engine hot	2-5 ms	10 V/2 ms	⟋⟍ 35
Injector 3	58	⊐▷	Ignition ON	11-14 V briefly then 0 V		
Injector 3 – A3	58	⊐▷	Engine idling – engine hot	2-4,1 ms	10 V/2 ms	⟋⟍ 35
Injector 3 – A4	58	⊐▷	Engine idling – engine hot	2-5 ms	10 V/2 ms	⟋⟍ 35
Injector 4	65	⊐▷	Ignition ON	11-14 V briefly then 0 V		
Injector 4 – A3	65	⊐▷	Engine idling – engine hot	2-4,1 ms	10 V/2 ms*	⟋⟍ 35

* Suggested settings - Voltage/time per division

Component/circuit description	ECM pin	Signal	Condition	Typical value	Oscilloscope setting*	Wave form
Injector 4 – A4	65	⊣▷	Engine idling – engine hot	2-5 ms	10 V/2 ms	∿∿ 35
Instrumentation control module, engine RPM signal	6	⇨	Engine idling	30 Hz		
	6	⇨	3000 rpm	100 Hz		
Instrumentation control module, fuel consumption signal – some models	18	⇨		1		
Instrumentation control module, immobilization/diagnosis signal – except A4 →07/97	19	⬄		1		
Instrumentation control module, vehicle speed signal	20	⬅	Ignition ON – vehicle pushed	0 V or 11-14 V switching		
Intake air temperature (IAT) sensor – →07/97	54	⬅	Ignition ON – air temp. 15°C	1,5 V		
	67	⊣⊢	Engine idling	0 V		
Intake manifold air control solenoid – except A4 →07/97	64	⊣▷	Ignition ON	11-14 V briefly then 0 V		
	64	⊣▷	Engine idling	11-14 V		
	64	⊣▷	Engine idling – full throttle briefly	0-1 V briefly then 11-14 V		
Knock sensor (KS)	67	⊣⊢	Engine idling	0 V		
	68	⬅	Engine idling – full throttle briefly		50 mV/1 ms	∿∿ 58
Knock sensor (KS), shield wire – A3	67	⊣⊢	Engine idling	0 V		
Mass air flow (MAF) sensor	12	⊣⊢	Engine idling	0 V		
	13	⬅	Engine idling	1 V		
	13	⬅	Engine idling – full throttle briefly	4,2 V		
Mass air flow (MAF) sensor, IAT signal – 08/97→, AEH/AKL/ARM	9	⬅	Ignition ON – air temp. 15°C	1,5 V		
Mass air flow (MAF) sensor, IAT signal – 08/97→, AHL	54	⬅	Ignition ON – air temp. 15°C	1,5 V		
Power steering pressure (PSP) switch – A3 08/97→	14	⬅		1		
	24	⬅		1		
Starter motor relay/reversing lamp/s relay – AT	22	⬅		1		
Throttle position (TP) sensor	62	⇨	Ignition ON	5 V		
	75	⬅	Ignition ON – throttle closed	4,3 V		
	75	⬅	Ignition ON – throttle fully open	0,6 V		
Throttle position (TP) sensor – A3 08/97→	70	⊣⊢	Engine idling	0 V		
Throttle position (TP) sensor – except A3 08/97→	67	⊣⊢	Engine idling	0 V		
Transmission control module (TCM), torque reduction signal – some models	23	⬅		1		
Transmission control module (TCM), TP signal – some models	7	⇨		1		
Transmission control module (TCM), engine RPM signal – some models	6	⇨	Engine idling	30 Hz		
	6	⇨	3000 rpm	100 Hz		

*Suggested settings - Voltage/time per division

1 Connected pin - no test data available or random digital signal

Model:	Engine code:	Year:
A3 1,8/Turbo	AGN/AGU	1996-03
A4 1,8/Turbo	ADR/AEB/AJL	7/96-01
A6 1,8/Turbo	AEB/AJP	1997-05

AUDI
Bosch Motronic M3.8.2/4/5

ECM harness multi-plug

Terminal side

```
80 79 78 77 76 75 74        52 51 50 49 48 47 46 45 44 43 42 41
   73 72 71 70 69 68 67         40 39 38 37 36 35 34 33 32 31 30 29    28 27
66 65 64 63 62 61 60        26 25 24 23 22 21 20 19 18 17 16 15
   59 58 57 56 55 54 53         14 13 12 11 10 9  8  7  6  5  4  3    2  1
AD42344
```

Wire side

```
           41 42 43 44 45 46 47 48 49 50 51 52        74 75 76 77 78 79 80
         29 30 31 32 33 34 35 36 37 38 39 40        67 68 69 70 71 72 73
   27 28   15 16 17 18 19 20 21 22 23 24 25 26        60 61 62 63 64 65 66
  1  2     3  4  5  6  7  8  9  10 11 12 13 14        53 54 55 56 57 58 59
AD42345
```

Component/circuit description	ECM pin	Signal	Condition	Typical value	Oscilloscope setting*	Wave form
Air conditioning, compressor clutch signal	8	←	Engine idling – AC OFF	0 V		
	8	←	Engine idling – AC ON, AC compressor OFF	0 V		
	8	←	Engine idling – AC ON, AC compressor ON	11-14 V		
Air conditioning, load signal	10	←	Engine idling – AC OFF	0 V		
	10	←	Engine idling – AC ON	11-14 V		
Air conditioning, engine RPM signal – some models	6	⇒	Engine idling	30 Hz		
Automatic transmission (AT) – except A3 08/97→	7			1		
	22			1		
	23			1		
Automatic transmission (AT) – A4, some models	18			1		
Automatic transmission (AT) – A4 Turbo	5			1		
	49			1		
Automatic transmission (AT), engine RPM signal – some models	6	⇒	Engine idling	30 Hz		
Barometric pressure (BARO) sensor – Turbo	61	←	Ignition ON – at sea level	4 V		
	61	←	Ignition ON – 1000 m above sea level	3 V		
	61	←	Ignition ON – 2000 m above sea level	2,1 V		
	62	⇒	Ignition ON	5 V		
	67	⌐	Ignition ON	0 V		
Battery	3	←	Ignition OFF	11-14 V		
Camshaft position (CMP) actuator – non-Turbo	55	⌐▷	Engine idling	11-14 V		
	55	⌐▷	Vehicle moving, in second gear – accelerator pedal fully depressed from 1000 rpm	0-1 V briefly		
Camshaft position (CMP) sensor	67	⌐	Ignition ON	0 V		
Camshaft position (CMP) sensor – Motronic M3.8.2/4	76	←	Engine idling		5 V/20 ms	〰〰 12
Camshaft position (CMP) sensor – Motronic M3.8.5	76	←	Engine idling		5 V/20 ms	〰〰 14
Camshaft position (CMP) sensor – except A4 Turbo	62	⇒	Ignition ON	5 V		
Camshaft position (CMP) sensor – A4 Turbo	11	⇒	Ignition ON	5 V		

* Suggested settings - Voltage/time per division

Component/circuit description	ECM pin	Signal	Condition	Typical value	Oscilloscope setting*	Wave form
CAN data bus – A3 08/97→	29	◄⇨		1		
	41	◄⇨		1		
Closed throttle position (CTP) switch	67	⌐—	Ignition ON	0 V		
	69	◄—	Ignition ON – throttle closed	0 V		
	69	◄—	Ignition ON – throttle open	11-14 V		
Clutch pedal position (CPP) switch – A3 non-Turbo 08/97→	9	◄—		1		
Clutch pedal position (CPP) switch – A3 Turbo 08/99→	9	◄—	Engine idling – clutch pedal released	11-14 V		
	9	◄—	Engine idling – clutch pedal depressed	0 V		
Crankshaft position (CKP) sensor	56	◄—	Engine idling		2 V/1 ms	∿ 2
	63	◄—	Engine idling		2 V/1 ms	∿ 2
Crankshaft position (CKP) sensor, shield wire – A3	67	⌐—	Ignition ON	0 V		
Data link connector (DLC) – A4 Turbo 1996-97	43			1		
Diagnostic module – A4/A6	18			1		
Diagnostic module – A4 Turbo	5			1		
Earth	2		Ignition ON	0 V		
Earth – A3 MT →07/97	22		Ignition ON	0 V		
Engine coolant temperature (ECT) sensor	53	◄—	Ignition ON – coolant temp. 10°C	2 V		
	53	◄—	Ignition ON – coolant temp. 80°C	0,4 V		
	67	⌐—	Ignition ON	0 V		
Evaporative emission (EVAP) canister purge valve	15	⌐⇨	Engine hot – valve operating		10 V/20 ms	∿ 20
Fuel pump relay	4	⌐⇨	Engine cranking	0-1 V		
Heated oxygen sensor (HO2S)	25	⌐—	Engine idling	0 V		
	26	◄—	Engine idling – engine hot	0,1-1 V fluctuating	0,2 V/1 sec.	∿ 21
	27	⌐⇨	Engine idling	0-1 V		
Heated rear window switch, load signal – A4 without AC, some models	10			1		
Idle speed control (ISC) actuator	59 (66)	⇨	Engine idling		2 V/2 ms	∿ 64
	66 (59)	⇨	Engine idling		2 V/2 ms	∿ 64
Idle speed control (ISC) actuator position sensor	67	⌐—	Ignition ON	0 V		
	74	◄—	Engine idling – engine hot	3,6-3,9 V		
Idle speed control (ISC) actuator position sensor – except A4 Turbo	62	⇨	Ignition ON	5 V		
Idle speed control (ISC) actuator position sensor – A4 Turbo	11	⇨	Ignition ON	5 V		
Ignition amplifier	71	⇨	Engine idling		1 V/10 ms	∿ 32
	78	⇨	Engine idling		1 V/10 ms	∿ 32
Ignition amplifier – Turbo/A6 non-Turbo	70	⇨	Engine idling		1 V/10 ms	∿ 32
	77	⇨	Engine idling		1 V/10 ms	∿ 32
Ignition switch	1	◄—	Ignition OFF	0 V		
	1	◄—	Ignition ON	11-14 V		
Immobilizer control module – A4 1996-97	19	◄—	Engine idling	11-14 V		
Injector 1 – non-Turbo	73	⌐⇨	Engine idling – engine hot	2-5 ms	10 V/2 ms	∿ 35
Injector 1 – Turbo	73	⌐⇨	Engine idling – engine hot	1-3 ms	10 V/2 ms	∿ 35
Injector 2 – non-Turbo	80	⌐⇨	Engine idling – engine hot	2-5 ms	10 V/2 ms	∿ 35
Injector 2 – Turbo	80	⌐⇨	Engine idling – engine hot	1-3 ms	10 V/2 ms	∿ 35
Injector 3 – non-Turbo	58	⌐⇨	Engine idling – engine hot	2-5 ms	10 V/2 ms	∿ 35
Injector 3 – Turbo	58	⌐⇨	Engine idling – engine hot	1-3 ms	10 V/2 ms	∿ 35
Injector 4 – non-Turbo	65	⌐⇨	Engine idling – engine hot	2-5 ms	10 V/2 ms	∿ 35

* Suggested settings - Voltage/time per division

Component/circuit description	ECM pin	Signal	Condition	Typical value	Oscilloscope setting*	Wave form
Injector 4 – Turbo	65	⊐⊅	Engine idling – engine hot	1-3 ms	10 V/2 ms	⋀⋁⋀ 35
Instrumentation control module, engine RPM signal	6	⇨	Engine idling	30 Hz		
Instrumentation control module, vehicle speed signal	20	⬅	Ignition ON – vehicle pushed	0 V or 11-14 V		
Instrumentation control module – A3 08/99→	18			1		
Instrumentation control module, immobilization/diagnosis signal – A3/A6	19	⬅	Engine idling	11-14 V		
Instrumentation control module, immobilization/diagnosis signal – A4 1997→	19	⬅	Engine idling	11-14 V		
Intake air temperature (IAT) sensor – except A3 non-Turbo 08/97→	54	⬅	Ignition ON – air temp. 10°C	2 V		
	67	⊐⊢	Ignition ON	0 V		
Intake air temperature (IAT) sensor, in MAF sensor – A3 non-Turbo 08/97→	40	⬅	Ignition ON – air temp. 10°C	2 V		
	12	⊐⊢	Ignition ON	0 V		
Intake manifold air control solenoid – non-Turbo 08/97→	64	⊐⊅	Engine idling	11-14 V		
	64	⊐⊅	Engine idling – throttle fully open briefly	0-1 V briefly		
Knock sensor (KS) 1	67	⊐⊢	Engine idling	0 V		
	68	⬅	Engine idling – accelerate briefly		50 mV/1 ms	⋀⋁⋀ 58
Knock sensor (KS) 1 – shield wire – A3	67	⊐⊢	Engine idling	0 V		
Knock sensor (KS) 2	60	⬅	Engine idling – accelerate briefly		50 mV/1 ms	⋀⋁⋀ 58
	67	⊐⊢	Engine idling	0 V		
Knock sensor (KS) 2, shield wire – A3	67	⊐⊢	Engine idling	0 V		
Mass air flow (MAF) sensor	12	⊐⊢	Engine idling	0 V		
	13	⬅	Engine idling – engine hot	0,8-1,1 V		
	13	⬅	3000 rpm	1,7-2 V		
Mass air flow (MAF) sensor – A3 non-Turbo 08/97→	11	⇨	Ignition ON	5 V		
Power steering pressure (PSP) switch – A3 08/97→	14			1		
	49			1		
Spare cable – A3 →07/99	18			1		
Spare cable – A3 08/97→	43			1		
Spare cable – A3 Turbo →07/99	9			1		
Throttle position (TP) sensor	67	⊐⊢	Ignition ON	0 V		
	75	⬅	Ignition ON – throttle closed	4,3 V after 20 seconds		
	75	⬅	Ignition ON – throttle fully open	0,6 V		
Throttle position (TP) sensor – except A4 Turbo	62	⇨	Ignition ON	5 V		
Throttle position (TP) sensor – A4 Turbo	11	⇨	Ignition ON	5 V		
Turbocharger (TC) wastegate regulating valve	64	⊐⊅	Engine idling	11-14 V		
	64	⊐⊅	Vehicle moving – accelerate, full load	1-99%		

*Suggested settings - Voltage/time per division

1 Connected pin - no test data available or random digital signal

AUDI

Bosch EDC 15V

Model:	Engine code:	Year:
A3 1,9 TDI	AGR, AHF, ALH	1996-07/99

ECM harness multi-plug

Terminal side

```
80 79 78 77 76 75 74          52 51 50 49 48 47 46 45 44 43 42 41
   73 72 71 70 69 68 67          40 39 38 37 36 35 34 33 32 31 30 29
66 65 64 63 62 61 60          26 25 24 23 22 21 20 19 18 17 16 15      28 27
   59 58 57 56 55 54 53          14 13 12 11 10  9  8  7  6  5  4  3      2  1
AD42344
```

Wire side

```
                 41 42 43 44 45 46 47 48 49 50 51 52        74 75 76 77 78 79 80
              29 30 31 32 33 34 35 36 37 38 39 40           67 68 69 70 71 72 73
27 28            15 16 17 18 19 20 21 22 23 24 25 26        60 61 62 63 64 65 66
 1  2          3  4  5  6  7  8  9 10 11 12 13 14           53 54 55 56 57 58 59
AD42345
```

Component/circuit description	ECM pin	Signal	Condition	Typical value	Oscilloscope setting*	Wave form
AC connector	16			[1]		
	48			[1]		
Accelerator pedal position (APP) sensor	11	⇨	Ignition ON	5 V		
	23	⅃	Ignition ON	0 V		
	24	⬅	Ignition ON – accelerator pedal released	0,4 V		
	24	⬅	Ignition ON – accelerator pedal fully depressed	4,4 V		
Accelerator pedal position (APP) switch	12	⬅	Ignition ON – accelerator pedal released	0 V		
	12	⬅	Ignition ON – accelerator pedal depressed	2,8 V		
	25	⅃	Ignition ON	0 V		
Alternator – MT with engine coolant heaters	22	⬅	Engine idling	0 V		
Brake pedal position (BPP) switch	9	⬅	Ignition OFF – brake pedal released	11-14 V		
	9	⬅	Ignition OFF – brake pedal depressed	0 V		
	20	⬅	Ignition OFF – brake pedal released	0 V		
	20	⬅	Ignition OFF – brake pedal depressed	11-14 V		
CAN data bus – high – 08/97→	68	⬌		[1]		
CAN data bus – low – 08/97→	75	⬌		[1]		
Clutch pedal position (CPP) switch	46	⬅	Ignition ON – clutch pedal released	11-14 V		
	46	⬅	Ignition ON – clutch pedal depressed	0 V		
Crankshaft position (CKP) sensor	67	⬅	Engine idling	3,8 V ac		
	67	⬅	Engine idling		5 V/5 ms	⎍⎍⎍ 6
	69	⅃	Engine idling	0 V		
	71	⅃	Engine idling	0 V		
Crankshaft position (CKP) sensor – screened lead	71	⅃	Engine idling	0 V		
Cruise control master switch	19			[1]		
	21			[1]		
	35			[1]		
Cruise control selector switch	10			[1]		
	19			[1]		

★ Suggested settings - Voltage/time per division

Component/circuit description	ECM pin	Signal	Condition	Typical value	Oscilloscope setting*	Wave form
Earth	1		Ignition ON	0 V		
	27		Ignition ON	0 V		
Earth – without engine coolant heaters	22		Ignition ON	0 V		
Engine control (EC) relay	2	←	Ignition OFF	0 V		
	2	←	Ignition ON	11-14 V		
	28	←	Ignition OFF	0 V		
	28	←	Ignition ON	11-14 V		
	33	⊐▷	Ignition OFF	11-14 V		
	33	⊐▷	Ignition ON	0-1 V		
Engine coolant blower timer relay – AHF	31	⊐▷		☐1		
Engine coolant heater relay 1, low output – if fitted	17	⊐▷	Engine idling – relay contacts open	11-14 V		
	17	⊐▷	Engine idling – relay contacts closed	0-1 V		
Engine coolant heater relay 2, high output – if fitted	34	⊐▷	Engine idling – relay contacts open	11-14 V		
	34	⊐▷	Engine idling – relay contacts closed	0-1 V		
Engine coolant temperature (ECT) sensor	54	←	Ignition ON – coolant temp. 20°C	3,5 V		
	54	←	Ignition ON – coolant temp. 80°C	1,4 V		
	70	⊣—	Ignition ON	0 V		
Exhaust gas recirculation (EGR) solenoid	29	⊐▷	Ignition ON	11-14 V		
	29	⊐▷	Engine running – valve operating		5 V/5 ms	⟋⟍⟋ 4
Fuel injection timing solenoid	79	⊐▷	Ignition ON	11-14 V		
	79	⊐▷	Engine idling		2 V/10 ms	⟋⟍⟋ 10
Fuel quantity adjuster	59	⊐▷	Ignition ON	11,3 V then 11-14 V		
	59	⊐▷	Engine idling		2 V/2 ms	⟋⟍⟋ 5
	66	⊐▷	Ignition ON	11,3 V then 11-14 V		
	66	⊐▷	Engine idling		2 V/2 ms	⟋⟍⟋ 5
	80	⊐▷	Ignition ON	11,3 V then 11-14 V		
	80	⊐▷	Engine idling		2 V/2 ms	⟋⟍⟋ 5
Fuel quantity adjuster position sensor	56	←	Ignition ON	2,5 V		
	56	←	Engine idling		0,5 V/0,1 ms	⟋⟍⟋ 8
	57	⇒	Ignition ON	2,5 V		
	64	←	Ignition ON	2,5 V		
	64	←	Engine idling		0,5 V/0,1 ms	⟋⟍⟋ 8
Fuel shut-off solenoid	77	⇒	Engine idling	11-14 V		
	77	⇒	Ignition ON	11-14 V then 0 V		
Fuel temperature sensor	53	←	Ignition ON – fuel temp. 20°C	3,5 V		
	76	⊣—	Ignition ON	0 V		
Glow plug relay	42	⊐▷	Ignition ON – glow plugs ON	0-1 V		
	42	⊐▷	Ignition ON – glow plugs OFF	11-14 V		
Glow plug warning lamp	41	⊐▷	Ignition ON – lamp ON	0-1 V		
	41	⊐▷	Ignition ON – lamp OFF	11-14 V		
Ignition switch	47	←	Ignition OFF	0 V		
	47	←	Ignition ON	11-14 V		
Injector needle lift sensor	55	⊣—	Engine idling	0 V		
	62	←	Engine idling	0,02 V ac		
	62	←	Engine idling		0,2 V/1 ms	⟋⟍⟋ 7
Injector needle lift sensor – screened lead	71	⊣—	Engine idling	0 V		

* Suggested settings - Voltage/time per division

Component/circuit description	ECM pin	Signal	Condition	Typical value	Oscilloscope setting*	Wave form
Instrument panel, immobilization/ diagnosis signal	45	⬅➡	Ignition ON	11-14 V		
	45	⬅➡	Engine idling	11-14 V		
Instrumentation control module	18			☐1		
Instrumentation control module – tachometer signal	6	➡	Engine idling	30 Hz		
	6	➡	Engine idling		5 V/10 ms	∿∿ 2
Instrumentation control module – vehicle speed signal	51	⬅	Ignition ON – vehicle pushed	0 V or 10 V min. (switching)		
Intake air temperature (IAT) sensor	13	⬅	Ignition ON – air temp. 20°C	3,75 V		
	25	⌐	Ignition ON	0 V		
Intake manifold air control solenoid – AHF/ALH	3	⌐➡	Ignition ON	11-14 V		
	3	⌐➡	Engine idling	11-14 V		
	3	⌐➡	Engine idling – switch ignition OFF	0-1 V for 2,5 secs., 11-14 V for 0,5 sec., then 0-1 V		
Manifold absolute pressure (MAP) sensor	25	⌐	Ignition ON	0 V		
	39	➡	Ignition ON	5 V		
	40	⬅	Ignition ON	1,9 V		
	40	⬅	Engine idling	1,85 V		
	40	⬅	Engine running – accelerator pedal briefly fully depressed	3,65 V (briefly)		
Mass air flow (MAF) sensor	50	➡	Ignition ON	5 V		
	52	⬅	Ignition ON	0,28 V		
	52	⬅	Engine idling	1 V		
	52	⬅	Engine running – accelerator pedal briefly fully depressed	4,35 V (briefly)		
Mass air flow (MAF) sensor – 08/98→	4	⌐	Ignition ON	0 V		
Transmission control module (TCM)	44			☐1		
Transmission control module (TCM) – →07/97	7			☐1		
	36			☐1		
Transmission kick-down switch	8	⬅		☐1		
	25	⌐	Ignition ON	0 V		
Turbocharger (TC) wastegate regulating valve	15	⌐➡	Ignition ON	11-14 V		
	15	⌐➡	Engine running – valve not operating	11-14 V		
	15	⌐➡	Engine running – valve operating	0-1 V		

*Suggested settings - Voltage/time per division

☐1 Connected pin - no test data available or random digital signal

ECM harness multi-plug

Terminal side

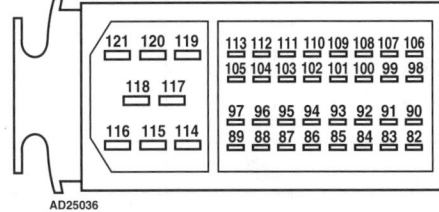
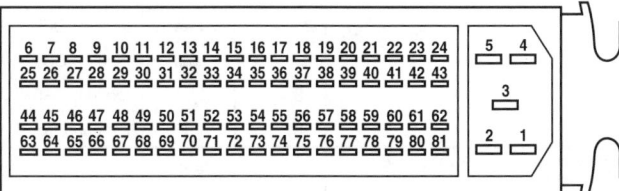

AD25036

Wire side

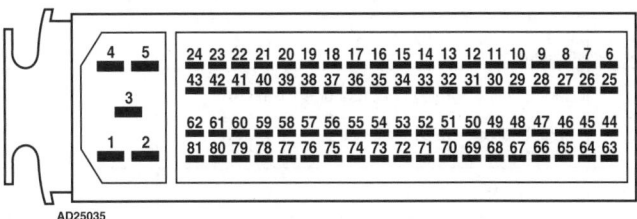

AD25035

Component/circuit description	ECM pin	Signal	Condition	Typical value	Oscilloscope setting*	Wave form
AC control module	29	⇨		1		
	34	⬅		1		
Accelerator pedal position (APP) sensor	12	⇨	Ignition ON	5 V		
	50	⌐⌐	Ignition ON	0 V		
	69	⬅	Ignition ON – accelerator pedal released	0,4 V		
	69	⬅	Ignition ON – accelerator pedal fully depressed	4,4 V		
Accelerator pedal position (APP) switch	51	⌐⌐	Ignition ON	0 V		
	70	⬅	Ignition ON – accelerator pedal released	0 V		
	70	⬅	Ignition ON – accelerator pedal depressed	2,8 V		
Alternator	38	⬅		1		
Brake pedal position (BPP) switch	32	⬅	Ignition OFF – brake pedal released	0 V		
	32	⬅	Ignition OFF – brake pedal depressed	11-14 V		
	65	⬅	Ignition OFF – brake pedal released	11-14 V		
	65	⬅	Ignition OFF – brake pedal depressed	0 V		
CAN data bus – high	6	⬅⇨		1		
CAN data bus – low	7	⬅⇨		1		
Clutch pedal position (CPP) switch	66	⬅	Ignition ON – clutch pedal released	11-14 V		
	66	⬅	Ignition ON – clutch pedal depressed	0 V		
Crankshaft position (CKP) sensor	102	⌐⌐	Engine idling	0 V		
	110	⬅	Engine idling	3,8 V ac		
	110	⬅	Engine idling		5 V/5 ms	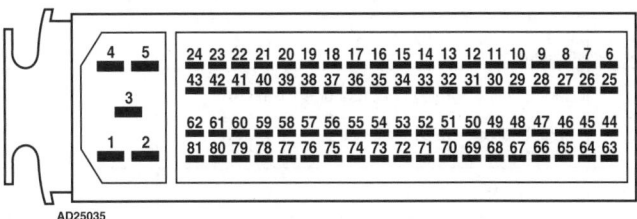 6
Crankshaft position (CKP) sensor – screened lead	86	⌐⌐	Engine idling	0 V		
Cruise control master switch	14			1		
	45			1		
	46			1		

* Suggested settings - Voltage/time per division

Component/circuit description	ECM pin	Signal	Condition	Typical value	Oscilloscope setting*	Wave form
Cruise control selector switch	14			1		
	44			1		
Earth	4		Ignition ON	0 V		
	5		Ignition ON	0 V		
Engine control (EC) relay	1	←	Ignition OFF	0 V		
	1	←	Ignition ON	11-14 V		
	2	←	Ignition OFF	0 V		
	2	←	Ignition ON	11-14 V		
	18	⇥▷	Ignition OFF	11-14 V		
	18	⇥▷	Ignition ON	0-1 V		
Engine coolant blower motor run-on relay – AHF/ASV	11	⇥▷		1		
Engine coolant heater relay 1, low output – if fitted	21	⇥▷	Engine idling – relay contacts open	11-14 V		
	21	⇥▷	Engine idling – relay contacts closed	0-1 V		
Engine coolant heater relay 2, high output – if fitted	22	⇥▷	Engine idling – relay contacts open	11-14 V		
	22	⇥▷	Engine idling – relay contacts closed	0-1 V		
Engine coolant temperature (ECT) sensor	104	⇥—	Ignition ON	0 V		
	112	←	Ignition ON – coolant temp. 20°C	3,5 V		
	112	←	Ignition ON – coolant temp. 80°C	1,4 V		
Exhaust gas recirculation (EGR) solenoid	61	⇥▷	Ignition ON	11-14 V		
	61	⇥▷	Engine running – valve operating		5 V/5 ms	⋀⋀ 4
Fuel injection timing solenoid	114	⇥▷	Ignition ON	11-14 V		
	114	⇥▷	Engine idling		2 V/10 ms	⋀⋀ 10
Fuel quantity adjuster	116	⇥▷	Ignition ON	11,3 V then 11-14 V		
	116	⇥▷	Engine idling		2 V/2 ms	⋀⋀ 5
	121	⇥▷	Ignition ON	11,3 V then 11-14 V		
	121	⇥▷	Engine idling		2 V/2 ms	⋀⋀ 5
Fuel quantity adjuster position sensor	99	←	Ignition ON	2,5 V		
	99	←	Engine idling		0,5 V/0,1 ms	⋀⋀ 8
	106	⇒	Ignition ON	2,5 V		
	108	←	Ignition ON	2,5 V		
	108	←	Engine idling		0,5 V/0,1 ms	⋀⋀ 8
Fuel shut-off solenoid	120	⇒	Engine idling	11-14 V		
	120	⇒	Ignition ON	11-14 V then 0 V		
Fuel temperature sensor	103	⇥—	Ignition ON	0 V		
	111	←	Ignition ON – fuel temp. 20°C	3,5 V		
Glow plug relay	42	⇥▷	Ignition ON – glow plugs ON	0-1 V		
	42	⇥▷	Ignition ON – glow plugs OFF	11-14 V		
Glow plug warning lamp	40	⇥▷	Ignition ON – lamp ON	0-1 V		
	40	⇥▷	Ignition ON – lamp OFF	11-14 V		
Ignition switch	37	←	Ignition OFF	0 V		
	37	←	Ignition ON	11-14 V		
	88	←	Ignition OFF	0 V		
	88	←	Ignition ON	11-14 V		
	88	←	Engine cranking	0 V		
	88	←	Engine idling	11-14 V		

★ Suggested settings - Voltage/time per division

Component/circuit description	ECM pin	Signal	Condition	Typical value	Oscilloscope setting*	Wave form
Injector needle lift sensor	101	⊣—	Engine idling	0 V		
	109	⟵	Engine idling	0,02 V ac		
	109	⟵	Engine idling		0,2 V/1 ms	ᗯ᙭ 7
Injector needle lift sensor – screened lead	86	⊣—	Engine idling	0 V		
Instrumentation control module	16			☐1		
Instrumentation control module – tachometer signal	27	⟹		☐1		
Instrumentation control module – vehicle speed signal	20	⟵	Ignition ON – vehicle pushed	0 V or 10 V min. (switching)		
Intake air temperature (IAT) sensor	52	⊣—	Ignition ON	0 V		
	73	⟵	Ignition ON – air temp. 20°C	3,75 V		
Intake manifold air control solenoid	81	⊣▷	Ignition ON	11-14 V		
	81	⊣▷	Engine idling	11-14 V		
	81	⊣▷	Engine idling – switch ignition OFF	0-1 V for 2,5 secs., 11-14 V for 0,5 sec., then 0-1 V		
Mass air flow (MAF) sensor	30	⟹	Ignition ON	5 V		
	49	⊣—	Ignition ON	0 V		
	68	⟵	Ignition ON	0,28 V		
	68	⟵	Engine idling	1 V		
	68	⟵	Engine running – accelerator pedal briefly fully depressed	4,35 V (briefly)		
Spare cable	28			☐1		
	33			☐1		
	80			☐1		
Supplementary restraint system (SRS) control module	47	⟵		☐1		
Transmission control module (TCM)	9			☐1		
	19			☐1		
	35			☐1		
Transmission kick-down switch	51	⊣—	Ignition ON	0 V		
	63	⟵		☐1		
Turbocharger (TC) boost pressure sensor	31	⟹	Ignition ON	5 V		
	52	⊣—	Ignition ON	0 V		
	71	⟵	Ignition ON	1,9 V		
	71	⟵	Engine idling	1,85 V		
	71	⟵	Engine running – accelerator pedal briefly fully depressed	3,65 V (briefly)		
Turbocharger (TC) wastegate regulating valve	62	⊣▷	Ignition ON	11-14 V		
	62	⊣▷	Engine running – valve not operating	11-14 V		
	62	⊣▷	Engine running – valve operating	0-1 V		

*Suggested settings - Voltage/time per division

☐1 Connected pin - no test data available or random digital signal

AUDI
Bosch EDC 15P/16

Model:	Engine code:	Year:
A3 1,9 TDI PD	ASZ/ATD/AXR	2001-03
A4 1,9 TDI PD	AJM/ATJ	1999-01
A6 1,9 TDI PD	AJM/AVF/AWX	2001-05

ECM harness multi-plug

Terminal side

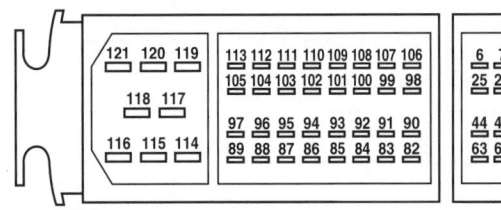
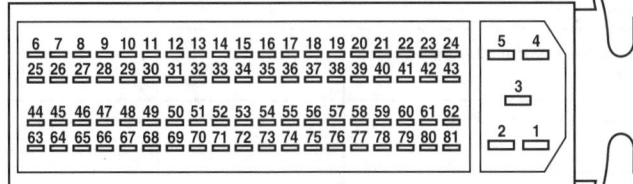

AD25036

Wire side

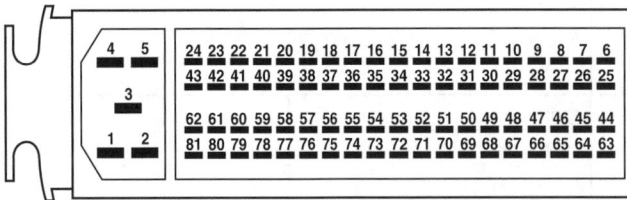

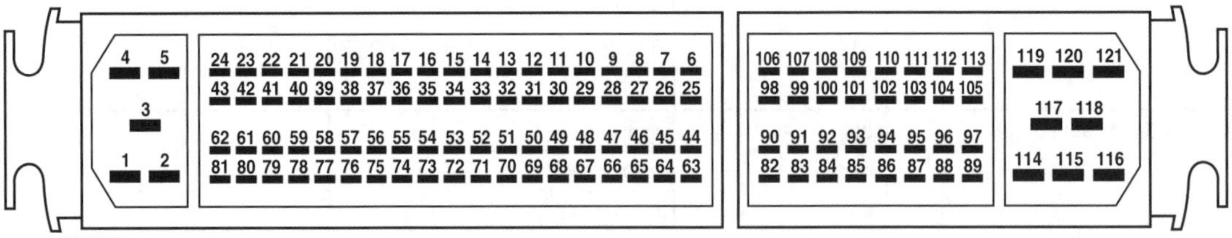

AD25035

Component/circuit description	ECM pin	Signal	Condition	Typical value	Oscilloscope setting*	Wave form
AC connection – some models	15			1		
AC connection, AC ON signal – some models	34	←	Engine idling – AC OFF	0 V		
	34	←	Engine idling – AC ON	11-14 V		
AC connection, compressor shut-off signal – some models	29	⇒	Engine idling – AC OFF	0 V		
	29	⇒	Engine idling – AC ON – compressor ON	11-14 V		
Accelerator pedal position (APP) sensor	12	⇒	Ignition ON	5 V		
	50	⌐	Ignition ON	0 V		
	69	←	Ignition ON – accelerator pedal released	0,4 V		
	69	←	Ignition ON – accelerator pedal fully depressed	4,4 V		
Accelerator pedal position (APP) switch	51	⌐	Ignition ON	0 V		
	70	←	Ignition ON – accelerator pedal released	0,2 V		
	70	←	Ignition ON – accelerator pedal depressed	5 V		
Airbag control module – crash signal	47			1		
Alternator, charging signal – some models	38	⇒	Ignition ON		2 V/20 ms	� 43
Auxiliary circuits relay – A4/A6	88	←	Ignition OFF	0 V		
	88	←	Ignition ON	11-14 V		
	88	←	Engine cranking	0 V		
	88	←	Engine idling	11-14 V		
Brake pedal position (BPP) switch 1	32	←	Ignition OFF – brake pedal released	0 V		
	32	←	Ignition OFF – brake pedal depressed	11-14 V		
Brake pedal position (BPP) switch 2	65	←	Ignition ON – brake pedal released	11-14 V		
	65	←	Ignition ON – brake pedal depressed	0 V		
Camshaft position (CMP) sensor	101	⌐	Ignition ON	0 V		
	109	←	Engine idling	2 V/0,5 ms		� 58

* Suggested settings - Voltage/time per division

Component/circuit description	ECM pin	Signal	Condition	Typical value	Oscilloscope setting*	Wave form
CAN data bus – high	7	⟷		1		
CAN data bus – low	6	⟷		1		
Clutch pedal position (CPP) switch	66	←	Ignition ON – clutch pedal released	11-14 V		
	66	←	Ignition ON – clutch pedal depressed	0 V		
Crankshaft position (CKP) sensor	102	←	Ignition ON	2,5 V		
	102	←	Engine idling	1,9 V ac		
	102	←	Engine idling		2 V/1 ms	∿ 25
	102	←	3000 rpm	3,1 V		
	110	←	Ignition ON	2,5 V		
	110	←	Engine idling	1,9 V ac		
	110	←	Engine idling		2 V/1 ms	Reversed ∿ 25
	110	←	3000 rpm	3,1 V		
Cruise control master switch	14	←	Ignition ON – selector switch set to 'OFF'	0 V		
	14	←	Ignition ON – selector switch set to 'ON'	11-14 V		
	44	←	Ignition ON – master switch released	0 V		
	44	←	Ignition ON – master switch depressed	11-14 V		
Cruise control selector switch	14	←	Ignition ON – selector switch set to 'OFF'	0 V		
	14	←	Ignition ON – selector switch set to 'ON'	11-14 V		
	45	←	Ignition ON – selector switch set to 'ON'	0 V		
	45	←	Ignition ON – selector switch set to 'RES'	11-14 V		
	46	←	Ignition ON – selector switch set to 'OFF'	0 V		
	46	←	Ignition ON – selector switch set to 'ON'	11-14 V		
Data link connector (DLC) – A3 (some models)	16			1		
Earth	4		Ignition ON	0 V		
	5		Ignition ON	0 V		
Engine control (EC) relay	1	←	Ignition OFF	0 V		
	1	←	Ignition ON	11-14 V		
	2	←	Ignition OFF	0 V		
	2	←	Ignition ON	11-14 V		
	18	⇥▷	Ignition OFF	11-14 V		
	18	⇥▷	Ignition ON	0-1 V		
Engine coolant blower motor control module – if fitted	11			1		
Engine coolant blower motor run-on relay – if fitted	11			1		
Engine coolant heater relay 1, low output – if fitted	21	⇥▷		1		
Engine coolant heater relay 2, high output – if fitted	22	⇥▷		1		
Engine coolant temperature (ECT) sensor	104	⇥—	Ignition ON	0 V		
	112	←	Ignition ON – coolant temp. 10°C	4 V		
	112	←	Ignition ON – coolant temp. 80°C	1,2 V		
Exhaust gas recirculation (EGR) solenoid 1	61	⇥▷	Ignition ON	11-14 V		
	61	⇥▷	Engine idling		5 V/1 ms	∿ 2
Exhaust gas recirculation (EGR) solenoid 2 – AXR	59	⇥▷	Ignition ON	11-14 V		
	59	⇥▷	Engine running – valve not operating	11-14 V		
	59	⇥▷	Engine running – valve operating	0-1 V		

* Suggested settings - Voltage/time per division

Component/circuit description	ECM pin	Signal	Condition	Typical value	Oscilloscope setting*	Wave form
Fuel cooling pump motor relay – A6 AJM/A4	43	⊐▷	Ignition ON – pump motor OFF	11-14 V		
	43	⊐▷	Engine idling – pump motor ON	0-1 V		
Fuel lift pump relay	80	⊐▷	Ignition ON	0-1 V briefly, then 11-14 V		
	80	⊐▷	Engine idling	0-1 V		
Fuel temperature sensor	103	⊐—	Ignition ON	0 V		
	111	⬅	Ignition ON – fuel temp. 5°C	4,6 V		
Glow plug relay	42	⊐▷	Ignition ON – glow plugs ON	0-1 V		
	42	⊐▷	Ignition ON – glow plugs OFF	11-14 V		
Glow plug warning lamp	40	⊐▷	Ignition ON – warning lamp ON	0-1 V		
	40	⊐▷	Ignition ON – warning lamp OFF	11-14 V		
Ignition switch	37	⬅	Ignition OFF	0 V		
	37	⬅	Ignition ON	11-14 V		
	37	⬅	Engine cranking	11-14 V		
	37	⬅	Engine idling	11-14 V		
Ignition switch – A3	88	⬅	Ignition OFF	0 V		
	88	⬅	Ignition ON	11-14 V		
	88	⬅	Engine cranking	0 V		
	88	⬅	Engine idling	11-14 V		
Ignition switch – A6 AVF/AWX	79	⬅	Ignition OFF	0 V		
	79	⬅	Ignition ON	0 V		
	79	⬅	Engine cranking	11-14 V		
	79	⬅	Engine idling	0 V		
Injector 1	114	⟹	Ignition ON	0,3 V		
	116	⟹	Ignition ON	0,3 V		
	116 (114)	⟹	Engine idling	2,2 ms		
	116 (114)	⟹	Engine idling		10 V/0,5 ms	∿∿ 57
Injector 2	114	⟹	Ignition ON	0,3 V		
	117	⟹	Ignition ON	0,3 V		
	117 (114)	⟹	Engine idling	2,2 ms		
	117 (114)	⟹	Engine idling		10 V/0,5 ms	∿∿ 57
Injector 3	114	⟹	Ignition ON	0,3 V		
	118	⟹	Ignition ON	0,3 V		
	118 (114)	⟹	Engine idling	2,2 ms		
	118 (114)	⟹	Engine idling		10 V/0,5 ms	∿∿ 57
Injector 4	114	⟹	Ignition ON	0,3 V		
	121	⟹	Ignition ON	0,3 V		
	121 (114)	⟹	Engine idling	2,2 ms		
	121 (114)	⟹	Engine idling		10 V/0,5 ms	∿∿ 57
Instrumentation control module – A3 except AT 2002→ – vehicle speed signal	20	⬅	Ignition ON – vehicle pushed	0 V or 10 V min. (switching)		
Instrumentation control module – A4/A6 – vehicle speed signal	20	⬅	Ignition ON – vehicle pushed	0 V or 10 V min. (switching)		
Instrumentation control module – diagnosis signal	16			1		
Instrumentation control module – some models	28			1		

★ Suggested settings - Voltage/time per division

Component/circuit description	ECM pin	Signal	Condition	Typical value	Oscilloscope setting*	Wave form
Instrumentation control module, engine RPM signal – some models	27	⇒	Engine idling	30 Hz		
	27	⇒	Engine idling		5 V/10 ms	∿ 2
	27	⇒	3000 rpm	100 Hz		
Intake air temperature (IAT) sensor	52	⊣	Ignition ON	0 V		
	73	⬅	Ignition ON – air temp. 10°C	3 V		
Intake manifold air control actuator – AXR	75			☐1		
	81			☐1		
Intake manifold air control solenoid – except AXR	81	⊣▷	Ignition ON	11-14 V		
	81	⊣▷	Engine idling	11-14 V		
	81	⊣▷	Engine idling – switch ignition OFF	0-1 V for 2,5 secs., 11-14 V for 0,5 sec then 0-1 V		
Mass air flow (MAF) sensor	30	⇒	Ignition ON	5 V		
	49	⊣	Ignition ON	0 V		
	68	⬅	Ignition ON	1 V		
	68	⬅	Engine idling	1,5-2,1 V		
	68	⬅	3000 rpm	3,2 V		
Spare cable, engine rear bulkhead – some models	28			☐1		
	33			☐1		
Transmission control module (TCM) – A3 AT 2002→ – vehicle speed signal	20	⬅	Ignition ON – vehicle pushed	0 V or 10 V min. (switching)		
Transmission control module (TCM) – A3 (some models)	9			☐1		
Transmission control module (TCM) – some models	19			☐1		
Transmission kick-down switch	51	⊣	Ignition ON	0 V		
	63	⬅	Ignition ON – accelerator pedal released	5 V		
	63	⬅	Ignition ON – accelerator pedal fully depressed	0 V		
Turbocharger (TC) boost pressure sensor	31	⇒	Ignition ON	5 V		
	52	⊣	Ignition ON	0 V		
	71	⬅	Ignition ON	1,6 V		
	71	⬅	Engine idling	1,7 V		
Turbocharger (TC) wastegate regulating valve	62	⊣▷	Ignition ON	11-14 V		
	62	⊣▷	Engine idling	11-14 V		
	62	⊣▷	Engine idling – accelerator pedal briefly fully depressed	0-1 V briefly		
	62	⊣▷	Engine running – valve not operating	11-14 V		
	62	⊣▷	Engine running – valve operating	0-1 V		

*Suggested settings - Voltage/time per division

☐1 Connected pin - no test data available or random digital signal

AUDI

Bosch Motronic M3.8.2

Model:	Engine code:	Year:
A4/quattro 2,4	AGA/AJG	1997-01
A4/quattro 2,8	ACK/ALG	1995-01
A6/quattro 2,4	AGA/AJG/ALF	1997-05
A6 2,4	ALF/ALN	1997-05
A6/quattro 2,8 30V	ACK/ALG	1995-01

ECM harness multi-plug

Terminal side

AD42344

Wire side

AD42345

Component/circuit description	ECM pin	Signal	Condition	Typical value	Oscilloscope setting*	Wave form
ABS control module – with traction control – some models	5			1		
	6			1		
	45		Engine idling	11-14 V		
Air conditioning	8		Engine idling – AC OFF	0 V		
	8		Engine idling – AC ON – AC compressor ON	11-14 V		
Air conditioning – some models	6			1		
	10			1		
	20			1		
Automatic transmission	18			1		
Automatic transmission – A4 – some models	49			1		
Automatic transmission – some models	5			1		
	6			1		
	7			1		
	8			1		
	22			1		
	23			1		
Battery	3	←	Ignition OFF	11-14 V		
Camshaft position (CMP) actuator, bank 1	55	⇥⊳	Engine idling	11-14 V		
Camshaft position (CMP) actuator, bank 2	55	⇥⊳	Engine idling	11-14 V		
Camshaft position (CMP) sensor, bank 1	11	⇨	Ignition ON	11-14 V		
	67	⇥–	Ignition ON	0 V		
	76	←	Ignition ON – engine turned	0 V or 11-14 V		
	76	←	Engine idling		5 V/20 ms	12
Camshaft position (CMP) sensor, bank 2	11	⇨	Ignition ON	11-14 V		
	14	⇥–	Engine idling	0 V		
	44	←	Ignition ON – engine turned	0 V or 11-14 V		
	44	←	Engine idling		5 V/20 ms	12

* Suggested settings - Voltage/time per division

Component/circuit description	ECM pin	Signal	Condition	Typical value	Oscilloscope setting*	Wave form
CAN data bus – "high" signal line – 1997-99	41	⟵⟩		[1]		
CAN data bus – "low" signal line – 1997-99	29	⟵⟩		[1]		
Closed throttle position (CTP) switch	67	⌐—	Ignition ON	0 V		
	69	⟵	Ignition ON – throttle closed	0 V		
	69	⟵	Ignition ON – throttle open	11-14 V		
Crankshaft position (CKP) sensor	56	⟵	Engine idling		2 V/1 ms	∿ 2
	63	⟵	Engine idling		2 V/1 ms	∿ 2
Crankshaft position (CKP) sensor – shield wire	67	⌐—	Engine idling	0 V		
Diagnostic module	18			[1]		
Earth	2		Ignition ON	0 V		
Engine coolant temperature (ECT) sensor	53	⟵	Ignition ON – coolant temp. 10°C	2,5 V		
	53	⟵	Ignition ON – coolant temp. 80°C	0,4 V		
	67	⌐—	Ignition ON	0 V		
Evaporative emission (EVAP) canister purge valve	15	⌐▷	Ignition ON	11-14 V briefly then 0 V		
	15	⌐▷	Engine hot – valve operating		10 V/20 ms	∿ 20
Fuel pump relay	4	⌐▷	Ignition ON	0-1 V briefly then 11-14 V		
	4	⌐▷	Engine cranking	0-1 V		
Heated oxygen sensor (HO2S) 1, bank 1 – RH	25	⌐—	Engine idling	0 V		
	26	⟵	Engine idling – engine hot	0,1-1,1 V fluctuating	0,2 V/1 sec.	∿ 21
Heated oxygen sensor (HO2S) 1, bank 1 – shield wire	14	⌐—	Engine idling	0 V		
Heated oxygen sensor (HO2S) 1, bank 2	39	⌐—	Engine idling	0 V		
	40	⟵	Engine idling – engine hot	0,1-1,1 V fluctuating	0,2 V/1 sec.	∿ 21
Heated oxygen sensor (HO2S) 1, bank 2 – shield wire	14	⌐—	Engine idling	0 V		
Heated rear window switch – without AC – 1995-97	10			[1]		
Idle speed control (ISC) actuator	59 (66)	⟹	Engine idling		2 V/2 ms	∿ 28
	66 (59)	⟹	Engine idling		2 V/2 ms	∿ 28
Idle speed control (ISC) actuator position sensor	62	⟹	Ignition ON	5 V		
	67	⌐—	Ignition ON	0 V		
	74	⟵	Engine idling – engine hot	3,8 V		
Ignition amplifier	70	⟹	Engine idling		1 V/10 ms	∿ 32
	71	⟹	Engine idling		1 V/10 ms	∿ 32
	78	⟹	Engine idling		1 V/10 ms	∿ 32
Ignition switch	1	⟵	Ignition OFF	0 V		
	1	⟵	Ignition ON	11-14 V		
Ignition switch – some models 1997-99	10		Ignition OFF	0 V		
	10		Ignition ON	11-14 V		
Immobilizer control module – 1995-97	19			[1]		
Injector 1	73	⌐▷	Ignition ON	11-14 V briefly then 5 V		
	73	⌐▷	Engine idling – engine hot	1-4 ms	10 V/2 ms	∿ 35
Injector 2	80	⌐▷	Ignition ON	11-14 V briefly then 5 V		
	80	⌐▷	Engine idling – engine hot	1-4 ms	10 V/2 ms	∿ 35

★ Suggested settings - Voltage/time per division

Component/circuit description	ECM pin	Signal	Condition	Typical value	Oscilloscope setting*	Wave form
Injector 3	58	→▷	Ignition ON	11-14 V briefly then 5 V		
	58	→▷	Engine idling – engine hot	1-4 ms	10 V/2 ms	∿∿ 35
Injector 4	65	→▷	Ignition ON	11-14 V briefly then 5 V		
	65	→▷	Engine idling – engine hot	1-4 ms	10 V/2 ms	∿∿ 35
Injector 5	72	→▷	Ignition ON	11-14 V briefly then 5 V		
	72	→▷	Engine idling – engine hot	1-4 ms	10 V/2 ms	∿∿ 35
Injector 6	79	→▷	Ignition ON	11-14 V briefly then 5 V		
	79	→▷	Engine idling – engine hot	1-4 ms	10 V/2 ms	∿∿ 35
Instrumentation control module	20	←	Ignition ON – vehicle pushed	0 V or 11-14 V		
Instrumentation control module – 1997-99	19		Engine idling	11-14 V		
Instrumentation control module – some models	6	⇨	Engine idling	8-10 V/40 Hz		
Intake air temperature (IAT) sensor	54	←	Ignition ON – air temp. 10°C	2,5 V		
	67	─	Ignition ON	0 V		
Intake manifold air control solenoid	64	→▷	Ignition ON	11-14 V briefly then 0 V		
	64	→▷	Engine idling	11-14 V		
Intake manifold air control solenoid – 2,4	64	→▷	Above 4500 rpm	0-1 V		
Intake manifold air control solenoid – 2,8	64	→▷	Above 4700 rpm	0-1 V		
Knock sensor (KS) 1	67	─	Engine idling	0 V		
	68	←	Engine idling – accelerate briefly		50 mV/1 ms	∿∿ 38
Knock sensor (KS) 1 – shield wire	67	─	Engine idling	0 V		
Knock sensor (KS) 2	60	←	Engine idling – accelerate briefly		50 mV/1 ms	∿∿ 38
	67	─	Engine idling	0 V		
Knock sensor (KS) 2 – shield wire	67	─	Engine idling	0 V		
Malfunction indicator lamp (MIL) – A6 1995-97	17		Ignition ON – MIL ON	0-1 V		
	17		Engine idling – MIL OFF	11-14 V		
Mass air flow (MAF) sensor	12	─	Engine idling	0 V		
	13	←	Engine idling	1,4 V		
	13	←	3000 rpm	2,1 V		
Mass air flow (MAF) sensor – shield wire	14	─	Ignition ON	0 V		
Secondary air injection (AIR) pump relay – if fitted	30	→▷	Engine idling – engine cold	0-1 V		
Secondary air injection (AIR) solenoid – if fitted	33	→▷		1		
Spare cable – A4 1995-97	17			1		
Throttle position (TP) sensor	62	⇨	Ignition ON	5 V		
	67	─	Ignition ON	0 V		
	75	←	Ignition ON – throttle closed	4,2 V after 20 seconds		
	75	←	Ignition ON – throttle fully open	0,6 V		

*Suggested settings - Voltage/time per division

1 Connected pin - no test data available or random digital signal

ECM harness multi-plug

Terminal side

D   C   B   A

AD20683

Wire side

A   B   C   D

AD20684

Component/circuit description	ECM pin	Signal	Condition	Typical value
AC control module – A4: 1998-99/A6	39D			☐1
AC control module – A6	28D			☐1
AC control module – tachometer signal	17D	⇨	Ignition ON	11-14 V
	17D	⇨	Engine idling	38 Hz
	17D	⇨	3000 rpm	150 Hz
AC control module	19D	⬄	Engine idling – AC ON – compressor OFF	0 V
	19D	⬄	Engine idling – AC ON – compressor ON	11-14 V
Accelerator pedal position (APP) sensor	7D	⌐	Ignition ON	0 V
	8D	⬅	Ignition ON – accelerator pedal released	0,36 V
	8D	⬅	Ignition ON – accelerator pedal fully depressed	4,5 V
	9D	⇨	Ignition ON	5 V
Accelerator pedal position (APP) switch	12D	⌐	Ignition ON	0 V
	13D	⬅	Ignition ON – accelerator pedal released	0 V
	13D	⬅	Ignition ON – accelerator pedal depressed	2,8 V
Alternator	12B	⬅		☐1
Alternator relay – A6 1997-98	14B	⌐⟩		☐1
Auxiliary heater control module – A6	20D			☐1
	52C			☐1
Brake pedal position (BPP) switch I	31D	⬅	Ignition ON – brake pedal released	11-14 V
	31D	⬅	Ignition ON – brake pedal depressed	0 V
Brake pedal position (BPP) switch II	24D	⬅	Ignition OFF – brake pedal released	0 V
	24D	⬅	Ignition OFF – brake pedal depressed	11-14 V
CAN data bus	46C	⬄		☐1
	47C	⬄		☐1

Component/circuit description	ECM pin	Signal	Condition	Typical value
Clutch pedal position (CPP) switch	23D	←	Ignition ON – clutch pedal released	11-14 V
	23D	←	Ignition ON – clutch pedal depressed	0 V
Crankshaft position (CKP) sensor	6C	←	Engine idling	3,35 V ac
	6C	←	Engine idling	5 V/5 ms per division ⎍ 6
	31C	⊣	Engine idling	0 V
Cruise control master switch	1D			1
	25D			1
Cruise control selector switch	2D			1
	25D			1
	40D			1
Diagnostic module – fuel consumption signal – some models	18D	⇒		1
Earth	4A		Ignition ON	0 V
	5A		Ignition ON	0 V
	6A		Ignition ON	0 V
Engine control relay	1A	←	Ignition ON	11-14 V
	8A	←	Ignition ON	11-14 V
	9A	⊐▷	Ignition ON	0-1 V
Engine coolant blower motor run-on relay	12C	⊐▷		1
Engine coolant heater relay I – low output – A6 (if fitted)	2B	⊐▷		1
Engine coolant heater relay II – high output – A6 (if fitted)	19B	⊐▷		1
Engine coolant temperature (ECT) sensor	28C	←	Ignition ON – coolant temp. 10°C	3,9 V
	28C	←	Ignition ON – coolant temp. 80°C	1,25 V
	32C	⊣	Ignition ON	0 V
Engine mounting control solenoid I/II	8B	⊐▷	Above 1100 rpm	0-1 V
Engine oil temperature sensor	27C	←	Ignition ON – oil temp. 10°C	4,4 V
	27C	←	Ignition ON – oil temp. 80°C	2,1 V
	34C	⊣	Ignition ON	0 V
Exhaust gas recirculation (EGR) solenoid	13B	⊐▷	Ignition ON	11-14 V
	13B	⊐▷	Engine idling – engine warm	50%
	13B	⊐▷	Engine idling	2 V/10 ms per division ⎍ 22
Fuel injection pump control module – engine cut-out signal	21C	⇒	Engine idling	0,2 V (with signal)
	21C	⇒	Engine idling – switch ignition OFF	11,3 V (without signal)
	21C	⇒	Engine idling	0,2 V/5 ms per division ⎍ 17
Fuel injection pump control module – engine speed signal	7C	⇒	Engine idling	5 V/10 ms per division ⎍ 12
	7C	⇒	Engine idling	76 Hz
	7C	⇒	3000 rpm	300 Hz
Fuel injection pump control module (data bus)	44C	⇆		1
	45C	⇆		1
Fuel low level sensor	5D	←	Ignition ON – fuel level OK	2,3 V
	15D	⊣	Ignition ON	0 V
Fuel transfer pump relay	10D	⊐▷	Engine cranking	0-1 V
	10D	⊐▷	Engine idling	0-1 V
	10D	⊐▷	Ignition ON	11-14 V
Glow plug relay	38D	⊐▷	Ignition ON – glow plugs ON	0-1 V
	38D	⊐▷	Ignition ON – glow plugs OFF	11-14 V
Glow plug warning lamp	30D	⊐▷	Ignition ON – lamp ON	0 V
	30D	⊐▷	Ignition ON – lamp OFF	10-14 V
Heater function control module – A6	28D			1

Component/circuit description	ECM pin	Signal	Condition	Typical value
Ignition switch – FWD – A4: 1997-98	39D	←	Ignition OFF	0 V
	39D	←	Ignition ON	11-14 V
Ignition switch	26D	←	Ignition OFF	0 V
	26D	←	Ignition ON	11-14 V
Injector needle lift sensor	5C	←	Engine idling	0,035 V ac
	5C	←	Engine idling	0,2 V/0,5 ms per division ⎍⎍ 55
	5C	←	Ignition ON	3,2 V
	18C	⌐	Engine idling	0 V
Instrument panel – immobilization/diagnosis signal	32D	←⇒	Ignition ON	11-14 V
	32D	←⇒	Engine idling	11-14 V
Instrumentation control module – fuel consumption signal – some models	18D	⇒		[1]
Instrumentation control module – fuel level signal	17B	←		[1]
Instrumentation control module – tachometer signal	17D	⇒	Ignition ON	11-14 V
	17D	⇒	Engine idling	38 Hz
	17D	⇒	3000 rpm	150 Hz
Instrumentation control module – vehicle speed signal	22D	←	Ignition ON – vehicle pushed	0 V or 10,65 V (switching)
Intake air temperature (IAT) sensor	3C	⌐	Ignition ON	0 V
	29C	←	Ignition ON – air temp. 20°C	2,4 V
Intake manifold air control solenoid – except A4 1997-98	20B	⌐⇒	Ignition ON	11-14 V
	20B	⌐⇒	Engine idling	11-14 V
	20B	⌐⇒	Engine idling – switch ignition OFF	0-1 V for 1-2 seconds then 11-14 V
Manifold absolute pressure (MAP) sensor	14C	⇒	Ignition ON	5 V
	15C	←	Engine idling	1,96 V
	15C	←	Engine running – accelerator pedal briefly fully depressed	3,5 V
	16C	⌐	Ignition ON	0 V
Mass air flow (MAF) sensor	1C	⇒	Ignition ON	5 V
	2C	←	3000 rpm	3,9 V
	2C	←	Engine idling	1,75 V
	2C	←	Ignition ON	1 V
	3C	⌐	Engine idling	0 V
Outside air temperature display – A6	33D	←		[1]
Spare cable, engine compartment rear – A4: 1997-98	33D			
Transmission kick-down switch	12D	⌐	Ignition ON	0 V
	34D	←	Ignition ON – accelerator pedal released	5 V
	34D	←	Ignition ON – accelerator pedal fully depressed	0 V
Turbocharger (TC) wastegate regulating valve	21B	⌐⇒	Ignition ON	11-14 V
	21B	⌐⇒	Engine idling	85%
	21B	⌐⇒	Engine idling	5 V/1 ms per division ⎍⎍ 29

[1] Connected pin - no test data available

AUDI
Bosch Motronic ME7.5

Model:	Engine code:	Year:
TT 1,8 Turbo	AJQ/APP/APX/ARY/AUM/AUQ/BAM	1998-06

ECM harness multi-plug

Terminal side

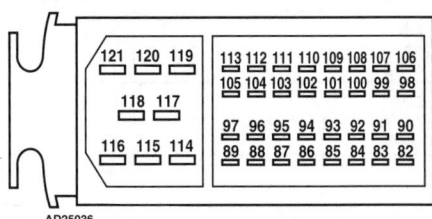

AD25036

Wire side

AD25035

Component/circuit description	ECM pin	Signal	Condition	Typical value	Oscilloscope setting*	Wave form
Accelerator pedal position (APP) sensor	33	⌐	Ignition ON	0 V		
	34	←	Ignition ON – accelerator pedal released	0,4 V		
	34	←	Ignition ON – accelerator pedal depressed	2 V		
	35	←	Ignition ON – accelerator pedal released	0,7 V		
	35	←	Ignition ON – accelerator pedal depressed	4,1 V		
	36	⌐	Ignition ON	0 V		
	72	⇒	Ignition ON	5 V		
	73	⇒	Ignition ON	5 V		
Air conditioning	40			1		
	41			1		
Air conditioning – 2001→	37			1		
Alternator – some models	28	⇒	Engine idling		5 V/50 ms	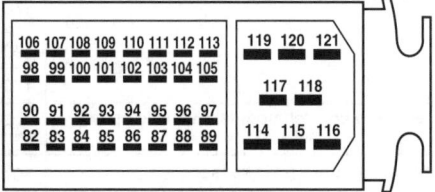 94
Battery	62	←	Ignition OFF	11-14 V		
Brake pedal position (BPP) switch 1	56	←	Ignition ON – brake pedal released	0 V		
	56	←	Ignition ON – brake pedal depressed	11-14 V		
Brake pedal position (BPP) switch 2	55	←	Ignition ON – brake pedal released	11-14 V		
	55	←	Ignition ON – brake pedal depressed	0 V		
Camshaft position (CMP) actuator – some models	115	⌐▷	Ignition ON	11-14 V briefly then 0-1 V		
	115	⌐▷	Engine idling	11-14 V		
Camshaft position (CMP) sensor	86	←	Ignition ON	0 or 11-14 V		
	86	←	Engine idling		5 V/20 ms	14
	98	⇒	Ignition ON	5 V		
	108	⌐	Ignition ON	0 V		
CAN data bus – high	60	←⇒		1		
CAN data bus – low	58	←⇒		1		

* Suggested settings - Voltage/time per division

Component/circuit description	ECM pin	Signal	Condition	Typical value	Oscilloscope setting*	Wave form
Clutch pedal position (CPP) switch	39	←	Ignition ON – clutch pedal released	11-14 V		
	39	←	Ignition ON – clutch pedal depressed	0 V		
Crankshaft position (CKP) sensor	82	←	Engine idling	3,1 V ac		
	82	←	Engine idling		2 V/2 ms	∿ 2
	90	←	Engine idling	3,1 V ac		
	90	←	Engine idling		2 V/2 ms	Reversed ∿ 2
	108	⌐	Ignition ON	0 V		
Cruise control master switch	38			1		
	57			1		
Cruise control selector switch	38			1		
	75			1		
	76			1		
Earth	1		Ignition ON	0 V		
	2		Ignition ON	0 V		
Engine control (EC) relay – 2000→	21	⌐▷	Ignition ON	0-1 V		
	21	⌐▷	Engine idling	0-1 V		
	121	←	Ignition ON	11-14 V		
Engine coolant blower motor/ AC compressor control module – AJQ/APP/APX	61			1		
Engine coolant temperature (ECT) sensor	93	←	Ignition ON – coolant temp. 20°C	2,2 V		
	93	←	Ignition ON – coolant temp. 80°C	0,4 V		
	108	⌐	Ignition ON	0 V		
Engine malfunction indicator lamp (MIL) – without CAN data bus	47	⌐▷	Ignition ON – MIL ON	0-1 V		
	47	⌐▷	Engine idling – MIL OFF	11-14 V		
Evaporative emission (EVAP) canister purge valve	64	⌐▷	Ignition ON	11-14 V briefly then 0-1 V		
	64	⌐▷	Engine running – engine hot – valve operating		10 V/5 ms	∿ 35
Exhaust gas temperature sensor – BAM	61			1		
Exhaust gas temperature sensor – BAM – →2001	50	⌐	Ignition ON	0 V		
Fuel pump (FP) relay	65	⌐▷	Ignition ON	0-1 V briefly then 11-14 V		
	65	⌐▷	Engine idling	0-1 V		
Heated oxygen sensor (HO2S) 1 – AJQ/APP/APX	5	⌐▷			5 V/50 ms	∿ 18
	51	⌐	Engine idling	0 V		
	70	←	Engine idling	0,1-1 V fluctuating	0,2 V/1 sec.	∿ 21
Heated oxygen sensor (HO2S) 1 – ARY/AUM/AUQ/BAM	5	⌐▷			2 V/0,2 sec.	∿ 55
	51	←	Engine idling	2,5 V		
	51 (70)	←	Engine idling	0,45 V		
	52	←▷	Engine idling	2,34-2,55 V		
	70	←	Engine idling	2,9 V		
	70 (51)	←	Engine idling	0,45 V		
	71	←▷	Engine idling	2,34-2,55 V		
Heated oxygen sensor (HO2S) 2 – APP/ARY/AUM/AUQ/BAM	63	⌐▷	Ignition ON	11-14 V briefly then 0-1 V		
	63	⌐▷	Engine idling	0-1 V		
	68	⌐	Ignition ON	0 V		
	69	←	Engine idling – engine hot	0,6 V		

* Suggested settings - Voltage/time per division

Component/circuit description	ECM pin	Signal	Condition	Typical value	Oscilloscope setting*	Wave form
Ignition coil 1	102	⇒	Ignition ON	0 V		
	102	⇒	Engine idling		2 V/20 ms	∿∿ 62
Ignition coil 2	95	⇒	Ignition ON	0 V		
	95	⇒	Engine idling		2 V/20 ms	∿∿ 62
Ignition coil 3	103	⇒	Ignition ON	0 V		
	103	⇒	Engine idling		2 V/20 ms	∿∿ 62
Ignition coil 4	94	⇒	Ignition ON	0 V		
	94	⇒	Engine idling		2 V/20 ms	∿∿ 62
Ignition switch	3	⇐	Ignition OFF	0 V		
	3	⇐	Ignition ON	11-14 V		
Injector 1	96	⊐▷	Ignition ON	11-14 V briefly then 0-1 V		
	96	⊐▷	Engine idling	2,5 ms	10 V/2 ms	∿∿ 35
Injector 2	89	⊐▷	Ignition ON	11-14 V briefly then 0-1 V		
	89	⊐▷	Engine idling	2,5 ms	10 V/2 ms	∿∿ 35
Injector 3	97	⊐▷	Ignition ON	11-14 V briefly then 0-1 V		
	97	⊐▷	Engine idling	2,5 ms	10 V/2 ms	∿∿ 35
Injector 4	88	⊐▷	Ignition ON	11-14 V briefly then 0-1 V		
	88	⊐▷	Engine idling	2,5 ms	10 V/2 ms	∿∿ 35
Instrumentation control module – diagnosis signal	43			[1]		
Instrumentation control module – engine RPM signal – →2001	37	⇒	Engine idling	28 Hz		
Instrumentation control module – vehicle speed signal	54	⇐		[1]		
Instrumentation control module – some models	30			[1]		
	81			[1]		
Intake air temperature (IAT) sensor	85	⇐	Ignition ON – air temp. 20°C	2,1 V		
	108	⊐─	Ignition ON	0 V		
Knock sensor (KS) 1	99	⊐─	Engine idling	0 V		
	106	⇐	Engine idling – accelerate briefly		50 mV/1 ms	∿∿ 38
	108	⊐─	Ignition ON	0 V		
Knock sensor (KS) 2	99	⊐─	Engine idling	0 V		
	107	⇐	Engine idling – accelerate briefly		50 mV/1 ms	∿∿ 38
	108	⊐─	Ignition ON	0 V		
Mass air flow (MAF) sensor	27	⊐─	Ignition ON	0 V		
	29	⇐	Engine idling	1,4 V		
	53	⇒	Ignition ON	5 V		
Power steering pressure (PSP) switch – some models	49	⇐	Engine idling – steering wheel not turned	11-14 V		
	49	⇐	Engine idling – steering wheel turned	0 V		
	50	⊐─	Ignition ON	0 V		
Secondary air injection (AIR) pump relay – except AJQ	66	⊐▷	Ignition ON	11-14 V briefly then 0-1 V		
	66	⊐▷	Engine running – pump OFF	11-14 V		
	66	⊐▷	Engine running – pump ON	0-1 V		
Secondary air injection (AIR) solenoid – except AJQ	9	⊐▷	Ignition ON	11-14 V briefly then 0-1 V		
	9	⊐▷	Engine running – solenoid OFF	11-14 V		
	9	⊐▷	Engine running – solenoid ON	0-1 V		

★ Suggested settings - Voltage/time per division

Component/circuit description	ECM pin	Signal	Condition	Typical value	Oscilloscope setting*	Wave form
Supplementary restraint system (SRS) control module	67			[1]		
Throttle control system warning lamp – without CAN data bus	48	⨼▷	Ignition ON – warning lamp ON	0-1 V		
	48	⨼▷	Engine idling – warning lamp OFF	11-14 V		
Throttle motor	117	⇨	Ignition ON	11-14 V for 30 seconds then 3 V		
	117	⇨	Ignition ON – accelerator pedal released		2 V/0,5 ms	64
	117	⇨	Ignition ON – accelerator pedal depressed		2 V/0,5 ms	71
	118	⇨	Ignition ON	11-14 V		
	118	⇨	Engine idling	11-14 V		
Throttle motor position sensor	83	⇨	Ignition ON	5 V		
	84	⬅	Ignition ON – accelerator pedal released	4,3 V		
	84	⬅	Ignition ON – accelerator pedal depressed	0,7 V		
	91	⨼―	Ignition ON	0 V		
	92	⬅	Ignition ON – accelerator pedal released	0,7 V		
	92	⬅	Ignition ON – accelerator pedal depressed	4,3 V		
Turbocharger (TC) boost pressure sensor	98	⇨	Ignition ON	5 V		
	101	⬅	Ignition ON	1,9 V		
	101	⬅	Engine idling	1,9 V		
	108	⨼―	Ignition ON	0 V		
Turbocharger (TC) intake divert valve	105	⨼▷	Ignition ON	11-14 V briefly then 0-1 V		
	105	⨼▷	Engine idling	11-14 V		
Turbocharger (TC) wastegate regulating valve	104	⨼▷	Ignition ON	11-14 V briefly then 0-1 V		
	104	⨼▷	Engine idling	11-14 V		

*Suggested settings - Voltage/time per division

[1] Connected pin - no test data available or random digital signal

BMW

Bosch Motronic M1.7.3

Model:	Engine code:	Year:
316i (E36)	16 4E 2	1995-00
318i (E36)	18 4E 2	1995-99

ECM harness multi-plug

Terminal side

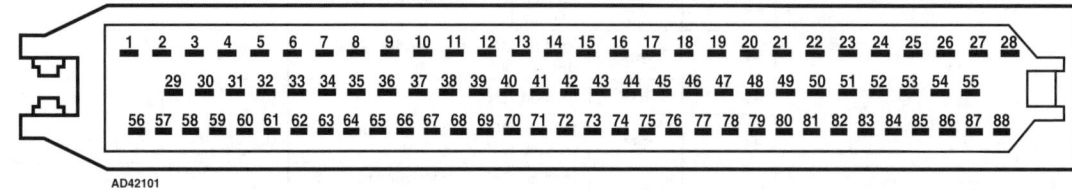

AD79776

Wire side

AD42101

Component/circuit description	ECM pin	Signal	Condition	Typical value	Oscilloscope setting★	Wave form
AC compressor clutch relay – if fitted	48	⊐▷		[1]		
AC condenser blower motor relay – if fitted	46	⊐▷		[1]		
AC control module – if fitted	83	▭▷		[1]		
AC engine coolant temperature switch – if fitted	62			[1]		
AC refrigerant pressure switch	82	◀		[1]		
Battery	26	◀	Ignition OFF	11-14 V		
Camshaft position (CMP) sensor	16	⊐	Ignition ON	0 V		
	44	◀	Engine cranking	0,4 V ac		
	44	◀	Engine idling	1,3 V ac	5 V/20 ms	⟋⟍⟋⟍ 11
Crankshaft position (CKP) sensor	67	◀	Engine cranking	2,9 V ac		
	67	◀	Engine idling	8 V ac	5 V/2 ms	⟋⟍⟋⟍ 2
	68	⊐	Ignition ON	0 V		
Data link connector (DLC)	60	◀▷		[1]		
	74	⊐▷	Engine idling	30 Hz		
	87	◀	Ignition ON	11-14 V		
	88	▭▷	Ignition ON	0-1 V		
Earth	6		Ignition ON	0 V		
	28		Ignition ON	0 V		
	34		Ignition ON	0 V		
	55		Ignition ON	0 V		
Engine control relay	27	⊐▷	Ignition OFF	11-14 V		
	27	⊐▷	Ignition ON	0 V		
	54	◀	Ignition ON	11-14 V		

★ Suggested settings - Voltage/time per division

Component/circuit description	ECM pin	Signal	Condition	Typical value	Oscilloscope setting*	Wave form
Engine coolant temperature (ECT) sensor	43	⊐—	Ignition ON	0 V		
	78	⟵	Ignition ON – 20°C	3,6 V		
	78	⟵	Ignition ON – 80°C	0,7 V		
Evaporative emission (EVAP) canister purge valve	36	⊐▷	Ignition ON	11-14 V		
	36	⊐▷	Engine idling	0 V		
	36	⊐▷	Engine hot – valve operating		10 V/20 ms	20
Fuel pump relay	1	⊐▷	Ignition ON	11-14 V		
	1	⊐▷	Engine idling	0 V		
Heated oxygen sensor (HO2S)	70	⟵	Engine idling – engine hot	0,1-1,0 V fluctuating	0,2 V/1 sec.	21
	71	⊐—	Ignition ON	0 V		
Idle air control (IAC) valve	2	⊐▷	Ignition ON	11-14 V		
	2	⊐▷	Engine idling	62%	5 V/5 ms	25
	29	⊐▷	Ignition ON	1 V		
	29	⊐▷	Engine idling	32%	5 V/5 ms	25
Ignition coil – cylinder 1	25	⊐▷	Ignition ON	11-14 V		
	25	⊐▷	Engine cranking	9 V		
	25	⊐▷	Engine idling		5 V/2 ms	33
Ignition coil – cylinder 2	52	⊐▷	Ignition ON	11-14 V		
	52	⊐▷	Engine cranking	9 V		
	52	⊐▷	Engine idling		5 V/2 ms	33
Ignition coil – cylinder 3	24	⊐▷	Ignition ON	11-14 V		
	24	⊐▷	Engine cranking	9 V		
	24	⊐▷	Engine idling		5 V/2 ms	33
Ignition coil – cylinder 4	51	⊐▷	Ignition ON	11-14 V		
	51	⊐▷	Engine cranking	9 V		
	51	⊐▷	Engine idling		5 V/2 ms	33
Ignition switch	56	⟵	Ignition ON	11-14 V		
Immobilizer control module	81	⟵		[1]		
Injector 1	32	⊐▷	Ignition ON	11-14 V		
	32	⊐▷	Engine idling – engine hot	3,5 ms	10 V/2 ms	35
Injector 2	3	⊐▷	Ignition ON	11-14 V		
	3	⊐▷	Engine idling – engine hot	3,5 ms	10 V/2 ms	35
Injector 3	31	⊐▷	Ignition ON	11-14 V		
	31	⊐▷	Engine idling – engine hot	3,5 ms	10 V/2 ms	35
Injector 4	4	⊐▷	Ignition ON	11-14 V		
	4	⊐▷	Engine idling – engine hot	3,5 ms	10 V/2 ms	35
Instrument panel	17	⇨	Engine idling	15 Hz		
	73	⟵	Ignition ON	10 V		
	74	⊐▷	Engine idling	30 Hz		
Intake air temperature (IAT) sensor	77	⟵	Ignition ON – 20°C	3,5 V		

* Suggested settings - Voltage/time per division

Component/circuit description	ECM pin	Signal	Condition	Typical value	Oscilloscope setting*	Wave form
Intake manifold air control solenoid	18	⊐⊢▷	Ignition ON	11-14 V		
	18	⊐⊢▷	Engine idling	0,1 V		
	18	⊐⊢▷	Engine idling – full throttle briefly	11-14 V		
Knock sensor (KS) 1 – cylinders 1 & 2	15	⬅	Engine idling	2,4-3,8 mV		
	15	⬅	Accelerate briefly		50 mV/1 ms	〰〰 38
Knock sensor (KS) 2 – cylinders 3 & 4	42	⬅	Engine idling	2,4-3,8 mV		
	42	⬅	Accelerate briefly		50 mV/1 ms	〰〰 38
Oxygen sensor heater relay	37	⊐⊢▷	Ignition ON	11-14 V		
	37	⊐⊢▷	Engine idling	0 V		
Throttle position (TP) sensor	12	⬅	Ignition ON – throttle closed	0,4 V		
	12	⬅	Ignition ON – throttle fully open	4,2 V		
	43	⊐⊢	Ignition ON	0 V		
	59	⇨	Ignition ON	5 V		
Traction control module – if fitted	85	⬌		1		
	86	⬌		1		
Transmission control module (TCM) – AT	11			1		
	17	⇨	Engine idling	15 Hz		
	64	⬅		1		
	85	⬌		1		
	86	⬌		1		
Transmission shift position switch – AT	65	⬅		1		
Trip computer	17	⇨	Engine idling	15 Hz		
Volume air flow (VAF) sensor	14	⊐⊢	Ignition ON	0 V		
	41	⬅	Ignition ON	0,25 V		
	41	⬅	Engine idling	0,77 V		
	41	⬅	Engine idling – full throttle briefly	3,4 V		
	59	⇨	Ignition ON	5 V		
	76	⬅	Ignition ON	0,5 V		
	76	⬅	Engine idling	0-1 V fluctuating		

*Suggested settings - Voltage/time per division

1 Connected pin - no test data available or random digital signal

Model:	Engine code:	Year:
316i (E46)	19 4E 1	1999-04
316i Compact (E36)	19 4E 1	1998-02
318i (E46)	19 4E 1	1998-02

ECM harness multi-plug

Terminal side

Wire side

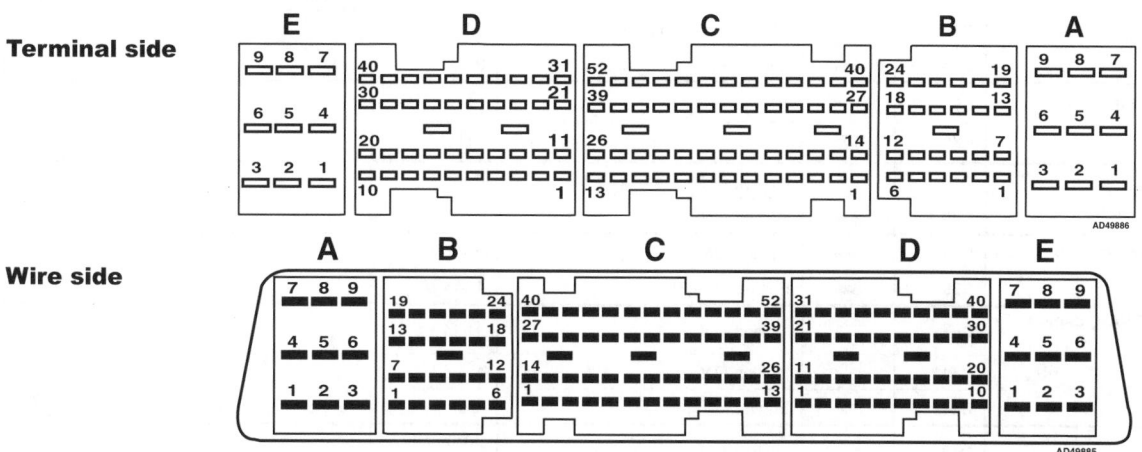

Component/circuit description	ECM pin	Signal	Condition	Typical value	Oscilloscope setting*	Wave form
ABS control module – vehicle speed signal	D22	←	Ignition ON – vehicle moving	0 V or 10 V		
AC compressor clutch relay	D29	⌐▷	Engine idling – AC OFF	11-14 V		
	D29	⌐▷	Engine idling – AC ON	0 V		
Alternator – charging signal	C13	←	Ignition ON	1 V		
	C13	←	Engine idling	11-14 V		
Battery	A7	←	Ignition OFF	11-14 V		
Brake booster vacuum valve	C17			1		
	C21			1		
Camshaft position (CMP) sensor	C4	▷	Ignition ON	11-14 V		
	C37	⌐	Ignition ON	0 V		
	C38	←	Ignition ON – engine turned	0 V or 5 V		
	C38	←	Engine idling		2 V/0,1 sec.	〰 45
CAN data bus	D36	←▷		1		
	D37	←▷		1		
Crankshaft position (CKP) sensor	C16	▷	Ignition ON	11-14 V		
	C35	←	Ignition ON – engine turned	0 V or 5 V		
	C35	←	Engine idling		2 V/0,1 sec.	〰 45
	C36	⌐	Ignition ON	0 V		
Data link connector (DLC) – engine RPM signal	D17	▷	Engine idling	27 Hz		
Data link connector (DLC) – supply voltage	D32	▷	Ignition ON	11-14 V		
Earth	A4		Ignition ON	0 V		
	A5		Ignition ON	0 V		
	A6		Ignition ON	0 V		
Engine control relay	A8	←	Ignition OFF	0 V after 5 seconds		
	A8	←	Ignition ON	11-14 V		
	A9	←	Ignition OFF	0 V after 5 seconds		
	A9	←	Ignition ON	11-14 V		
	B23	⌐▷	Ignition OFF	11-14 V		
	B23	⌐▷	Ignition ON	0 V		

* Suggested settings - Voltage/time per division

Component/circuit description	ECM pin	Signal	Condition	Typical value	Oscilloscope setting*	Wave form
Engine coolant blower motor	D4	⇨	Engine idling	6,8%	5 V/5 ms	68
Engine coolant blower motor temperature sensor	D38	⊣	Ignition ON	0 V		
	D39	←	Ignition ON – coolant temp. 17°C	3,6 V		
	D39	←	Engine idling – engine hot	1,6 V		
Engine coolant temperature (ECT) sensor	C22	⊣	Ignition ON	0 V		
	C28	←	Ignition ON – coolant temp. 17°C	3,2 V		
	C28	←	Engine idling – engine hot	0,5 V		
Engine coolant thermostat	C9	⊣		1		
	C43	⇨		1		
Engine oil level sensor	C10	⊣	Ignition ON	0 V		
	C39	←	Ignition ON		2 V/1 sec.	74
Engine oil pressure warning lamp switch	C26	←	Ignition ON	0 V		
	C26	←	Engine idling	11-14 V		
Evaporative emission (EVAP) canister purge valve	C6	⇨	Ignition ON	11-14 V		
	C44	⊣▷	Ignition ON	11-14 V		
	C44	⊣▷	Engine idling	9%	10 V/50 ms	59
Fuel pump relay	D10	⊣▷	Ignition ON	0 V briefly then 11-14 V		
	D10	⊣▷	Engine idling	0 V		
Heated oxygen sensor (HO2S) 1	B9	⊣	Ignition ON	0 V		
	B18	←	Engine idling	0,1-0,9 V fluctuating	0,2 V/1 sec.	21
Heated oxygen sensor (HO2S) 1 – heater control	B7	⊣	Ignition ON	0 V		
	B24	⇨	Ignition ON	0 V		
	B24	⇨	Engine idling	11-14 V		
Heated oxygen sensor (HO2S) 2	B14	⊣	Ignition ON	0 V		
	B16	←	Engine idling	0,3-0,7 V	0,2 V/0,5 sec.	76
Heated oxygen sensor (HO2S) 2 – heater control	B8	⊣	Ignition ON	0 V		
	B22	⊣▷	Ignition ON	0 V		
	B22	⊣▷	Engine idling – engine cold	77%	2 V/50 ms	32
	B22	⊣▷	Engine idling – engine hot	11-14 V		
Idle air control (IAC) valve	C23	⊣	Ignition ON	0 V		
	C40	⊣▷	Ignition ON	0 V		
	C40	⊣▷	Engine idling	70%	5 V/5 ms	45
	C41	⊣▷	Ignition ON	0 V		
	C41	⊣▷	Engine idling	45%	5 V/5 ms	45
Ignition coil 1	E6	⊣▷	Ignition ON	11-14 V		
	E6	⊣▷	Engine idling		5 V/2 ms	33
Ignition coil 2	E4	⊣▷	Ignition ON	11-14 V		
	E4	⊣▷	Engine idling		5 V/2 ms	33
Ignition coil 3	E8	⊣▷	Ignition ON	11-14 V		
	E8	⊣▷	Engine idling		5 V/2 ms	33
Ignition coil 4	E9	⊣▷	Ignition ON	11-14 V		
	E9	⊣▷	Engine idling		5 V/2 ms	33
Ignition switch	D26	←	Ignition ON	11-14 V		
Immobilizer control module	D33			1		
Injector 1	C2	⇨	Ignition ON	11-14 V		
	C51	⊣▷	Ignition ON	11-14 V		
	C51	⊣▷	Engine idling	4 ms	10 V/2 ms	35

* Suggested settings - Voltage/time per division

Component/circuit description	ECM pin	Signal	Condition	Typical value	Oscilloscope setting*	Wave form
Injector 2	C1	⇨	Ignition ON	11-14 V		
	C50	⇥	Ignition ON	11-14 V		
	C50	⇥	Engine idling	4 ms	10 V/2 ms	⩗ 35
Injector 3	C15	⇨	Ignition ON	11-14 V		
	C49	⇥	Ignition ON	11-14 V		
	C49	⇥	Engine idling	4 ms	10 V/2 ms	⩗ 35
Injector 4	C14	⇨	Ignition ON	11-14 V		
	C48	⇥	Ignition ON	11-14 V		
	C48	⇥	Engine idling	4 ms	10 V/2 ms	⩗ 35
Instrumentation control module – charging signal	D1	⇨	Ignition ON	1 V		
	D1	⇨	Engine idling	11-14 V		
Instrumentation control module – engine oil level signal	D21	⇦	Ignition ON		2 V/1 sec.	⩗ 74
Instrumentation control module – oil pressure signal	D11	⇨	Ignition ON	0 V		
	D11	⇨	Engine idling	11-14 V		
Instrumentation control module – start signal	D2	⇨	Ignition ON	0 V		
	D2	⇨	Engine cranking	9 V min.		
Intake air temperature (IAT) sensor – in MAF sensor	C29	⇦	Ignition ON – air temp. 20°C	2,4 V		
Intake manifold air control valve	C5	⇨	Ignition ON	11-14 V		
	C45	⇥	Ignition ON	11-14 V		
	C45	⇥	Engine idling – full throttle briefly	0 V		
Knock sensor (KS) – signal 1	C18	⊣	Engine idling – accelerate briefly		50 mV/1 ms	⩗ 58
Knock sensor (KS) – signal 2	C19	⊣	Engine idling – accelerate briefly		50 mV/1 ms	⩗ 58
Knock sensor (KS) – signal 3	C31	⇦	Engine idling – accelerate briefly		50 mV/1 ms	⩗ 58
Knock sensor (KS) – signal 4	C32	⇦	Engine idling – accelerate briefly		50 mV/1 ms	⩗ 58
Mass air flow (MAF) sensor	C3	⇨	Ignition ON	11-14 V		
	C8	⊣	Ignition ON	0 V		
	C27	⇨	Ignition ON	5 V		
	C30	⇦	Ignition ON	1 V		
	C30	⇦	Engine idling	1,4 V		
	C30	⇦	Engine idling – full throttle briefly	4 V		
Secondary air injection (AIR) pump/ solenoid relay	D3	⇥	Ignition ON	11-14 V		
	D3	⇥	Engine idling – engine cold	0 V		
Secondary air injection (AIR) solenoid	C7	⊣	Ignition ON	11-14 V		
	C52	⇨	Ignition ON	11-14 V		
	C52	⇨	Engine idling – engine cold	0 V		
Starter motor	C12	⇦	Ignition ON	0 V		
	C12	⇦	Engine cranking	9 V min.		
Throttle position (TP) sensor	C33	⇦	Ignition ON – throttle closed	0,5 V		
	C33	⇦	Ignition ON – throttle fully open	4,2 V		
	C20	⊣	Ignition ON	0 V		
	C46	⇨	Ignition ON	4,7 V		
Transmission control module (TCM)	B6	⇆		1		
Transmission control module (TCM) – data bus	B3	⇆		1		
	B4	⇆		1		

*Suggested settings - Voltage/time per division

1 Connected pin - no test data available or random digital signal

BMW

Bosch ME9.2

Model:	Engine code:	Year:
316i (E46)	N42 B18A	2001-05
316ti Compact (E46)	N42 B18A	2001-05

ECM harness multi-plug

Terminal side

Wire side

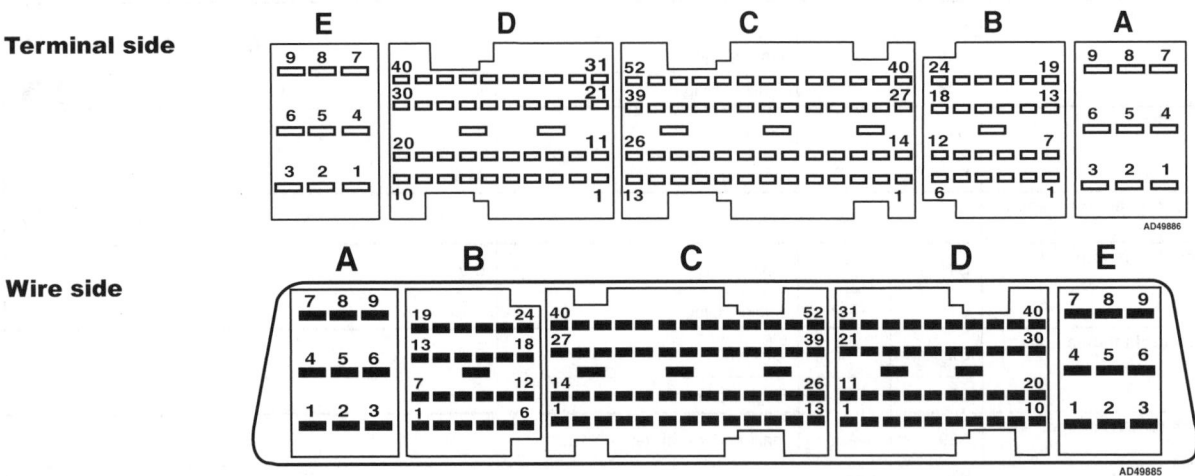

AD49886

AD49885

Component/circuit description	ECM pin	Signal	Condition	Typical value	Oscilloscope setting★	Wave form
ABS control module	D36	◄▭▷		1		
	D37	◄▭▷		1		
ABS control module – vehicle speed sensor (VSS)	D22	◄▬	Ignition ON – vehicle pushed	0-11 V switching		
AC compressor clutch relay	D29	⊐▷	Ignition ON – AC OFF	11-14 V		
	D29	⊐▷	Engine idling – AC ON	0-1 V		
Accelerator pedal position (APP) sensor	D7	⌐	Ignition ON	0 V		
	D8	◄▬	Ignition ON – pedal released	0,7 V		
	D8	◄▬	Ignition ON – pedal depressed	3,9 V		
	D9	▭▷	Ignition ON	5 V		
	D12	⌐	Ignition ON	0 V		
	D13	◄▬	Ignition ON – pedal released	0,4 V		
	D13	◄▬	Ignition ON – pedal depressed	1,9 V		
	D14	▭▷	Ignition ON	5 V		
Airbag spiral cable	D27	◄▭▷		1		
Alternator	C19	◄▬	Engine idling	1210 Hz	2 V/0,5 ms	⩘⩘ 71
	C19	◄▬	Engine idling – accelerate briefly		2 V/0,5 ms	⩘⩘ 55
Battery	A7	◄▬	Ignition OFF	11-14 V		
Brake pedal position (BPP) switch	D24	◄▬	Ignition ON – pedal released	0,1 V		
	D24	◄▬	Ignition ON – pedal depressed	9,8 V		
	D28	◄▬	Ignition ON – pedal released	0 V		
	D28	◄▬	Ignition ON – pedal depressed	11-14 V		
Camshaft position (CMP) actuator 1	C10	◄▬	Engine idling		2 V/2 ms	⩘⩘ 55
	C10	◄▬	Engine idling – accelerate briefly		2 V/4 ms	⩘⩘ 71

★ Suggested settings - Voltage/time per division

Component/circuit description	ECM pin	Signal	Condition	Typical value	Oscilloscope setting*	Wave form
Camshaft position (CMP) actuator 2	C9	←	Engine idling	244 Hz	2 V/4 ms	71
	C9	←	Engine idling – accelerate briefly		2 V/2 ms	55
Camshaft position (CMP) sensor 1	C29	←	Engine idling		5 V/20 ms	14
	C48	⅂	Ignition ON	0 V		
Camshaft position (CMP) sensor 2	C30	←	Engine idling		5 V/20 ms	14
	C36	⅂	Ignition ON	0 V		
Clutch control module	D23	←	Ignition ON – pedal released	0 V		
	D23	←	Ignition ON – pedal depressed	11-14 V		
Crankshaft position (CKP) sensor	C27	←	Engine running		5 V/1 ms	5
	C37	⅂	Ignition ON	0 V		
Data link connector (DLC)	D32	↔		[1]		
Earth	A4		Ignition ON	0 V		
	A6		Ignition ON	0 V		
	E5		Ignition ON	0 V		
Engine control (EC) relay	A8	←	Ignition OFF	0 V		
	A8	←	Ignition ON	11-14 V		
	B23	⅂→	Ignition OFF	11-14 V		
	B23	⅂→	Ignition ON	0-1 V		
Engine coolant blower motor	D4	←	Ignition ON – coolant blower motor OFF	11,6 V		
	D4	←	Ignition ON – coolant blower motor OFF		5 V/5 ms	67
Engine coolant temperature (ECT) sensor	C28	←	Ignition ON – coolant temp. 18°C	3,7 V		
	C35	⅂	Ignition ON	0 V		
	D38	⅂	Ignition ON	0 V		
	D39	←	Ignition ON – coolant temp. 18°C	3,7 V		
	D39	←	Engine idling – coolant temp. 90°C	1,6 V		
Engine coolant thermostat	C12	⅂→	Engine idling – coolant blower motor OFF	11-14 V		
	C12	⅂→	Engine idling – coolant blower motor ON	0-1 V		
Engine oil level sensor	C5	↔		[1]		
Evaporative emission (EVAP) canister purge valve	C21	⅂→	Ignition ON	11-14 V		
	C21	⅂→	Engine running – valve operating		10 V/20 ms	20
Fuel pump (FP) relay	D10	⅂→	Ignition ON	11-14 V		
	D10	⅂→	Engine idling	0-1 V		
Heated oxygen sensor (HO2S) 1	B1	⅂→	Ignition ON	11-14 V		
	B1	⅂→	Engine idling – engine cold		2 V/0,5 sec.	5
	B7	⅂	Ignition ON	0 V		
	B13	↔		[1]		
	B19	↔		[1]		
	B20	↔		[1]		

* Suggested settings - Voltage/time per division

Component/circuit description	ECM pin	Signal	Condition	Typical value	Oscilloscope setting*	Wave form
Heated oxygen sensor (HO2S) 2	B2	⊐⊳	Ignition ON	11-14 V		
	B2	⊐⊳	Engine idling – engine cold		2 V/0,5 sec.	⋀⋁⋀ 5
	B9	⊐―	Ignition ON	0 V		
	B15	⬅⇨		1		
	B21	⬅⇨		1		
	B22	⬅⇨		1		
Heated oxygen sensor (HO2S) 3	B6	⊐⊳	Ignition ON	11-14 V		
	B6	⊐⊳	Engine idling	2,5 V		
	B10	⊐―	Ignition ON	0 V		
	B16	⬅	Engine idling – engine hot	0,5 V		
Heated oxygen sensor (HO2S) 4	B8	⊐―	Ignition ON	0 V		
	B12	⊐⊳	Ignition ON	11-14 V		
	B12	⊐⊳	Engine idling	2,5 V		
	B14	⬅	Engine idling – engine hot	0,5 V		
Ignition coil 1	E3	⊐⊳	Ignition ON	11-14 V		
	E3	⊐⊳	Engine idling		5 V/2 ms	⋀⋁⋀ 33
Ignition coil 2	E6	⊐⊳	Ignition ON	11-14 V		
	E6	⊐⊳	Engine idling		5 V/2 ms	⋀⋁⋀ 33
Ignition coil 3	E9	⊐⊳	Ignition ON	11-14 V		
	E9	⊐⊳	Engine idling		5 V/2 ms	⋀⋁⋀ 33
Ignition coil 4	E2	⊐⊳	Ignition ON	11-14 V		
	E2	⊐⊳	Engine idling		5 V/2 ms	⋀⋁⋀ 33
Ignition switch	D26	⬅	Ignition OFF	0 V		
	D26	⬅	Ignition ON	11-14 V		
Immobilizer control module	D33	⬅	Ignition ON		2 V/10 ms	⋀⋁⋀ 61
Injector 1	C13	⊐⊳	Ignition ON	11-14 V		
	C13	⊐⊳	Engine idling	3,1 ms	10 V/2 ms	⋀⋁⋀ 35
Injector 2	C25	⊐⊳	Ignition ON	11-14 V		
	C25	⊐⊳	Engine idling	3,1 ms	10 V/2 ms	⋀⋁⋀ 35
Injector 3	C7	⊐⊳	Ignition ON	11-14 V		
	C7	⊐⊳	Engine idling	3,1 ms	10 V/2 ms	⋀⋁⋀ 35
Injector 4	C6	⊐⊳	Ignition ON	11-14 V		
	C6	⊐⊳	Engine idling	3,1 ms	10 V/2 ms	⋀⋁⋀ 35
Instrument panel	D36	⬅⇨		1		
	D37	⬅⇨		1		
Intake air flap control actuator	C40	⬅	Engine idling		5 V/5 ms	⋀⋁⋀ 24
	C41	⇨	Ignition ON	0 V		
	C41	⇨	Engine idling	11-14 V		
Intake air temperature (IAT) sensor	C3	⬅	Ignition ON – air temp. 18°C	2,5 V		

* Suggested settings - Voltage/time per division

Component/circuit description	ECM pin	Signal	Condition	Typical value	Oscilloscope setting*	Wave form
Knock sensor (KS)	**C33**	←	Engine idling – accelerate briefly		50 mV/20 ms	58
	C34	←	Engine idling – accelerate briefly		50 mV/20 ms	58
	C46	←	Engine idling – accelerate briefly		50 mV/20 ms	58
	C47	←	Engine idling – accelerate briefly		50 mV/20 ms	58
Manifold absolute pressure (MAP) sensor	**C2**	←	Ignition ON	0,7 V		
	C2	←	Engine idling	0,9 V		
	C4	⇨	Ignition ON	5 V		
	C14	⏚	Ignition ON	0 V		
Mass air flow (MAF) sensor	**C1**	←	Ignition ON	0,9 V		
	C1	←	Engine idling	1,3 V		
	C4	⇨	Ignition ON	5 V		
	C14	⏚	Ignition ON	0 V		
Secondary air injection (AIR) pump relay	**D3**	⏚⇨	Ignition ON	11-14 V		
	D3	⏚⇨	Engine idling – valve operating	0 V		
Throttle motor	**C42**	←	Ignition ON – throttle slightly open		2 V/0,5 ms	71
	C42	←	Ignition ON – throttle fully open		2 V/0,5 ms	64
	C43	⇨	Ignition ON – throttle slightly open	11-14 V		
	C43	⇨	Ignition ON – throttle fully open	11-14 V		
Throttle motor position sensor	**C50**	⇨	Ignition ON	5 V		
	C52	⏚	Ignition ON	0 V		
Throttle motor position sensor 1	**C31**	←	Ignition ON – pedal released	0,6 V		
	C31	←	Ignition ON – pedal depressed	4,4 V		
Throttle motor position sensor 2	**C32**	←	Ignition ON – pedal released	4,4 V		
	C32	←	Ignition ON – pedal depressed	0,5 V		
Transmission control module (TCM)	**A3**	⇦⇨		[1]		
	B3	⇦⇨		[1]		
	B4	⇦⇨		[1]		
Variable valve lift control module	**C18**	⇨	Engine idling	11-14 V		
	C38	⇦⇨		[1]		
	C51	⇦⇨		[1]		

*Suggested settings - Voltage/time per division

[1] Connected pin - no test data available or random digital signal

BMW

Bosch Motronic 5.2

Model:	Engine code:	Year:
318iS/Coupe (E36)	19 4S 1	1996-99
318ti Compact (E36)	19 4S 1	1996-01

ECM harness multi-plug

Terminal side

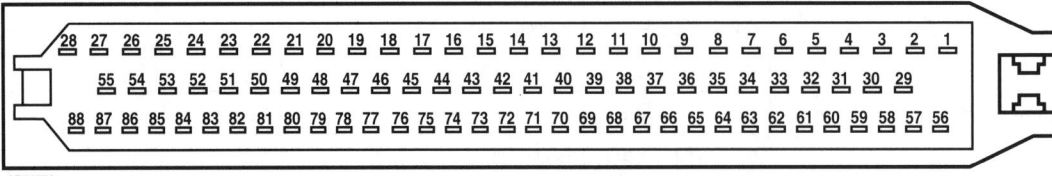

AD79776

Wire side

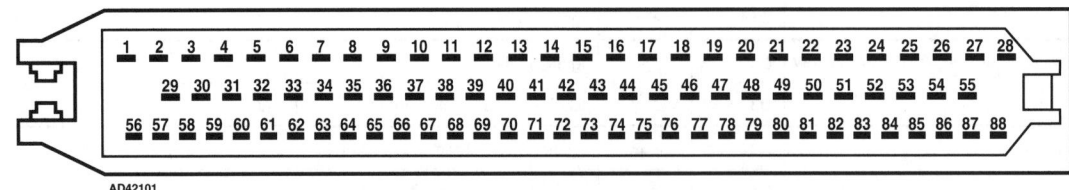

AD42101

Component/circuit description	ECM pin	Signal	Condition	Typical value	Oscilloscope setting*	Wave form
AC compressor clutch relay – if fitted	36	⊐⊳		1		
AC condenser blower motor relay – if fitted	57	⊐⊳		1		
AC control module – if fitted	69	⊐⊳		1		
	80	⇨		1		
AC engine coolant temperature switch – if fitted	68			1		
AC refrigerant pressure switch	11	⬅		1		
Battery	26	⬅	Ignition OFF	11-14 V		
Camshaft position (CMP) sensor	21	⬅	Ignition ON	11-14 V		
	21	⬅	Engine idling		5 V/20 ms	〰 14
Crankshaft position (CKP) sensor	20	⊐⊢	Ignition ON	0 V		
	78	⬅	Engine idling	5,7 V ac		
	78	⬅	Engine idling		5 V/2 ms	〰 2
Cruise control module – if fitted	80	⇨		1		
Data link connector (DLC)	60	⬅		1		
	80	⇨		1		
	87	⇨		1		
	88	⬄		1		
Earth	6		Ignition ON	0 V		
	28		Ignition ON	0 V		
	34		Ignition ON	0 V		
	55		Ignition ON	0 V		

* Suggested settings - Voltage/time per division

Component/circuit description	ECM pin	Signal	Condition	Typical value	Oscilloscope setting*	Wave form
Engine control relay	27	→▷	Ignition OFF	11-14 V		
	27	→▷	Ignition ON	0-1 V		
	54	←	Ignition OFF	0 V		
	54	←	Ignition ON	11-14 V		
Engine coolant temperature (ECT) sensor	71	⊣—	Ignition ON	0 V		
	74	←	Ignition ON – 10°C	3,8 V		
	74	←	Ignition ON – 80°C	0,8 V		
Evaporative emission (EVAP) canister purge valve	61	→▷	Ignition ON	11-14 V		
	61	→▷	Engine hot – valve operating		10 V/20 ms	〰 20
Fuel pump relay	63	→▷	Ignition ON	11-14 V		
	63	→▷	Engine idling	0-1 V		
Heated oxygen sensor (HO2S)	19	←	Engine idling – engine hot	0,8-1,5 V fluctuating	0,5 V/1 sec.	〰 22
	30	→▷	Ignition ON	11-14 V		
	30	→▷	Engine idling	0-1 V		
	46	⊣—	Ignition ON	0 V		
Idle air control (IAC) valve	2	→▷	Engine idling	63%	5 V/5 ms	〰 25
	29	→▷	Engine idling	37%	5 V/5 ms	〰 25
Ignition coil – cylinder 1	49	→▷	Ignition ON	11-14 V		
	49	→▷	Engine cranking	9 V		
	49	→▷	Engine idling		5 V/2 ms	〰 33
Ignition coil – cylinder 2	50	→▷	Ignition ON	11-14 V		
	50	→▷	Engine cranking	9 V		
	50	→▷	Engine idling		5 V/2 ms	〰 33
Ignition coil – cylinder 3	22	→▷	Ignition ON	11-14 V		
	22	→▷	Engine cranking	9 V		
	22	→▷	Engine idling		5 V/2 ms	〰 33
Ignition coil – cylinder 4	23	→▷	Ignition ON	11-14 V		
	23	→▷	Engine cranking	9 V		
	23	→▷	Engine idling		5 V/2 ms	〰 33
Ignition switch	56	←	Ignition ON	11-14 V		
Immobilizer control module	10	←		[1]		
	80	⇒		[1]		
Injector 1	3	→▷	Ignition ON	11-14 V		
	3	→▷	Engine idling – engine hot	3,7 ms	10 V/2 ms	〰 35
Injector 2	32	→▷	Ignition ON	11-14 V		
	32	→▷	Engine idling – engine hot	3,7 ms	10 V/2 ms	〰 35
Injector 3	31	→▷	Ignition ON	11-14 V		
	31	→▷	Engine idling – engine hot	3,7 ms	10 V/2 ms	〰 35
Injector 4	4	→▷	Ignition ON	11-14 V		
	4	→▷	Engine idling – engine hot	3,7 ms	10 V/2 ms	〰 35
Instrument panel	80	⇒		[1]		
	83	⇒	Ignition ON	11-14 V		

* Suggested settings - Voltage/time per division

Component/circuit description	ECM pin	Signal	Condition	Typical value	Oscilloscope setting*	Wave form
Intake air temperature (IAT) sensor	16	←	Ignition ON – 10°C	3,9 V		
Intake manifold air control solenoid	58	→⊦▷	Ignition ON	11-14 V		
	58	→⊦▷	Engine idling	0-1 V		
	58	→⊦▷	Engine idling – full throttle briefly	11-14 V		
Knock sensor (KS) – cylinders 1 & 2	70	←	Engine idling – accelerate briefly		50 mV/1 ms	⋀⋁⋀ 38
Knock sensor (KS) – cylinders 3 & 4	40	←	Engine idling – accelerate briefly		50 mV/1 ms	⋀⋁⋀ 38
Mass air flow (MAF) sensor	17	←	Ignition ON	0,1 V		
	17	←	Engine idling	0,9 V		
	17	←	Engine idling – accelerate briefly	4 V briefly		
	45	⊦⊢	Ignition ON	0 V		
Throttle position (TP) sensor	44	←	Ignition ON – throttle closed	0,5 V		
	44	←	Ignition ON – throttle fully open	4 V		
	53	⇨	Ignition ON	5 V		
	71	⊦⊢	Ignition ON	0 V		
Traction control module – if fitted	79	←		1		
	85	◄▷		1		
	86	◄▷		1		
Transmission control module (TCM) – AT	36			1		
	80	⇨		1		
	60	←		1		
	87	⇨		1		
	88	◄▷		1		

*Suggested settings - Voltage/time per division

1 Connected pin - no test data available or random digital signal

ECM harness multi-plug

Terminal side

Wire side

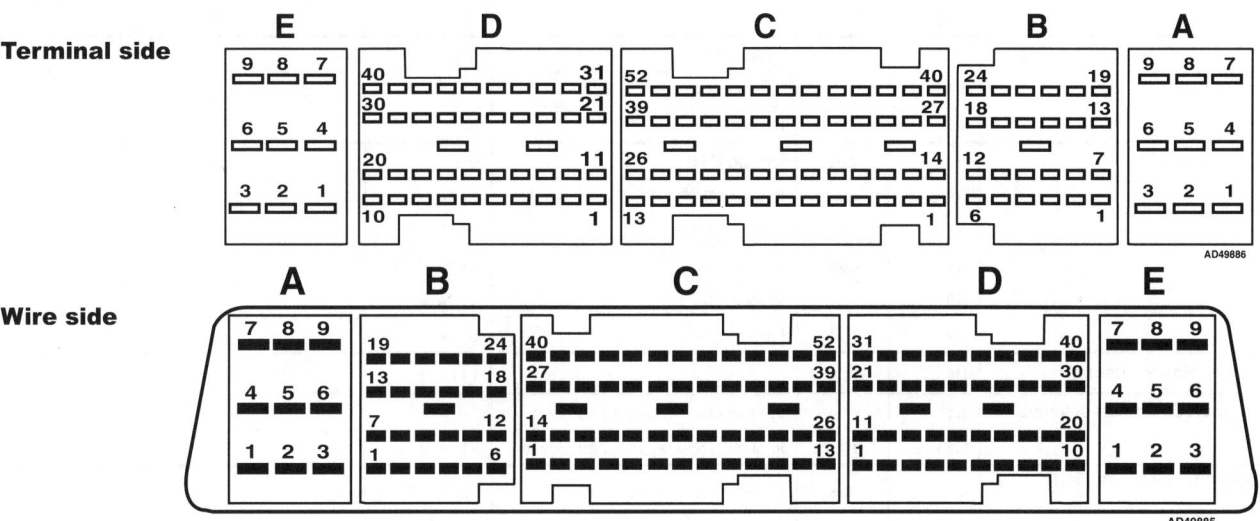

AD49886

AD49885

Component/circuit description	ECM pin	Signal	Condition	Typical value	Oscilloscope setting*	Wave form
ABS control module	D22	⬅▷		1		
AC compressor clutch relay	D29	⬅	Engine idling – AC OFF	11-14 V		
	D29	⬅	Engine idling – AC ON	0 V		
AC control module	D31	⬅▷		1		
Accelerator pedal position (APP) sensor	D7	⅃	Ignition ON	0 V		
	D8	⬅	Ignition ON – accelerator pedal released	0,3 V		
	D8	⬅	Ignition ON – accelerator pedal depressed	3,2 V		
	D9	▷	Ignition Off	0 V		
	D9	▷	Ignition ON	4,5-5,5 V		
	D12	⅃	Ignition ON	0 V		
	D16	⬅	Ignition ON – accelerator pedal released	2,7 V		
	D16	⬅	Ignition ON – accelerator pedal depressed	0 V		
Alternator	C24			1		
	C50	⬅	Engine idling	11-14 V		
	C50	⬅	Ignition ON	1,3 V		
Alternator warning lamp	D1	▷	Engine idling	11-14 V		
	D1	▷	Ignition ON	1,3 V		
Auxiliary heater control module	D20	⬅▷		1		
Brake pedal position (BPP) switch	D24	⬅	Ignition ON – brake pedal depressed	9,8 V		
	D24	⬅	Ignition ON – brake pedal released	0 V		
	D28	⬅	Ignition ON – brake pedal released	0 V		
	D28	⬅	Ignition ON – brake pedal depressed	11-14 V		
Clutch pedal position (CPP) switch	D23	⬅	Ignition ON – clutch pedal depressed	11-14 V		
	D23	⬅	Ignition ON – clutch pedal released	0 V		

* Suggested settings - Voltage/time per division

BMW

Component/circuit description	ECM pin	Signal	Condition	Typical value	Oscilloscope setting*	Wave form
Crankshaft position (CKP) sensor	C6	←	Engine idling	2,7 V ac		
	C6	←	Engine idling		5 V/5 ms	6
	C31	⌐	Ignition ON	0 V		
Data link connector (DLC)	D17	⇨	Engine idling		5 V/10 ms	2
	D17	⇨	Ignition ON	11-14 V		
	D32	⇨	Ignition OFF	11-14 V		
	D32	⇨	Ignition ON	11-14 V		
Earth	A4		Ignition ON	0 V		
	A5		Ignition ON	0 V		
	A6		Ignition ON	0 V		
Engine control relay	A1	←	Ignition OFF	0 V		
	A1	←	Ignition ON	11-14 V		
	A8	←	Ignition OFF	0 V		
	A8	←	Ignition ON	11-14 V		
	A9	⇾	Ignition OFF	11-14 V		
	A9	⇾	Ignition ON	0-1 V		
Engine coolant blower motor	D4	↔		1		
Engine coolant radiator flap solenoid	C13	⇾	Ignition ON – radiator flap open	0-1 V		
	C13	⇾	Ignition ON – radiator flap closed	11-14 V		
Engine coolant temperature (ECT) sensor	C28	←	Ignition ON – engine cold	3,3 V		
	C28	←	Ignition ON – engine hot	1 V		
	C32	⌐	Ignition ON	0 V		
Engine oil level sensor	C40	←	Ignition OFF	0 V		
	C40	←	Ignition ON	0-2 V (fluctuating)		
	D21	⇨	Ignition OFF	0 V		
	D21	⇨	Ignition ON	0-2 V (fluctuating)		
Engine oil pressure switch	C41	←	Engine idling	11-14 V		
	C41	←	Ignition ON	0 V		
Engine oil pressure warning lamp	D11	⇨	Engine idling	11-14 V		
	D11	⇨	Ignition ON	0 V		
Exhaust gas recirculation (EGR) solenoid	C10	⇾	Ignition OFF	0-1 V		
	C10	⇾	Ignition ON	11-14 V		
	C10	⇾	Engine idling		5 V/2 ms	31
Fuel injection pump control module	C7	←	Engine idling		2 V/5 ms	15
	C7	←	Ignition ON	0 V		
	C21	←	Ignition ON	0 V		
	C21	←	Engine idling	0 V		
Fuel injection pump control module – databus connection	C44	↔		1		
	C45	↔		1		
Fuel lift pump relay	D10	⇾	Engine idling	0-1 V		
	D10	⇾	Ignition ON	11-14 V		
Glow plug control module	C12	⇨	Engine idling	11-14 V		
	C12	⇨	Ignition OFF	0 V		
	C12	⇨	Ignition ON	11-14 V		
	C52	⇾	Ignition OFF	0-1 V		
	C52	⇾	Ignition ON	0-1 V		
Ignition switch	D26	←	Ignition OFF	0 V		
	D26	←	Ignition ON	11-14 V		
Immobilizer control module	D33	↔		1		

* Suggested settings - Voltage/time per division

Component/circuit description	ECM pin	Signal	Condition	Typical value	Oscilloscope setting*	Wave form
Injector needle lift sensor	C5	←	Engine idling	3,35 V		
	C5	←	Ignition OFF	0 V		
	C5	←	Ignition ON	3,3 V		
	C18	⌐	Ignition ON	0 V		
Instrument panel	D2	←⇒		1		
Instrument panel/ABS control module – databus connection	D36	←⇒		1		
	D37	←⇒		1		
Manifold absolute pressure (MAP) sensor	C14	⇒	Ignition OFF	0 V		
	C14	⇒	Ignition ON	5 V		
	C15	←	Ignition ON	1,7 V		
	C15	←	Engine idling	1,7 V		
	C15	←	Engine under load	4,5 V		
	C16	⌐	Ignition ON	0 V		
Mass air flow (MAF) sensor	C2	←	Engine idling	1,7 V		
	C2	←	Engine running – accelerate briefly	4,3 V briefly		
	C2	←	Ignition OFF	0 V		
	C2	←	Ignition ON	0,9 V		
	C3	⌐	Ignition ON	0 V		
	C33	⇒	Ignition OFF	0 V		
	C33	⇒	Ignition ON	5 V		
Starter motor	C51	←	Engine cranking	10 V		
	C51	←	Ignition ON	0 V		
Steering wheel multifunction switch	D27	←⇒		1		
Transmission control module (TCM)	A3	←⇒		1		
Turbocharger (TC) wastegate regulating valve	C9	⌐⇒	Ignition OFF	0-1 V		
	C9	⌐⇒	Ignition ON	0,8 V		
	C9	⌐⇒	Engine idling	1,2 V		
	C9	⌐⇒	Engine idling		2 V/1 ms	∿∿ 20

*Suggested settings - Voltage/time per division

1 Connected pin - no test data available or random digital signal

Model:	Engine code:	Year:
320i Vanos (E36)	20 6S 3	1994-99
323i/Compact (E36)	25 6S 3	1995-01
328i (E36)	28 6S 1	1995-99
520i 24V Vanos (E39)	20 6S 3	1996-00
523i (E39)	25 6S 3	1996-00
528i (E39)	28 6S 1	1996-00

ECM harness multi-plug

Terminal side

Wire side

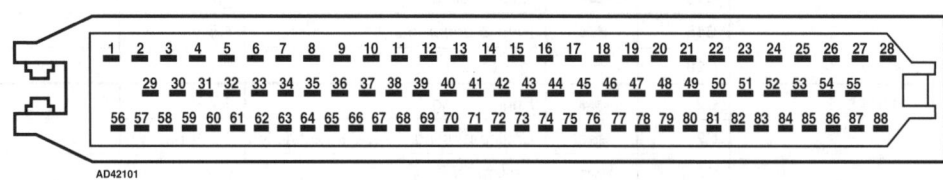

Component/circuit description	ECM pin	Signal	Condition	Typical value	Oscilloscope setting*	Wave form
ABS control module – some models	15			1		
ABS/traction control module – if fitted	15			1		
	36	⇨	Ignition ON	11 V		
	45			1		
	80			1		
	81			1		
	82			1		
AC compressor clutch relay – if fitted	74	⊐▷		1		
AC control module – if fitted	19			1		
	36	⇨	Ignition ON	11 V		
AC refrigerant pressure switch	16	⟵		1		
Battery	26	⟵	Ignition OFF	11-14 V		
Camshaft position (CMP) actuator	21	⊐▷	Ignition ON	11-14 V		
	21	⊐▷	Engine idling	11-14 V		
	21	⊐▷	Engine idling – full throttle briefly	0-1 V		
Camshaft position (CMP) sensor	43	⟵	Ignition ON	0 V		
	43 (65)	⟵	Engine idling		1 V/20 ms	⌁ 13
	64	⊐–	Ignition ON	0 V		
	65	⟵	Ignition ON	0 V		
	65 (43)	◀	Engine idling		1 V/20 ms	⌁ 13
Camshaft position (CMP) sensor – shield wire	41	⊐–	Ignition ON	0 V		
Crankshaft position (CKP) sensor	40	⊐–	Ignition ON	0 V		
	40	⊐–	Ignition ON	5 kHz		
	48	⇨	Ignition ON	5 V		
	48	⇨	Ignition ON	5 kHz		
	83	⟵	Ignition ON	5 V		
	83	⟵	Engine idling		2 V/2 ms	⌁ 6
Cruise control module – if fitted	36	⇨	Ignition ON	11 V		
Data link connector (DLC)	36	⇨	Ignition ON	11 V		
	60		Ignition ON	2,6 V		
	88	◀▷		1		

* Suggested settings - Voltage/time per division

Component/circuit description	ECM pin	Signal	Condition	Typical value	Oscilloscope setting*	Wave form
Earth	4		Ignition ON	0 V		
	28		Ignition ON	0 V		
	32		Ignition ON	0 V		
	34		Ignition ON	0 V		
Engine control relay	54	←	Ignition ON	11-14 V		
	73	⊐⊳	Ignition OFF	11-14 V		
	73	⊐⊳	Ignition ON	0-1 V		
	73	⊐⊳	Engine cranking	0-1 V		
	87	←	Ignition ON	11-14 V		
Engine coolant temperature (ECT) sensor	10	←	Ignition ON – 10°C	4 V		
	10	←	Ignition ON – 80°C	1 V		
	39	⊐—	Ignition ON	0 V		
Evaporative emission (EVAP) canister purge valve	68	⊐⊳	Ignition ON	11-14 V		
	68	⊐⊳	Engine hot – valve operating		10 V/20 ms	∿ 20
Exhaust gas control solenoid	52	⊐⊳	Ignition ON	4,4 V		
	52	⊐⊳	Engine idling	33%		
Fuel pump relay	69	⊐⊳	Ignition ON	0-1 V briefly then 11-14 V		
	69	⊐⊳	Engine idling	0-1 V		
Heated oxygen sensor (HO2S) 1	25	⊐⊳	Ignition ON	11-14 V		
	25	⊐⊳	Engine idling	10 Hz		
	67	⊐—	Ignition ON	0 V		
	75	←	Ignition ON	5 V		
	75	←	Engine idling – engine hot	0-4,6 V fluctuating	1 V/2 secs.	∿ 22
Heated oxygen sensor (HO2S) 2	55	⊐⊳	Ignition ON	11-14 V		
	55	⊐⊳	Engine idling	10 Hz		
	70	⊐—	Ignition ON	0 V		
	76	←	Ignition ON	5 V		
	76	←	Engine idling – engine hot	0-4,6 V fluctuating	1 V/2 secs.	∿ 22
Idle air control (IAC) valve	27	⊐⊳	Ignition ON	6-9 V fluctuating		
	27	⊐⊳	Engine idling	66%	5 V/5 ms	∿ 25
	53	⊐⊳	Ignition ON	3-6 V fluctuating		
	53	⊐⊳	Engine idling	30%	5 V/5 ms	∿ 25
Ignition coil – cylinder 1	29	⊐⊳	Ignition ON	11-14 V		
	29	⊐⊳	Engine cranking	9 V		
	29	⊐⊳	Engine idling		5 V/2 ms	∿ 33
	56	⇒		[1]		
Ignition coil – cylinder 2	1	⊐⊳	Ignition ON	11-14 V		
	1	⊐⊳	Engine cranking	9 V		
	1	⊐⊳	Engine idling		5 V/2 ms	∿ 33
	56	⇒		[1]		
Ignition coil – cylinder 3	30	⊐⊳	Ignition ON	11-14 V		
	30	⊐⊳	Engine cranking	9 V		
	30	⊐⊳	Engine idling		5 V/2 ms	∿ 33
	56	⇒		[1]		
Ignition coil – cylinder 4	2	⊐⊳	Ignition ON	11-14 V		
	2	⊐⊳	Engine cranking	9 V		
	2	⊐⊳	Engine idling		5 V/2 ms	∿ 33
	56	⇒		[1]		

* Suggested settings - Voltage/time per division

Component/circuit description	ECM pin	Signal	Condition	Typical value	Oscilloscope setting*	Wave form
Ignition coil – cylinder 5	31	⏚⇨	Ignition ON	11-14 V		
	31	⏚⇨	Engine cranking	9 V		
	31	⏚⇨	Engine idling		5 V/2 ms	33
	56	⇨		[1]		
Ignition coil – cylinder 6	3	⏚⇨	Ignition ON	11-14 V		
	3	⏚⇨	Engine cranking	9 V		
	3	⏚⇨	Engine idling		5 V/2 ms	33
	56	⇨		[1]		
Ignition switch	49	⬅	Ignition ON	11-14 V		
Immobilizer control module	18	⬅	Ignition ON	0-9 V fluctuating		
	36	⇨	Ignition ON	11 V		
Injector 1	6	⏚⇨	Ignition ON	11-14 V		
	6	⏚⇨	Engine idling – engine hot	3,4 ms	10 V/2 ms	35
Injector 2	5	⏚⇨	Ignition ON	11-14 V		
	5	⏚⇨	Engine idling – engine hot	3,4 ms	10 V/2 ms	35
Injector 3	22	⏚⇨	Ignition ON	11-14 V		
	22	⏚⇨	Engine idling – engine hot	3,4 ms	10 V/2 ms	35
Injector 4	24	⏚⇨	Ignition ON	11-14 V		
	24	⏚⇨	Engine idling – engine hot	3,4 ms	10 V/2 ms	35
Injector 5	33	⏚⇨	Ignition ON	11-14 V		
	33	⏚⇨	Engine idling – engine hot	3,4 ms	10 V/2 ms	35
Injector 6	23	⏚⇨	Ignition ON	11-14 V		
	23	⏚⇨	Engine idling – engine hot	3,4 ms	10 V/2 ms	35
Instrument panel	9	⇨	Ignition ON	11-14 V		
	36	⇨	Ignition ON	11 V		
Intake air temperature (IAT) sensor	14	⬅	Ignition ON – 10°C	4 V		
	39	⏚	Ignition ON	0 V		
Knock sensor (KS) – shield wire	38	⏚	Ignition ON	0 V		
Knock sensor (KS) 1 – cylinders 1 & 3	57	⬅	Ignition ON	2,5 V		
	57	⬅	Engine idling – accelerate briefly		50 mV/1 ms	38
	58	⬅	Ignition ON	2,5 V		
	58	⬅	Engine idling – accelerate briefly		50 mV/1 ms	38
Knock sensor (KS) 2 – cylinders 4 & 6	59	⬅	Ignition ON	2,5 V		
	59	⬅	Engine idling – accelerate briefly		50 mV/1 ms	38
	63	⬅	Ignition ON	2,5 V		
	63	⬅	Engine idling – accelerate briefly		50 mV/1 ms	38
Mass air flow (MAF) sensor	7	⏚	Ignition ON	0 V		
	8	⬅	Ignition ON	0 V		
	8	⬅	Engine idling	0,6 V		
	8	⬅	3000 rpm	1,5 V		
Throttle position (TP) sensor	12	⬅	Ignition ON – throttle closed	0,7 V		
	12	⬅	Ignition ON – throttle fully open	4,5 V		
	42	⏚	Ignition ON	0 V		
	44	⇨	Ignition ON	5 V		
Transmission control module (TCM) – AT	85			[1]		
	86			[1]		
	88	⬅⇨		[1]		

*Suggested settings - Voltage/time per division

[1] Connected pin - no test data available or random digital signal

Model:	Engine code:	Year:
320i/323i (E46)	20 6S 4/25 6S 4	1998-03
328i (E46)	28 6S 2	1998-03
520i/523i (E39)	20 6S 4/25 6S 4	1998-03
528i (E39)	28 6S 2	1998-03
728i (E38)	28 6S 2	1998-02
Z3 2,0/2,8	20 6S 4/28 6S 2	1999-03

ECM harness multi-plug

Terminal side

Wire side

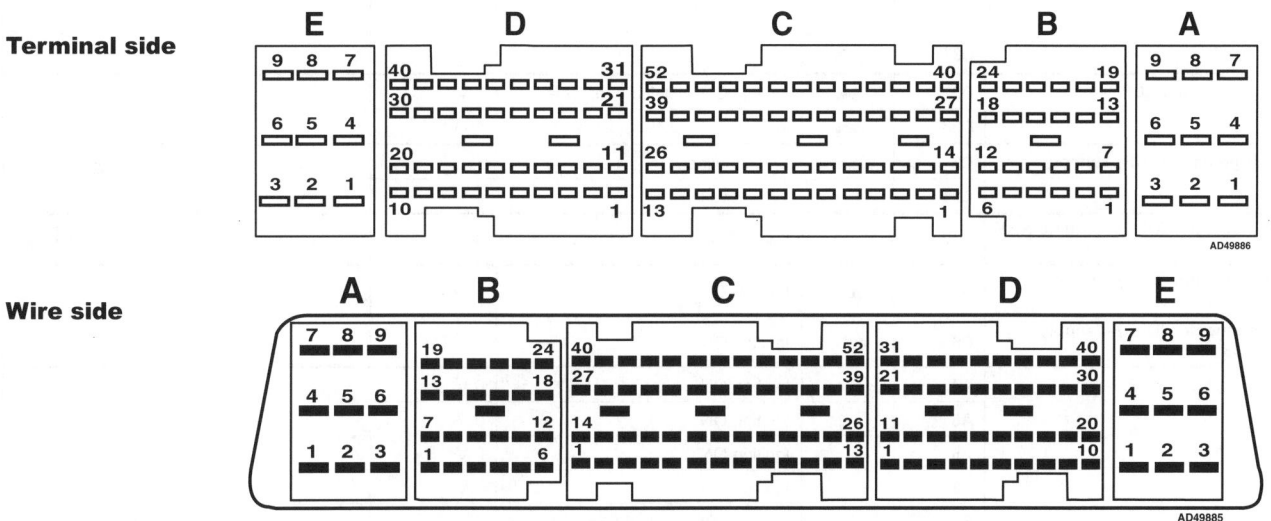

AD49886

AD49885

Component/circuit description	ECM pin	Signal	Condition	Typical value	Oscilloscope setting*	Wave form
ABS control module – vehicle speed signal	D22			$\boxed{1}$		
AC compressor clutch relay	D29		Engine idling – AC OFF	11-14 V		
	D29		Engine idling – AC ON	0 V		
Accelerator pedal position (APP) sensor 1 – in throttle control unit	C4	⟹	Ignition ON	5 V		
	C14		Ignition ON	0 V		
	C16	⟸	Ignition ON – accelerator pedal released	0,7 V		
	C16	⟸	Ignition ON – accelerator pedal fully depressed	4 V		
Accelerator pedal position (APP) sensor 2 – in throttle control unit	C7	⟹	Ignition ON	5 V		
	C9	⟸	Ignition ON – accelerator pedal released	0,8 V		
	C9	⟸	Ignition ON – accelerator pedal fully depressed	4 V		
	C20		Ignition ON	0 V		
Alternator – charging signal	C13	⟸	Ignition ON	1 V		
	C13	⟸	Engine idling	11-14 V		
Battery	A7	⟸	Ignition OFF	11-14 V		
Brake booster vacuum valve – except E38/E39	C3	⟸		$\boxed{1}$		
Brake pedal position (BPP) switch	D24	⟸	Ignition ON – brake pedal released	0 V		
	D24	⟸	Ignition ON – brake pedal depressed	9,8 V		
	D28	⟸	Ignition ON – brake pedal released	0 V		
	D28	⟸	Ignition ON – brake pedal depressed	11-14 V		
Camshaft position (CMP) actuator – inlet valve	C40		Ignition ON	10,6 V		
	C40		Engine idling	200 Hz		
	C40		Engine idling – accelerate briefly	0 V		
Camshaft position (CMP) actuator – outlet valve	C41		Ignition ON	10,7 V		
	C41		Engine idling	200 Hz		
	C41		Engine idling – accelerate briefly	0 V		

* Suggested settings - Voltage/time per division

Component/circuit description	ECM pin	Signal	Condition	Typical value	Oscilloscope setting*	Wave form
Camshaft position (CMP) sensor 1	C5	←	Ignition ON – engine turned	0 V or 5 V		
	C5	←	Engine idling		2 V/0,1 sec.	⎍ 45
	C18	⊣—	Ignition ON	0 V		
Camshaft position (CMP) sensor 2	C2	←	Ignition ON – engine turned	0 V or 5 V		
	C2	←	Engine idling		2 V/0,1 sec.	⎍ 45
	C15	⊣—	Ignition ON	0 V		
CAN data bus	D36	⇄		[1]		
	D37	⇄		[1]		
Clutch pedal position (CPP) switch	D23	←	Ignition ON – clutch pedal released	0 V		
	D23	←	Ignition ON – clutch pedal depressed	11-14 V		
Crankshaft position (CKP) sensor	C8	←	Engine idling		2 V/2 ms	⎍ 73
	C21	⊣—	Ignition ON	0 V		
Data link connector (DLC) – engine RPM signal	D17	⇒	Engine idling	39 Hz	5 V/10 ms	⎍ 45
Data link connector (DLC) – supply voltage	D32	⇄	Ignition ON	11-14 V		
Data link connector (DLC) – supply voltage – E38	B6	⇄	Ignition ON	11-14 V		
Earth	A4		Ignition ON	0 V		
	A5		Ignition ON	0 V		
	A6		Ignition ON	0 V		
	E5		Ignition ON	0 V		
	E6		Ignition ON – except E39	0 V		
Engine control (EC) relay	A8	←	Ignition OFF	0 V after 5 seconds		
	A8	←	Ignition ON	11-14 V		
	A9	←	Ignition OFF	0 V after 5 seconds		
	A9	←	Ignition ON	11-14 V		
	B23	⊣→	Ignition OFF	11-14 V		
	B23	⊣→	Ignition ON	0 V		
Engine coolant blower motor	D4	⊣→	Engine idling		5 V/5 ms	⎍ 68
Engine coolant blower motor temperature sensor	D38	⊣—	Ignition ON	0 V		
	D39	←	Ignition ON – coolant temp. 10°C	4,1 V		
	D39	←	Ignition ON – engine hot	2 V		
Engine coolant temperature (ECT) sensor	C24	←	Ignition ON – coolant temp. 10°C	4 V		
	C24	←	Engine idling – engine hot	0,9 V		
	C25	⊣—	Ignition ON	0 V		
Engine coolant thermostat	C45	⊣→	Ignition ON	11,5 V		
	C45	⊣→	Engine idling		5 V/0,5 ms	⎍ 67
Engine oil level sensor	C39	←	Ignition ON		2 V/1 sec.	⎍ 74
Engine oil pressure warning lamp switch	C26	←	Ignition ON	0 V		
	C26	←	Engine idling	11-14 V		
Engine oil temperature (EOT) sensor	C27	←	Ignition ON – oil temp. 10°C	4 V		
	C27	←	Ignition ON – engine hot	1 V		
	C28	⊣—	Ignition ON	0 V		
Evaporative emission (EVAP) canister purge valve	C42	⊣→	Ignition ON	11-14 V		
	C42	⊣→	Engine idling	7,5%	10 V/20 ms	⎍ 59
Exhaust gas control solenoid – except E39/E38	D18	⊣→	Engine idling	11-14 V		
	D18	⊣→	Vehicle moving – engine under load	0 V		
Fuel pump (FP) relay	D10	⊣→	Ignition ON	0 V briefly then 11-14 V		
	D10	⊣→	Engine idling	0 V		

* Suggested settings - Voltage/time per division

Component/circuit description	ECM pin	Signal	Condition	Typical value	Oscilloscope setting*	Wave form
Heated oxygen sensor (HO2S) 1, bank 1	B1	⊐▷	Ignition ON	11-14 V		
	B1	⊐▷	Engine idling		2 V/0,2 sec.	65
	B14	⟵	Engine idling	0,1-0,9 V fluctuating	0,2 V/1 sec.	21
	B20	⊐—	Ignition ON	0 V		
Heated oxygen sensor (HO2S) 1, bank 2	B13	⊐▷	Ignition ON	11-14 V		
	B13	⊐▷	Engine idling		2 V/0,2 sec.	65
	B15	⟵	Engine idling	0,1-0,9 V fluctuating	0,2 V/1 sec.	21
	B21	⊐—	Ignition ON	0 V		
Heated oxygen sensor (HO2S) 2, bank 1	B7	⊐▷	Ignition ON	11-14 V		
	B7	⊐▷	Engine idling		2 V/1 sec.	72
	B16	⟵	Engine idling	0,5 V		
	B22	⊐—	Ignition ON	0 V		
Heated oxygen sensor (HO2S) 2, bank 2	B18	⟵	Engine idling	0,5 V		
	B19	⊐▷	Ignition ON	11-14 V		
	B19	⊐▷	Engine idling		2 V/1 sec.	72
	B24	⊐—	Ignition ON	0 V		
Idle air control (IAC) valve	C46	⊐▷	Ignition ON	6 V		
	C46	⊐▷	Engine idling		5 V/5 ms	45
	C47	⊐▷	Ignition ON	6 V		
	C47	⊐▷	Engine idling		5 V/5 ms	45
Ignition coil 1	E3	⊐▷	Ignition ON	11-14 V		
	E3	⊐▷	Engine idling		10 V/1 ms	75
Ignition coil 2	E2	⊐▷	Ignition ON	11-14 V		
	E2	⊐▷	Engine idling		10 V/1 ms	75
Ignition coil 3	E1	⊐▷	Ignition ON	11-14 V		
	E1	⊐▷	Engine idling		10 V/1 ms	75
Ignition coil 4	E9	⊐▷	Ignition ON	11-14 V		
	E9	⊐▷	Engine idling		10 V/1 ms	75
Ignition coil 5	E8	⊐▷	Ignition ON	11-14 V		
	E8	⊐▷	Engine idling		10 V/1 ms	75
Ignition coil 6	E7	⊐▷	Ignition ON	11-14 V		
	E7	⊐▷	Engine idling		10 V/1 ms	75
Ignition switch	D26	⟵	Ignition ON	11-14 V		
Ignition switch relay	A1	⟵	Ignition OFF	0 V		
	A1	⟵	Ignition ON	11-14 V		
Immobilizer control module	D33	⟵		[1]		
Injector 1	C33	⊐▷	Ignition ON	11-14 V		
	C33	⊐▷	Engine idling	3,6 ms	10 V/2 ms	35
Injector 2	C34	⊐▷	Ignition ON	11-14 V		
	C34	⊐▷	Engine idling	3,6 ms	10 V/2 ms	35
Injector 3	C35	⊐▷	Ignition ON	11-14 V		
	C35	⊐▷	Engine idling	3,6 ms	10 V/2 ms	35
Injector 4	C36	⊐▷	Ignition ON	11-14 V		
	C36	⊐▷	Engine idling	3,6 ms	10 V/2 ms	35
Injector 5	C37	⊐▷	Ignition ON	11-14 V		
	C37	⊐▷	Engine idling	3,6 ms	10 V/2 ms	35
Injector 6	C38	⊐▷	Ignition ON	11-14 V		
	C38	⊐▷	Engine idling	3,6 ms	10 V/2 ms	35
Instrumentation control module – charging signal	D1	⟹	Ignition ON	1 V		
	D1	⟹	Engine idling	11-14 V		
Instrumentation control module – engine oil level signal	D21	⟵	Ignition ON		2 V/1 sec.	74

* Suggested settings - Voltage/time per division

Component/circuit description	ECM pin	Signal	Condition	Typical value	Oscilloscope setting*	Wave form
Instrumentation control module – oil pressure signal	D11	⇒	Ignition ON	0 V		
	D11	⇒	Engine idling	11-14 V		
Instrumentation control module – start signal	D2	⇒	Ignition ON	0 V		
	D2	⇒	Engine cranking	9 V min.		
Intake air temperature (IAT) sensor	C22	←	Ignition ON – air temp. 10°C	3,8 V		
	C23	⊣	Ignition ON	0 V		
Intake manifold air control valve	C49	⊐▷	Engine idling – full throttle briefly	0 V		
	C49	⊐▷	Ignition ON	11-14 V		
Knock sensor (KS) – signal 1	C29	←	Engine idling – accelerate briefly		50 mV/1 ms	〰58
Knock sensor (KS) – signal 2	C30	←	Engine idling – accelerate briefly		50 mV/1 ms	〰58
Knock sensor (KS) – signal 3	C31	←	Engine idling – accelerate briefly		50 mV/1 ms	〰58
Knock sensor (KS) – signal 4	C32	←	Engine idling – accelerate briefly		50 mV/1 ms	〰58
Knock sensor (KS), shield wire	C48	⊣	Ignition ON	0 V		
Mass air flow (MAF) sensor	C1	←	Ignition ON	0 V		
	C1	←	Engine idling – full throttle briefly	4 V		
	C17	⊣		0 V		
Reverse gear position switch – except E46	B2			[1]		
	D19			[1]		
Secondary air injection (AIR) pump/ solenoid relay	D3	⊐▷	Ignition ON	11-14 V		
	D3	⊐▷	Engine idling – engine cold	0 V		
Secondary air injection (AIR) solenoid	C52	⊐▷	Ignition ON	11-14 V		
	C52	⊐▷	Engine idling – engine cold	0 V		
Spare cable	D30			[1]		
	D34			[1]		
Starter motor	C12	←	Ignition ON	0 V		
	C12	←	Engine cranking	9 V min.		
Steering wheel multifunction switch	D27			[1]		
Throttle position (TP) sensor 1 – in throttle control unit	C4	⇒	Ignition ON	5 V		
	C14	⊣	Ignition ON	0 V		
	C19	←	Ignition ON – throttle closed	0,9 V		
	C19	←	Ignition ON – throttle fully open	4,1 V		
Throttle position (TP) sensor 2 – in throttle control unit	C7	⇒	Ignition ON	5 V		
	C10	←	Ignition ON – throttle closed	0,9 V		
	C10	←	Ignition ON – throttle fully open	4,1 V		
	C20	⊣	Ignition ON	0 V		
Throttle position motor – in throttle control unit	C43	⇒	Ignition ON	8,5 V		
	C43	⇒	Engine idling	600 Hz	2 V/1 ms	〰71
	C44	⇒	Ignition ON	11 V		
	C44	⇒	Engine idling	11-14 V		
Transmission control module (TCM)	B6	◀▷		[1]		
Transmission control module (TCM) – data bus	B3	◀▷		[1]		
	B4	◀▷		[1]		

*Suggested settings - Voltage/time per division

[1] Connected pin - no test data available or random digital signal

ECM harness multi-plug

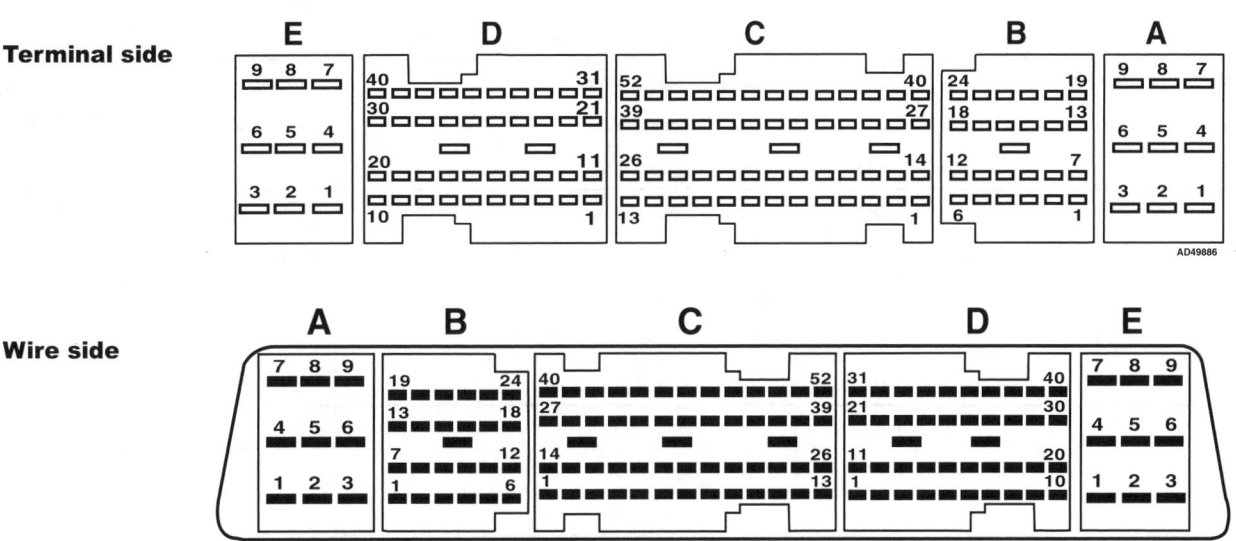

Terminal side

Wire side

Component/circuit description	ECM pin	Signal	Condition	Typical value
ABS control module	D22			1
AC compressor clutch relay	D29	←	Engine idling – AC OFF	11-14 V
	D29	←	Engine idling – AC ON	0 V
Accelerator pedal position (APP) sensor	D8	←	Ignition ON – accelerator pedal released	0,3 V
	D8	←	Ignition ON – accelerator pedal depressed	3,2 V
	D9	⇒	Ignition OFF	0 V
	D9	⇒	Ignition ON	4,5-5,5 V
	D12	⊣⌐	Ignition ON	0 V
Accelerator pedal position (APP) switch	D7	⊣⌐	Ignition ON	0 V
	D16	←	Ignition ON – accelerator pedal released	2,7 V
	D16	←	Ignition ON – accelerator pedal slightly depressed	0 V
Accessories connector	D20			1
	D31			1
Alternator	C50	←	Engine idling	11-14 V
	C50	←	Ignition ON	1,3 V
Alternator warning lamp	D1	⇒	Engine idling	11-14 V
	D1	⇒	Ignition ON	1,3 V
Brake pedal position (BPP) switch	D24	←	Ignition ON – brake pedal depressed	9,8 V
	D24	←	Ignition ON – brake pedal released	0 V
	D28	←	Ignition ON – brake pedal released	0 V
	D28	←	Ignition ON – brake pedal depressed	11-14 V

Component/circuit description	ECM pin	Signal	Condition	Typical value
CAN data bus connection	C44			1
	C45			1
	D36			1
	D37			1
Clutch pedal position (CPP) switch	D23	←	Ignition ON – clutch pedal depressed	11-14 V
	D23	←	Ignition ON – clutch pedal released	0 V
Crankshaft position (CKP) sensor	C6	←	Engine idling	2,7 V ac
	C6	←	Engine idling	5 V/5 ms per division 〜〜 6
	C31	⌐–	Ignition ON	0 V
Data link connector (DLC)	D17	⇒	Engine idling	5 V/10 ms per division 〜〜 2
	D17	⇒	Ignition ON	11-14 V
	D27	⟷	Ignition ON	0 V
	D32	⇒	Ignition OFF	11-14 V
	D32	⇒	Ignition ON	11-14 V
Earth	A4		Ignition ON	0 V
	A5		Ignition ON	0 V
	A6		Ignition ON	0 V
Engine control relay	A1	←	Ignition OFF	0 V
	A1	←	Ignition ON	11-14 V
	A8	←	Ignition OFF	0 V
	A8	←	Ignition ON	11-14 V
	A9	⊣⇒	Ignition OFF	11-14 V
	A9	⊣⇒	Ignition ON	0 V
Engine coolant blower motor	D4			1
Engine coolant radiator flap solenoid	C13	⊣⇒	Ignition ON – radiator flap open	0 V
	C13	⊣⇒	Ignition ON – radiator flap closed	11-14 V
Engine coolant temperature (ECT) sensor	C28	←	Ignition ON – engine cold	3,3 V
	C28	←	Engine idling – engine hot	1 V
	C32	⌐–	Ignition ON	0 V
Engine oil level sensor	C40	←	Ignition OFF	0 V
	C40	←	Ignition ON	0-2 V (fluctuating)
	D21	⇒	Ignition OFF	0 V
	D21	⇒	Ignition ON	0-2 V (fluctuating)
Engine oil pressure switch	C41	←	Engine idling	11-14 V
	C41	←	Ignition ON	0 V
Engine oil pressure warning lamp	D11	⇒	Engine idling	11-14 V
	D11	⇒	Ignition ON	0 V
Exhaust gas recirculation (EGR) solenoid	C10	⊣⇒	Ignition OFF	0 V
	C10	⊣⇒	Ignition ON	11-14 V
	C10	⊣⇒	Engine idling	5 V/2 ms per division 〜〜 31

Component/circuit description	ECM pin	Signal	Condition	Typical value
Fuel injection pump control module	C7	←	Engine idling	2 V/5 ms per division ⌁ 15
	C7	←	Ignition ON	0 V
	C21	⇒	Ignition ON	0 V
	C21	⇒	Engine idling	0 V
Fuel lift pump relay	D10	⇥▷	Engine idling	0 V
	D10	⇥▷	Ignition ON	11-14 V
Glow plug control module	C12	⇒	Engine idling	11-14 V
	C12	⇒	Ignition OFF	0 V
	C12	⇒	Ignition ON	11-14 V
	C52	⇥▷	Ignition OFF	0 V
	C52	⇥▷	Ignition ON	0,9 V
Ignition switch	D26	←	Ignition OFF	0 V
	D26	←	Ignition ON	11-14 V
Immobilizer control module	D33			[1]
Injector needle lift sensor	C5	←	Engine idling	3,35 V
	C5	←	Ignition OFF	0 V
	C5	←	Ignition ON	3,3 V
	C18	⇥—	Ignition ON	0 V
Instrument panel	D2			[1]
Manifold absolute pressure (MAP) sensor	C14	⇒	Ignition OFF	0 V
	C14	⇒	Ignition ON	5 V
	C15	←	Ignition ON	1,7 V
	C15	←	Engine idling	1,7 V
	C15	←	Engine under load	4,5 V
	C16	⇥—	Ignition ON	0 V
Mass air flow (MAF) sensor	C2	←	Engine idling	1,7 V
	C2	←	Engine running – accelerate briefly	4,3 V
	C2	←	Ignition OFF	0 V
	C2	←	Ignition ON	0,9 V
	C3	⇥—	Ignition ON	0 V
	C33	⇒	Ignition OFF	0 V
	C33	⇒	Ignition ON	5 V
Starter motor	C51	←	Engine cranking	10 V
	C51	←	Ignition ON	0 V
Turbocharger (TC) wastegate regulating valve	C9	⇥▷	Ignition OFF	0 V
	C9	⇥▷	Ignition ON	0,8 V
	C9	⇥▷	Engine idling	1,2 V
	C9	⇥▷	Engine idling	2 V/1 ms per division ⌁ 20

[1] Connected pin - no test data available

BMW

Bosch DDE7

Model:	Engine code:	Year:
320d (E46) - AT	20 4D 4	2001-06

ECM harness multi-plug

Terminal side

A

```
96 95 94 93 92 91 90 89 88 87 86 85 84 83 82 81 80 79 78 77 76 75 74 73
72 71 70 69 68 67 66 65 64 63 62 61 60 59 58 57 56 55 54 53 52 51 50 49

48 47 46 45 44 43 42 41 40 39 38 37 36 35 34 33 32 31 30 29 28 27 26 25
24 23 22 21 20 19 18 17 16 15 14 13 12 11 10 9 8 7 6 5 4 3 2 1
```

B

```
58 57 56 55 54 53 52 51 50 49 48 47 46   6   5
45 44 43 42 41 40 39 38 37 36 35 34 33   4   3

32 31 30 29 28 27 26 25 24 23 22 21 20   2   1
19 18 17 16 15 14 13 12 11 10 9 8 7
```

AD106092

Wire side

B

```
5   6   46 47 48 49 50 51 52 53 54 55 56 57 58
        33 34 35 36 37 38 39 40 41 42 43 44 45
3   4
1   2   20 21 22 23 24 25 26 27 28 29 30 31 32
        7  8  9  10 11 12 13 14 15 16 17 18 19
```

AD106117

A

```
73 74 75 76 77 78 79 80 81 82 83 84 85 86 87 88 89 90 91 92 93 94 95 96
49 50 51 52 53 54 55 56 57 58 59 60 61 62 63 64 65 66 67 68 69 70 71 72

25 26 27 28 29 30 31 32 33 34 35 36 37 38 39 40 41 42 43 44 45 46 47 48
1  2  3  4  5  6  7  8  9  10 11 12 13 14 15 16 17 18 19 20 21 22 23 24
```

Component/circuit description	ECM pin	Signal	Condition	Typical value	Oscilloscope setting★	Wave form
ABS control module	B49	⬌		1		
AC compressor clutch relay	B58	⊐▷	Ignition ON – AC OFF	11-14 V		
	B58	⊐▷	Ignition ON – AC ON	0-1 V		
Accelerator pedal position (APP) sensor	B29	⅂	Ignition ON	0 V		
	B30	⅂	Ignition ON	0 V		
	B39	⬅	Ignition ON – accelerator pedal released	0,35 V		
	B39	⬅	Ignition ON – accelerator pedal depressed	2 V		
	B43	⇨	Ignition ON	5 V		
	B52	⬅	Ignition ON – accelerator pedal released	0,7 V		
	B52	⬅	Ignition ON – accelerator pedal depressed	4 V		
	B56	⇨	Ignition ON	5 V		
Alternator	A13			1		
	A37	⬅	Ignition ON		1,5 V/10 ms	〰 43
	A37	⬅	Engine idling		2 V/10 ms	〰 5
Auxiliary heater control module	B12	⬅	Ignition ON – auxiliary heater ON	9,6 V		
	B44	⇨	Ignition ON		3 V/2 ms	〰 31
Brake pedal position (BPP) switch	B23	⬅	Ignition ON – brake pedal depressed	11-14 V		
	B36	⇨	Ignition ON – brake pedal released	0 V		
	B36	⇨	Ignition ON – brake pedal depressed	11-14 V		
Camshaft position (CMP) sensor	A14	⅂	Ignition ON	0 V		
	A62	⬅	Ignition ON	5 V		
	A62	⬅	Engine idling		2 V/50 ms	〰 3

★ Suggested settings - Voltage/time per division

Component/circuit description	ECM pin	Signal	Condition	Typical value	Oscilloscope setting*	Wave form
CAN data bus connection	A65	⟷		[1]		
	A66	⟷		[1]		
	A67	⟷		[1]		
	A89	⟷		[1]		
	A90	⟷		[1]		
	A91	⟷		[1]		
	B33	⟷		[1]		
	B46	⟷		[1]		
Crankshaft position (CKP) sensor	A15	⊣—	Ignition ON	0 V		
	A39	⇒	Ignition ON	5 V		
	A87	⟵	Ignition ON	5 V		
	A87	⟵	Engine idling		1 V/2 ms	MvM 72
Cruise control module	B37	⟷		[1]		
Data link connector (DLC)	B8	⟷		[1]		
	B53	⟷		[1]		
Earth	B2		Ignition ON	0 V		
	B4		Ignition ON	0 V		
	B6		Ignition ON	0 V		
Engine control relay	A44	⊣▷	Ignition OFF	11-14 V		
	A44	⊣▷	Ignition ON	0-1 V		
	B1	⟵	Ignition ON	11-14 V		
	B3	⟵	Ignition ON	11-14 V		
	B5	⟵	Ignition ON	11-14 V		
Engine coolant blower motor	B40	⟷		[1]		
Engine coolant temperature (ECT) sensor	A7	⊣—	Ignition ON	0 V		
	A82	⟵	Ignition ON – 14°C	3,8 V		
Engine oil level sensor	A86	⊣▷	Ignition ON	0-1 V		
Engine oil pressure switch	A10	⟵	Ignition ON	0 V		
Engine oil pressure warning lamp	B45	⊣▷	Ignition ON	0-1 V		
Exhaust gas recirculation (EGR) solenoid	A94	⊣▷	Ignition ON	11-14 V		
	A94	⊣▷	Engine idling	50%	2 V/2 ms	MvM 10
Fuel pump relay	B32	⊣▷	Ignition ON – fuel pump ON	0-1 V		
	B32	⊣▷	Ignition ON – fuel pump OFF	11-14 V		
Fuel quantity adjuster	A71	⊣▷	Engine idling		2 V/5 ms	MvM 10
Fuel rail pressure (FRP) control valve	A72	⊣▷	Engine idling		2 V/5 ms	MvM 37
Fuel rail pressure (FRP) sensor	A30	⇒	Ignition ON	5 V		
	A56	⟵	Ignition ON	0,5 V		
	A56	⟵	Engine idling	1,2 V		
	A56	⟵	Engine running – 3000 rpm	1,2 V		
	A78	⊣—	Ignition ON	0 V		
Fuse box/relay plate cooling fan motor – if fitted	B19	⟷		[1]		
Glow plug control module	A68	⟷		[1]		
	A70	⊣▷	Ignition ON	0-1 V		
Ignition switch	B7	⟵	Ignition ON	11-14 V		
Immobilizer control module	B10	⟷		[1]		
Injector 1	A49 (A73)	⇒	Engine idling – engine hot	0,3 ms pilot + 1 ms main	10 V/0,5 ms	BvM 13
	A73 (A49)	⇒	Engine idling – engine hot	0,3 ms pilot + 1 ms main	10 V/0,5 ms	MvM 13

* Suggested settings - Voltage/time per division

Component/circuit description	ECM pin	Signal	Condition	Typical value	Oscilloscope setting*	Wave form
Injector 2	A51 (A75)	⇒	Engine idling – engine hot	0,3 ms pilot + 1 ms main	10 V/0,5 ms	13
	A75 (A51)	⇒	Engine idling – engine hot	0,3 ms pilot + 1 ms main	10 V/0,5 ms	13
Injector 3	A3 (A27)	⇒	Engine idling – engine hot	0,3 ms pilot + 1 ms main	10 V/0,5 ms	13
	A27 (A3)	⇒	Engine idling – engine hot	0,3 ms pilot + 1 ms main	10 V/0,5 ms	13
Injector 4	A50 (A74)	⇒	Engine idling – engine hot	0,3 ms pilot + 1 ms main	10 V/0,5 ms	13
	A74 (A50)	⇒	Engine idling – engine hot	0,3 ms pilot + 1 ms main	10 V/0,5 ms	13
Intake air temperature (IAT) sensor	A57	⇐	Ignition ON – 14°C	2,4 V		
Intake manifold air control solenoid	A95	⇥▷	Ignition ON	11-14 V		
	A95	⇥▷	Engine idling	0,2 V		
	A95	⇥▷	Engine idling – accelerate briefly	11-14 V briefly		
Mass air flow (MAF) sensor	A31	⇒	Ignition ON	5 V		
	A55	⇐	Ignition ON	1 V		
	A55	⇐	Engine idling	1,5 V		
	A55	⇐	Engine idling – full throttle briefly	3,7 V briefly		
	A79	⊣	Ignition ON	0 V		
Transmission control module (TCM)	A19	⇔		1		
	A22	⇔		1		
Turbocharger (TC) boost air temperature sensor	A6	⊣	Ignition ON	0 V		
	A83	⇐	Ignition ON – 14°C	4,3 V		
Turbocharger (TC) boost pressure sensor	A32	⇒	Ignition ON	5 V		
	A54	⇐	Ignition ON	1,3 V		
	A54	⇐	Engine idling	1,3 V		
	A54	⇐	Engine idling – accelerate briefly	2,3 V briefly		
	A80	⊣	Ignition ON	0 V		
Turbocharger (TC) wastegate regulating valve	A93	⇥▷	Ignition ON		2 V/5 ms	49
	A93	⇥▷	Engine idling		2 V/2 ms	64

*Suggested settings - Voltage/time per division

1 Connected pin - no test data available or random digital signal

ECM harness multi-plug

Terminal side

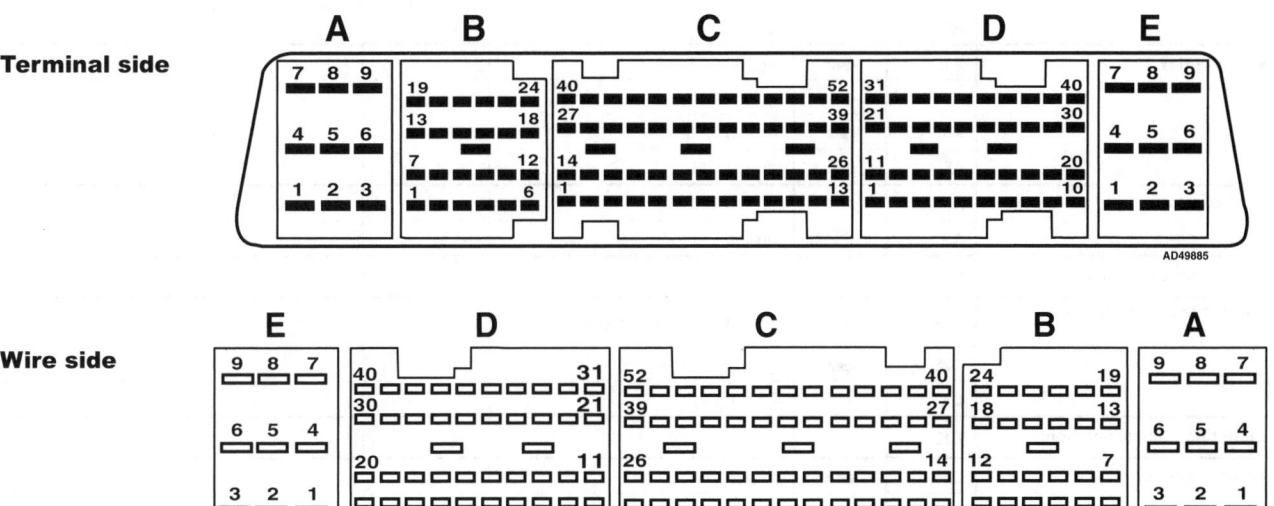

Wire side

Component/circuit description	ECM pin	Signal	Condition	Typical value	Oscilloscope setting*	Wave form
ABS control module	D22	⇔		1		
AC control module	D29	⇔		1		
	D29	⇔		1		
Accelerator pedal position (APP) sensor	D7	⌐	Ignition ON	0 V		
	D8	←	Ignition ON – accelerator pedal released	0,3 V		
	D8	←	Ignition ON – accelerator pedal fully depressed	3,2 V		
	D9	⇒	Ignition Off	0 V		
	D9	⇒	Ignition ON	5 V		
	D12	⌐	Ignition ON	0 V		
	D16	←	Ignition ON – accelerator pedal released	2,7 V		
	D16	←	Ignition ON – accelerator pedal depressed	0 V		
Alternator	C50	←	Engine idling	11-14 V		
	C50	←	Ignition ON	1,3 V		
Brake pedal position (BPP) switch	D28	←	Ignition ON – brake pedal released	0 V		
	D28	←	Ignition ON – brake pedal depressed	11-14 V		
CAN data bus – high	D36	⇔		1		
CAN data bus – low	D37	⇔		1		
Clutch pedal position (CPP) switch	D23	←	Ignition ON – clutch pedal depressed	11-14 V		
	D23	←	Ignition ON – clutch pedal released	0 V		
Crankshaft position (CKP) sensor	C6	←	Engine idling	2,7 V ac	5 V/5 ms	6
	C31	⌐	Ignition ON	0 V		

* Suggested settings - Voltage/time per division

Component/circuit description	ECM pin	Signal	Condition	Typical value	Oscilloscope setting*	Wave form
Data link connector (DLC)	D17	⇒	Engine idling		5 V/10 ms	〰️〰️ 2
	D17	⇒	Ignition ON	11-14 V		
	D32	⇒	Ignition OFF	11-14 V		
	D32	⇒	Ignition ON	11-14 V		
Earth	A4		Ignition ON	0 V		
	A5		Ignition ON	0 V		
	A6		Ignition ON	0 V		
Engine control relay	A1	⬅	Ignition OFF	0 V		
	A1	⬅	Ignition ON	11-14 V		
	A8	⬅	Ignition OFF	0 V		
	A8	⬅	Ignition ON	11-14 V		
Engine control relay	A9	⥅	Ignition OFF	11-14 V		
	A9	⥅	Ignition ON	0-1 V		
Engine coolant blower motor	D4	⇒		1		
Engine coolant temperature (ECT) sensor	C28	⬅	Ignition ON – engine cold	3,3 V		
	C28	⬅	Ignition ON – engine hot	1 V		
	C32	⊣	Ignition ON	0 V		
Engine mounting control solenoid	C13	⥅		1		
Engine oil level sensor	C40	⬅	Ignition OFF	0 V		
	C40	⬅	Ignition ON	0-2 V (fluctuating)		
Engine oil pressure switch	C41	⬅	Engine idling	11-14 V		
	C41	⬅	Ignition ON	0 V		
Engine oil pressure warning lamp	D11	⇒	Engine idling	11-14 V		
	D11	⇒	Ignition ON	0 V		
Exhaust gas recirculation (EGR) solenoid	C10	⥅	Ignition OFF	0 V		
	C10	⥅	Ignition ON	11-14 V		
	C10	⥅	Engine idling		5 V/2 ms	〰️〰️ 31
Fuel injection pump control module	C7	⬅	Engine idling		2 V/5 ms	〰️〰️ 15
	C7	⬅	Ignition ON	0 V		
	C21	⇒	Ignition ON	0 V		
	C21	⇒	Engine idling – switch ignition OFF	11-14 V briefly		
Fuel injection pump control module – CAN data bus – low	C44	⬌		1		
Fuel injection pump control module – CAN data bus – high	C45	⬌		1		
Fuel lift pump relay	D10	⥅	Engine idling	0-1 V		
	D10	⥅	Ignition ON	11-14 V		
Glow plug control module	C12	⇒	Engine idling	11-14 V		
	C12	⇒	Ignition OFF	0 V		
	C12	⇒	Ignition ON	11-14 V		
	C52	⥅	Ignition OFF	0 V		
	C52	⥅	Ignition ON	0-1 V		
Ignition switch	D26	⬅	Ignition OFF	0 V		
	D26	⬅	Ignition ON	11-14 V		
Immobilizer control module	D33	⬌		1		
Injector needle lift sensor	C5	⬅	Engine idling	3,35 V		
	C5	⬅	Ignition OFF	0 V		
	C5	⬅	Ignition ON	3,3 V		
	C18	⊣	Ignition ON	0 V		

* Suggested settings - Voltage/time per division

Component/circuit description	ECM pin	Signal	Condition	Typical value	Oscilloscope setting*	Wave form
Instrument panel	**D1**	⇨		[1]		
	D2	⇨		[1]		
	D19	⬅⇨		[1]		
Lamps control module	**D21**	⬅⇨		[1]		
	D21	⬅⇨		[1]		
Mass air flow (MAF) sensor	**C2**	⬅	Engine idling	1,7 V		
	C2	⬅	Engine idling – accelerate briefly	4,3 V briefly		
	C2	⬅	Ignition OFF	0 V		
	C2	⬅	Ignition ON	0,9 V		
	C3	⏚	Ignition ON	0 V		
	C33	⇨	Ignition OFF	0 V		
	C33	⇨	Ignition ON	5 V		
Starter motor	**C51**	⬅	Engine cranking	10 V		
	C51	⬅	Ignition ON	0 V		
Steering wheel multifunction switch	**D27**	⬅⇨		[1]		
Turbocharger (TC) boost pressure sensor	**C14**	⇨	Ignition OFF	0 V		
	C14	⇨	Ignition ON	5 V		
	C15	⬅	Ignition ON	1,7 V		
	C15	⬅	Engine idling	1,7 V		
	C15	⬅	Engine under load	4,5 V		
	C16	⏚	Ignition ON	0 V		
Turbocharger (TC) wastegate regulating valve	**C9**	⏚⇨	Ignition OFF	0 V		
	C9	⏚⇨	Ignition ON	0,8 V		
	C9	⏚⇨	Engine idling	1,2 V	2 V/1 ms	20

*Suggested settings - Voltage/time per division

[1] Connected pin - no test data available or random digital signal

BMW

Bosch DDE7

Model:	Engine code:	Year:
525d (E60/61)	25 6D 2	2003-06

ECM harness multi-plug

Terminal side

B

```
58 57 56 55 54 53 52 51 50 49 48 47 46   6  5
45 44 43 42 41 40 39 38 37 36 35 34 33   4  3
32 31 30 29 28 27 26 25 24 23 22 21 20   2  1
19 18 17 16 15 14 13 12 11 10  9  8  7
```

A

```
96 95 94 93 92 91 90 89 88 87 86 85 84 83 82 81 80 79 78 77 76 75 74 73
72 71 70 69 68 67 66 65 64 63 62 61 60 59 58 57 56 55 54 53 52 51 50 49
48 47 46 45 44 43 42 41 40 39 38 37 36 35 34 33 32 31 30 29 28 27 26 25
24 23 22 21 20 19 18 17 16 15 14 13 12 11 10  9  8  7  6  5  4  3  2  1
```

AD106504

Wire side

A

```
73 74 75 76 77 78 79 80 81 82 83 84 85 86 87 88 89 90 91 92 93 94 95 96
49 50 51 52 53 54 55 56 57 58 59 60 61 62 63 64 65 66 67 68 69 70 71 72
25 26 27 28 29 30 31 32 33 34 35 36 37 38 39 40 41 42 43 44 45 46 47 48
 1  2  3  4  5  6  7  8  9 10 11 12 13 14 15 16 17 18 19 20 21 22 23 24
```

AD106503

B

```
 5  6   46 47 48 49 50 51 52 53 54 55 56 57 58
        33 34 35 36 37 38 39 40 41 42 43 44 45
 3  4
 1  2   20 21 22 23 24 25 26 27 28 29 30 31 32
         7  8  9 10 11 12 13 14 15 16 17 18 19
```

Component/circuit description	ECM pin	Signal	Condition	Typical value	Oscilloscope setting*	Wave form
AC control module	B44	⇒	Ignition ON		3 V/2 ms	
Accelerator pedal position (APP) sensor	B29	⊣⟋	Ignition ON	0 V		
	B30	⊣⟋	Ignition ON	0 V		
	B39	⟵	Ignition ON – accelerator pedal released	0,2 V		
	B39	⟵	Ignition ON – accelerator pedal depressed	1,7 V		
	B43	⇒	Ignition ON	5 V		
	B52	⟵	Ignition ON – accelerator pedal released	0,5 V		
	B52	⟵	Ignition ON – accelerator pedal depressed	3,6 V		
	B56	⇒	Ignition ON	5 V		
Alternator	A69			▢1		
Battery condition sensor	B14	⟵		▢1		
Brake pedal position (BPP) switch	B23	⟵	Ignition ON – brake pedal released	0 V		
	B23	⟵	Ignition ON – brake pedal depressed	11-14 V		
	B36	⇒	Ignition ON – brake pedal released	0 V		
Camshaft position (CMP) sensor	A14	⊣⟋	Ignition ON	0 V		
	A62	⟵	Ignition ON	5 V		
	A62	⟵	Engine idling		2 V/0,1 s	
CAN data bus connection	B33	⬌		▢1		
	B46	⬌		▢1		
Clutch pedal position (CPP) switch	B50	⟵	Ignition ON – clutch pedal released	0 V		
	B50	⟵	Ignition ON – clutch pedal depressed	11-14 V		
Crankshaft position (CKP) sensor	A15	⊣⟋	Ignition ON	0 V		
	A39	⇒	Ignition ON	5 V		
	A87	⟵	Engine idling		1 V/2 ms	
Data link connector (DLC)	B53	⟵		▢1		

* Suggested settings - Voltage/time per division

Autodata

Component/circuit description	ECM pin	Signal	Condition	Typical value	Oscilloscope setting*	Wave form
Earth	B2		Ignition ON	0 V		
	B4		Ignition ON	0 V		
	B6		Ignition ON	0 V		
Engine control (EC) relay	A44	⇥▷	Ignition OFF	11-14 V		
	A44	⇥▷	Ignition ON	0-1 V		
	B1	←	Ignition ON	11-14 V		
	B3	←	Ignition ON	11-14 V		
	B5	←	Ignition ON	11-14 V		
Engine coolant blower motor	B40			1		
Engine coolant radiator flap solenoid	B31	⇥▷	Ignition ON – 14°C	0-1 V		
Engine coolant temperature (ECT) sensor	A7	⇥–	Ignition ON	0 V		
	A82	←	Ignition ON – 12°C	4,1 V		
	A82	←	Engine idling – 70°C	1,5 V		
Engine mounting control solenoid	A24	⇥▷	Ignition ON	11-14 V		
	A24	⇥▷	Engine running	0-1 V – when operating		
Engine oil level sensor	A38	←	Engine idling		2 V/0,1 ms	⦿ 20
	A86	⇥–	Ignition ON	0 V		
Engine oil pressure switch	A10	←	Ignition ON	0 V		
	A10	←	Engine idling	5 V		
Exhaust gas pressure sensor	A33	⇨	Ignition ON	5 V		
	A59	←	Ignition ON	2,5 V		
	A81	⇥–	Ignition ON	0 V		
Exhaust gas recirculation (EGR) solenoid	A94	⇥▷	Engine idling		2 V/1 ms	⦿ 66
Exhaust gas temperature sensor 1	A8	⇥–	Ignition ON	0 V		
	A58	←	Ignition ON – 12°C	4,6 V		
Exhaust gas temperature sensor 2	A9	⇥–	Ignition ON	0 V		
	A34	←	Ignition ON – 12°C	4,6 V		
Fuel filter heater	B11			1		
Fuel quantity adjuster	A71	⇥▷	Ignition ON	11-14 V		
	A71	⇥▷	Engine idling		2 V/5 ms	⦿ 10
Fuel rail pressure (FRP) control valve	A72	⇥▷	Engine idling		2 V/0,5 ms	⦿ 37
Fuel rail pressure (FRP) sensor	A30	⇨	Ignition ON	5 V		
	A56	←	Ignition ON	0,3 V		
	A56	←	Engine idling	1 V		
	A56	←	Engine running – 3000 rpm	1,4 V		
	A78	⇥–	Ignition ON	0 V		
Fuel temperature sensor	A11	⇥–	Ignition ON	0 V		
	A57	←	Ignition ON – 12°C	3,8 V		
Glow plug control module	A68	◄▷	Ignition ON		2 V/1 ms	⦿ 37
	A68	◄▷	Engine idling		2 V/1 ms	⦿ 37
	A70	⇥▷	Ignition ON	0-1 V		
Heated oxygen sensor (HO2S)	A12		Engine idling	2,3 V		
	A16	⇥▷	Engine idling	2,3 V		
	A36		Engine running	1,8-3 V		
	A60		Engine running	3 V		
	A84		Engine running	2,8 V		
Injector 1	A49 (A73)	⇨	Engine idling	0,5 ms pilot + 0,8 ms main	10 V/0,5 ms	⦿ 59
	A73 (A49)	⇨	Engine idling	0,5 ms pilot + 0,8 ms main	10 V/0,5 ms	⦿ 59

* Suggested settings - Voltage/time per division

Component/circuit description	ECM pin	Signal	Condition	Typical value	Oscilloscope setting*	Wave form
Injector 2	A51 (A75)	⇒	Engine idling	0,5 ms pilot + 0,8 ms main	10 V/0,5 ms	59
	A75 (A51)	⇒	Engine idling	0,5 ms pilot + 0,8 ms main	10 V/0,5 ms	59
Injector 3	A50 (A74)	⇒	Engine idling	0,5 ms pilot + 0,8 ms main	10 V/0,5 ms	59
	A74 (A50)	⇒	Engine idling	0,5 ms pilot + 0,8 ms main	10 V/0,5 ms	59
Injector 4	A1 (A25)	⇒	Engine idling	0,5 ms pilot + 0,8 ms main	10 V/0,5 ms	59
	A25 (A1)	⇒	Engine idling	0,5 ms pilot + 0,8 ms main	10 V/0,5 ms	59
Injector 5	A3 (A27)	⇒	Engine idling	0,5 ms pilot + 0,8 ms main	10 V/0,5 ms	59
	A27 (A3)	⇒	Engine idling	0,5 ms pilot + 0,8 ms main	10 V/0,5 ms	59
Injector 6	A2 (A26)	⇒	Engine idling	0,5 ms pilot + 0,8 ms main	10 V/0,5 ms	59
	A26 (A2)	⇒	Engine idling	0,5 ms pilot + 0,8 ms main	10 V/0,5 ms	59
Intake air temperature (IAT) sensor	A46	⬅	Ignition ON – 12°C	20 %	2 V/20 ms	48
Intake manifold air control solenoid	A95	⤙⇥	Engine idling		2 V/0,5 ms	49
	A95	⤙⇥	Engine idling – accelerate briefly	11-14 V briefly		
Mass air flow (MAF) sensor	A45	⬅	Ignition ON	1,2 Hz	2 V/0,5 ms	9
	A45	⬅	Engine running	1,2-14 Hz	2 V/0,5 ms	9
	A47	⤙⎯	Ignition ON	0 V		
Multifunction control module 2	B7	⬅	Ignition ON	11-14 V		
	B10	⬅		[1]		
	B34	⬅	Ignition ON	11-14 V		
Throttle control unit	A96	⤙⇥	Engine idling		2 V/1 ms	66
Turbocharger (TC) boost air temperature sensor	A6	⤙⎯	Ignition ON	0 V		
	A83	⬅	Ignition ON – 14°C	3,8 V		
Turbocharger (TC) boost pressure actuator	A93	⤙⇥	Ignition ON		2 V/1 ms	20
Turbocharger (TC) boost pressure sensor	A32	⇒	Ignition ON	5 V		
	A54	⬅	Ignition ON	0,9 V		
	A54	⬅	Engine idling	0,9 V		
	A54	⬅	Engine idling – accelerate briefly	1,5 V		
	A80	⤙⎯	Ignition ON	0 V		

*Suggested settings - Voltage/time per division

[1] Connected pin - no test data available or random digital signal

Model:	Engine code:	Year:
Saxo 1,0i	CDY (TU9M/L3)	1996-03
Saxo 1,0i	CDZ (TU9M/L)	1996-03
Saxo 1,1i	HDY (TU1M/L3)	1996-02
Saxo 1,1i	HDZ (TU1M/L)	1996-02
Berlingo 1,1i	HDY/HDZ (TU1M/L3)	1997-02

ECM harness multi-plug

Terminal side

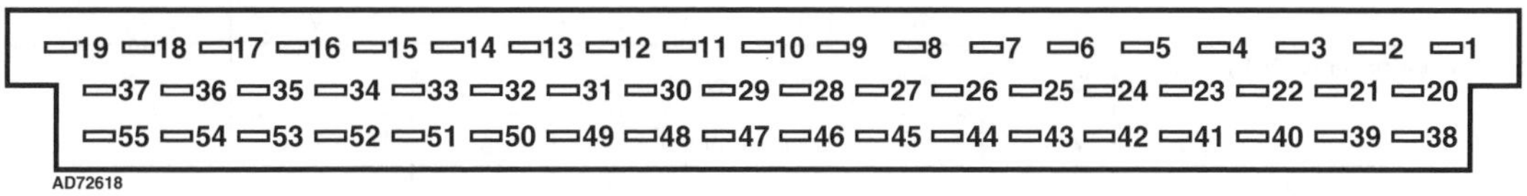

Wire side

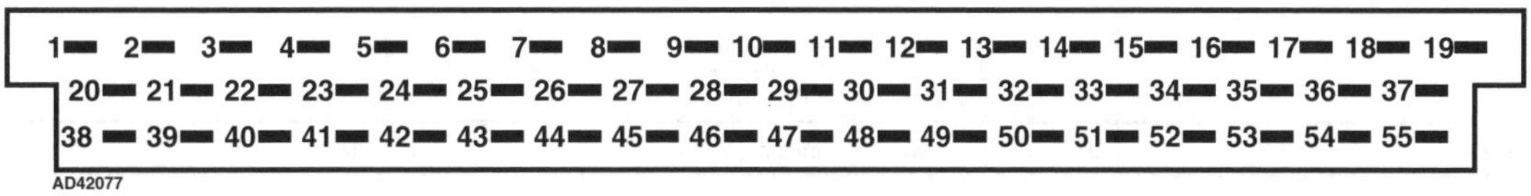

Component/circuit description	ECM pin	Signal	Condition	Typical value	Oscilloscope setting*	Wave form
Battery	18	⬅	Ignition OFF	11-14 V		
Closed throttle position (CTP) switch	31	⬅	Ignition ON – throttle closed	0 V		
	31	⬅	Ignition ON – throttle slightly open	11-14 V		
Crankshaft position (CKP) sensor	11	⊣—	Ignition ON	0 V		
	30	⬅	Engine idling	9 V ac	2 V/1 ms	2
Data link connector (DLC)	13			[1]		
	16			[1]		
Data link connector (DLC) – some models	6	⇨	Engine idling	30 Hz		
	6	⇨	3000 rpm	100 Hz		
	22			[1]		
Earth	2		Ignition ON	0 V		
	14		Ignition ON	0 V		
	19		Ignition ON	0 V		
Engine coolant temperature (ECT) sensor	25	⬅	Ignition ON – coolant temp. 20°C	2,5 V		
	25	⬅	Ignition ON – coolant temp. 80°C	0,4 V		
	26	⊣—	Ignition ON	0 V		
Evaporative emission (EVAP) canister purge valve	5	⊣▷	Ignition OFF	11-14 V		
	5	⊣▷	Engine idling	1-99%	10 V/50 ms	20
Heated oxygen sensor (HO2S)	10	⊣—	Ignition ON	0 V		
	28	⬅	Engine idling – accelerate briefly	0,1-1,0 V fluctuating	0,2 V/1 sec.	21
Idle speed control (ISC) actuator	15 (33)	⇨	Engine idling		5 V/0,5 sec.	Intermittent 27
	33 (15)	⇨	Engine idling		5 V/0,5 sec.	Intermittent 27
Idle speed control (ISC) actuator position sensor – HDY/HDZ	24	⬅	Engine idling		2 V/20 ms	Intermittent 31
Ignition coil – cylinders 1 & 4	1	⊣▷	Engine idling		5 V/2 ms	33
Ignition coil – cylinders 2 & 3	20	⊣▷	Engine idling		5 V/2 ms	33
Immobilizer control module – some models	22			[1]		
	34	⬅		[1]		
Inertia fuel shut-off (IFS) switch – some models	3	⊣▷	Ignition ON	0-1 V briefly then 11-14 V		
	3	⊣▷	Engine cranking	0-1 V		
	3	⊣▷	Engine running	0-1 V		

* Suggested settings - Voltage/time per division

Component/circuit description	ECM pin	Signal	Condition	Typical value	Oscilloscope setting*	Wave form
Injector	17	⊐▷	Engine idling	1,9 ms	10 V/2 ms	∿∿ 35
	17	⊐▷	3000 rpm	2,2 ms	10 V/2 ms	∿∿ 35
Intake air temperature (IAT) sensor	26	⊐—	Ignition ON	0 V		
	27	◀—	Ignition ON – air temp. 20°C	2,8 V		
Intake manifold heater relay – HDY/HDZ	36	⊐▷	Ignition ON	11-14 V		
	36	⊐▷	Engine running – engine cold	0-1 V		
	36	⊐▷	Engine running – engine hot	11-14 V		
Malfunction indicator lamp (MIL) – some models	22	⊐▷	Ignition ON – MIL ON	0-1 V		
	22	⊐▷	Engine running – MIL OFF	11-14 V		
Multifunction control module – some models	22			1		
	34	◀—		1		
	6	⇨	Engine idling	30 Hz		
	6	⇨	3000 rpm	100 Hz		
Relay module	37	◀—	Ignition ON	11-14 V		
Relay module – some models	3	⊐▷	Ignition ON	0-1 V briefly then 11-14 V		
	3	⊐▷	Engine cranking	0-1 V		
	3	⊐▷	Engine running	0-1 V		
Tachometer – some models	6	⇨	Engine idling	30 Hz		
	6	⇨	3000 rpm	100 Hz		
Throttle position (TP) sensor	7	◀—	Ignition ON – throttle closed	1,8 V		
	7	◀—	Ignition ON – throttle fully open	4,9 V		
	12	⇨	Ignition ON	5 V		
	26	⊐—	Ignition ON	0 V		
	29	◀—	Ignition ON – throttle closed	0 V		
	29	◀—	Ignition ON – throttle fully open	4 V		
Vehicle speed sensor (VSS)	9	◀—	Vehicle moving	Voltage varies with vehicle speed		

*Suggested settings - Voltage/time per division

1 Connected pin - no test data available or random digital signal

Model:	Engine code:	Year:
Saxo 1,4	KFX (TU3JP/L3)	1996-02
Saxo 1,6 16V	NFX (TU5JP4/L3)	1997-03
Xsara 1,4i	KFX (TU3JP)	1997-02
Xsara 1,8i (MT)	LFX (TXU7JB)	1997-02
Berlingo 1,4	KFX (TU3JP/L3)	1997-02
Berlingo 1,8	LFX (XU7JB/L3)	1997-02

CITROEN
Magneti Marelli
1AP.20/40/41

ECM harness multi-plug

Terminal side

19 18 17 16 15 14 13 12 11 10 9 8 7 6 5 4 3 2 1
37 36 35 34 33 32 31 30 29 28 27 26 25 24 23 22 21 20
55 54 53 52 51 50 49 48 47 46 45 44 43 42 41 40 39 38
AD72618

Wire side

1 2 3 4 5 6 7 8 9 10 11 12 13 14 15 16 17 18 19
20 21 22 23 24 25 26 27 28 29 30 31 32 33 34 35 36 37
38 39 40 41 42 43 44 45 46 47 48 49 50 51 52 53 54 55
AD42077

Component/circuit description	ECM pin	Signal	Condition	Typical value	Oscilloscope setting*	Wave form
Air conditioning	26			[1]		
	50			[1]		
Crankshaft position (CKP) sensor	30	←	Engine cranking	2 V ac	2 V/1 ms	[2]
	30	←	Engine idling	5 V ac	2 V/1 ms	[2]
	30	←	3000 rpm	12 V ac	2 V/1 ms	[2]
	49	←	Engine cranking	2 V ac	2 V/1 ms	[2]
	49	←	Engine idling	5 V ac	2 V/1 ms	[2]
	49	←	3000 rpm	12 V ac	2 V/1 ms	[2]
Crankshaft position (CKP) sensor – some models – shield wire	19	⊣	Ignition ON	0 V		
Data link connector (DLC)	12	←		[1]		
	31			[1]		
Data link connector (DLC) – some models	42	⇒		[1]		
Earth	36	⊣	Ignition ON	0 V		
	54	⊣	Ignition ON	0 V		
Earth – some models	19	⊣	Ignition ON	0 V		
Engine coolant temperature (ECT) sensor	47	←	Ignition ON – coolant temp. 20°C	1,7 V		
	47	←	Ignition ON – coolant temp. 80°C	0,4 V		
	53	⊣	Ignition ON	0 V		
Evaporative emission (EVAP) canister purge valve	24	⊣▷	Engine running	1-99%	10 V/50 ms	[20]
Heated oxygen sensor (HO2S)	4	⊣	Ignition ON	0 V		
	22	←	Engine idling – accelerate briefly	0-1 V fluctuating	0,2 V/1 sec.	[21]
Heated oxygen sensor (HO2S) – some models – shield wire	19	⊣	Ignition ON	0 V		
Idle air control (IAC) valve	21 (40)	⇒	Engine idling		5 V/0,5 sec.	Intermittent [26]
	3 (20)	⇒	Engine idling		5 V/0,5 sec.	Intermittent [26]
	20 (3)	⇒	Engine idling		5 V/0,5 sec.	Intermittent [26]
	40 (21)	⇒	Engine idling		5 V/0,5 sec.	Intermittent [26]
Ignition coil – cylinders 1 & 4	55	⊣▷	Engine idling		5 V/2 ms	[33]
Ignition coil – cylinders 2 & 3	37	⊣▷	Engine idling		5 V/2 ms	[33]
Immobilizer control module – some models	13	←	Ignition ON	11-14 V		
	27			[1]		
	48			[1]		

* Suggested settings - Voltage/time per division

Component/circuit description	ECM pin	Signal	Condition	Typical value	Oscilloscope setting*	Wave form
Inertia fuel shut-off (IFS) switch	7	⊐▷	Ignition ON	0-1 V briefly then 11-14 V		
Injectors 1 & 4	2	⊐▷	Engine idling	4,2 ms	10 V/1 ms	ᴡᴡ 35
Injectors 2 & 3	1	⊐▷	Engine idling	4,2 ms	10 V/1 ms	ᴡᴡ 35
Intake air temperature (IAT) sensor	17	⊐—	Ignition ON	0 V		
	29	⬅	Ignition ON – air temp. 20°C	2,5 V		
Knock sensor (KS)	15	⬅	Engine idling – accelerate briefly		50 mV/1 ms	ᴡᴡ 38
	18	⊐—	Ignition ON	0-1 V		
Knock sensor (KS) – some models – shield wire	18	⊐—	Ignition ON	0 V		
Malfunction indicator lamp (MIL)	9	⊐▷	Ignition ON	0-1 V		
Manifold absolute pressure (MAP) sensor	17	⊐—	Ignition ON	0 V		
	34	⇨	Ignition ON	5 V		
	41	⬅	Ignition ON	4,5 V		
	41	⬅	Engine idling	1,3 V		
Power steering pressure (PSP) switch – some models	14	⬅	Engine running – steering wheel not turned	0 V		
	14	⬅	Engine running – steering wheel turned	11-14 V		
Relay module	13	⬅	Ignition ON	11-14 V		
	35	⬅	Ignition ON	11-14 V		
	35	⬅	Engine running	11-14 V		
	52	⊐▷	Ignition ON	0-1 V		
	52	⊐▷	Engine running	0-1 V		
Tachometer – some models	42	⇨	Engine idling	28 Hz		
	42	⇨	3000 rpm	100 Hz		
Throttle position (TP) sensor	16	⇨	Ignition ON	5 V		
	23	⬅	Ignition ON – throttle closed	0,7 V		
	23	⬅	Ignition ON – throttle fully open	4,7 V		
	53	⊐—	Ignition ON	0 V		
Vehicle speed sensor (VSS)	28	⬅	Ignition ON – vehicle moving	0-12 V fluctuating		

*Suggested settings - Voltage/time per division

1 Connected pin - no test data available or random digital signal

Model:	Engine code:	Year:
Saxo 1,6i (MT)	NFZ (TU5JP/L3)	1996-02
ZX 1,8	LFZ (XU7JP/LZ)	1992-98
Xantia 1,8i	LFZ (XU7JP/Z)	1993-97

ECM harness multi-plug

Terminal side

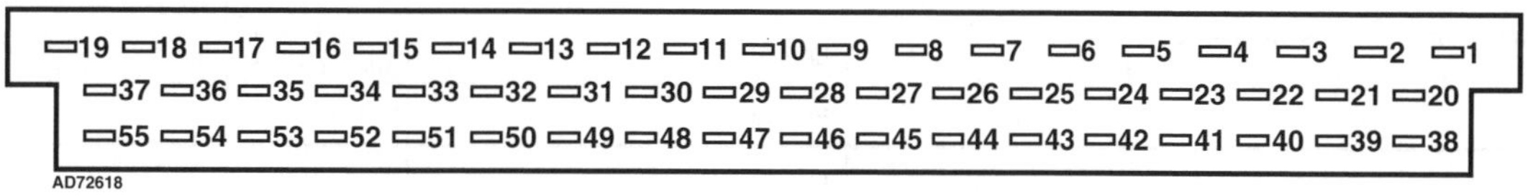
19 18 17 16 15 14 13 12 11 10 9 8 7 6 5 4 3 2 1
37 36 35 34 33 32 31 30 29 28 27 26 25 24 23 22 21 20
55 54 53 52 51 50 49 48 47 46 45 44 43 42 41 40 39 38
AD72618

Wire side

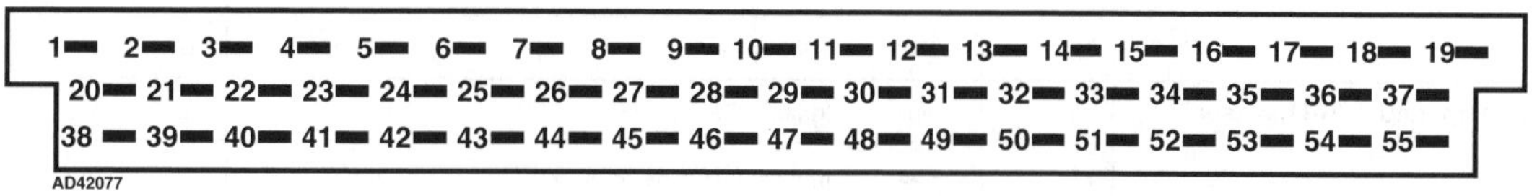
1 2 3 4 5 6 7 8 9 10 11 12 13 14 15 16 17 18 19
20 21 22 23 24 25 26 27 28 29 30 31 32 33 34 35 36 37
38 39 40 41 42 43 44 45 46 47 48 49 50 51 52 53 54 55
AD42077

Component/circuit description	ECM pin	Signal	Condition	Typical value	Oscilloscope setting*	Wave form
Air conditioning	23			[1]		
	32			[1]		
	34			[1]		
Battery	18	←	Ignition OFF	11-14 V		
Coded keypad – some models	22		Ignition ON – MIL ON	0 V		
	22		Engine idling – MIL OFF	11-14 V		
	35			[1]		
Crankshaft position (CKP) sensor	11	⏚	Ignition ON	0 V		
	30	←	Engine idling	6 V ac	2 V/1 ms	2
	30	←	3000 rpm	17 V ac	2 V/1 ms	2
Crankshaft position (CKP) sensor – shield wire	19	⏚	Ignition ON	0 V		
Data link connector (DLC)	13	⇨	Ignition ON – MIL ON	0-1 V		
	13	⇨	Engine idling – MIL OFF	11-14 V		
	16			[1]		
Data link connector (DLC) – some models	6	⇨	Engine idling	30 Hz		
	6	⇨	3000 rpm	100 Hz		
Earth	2		Ignition ON	0 V		
	14		Ignition ON	0 V		
	19		Ignition ON	0 V		
Engine coolant temperature (ECT) sensor	25	←	Ignition ON – coolant temp. 20°C	3,5 V		
	25	←	Ignition ON – coolant temp. 80°C	1 V		
	26	⏚	Ignition ON	0 V		
Evaporative emission (EVAP) canister purge valve	5	⏚▷	Ignition OFF	11-14 V		
	5	⏚▷	Engine running		10 V/50 ms	20
Heated oxygen sensor (HO2S)	10	⏚	Ignition ON	0 V		
	28	←	Engine idling – accelerate briefly	0,1-1 V fluctuating	0,2 V/1 sec.	21

* Suggested settings - Voltage/time per division

Component/circuit description	ECM pin	Signal	Condition	Typical value	Oscilloscope setting*	Wave form
Heated oxygen sensor (HO2S) – shield wire – some models	19	⊣⊢	Ignition ON	0 V		
Idle air control (IAC) valve	15	⇨	Engine idling	40%	5 V/5 ms	⩗⩗ 25
	33	⇨	Engine idling	57%	5 V/5 ms	⩗⩗ 25
Ignition coil – cylinders 1 & 4	1	⊣⊳	Engine idling		5 V/2 ms	⩗⩗ 33
Ignition coil – cylinders 2 & 3	20	⊣⊳	Engine idling		5 V/2 ms	⩗⩗ 33
Inertia fuel shut-off (IFS) switch – some models	3	⊣⊳	Ignition ON	0-1 V briefly then 11-14 V		
	3	⊣⊳	Engine cranking	0-1 V		
Injectors	17	⊣⊳	Ignition ON	11-14 V		
	17	⊣⊳	Engine idling	2,1 ms	10 V/2 ms	⩗⩗ 35
	17	⊣⊳	3000 rpm	1,8 ms	10 V/2 ms	⩗⩗ 35
Intake air temperature (IAT) sensor	26	⊣—	Ignition ON	0 V		
	27	⟵	Ignition ON – air temp. 20°C	3,5 V		
Malfunction indicator lamp (MIL)	22	⊣⊳	Ignition ON – MIL ON	0-1 V		
	22	⊣⊳	Engine idling – MIL OFF	11-14 V		
Manifold absolute pressure (MAP) sensor	7	⟵	Engine idling	1,2 V		
	7	⟵	Engine idling – accelerate briefly	4,4 V briefly		
	12	⇨	Ignition ON	5 V		
	26	⊣—	Ignition ON	0 V		
Relay module	37	⟵	Ignition ON	11-14 V		
Relay module – some models	3	⊣⊳	Ignition ON	0-1 V briefly then 11-14 V		
	3	⊣⊳	Engine cranking	0-1 V		
Tachometer	6	⇨	Engine idling	30 Hz		
	6	⇨	3000 rpm	100 Hz		
Throttle position (TP) sensor	12	⇨	Ignition ON	5 V		
	26	⊣—	Ignition ON	0 V		
	29	⟵	Ignition ON – throttle closed	0,3 V		
	29	⟵	Ignition ON – throttle fully open	5 V		
Vehicle speed sensor (VSS)	9	⟵	Ignition ON – vehicle moving	Voltage varies with vehicle speed		

*Suggested settings - Voltage/time per division

1 Connected pin - no test data available or random digital signal

Model:	Engine code:	Year:
Saxo 1,6 (MT)	NFZ (TU5JP/L3)	1998-02
Xsara 1,6 (MT)	NFZ (TU5JP/L3)	1998-02
Xsara 1,6 (AT)	NFZ (TU5JP/L3)	1999-02
Xsara Picasso 1,6 (MT)	NFZ (TU5JP/L3)	1999-02
Synergie 2,0 16V	RFV (XU10J4R)	1998-01
Berlingo 1,4	KFX (TU3JP/IFL4)	1999-02

ECM harness multi-plug

Terminal side

Wire side

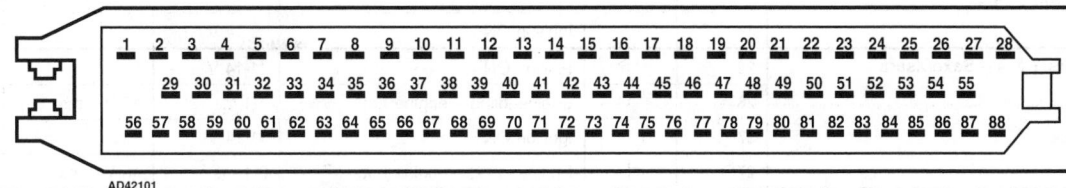

Component/circuit description	ECM pin	Signal	Condition	Typical value	Oscilloscope setting★	Wave form
AC control module	24			①1		
	36			①1		
Acceleration sensor – Synergie	72	←		①1		
	37	⌐	Ignition ON	0 V		
	42	⇨	Ignition ON	5 V		
Battery	49	←	Ignition OFF	11-14 V		
Camshaft position (CMP) sensor – Synergie	45	←	Engine idling		2 V/20 ms	Ⓜ12
	75	⌐	Ignition ON	0 V		
Camshaft position (CMP) sensor – Berlingo	45	←	Engine idling		2 V/20 ms	Ⓜ12
	37	⌐	Ignition ON	0 V		
Crankshaft position (CKP) sensor	18	←	Engine idling	2,6 V ac	2 V/1 ms	Ⓜ2
	46	←	Engine idling	2,6 V ac	2 V/1 ms	Reversed Ⓜ2
Data link connector (DLC)	19	←⇨	Ignition ON	0 V		
	20	←⇨	Ignition ON	0 V		
	44	⇨	Engine idling	30 Hz	5V/50 ms	Ⓜ4
Earth	1		Ignition ON	0 V		
	6		Ignition ON	0 V		
	23		Ignition ON	0 V		
	28		Ignition ON	0 V		
Engine coolant temperature (ECT) sensor	37	⌐	Ignition ON	0 V		
	39	←	Ignition ON – coolant temp. 20°C	3,3 V		
	39	←	Ignition ON – coolant temp. 80°C	0,9 V		
Evaporative emission (EVAP) canister purge valve	51	⌐⇨	Engine idling	10-15%		
Heated oxygen sensor (HO2S) front	13	←	Engine idling – accelerate briefly	0,1-0,9 V fluctuating	0,2 V/1 sec.	Ⓜ21
	40	⌐	Ignition ON	0 V		
	55	⌐⇨	Engine idling	90%		

★ Suggested settings - Voltage/time per division

Component/circuit description	ECM pin	Signal	Condition	Typical value	Oscilloscope setting*	Wave form
Heated oxygen sensor (HO2S) rear – Synergie/Berlingo	71	←	Engine idling – accelerate briefly	0,6 V	0,2 V/0,5 sec.	⟿ 76
	70	⊐⊢	Ignition ON	0 V		
	86	⊐▷	Engine idling	90%		
Idle air control (IAC) valve	3 (31)	⇒	Engine idling		5 V/0,5 sec.	Intermittent ⟿ 26
	4 (32)	⇒	Engine idling		5 V/0,5 sec.	Intermittent ⟿ 26
	31 (3)	⇒	Engine idling		5 V/0,5 sec.	Intermittent ⟿ 26
	32 (4)	⇒	Engine idling		5 V/0,5 sec.	Intermittent ⟿ 26
Ignition coil – cylinder 1 & 4	30	⊐▷	Engine idling		5 V/2 ms	⟿ 33
Ignition coil – cylinder 2 & 3	29	⊐▷	Engine idling		5 V/2 ms	⟿ 33
Ignition switch	21	←	Ignition OFF	0 V		
	21	←	Ignition ON	11-14 V		
Immobilizer control module – except Picasso/Berlingo	22		Engine idling	11-14 V		
	48		Ignition ON	11-14 V		
Injectors 1 & 4 – Saxo/Xsara	26	⊐▷	Ignition ON	11-14 V		
	26	⊐▷	Engine idling – engine hot	3,1 ms	10 V/2 ms	⟿ 35
	27	⊐▷	Ignition ON	11-14 V		
	27	⊐▷	Engine idling – engine hot	3,1 ms	10 V/2 ms	⟿ 35
Injectors 2 & 3 – Saxo/Xsara	53	⊐▷	Ignition ON	11-14 V		
	53	⊐▷	Engine idling – engine hot	3,1 ms	10 V/2 ms	⟿ 35
	54	⊐▷	Ignition ON	11-14 V		
	54	⊐▷	Engine idling – engine hot	3,1 ms	10 V/2 ms	⟿ 35
	26	⊐▷	Engine idling – engine hot	3,1 ms	10 V/2 ms	⟿ 35
Injector 1 – Synergie/Berlingo	27	⊐▷	Ignition ON	11-14 V		
	27	⊐▷	Engine idling – engine hot	3,1 ms	10 V/2 ms	⟿ 35
Injector 2 – Synergie/Berlingo	53	⊐▷	Ignition ON	11-14 V		
	53	⊐▷	Engine idling – engine hot	3,1 ms	10 V/2 ms	⟿ 35
Injector 3 – Synergie/Berlingo	54	⊐▷	Ignition ON	11-14 V		
	54	⊐▷	Engine idling – engine hot	3,1 ms	10 V/2 ms	⟿ 35
Injector 4 – Synergie/Berlingo	26	⊐▷	Ignition ON	11-14 V		
	26	⊐▷	Engine idling – engine hot	3,1 ms	10 V/2 ms	⟿ 35
Instrument panel – Xsara 2000→/ Synergie	47			[1]		
Instrumentation control module – engine speed signal – except Synergie/Berlingo	44	⇒	Engine idling	30 Hz	5 V/50 ms	⟿ 4
Intake air temperature (IAT) sensor	12	←	Ignition ON – air temp. 22°C	3,3 V		
Intake air temperature (IAT) sensor – Saxo/Xsara/Berlingo	37	⊐⊢	Ignition ON	0 V		
Intake air temperature (IAT) sensor – Synergie	68	⊐⊢	Ignition ON	0 V		
Knock sensor (KS)	10	←	Engine idling – accelerate briefly		50 mV/1 ms	⟿ 38
	38	←	Engine idling – accelerate briefly		50 mV/1 ms	⟿ 38
Malfunction indicator lamp (MIL) – except Berlingo	43	⊐▷	Ignition ON – MIL ON	0-1 V		
	43	⊐▷	Engine idling – MIL OFF	11-14 V		
Manifold absolute pressure (MAP) sensor	14	←	Ignition ON	4,5 V		
	14	←	Engine idling	1,2 V		
	14	←	Engine idling – accelerate briefly	4,7 V briefly		
	37	⊐⊢	Ignition ON	0 V		
	42	⇒	Ignition ON	5 V		
Multifunction control module – if fitted – except Synergie	43			[1]		
	44	⇒	Engine idling	30 Hz	5 V/50 ms	⟿ 4

★ Suggested settings - Voltage/time per division

Component/circuit description	ECM pin	Signal	Condition	Typical value	Oscilloscope setting*	Wave form
Multifunction control module – Picasso/Berlingo	22			1		
	48			1		
Multifunction control module – Picasso	47			1		
Power steering pressure (PSP) switch – except Saxo	9	←	Engine running – steering wheel not turned	0 V		
	9	←	Engine running – steering wheel turned	11-14 V		
	37	⊣—	Ignition ON	0 V		
Pulsed secondary air injection (PAIR) relay – Synergie/Berlingo	84	⊣▷	Ignition ON	11-14 V		
	84	⊣▷	Engine idling – hot	11-14 V		
Relay module	33	←	Ignition ON	11-14 V		
Relay module – except Berlingo	50	⊣▷	Ignition OFF	11-14 V		
	50	⊣▷	Ignition ON	0-1 V		
Relay module – through inertia fuel shut-off (IFS) switch – Berlingo	50	⊣▷	Ignition OFF	11-14 V		
	50	⊣▷	Ignition ON	0-1 V		
Relay module – Berlingo	15	⊣▷	Ignition ON	11-14 V		
	15	⊣▷	Engine cranking	0-1 V		
	15	⊣▷	Engine running	0-1 V		
Relay module – through inertia fuel shut-off (IFS) switch – except Berlingo	15	⊣▷	Ignition ON	11-14 V		
	15	⊣▷	Engine cranking	0-1 V		
	15	⊣▷	Engine running	0-1 V		
Throttle position (TP) sensor	41	←	Ignition ON – throttle closed	0,6 V		
	41	←	Ignition ON – throttle fully open	4,7 V		
Throttle position (TP) sensor – except Synergie/Berlingo	37	⊣—	Ignition ON	0 V		
	42	⇒	Ignition ON	5 V		
Throttle position (TP) sensor – Synergie	68	⊣—	Ignition ON	0 V		
	74	⇒	Ignition ON	5 V		
Throttle position (TP) sensor – Berlingo	37	⊣—	Ignition ON	0 V		
	74	⇒	Ignition ON	5 V		
Transmission control module (TCM) – AT – except Synergie/Berlingo	7		Ignition ON	10,8 V		
	7		Engine idling	11-14 V		
	16		Ignition ON	9,5 V		
	16		Engine idling	50 Hz		
	19	←⇒	Ignition ON	0 V		
	20	←⇒	Ignition ON	0 V		
	25		Ignition ON	5-8 V fluctuating		
	25		Engine idling	100 Hz		
	35		Ignition ON	10,6 V		
	35		Engine idling	11-14 V		
Transmission control module (TCM) – engine speed signal – except Synergie/Berlingo	44	⇒	Engine running		5 V/50 ms	∿∿ 4
Vehicle speed sensor (VSS)	17	←	Ignition ON – vehicle pushed	0 V or 11-14 V fluctuating		

*Suggested settings - Voltage/time per division

1 Connected pin - no test data available or random digital signal

CITROEN

Sagem SL96

Model:	Engine code:	Year:
Xsara 1,4	KFX (TU3JP/L3)	1998-02
Xsara 1,8 16V	LFY (XU7JP4)	1997-02
Xantia 1,8 16V	LFY (XU7JP4/L3)	1997-01

ECM harness multi-plug

Terminal side

19 18 17 16 15 14 13 12 11 10 9 8 7 6 5 4 3 2 1
37 36 35 34 33 32 31 30 29 28 27 26 25 24 23 22 21 20
55 54 53 52 51 50 49 48 47 46 45 44 43 42 41 40 39 38

AD72618

Wire side

1 2 3 4 5 6 7 8 9 10 11 12 13 14 15 16 17 18 19
20 21 22 23 24 25 26 27 28 29 30 31 32 33 34 35 36 37
38 39 40 41 42 43 44 45 46 47 48 49 50 51 52 53 54 55

AD42077

Component/circuit description	ECM pin	Signal	Condition	Typical value	Oscilloscope setting*	Wave form
Air conditioning	26	⊐▷	Engine idling – AC OFF	0-1 V		
	26	⊐▷	Engine idling – AC ON	11-14 V		
	50	▷	Engine idling – AC OFF	0-1 V		
	50	▷	Engine idling – AC ON	11-14 V		
Alarm system signal sensor	27		Ignition ON	10,6 V		
	48		Engine idling	11-14 V		
Crankshaft position (CKP) sensor	30	←	Engine idling	2,5 V ac	2 V/1 ms	Reversed ⋀⋀ 2
	49	←	Engine idling	2,5 V ac	2 V/1 ms	⋀⋀ 2
Crankshaft position (CKP) sensor – shield wire	19	⊐	Ignition ON	0 V		
Data link connector (DLC)	12		Ignition ON	9,5 V		
	31		Ignition ON	9,6 V		
	31		Engine idling	0 V		
Data link connector (DLC) – engine speed signal	42	▷	Ignition ON	11-14 V		
	42	▷	Engine idling	29 Hz		
Earth	36		Ignition ON	0 V		
	54		Ignition ON	0 V		
Engine coolant temperature (ECT) sensor	47	←	Ignition ON – coolant temp. 15°C	2,6 V		
	47	←	Ignition ON – coolant temp. 80-85°C	0,5 V		
	53	⊐	Ignition ON	0 V		
Evaporative emission (EVAP) canister purge valve	24	⊐▷	Ignition ON	11-14 V		
Heated oxygen sensor (HO2S)	4	⊐	Ignition ON	0 V		
	22	←	Engine running	0,1-1 V	0,2 V/1 sec.	⋀⋀ 21
Heated oxygen sensor (HO2S) – shield wire	19	⊐	Ignition ON	0 V		
Idle air control (IAC) valve	3	▷	Engine idling		5 V/0,2 ms	⋀⋀ 51
	20	▷	Engine idling		5 V/0,2 ms	⋀⋀ 51
	21	▷	Engine idling		5 V/0,2 ms	⋀⋀ 51
	40	▷	Engine idling		5 V/0,2 ms	⋀⋀ 51
Ignition coil – cylinders 1 & 4	55	⊐▷	Engine idling		5 V/1 ms	⋀⋀ 33
Ignition coil – cylinders 2 & 3	37	⊐▷	Engine idling		5 V/1 ms	⋀⋀ 33
Injector 1	2	⊐▷	Ignition ON	11-14 V		
	2	⊐▷	Engine idling – engine hot	2,1 ms	10 V/2 ms	⋀⋀ 35

* Suggested settings - Voltage/time per division

Autodata

Component/circuit description	ECM pin	Signal	Condition	Typical value	Oscilloscope setting*	Wave form
Injector 2	1	⊐▷	Ignition ON	11-14 V		
	1	⊐▷	Engine idling – engine hot	2,1 ms	10 V/2 ms	〰 35
Injector 3	1	⊐▷	Ignition ON	11-14 V		
	1	⊐▷	Engine idling – engine hot	2,1 ms	10 V/2 ms	〰 35
Injector 4	2	⊐▷	Ignition ON	11-14 V		
	2	⊐▷	Engine idling – engine hot	2,1 ms	10 V/2 ms	〰 35
Instrument panel – Xsara →12/99/ Xantia – engine speed signal	42	⇨	Ignition ON	11-14 V		
	42	⇨	Engine idling	29 Hz		
Intake air temperature (IAT) sensor	17	⊐—	Ignition ON	0 V		
	29	◀	Ignition ON – air temp. 15°C	2,79 V		
Knock sensor (KS)	15	◀	Engine idling – accelerate briefly		50 mV/1 ms	〰 58
	18	⊐—	Ignition ON	0 V		
Malfunction indicator lamp (MIL)	9	⊐▷	Ignition ON – MIL ON	0-1 V		
	9	⊐▷	Ignition ON – MIL OFF	11-14 V		
Manifold absolute pressure (MAP) sensor	17	⊐—	Ignition ON	0 V		
	34	⇨	Ignition ON	5 V		
	41	◀	Ignition ON	4,5 V		
	41	◀	Engine idling	1,2 V		
	41	◀	Engine idling – accelerate briefly	4,5 V briefly		
Multifunction control module – Xsara 12/99→	9	⊐▷	Ignition ON – MIL ON	0-1 V		
	9	⊐▷	Ignition ON – MIL OFF	11-14 V		
Multifunction control module – Xsara 12/99→ – engine speed signal	42	⇨	Ignition ON	11-14 V		
	42	⇨	Engine idling	29 Hz		
Power steering pressure (PSP) switch – Xsara 1,4	14	◀		1		
	17	⊐—	Ignition ON	0 V		
Power steering pressure (PSP) switch – Xsara 1,8 12/99→	10	◀		1		
Relay module	13	◀	Ignition ON	11-14 V		
	35	◀	Ignition ON	11-14 V		
	52	⊐▷	Ignition OFF	11-14 V		
	52	⊐▷	Ignition ON	0-1 V		
Relay module – through inertia fuel shut-off (IFS) switch	7	⊐▷	Ignition ON	0-1 V briefly then 11-14 V		
Throttle position (TP) sensor	16	⇨	Ignition ON	5 V		
	23	◀	Ignition ON – throttle closed	0,6 V		
	23	◀	Ignition ON – throttle fully open	4,7 V		
	53	⊐—	Ignition ON	0 V		
Trip computer – Xsara 12/99→	5	⇨	Ignition ON	11-14 V		
Vehicle speed sensor (VSS)	28	◀	Ignition ON – vehicle moving	0 V or 9-12 V fluctuating		

*Suggested settings - Voltage/time per division

1 Connected pin - no test data available or random digital signal

CITROEN
Sagem S2000

Model:	Engine code:	Year:
Xsara 1,4	KFW (TU3JP/L4)	07/01-2004

ECM harness multi-plug

Terminal side – A – Brown, B – Black, C – Grey

AD100217

Wire side – A – Brown, B – Black, C – Grey

AD100218

Component/circuit description	ECM pin	Signal	Condition	Typical value	Oscilloscope setting*	Wave form
AC refrigerant pressure sensor	Aa3			1		
	Ad4			1		
	Ae4			1		
Alternator	Bc4			1		
Crankshaft position (CKP) sensor	Cb1	←	Engine idling	2,3 V ac	2 V/1 ms	2
	Cb2	←	Engine idling	2,3 V ac	2 V/1 ms	Reversed 2
Data link connector (DLC)	Ab3			1		
	Ah2			1		
Earth	Al4	⅂	Ignition ON	0 V		
	Am4	⅂	Ignition ON	0 V		
	Bh4	⅂	Ignition ON	0 V		
	Ch1	⅂	Ignition ON	0 V		
Engine coolant blower motor relay 1 – without AC	Af2	⇒	Coolant blower motor OFF	0 V		
	Af2	⇒	Coolant blower motor ON	11-14 V		
Engine coolant blower motor relay 1 – with AC	Ak4	⅂▷	Ignition OFF	0-1 V		
	Ak4	⅂▷	Ignition ON – engine coolant blower motor OFF	11-14 V		
	Ak4	⅂▷	Ignition ON – engine coolant blower motor ON	0 V		
Engine coolant blower motor relay 2 – with AC	Af2	⇒	Coolant blower motor OFF	0 V		
	Af2	⇒	Coolant blower motor ON	11-14 V		
	Aj4	←	Engine running – coolant blower motor OFF	11-14 V		
	Aj4	←	Engine running – coolant blower motor ON	0 V		

* Suggested settings - Voltage/time per division

Component/circuit description	ECM pin	Signal	Condition	Typical value	Oscilloscope setting*	Wave form
Engine coolant temperature (ECT) sensor	Bd4	⊣⌐	Ignition ON	0 V		
	Be4	⬅	Engine idling – coolant temp. 10°C	3-3,5 V switching	2 V/0,1 sec.	101
	Be4	⬅	Engine idling – coolant temp. 80°C	3-3,5 V switching	2 V/0,2 sec.	18
Evaporative emission (EVAP) canister purge valve	Cf2	⊣▷	Ignition ON	11-14 V briefly then 0-1 V		
	Cf2	⊣▷	Engine running		10 V/50 ms	20
Heated oxygen sensor (HO2S) 1 – before cat	Be2	⬅	Engine idling	0,1-0,9 V	4 V/0,2 sec.	4
	Ca3	⬅	Engine idling	0,1-0,8 V		
	Cb3	⊣⌐	Engine idling	0 V		
Heated oxygen sensor (HO2S) 2 – after cat	Bd2	⊣▷	Ignition ON	11-14 V briefly then 0-1 V		
	Bd2	⊣▷	Engine idling	0-1 V		
	Bd3	⊣⌐	Engine idling	0 V		
	Be3	⬅	Engine idling	0,1-0,8 V		
Idle air control (IAC) valve	Cd1	⇨	Engine idling		5 V/0,5 sec.	Intermittent 26
	Cd2	⇨	Engine idling		5 V/0,5 sec.	Intermittent 26
	Cd3	⇨	Engine idling		5 V/0,5 sec.	Intermittent 26
	Ce3	⇨	Engine idling		5 V/0,5 sec.	Intermittent 26
Ignition coil	Bf3	⬅	Ignition ON	11-14 V briefly then 0-1 V		
	Bf3	⬅	Engine running		5 V/50 μs	100
	Bg3	⊣▷	Ignition ON	11-14 V briefly then 0-1 V		
	Bg3	⊣▷	Engine idling		5 V/2 ms	33
	Bh3	⊣▷	Ignition ON	11-14 V briefly then 0-1 V		
	Bh3	⊣▷	Engine idling		5 V/2 ms	33
Injector 1	Ch2	⊣▷	Ignition ON	11-14 V briefly then 0-1 V		
	Ch2	⊣▷	Engine idling	4 ms	10 V/2 ms	35
Injector 2	Cg3	⊣▷	Ignition ON	11-14 V briefly then 0-1 V		
	Cg3	⊣▷	Engine idling	4 ms	10 V/2 ms	35
Injector 3	Cg2	⊣▷	Ignition ON	11-14 V briefly then 0-1 V		
	Cg2	⊣▷	Engine idling	4 ms	10 V/2 ms	35
Injector 4	Ch3	⊣▷	Ignition ON	11-14 V briefly then 0-1 V		
	Ch3	⊣▷	Engine idling	4 ms	10 V/2 ms	35
Intake air temperature (IAT) sensor	Ba2	⬅	Ignition ON – air temp. 20°C	2,35 V		
	Ca2	⊣⌐	Ignition ON	0 V		
Knock sensor (KS)	Bb3	⬅	Ignition ON	2,5 V		
	Bb3	⬅	Engine idling – accelerate briefly		50 mV/1 ms	38
	Bc3	⬅	Ignition ON	2,5 V		
	Bc3	⬅	Engine idling – accelerate briefly		50 mV/1 ms	38

* Suggested settings - Voltage/time per division

Component/circuit description	ECM pin	Signal	Condition	Typical value	Oscilloscope setting*	Wave form
Manifold absolute pressure (MAP) sensor	Ca2	⌐—	Ignition ON	0 V		
	Cc1	⬅	Ignition ON	4,2 V		
	Cc1	⬅	Engine idling	1,8 V		
	Cc1	⬅	Engine idling – accelerate briefly	4,4 V		
	Ce1	⇨	Ignition ON	5 V		
Multifunction control module 1 – CAN data bus	Ah3	⬅⇨		1		
	Ah4	⬅⇨		1		
Multifunction control module 2	Ab4	⬅	Ignition ON	11-14 V		
	Ba4	⬅	Ignition ON	11-14 V		
	Bf2	⊐⇨	Ignition OFF	11-14 V		
	Bf2	⊐⇨	Ignition ON	0-1 V		
	Cf3	⊐⇨	Ignition ON	0,1 V briefly then 11-14 V		
Power steering pressure (PSP) switch	Ae3	⬅	Engine running – steering wheel not turned	0 V		
	Ae3	⬅	Engine running – steering wheel turned	11-14 V		
Throttle position (TP) sensor	Ba3	⌐—	Ignition ON	0 V		
	Bb4	⬅	Ignition ON – throttle closed	0,5 V		
	Bb4	⬅	Ignition ON – throttle fully open	4 V		
	Cc3	⇨	Ignition ON	5 V		
Vehicle speed sensor (VSS)	Ag2	⬅	Ignition OFF	10,8 V		
	Ag2	⬅	Ignition ON – vehicle pushed	0 V or 11-14 V switching		
	Bh4	⌐—		0 V		

*Suggested settings - Voltage/time per division

1 Connected pin - no test data available or random digital signal

Model:	Engine code:	Year:
Xsara 2,0	RFV (XU10J4R)	1998-02
Xantia 2,0 16V	RFV (XU10J4R)	1995-01
XM 2,0 16V	RFV (XU10J4R)	1993-00

CITROEN
Bosch Motronic
MP5.1.1/5.2

ECM harness multi-plug

Terminal side

19 18 17 16 15 14 13 12 11 10 9 8 7 6 5 4 3 2 1
37 36 35 34 33 32 31 30 29 28 27 26 25 24 23 22 21 20
55 54 53 52 51 50 49 48 47 46 45 44 43 42 41 40 39 38

AD72618

Wire side

1 2 3 4 5 6 7 8 9 10 11 12 13 14 15 16 17 18 19
20 21 22 23 24 25 26 27 28 29 30 31 32 33 34 35 36 37
38 39 40 41 42 43 44 45 46 47 48 49 50 51 52 53 54 55

AD42077

Component/circuit description	ECM pin	Signal	Condition	Typical value	Oscilloscope setting★	Wave form
Air conditioning	23			1		
	32			1		
Air conditioning – XM	34			1		
Battery	18	←	Ignition OFF	11-14 V		
Coded keypad – some models	22			1		
	35	←		1		
Crankshaft position (CKP) sensor	11	⌐	Ignition ON	0 V		
	30	←	Engine idling	2,3 V ac	2 V/1 ms	2
	30	←	3000 rpm	3,9 V ac	2 V/1 ms	2
Data link connector (DLC)	6	⇒		1		
	13			1		
	16			1		
Earth	2		Ignition ON	0 V		
	14		Ignition ON	0 V		
	19		Ignition ON	0 V		
Engine coolant temperature (ECT) sensor	25	←	Ignition ON – coolant temp. 20°C	3,5 V		
	25	←	Ignition ON – coolant temp. 80°C	1 V		
	26	⌐	Ignition ON	0 V		
Evaporative emission (EVAP) canister purge valve	5	⌐▷	Ignition OFF	11-14 V		
	5	⌐▷	Engine running		10 V/50 ms	20
Heated oxygen sensor (HO2S)	10	⌐	Ignition ON	0 V		
	28	←	Engine idling – accelerate briefly	0,1-1 V fluctuating	0,2 V/1 sec.	21
Idle air control (IAC) valve	15 (33)	⇒	Engine idling		5 V/0,5 sec.	Intermittent 26
	21 (24)	⇒	Engine idling		5 V/0,5 sec.	Intermittent 26
	24 (21)	⇒	Engine idling		5 V/0,5 sec.	Intermittent 26
	33 (15)	⇒	Engine idling		5 V/0,5 sec.	Intermittent 26
Ignition coil – cylinders 1 & 4	1	⌐▷	Engine idling		5 V/2 ms	33
Ignition coil – cylinders 2 & 3	20	⌐▷	Engine idling		5 V/2 ms	33
Ignition switch – through relay module – except XM	34	←	Ignition ON	11-14 V		
Immobilizer control module – some models	22			1		
	35	←		1		

★ Suggested settings - Voltage/time per division

Component/circuit description	ECM pin	Signal	Condition	Typical value	Oscilloscope setting*	Wave form
Inertia fuel shut-off (IFS) switch – some models	3	⊐⊳	Ignition ON	0-1 V briefly then 11-14 V		
	3	⊐⊳	Engine cranking	0-1 V		
	3	⊐⊳	Engine running	0-1 V		
Injectors	17	⊐⊳	Ignition ON	11-14 V		
	17	⊐⊳	Engine idling	2,1 ms	10 V/2 ms	Ⓜ 35
	17	⊐⊳	3000 rpm	1,8 ms	10 V/2 ms	Ⓜ 35
Intake air temperature (IAT) sensor	26	⊐⊢	Ignition ON	0 V		
	27	⇐	Ignition ON – air temp. 20°C	3,5 V		
Knock sensor (KS)	8	⇐	Engine idling – accelerate briefly		50 mV/1 ms	Ⓜ 38
	26	⊐⊢	Ignition ON	0 V		
Malfunction indicator lamp (MIL) – some models	22	⊐⊳	Ignition ON – MIL ON	0-1 V		
	22	⊐⊳	Engine idling – MIL OFF	11-14 V		
Manifold absolute pressure (MAP) sensor	7	⇐	Ignition ON	4,4 V		
	7	⇐	Engine idling	1,3 V		
	7	⇐	Accelerate briefly	1,3-4,4 V		
	12	⇒	Ignition ON	5 V		
	26	⊐⊢	Ignition ON	0 V		
Power steering pressure (PSP) switch – some models	50	⇐	Ignition ON – steering wheel not turned	0 V		
	50	⇐	Ignition ON – steering wheel turned	11-14 V		
Relay module – some models	3	⊐⊳	Ignition ON	0-1 V briefly then 11-14 V		
	3	⊐⊳	Engine cranking	0-1 V		
	3	⊐⊳	Engine running	0-1 V		
	36	⊐⊳	Ignition OFF	11-14 V		
	36	⊐⊳	Ignition ON	0-1 V		
Relay module	37	⇐	Ignition ON	11-14 V		
Starter motor inhibitor switch relay – AT	31			[1]		
Tachometer	6	⇒	Engine idling	30 Hz		
	6	⇒	3000 rpm	100 Hz		
Throttle position (TP) sensor	12	⇒	Ignition ON	5 V		
	26	⊐⊢	Ignition ON	0 V		
	29	⇐	Ignition ON – throttle closed	0,4 V		
	29	⇐	Ignition ON – throttle fully open	4,5 V		
Trip computer	4			[1]		
Vehicle speed sensor (VSS)	9	⇐	Ignition ON – vehicle moving	Voltage varies with vehicle speed		

*Suggested settings - Voltage/time per division

[1] Connected pin - no test data available or random digital signal

Model:	Engine code:	Year:
Xsara 2,0 HDi	RHY (DW10TD)	2001-06
C5 2,0 HDi	RHY (DW10TD)	2001-04

CITROEN

Siemens SID 801

ECM harness multi-plug

Terminal side – A – Grey, B – Brown, C – Black

C

h1	g1	f1	e1	d1	c1	b1	a1
h2	g2	f2	e2	d2	c2	b2	a2
h3	g3	f3	e3	d3	c3	b3	a3
h4	g4	f4	e4	d4	c4	b4	a4

B

m1	l1	k1	j1	h1	g1	f1	e1	d1	c1	b1	a1
m2	l2	k2	j2	h2	g2	f2	e2	d2	c2	b2	a2
m3	l3	k3	j3	h3	g3	f3	e3	d3	c3	b3	a3
m4	l4	k4	j4	h4	g4	f4	e4	d4	c4	b4	a4

A

a4	b4	c4	d4	e4	f4	g4	h4
a3	b3	c3	d3	e3	f3	g3	h3
a2	b2	c2	d2	e2	f2	g2	h2
a1	b1	c1	d1	e1	f1	g1	h1

AD22744

Wire side – A – Grey, B – Brown, C – Black

A

h4	g4	f4	e4	d4	c4	b4	a4
h3	g3	f3	e3	d3	c3	b3	a3
h2	g2	f2	e2	d2	c2	b2	a2
h1	g1	f1	e1	d1	c1	b1	a1

B

a1	b1	c1	d1	e1	f1	g1	h1	j1	k1	l1	m1
a2	b2	c2	d2	e2	f2	g2	h2	j2	k2	l2	m2
a3	b3	c3	d3	e3	f3	g3	h3	j3	k3	l3	m3
a4	b4	c4	d4	e4	f4	g4	h4	j4	k4	l4	m4

C

a1	b1	c1	d1	e1	f1	g1	h1
a2	b2	c2	d2	e2	f2	g2	h2
a3	b3	c3	d3	e3	f3	g3	h3
a4	b4	c4	d4	e4	f4	g4	h4

AD22743

Component/circuit description	ECM pin	Signal	Condition	Typical value	Oscilloscope setting*	Wave form
AC refrigerant pressure sensor	Cf2	⇒	Ignition ON	5 V		
	Cf4	⌐	Ignition ON	0 V		
	Ch2	⟵	Ignition OFF	0 V		
	Ch2	⟵	Ignition ON	0,8 V		
Accelerator pedal position (APP) sensor	Cc2	⟵	Ignition ON – accelerator pedal released	0,2 V		
	Cc2	⟵	Ignition ON – accelerator pedal depressed	1,85 V		
	Cg2	⇒	Ignition ON	5 V		
	Cg3	⟵	Ignition ON – accelerator pedal released	0,4 V		
	Cg3	⟵	Ignition ON – accelerator pedal depressed	3,7 V		
	Ch3	⌐	Ignition ON	0 V		
Camshaft position (CMP) sensor	Aa1	⌐	Ignition ON	0 V		
	Ad1	⟵	Engine idling		2 V/50 ms	∿ 64
	Bc3	⇒	Ignition ON	5 V		
Clutch pedal position (CPP) switch	Ce3	⟵	Ignition ON – clutch pedal released	11-14 V		
	Ce3	⟵	Ignition ON – clutch pedal depressed	0 V		
Crankshaft position (CKP) sensor	Bj4	⟵	Engine idling	1,4 V ac	1 V/2 ms	Reversed ∿ 1
	Bk4	⟵	Engine idling	1,4 V ac	1 V/2 ms	∿ 1
Data link connector (DLC)	Cb4	⟷	Ignition ON	0 V		
Earth	Ah2		Ignition ON	0 V		
	Bk2		Ignition ON	0 V		
	Cg4		Ignition ON	0 V		
	Ch4		Ignition ON	0 V		

* Suggested settings - Voltage/time per division

Component/circuit description	ECM pin	Signal	Condition	Typical value	Oscilloscope setting*	Wave form
Engine coolant blower motor relay I	Cd4		Ignition ON	11-14 V		
Engine coolant blower motor relay II	Cb2	⊐▷	Ignition ON	11-14 V		
	Cc4		Ignition ON	0 V		
Engine coolant heater relay	Cb1	⊐▷	Ignition ON	11-14 V		
	Cc1	⊐▷	Ignition ON	11-14 V		
Engine coolant temperature (ECT) sensor	Be1	⊐—	Ignition ON	0 V		
	Be4	◀—	Coolant temp. 85°C	0,9 V		
Exhaust gas recirculation (EGR) solenoid 1	Ag1	⊐▷	Ignition ON		2 V/2 ms	66
	Ag1	⊐▷	Engine idling	41%	2 V/5 ms	10
Exhaust gas recirculation (EGR) solenoid 2	Ah3	⊐▷	Engine idling		2 V/5 ms	37
Fuel pressure control solenoid	Ah1	⊐▷	Ignition ON	11-14 V		
	Ah1	⊐▷	Engine idling		2 V/2 ms	37
Fuel pressure sensor	Ad3	◀—	Ignition ON	0,5 V		
	Bd1	⇨	Ignition ON	5 V		
	Bf2	⊐—	Ignition ON	0 V		
Fuel temperature sensor	Bf3	◀—	Engine idling – coolant temp. 85°C	1,3 V		
	Bh4	⊐—	Ignition ON	0 V		
Glow plug timer relay	Ac1		Ignition ON	0 V		
	Be2		Ignition ON	11-14 V		
Injector 1	Bl3	⇨	Ignition ON	110 V		
	Bl3	⇨	Engine idling	0,4 ms pilot + 0,7 ms main		
	Bl3	⇨	Engine idling		20 V/0,5 ms	68
	Bm2	⇨	Ignition ON	110 V		
	Bm2	⇨	Engine idling	0,4 ms pilot + 0,7 ms main		
	Bm2	⇨	Engine idling		20 V/0,5 ms	68
Injector 2	Bl1	⇨	Ignition ON	110 V		
	Bl1	⇨	Engine idling	0,4 ms pilot + 0,7 ms main		
	Bl1	⇨	Engine idling		20 V/0,5 ms	68
	Bl4	⇨	Ignition ON	110 V		
	Bl4	⇨	Engine idling	0,4 ms pilot + 0,7 ms main		
	Bl4	⇨	Engine idling		20 V/0,5 ms	68
Injector 3	Bl2	⇨	Ignition ON	110 V		
	Bl2	⇨	Engine idling	0,4 ms pilot + 0,7 ms main		
	Bl2	⇨	Engine idling		20 V/0,5 ms	68
	Bm3	⇨	Ignition ON	110 V		
	Bm3	⇨	Engine idling	0,4 ms pilot + 0,7 ms main		
	Bm3	⇨	Engine idling		20 V/0,5 ms	68

* Suggested settings - Voltage/time per division

Component/circuit description	ECM pin	Signal	Condition	Typical value	Oscilloscope setting*	Wave form
Injector 4	Bm1	⇒	Ignition ON	110 V		
	Bm1	⇒	Engine idling	0,4 ms pilot + 0,7 ms main		
	Bm1	⇒	Engine idling		20 V/0,5 ms	∿∿ 68
	Bm4	⇒	Ignition ON	110 V		
	Bm4	⇒	Engine idling	0,4 ms pilot + 0,7 ms main		
	Bm4	⇒	Engine idling		20 V/0,5 ms	∿∿ 68
Intake air temperature (IAT) sensor	Be3	⇐	Ignition ON – air temp. 19°C	2,5 V		
Mass air flow (MAF) sensor	Aa3	⇐	Ignition ON	0,6 V		
	Aa3	⇐	Engine idling	2,6 V		
	Ab3	�;⊣	Ignition ON	0 V		
	Bg2	⊣	Ignition ON	0 V		
Multifunction control module 1 – CAN data bus – high	Ca4	⇔		1		
Multifunction control module 1 – CAN data bus – low	Ca3	⇔		1		
Multifunction control module 2	Ae3	⇐	Ignition ON	11-14 V		
	Af2	⇐	Ignition ON	11-14 V		
	Af3	⇐	Ignition ON	11-14 V		
	Cc3	⇐	Ignition ON	11-14 V		
3rd piston cut-off solenoid	Ag3	⊣⇒	Ignition ON	11-14 V for 2 secs then 0 V		
	Ag3	⊣⇒	Engine idling	11-14 V		
	Ag3	⊣⇒	Engine under full load	0-1 V		

*Suggested settings - Voltage/time per division

1 Connected pin - no test data available or random digital signal

CITROEN

Bosch Motronic MP5.1.1

Model:	Engine code:	Year:
Xantia 1,8 16V	LFY (XU7JP4)	1995-01

ECM harness multi-plug

Terminal side

19 18 17 16 15 14 13 12 11 10 9 8 7 6 5 4 3 2 1
37 36 35 34 33 32 31 30 29 28 27 26 25 24 23 22 21 20
55 54 53 52 51 50 49 48 47 46 45 44 43 42 41 40 39 38

AD72618

Wire side

1 2 3 4 5 6 7 8 9 10 11 12 13 14 15 16 17 18 19
20 21 22 23 24 25 26 27 28 29 30 31 32 33 34 35 36 37
38 39 40 41 42 43 44 45 46 47 48 49 50 51 52 53 54 55

AD42077

Component/circuit description	ECM pin	Signal	Condition	Typical value	Oscilloscope setting*	Wave form
Air conditioning	23			1		
	32			1		
Battery	18	←	Ignition OFF	11-14 V		
Coded keypad – some models	22			1		
	35	←		1		
Crankshaft position (CKP) sensor	11	⌐—	Ignition ON	0 V		
	30	←	Engine idling	2,3 V ac	2 V/1 ms	2
Data link connector (DLC)	6	⇨		1		
	13			1		
	16			1		
	22	⌐⇨	Ignition ON – MIL ON	0-1 V		
	22	⌐⇨	Engine idling – MIL OFF	11-14 V		
Earth	2		Ignition ON	0 V		
	14		Ignition ON	0 V		
	19		Ignition ON	0 V		
Engine coolant temperature (ECT) sensor	25	←	Ignition ON – coolant temp. 20°C	3,5 V		
	25	←	Ignition ON – coolant temp. 80°C	1 V		
	26	⌐—	Ignition ON	0 V		
Evaporative emission (EVAP) canister purge valve	5	⌐⇨	Ignition ON	11-14 V		
	5	⌐⇨	Engine running		10 V/50 ms	20
Heated oxygen sensor (HO2S)	10	⌐—	Ignition ON	0 V		
	28	←	Engine idling – accelerate briefly	0,1-1 V fluctuating	0,2 V/1 sec.	21
Idle air control (IAC) valve	15 (33)	⇨	Engine idling		5 V/0,5 sec.	Intermittent 26
	21 (24)	⇨	Engine idling		5 V/0,5 sec.	Intermittent 26
	24 (21)	⇨	Engine idling		5 V/0,5 sec.	Intermittent 26
	33 (15)	⇨	Engine idling		5 V/0,5 sec.	Intermittent 26
Ignition coil – cylinders 1 & 4	1	⌐⇨	Engine idling		5 V/2 ms	33
Ignition coil – cylinders 2 & 3	20	⌐⇨	Engine idling		5 V/2 ms	33

* Suggested settings - Voltage/time per division

Autodata

Component/circuit description	ECM pin	Signal	Condition	Typical value	Oscilloscope setting*	Wave form
Ignition switch – some models	35	⬅	Ignition ON	11-14 V		
Injectors	17	⊐▷	Ignition ON	11-14 V		
	17	⊐▷	Engine idling	2,1 ms	10 V/2 ms	∿ 35
	17	⊐▷	3000 rpm	1,8 ms	10 V/2 ms	∿ 35
Intake air temperature (IAT) sensor	26	⊐⊢	Ignition ON	0 V		
	27	⬅	Ignition ON – air temp. 20°C	3,5 V		
Knock sensor (KS)	8	⬅	Engine idling – accelerate briefly		50 mV/1 ms	∿ 38
	26	⊐⊢	Ignition ON	0 V		
Malfunction indicator lamp (MIL)	22	⊐▷	Ignition ON – MIL ON	0-1 V		
	22	⊐▷	Engine idling – MIL OFF	11-14 V		
Manifold absolute pressure (MAP) sensor	7	⬅	Ignition ON	4,4 V		
	7	⬅	Engine idling	1,3 V		
	7	⬅	Accelerate briefly	1,3-4,4 V		
	12	⇨	Ignition ON	5 V		
	26	⊐⊢	Ignition ON	0 V		
Relay module	3	⊐▷	Ignition ON	0-1 V briefly then 11-14 V		
	3	⊐▷	Engine cranking	0-1 V		
	37	⬅	Ignition ON	11-14 V		
Relay module – some models	36	⊐▷	Ignition OFF	11-14 V		
	36	⊐▷	Ignition ON	0-1 V		
Starter motor inhibitor switch relay	31			1		
Tachometer	6	⇨	Engine idling	30 Hz		
	6	⇨	3000 rpm	100 Hz		
Throttle position (TP) sensor	12	⇨	Ignition ON	5 V		
	26	⊐⊢	Ignition ON	0 V		
	29	⬅	Ignition ON – throttle closed	0,4 V		
	29	⬅	Ignition ON – throttle fully open	4,5 V		
Vehicle speed sensor (VSS) – some models	9	⬅	Ignition ON – vehicle moving	Voltage varies with vehicle speed		

*Suggested settings - Voltage/time per division

1 Connected pin - no test data available or random digital signal

CITROEN

Bosch Motronic MP3.2

Model:	Engine code:	Year:
Xantia 2,0 16V	RFY	1993-97
Xantia 2,0 Turbo	RGX	1995-01
XM 2,0 Turbo	RGX (XU10J2TE)	1994-00
Synergie 2,0 Turbo	RGX (XU10J2CTE)	1994-00

ECM harness multi-plug

Terminal side

19 18 17 16 15 14 13 12 11 10 9 8 7 6 5 4 3 2 1
37 36 35 34 33 32 31 30 29 28 27 26 25 24 23 22 21 20
55 54 53 52 51 50 49 48 47 46 45 44 43 42 41 40 39 38

AD72618

Wire side

1 2 3 4 5 6 7 8 9 10 11 12 13 14 15 16 17 18 19
20 21 22 23 24 25 26 27 28 29 30 31 32 33 34 35 36 37
38 39 40 41 42 43 44 45 46 47 48 49 50 51 52 53 54 55

AD42077

Component/circuit description	ECM pin	Signal	Condition	Typical value	Oscilloscope setting*	Wave form
Air conditioning	41	←		1		
	40	←		1		
Air conditioning – some models	23	←		1		
Battery	18	←	Ignition OFF	11-14 V		
Coded keypad – some models	2			1		
	13			1		
	50			1		
Camshaft position (CMP) sensor – RFY	8	←	Ignition ON	0 V or 5 V		
	8	←	Engine idling	4 V	2 V/20 ms	⎍ 12
Crankshaft position (CKP) sensor	48 (49)	←	Engine idling		2 V/1 ms	⎍ 2
Data link connector (DLC)	13			1		
	43	⇒		1		
	55	⇒		1		
Data link connector (DLC) – some models	2			1		
Earth	14		Ignition ON	0 V		
	19		Ignition ON	0 V		
	24		Ignition ON	0 V		
Earth – some models	54		Ignition ON	0 V		
Earth – XM – AT	47		Ignition ON	0 V		
Engine coolant temperature (ECT) sensor	26	⅂	Ignition ON	0 V		
	45	←	Ignition ON – coolant temp. 10°C	3,2 V		
	45	←	Ignition ON – coolant temp. 80°C	0,7 V		
Evaporative emission (EVAP) canister purge valve	5	⅂▷	Ignition ON	11-14 V		
	5	⅂▷	Engine idling – engine hot	0%		
	5	⅂▷	Engine running – accelerate briefly	1-99%	10 V/50 ms	⎍ 20
Heated oxygen sensor (HO2S)	10	⅂	Ignition ON	0 V		
	28	←	Engine idling – accelerate briefly	0-1 V fluctuating	0,2 V/1 sec.	⎍ 21
Heated oxygen sensor (HO2S) – shield wire – some models	19	⅂	Ignition ON	0 V		
	47	⅂	Ignition ON	0 V		
Idle air control (IAC) valve	4	⅂▷	Engine idling		5 V/5 ms	Intermittent ⎍ 25
	22	⅂▷	Engine idling		5 V/5 ms	Intermittent ⎍ 25

★ Suggested settings - Voltage/time per division

Component/circuit description	ECM pin	Signal	Condition	Typical value	Oscilloscope setting*	Wave form
Ignition amplifier – RFY – cylinders 1 & 4	1	⇨	Engine idling		2 V/0,1 sec.	〰 32
Ignition amplifier – RFY – cylinders 1 & 4	20	⇨	Engine idling		2 V/0,1 sec.	〰 32
Ignition amplifier – RFY – cylinders 2 & 3	38	⇨	Engine idling		2 V/0,1 sec.	〰 32
Ignition amplifier – RFY – cylinders 2 & 3	21	⇨	Engine idling		2 V/0,1 sec.	〰 32
Ignition amplifier – RGX	1	⇨	Engine idling		2 V/0,1 sec.	〰 32
Ignition amplifier – RGX	20	⇨	Engine idling		2 V/0,1 sec.	〰 32
Ignition switch – through relay module	27	⇦	Ignition OFF	0 V		
	27	⇦	Ignition ON	11-14 V		
Immobilizer control module – some models	2			[1]		
	50			[1]		
Inertia fuel shut-off (IFS) switch – some models	3	⌐▷	Ignition ON	0-1 V briefly then 11-14 V		
	3	⌐▷	Engine cranking	0-1 V		
	3	⌐▷	Engine idling	0-1 V		
Injector 1	17	⌐▷	Ignition ON	11-14 V		
	17	⌐▷	Engine idling	2,7 ms	10 V/2 ms	〰 35
Injector 2	34	⌐▷	Ignition ON	11-14 V		
	34	⌐▷	Engine idling	2,7 ms	10 V/2 ms	〰 35
Injector 3	16	⌐▷	Ignition ON	11-14 V		
	16	⌐▷	Engine idling	2,7 ms	10 V/2 ms	〰 35
Injector 4	35	⌐▷	Ignition ON	11-14 V		
	35	⌐▷	Engine idling	2,7 ms	10 V/2 ms	〰 35
Intake air temperature (IAT) sensor	26	⌐	Ignition ON	0 V		
	44	⇦	Ignition ON – air temp. 10°C	3,2 V		
Intake manifold air control solenoid – RFY	6	⌐▷	Ignition ON	11-14 V		
	6	⌐▷	Engine idling	11-14 V		
	6	⌐▷	Engine idling – accelerate briefly	0-1 V – briefly		
Knock sensor (KS)	11 (30)	⇦	Engine idling – accelerate briefly		50 mV/1 ms	〰 38
Malfunction indicator lamp (MIL) – some models	2	⌐▷	Ignition ON – MIL ON	0 V		
	2	⌐▷	Engine running – MIL OFF	11-14 V		
Park/neutral position (PNP) switch – AT	47	⇦	Ignition ON – AT in P or N	11-14 V		
	47	⇦	Ignition ON – AT not in P or N	0 V		
Relay module	3	⌐▷	Ignition ON	0-1 V briefly then 11-14 V		
	3	⌐▷	Engine idling	0-1 V		
	36	⌐▷	Ignition OFF	11-14 V		
	36	⌐▷	Ignition ON	0-1 V		
	37	⇦	Ignition ON	11-14 V		
Tachometer	43	⇨	Engine idling	30 Hz		
	43	⇨	3000 rpm	100 Hz		
Throttle position (TP) sensor	12	⇨	Ignition ON	5 V		
	26	⌐	Ignition ON	0 V		
	53	⇦	Ignition ON – throttle closed	0,4 V		
	53	⇦	Ignition ON – throttle fully open	4,5 V		
Turbocharger (TC) wastegate regulating valve – RGX	6	⌐▷	Engine idling	11-14 V		
	6	⌐▷	Engine idling – full load	0-1 V		
Vehicle speed sensor (VSS)	9	⇦	Vehicle pushed		5 V/2 secs.	〰 43

*Suggested settings - Voltage/time per division

[1] Connected pin - no test data available or random digital signal

CITROEN

Bosch EDC 15C2 HDI

Model:	Engine code:	Year:
Xantia 2,0 HDi	DW10TD (RHY)	1998-01
Xantia 2,0 HDi	DW10ATED (RHZ)	1998-01
Berlingo 2,0 HDi	DW10TD (RHY)	1999-06

ECM harness multi-plug

Terminal side

AD20174

Wire side

AD20176

Component/circuit description	ECM pin	Signal	Condition	Typical value
AC compressor clutch relay	78	←		1
AC control module	84	⇥▷		1
AC control module – Xantia	47	←		1
AC refrigerant triple pressure switch – Berlingo	47	←		1
Accelerator pedal position (APP) sensor	15	←	Ignition ON – accelerator pedal released	0,5 V
	15	←	Ignition ON – accelerator pedal depressed	3,5 V
	22	⊣⁻	Engine idling	0 V
	44	⇨	Ignition ON	5 V
	68	←	Ignition ON – accelerator pedal released	0,2 V
	68	←	Ignition ON – accelerator pedal depressed	2 V
Brake pedal position (BPP) switch	48	←	Ignition ON – brake pedal released	0 V
	48	←	Ignition ON – brake pedal depressed	11-14 V
Camshaft position (CMP) sensor	12	⇨	Ignition ON	5 V
	18	←	Engine idling	5 V/50 ms per division ∿ 26
	18	←	Ignition ON	11 V
	40	⊣⁻	Engine idling	0 V
Clutch pedal position (CPP) switch	21	←	Engine idling – clutch pedal released	11-14 V
	21	←	Engine idling – clutch pedal depressed	0 V
Crankshaft position (CKP) sensor	14	←	Engine idling	1,7 V ac
	14 (41)	←	Engine idling	2 V/1 ms per division ∿ 6
	41	←	Engine idling	1,72 V ac
	41 (14)	←	Engine idling	2 V/1 ms per division – wave form reversed ∿ 6
Data link connector (DLC)	10		Ignition ON	0 V
	38		Ignition ON	0 V
	62	⇨	Engine idling	28 Hz
	62	⇨	Ignition ON	0 V

Autodata

Component/circuit description	ECM pin	Signal	Condition	Typical value
Data link connector (DLC) – some models	8	←	Ignition ON – coolant blower motor OFF	0 V
	8	←	Ignition ON – coolant blower motor ON	11-14 V
Earth	33		Ignition ON	0 V
	49		Ignition ON	0 V
	51		Ignition ON	0 V
	53		Ignition ON	0 V
Engine coolant blower motor relay I – Berlingo – without AC	25	⊐▷	Engine idling – coolant blower motor OFF	11-14 V
	25	⊐▷	Engine idling – coolant blower motor ON	0-1 V
Engine coolant blower motor relay I/III – except Berlingo – without AC	25	⊐▷	Engine idling – coolant blower motor OFF	11-14 V
	25	⊐▷	Engine idling – coolant blower motor ON	0-1 V
Engine coolant blower motor relay I/III – some models	8		Ignition ON – coolant blower motor OFF	0 V
	8		Ignition ON – coolant blower motor ON	11-14 V
Engine coolant blower motor relay II	83	⊐▷	Ignition OFF	0 V
	83	⊐▷	Ignition ON	11-14 V
	83	⊐▷	Engine idling – coolant blower motor OFF	11-14 V
	83	⊐▷	Engine idling – coolant blower motor ON	0-1 V
Engine coolant heater relay – Berlingo	58	⊐▷	Ignition ON – engine coolant heater OFF	11-14 V
	58	⊐▷	Ignition ON – engine coolant heater ON	0-1 V
	85	⊐▷	Ignition ON – engine coolant heater OFF	11-14 V
	85	⊐▷	Ignition ON – engine coolant heater ON	0-1 V
Engine coolant heater relay II – Xantia	58	⊐▷	Ignition ON – engine coolant heater OFF	11-14 V
	58	⊐▷	Ignition ON – engine coolant heater ON	0-1 V
	85	⊐▷	Ignition ON – engine coolant heater OFF	11-14 V
	85	⊐▷	Ignition ON – engine coolant heater ON	0-1 V
Engine coolant temperature (ECT) sensor	45	⊐	Engine idling	0 V
	46	←	Ignition ON – coolant temp. 20°C	3,2 V
	46	←	Ignition ON – coolant temp. 80°C	0,7 V
Exhaust gas recirculation (EGR) solenoid I	52	⊐▷	Ignition ON	11-14 V for 2 seconds then 0 V
	52	⊐▷	Engine idling	25%
	52	⊐▷	Engine idling	5 V/2 ms per division 〰 29
Exhaust gas recirculation (EGR) solenoid II – some models	55	⊐▷	Ignition ON	11-14 V for 2 seconds then 0 V
Fuel pressure control solenoid	50	⊐▷	4000 rpm	23-25%
	50	⊐▷	Engine idling	11-14 V
	50	⊐▷	Engine idling	1000 Hz
	50	⊐▷	Engine idling	15-17%
	50	⊐▷	Engine idling	2 V/1 ms per division 〰 37
	50	⊐▷	Ignition ON	10 V

Component/circuit description	ECM pin	Signal	Condition	Typical value
Fuel pressure sensor	34	⌐⌐	Engine idling	0 V
	44	⇨	Ignition ON	5 V
	74	⟵	3000 rpm	1,97 V
	74	⟵	Engine cranking	1,3 V
	74	⟵	Engine idling	1,3 V
	74	⟵	Ignition ON	0,5 V
Fuel temperature sensor	39	⟵	Ignition ON – air temp. 20°C	2,7 V
	40	⌐⌐	Engine idling	0 V
Glow plug timer relay	67		Ignition ON – glow plugs OFF	0 V
	67		Ignition ON – glow plugs ON	11-14 V
	88		Ignition ON – glow plugs OFF	11-14 V
	88		Ignition ON – glow plugs ON	0 V
Glow plug warning lamp	56	⇨	Ignition ON – lamp ON	11-14 V
	56	⇨	Ignition ON – lamp OFF	0 V
Ignition switch	69	⟵	Ignition OFF	0 V
	69	⟵	Ignition ON	11-14 V
Immobilizer control module	36	⟺		1
	66			1
Inertia fuel shut-off (IFS) switch	87	⟵	Engine idling – button depressed	0-1 V
	87	⟵	Ignition ON – button depressed	0-1 V for 2 seconds then 11-14 V
	87	⟵	Ignition ON – button released	0 V
Injector 1	2	⇨	Ignition ON	7 V
	2 (30)	⇨	Engine idling	1 ms pilot + 1 ms main
	2 (30)	⇨	Engine idling	10 V/0,5 ms per division 〰24
	30	⇨	Ignition ON	7 V
	30 (2)	⇨	Engine idling	1 ms pilot + 1 ms main
	30 (2)	⇨	Engine idling	10 V/0,5 ms per division 〰24
Injector 2	5	⇨	Ignition ON	7 V
	5 (6)	⇨	Engine idling	1 ms pilot + 1 ms main
	5 (6)	⇨	Engine idling	10 V/0,5 ms per division 〰24
	6	⇨	Ignition ON	7 V
	6 (5)	⇨	Engine idling	1 ms pilot + 1 ms main
	6 (5)	⇨	Engine idling	10 V/0,5 ms per division 〰24
Injector 3	3	⇨	Ignition ON	7 V
	3 (31)	⇨	Engine idling	1 ms pilot + 1 ms main
	3 (31)	⇨	Engine idling	10 V/0,5 ms per division 〰24
	31	⇨	Ignition ON	7 V
	31 (3)	⇨	Engine idling	1 ms pilot + 1 ms main
	31 (3)	⇨	Engine idling	10 V/0,5 ms per division 〰24

Component/circuit description	ECM pin	Signal	Condition	Typical value
Injector 4	4	⇒	Ignition ON	7 V
	4 (32)	⇒	Engine idling	1 ms pilot + 1 ms main
	4 (32)	⇒	Engine idling	10 V/0,5 ms per division ⎓24
	32	⇒	Ignition ON	7 V
	32 (4)	⇒	Engine idling	1 ms pilot + 1 ms main
	32 (4)	⇒	Engine idling	10 V/0,5 ms per division ⎓24
Instrument panel	23	⊐⊳		[1]
Instrument panel – tachometer	62	⇒	Engine idling	28 Hz
	62	⇒	Ignition ON	0 V
Intake air temperature (IAT) sensor	11	⇐	Ignition ON – air temp. 18°C	2,4 V
Malfunction indicator lamp (MIL)	82	⊐⊳	Engine idling – MIL OFF	11-14 V
	82	⊐⊳	Ignition ON – MIL ON	0-1 V
Manifold absolute pressure (MAP) sensor – RHZ	34	⊐—	Engine idling	0 V
	44	⇒	Ignition ON	5 V
	71	⇐	Ignition ON	2,4 V
	71	⇐	Engine idling	2,4 V
	71	⇐	Engine running – accelerator pedal briefly fully depressed	3,35 V (briefly)
Mass air flow (MAF) sensor	13	⇐	Engine idling	2 V
	13	⇐	Engine idling – accelerate briefly	4,4 V (briefly)
	13	⇐	Ignition ON	0,5 V
	40	⊐—	Engine idling	0 V
Relay module	1	⇐	Ignition OFF	0 V
	1	⇐	Ignition ON	11-14 V
	29	⇐	Ignition OFF	0 V
	29	⇐	Ignition ON	11-14 V
	86	⊐⊳	Ignition OFF	11-14 V
	86	⊐⊳	Ignition ON	0-1 V
Turbocharger (TC) wastegate regulating valve – RHZ	26	⊐⊳	Ignition ON	11-14 V for 2 seconds then 0 V
	26	⊐⊳	Engine idling	5 V/2 ms per division ⎓29
Vehicle speed sensor (VSS)	19	⇐	Ignition ON – vehicle pushed	0 V or 10 V
3rd piston cut-off solenoid	80	⊐⊳	Engine idling	11-14 V
	80	⊐⊳	Engine under full load	0-1 V
	80	⊐⊳	Ignition ON	11-14 V for 2 seconds then 0 V

[1] Connected pin - no test data available

CITROEN

Bosch EDC 15C2

Model:	Engine code:	Year:
C5 2,0 HDi	RHZ (DW10ATED)	2000-04

ECM harness multi-plug

Terminal side – A – Grey, B – Brown, C – Black

AD22744

Wire side – A – Grey, B – Brown, C – Black

AD22743

Component/circuit description	ECM pin	Signal	Condition	Typical value	Oscilloscope setting*	Wave form
AC refrigerant pressure sensor	Af2	↔		1		
	Af4	↔		1		
	Ah2	↔		1		
	Ah2	↔		1		
Accelerator pedal position (APP) sensor	Ac2	←	Ignition ON – accelerator pedal released	0,2 V		
	Ac2	←	Ignition ON – accelerator pedal depressed	1,85 V		
	Ag2	⇒	Ignition ON	5 V		
	Ag3	←	Ignition ON – accelerator pedal released	0,4 V		
	Ag3	←	Ignition ON – accelerator pedal depressed	3,7 V		
	Ah3	⌐	Ignition ON	0 V		
Brake pedal position (BPP) switch 2	Ae4	←	Ignition ON – brake pedal released	11-14 V		
	Ae4	←	Ignition ON – brake pedal depressed	0 V		
Camshaft position (CMP) sensor	Bf2	⌐	Ignition ON	0 V		
	Bg2	←	Engine idling		2 V/50 ms	64
	Bh2	⇒	Ignition ON	5 V		
CAN data bus – high	Aa3	↔		1		
CAN data bus – low	Aa4	↔		1		
Clutch pedal position (CPP) switch	Ae3	←	Ignition ON – clutch pedal released	11-14 V		
	Ae3	←	Ignition ON – clutch pedal depressed	0 V		
Crankshaft position (CKP) sensor	Bj1	←	Engine idling	1,5 V ac	1 V/2 ms	1
	Bk1	←	Engine idling	1,5 V ac	1 V/2 ms	Reversed 1
Data link connector (DLC)	Ab4	↔	Ignition ON	0 V		

★ Suggested settings - Voltage/time per division

Autodata

Component/circuit description	ECM pin	Signal	Condition	Typical value	Oscilloscope setting*	Wave form
Earth	Ag1		Ignition ON	0 V		
	Ah1		Ignition ON	0 V		
	Bl4		Ignition ON	0 V		
	Bm4		Ignition ON	0 V		
Engine coolant blower motor relay 1	Ad4	⊣▷	Ignition ON	11-14 V		
Engine coolant blower motor relay 2	Ab2	⊣▷	Ignition ON	0-1 V		
	Ab2	⊣▷	Engine idling	11-14 V		
	Ac4	⬅	Ignition ON	0 V		
Engine coolant temperature (ECT) sensor	Bd1	⊣―	Ignition ON	0 V		
	Be1	⬅	Ignition ON – coolant temp. 20°C	3 V		
	Be1	⬅	Ignition ON – coolant temp. 85°C	0,6 V		
Exhaust gas recirculation (EGR) solenoid 1	Ba3	⊣▷	Ignition ON	Wave pattern for 5 secs then 0-1 V	2 V/2 ms	〰 66
	Ba3	⊣▷	Engine idling	61%	2 V/5 ms	〰 64
Exhaust gas recirculation (EGR) solenoid 2	Ca4	⊣▷	Ignition ON	Wave pattern for 5 secs then 0-1 V	2 V/2 ms	〰 66
	Ca4	⊣▷	Engine idling		2 V/5 ms	〰 37
Fuel pressure control solenoid	Bl2	⊣▷	Ignition ON		2 V/0,5 ms	〰 43
	Bl2	⊣▷	Engine idling		2 V/1 ms	〰 37
Fuel pressure sensor	Bf1	⊣―	Ignition ON	0 V		
	Bg1	⬅	Ignition ON	0,5 V		
	Bg1	⬅	Engine idling	1,3 V		
	Bg1	⬅	3000 rpm	1,8 V		
	Bh1	⇨	Ignition ON	5 V		
Fuel temperature sensor	Bd2	⊣―	Ignition ON	0 V		
	Be2	⬅	Engine idling	2,2 V		
Fuse box/relay plate, engine bay 3	Ab1	⬅⇨		1		
	Ac1	⬅⇨		1		
Glow plug timer relay	Cb1			140 Hz	5 V/5 ms	〰 12
	Cf1		Ignition ON	1,1 V		
Injector 1	Cg1	⇨	Ignition ON	1 V		
	Cg1	⇨	Engine idling	0,25 ms pilot + 0,5 ms main		
	Cg1	⇨	Engine idling		20 V/0,5 ms	〰 67
	Ch2	⇨	Ignition ON	1 V		
	Ch2	⇨	Engine idling	0,25 ms pilot + 0,5 ms main		
	Ch2	⇨	Engine idling		20 V/0,5 ms	〰 67
Injector 2	Ch3	⇨	Ignition ON	1 V		
	Ch3	⇨	Engine idling	0,25 ms pilot + 0,5 ms main		
	Ch3	⇨	Engine idling		20 V/0,5 ms	〰 67
	Ch4	⇨	Ignition ON	1 V		
	Ch4	⇨	Engine idling	0,25 ms pilot + 0,5 ms main		
	Ch4	⇨	Engine idling		20 V/0,5 ms	〰 67

★ Suggested settings - Voltage/time per division

Component/circuit description	ECM pin	Signal	Condition	Typical value	Oscilloscope setting*	Wave form
Injector 3	Cg3	⇨	Ignition ON	1 V		
	Cg3	⇨	Engine idling	0,25 ms pilot + 0,5 ms main		
	Cg3	⇨	Engine idling		20 V/0,5 ms	〰️ 67
	Cg4	⇨	Ignition ON	1 V		
	Cg4	⇨	Engine idling	0,25 ms pilot + 0,5 ms main		
	Cg4	⇨	Engine idling		20 V/0,5 ms	〰️ 67
Injector 4	Cg2	⇨	Ignition ON	1 V		
	Cg2	⇨	Engine idling	0,25 ms pilot + 0,5 ms main		
	Cg2	⇨	Engine idling		20 V/0,5 ms	〰️ 67
	Ch1	⇨	Ignition ON	1 V		
	Ch1	⇨	Engine idling	0,25 ms pilot + 0,5 ms main		
	Ch1	⇨	Engine idling		20 V/0,5 ms	〰️ 67
Intake air temperature (IAT) sensor	Bj3	⬅	Ignition ON – air temp. 18°C	2,3 V		
Manifold absolute pressure (MAP) sensor	Bb2	⇨	Ignition ON	5 V		
	Bc4	⌐	Ignition ON	0 V		
	Bd4	⬅	Engine idling	2,4 V		
	Bd4	⬅	Engine idling – accelerate briefly	3,9 V briefly		
Mass air flow (MAF) sensor	Bg3	⌐	Ignition ON	0 V		
	Bh3	⬅	Ignition ON	0,5 V		
	Bh3	⬅	Engine idling	2,1 V		
	Bh3	⬅	Engine idling – accelerate briefly	4 V briefly		
Multifunction control module 1	Aa3	⬌		1		
	Aa4	⬌		1		
Multifunction control module 2	Ac3	⬅	Ignition OFF	0 V		
	Ac3	⬅	Ignition ON	11-14 V		
	Ba2	⌐⊳	Ignition OFF	11-14 V		
	Ba2	⌐⊳	Ignition ON	0-1 V		
	Ba4	⌐⊳	Ignition ON	0-1 V for 5 secs then 10,6 V		
	Bl1	⬅	Ignition ON	11-14 V		
	Bm1	⬅	Ignition ON	11-14 V		
Turbocharger (TC) wastegate regulating valve	Cb4	⌐⊳	Ignition ON	Wave pattern for 5 secs then 0-1 V	2 V/2 ms	〰️ 66
3rd piston cut-off solenoid	Bc3	⌐⊳	Ignition ON	11-14 V for 5 secs then 0-1 V		
	Bc3	⌐⊳	Engine idling	11-14 V		
	Bc3	⌐⊳	Engine under full load	0-1 V		

*Suggested settings - Voltage/time per division

1 Connected pin - no test data available or random digital signal

Model:	Engine code:	Year:
Synergie 1,8	LFW (XU7JP/L3)	1997-02
Synergie 2,0	RFU (XU10J2C/Z)	1997-02

CITROEN
Magneti Marelli
8P.15/8P.22

ECM harness multi-plug

Terminal side

1 2 3 4 5 6 7 8 9 10 11 12 13 14 15 16 17 18
19 20 21 22 23 24 25 26 27 28 29 30 31 32 33 34 35

AD71594

Wire side

18 17 16 15 14 13 12 11 10 9 8 7 6 5 4 3 2 1
35 34 33 32 31 30 29 28 27 26 25 24 23 22 21 20 19

AD42073

Component/circuit description	ECM pin	Signal	Condition	Typical value	Oscilloscope setting★	Wave form
Air conditioning	9			1		
	24			1		
Air conditioning – some models	8			1		
Coded keypad – some models	10		Ignition ON	11-14 V		
	15		Ignition OFF	0 V		
	15		Ignition ON	11-14 V		
Crankshaft position (CKP) sensor	11	←	Engine idling	3 V ac	2 V/1 ms	2
	11	←	3000 rpm	8,5 V ac	2 V/1 ms	2
	28	←	Engine idling	3 V ac	2 V/1 ms	Reversed 2
	28	←	3000 rpm	8,5 V ac	2 V/1 ms	Reversed 2
Data link connector (DLC) – some models	5	⇒	Engine idling	30 Hz		
	5	⇒	3000 rpm	100 Hz		
	10		Ignition ON	11-14 V		
	15	⇒	Ignition OFF	0 V		
	15	⇒	Ignition ON	11-14 V		
	6	⇁▷	Ignition ON – MIL ON	0-1 V		
	6	⇁▷	Engine running – MIL OFF	11-14 V		
Earth	17		Ignition ON	0 V		
	34		Ignition ON	0 V		
Engine coolant temperature (ECT) sensor	13	←	Ignition ON – coolant temp. 13°C	3 V		
	13	←	Ignition ON – coolant temp. 80°C	0,5 V		
Evaporative emission (EVAP) canister purge valve	22	⇁▷	Ignition ON	0 V		
	22	⇁▷	Engine idling	1-99%	10 V/50 ms	20
Heated oxygen sensor (HO2S)	12	⇁—	Ignition ON	0 V		
	29	←	Engine idling – accelerate briefly	0-1 V fluctuating	0,2 V/1 sec.	21
Heated oxygen sensor (HO2S) – shield wire	16	⇁—	Ignition ON	0 V		

★ Suggested settings - Voltage/time per division

Component/circuit description	ECM pin	Signal	Condition	Typical value	Oscilloscope setting*	Wave form
Idle air control (IAC) valve	2	⇒	Ignition ON	1 V		
	2 (20)	⇒	Engine idling		5 V/0,5 sec.	Intermittent 〰 26
	3	⇒	Ignition ON	11-14 V		
	3 (21)	⇒	Engine idling		5 V/0,5 sec.	Intermittent 〰 26
	20	⇒	Ignition ON	11-14 V		
	20 (2)	⇒	Engine idling		5 V/0,5 sec.	Intermittent 〰 26
	21	⇒	Ignition ON	1 V		
	21 (3)	⇒	Engine idling		5 V/0,5 sec.	Intermittent 〰 26
Ignition coil	1	⊐⊳	Ignition ON	11-14 V briefly then 0 V		
	1	⊐⊳	Engine idling		5 V/2 ms	〰 33
	19	⊐⊳	Ignition ON	11-14 V briefly then 0 V		
	19	⊐⊳	Engine idling		5 V/2 ms	〰 33
Immobilizer control module – some models	10		Ignition ON	11-14 V		
	15		Ignition OFF	0 V		
	15		Ignition ON	11-14 V		
Inertia fuel shut-off (IFS) switch	23	⊐⊳	Ignition ON	0 V briefly then 11-14 V		
	23	⊐⊳	Engine cranking	0-1 V		
	23	⊐⊳	Engine idling	0-1 V		
Injectors	18	⊐⊳	Ignition ON	11-14 V briefly then 0 V		
	18	⊐⊳	Engine idling	2,4 ms	10 V/2 ms	〰 35
Intake air temperature (IAT) sensor	16	⊐−	Ignition ON	0 V		
	16	⊐−	Ignition ON	0 V		
	31	←	Ignition ON – air temp. 13°C	3 V		
Knock sensor (KS) – some models	16	⊐−	Ignition ON	0 V		
	33	←	Engine idling – accelerate briefly		50 mV/1 ms	〰 38
	34	⊐−	Ignition ON	0 V		
Malfunction indicator lamp (MIL)	6	⊐⊳	Ignition ON – MIL ON	0-1 V		
	6	⊐⊳	Engine running – MIL OFF	11-14 V		
Manifold absolute pressure (MAP) sensor	14	⇒	Ignition ON	5 V		
	16	⊐−	Ignition ON	0 V		
	32	←	Ignition ON	4,6 V		
	32	←	Engine idling	1,5 V		
	32	←	Engine idling – accelerate briefly	4,5 V briefly		
Relay module	4	⊐⊳	Ignition ON	0-1 V		
	4	⊐⊳	Engine cranking	0-1 V		
	4	⊐⊳	Engine idling	0-1 V		
	35	←	Ignition ON	11-14 V		
	35	←	Engine running	11-14 V		
Tachometer – some models	5	⇒	Engine idling	30 Hz		
	5	⇒	3000 rpm	100 Hz		
Throttle position (TP) sensor	14	⇒	Ignition ON	5 V		
	16	⊐−	Ignition ON	0 V		
	30	←	Ignition ON – throttle closed	0,3 V		
	30	←	Ignition ON – throttle fully open	4,5 V		
Vehicle speed sensor (VSS)	27	←	Vehicle moving	1,5 V or 11-14 V fluctuating		

*Suggested settings - Voltage/time per division

[1] Connected pin - no test data available or random digital signal

ECM harness multi-plug

Terminal side

AD20174

Wire side

AD20176

Component/circuit description	ECM pin	Signal	Condition	Typical value	Oscilloscope setting*	Wave form
AC refrigerant triple pressure switch	78	←		1		
Accelerator pedal position (APP) sensor	15	←	Ignition ON – accelerator pedal released	0,5 V		
	15	←	Ignition ON – accelerator pedal fully depressed	3,5 V		
	22	⌐	Engine idling	0 V		
	44	⇨	Ignition ON	5 V		
	68	←	Ignition ON – accelerator pedal released	0,2 V		
	68	←	Ignition ON – accelerator pedal fully depressed	2 V		
Brake pedal position (BPP) switch	48	←	Ignition ON – brake pedal released	0 V		
	48	←	Ignition ON – brake pedal depressed	11-14 V		
Camshaft position (CMP) sensor	12	⇨	Ignition ON	5 V		
	18	←	Engine idling		5 V/50 ms	⌁ 26
	18	←	Ignition ON	11 V		
	40	⌐	Engine idling	0 V		
Clutch pedal position (CPP) switch	21	←	Ignition ON – clutch pedal released	11-14 V		
	21	←	Ignition ON – clutch pedal fully depressed	0 V		
Crankshaft position (CKP) sensor	14	←	Engine idling	1,72 V ac		
	14	←	Engine idling		2 V/1 ms	⌁ 6
	41	←	Engine idling	1,72 V		
	41	←	Engine idling		2 V/1 ms	⌁ 6
Cruise control brake pedal switch	73	←	Ignition ON – brake pedal released	11-14 V		
	73	←	Ignition ON – brake pedal depressed	0 V		
Cruise control switch	17	←⇨		1		
	60	←⇨		1		
	61	←⇨		1		

* Suggested settings - Voltage/time per division

Component/circuit description	ECM pin	Signal	Condition	Typical value	Oscilloscope setting*	Wave form
Data link connector (DLC)	10		Ignition ON	0 V		
	38		Ignition ON	0 V		
	62	⟹	Ignition ON	0 V		
	62	⟹	Engine idling	27 Hz		
	62	⟹	3000 rpm	97 Hz		
	81	⟺		☐1		
Earth	33		Ignition ON	0 V		
	49		Ignition ON	0 V		
	51		Ignition ON	0 V		
	53		Ignition ON	0 V		
Engine coolant blower motor relay 1	83	⊐▷	Ignition OFF	11-14 V		
	83	⊐▷	Ignition ON	11-14 V		
	83	⊐▷	Engine idling – coolant blower motor OFF	11-14 V		
	83	⊐▷	Engine idling – coolant blower motor ON	0-1 V		
Engine coolant blower motor relay 2	8	⊐▷	Ignition ON – coolant blower motor OFF	0 V		
	8	⊐▷	Ignition ON – coolant blower motor ON	11-14 V		
	25	⊐▷	Engine idling – coolant blower motor OFF	11-14 V		
	25	⊐▷	Engine idling – coolant blower motor ON	0-1 V		
Engine coolant heater relay	85	⊐▷	Ignition ON – engine coolant heater OFF	11-14 V		
	85	⊐▷	Ignition ON – engine coolant heater ON	0-1 V		
Engine coolant temperature (ECT) sensor	45	⊐─	Engine idling	0 V		
	46	⬅	Ignition ON – coolant temp. 20°C	3,2 V		
	46	⬅	Ignition ON – coolant temp. 80°C	0,7 V		
Exhaust gas recirculation (EGR) solenoid 1	52	⊐▷	Ignition ON	11-14 V for 2 seconds then 0-1 V		
	52	⊐▷	Engine idling		25%	
	52	⊐▷	Engine idling		5 V/2 ms	∿ 29
Exhaust gas recirculation (EGR) solenoid 2	55	⊐▷	Ignition ON	11-14 V for 2 seconds then 0-1 V		
Fuel pressure regulator control solenoid	50	⊐▷	Ignition ON	10 V		
	50	⊐▷	Engine idling	11-14 V		
	50	⊐▷	Engine idling	1000 Hz		
	50	⊐▷	Engine idling	15-17%		
	50	⊐▷	4000 rpm	23-25%		
	50	⊐▷	Engine idling		2 V/1 ms	∿ 37
Fuel pressure sensor	74	⬅	3000 rpm	1,97 V		
Fuel rail pressure (FRP) sensor	34	⊐─	Engine idling	0 V		
	44	⟹	Ignition ON	5 V		
	74	⬅	Ignition ON	0,5 V		
	74	⬅	Engine cranking	1,3 V		
	74	⬅	Engine idling	1,3 V		
Fuel temperature sensor	39	⬅	Ignition ON – air temp. 20°C	2,7 V		

★ Suggested settings - Voltage/time per division

Component/circuit description	ECM pin	Signal	Condition	Typical value	Oscilloscope setting*	Wave form
Glow plug timer relay	67		Ignition ON – glow plugs OFF	0 V		
	67		Ignition ON – glow plugs ON	11-14 V		
	88		Ignition ON – glow plugs OFF	11-14 V		
	88		Ignition ON – glow plugs ON	0 V		
Glow plug warning lamp	56	⇒	Ignition ON – lamp ON	11-14 V		
	56	⇒	Ignition ON – lamp OFF	0 V		
Ignition switch	69	⇐	Ignition OFF	0 V		
	69	⇐	Ignition ON	11-14 V		
Immobiliser control module	36	⇐⇒		1		
	66	⇐⇒		1		
Inertia fuel shut-off (IFS) switch	87	⇐	Ignition ON – button depressed	0-1 V for 2 seconds then 11-14 V		
	87	⇐	Ignition ON – button released	0 V		
	87	⇐	Engine idling – button depressed	0-1 V		
Injector 1	2	⇒	Ignition ON	7 V		
	2	⇒	Engine idling	1 ms pilot + 1 ms main		
	2	⇒	Engine idling		10 V/0,5 ms	24
	30	⇒	Ignition ON	7 V		
	30	⇒	Engine idling	1 ms pilot + 1 ms main		
	30	⇒	Engine idling		10 V/0,5 ms	24
Injector 2	5	⇒	Ignition ON	7 V		
	5	⇒	Engine idling	1 ms pilot + 1 ms main		
	5	⇒	Engine idling		10 V/0,5 ms	24
	6	⇒	Ignition ON	7 V		
	6	⇒	Engine idling	1 ms pilot + 1 ms main		
	6	⇒	Engine idling		10 V/0,5 ms	24
Injector 3	3	⇒	Ignition ON	7 V		
	3	⇒	Engine idling	1 ms pilot + 1 ms main		
	3	⇒	Engine idling		10 V/0,5 ms	24
	31	⇒	Ignition ON	7 V		
	31	⇒	Engine idling	1 ms pilot + 1 ms main		
	31	⇒	Engine idling		10 V/0,5 ms	24
Injector 4	4	⇒	Ignition ON	7 V		
	4	⇒	Engine idling	1 ms pilot + 1 ms main		
	4	⇒	Engine idling		10 V/0,5 ms	24
	32	⇒	Ignition ON	7 V		
	32	⇒	Engine idling	1 ms pilot + 1 ms main		
	32	⇒	Engine idling		10 V/0,5 ms	24
Instrument panel	23	⇒		1		
	63	⇐⇒		1		
Intake air temperature (IAT) sensor	11	⇐	Ignition ON – air temp. 18°C	2,4 V		
Intake manifold air control solenoid	24	⇒		1		

* Suggested settings - Voltage/time per division

Component/circuit description	ECM pin	Signal	Condition	Typical value	Oscilloscope setting*	Wave form
Malfunction indicator lamp (MIL)	82	⌐▷	Ignition ON – MIL ON	0-1 V		
	82	⌐▷	Engine idling – MIL OFF	11-14 V		
Manifold absolute pressure (MAP) sensor	22	⌐	Engine idling	0 V		
	44	⇨	Ignition ON	5 V		
	71	⬅	Ignition ON	2,4 V		
	71	⬅	Engine idling	2,4 V		
	71	⬅	Engine idling – accelerator pedal briefly fully depressed	3,35 V briefly		
Mass air flow (MAF) sensor	13	⬅	Engine idling	2 V		
	13	⬅	Engine idling – accelerate briefly	4,4 V briefly		
	13	⬅	Ignition ON	0,5 V		
	22	⌐	Engine idling	0 V		
Relay module (RM)	1	⬅	Ignition OFF	0 V		
	1	⬅	Ignition ON	11-14 V		
	29	⬅	Ignition OFF	0 V		
	29	⬅	Ignition ON	11-14 V		
	86	⌐▷	Ignition OFF	0-1 V		
	86	⌐▷	Ignition ON	11-14 V		
Turbocharger (TC) wastegate regulating valve	26	⌐▷	Ignition ON	11-14 V for 2 seconds then 0-1 V		
	26	⌐▷	Engine idling		5 V/2 ms	〰〰 29
Vehicle speed sensor (VSS)	19	⬅	Ignition ON – vehicle pushed	0 V or 10 V		
Wide open throttle (WOT) relay	47	⬅		1		
	84	⌐▷		1		
3rd piston cut-off solenoid	80	⌐▷	Engine idling	11-14 V		
	80	⌐▷	Engine under full load	0-1 V		
	80	⌐▷	Ignition ON	11-14 V for 2 seconds then 0-1 V		

*Suggested settings - Voltage/time per division

1 Connected pin - no test data available or random digital signal

ECM harness multi-plug

Terminal side – A – Brown, B – Black, C – Grey

B

h1	g1	f1	e1	d1	c1	b1	a1
h2	g2	f2	e2	d2	c2	b2	a2
h3	g3	f3	e3	d3	c3	b3	a3
h4	g4	f4	e4	d4	c4	b4	a4

A

m1	l1	k1	j1	h1	g1	f1	e1	d1	c1	b1	a1
m2	l2	k2	j2	h2	g2	f2	e2	d2	c2	b2	a2
m3	l3	k3	j3	h3	g3	f3	e3	d3	c3	b3	a3
m4	l4	k4	j4	h4	g4	f4	e4	d4	c4	b4	a4

C

a4	b4	c4	d4	e4	f4	g4	h4
a3	b3	c3	d3	e3	f3	g3	h3
a2	b2	c2	d2	e2	f2	g2	h2
a1	b1	c1	d1	e1	f1	g1	h1

AD100217

Wire side – A – Brown, B – Black, C – Grey

C

h4	g4	f4	e4	d4	c4	b4	a4
h3	g3	f3	e3	d3	c3	b3	a3
h2	g2	f2	e2	d2	c2	b2	a2
h1	g1	f1	e1	d1	c1	b1	a1

A

a1	b1	c1	d1	e1	f1	g1	h1	j1	k1	l1	m1
a2	b2	c2	d2	e2	f2	g2	h2	j2	k2	l2	m2
a3	b3	c3	d3	e3	f3	g3	h3	j3	k3	l3	m3
a4	b4	c4	d4	e4	f4	g4	h4	j4	k4	l4	m4

B

a1	b1	c1	d1	e1	f1	g1	h1
a2	b2	c2	d2	e2	f2	g2	h2
a3	b3	c3	d3	e3	f3	g3	h3
a4	b4	c4	d4	e4	f4	g4	h4

AD100218

Component/circuit description	ECM pin	Signal	Condition	Typical value	Oscilloscope setting*	Wave form
AC refrigerant triple pressure switch	Ae2			1		
Air conditioning	Ac3			1		
	Ad3			1		
Alternator	Bc4			1		
Crankshaft position (CKP) sensor	Cb1	←	Engine idling	2,3 V ac	2 V/1 ms	2
	Cb2	←	Engine idling	2,3 V ac	2 V/1 ms	Reversed 2
Data link connector (DLC)	Ab3	←⇨	Ignition ON	0 V		
	Ah2			1		
	Aj2	←⇨	Ignition ON	0 V		
	Aj2	←⇨	Engine idling	25 Hz		
	Aj2	←⇨	3000 rpm	100 Hz		
Earth	Al4		Ignition ON	0 V		
	Am4		Ignition ON	0 V		
	Ch1		Ignition ON	0 V		
Engine coolant blower motor	Af2	⇨	Coolant blower motor OFF	0 V		
	Af2	⇨	Coolant blower motor ON	11-14 V		
Engine coolant blower motor relay 1/2	Aj4	←	Engine running – coolant blower motor OFF	11-14 V		
	Aj4	←	Engine running – coolant blower motor ON	0 V		
Engine coolant blower motor relay 3 – low speed	Ak4	⫤⇨	Ignition OFF	0-1 V		
	Ak4	⫤⇨	Ignition ON – engine coolant blower motor OFF	11-14 V		
	Ak4	⫤⇨	Ignition ON – engine coolant blower motor ON	0-1 V		

* Suggested settings - Voltage/time per division

Component/circuit description	ECM pin	Signal	Condition	Typical value	Oscilloscope setting*	Wave form
Engine coolant temperature (ECT) sensor	Bd4		Ignition ON	0 V		
	Be4	←	Engine idling – coolant temp. 10°C	3-3,5 V switching	2 V/0,1 sec.	101
	Be4	←	Engine idling – coolant temp. 80°C	3-3,5 V switching	2 V/0,2 sec.	18
Evaporative emission (EVAP) canister purge valve	Cf2	⊐▷	Ignition ON	11-14 V briefly then 0-1 V		
	Cf2	⊐▷	Engine running		10 V/50 ms	20
Heated oxygen sensor (HO2S) 1 – before cat	Be2	⊐▷	Engine idling	0-1 V	4 V/0,2 sec.	4
	Ca3	←	Engine idling	0,1-0,8 V		
	Cb3		Engine idling	0 V		
Heated oxygen sensor (HO2S) 2 – after cat	Bd2	⊐▷	Ignition ON	11-14 V briefly then 0-1 V		
	Bd2	⊐▷	Engine idling	0-1 V		
	Bd3		Engine idling	0 V		
	Be3	←	Engine idling	0,1-0,8 V		
Idle air control (IAC) valve	Cd1	⇨	Engine idling		5 V/0,5 sec.	Intermittent 26
	Cd2	⇨	Engine idling		5 V/0,5 sec.	Intermittent 26
	Cd3	⇨	Engine idling		5 V/0,5 sec.	Intermittent 26
	Ce3	⇨	Engine idling		5 V/0,5 sec.	Intermittent 26
Ignition coil	Bf3	←	Ignition ON	11-14 V briefly then 0-1 V		
	Bf3	←	Engine running		5 V/50 μs	100
	Bg3	⊐▷	Ignition ON	11-14 V briefly then 0-1 V		
	Bg3	⊐▷	Engine idling		5 V/2 ms	33
	Bh3	⊐▷	Ignition ON	11-14 V briefly then 0-1 V		
	Bh3	⊐▷	Engine idling		5 V/2 ms	33
Ignition switch	Ab4	←	Ignition ON	9 V min.		
Inertia fuel shut-off (IFS) switch	Cf3	⊐▷	Ignition ON	0-1 V briefly then 11-14 V		
	Cf3	⊐▷	Engine idling	0-1 V		
Injector 1	Ch2	⊐▷	Ignition ON	11-14 V briefly then 0-1 V		
	Ch2	⊐▷	Engine idling	4 ms	10 V/2 ms	35
Injector 2	Cg3	⊐▷	Ignition ON	11-14 V briefly then 0-1 V		
	Cg3	⊐▷	Engine idling	4 ms	10 V/2 ms	35
Injector 3	Cg2	⊐▷	Ignition ON	11-14 V briefly then 0-1 V		
	Cg2	⊐▷	Engine idling	4 ms	10 V/2 ms	35
Injector 4	Ch3	⊐▷	Ignition ON	11-14 V briefly then 0-1 V		
	Ch3	⊐▷	Engine idling	4 ms	10 V/2 ms	35
Intake air temperature (IAT) sensor	Ba2	←	Ignition ON – air temp. 20°C	2,35 V		
	Ca2		Ignition ON	0 V		

* Suggested settings - Voltage/time per division

Component/circuit description	ECM pin	Signal	Condition	Typical value	Oscilloscope setting*	Wave form
Knock sensor (KS)	Bb3	←	Ignition ON	2,5 V		
	Bb3	←	Engine idling – accelerate briefly		50 mV/1 ms	⩗⩗⩗ 38
	Bc3	←	Ignition ON	2,5 V		
	Bc3	←	Engine idling – accelerate briefly		50 mV/1 ms	⩗⩗⩗ 38
Manifold absolute pressure (MAP) sensor	Ca2	⊐⌐	Ignition ON	0 V		
	Cc1	←	Ignition ON	4,2 V		
	Cc1	←	Engine idling	1,8 V		
	Cc1	←	Engine idling – accelerate briefly	4,4 V briefly		
	Ce1	⇒	Ignition ON	5 V		
Multifunction control module	Ac4	⬄	Ignition OFF	0 V		
	Af3	⬄	Ignition OFF	0 V		
	Af3	⬄	Ignition ON	11-14 V		
	Af4	⬄	Ignition OFF	0 V		
	Af4	⬄	Ignition ON	11-14 V		
	Aj3			[1]		
	Ak3			[1]		
Power steering pressure (PSP) switch	Ae3	←	Engine running – steering wheel not turned	0 V		
	Ae3	←	Engine running – steering wheel turned	11-14 V		
Relay module (RM)	Ba4	←	Ignition ON	11-14 V		
	Bf2	⊐⇒	Ignition OFF	11-14 V		
	Bf2	⊐⇒	Ignition ON	0-1 V		
Throttle position (TP) sensor	Ba3	⊐⌐	Ignition ON	0 V		
	Bb4	←	Ignition ON – throttle closed	0,5 V		
	Bb4	←	Ignition ON – throttle fully open	4 V		
	Cc3	⇒	Ignition ON	5 V		
Vehicle speed sensor (VSS)	Ag2	←	Ignition OFF	10,8 V		
	Ag2	←	Ignition ON – vehicle pushed	0 V or 11-14 V switching		
	Bh4	⊐⌐		0 V		

*Suggested settings - Voltage/time per division

[1] Connected pin - no test data available or random digital signal

CITROEN

Siemens SID 801

Model:	Engine code:	Year:
Berlingo 2,0 HDi	RHY (DW10TD)	2002-06

ECM harness multi-plug

Terminal side – A – Grey, B – Brown, C – Black

AD22744

Wire side – A – Grey, B – Brown, C – Black

AD22743

Component/circuit description	ECM pin	Signal	Condition	Typical value	Oscilloscope setting*	Wave form
AC refrigerant triple pressure switch	Cf2	⟹	Ignition ON	5 V		
	Cf4	⌐⌐	Ignition ON	0 V		
	Ch2	⟸	Ignition OFF	0 V		
	Ch2	⟸	Ignition ON	0,8 V		
Accelerator pedal position (APP) sensor	Cc2	⟸	Ignition ON – accelerator pedal released	0,2 V		
	Cc2	⟸	Ignition ON – accelerator pedal depressed	1,85 V		
	Cg2	⟹	Ignition ON	5 V		
	Cg3	⟸	Ignition ON – accelerator pedal released	0,4 V		
	Cg3	⟸	Ignition ON – accelerator pedal depressed	3,7 V		
	Ch3	⌐⌐	Ignition ON	0 V		
Battery	Bg4	⟸	Ignition OFF	11-14 V		
	Cc1	⟸	Ignition ON	11-14 V		
Brake pedal position (BPP) switch	Ce4	⟸	Ignition ON – brake pedal released	11-14 V		
	Ce4	⟸	Ignition ON – brake pedal depressed	0 V		
Camshaft position (CMP) sensor	Aa1	⌐⌐	Ignition ON	0 V		
	Ad1	⟸	Engine idling		2 V/50 ms	〰64
	Bc3	⟹	Ignition ON	5 V		
Clutch pedal position (CPP) switch	Ce3	⟸	Ignition ON – clutch pedal released	11-14 V		
	Ce3	⟸	Ignition ON – clutch pedal depressed	0 V		
Crankshaft position (CKP) sensor	Bj4	⟸	Engine idling	1,4 V ac	1 V/2 ms	Reversed 〰1
	Bk4	⟸	Engine idling	1,4 V ac	1 V/2 ms	〰1

* Suggested settings - Voltage/time per division

Component/circuit description	ECM pin	Signal	Condition	Typical value	Oscilloscope setting*	Wave form
Data link connector (DLC)	Cb4	⬅⇨	Ignition ON	0 V		
Earth	Ah2		Ignition ON	0 V		
	Bk2		Ignition ON	0 V		
	Cg4		Ignition ON	0 V		
	Ch4		Ignition ON	0 V		
Engine coolant blower motor relay I	Cc4	⊐⇾	Ignition ON	0 V		
	Cd4	⊐⇾	Ignition ON	11-14 V		
Engine coolant blower motor relay II	Cb2	⊐⇾	Ignition ON	11-14 V		
Engine coolant temperature (ECT) sensor	Be1	⊐—	Ignition ON	0 V		
	Be4	⬅	Coolant temp. 85°C	0,9 V		
Exhaust gas recirculation (EGR) solenoid	Ag1	⊐⇾	Ignition ON		2 V/2 ms	〰 66
	Ag1	⊐⇾	Engine idling	41%	2 V/5 ms	〰 10
Fuel flow control valve	Ag3	⊐⇾	Ignition ON	11-14 V		
	Ag3	⊐⇾	Engine idling	10%	2 V/5 ms	〰 37
Fuel pressure control solenoid	Ah1	⊐⇾	Ignition ON	11-14 V		
	Ah1	⊐⇾	Engine idling	0	2 V/2 ms	〰 37
Fuel pressure sensor	Ad3	⬅	Ignition ON	0,5 V		
	Bd1	⇨	Ignition ON	5 V		
	Bf2	⊐—	Ignition ON	0 V		
Fuel temperature sensor	Bf3	⬅	Engine idling – coolant temp. 85°C	1,3 V		
	Bh4	⊐—	Ignition ON	0 V		
Glow plug timer relay	Ac1		Ignition ON	0 V		
	Be2		Ignition ON	11-14 V		
Injector 1	Bl3	⇨	Ignition ON	110 V		
	Bl3	⇨	Engine idling	0,4 ms pilot + 0,7 ms main		
	Bl3	⇨	Engine idling		20 V/0,5 ms	〰 68
	Bm2	⇨	Ignition ON	110 V		
	Bm2	⇨	Engine idling	0,4 ms pilot + 0,7 ms main		
	Bm2	⇨	Engine idling		20 V/0,5 ms	〰 68
Injector 2	Bl1	⇨	Ignition ON	110 V		
	Bl1	⇨	Engine idling	0,4 ms pilot + 0,7 ms main		
	Bl1	⇨	Engine idling		20 V/0,5 ms	〰 68
	Bl4	⇨	Ignition ON	110 V		
	Bl4	⇨	Engine idling	0,4 ms pilot + 0,7 ms main		
	Bl4	⇨	Engine idling		20 V/0,5 ms	〰 68
Injector 3	Bl2	⇨	Ignition ON	110 V		
	Bl2	⇨	Engine idling	0,4 ms pilot + 0,7 ms main		
	Bl2	⇨	Engine idling		20 V/0,5 ms	〰 68
	Bm3	⇨	Ignition ON	110 V		
	Bm3	⇨	Engine idling	0,4 ms pilot + 0,7 ms main		
	Bm3	⇨	Engine idling		20 V/0,5 ms	〰 68

* Suggested settings - Voltage/time per division

Component/circuit description	ECM pin	Signal	Condition	Typical value	Oscilloscope setting*	Wave form
Injector 4	Bm1	⟹	Ignition ON	110 V		
	Bm1	⟹	Engine idling	0,4 ms pilot + 0,7 ms main		
	Bm1	⟹	Engine idling		20 V/0,5 ms	〰68
	Bm4	⟹	Ignition ON	110 V		
	Bm4	⟹	Engine idling	0,4 ms pilot + 0,7 ms main		
	Bm4	⟹	Engine idling		20 V/0,5 ms	〰68
Intake air temperature (IAT) sensor	Be3	⟸	Ignition ON – air temp. 19°C	2,5 V		
Mass air flow (MAF) sensor	Aa3	⟸	Ignition ON	0,57 V		
	Aa3	⟸	Engine idling	2,6 V		
	Ab3	⌐	Ignition ON	0 V		
	Bg2	⌐	Ignition ON	0 V		
Multifunction control module 1 – CAN data bus – high	Ca4	⟺		1		
Multifunction control module 1 – CAN data bus – low	Ca3	⟺		1		
Multifunction control module 2	Ae3	⟸	Ignition ON	11-14 V		
	Af2	⟸	Ignition ON	11-14 V		
	Af3	⟸	Ignition ON	11-14 V		
	Bf1	⌐⟹	Ignition OFF	11-14 V		
	Bf1	⌐⟹	Ignition ON	0-1 V		
	Bh1		Ignition ON	0 V		
	Cc3	⟸	Ignition ON	11-14 V		
Vehicle speed sensor (VSS)	Ab1	⟸	Ignition OFF	10,8 V		
	Ab1	⟸	Ignition ON – vehicle pushed	0 V or 11-14 V switching		

*Suggested settings - Voltage/time per division

1 Connected pin - no test data available or random digital signal

ECM harness multi-plug

Terminal side

27 26 25 24 23 22 21 20 19 18 17 16 15 14 13 12 11 10 9 8 7 6 5 4 3 2 1
55 54 53 52 51 50 49 48 47 46 45 44 43 42 41 40 39 38 37 36 35 34 33 32 31 30 29 28

AD81647

Wire side

1 2 3 4 5 6 7 8 9 10 11 12 13 14 15 16 17 18 19 20 21 22 23 24 25 26 27
28 29 30 31 32 33 34 35 36 37 38 39 40 41 42 43 44 45 46 47 48 49 50 51 52 53 54 55

AD42110

Component/circuit description	ECM pin	Signal	Condition	Typical value	Oscilloscope setting*	Wave form
AC compressor clutch relay	51	⊐▷	Ignition ON	11-14 V		
	51	⊐▷	Engine idling – AC OFF	11-14 V		
	51	⊐▷	Engine idling – AC ON – AC compressor ON	0-1 V		
AC evaporator temperature sensor	21	◀—		1		
	44	⊐—	Ignition ON	0 V		
AC master switch	7	◀—		1		
Battery	32	◀—	Ignition OFF	11-14 V		
Camshaft position (CMP) sensor	5	◀—	Ignition ON	0,28 V		
	5	◀—	Engine idling	8 Hz	2 V/10 ms	〜〜 62
Camshaft position (CMP) sensor – shield wire	31	⊐—	Ignition ON	0 V		
Clutch control module – engine speed signal – with automatic clutch	41	⇨		1		
Clutch control module – throttle position signal – with automatic clutch	48	⇨		1		
Crankshaft position (CKP) sensor	33	◀—	Ignition ON	0 V or 5 V		
	33	◀—	Engine idling		2 V/1 ms	〜〜 4
Crankshaft position (CKP) sensor – shield wire	31	⊐—	Ignition ON	0 V		
Data link connector (DLC)	11	◀⇨		1		
	13	◀⇨		1		
	38	◀⇨		1		
Earth	2		Ignition ON	0 V		
	3		Ignition ON	0 V		
Earth – without HO2S	18		Ignition ON	0 V		
Engine control (EC) relay	14	⊐▷	Ignition ON	0-1 V briefly then 11-14 V		
	14	⊐▷	Engine running	0-1 V		
	52	◀—	Ignition ON	11-14 V briefly then 0 V		
	52	◀—	Engine idling	11-14 V		

* Suggested settings - Voltage/time per division

Component/circuit description	ECM pin	Signal	Condition	Typical value	Oscilloscope setting*	Wave form
Engine coolant blower motor relay 1	47	⊐⊢▷	Engine idling – coolant blower motor OFF	11-14 V		
	47	⊐⊢▷	Engine idling – coolant blower motor ON – low speed	0-1 V		
Engine coolant blower motor relay 2	50	⊐⊢▷	Engine idling – coolant blower motor OFF	11-14 V		
	50	⊐⊢▷	Engine idling – coolant blower motor ON – high speed	0-1 V		
Engine coolant temperature (ECT) sensor	15	◀	Ignition ON – coolant temp. 10°C	2,8 V		
	15	◀	Ignition ON – coolant temp. 80°C	0,5 V		
	44	⊐⊢	Ignition ON	0 V		
Engine malfunction indicator lamp (MIL)	43	⊐⊢▷	Ignition ON – lamp ON	0-1 V		
	43	⊐⊢▷	Engine idling – lamp OFF	11-14 V		
Evaporative emission (EVAP) canister purge valve	10	⊐⊢▷	Ignition ON	11-14 V briefly then 0-1 V		
	10	⊐⊢▷	Engine running – engine hot – valve operating		10 V/20 ms	〜〜 59
Exhaust gas recirculation (EGR) solenoid	42	⊐⊢▷	Ignition ON	11-14 V briefly then 0-1 V		
	42	⊐⊢▷	Engine idling	11-14 V		
Headlamp relay	26	◀	Ignition ON – headlamps OFF	0 V		
	26	◀	Ignition ON – headlamps ON	11-14 V		
Heated oxygen sensor(HO2S)/oxygen sensor (O2S)	17	◀	Engine idling – engine hot	0-1 V fluctuating	0,2 V/1 sec.	〜〜 21
Heated oxygen sensor (HO2S)	18	⊐⊢	Engine idling	0 V		
Idle air control (IAC) valve	9 (35)	⇨	Engine idling		5 V/0,5 sec.	Intermittent 〜〜 26
	35 (9)	⇨	Engine idling		5 V/0,5 sec.	Intermittent 〜〜 26
	36 (40)	⇨	Engine idling		5 V/0,5 sec.	Intermittent 〜〜 26
	40 (36)	⇨	Engine idling		5 V/0,5 sec.	Intermittent 〜〜 26
Ignition coil	28	⊐⊢▷	Ignition ON	11-14 V		
	28	⊐⊢▷	Engine idling	11-14 V	5 V/2 ms	〜〜 33
Ignition coil – shield wire	31	⊐⊢	Ignition ON	0 V		
Ignition switch	24	◀	Ignition OFF	0-1 V		
	24	◀	Ignition ON	11-14 V		
Injector 1	30	⊐⊢▷	Ignition ON	11-14 V briefly then 0-1 V		
	30	⊐⊢▷	Engine idling	3,8 ms	10 V/2 ms	〜〜 35
Injector 2	1	⊐⊢▷	Ignition ON	11-14 V briefly then 0-1 V		
	1	⊐⊢▷	Engine idling	3,8 ms	10 V/2 ms	〜〜 35
Injector 3	4	⊐⊢▷	Ignition ON	11-14 V briefly then 0-1 V		
	4	⊐⊢▷	Engine idling	3,8 ms	10 V/2 ms	〜〜 35
Intake air temperature (IAT) sensor	20	◀	Ignition ON – air temp. 15°C	2,8 V		
	46	⊐⊢	Ignition ON	0 V		
Knock sensor (KS)	8	◀	Engine idling – accelerate briefly		0,5 V/0,5 ms	〜〜 38
	44	⊐⊢	Ignition ON	0 V		
Knock sensor (KS) – shield wire	31	⊐⊢	Ignition ON	0 V		

* Suggested settings - Voltage/time per division

Component/circuit description	ECM pin	Signal	Condition	Typical value	Oscilloscope setting*	Wave form
Manifold absolute pressure (MAP) sensor	16	⬅	Ignition ON	4,8 V		
	16	⬅	Engine idling	1,7 V		
	16	⬅	Engine idling – accelerate briefly	4,7 V		
	44	⅃—	Ignition ON	0 V		
	45	⇨	Ignition ON	5 V		
Octane coding plug	22	⬅		☐1		
	25	⬅		☐1		
Overspeed warning buzzer	27	⇨		☐1		
Oxygen sensor (O2S)/heated oxygen sensor (HO2S)	17	⬅	Engine idling – engine hot	0-1 V fluctuating	0,2 V/1 sec.	〰 21
Power steering pressure (PSP) switch	37	⬅	Engine idling – steering wheel not turned	5 V		
	37	⬅	Engine idling – steering wheel turned	0 V		
Throttle position (TP) sensor	45	⇨	Ignition ON	5 V		
	46	⅃—	Ignition ON	0 V		
	19	⬅	Ignition ON – throttle closed	0,6 V		
	19	⬅	Ignition ON – throttle fully open	4,6 V		
Vehicle speed sensor (VSS)	12	⬅	Ignition ON – vehicle moving	0-5 V fluctuating		

*Suggested settings - Voltage/time per division

☐1 Connected pin - no test data available or random digital signal

DAEWOO

Daewoo EIFI-6

Model:	Engine code:	Year:
Lanos 1,6i	A16DM	1997-01

ECM harness multi-plug

Terminal side

C1 C2 C3 C4 C5 C6 C7 C8 C9 C10 C11 C12 C13 C14 C15 C16
D1 D2 D3 D4 D5 D6 D7 D8 D9 D10 D11 D12 D13 D14 D15 D16

A1 A2 A3 A4 A5 A6 A7 A8 A9 A10 A11 A12 A13 A14 A15 A16
B1 B2 B3 B4 B5 B6 B7 B8 B9 B10 B11 B12 B13 B14 B15 B16

AD42236

Wire side

A16 A15 A14 A13 A12 A11 A10 A9 A8 A7 A6 A5 A4 A3 A2 A1
B16 B15 B14 B13 B12 B11 B10 B9 B8 B7 B6 B5 B4 B3 B2 B1

C16 C15 C14 C13 C12 C11 C10 C9 C8 C7 C6 C5 C4 C3 C2 C1
D16 D15 D14 D13 D12 D11 D10 D9 D8 D7 D6 D5 D4 D3 D2 D1

AD42237

Component/circuit description	ECM pin	Signal	Condition	Typical value	Oscilloscope setting*	Wave form
AC refrigerant pressure sensor	C15	←	Ignition ON	0,7 V		
	C15	←	Engine idling – AC ON	1 V		
	D8	⇒	Ignition ON	5 V		
	D15	⌐	Ignition ON	0 V		
Battery	A6	←	Ignition OFF	11-14 V		
Crankshaft position (CKP) sensor	A16	←	Engine running		5 V/2 ms	2
	B14	←	Engine running		5 V/2 ms	Reversed 2
Data link connector (DLC)	B9		Ignition ON	11-14 V		
	D11		Ignition ON	5 V		
Earth	B1		Ignition ON	0 V		
	C7		Ignition ON	0 V		
	C9		Ignition ON	0 V		
	D7		Ignition ON	0 V		
	D16		Ignition ON	0 V		
Engine coolant temperature (ECT) sensor	B2	⌐	Ignition ON	0 V		
	B3	←	Ignition ON – coolant temp. 12°C	2,4 V		
	B3	←	Ignition ON – coolant temp. 80°C	1,94 V		
Evaporative emission (EVAP) canister purge valve	A13	⌐▷	Ignition ON	11-14 V		
	A13	⌐▷	Engine running – valve not operating	0%		
	A13	⌐▷	Engine running – valve operating	1-99%	10 V/20 ms	20
Exhaust gas recirculation (EGR) solenoid	A11	⌐▷	Ignition ON	11-14 V		
	A11	⌐▷	Engine idling	11-14 V		
Fuel pump relay	A12	⌐▷	Ignition ON	0 V briefly then 11-14 V		
	A12	⌐▷	Engine cranking	0 V		
	A12	⌐▷	Engine running	0 V		
Heated oxygen sensor (HO2S)	D9	←	Engine idling – accelerate briefly	0-1 V fluctuating	0,2 V/1 sec.	21

* Suggested settings - Voltage/time per division

Autodata

Component/circuit description	ECM pin	Signal	Condition	Typical value	Oscilloscope setting*	Wave form
Idle air control (IAC) valve	A1	⇨	Ignition ON	10 V		
	A1 (A2)	⇨	Engine idling		5 V/0,1 sec.	Intermittent ⋀⋁⋀ 26
	A2	⇨	Ignition ON	1 V		
	A2 (A1)	⇨	Engine idling		5 V/0,1 sec.	Intermittent ⋀⋁⋀ 26
	A3	⇨	Ignition ON	10 V		
	A3 (A4)	⇨	Engine idling		5 V/0,1 sec.	Intermittent ⋀⋁⋀ 26
	A4	⇨	Ignition ON	1 V		
	A4 (A3)	⇨	Engine idling		5 V/0,1 sec.	Intermittent ⋀⋁⋀ 26
Ignition coil	C14	⇨	Ignition ON	0 V		
	C14	⇨	Engine idling	14 Hz	2 V/20 ms	⋀⋁⋀ 32
	D14	⇨	Ignition ON	0 V		
	D14	⇨	Engine idling	14 Hz	2 V/20 ms	⋀⋁⋀ 32
Ignition switch	C16	⇦	Ignition ON	11-14 V		
Injectors 1 & 4	C4	⇨	Ignition ON	11-14 V		
	C4	⇨	Engine idling	2,1 ms	10 V/2 ms	⋀⋁⋀ 35
Injectors 2 & 3	C6	⇨	Ignition ON	11-14 V		
	C6	⇨	Engine idling	2,1 ms	10 V/2 ms	⋀⋁⋀ 35
Intake air temperature (IAT) sensor	B4	⇦	Ignition ON – air temp. 12°C	2,5 V		
	D15	⅃—	Ignition ON	0 V		
Intake manifold air control solenoid	B11	⅃⇨	Ignition ON	11-14 V		
	B11	⅃⇨	Engine idling	0 V		
	B11	⅃⇨	Engine idling – accelerate briefly	11-14 V briefly		
Knock sensor (KS)	C11	⇦	Engine idling – accelerate briefly		50 mV/1 ms	⋀⋁⋀ 38
	D15	⅃—	Ignition ON	0 V		
Malfunction indicator lamp (MIL)	B10	⅃⇨	Ignition ON – MIL ON	0 V		
	B10	⅃⇨	Engine running – MIL OFF	11-14 V		
Manifold absolute pressure (MAP) sensor	A7	⇦	Ignition ON	5 V approx.		
	A7	⇦	Engine idling	1,5 V		
	A7	⇦	Engine idling – accelerate briefly	4,9 V briefly	1 V/2 secs.	⋀⋁⋀ 40
	D8	⇨	Ignition ON	5 V		
	D15	⅃—	Ignition ON	0 V		
Octane coding plug	C13	⇦	Ignition ON	0 V		
	D6	⇨	Ignition ON	5 V		
Tachometer	B13	⇨	Ignition ON	11-14 V		
	B13	⇨	Engine idling	30 Hz		
	B13	⇨	Engine idling	100 Hz		
Throttle position (TP) sensor	B2	⅃—	Ignition ON	0 V		
	D5	⇦	Ignition ON – throttle closed	0,65 V		
	D5	⇦	Ignition ON – throttle fully open	4,6 V		
	D8	⇨	Ignition ON	5 V		
Vehicle speed sensor (VSS)	D10	⇦	Ignition ON – vehicle pushed	0-9,5 V fluctuating		

*Suggested settings - Voltage/time per division

1 Connected pin - no test data available or random digital signal

DAEWOO

GM ITMS-6F

Model:	Engine code:	Year:
Nubira 1,6	A16DM	1997-03
Nubira 2,0	C20SE/X20SED	1997-03

ECM harness multi-plug

Terminal side

C1 C2 C3 C4 C5 C6 C7 C8 C9 C10 C11 C12 C13 C14 C15 C16

D1 D2 D3 D4 D5 D6 D7 D8 D9 D10 D11 D12 D13 D14 D15 D16

A1 A2 A3 A4 A5 A6 A7 A8 A9 A10 A11 A12 A13 A14 A15 A16

B1 B2 B3 B4 B5 B6 B7 B8 B9 B10 B11 B12 B13 B14 B15 B16

AD42236

Wire side

A16 A15 A14 A13 A12 A11 A10 A9 A8 A7 A6 A5 A4 A3 A2 A1

B16 B15 B14 B13 B12 B11 B10 B9 B8 B7 B6 B5 B4 B3 B2 B1

C16 C15 C14 C13 C12 C11 C10 C9 C8 C7 C6 C5 C4 C3 C2 C1

D16 D15 D14 D13 D12 D11 D10 D9 D8 D7 D6 D5 D4 D3 D2 D1

AD42237

Component/circuit description	ECM pin	Signal	Condition	Typical value	Oscilloscope setting*	Wave form
AC compressor clutch relay	A15	⅃▷	Ignition ON	11-14 V		
	A15	⅃▷	Engine idling – AC compressor OFF	11-14 V		
	A15	⅃▷	Engine idling – AC compressor ON	0-1 V		
AC control module	A8	←	Engine idling – AC OFF	0 V		
	A8	←	Engine idling – AC ON	11-14 V		
AC refrigerant pressure sensor	C15	←	Ignition ON	0 V		
	D8	⇒	Ignition ON	5 V		
	D15	⅃	Ignition ON	0 V		
Battery	A6	←	Ignition OFF	11-14 V		
Crankshaft position (CKP) sensor	A16 (B14)	←	Engine idling	4,8 V ac	2 V/1 ms	∿∿ 2
	B14 (A16)	←	Engine idling	4,8 V ac	2 V/1 ms	∿∿ 2
Data link connector (DLC)	B9		Ignition ON	9 V		
	D11		Ignition ON	5 V		
Earth	B1		Ignition ON	0 V		
	C7		Ignition ON	0 V		
	C9		Ignition ON	0 V		
	D7		Ignition ON	0 V		
	D16		Ignition ON	0 V		
Engine coolant blower motor relay 1 – without AC	A10	⅃▷	Engine running – coolant blower motor OFF	11-14 V		
	A10	⅃▷	Engine running – coolant blower motor ON, 1st speed	0-1 V		
	A10	⅃▷	Engine running – coolant blower motor ON, 2nd speed	11-14 V		
Engine coolant blower motor relay 1 – with AC	A10	⅃▷	Engine running – coolant blower motors OFF	11-14 V		
	A10	⅃▷	Engine running – coolant blower motors ON, 1st speed	0-1 V		
	A10	⅃▷	Engine running – coolant blower motor 2 ON, 2nd speed	0-1 V		

★ Suggested settings - Voltage/time per division

Component/circuit description	ECM pin	Signal	Condition	Typical value	Oscilloscope setting*	Wave form
Engine coolant blower motor relay 2 – without AC	A14	⊣▷	Engine running – coolant blower motor OFF	11-14 V		
	A14	⊣▷	Engine running – coolant blower motor ON, 1st speed	11-14 V		
	A14	⊣▷	Engine running – coolant blower motor ON, 2nd speed	0-1 V		
Engine coolant blower motor relays 2 & 3 – with AC	A14	⊣▷	Engine running – coolant blower motors OFF	11-14 V		
	A14	⊣▷	Engine running – coolant blower motors ON, 1st speed	11-14 V		
	A14	⊣▷	Engine running – coolant blower motors ON, 2nd speed	0-1 V		
Engine coolant temperature (ECT) sensor	B2	⊣–	Ignition ON	0 V		
	B3	◀—	Ignition ON – engine cold	2,8 V		
	B3	◀—	Ignition ON – engine hot	1,5-2 V		
Evaporative emission (EVAP) canister purge valve	A13	⊣▷	Ignition ON	11-14 V		
	A13	⊣▷	Engine running – engine hot – valve operating		10 V/50 ms	Intermittent ⩗⩗ 20
Exhaust gas recirculation (EGR) solenoid	A11	⊣▷	Ignition ON	11-14 V		
	A11	⊣▷	Engine idling	11-14 V		
Fuel pump (FP) relay	A12	⊣▷	Ignition ON	11-14 V		
	A12	⊣▷	Engine idling	0-1 V		
Idle air control (IAC) valve	A1	⇨	Ignition ON	11 V		
	A1 (A2)	⇨	Engine idling		5 V/50 ms	Intermittent ⩗⩗ 80
	A2	⇨	Ignition ON	0,9 V		
	A2 (A1)	⇨	Engine idling		5 V/50 ms	Intermittent ⩗⩗ 80
	A3	⇨	Ignition ON	0,9 V		
	A3 (A4)	⇨	Engine idling		5 V/50 ms	Intermittent ⩗⩗ 80
	A4	⇨	Ignition ON	11 V		
	A4 (A3)	⇨	Engine idling		5 V/50 ms	Intermittent ⩗⩗ 80
Ignition amplifier	C14	⇨	Engine idling	13 Hz	1 V/20 ms	⩗⩗ 32
	D14	⇨	Engine idling	13 Hz	1 V/20 ms	⩗⩗ 32
Ignition switch	C16	◀—	Ignition ON	11-14 V		
Injectors 1 & 4	C4	⊣▷	Ignition ON	11-14 V		
	C4	⊣▷	Engine idling – engine hot	1,9 ms	10 V/2 ms	⩗⩗ 35
Injectors 2 & 3	C6	⊣▷	Ignition ON	11-14 V		
	C6	⊣▷	Engine idling – engine hot	1,9 ms	10 V/2 ms	⩗⩗ 35
Intake air temperature (IAT) sensor	B4	◀—	Ignition ON – 10°C	2,7 V		
	D15	⊣–	Ignition ON	0 V		
Intake manifold air control solenoid – 1,6	B11	⊣▷	Ignition ON	11-14 V		
	B11	⊣▷	Engine idling	11-14 V		
	B11	⊣▷	Engine running – solenoid ON	0-1 V		
Knock sensor (KS)	C11	◀—	Engine idling – accelerate briefly		50 mV/0,5 ms	⩗⩗ 38
	D15	⊣▷	Ignition ON	0-1 V		
Malfunction indicator lamp (MIL)	B10	⇨	Ignition ON – lamp ON	0 V		
	B10	⇨	Engine idling – lamp OFF	11-14 V		

* Suggested settings - Voltage/time per division

DAEWOO

Component/circuit description	ECM pin	Signal	Condition	Typical value	Oscilloscope setting*	Wave form
Manifold absolute pressure (MAP) sensor	A7	←	Ignition ON	0 V		
	A7	←	Engine idling	1,2 V		
	A7	←	3000 rpm	1 V		
	A7	←	Engine idling – full throttle briefly	4,8 V		
	D8	⇒	Ignition ON	5 V		
	D15	⌐	Ignition ON	0 V		
Octane coding plug	C13	←		[1]		
	D6	←		[1]		
	D15	⌐	Ignition ON	0 V		
Oxygen sensor (O2S)	D9	←	Ignition ON	0,4-0,6 V		
	D9	←	Engine idling – engine hot	0,1-0,9 V fluctuating	0,2 V/1 sec.	⩗⩘ 21
Transmission range (TR) switch – AT	B8	⇒	Ignition ON – AT in P or N	0 V		
	B8	⇒	Ignition ON – AT not in P or N	11-14 V		
Throttle position (TP) sensor	B2	⌐	Ignition ON	0 V		
	D5	←	Ignition ON – throttle closed	0,4 V		
	D5	←	Ignition ON – throttle fully open	4,5 V		
	D8	⇒	Ignition ON	5 V		
Transmission control module (TCM) – AT →1999	A9	⇒	Ignition ON	6 V		
	B12	⇒	Ignition ON	0,7 V		
	B12	⇒	Engine idling	4,7 V		
Transmission control module (TCM) – AT →1999 – engine speed signal	B13	⇒	Ignition ON	9,5 V		
	B13	⇒	Engine idling	27 Hz		
	B13	⇒	3000 rpm	100 Hz		
Transmission control module (TCM) – AT →1999 – vehicle speed signal	D10	←	Ignition ON – vehicle pushed	0 V or 11 V switching		
Vehicle speed sensor (VSS) – AT 1999→	D10	←	Ignition ON – vehicle pushed	0 V or 11 V switching		
Vehicle speed sensor (VSS) – MT	D10	←	Ignition ON – vehicle pushed	0 V or 11 V switching		

*Suggested settings - Voltage/time per division

[1] Connected pin - no test data available or random digital signal

Autodata

Model:	Engine code:	Year:
Cinquecento	1170 A1 046	1991-98
Cinquecento 900	170 A1 046	1991-97
Cinquecento Sporting	176 B2 000	1994-98
Punto 55	176 A6 000/B2 000	1993-99
Punto 60	176 A7 000/B4 000	1994-99

ECM harness multi-plug

Terminal side

35 34 33 32 31 30 29 28 27 26 25 24 23 22 21 20 19
18 17 16 15 14 13 12 11 10 9 8 7 6 5 4 3 2 1

AD78538

Wire side

19 20 21 22 23 24 25 26 27 28 29 30 31 32 33 34 35
1 2 3 4 5 6 7 8 9 10 11 12 13 14 15 16 17 18

AD42096

Component/circuit description	ECM pin	Signal	Condition	Typical value	Oscilloscope setting*	Wave form
AC compressor clutch relay – if fitted	24	⊐→	Engine idling – AC OFF	11-14 V		
	24	⊐→	Engine idling – AC ON – AC compressor ON	0-1 V		
AC control module – Punto – if fitted	8			1		
AC refrigerant pressure switch – Cinquecento/Seicento – if fitted	8			1		
Alarm system control module – if fitted	23	⊐→	Engine cranking	0 V		
	26	←	Ignition ON	11-14 V		
Crankshaft position (CKP) sensor	11 (28)	←	Engine cranking	2,5 V ac		
	11 (28)	←	Engine idling	5,6 V ac	2 V/2 ms	2
	11 (28)	←	3000 rpm	12,4 V ac		
	28 (11)	←	Engine cranking	2,5 V ac		
	28 (11)	←	Engine idling	5,6 V ac	2 V/2 ms	Reversed 2
	28 (11)	←	3000 rpm	12,4 V ac		
Data link connector (DLC)	10	←→	Ignition ON	11-14 V		
	15	←→	Ignition ON	11-14 V		
	16	⊐—	Ignition ON	0 V		
Earth	17		Ignition ON	0 V		
	34		Ignition ON	0 V		
Engine control relay – 899/903 cc	4	⊐→	Ignition OFF	11-14 V after 1 minute		
	4	⊐→	Ignition ON	0-1 V		
	35	←	Ignition OFF	0 V after 1 minute		
	35	←	Ignition ON	11-14 V		
Engine coolant temperature (ECT) sensor	13	←	Ignition ON – coolant temp. 20°C	2,8 V		
	13	←	Ignition ON – coolant temp. 80°C	0,56 V		
	16	⊐—	Ignition ON	0 V		
Evaporative emission (EVAP) canister purge valve	22	⇒	Ignition ON	11-14 V briefly then 0 V		
	22	⇒	Engine idling – engine hot – valve not operating	11-14 V		
	22	⇒	Engine under load – engine hot – valve operating		10 V/20 ms	20
Fuel pump relay – 899/903 cc	23	⊐→	Ignition ON	0-1 V briefly then 11-14 V		
	23	⊐→	Engine cranking	0 V		

* Suggested settings - Voltage/time per division

Component/circuit description	ECM pin	Signal	Condition	Typical value	Oscilloscope setting*	Wave form
Heated oxygen sensor (HO2S)	12	⌐—	Engine idling	0 V		
	29	⟵	Engine idling – engine hot	0,1-1,0 V fluctuating	0,2 V/1 sec.	MMM 21
Idle speed control (ISC) actuator	2 (20)	⟹	Engine idling		5 V/0,1 sec.	Intermittent MMM 26
	3 (21)	⟹	Engine idling		5 V/0,1 sec.	Intermittent MMM 26
	2	⟹	Ignition ON	0,2 V or 11-14 V		
	2	⟹	Engine idling	0,2 V or 11-14 V		
	3	⟹	Ignition ON	0,2 V or 11-14 V		
	3	⟹	Engine idling	0,2 V or 11-14 V		
	20 (2)	⟹	Ignition ON	0,2 V or 11-14 V		
	20 (2)	⟹	Engine idling	0,2 V or 11-14 V		
	20 (2)	⟹	Engine idling		5 V/0,1 sec.	Intermittent MMM 26
	21 (3)	⟹	Ignition ON	0,2 V or 11-14 V		
	21 (3)	⟹	Engine idling	0,2 V or 11-14 V		
	21 (3)	⟹	Engine idling		5 V/0,1 sec.	Intermittent MMM 26
Ignition coil – cylinders 1 & 4	19	⊐▷	Ignition ON	11-14 V briefly then 0 V		
	19	⊐▷	Engine cranking	10,5 V		
	19	⊐▷	Engine idling		5 V/2 ms	MMM 33
Ignition coil – cylinders 2 & 3	1	⊐▷	Ignition ON	11-14 V briefly then 0 V		
	1	⊐▷	Engine cranking	9 V		
	1	⊐▷	Engine idling		5 V/2 ms	MMM 33
Ignition switch	26	⟵	Ignition ON	11-14 V		
Immobilizer control module – if fitted	7	⟵	Ignition ON	11-14 V/0 V after 1 minute		
Injector	18	⊐▷	Ignition ON	11-14 V briefly then 0 V		
	18	⊐▷	Engine idling	1,4 ms	10 V/2 ms	MMM 35
Intake air temperature (IAT) sensor	16	⌐—	Ignition ON	0 V		
	31	⟵	Ignition ON – air temp. 20°C	3,1 V		
Malfunction indicator lamp (MIL)	6	⟹	Ignition ON – MIL ON	0,8 V		
	6	⟹	Ignition ON – MIL OFF	11-14 V		
Manifold absolute pressure (MAP) sensor	14	⟹	Ignition ON	5 V		
	16	⌐—	Ignition ON	0 V		
	32	⟵	Ignition ON	4,5 V		
	32	⟵	Engine idling	1,5 V		
	32	⟵	3000 rpm	1,2 V		
Relay module – 1108/1242 cc	4	⊐▷	Ignition OFF	11-14 V after 1 minute		
	4	⊐▷	Ignition ON	0-1 V		
	23	⊐▷	Ignition ON	0-1 V briefly then 11-14 V		
	23	⊐▷	Engine cranking	0 V		
	35	⟵	Ignition OFF	0 V after 1 minute		
	35	⟵	Ignition ON	11-14 V		
Throttle position (TP) sensor	14	⟹	Ignition ON	5 V		
	16	⌐—	Ignition ON	0 V		
	30	⟵	Ignition ON – throttle closed	0,2-0,6 V		
	30	⟵	Ignition ON – throttle fully open	4,2-5 V		
Transmission control module (TCM) – AT	5			1		

*Suggested settings - Voltage/time per division

1 Connected pin - no test data available or random digital signal

Model:	Engine code:	Year:
Seicento 900	1170 A1 046	1998-01
Seicento Sporting	176 B2 000	1998-02

FIAT
Weber-Marelli IAW 06F/16F

ECM harness multi-plug

Terminal side

35 34 33 32 31 30 29 28 27 26 25 24 23 22 21 20 19

18 17 16 15 14 13 12 11 10 9 8 7 6 5 4 3 2 1

AD78538

Wire side

19 20 21 22 23 24 25 26 27 28 29 30 31 32 33 34 35

1 2 3 4 5 6 7 8 9 10 11 12 13 14 15 16 17 18

AD42096

Component/circuit description	ECM pin	Signal	Condition	Typical value	Oscilloscope setting*	Wave form
AC compressor clutch relay – if fitted	24	→⊃	Engine idling – AC OFF	11-14 V		
	24	→⊃	Engine idling – AC ON – AC compressor ON	0-1 V		
AC refrigerant pressure switch – if fitted	8	←		1		
Clutch control module – if fitted	23	⊃		1		
Crankshaft position (CKP) sensor	11 (28)	←	Engine idling	6 V ac	2 V/2 ms	2
	28 (11)	←	Engine idling	6 V ac	2 V/2 ms	2
Data link connector (DLC)	10	⇆	Ignition ON	11-14 V		
	15	⇆	Ignition ON	11-14 V		
	16	⊣	Ignition ON	0 V		
Earth	17		Ignition ON	0 V		
	34		Ignition ON	0 V		
Engine control relay – without AC or automatic clutch control	4	→⊃	Ignition OFF	11-14 V after 1 minute		
	4	→⊃	Ignition ON	0-1 V		
	35	←	Ignition OFF	0 V after 1 minute		
	35	←	Ignition ON	11-14 V		
Engine coolant temperature (ECT) sensor	13	←	Ignition ON – coolant temp. 20°C	2,8 V		
	13	←	Ignition ON – coolant temp. 80°C	0,56 V		
	16	⊣	Ignition ON	0 V		
Evaporative emission (EVAP) canister purge valve	22	⊃	Ignition ON	11-14 V briefly then 0 V		
	22	⊃	Engine idling – engine hot – valve not operating	11-14 V		
	22	⊃	Engine under load – engine hot – valve operating		10 V/20 ms	20
Fuel pump relay – without AC or automatic clutch control	23	→⊃	Ignition ON	0-1 V briefly then 11-14 V		
	23	→⊃	Engine cranking	0 V		
Heated oxygen sensor (HO2S)	12	⊣	Engine idling	0 V		
	29	←	Engine idling – engine hot	0,1-1,0 V fluctuating	0,2 V/1 sec.	21

* Suggested settings - Voltage/time per division

Component/circuit description	ECM pin	Signal	Condition	Typical value	Oscilloscope setting*	Wave form
Idle air control (IAC) valve	**2 (20)**	⇨	Engine idling		5 V/0,1 sec.	Intermittent 26
	3 (21)	⇨	Engine idling		5 V/0,1 sec.	Intermittent 26
	2	⇨	Ignition ON	0,2 V or 11-14 V		
	2	⇨	Engine idling	0,2 V or 11-14 V		
	3	⇨	Ignition ON	0,2 V or 11-14 V		
	3	⇨	Engine idling	0,2 V or 11-14 V		
	20 (2)	⇨	Ignition ON	0,2 V or 11-14 V		
	20 (2)	⇨	Engine idling	0,2 V or 11-14 V	5 V/0,1 sec.	Intermittent 26
	21 (3)	⇨	Ignition ON	0,2 V or 11-14 V		
	21 (3)	⇨	Engine idling	0,2 V or 11-14 V	5 V/0,1 sec.	Intermittent 26
Ignition coil – cylinders 1 & 4	**1**	⊣▷	Ignition ON	11-14 V briefly then 0 V		
	1	⊣▷	Engine idling		5 V/2 ms	33
Ignition coil – cylinders 2 & 3	**19**	⊣▷	Ignition ON	11-14 V briefly then 0 V		
	19	⊣▷	Engine idling		5 V/2 ms	33
Ignition switch	**26**	⬅	Ignition ON	11-14 V		
Immobilizer control module	**7**			[1]		
Injector	**18**	⊣▷	Ignition ON	11-14 V briefly then 0 V		
	18	⊣▷	Engine idling	1,5 ms	10 V/2 ms	35
Intake air temperature (IAT) sensor	**16**	⊣—	Ignition ON	0 V		
	31	⬅	Ignition ON – air temp. 20°C	3,1 V		
Malfunction indicator lamp (MIL)	**6**	⇨	Ignition ON – MIL ON	0,8 V		
	6	⇨	Ignition ON – MIL OFF	11-14 V		
Manifold absolute pressure (MAP) sensor	**14**	⇨	Ignition ON	5 V		
	16	⊣—	Ignition ON	0 V		
	32	⬅	Ignition ON	4,5 V		
	32	⬅	Engine idling	1,5 V		
	32	⬅	3000 rpm	1,2 V		
Relay module – with AC or automatic clutch control	**4**	⊣▷	Ignition OFF	11-14 V after 1 minute		
	4	⊣▷	Ignition ON	0-1 V		
	23	⇨		[1]		
	35	⬅	Ignition OFF	0 V after 1 minute		
	35	⬅	Ignition ON	11-14 V		
Tachometer – with AC	**23**	⇨		[1]		
Throttle position (TP) sensor	**14**	⇨	Ignition ON	5 V		
	16	⊣—	Ignition ON	0 V		
	30	⬅	Ignition ON – throttle closed	0,2-0,6 V		
	30	⬅	Ignition ON – throttle fully open	4,2-5 V		

*Suggested settings - Voltage/time per division

[1] Connected pin - no test data available or random digital signal

ECM harness multi-plug

Terminal side

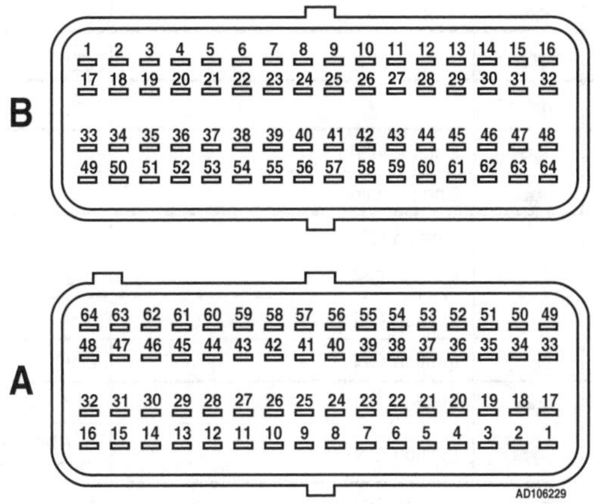

Wire side

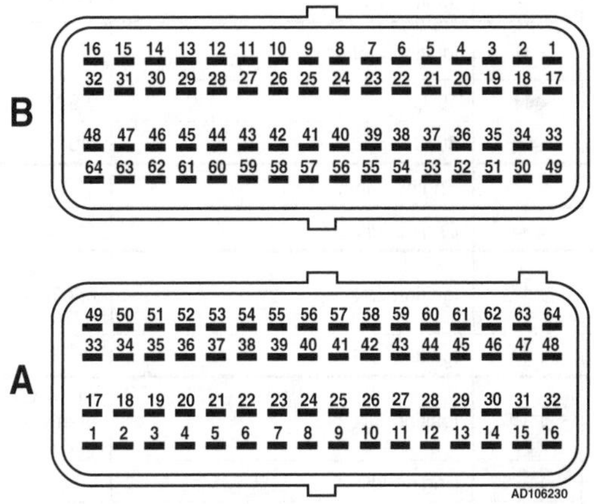

Component/circuit description	ECM pin	Signal	Condition	Typical value	Oscilloscope setting*	Wave form
AC compressor clutch relay	B12	⊣▷	Engine idling – AC OFF	11-14 V		
	B12	⊣▷	Engine idling – AC ON	0-1 V		
AC control module	B26			[1]		
AC refrigerant pressure sensor – if fitted	B3	⇨	Ignition ON	5 V		
	B5	⬅		[1]		
	B15	⏚	Ignition ON	0 V		
Accelerator pedal position (APP) sensor	B2	⇨	Ignition ON	5 V		
	B3	⇨	Ignition ON	5 V		
	B15	⏚	Ignition ON	0 V		
	B40	⬅	Ignition ON – accelerator pedal released	0,37 V		
	B40	⬅	Ignition ON – accelerator pedal depressed	2,2 V		
	B42	⬅	Ignition ON – accelerator pedal released	0,7 V		
	B42	⬅	Ignition ON – accelerator pedal depressed	4,48 V		
	B46	⏚	Ignition ON	0 V		
Battery	B16	⬅	Ignition OFF	11-14 V		
	B16	⬅	Ignition ON	11-14 V		

* Suggested settings - Voltage/time per division

Component/circuit description	ECM pin	Signal	Condition	Typical value	Oscilloscope setting*	Wave form
Brake pedal position (BPP) switch	B34	←	Ignition ON – pedal released	11-14 V		
	B34	←	Ignition ON – pedal depressed	0 V		
	B35	←	Ignition ON – pedal released	0 V		
	B35	←	Ignition ON – pedal depressed	11-14 V		
Camshaft position (CMP) sensor	A7	⌐—	Ignition ON	0 V		
	A13	⇨	Ignition ON	5 V		
	A24	←	Engine idling		2 V/50 ms	〰 34
CAN data bus – high	B52	⬌		[1]		
CAN data bus – low	B36	⬌		[1]		
Crankshaft position (CKP) sensor	A9	←	Engine idling		2 V/1ms	〰 2
	A23	←	Engine idling		2 V/1 ms	Reversed 〰 2
Earth	A5		Ignition ON	0 V		
	A6		Ignition ON	0 V		
	A21		Ignition ON	0 V		
	A22		Ignition ON	0 V		
Engine control (EC) relay	B6	←	Ignition ON	11-14 V		
	B62	←	Ignition ON	0 V briefly then 11-14 V		
Engine coolant blower motor relay 1	B55	⌐⊳	Ignition ON	11-14 V		
Engine coolant blower motor relay 2	B59	⌐⊳	Ignition ON	11-14 V		
Engine coolant temperature (ECT) sensor	A36	⌐—	Ignition ON	0 V		
	A45	←	10°C	3,9 V		
	A45	←	80°C	0,9 V		
Engine malfunction indicator lamp (MIL)	B58	⌐⊳	Engine idling	11-14 V		
Engine oil pressure sensor	B7	←	Engine idling	11-14 V		
Evaporative emission (EVAP) canister purge valve	A51	⌐⊳	Ignition ON	11-14 V briefly then 0 V		
	A51	⌐⊳	Ignition ON		10 V/20 ms	〰 20
Heated oxygen sensor (HO2S) 1	A32	⌐⊳	Ignition ON	11-14 V briefly then 0 V		
	A32	⌐⊳	Engine idling		2 V/50 ms	〰 72
	A43	←	Engine idling	0-1 V fluctuating		
	A60	⌐—	Ignition OFF	0 V		
	A60	⌐—	Ignition ON	0 V		
Heated oxygen sensor (HO2S) 2	A42	←	Engine idling	0,6 V		
	A58	⌐—	Ignition OFF	0 V		
	A58	⌐—	Ignition ON	0 V		
	A64	⌐⊳	Ignition ON	11-14 V briefly then 0 V		
	A64	⌐⊳	Engine idling		2 V/50 ms	〰 72
Ignition coil 1	A17	⌐⊳	Engine idling		10 V/1 ms	〰 33
Ignition coil 2	A19	⌐⊳	Engine idling		10 V/1 ms	〰 33
Ignition switch	B17	←	Ignition ON	11-14 V		
	B29	←	Ignition ON	11-14 V		
Injector 1	A50	⌐⊳	Ignition ON	11-14 V briefly then 0 V		
	A50	⌐⊳	Engine idling	2,6 ms	10 V/2 ms	〰 35
Injector 2	A34	⌐⊳	Ignition ON	11-14 V briefly then 0 V		
	A34	⌐⊳	Engine idling	2,6 ms	10 V/2 ms	〰 35

* Suggested settings - Voltage/time per division

Component/circuit description	ECM pin	Signal	Condition	Typical value	Oscilloscope setting*	Wave form
Injector 3	A49	⊐▷	Ignition ON	11-14 V briefly then 0 V		
	A49	⊐▷	Engine idling	2,6 ms	10 V/2 ms	〰️ 35
Injector 4	A33	⊐▷	Ignition ON	11-14 V briefly then 0 V		
	A33	⊐▷	Engine idling	2,6 ms	10 V/2 ms	〰️ 35
Intake air temperature (IAT) sensor	A7	⊐─	Ignition ON	0 V		
	A63	⬅	Ignition ON – air temp. 11°C	3,2 V		
	A63	⬅	Engine idling – air temp. 28°C	2,4 V		
Knock sensor	A41	⬅	Ignition ON	1,5 V		
	A41	⬅	Engine idling		50 mv/1 ms	〰️ 38
	A48	⬅	Ignition ON	1,5 V		
Manifold absolute pressure (MAP) sensor	A7	⊐─	Ignition ON	0 V		
	A13	⇨	Ignition ON	5 V		
	A31	⬅	Ignition ON	4,1 V		
	A31	⬅	Engine idling – accelerate briefly	4 V briefly		
Multifunction control module III	B10			☐1		
	B10			☐1		
	B11			☐1		
	B11			☐1		
Throttle motor	A52	⬅	Ignition ON		5 V/1 ms	〰️ 69
	A57	⬅	Ignition ON		5 V/1 ms	〰️ 69
	A57	⬅	Engine idling	0,1 V		
	A57	⬅	Engine idling – accelerate briefly	11-14 V briefly		
Throttle motor position sensor	A15	⇨	Ignition ON	5 V		
	A15	⇨	Engine idling	5 V		
	A30	⬅	Ignition ON	3,8 V		
	A30	⬅	Engine idling	4,3 V		
	A30	⬅	Engine idling – accelerate briefly	1,9 V briefly		
	A35	⊐─	Ignition ON	0 V		
	A44	⬅	Ignition ON	1 V		
	A44	⬅	Engine idling	0,6 V		
	A44	⬅	Engine idling – accelerate briefly	0,9 V briefly		
Transmission control module (TCM)	B63			☐1		

*Suggested settings - Voltage/time per division

☐1 Connected pin - no test data available or random digital signal

FIAT
Weber-Marelli IAW 08F/18F

Model:	Engine code:	Year:
Punto 75	176 A8 000	1993-99

Autodata

ECM harness multi-plug

Terminal side

AD78538

Wire side

AD42096

Component/circuit description	ECM pin	Signal	Condition	Typical value	Oscilloscope setting*	Wave form
AC compressor clutch relay – if fitted	24	⊐→		1		
AC control module – if fitted	8			1		
Alarm system control module – if fitted	23	⊐→	Ignition ON	0-1 V briefly then 11-14 V		
	23	⊐→	Engine cranking	0 V		
Crankshaft position (CKP) sensor	11 (28)	←	Engine cranking	2 V ac		
	11 (28)	←	Engine idling	3 V ac	2 V/2 ms	2
	11 (28)	←	3000 rpm	6 V ac		
	28 (11)	←	Engine cranking	2 V ac		
	28 (11)	←	Engine idling	3 V ac	2 V/2 ms	Reversed 2
	28 (11)	←	3000 rpm	6 V ac		
Data link connector (DLC)	10	←→	Ignition ON	11-14 V		
	15	←→	Ignition ON	11-14 V		
	16	⊐−	Ignition ON	0 V		
Earth	17		Ignition ON	0 V		
	34		Ignition ON	0 V		
Engine coolant temperature (ECT) sensor	13	←	Ignition ON – coolant temp. 20°C	2,8 V		
	13	←	Ignition ON – coolant temp. 80°C	0,56 V		
	16	⊐−	Ignition ON	0 V		
Evaporative emission (EVAP) canister purge valve	22	⇨	Ignition ON	11-14 V briefly then 0 V		
	22	⊐→	Engine hot – valve operating		10 V/20 ms	20
Heated oxygen sensor (HO2S)	12	⊐−	Engine idling	0 V		
	29	←	Engine idling – engine hot	0,1-1,0 V fluctuating	0,2 V/1 sec.	21

* Suggested settings - Voltage/time per division

Autodata

Component/circuit description	ECM pin	Signal	Condition	Typical value	Oscilloscope setting*	Wave form
Idle air control (IAC) valve	2 (20)	⇨	Engine idling		5 V/0,1 sec.	Intermittent 26
	3 (21)	⇨	Engine idling		5 V/0,1 sec.	Intermittent 26
	2	⇨	Ignition ON	0,2 V or 11-14 V		
	2	⇨	Engine idling	0,2 V or 11-14 V		
	3	⇨	Ignition ON	0,2 V or 11-14 V		
	3	⇨	Engine idling	0,2 V or 11-14 V		
	20 (2)	⇨	Engine idling		5 V/0,1 sec.	Intermittent 26
	21 (3)	⇨	Engine idling		5 V/0,1 sec.	Intermittent 26
	20	⇨	Ignition ON	0,2 V or 11-14 V		
	20	⇨	Engine idling	0,2 V or 11-14 V		
	21	⇨	Ignition ON	0,2 V or 11-14 V		
	21	⇨	Engine idling	0,2 V or 11-14 V		
Ignition coil – cylinders 1 & 4	19	⊐▷	Ignition ON	11-14 V briefly then 0 V		
	19	⊐▷	Engine cranking	9 V		
	19	⊐▷	Engine idling		5 V/2 ms	33
Ignition coil – cylinders 2 & 3	1	⊐▷	Ignition ON	11-14 V briefly then 0 V		
	1	⊐▷	Engine cranking	9 V		
	1	⊐▷	Engine idling		5 V/2 ms	33
Immobilizer control module – if fitted	7	⬅	Ignition OFF	11-14 V/0 V after 3 minutes		
	7	⬅	Ignition ON	11-14 V/0 V after 1 minute		
	7	⬅	Engine idling	11-14 V		
Injectors	18	⊐▷	Ignition ON	11-14 V briefly then 0 V		
	18	⊐▷	Engine idling	2,4 ms	10 V/2 ms	35
Intake air temperature (IAT) sensor	16	⊐—	Ignition ON	0 V		
	31	⬅	Ignition ON – air temp. 20°C	3,1 V		
Malfunction indicator lamp (MIL)	6	⊐▷	Ignition ON – MIL ON	0,8 V		
	6	⊐▷	Ignition ON – MIL OFF	11-14 V		
Manifold absolute pressure (MAP) sensor	14	⇨	Ignition ON	5 V		
	16	⊐—	Ignition ON	0 V		
	32	⬅	Ignition ON	4,5 V		
	32	⬅	Engine idling	1,5 V		
	32	⬅	Engine idling – full throttle briefly	4,5 V		
Relay module	4	⊐▷	Ignition OFF	11-14 V after 1 minute		
	4	⊐▷	Ignition ON	0-1 V		
	23	⊐▷	Ignition ON	0-1 V briefly then 11-14 V		
	23	⊐▷	Engine cranking	0 V		
	35	⬅	Ignition OFF	0 V after 2 minutes		
	35	⬅	Ignition ON	11-14 V		
Throttle position (TP) sensor	14	⇨	Ignition ON	5 V		
	16	⊐—	Ignition ON	0 V		
	30	⬅	Ignition ON – throttle closed	0,2-0,6 V		
	30	⬅	Ignition ON – throttle fully open	4,2-5 V		

*Suggested settings - Voltage/time per division

1 Connected pin - no test data available or random digital signal

FIAT

Weber-Marelli IAW 18FD

Model:	Engine code:	Year:
Punto 85	176 B9 000	1997-99

ECM harness multi-plug

Terminal side

AD71594

Wire side

AD42073

Component/circuit description	ECM pin	Signal	Condition	Typical value	Oscilloscope setting*	Wave form
AC compressor clutch relay – if fitted	24	⊐▷		1		
AC control module – if fitted	8			1		
Crankshaft position (CKP) sensor	11	←	Engine idling		2 V/2 ms	2
	28	←	Engine idling		2 V/2 ms	Reversed 2
Data link connector (DLC)	10	◄▷	Ignition ON	11-14 V		
	15	◄▷	Ignition ON	10-11 V		
	16	⊐	Ignition ON	0 V		
Earth	17		Ignition ON	0 V		
	34		Ignition ON	0 V		
Engine coolant temperature (ECT) sensor	13	←	Ignition ON – coolant temp. 10°C	3,5 V		
	13	←	Ignition ON – coolant temp. 80°C	0,6 V		
	16	⊐	Ignition ON	0 V		
Evaporative emission (EVAP) canister purge valve	22	⊐▷	Ignition ON	11-14 V briefly then 0 V		
	22	⊐▷	Engine idling	11-14 V		
	22	⊐▷	Engine hot – valve operating		10 V/20 ms	20
Heated oxygen sensor (HO2S)	12	⊐	Engine idling	0 V		
	29	←	Engine idling – engine hot	0,1-1,0 V fluctuating	0,2 V/1 sec.	21
Idle air control (IAC) valve	2 (20)	⇒	Engine idling		5 V/0,1 sec.	Intermittent 26
	3 (21)	⇒	Engine idling		5 V/0,1 sec.	Intermittent 26
	2	⇒	Ignition ON	0,2 V or 11-14 V		
	3	⇒	Ignition ON	0,2 V or 11-14 V		
	20 (2)	⇒	Engine idling		5 V/0,1 sec.	Intermittent 26
	21 (3)	⇒	Engine idling		5 V/0,1 sec.	Intermittent 26
	20	⇒	Ignition ON	2,5 V		
	21	⇒	Ignition ON	11-14 V briefly then 2,5 V		
Ignition coil – cylinders 1 & 4	19	⊐▷	Ignition ON	11-14 V briefly then 0 V		
	19	⊐▷	Engine cranking	9 V		
	19	⊐▷	Engine idling		5 V/2 ms	33

* Suggested settings - Voltage/time per division

Component/circuit description	ECM pin	Signal	Condition	Typical value	Oscilloscope setting*	Wave form
Ignition coil – cylinders 2 & 3	1	⊐▷	Ignition ON	11-14 V briefly then 0 V		
	1	⊐▷	Engine cranking	9 V		
	1	⊐▷	Engine idling		5 V/2 ms	∿〰 33
Immobilizer control module	7	←	Ignition ON	11-14 V		
Injectors 1 & 4	18	⊐▷	Ignition ON	11-14 V briefly then 0 V		
	18	⊐▷	Engine idling	2,6 ms	10 V/2 ms	∿〰 35
Injectors 2 & 3	33	⊐▷	Ignition ON	11-14 V briefly then 0 V		
	33	⊐▷	Engine idling	2,8 ms	10 V/2 ms	∿〰 35
Intake air temperature (IAT) sensor	16	⊐—	Ignition ON	0 V		
	31	←	Ignition ON – air temp. 10°C	3,2 V		
Malfunction indicator lamp (MIL)	6	⇨	Ignition ON – MIL ON	0,8 V		
	6	⇨	Ignition ON – MIL OFF	11-14 V		
Manifold absolute pressure (MAP) sensor	14	⇨	Ignition ON	5 V		
	16	⊐—	Ignition ON	0 V		
	32	←	Ignition ON	4,5 V		
	32	←	Engine idling	1,5 V		
	32	←	3000 rpm	0,9 V		
	32	←	Engine idling – full throttle briefly	4,8 V		
Relay module	4	⊐▷	Ignition OFF	11-14 V after 1 minute		
	4	⊐▷	Ignition ON	0-1 V		
	23	⊐▷	Ignition ON	0-1 V briefly then 11-14 V		
	23	⊐▷	Engine cranking	0-1 V		
	35	←	Ignition OFF	0 V after 2 minutes		
	35	←	Ignition ON	11-14 V		
Throttle position (TP) sensor	14	⇨	Ignition ON	5 V		
	16	⊐—	Ignition ON	0 V		
	30	←	Ignition ON – throttle closed	0,5 V		
	30	←	Ignition ON – throttle fully open	4,5 V		

*Suggested settings - Voltage/time per division

1 Connected pin - no test data available or random digital signal

FIAT

Weber-Marelli IAW 59F

Model:	Engine code:	Year:
Punto 1,2 8V	188 A4 000	1999-06

ECM harness multi-plug

Terminal side

B

```
38 37 36 35 34 33 32 31 30 29
○  ○  ○  ○  ○  ○  ○  ○  ○  ○
28 27 26 25 24 23 22 21 20
○  ○  ○  ○  ○  ○  ○  ○  ○
19 18 17 16 15 14 13 12 11
○  ○  ○  ○  ○  ○  ○  ○  ○
10 9  8  7  6  5  4  3  2  1
○  ○  ○  ○  ○  ○  ○  ○  ○  ○
```

A

```
1  2  3  4  5  6  7  8  9  10
○  ○  ○  ○  ○  ○  ○  ○  ○  ○
11 12 13 14 15 16 17 18 19
○  ○  ○  ○  ○  ○  ○  ○  ○
20 21 22 23 24 25 26 27 28
○  ○  ○  ○  ○  ○  ○  ○  ○
29 30 31 32 33 34 35 36 37 38
○  ○  ○  ○  ○  ○  ○  ○  ○  ○
```

AD20078

Wire side

A

```
10 9  8  7  6  5  4  3  2  1
●  ●  ●  ●  ●  ●  ●  ●  ●  ●
19 18 17 16 15 14 13 12 11
●  ●  ●  ●  ●  ●  ●  ●  ●
28 27 26 25 24 23 22 21 20
●  ●  ●  ●  ●  ●  ●  ●  ●
38 37 36 35 34 33 32 31 30 29
●  ●  ●  ●  ●  ●  ●  ●  ●  ●
```

B

```
29 30 31 32 33 34 35 36 37 38
●  ●  ●  ●  ●  ●  ●  ●  ●  ●
20 21 22 23 24 25 26 27 28
●  ●  ●  ●  ●  ●  ●  ●  ●
11 12 13 14 15 16 17 18 19
●  ●  ●  ●  ●  ●  ●  ●  ●
1  2  3  4  5  6  7  8  9  10
●  ●  ●  ●  ●  ●  ●  ●  ●  ●
```

AD23420

Component/circuit description	ECM pin	Signal	Condition	Typical value	Oscilloscope setting*	Wave form
AC compressor clutch relay	B12	⊐▷	Engine idling – AC OFF	11-14 V		
	B12	⊐▷	Engine idling – AC ON – AC compressor ON	0-1 V		
AC refrigerant quadruple pressure switch	B27			1		
	B28			1		
	B38			1		
Battery	B4	←	Ignition OFF	11-14 V		
Crankshaft position (CKP) sensor	A25	←	Engine idling	1,2 V ac	2 V/2 ms	⋀⋁⋀ 2
	A35	←	Engine idling	1,2 V ac	2 V/2 ms	Reversed ⋀⋁⋀ 2
Crankshaft position (CKP) sensor – shield wire	A34	⊐—	Ignition ON	0 V		
Engine control module (ECM) – case		⊐—	Ignition ON	0 V		
Engine control relay	B6	⊐▷	Ignition OFF	0 V		
	B6	⊐▷	Ignition ON	0-1 V briefly then 11-14 V		
	B6	⊐▷	Engine cranking	0-1 V		
Engine coolant blower motor relay – without AC	B8	⊐▷	Engine idling – coolant blower motor OFF	11-14 V		
	B8	⊐▷	Engine idling – coolant blower motor ON	0-1 V		
Engine coolant blower motor relay 1 – with AC	B8	⊐▷	Engine idling – coolant blower motor OFF	11-14 V		
	B8	⊐▷	Engine idling – coolant blower motor ON – low speed	0-1 V		

* Suggested settings - Voltage/time per division

Component/circuit description	ECM pin	Signal	Condition	Typical value	Oscilloscope setting*	Wave form
Engine coolant blower motor relay 2 – with AC	B18	→▷	Engine idling – coolant blower motor OFF	11-14 V		
	B18	→▷	Engine idling – coolant blower motor ON – high speed	0-1 V		
Engine coolant temperature (ECT) sensor	A5	◀	Ignition ON – coolant temp. 10°C	3,5 V		
	A5	◀	Ignition ON – coolant temp. 80°C	0,8 V		
	A29	⊣−	Ignition ON	0 V		
Engine oil pressure switch	A23	◀	Ignition ON	0 V		
	A23	◀	Engine running	11-14 V		
Evaporative emission (EVAP) canister purge valve	A26	→▷	Ignition ON	11-14 V briefly then 0 V		
	A26	→▷	Engine running – valve operating		10 V/20 ms	⋀⋁⋀ 59
Heated oxygen sensor (HO2S)	B22	◀	Engine idling – engine hot	0-1 V fluctuating	0,2 V/1 sec.	⋀⋁⋀ 21
	B32	⊣−	Engine idling	0 V		
Heated oxygen sensor (HO2S) – heater control	B11	→▷	Ignition ON	11-14 V briefly then 0 V		
	B11	→▷	Engine idling – engine hot	94%	2 V/20 ms	⋀⋁⋀ 65
Heated oxygen sensor (HO2S) – shield wire	B34	⊣−	Ignition ON	0 V		
Idle speed control (ISC) actuator	A9	⇨	Ignition ON	0,2 V or 11-14 V		
	A9 (A18)	⇨	Engine idling		5 V/0,2 sec.	Intermittent ⋀⋁⋀ 26
	A17	⇨	Ignition ON	0,2 V or 11-14 V		
	A17 (A19)	⇨	Engine idling		5 V/0,2 sec.	Intermittent ⋀⋁⋀ 26
	A18	⇨	Ignition ON	0,2 or 11-14 V		
	A18 (A9)	⇨	Engine idling		5 V/0,2 sec.	Intermittent ⋀⋁⋀ 26
	A19	⇨	Ignition ON	0,2 V or 11-14 V		
	A19 (A17)	⇨	Engine idling		5 V/0,2 sec.	Intermittent ⋀⋁⋀ 26
Ignition coil – cylinder 1/4	A38	→▷	Ignition ON	11-14 V briefly then 0 V		
	A38	→▷	Engine idling		5 V/2 ms	⋀⋁⋀ 33
Ignition coil – cylinder 2/3	A10	→▷	Ignition ON	11-14 V briefly then 0 V		
	A10	→▷	Engine idling		5 V/2 ms	⋀⋁⋀ 33
Ignition switch	B17	◀	Ignition OFF	0 V		
	B17	◀	Ignition ON	11-14 V		
Injector 1	A28	→▷	Ignition ON	11-14 V briefly then 0 V		
	A28	→▷	Engine idling	3,2 ms	10 V/2 ms	⋀⋁⋀ 35
Injector 2	A36	→▷	Ignition ON	11-14 V briefly then 0 V		
	A36	→▷	Engine idling	3,2 ms	10 V/2 ms	⋀⋁⋀ 35
Injector 3	A37	→▷	Ignition ON	11-14 V briefly then 0 V		
	A37	→▷	Engine idling	3,2 ms	10 V/2 ms	⋀⋁⋀ 35

* Suggested settings - Voltage/time per division

Component/circuit description	ECM pin	Signal	Condition	Typical value	Oscilloscope setting*	Wave form
Injector 4	A27	⅃▷	Ignition ON	11-14 V briefly then 0 V		
	A27	⅃▷	Engine idling	3,2 ms	10 V/2 ms	⩗⩗⩘ 35
Intake air temperature (IAT) sensor	A14	⬅	Ignition ON – air temp. 20°C	2,7 V		
Knock sensor (KS)	A6	⬅	Engine idling – accelerate briefly		0,5 V/0,5 ms	⩗⩗⩘ 38
	A15	⬅	Engine idling – accelerate briefly		0,5 V/0,5 ms	⩗⩗⩘ 38
Knock sensor (KS) – shield wire	A8	⅃—	Ignition ON	0 V		
Manifold absolute pressure (MAP) sensor	A13	⬅	Ignition ON	4,5 V		
	A13	⬅	Engine idling	1,3 V		
	A13	⬅	Engine idling – accelerate briefly	4,5 V		
	A20	⅃—	Ignition ON	0 V		
	A22	⇨	Ignition ON	5 V		
Manifold absolute pressure (MAP) sensor – shield wire	A20	⅃—	Ignition ON	0 V		
Multifunction control module – CAN data bus	B20	⬅⇨		1		
	B29	⬅⇨		1		
Multifunction control module – diagnostic link	B16	⬅⇨		1		
Throttle position (TP) sensor	A3	⬅	Ignition ON – throttle closed	0,6 V		
	A3	⬅	Ignition ON – throttle fully open	4,7 V		
	A20	⅃—	Ignition ON	0 V		
	A32	⇨	Ignition ON	5 V		
Throttle position (TP) sensor – shield wire	A20	⅃—	Ignition ON	0 V		

*Suggested settings - Voltage/time per division

1 Connected pin - no test data available or random digital signal

ECM harness multi-plug

Terminal side

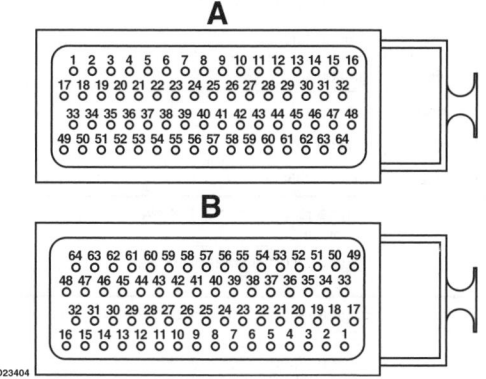

Wire side

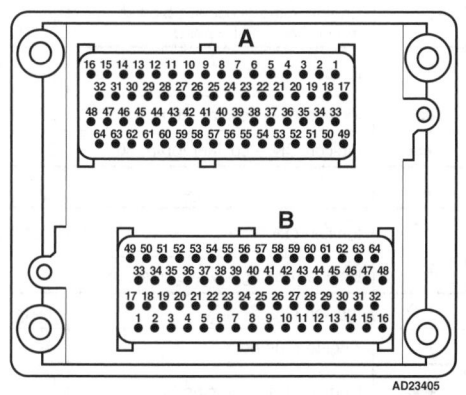

Component/circuit description	ECM pin	Signal	Condition	Typical value	Oscilloscope setting*	Wave form
AC compressor clutch relay	B46	⌐⊳	Engine idling – AC OFF	11-14 V		
	B46	⌐⊳	Engine idling – AC ON – AC compressor ON	0-1 V		
AC refrigerant quadruple pressure switch	B24			1		
	B40	⬅		1		
	B56			1		
Accelerator pedal position (APP) sensor	B4	⇨	Ignition ON	5 V		
	B5	⌐⊢	Ignition ON	0 V		
	B21	⇨	Ignition ON	5 V		
	B22	⌐⊢	Ignition ON	0 V		
	B37	⬅	Ignition ON – accelerator pedal released	0,3 V		
	B37	⬅	Ignition ON – accelerator pedal fully depressed	2,1 V		
	B54	⬅	Ignition ON – accelerator pedal released	0,7 V		
	B54	⬅	Ignition ON – accelerator pedal fully depressed	4,2 V		
Battery	B18	⬅	Ignition OFF	11-14 V		
Clutch pedal position (CPP) switch	B7	⬅	Ignition ON – clutch pedal released	11-14 V		
	B7	⬅	Ignition ON – clutch pedal depressed	0-1 V		

★ Suggested settings - Voltage/time per division

Component/circuit description	ECM pin	Signal	Condition	Typical value	Oscilloscope setting*	Wave form
Crankshaft position (CKP) sensor	A10	←	Engine idling	1,4 V ac	2 V/2 ms	Reversed 2
	A42	←	Engine idling	1,4 V ac	2 V/2 ms	2
Engine control module (ECM) – case		⊣	Ignition ON	0 V		
Engine control relay	B17	←	Ignition OFF	0 V		
	B17	←	Ignition ON	11-14 V		
	B19	⊣▷	Ignition OFF	0 V		
	B19	⊣▷	Ignition ON	0-1 V		
	B33	←	Ignition OFF	0 V		
	B33	←	Ignition ON	11-14 V		
	B49	←	Ignition OFF	0 V		
	B49	←	Ignition ON	11-14 V		
Engine coolant blower motor relay – without AC	B14	⊣▷	Engine idling – coolant blower motor OFF	11-14 V		
	B14	⊣▷	Engine idling – coolant blower motor ON	0-1 V		
Engine coolant blower motor relay 1 – with AC	B14	⊣▷	Engine idling – coolant blower motor OFF	11-14 V		
	B14	⊣▷	Engine idling – coolant blower motor ON – low speed	0-1 V		
Engine coolant blower motor relay 2 – with AC	B30	⊣▷	Engine idling – coolant blower motor OFF	11-14 V		
	B30	⊣▷	Engine idling – coolant blower motor ON – high speed	0-1 V		
Engine coolant temperature (ECT) sensor	A9	⊣	Ignition ON	0 V		
	A38	←	Ignition ON – coolant temp. 10°C	3,5 V		
	A38	←	Ignition ON – coolant temp. 80°C	0,9 V		
Engine oil pressure switch	B42	←		[1]		
Evaporative emission (EVAP) canister purge valve	A33	⊣▷	Ignition ON	11-14 V		
	A33	⊣▷	Engine running – valve operating		10 V/20 ms	59
Fuel pump relay	B62	⊣▷	Ignition ON	11-14 V		
	B62	⊣▷	Engine running	0-1 V		
Heated oxygen sensor (HO2S)	A8	←	Engine idling – engine hot	0-1 V fluctuating	0,2 V/1 sec.	21
	A25	⊣	Engine idling	0 V		
Heated oxygen sensor (HO2S) – heater control	A49	⊣▷	Ignition ON	11-14 V		
	A49	⊣▷		[1]		
Ignition coil – cylinder 1/4	A32	⊣▷	Ignition ON	11-14 V		
	A32	⊣▷	Engine idling		5 V/2 ms	33
Ignition coil – cylinder 2/3	A31	⊣▷	Ignition ON	11-14 V		
	A31	⊣▷	Engine idling		5 V/2 ms	33
Ignition switch	B51	←	Ignition OFF	0 V		
	B51	←	Ignition ON	11-14 V		
Injector 1	A51	⊣▷	Ignition ON	11-14 V		
	A51	⊣▷	Engine idling	3,1 ms	10 V/2 ms	35
Injector 2	A18	⊣▷	Ignition ON	11-14 V		
	A18	⊣▷	Engine idling	3,1 ms	10 V/2 ms	35
Injector 3	A2	⊣▷	Ignition ON	11-14 V		
	A2	⊣▷	Engine idling	3,1 ms	10 V/2 ms	35
Injector 4	A34	⊣▷	Ignition ON	11-14 V		
	A34	⊣▷	Engine idling	3,1 ms	10 V/2 ms	35
Intake air temperature (IAT) sensor	A26	⊣	Ignition ON	0 V		
	A55	←	Ignition ON – air temp. 10°C	3,7 V		
Knock sensor (KS)	A21	⊣	Ignition ON	0 V		
	A37	←	Engine idling – accelerate briefly		0,5 V/0,5 ms	38

* Suggested settings - Voltage/time per division

Component/circuit description	ECM pin	Signal	Condition	Typical value	Oscilloscope setting*	Wave form
Manifold absolute pressure (MAP) sensor	A6	←	Ignition ON	4 V		
	A6	←	Engine idling	1 V		
	A6	←	Engine idling – accelerate briefly	4 V		
	A7	⇒	Ignition ON	5 V		
	A26	⌐	Ignition ON	0 V		
Multifunction control module – CAN data bus	B11	←⇒		①		
	B43	←⇒		①		
Multifunction control module – diagnostic link	B2	←⇒	Ignition OFF	0 V		
	B2	←⇒	Ignition ON	11-14 V		
Throttle motor position sensor 1	A39	←	Ignition ON – throttle closed	3,9 V		
	A39	←	Ignition ON – throttle fully open	3,1 V		
	A56	⇒	Ignition ON	11-14 V		
	A58	⌐	Ignition ON	0 V		
Throttle motor position sensor 2	A23	←	Ignition ON – throttle closed	1 V		
	A23	←	Ignition ON – throttle fully open	1,8 V		
	A56	⇒	Ignition ON	11-14 V		
	A58	⌐	Ignition ON	0 V		
Throttle position motor	A11	⇒	Ignition ON	0 V		
	A28	⇒	Ignition ON		2 V/2 ms	〰 64
	A28	⇒	Engine idling		2 V/2 ms	〰 71
	A43	⇒	Ignition ON	0 V		
	A60	⇒	Ignition ON		2 V/2 ms	〰 64
	A60	⇒	Engine idling		2 V/2 ms	〰 71
Transmission control module (TCM)	B3	⇒		①		
	B8	←		①		
	B10	←		①		
	B26	←		①		
	B29	⇒		①		
	B35	⇒		①		

*Suggested settings - Voltage/time per division

① Connected pin - no test data available or random digital signal

ECM harness multi-plug

Terminal side

```
19 18 17 16 15 14 13 12 11 10 9 8 7 6 5 4 3 2 1
  37 36 35 34 33 32 31 30 29 28 27 26 25 24 23 22 21 20
  55 54 53 52 51 50 49 48 47 46 45 44 43 42 41 40 39 38
AD72618
```

Wire side

```
1  2  3  4  5  6  7  8  9  10 11 12 13 14 15 16 17 18 19
  20 21 22 23 24 25 26 27 28 29 30 31 32 33 34 35 36 37
  38 39 40 41 42 43 44 45 46 47 48 49 50 51 52 53 54 55
AD42077
```

Component/circuit description	ECM pin	Signal	Condition	Typical value	Oscilloscope setting*	Wave form
AC compressor clutch relay – if fitted	32	⅂▷		1		
AC control module – if fitted	40			1		
AC refrigerant pressure switch – if fitted	41			1		
Alarm system control module – 1994-95 – if fitted	52		Ignition ON	11-14 V		
Barometric pressure (BARO) sensor	46	◀	Ignition ON – at sea level	4 V		
Battery	18	◀	Ignition OFF	11-14 V		
Camshaft position (CMP) sensor	8	◀	Engine idling		2 V/50 ms	⋀⋀ 12
	12	▷	Ignition ON	5 V		
Crankshaft position (CKP) sensor	47 (48)	◀	Engine idling		5 V/2 ms	⋀⋀ 2
	48 (47)	◀	Engine idling		5 V/2 ms	Reversed ⋀⋀ 2
Data link connector (DLC)	13	◀		1		
Data link connector (DLC) – 1994-95	55	◀▷		1		
Earth	14		Ignition ON	0 V		
	19		Ignition ON	0 V		
	24		Ignition ON	0 V		
Engine control relay	36	⅂▷	Ignition OFF	11-14 V		
	36	⅂▷	Ignition ON	0 V		
	37	◀	Ignition ON	11-14 V		
Engine coolant temperature (ECT) sensor	30	⅂	Engine running	0 V		
	45	◀	Engine idling – 87-114°C	0,6-1 V		
Evaporative emission (EVAP) canister purge valve	5	⅂▷	Ignition ON	11-14 V		
	5	⅂▷	Engine idling	11-14 V		
	5	⅂▷	Engine hot – valve operating		10 V/20 ms	⋀⋀ 20
Fuel pump relay	3	⅂▷	Ignition ON	0-1 V briefly then 11-14 V		
	3	⅂▷	Engine cranking	0-1 V		
Heated oxygen sensor (HO2S)	10	⅂	Engine idling	0 V		
	28	◀	Engine idling – engine hot	0,1-1 V – fluctuating	0,2 V/1 sec.	⋀⋀ 21
Idle air control (IAC) valve	4	⅂▷	Engine idling		5 V/5 ms	⋀⋀ 25
	22	⅂▷	Engine idling		5 V/5 ms	⋀⋀ 25

* Suggested settings - Voltage/time per division

Component/circuit description	ECM pin	Signal	Condition	Typical value	Oscilloscope setting*	Wave form
Ignition amplifier	1	⟹	Engine cranking	2,5 V min.		
	1	⟹	Engine idling		2 V/10 ms	∿∿ 32
	20	⟹	Engine idling		2 V/10 ms	∿∿ 32
Ignition switch	27	⟸	Ignition ON	11-14 V		
Immobilizer control module – 1996→	55	⟺		[1]		
Injector 1	17	⊐▷	Ignition ON	11-14 V		
	17	⊐▷	Engine idling – engine hot	2-2,8 ms	10 V/2 ms	∿∿ 35
Injector 2	34	⊐▷	Ignition ON	11-14 V		
	34	⊐▷	Engine idling – engine hot	2-2,8 ms	10 V/2 ms	∿∿ 35
Injector 3	16	⊐▷	Ignition ON	11-14 V		
	16	⊐▷	Engine idling – engine hot	2-2,8 ms	10 V/2 ms	∿∿ 35
Injector 4	35	⊐▷	Ignition ON	11-14 V		
	35	⊐▷	Engine idling – engine hot	2-2,8 ms	10 V/2 ms	∿∿ 35
Intake air temperature (IAT) sensor	30	⊐—	Engine running	0 V		
	44	⟸	Ignition ON – 10°C	4 V		
	44	⟸	Ignition ON – 74°C	1,4 V		
Knock sensor (KS)	11	⟸	Engine idling – accelerate briefly		50 mV/1 ms	∿∿ 38
	30	⊐—	Engine running	0 V		
Malfunction indicator lamp (MIL)	2	⊐▷	Ignition ON – MIL ON	0,1 V		
	2	⊐▷	Engine idling – MIL OFF	11-14 V		
Manifold absolute pressure (MAP) sensor	12	⟹	Ignition ON	5 V		
Mass air flow (MAF) sensor	7	⟸	Engine idling – engine hot	0,7-1 V		
	26	⊐—	Ignition ON	0 V		
Mass air flow (MAF) sensor – filament burn-off	25	⟹	Engine idling – engine hot	0 V		
	25	⟹	Ignition OFF	4 V after 1,5 secs.		
Tachometer – if fitted	6	⟹	Engine idling	30 Hz	2 V/20 ms	∿∿ 55
Throttle position (TP) sensor	12	⟹	Ignition ON	5 V		
	30	⊐—	Ignition ON	0 V		
	53	⟸	Ignition ON – throttle closed	0,1-0,7 V		
	53	⟸	Ignition ON – throttle fully open	3,5-4,7 V		
Turbocharger (TC) wastegate regulating valve	21	⊐▷	Ignition ON	11-14 V		
	21	⊐▷	Engine idling – engine hot	0%		
	21	⊐▷	Engine running – accelerate briefly	1% min.		
Vehicle speed sensor (VSS)	9	⟸	Ignition ON – vehicle pushed	0 V or 11-14 V		

*Suggested settings - Voltage/time per division

[1] Connected pin - no test data available or random digital signal

Model:	Engine code:	Year:
Punto 1,4	843A1.000	2003-06

ECM harness multi-plug

Terminal side

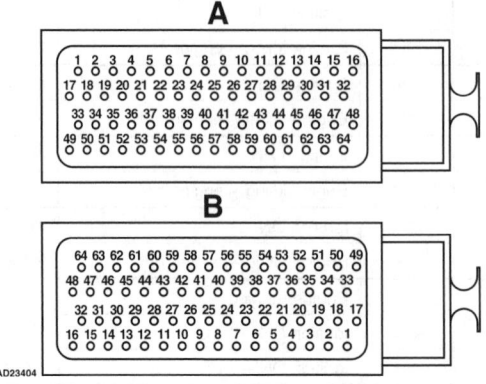

Wire side

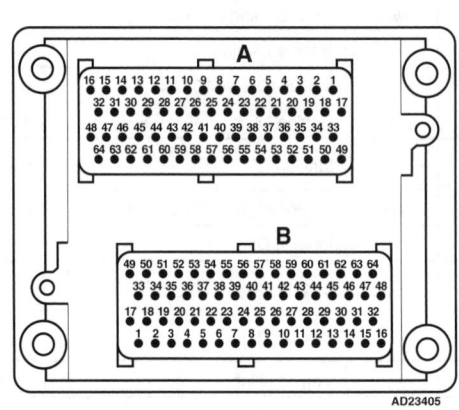

AD23405

Component/circuit description	ECM pin	Signal	Condition	Typical value	Oscilloscope setting★	Wave form
AC control module	B40			1		
AC compressor clutch relay	B46	⊐▷	Engine idling – AC OFF	11-14 V		
	B46	⊐▷	Engine idling – AC ON – AC compressor ON	0-1 V		
AC refrigerant pressure sensor	A54			1		
	B5	⊐	Ignition ON	0 V		
	B53	⬅		1		
Accelerator pedal position (APP) sensor	B4	⬅		1		
	B5	⊐	Ignition ON	0 V		
	B21	⇨	Ignition ON	5 V		
	B22	⊐	Ignition ON	0 V		
	B37	⇨	Ignition ON	5 V		
	B54	⬅		1		
Battery	B18	⬅	Ignition OFF	11-14 V		
Brake pedal position (BPP) switch	B57	⬅	Ignition ON – brake pedal released	11-14 V		
	B57	⬅	Ignition ON – brake pedal depressed	0 V		
Camshaft position (CMP) sensor	A7	⇨	Ignition ON	5 V		
	A9	⊐	Ignition ON	0 V		
	A36	⬅	Ignition ON – engine turned	0 V or 5 V switching		
	A36	⬅	Engine idling		2 V/20 ms	45

★ Suggested settings - Voltage/time per division

Autodata

Component/circuit description	ECM pin	Signal	Condition	Typical value	Oscilloscope setting*	Wave form
CAN data bus – low	B43	⬅▷		1		
CAN data bus – high	B11	⬅▷		1		
CAN data bus resistor – without ESP	B28	⬅▷		1		
	B60	⬅▷		1		
Clutch pedal position (CPP) switch	B7	⬅	Ignition ON – clutch pedal released	11-14 V		
	B7	⬅	Ignition ON – clutch pedal depressed	0-1 V		
Crankshaft position (CKP) sensor	A10	⬅	Engine idling	1,4 V ac	2 V/2 ms	Reversed 〰〰 2
	A42	⬅	Engine idling	1,4 V ac	2 V/2 ms	〰〰 2
Cruise control module	B8			1		
	B9			1		
	B41			1		
	B58			1		
Engine control module (ECM) – case		�	Ignition ON	0 V		
Engine control relay	B17	⬅	Ignition OFF	0 V		
	B17	⬅	Ignition ON	11-14 V		
	B19	片▷	Ignition OFF	0-1 V		
	B19	片▷	Ignition ON	0-1 V		
	B33	⬅	Ignition OFF	0 V		
	B33	⬅	Ignition ON	11-14 V		
	B49	⬅	Ignition OFF	0 V		
	B49	⬅	Ignition ON	11-14 V		
Engine coolant blower motor relay – without AC	B14	片▷	Engine idling – coolant blower motor OFF	11-14 V		
	B14	片▷	Engine idling – coolant blower motor ON	0-1 V		
Engine coolant blower motor relay 1 – with AC	B14	片▷	Engine idling – coolant blower motor OFF	11-14 V		
	B14	片▷	Engine idling – coolant blower motor ON – low speed	0-1 V		
Engine coolant blower motor relay 2 – with AC	B30	片▷	Engine idling – coolant blower motor OFF	11-14 V		
	B30	片▷	Engine idling – coolant blower motor ON – high speed	0-1 V		
Engine coolant temperature (ECT) sensor	A9	片	Ignition ON	0 V		
	A38	⬅	Ignition ON – coolant temp. 10°C	3,5 V		
	A38	⬅	Ignition ON – coolant temp. 80°C	0,9 V		
Engine malfunction indicator lamp (MIL)	B31	片▷	Ignition ON – MIL ON	11-14 V		
	B31	片▷	Engine running – MIL OFF	0-1 V		
Engine oil pressure switch	B42	⬅		1		
Evaporative emission (EVAP) canister purge valve	A33	片▷	Ignition ON	11-14 V		
	A33	片▷	Engine running – valve operating		10 V/20 ms	〰〰 59
Fuel pump relay	B62	片▷	Ignition ON	11-14 V		
	B62	片▷	Engine running	0-1 V		
Heated oxygen sensor (HO2S) 1	A8	⬅	Engine idling – engine hot	0-1 V fluctuating	0,2 V/1 sec.	〰〰 21
	A25	片	Engine idling	0 V		
Heated oxygen sensor (HO2S) 1 – heater control	A49	片▷	Ignition ON	11-14 V		
	A49	片▷	Engine idling	1		
Heated oxygen sensor (HO2S) 2	A57	⬅	Engine idling – engine hot	0,4-0,6 V		
	A41	片	Engine idling	0 V		
Heated oxygen sensor (HO2S) 2 – heater control	A17	片▷	Ignition ON	11-14 V		
	A17	片▷	Engine idling	1		

★ Suggested settings - Voltage/time per division

Component/circuit description	ECM pin	Signal	Condition	Typical value	Oscilloscope setting*	Wave form
Ignition coil 1	A32	⊐▷	Ignition ON	11-14 V		
	A32	⊐▷	Engine idling		5 V/1 ms	33
Ignition coil 2	A16	⊐▷	Ignition ON	11-14 V		
	A16	⊐▷	Engine idling		5 V/1 ms	33
Ignition coil 3	A31	⊐▷	Ignition ON	11-14 V		
	A31	⊐▷	Engine idling		5 V/1 ms	33
Ignition coil 4	A15	⊐▷	Ignition ON	11-14 V		
	A15	⊐▷	Engine idling		5 V/1 ms	33
Ignition switch	B51	◀	Ignition OFF	0 V		
	B51	◀	Ignition ON	11-14 V		
Immobilizer control module	B52			[1]		
Injector 1	A51	⊐▷	Ignition ON	11-14 V		
	A51	⊐▷	Engine idling	3,1 ms	10 V/2 ms	35
Injector 2	A18	⊐▷	Ignition ON	11-14 V		
	A18	⊐▷	Engine idling	3,1 ms	10 V/2 ms	35
Injector 3	A2	⊐▷	Ignition ON	11-14 V		
	A2	⊐▷	Engine idling	3,1 ms	10 V/2 ms	35
Injector 4	A34	⊐▷	Ignition ON	11-14 V		
	A34	⊐▷	Engine idling	3,1 ms	10 V/2 ms	35
Intake air temperature (IAT) sensor	A26	⊐—	Ignition ON	0 V		
	A55	◀	Ignition ON – air temp. 10°C	3,7 V		
Knock sensor (KS)	A21	⊐—	Ignition ON	0 V		
	A37	◀	Engine idling – accelerate briefly		0,5 V/0,5 ms	38
Manifold absolute pressure (MAP) sensor	A6	◀	Ignition ON	4 V		
	A6	◀	Engine idling	1 V		
	A6	◀	Engine idling – accelerate briefly	4 V briefly		
	A7	▷	Ignition ON	5 V		
	A26	⊐—	Ignition ON	0 V		
Multifunction control module	B25			[1]		
Multifunction control module – diagnostic link	B2	◀▷	Ignition OFF	0 V		
	B2	◀▷	Ignition ON	11-14 V		
Throttle motor position sensor	A23	◀	Ignition ON – throttle closed	1 V		
	A23	◀	Ignition ON – throttle fully open	1,8 V		
	A39	◀	Ignition ON – throttle closed	3,9 V		
	A39	◀	Ignition ON – throttle fully open	3,1 V		
	A56	▷	Ignition ON	5 V		
	A58	⊐—	Ignition ON	0 V		
Throttle motor	A11	▷	Ignition ON	0 V		
	A28	▷	Ignition ON		2 V/2 ms	64
	A28	▷	Engine idling		2 V/2 ms	71
	A43	▷	Ignition ON	0 V		
	A60	▷	Ignition ON		2 V/2 ms	64
	A60	▷	Engine idling		2 V/2 ms	71

*Suggested settings - Voltage/time per division

[1] Connected pin - no test data available or random digital signal

Model:	Engine code:	Year:
Punto 1,8	183 A1.000	1999-03
Bravo/Brava 1,8 16V	182 A2.000	1999-02
Marea/Marea Weekend 1,8 16V	182 A2.000	1999-03
Barchetta 1,8 16V	183 A1.000	1998-01
Coupe 1,8 16V	183 A1.000	1998-02

FIAT

Hitachi

ECM harness multi-plug

Terminal side

A

```
2  4  6  8  10 12 14 16 18 20 22 24 26 28 30 32 34 36 38 40
1  3  5  7  9  11 13 15 17 19 21 23 25 27 29 31 33 35 37 39
```

B

```
39 37 35 33 31 29 27 25 23 21 19 17 15 13 11  9  7  5  3  1
40 38 36 34 32 30 28 26 24 22 20 18 16 14 12 10  8  6  4  2
```

AD23450

Wire side

A

```
40 38 36 34 32 30 28 26 24 22 20 18 16 14 12 10  8  6  4  2
39 37 35 33 31 29 27 25 23 21 19 17 15 13 11  9  7  5  3  1
```

B

```
1  3  5  7  9  11 13 15 17 19 21 23 25 27 29 31 33 35 37 39
2  4  6  8  10 12 14 16 18 20 22 24 26 28 30 32 34 36 38 40
```

AD23451

Component/circuit description	ECM pin	Signal	Condition	Typical value	Oscilloscope setting*	Wave form
AC compressor clutch relay	B10	⊣▷	Ignition ON	11-14 V		
	B10	⊣▷	Engine idling – AC OFF	11-14 V		
	B10	⊣▷	Engine idling – AC ON	0 V		
AC refrigerant pressure switch	B9	⟵	Engine idling – AC OFF	0 V		
	B9	⟵	Engine idling – AC ON	11-14 V		
Air conditioning – some models	B26			1		
	B27	⊣		1		
	B28			1		
Battery	B5	⟵	Ignition OFF	11-14 V		
Camshaft position (CMP) actuator relay – 183 A1.000	B11	⊣▷	Ignition ON	11-14 V		
	B11	⊣▷	Engine idling	11-14 V		
	B11	⊣▷	Engine idling – throttle fully open briefly	0-1 V – briefly		
Camshaft position (CMP) sensor	A22	⟵	Engine idling	0-6 V switching	2 V/20 ms	〰 78
	A31	⊣	Ignition ON	0 V		
Crankshaft position (CKP) sensor	A23	⟵	Engine idling	4,3 V ac	5 V/10 ms	〰 79
	A24	⟵	Engine idling	4,3 V ac	5 V/10 ms	〰 79
Crankshaft position (CKP) sensor – shield wire	A28	⊣	Ignition ON	0 V		
Data link connector (DLC) 1 – except Punto	B32	⟺	Ignition ON	11-14 V		
	B32	⟺	Engine idling	11-14 V		
Data link connector (DLC) 2 – memory reprogramming – except Punto	B31	⟺	Ignition ON	0 V		

* Suggested settings - Voltage/time per division

Component/circuit description	ECM pin	Signal	Condition	Typical value	Oscilloscope setting*	Wave form
Earth	A5		Ignition ON	0 V		
	A6		Ignition ON	0 V		
	A21		Ignition ON	0 V		
	A25		Ignition ON	0 V		
	A26		Ignition ON	0 V		
	A35		Ignition ON	0 V		
Earth – non-AC – some models	B26		Ignition ON	0 V		
Engine control relay – through diode – except Barchetta	B1	⊣▷	Ignition OFF	11-14 V		
	B1	⊣▷	Ignition ON	0,1 V		
	B1	⊣▷	Engine idling	0,1 V		
	B3	◄	Ignition ON	11-14 V		
	B4	◄	Ignition ON	11-14 V		
Engine coolant blower motor relay – high speed	B15	⊣▷	Ignition ON	11-14 V		
	B15	⊣▷	Engine idling – coolant blower motor OFF	11-14 V		
	B15	⊣▷	Engine idling – coolant blower motor ON	0 V		
Engine coolant blower motor relay – low speed	B14	⊣▷	Ignition ON	11-14 V		
	B14	⊣▷	Engine idling – coolant blower motor OFF	11-14 V		
	B14	⊣▷	Engine idling – coolant blower motor ON	0 V		
Engine coolant temperature (ECT) sensor	A11	⊣─	Ignition ON	0 V		
	A16	◄	Ignition ON – coolant temp. 15°C	3,6 V		
	A16	◄	Engine idling – engine hot	0,9 V		
Engine oil pressure switch – Punto	B33	◄	Ignition ON	0 V		
	B33	◄	Engine running	11-14 V		
Evaporative emission (EVAP) canister purge valve	A27	⊣▷	Ignition ON	11-14 V		
	A27	⊣▷	Engine idling	11-14 V		
	A27	⊣▷	Engine running – above idle speed		10 V/50 ms	20
Fuel pump relay – except Barchetta	B7	⊣▷	Ignition ON	0 V briefly then 11-14 V		
	B7	⊣▷	Engine idling	0 V		
Heated oxygen sensor (HO2S)	B20	◄	Engine idling	0,1-0,9 V fluctuating	0,2 V/1 sec.	21
	B21	⊣─	Ignition ON	0 V		
Idle air control (IAC) valve	A37	⇨	Ignition ON	11-14 V		
	A37	⇨	Engine idling		2 V/0,1 sec.	52
	A38	⇨	Ignition ON	11-14 V		
	A38	⇨	Engine idling		2 V/0,1 sec.	52
	A39	⇨	Ignition ON	0,1 V		
	A39	⇨	Engine idling		2 V/0,1 sec.	52
	A40	⇨	Ignition ON	0,1 V		
	A40	⇨	Engine idling		2 V/0,1 sec.	52
Ignition coil 1	A7	⊣▷	Ignition ON	0 V		
	A7	⊣▷	Engine idling		1 V/50 ms	56
Ignition coil 2	A8	⊣▷	Ignition ON	0 V		
	A8	⊣▷	Engine idling		1 V/50 ms	56
Ignition coil 3	A9	⊣▷	Ignition ON	0 V		
	A9	⊣▷	Engine idling		1 V/50 ms	56
Ignition coil 4	A10	⊣▷	Ignition ON	0 V		
	A10	⊣▷	Engine idling		1 V/50 ms	56
Ignition switch	B2	◄	Ignition ON	11-14 V		

* Suggested settings - Voltage/time per division

Component/circuit description	ECM pin	Signal	Condition	Typical value	Oscilloscope setting*	Wave form
Ignition switch – except Punto	B6	←	Ignition ON – engine cranking	11-14 V		
Immobilizer control module – except Punto	B30	←→	Ignition ON	0,8 V		
	B30	←→	Engine idling	0 V		
Injector 1	A1	⅂▷	Ignition ON	11-14 V		
	A1	⅂▷	Engine idling	2,7 ms	10 V/2 ms	35
Injector 2	A2	⅂▷	Ignition ON	11-14 V		
	A2	⅂▷	Engine idling	2,7 ms	10 V/2 ms	35
Injector 3	A3	⅂▷	Ignition ON	11-14 V		
	A3	⅂▷	Engine idling	2,7 ms	10 V/2 ms	35
Injector 4	A4	⅂▷	Ignition ON	11-14 V		
	A4	⅂▷	Engine idling	2,7 ms	10 V/2 ms	35
Intake manifold air control solenoid – 183 A1.000	A29	⅂▷	Ignition ON	11-14 V		
	A29	⅂▷	Engine idling	11-14 V		
	A29	⅂▷	Engine idling – throttle fully open briefly	0-1 V – briefly		
Knock sensor (KS)	A19	←	Engine idling – accelerate briefly		50 mV/1 ms	58
	A20	⅂—	Ignition ON	0 V		
Malfunction indicator lamp (MIL) – except Punto	B8	⅂▷	Ignition ON – MIL ON	0 V		
	B8	⅂▷	Ignition ON – MIL OFF	11,3 V		
	B8	⅂▷	Engine idling – MIL OFF	11-14 V		
Mass air flow (MAF) sensor	A12	⅂—	Ignition ON	0 V		
	A14	←	Engine idling	1,2 V		
	A14	←	Engine idling – accelerate briefly	4,1 V		
Multifunction control module – CAN data bus	B37	←→		1		
	B38	←→		1		
Multifunction control module – diagnostic link	B32	←→		1		
Relay module – Barchetta	B1	⅂▷	Ignition OFF	11-14 V		
	B1	⅂▷	Ignition ON	0-1 V		
	B1	⅂▷	Engine idling	0-1 V		
	B3	←	Ignition ON	11-14 V		
	B4	←	Ignition ON	11-14 V		
	B7	⅂▷	Ignition OFF	11-14 V		
	B7	⅂▷	Ignition ON	0-1 V briefly then 11-14 V		
	B7	⅂▷	Engine cranking	0-1 V		
Tachometer – except Punto	B17	⇒	Engine idling	27 Hz		
	B17	⇒	3000 rpm	100 Hz		
	B17	⇒	Engine idling		5 V/20 ms	4
Throttle position (TP) sensor	A15	←	Ignition ON – throttle closed	0,6 V		
	A15	←	Ignition ON – throttle fully open	4,3 V		
	A17	⇒	Ignition ON	5 V		
	A18	⅂—	Ignition ON	0 V		
Vehicle speed sensor (VSS) – except Punto	B18	←	Ignition ON	5 V		
	B18	←	Ignition ON – vehicle pushed	0 V or 5 V		

*Suggested settings - Voltage/time per division

1 Connected pin - no test data available or random digital signal

FIAT

Bosch Motronic M1.5.5

Model:	Engine code:	Year:
Brava/Bravo 1,2 16V	182 B2000	1998-02

ECM harness multi-plug

Terminal side

Wire side

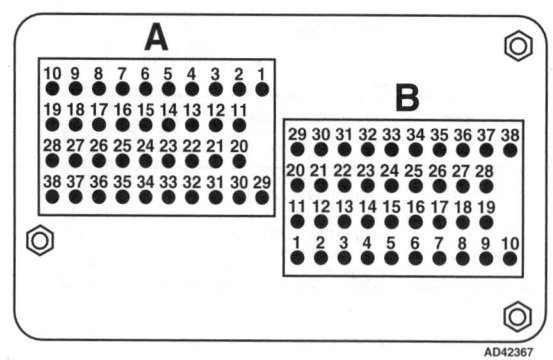

AD42368

AD42367

Component/circuit description	ECM pin	Signal	Condition	Typical value	Oscilloscope setting*	Wave form
AC compressor clutch relay	A19	⊐▷	Engine idling – AC OFF	11-14 V		
	A19	⊐▷	Engine idling – AC ON – AC compressor ON	0-1 V		
AC refrigerant pressure switch	A31	←		1		
	A34	←		1		
	A35	←		1		
Battery	A18	←	Ignition OFF	11-14 V		
Crankshaft position (CKP) sensor	B22	⊐	Ignition ON	0 V		
	B32	←	Engine idling	1,6 V ac		
	B32	←	Engine idling		1 V/2 ms	〰 2
Crankshaft position (CKP) sensor – shield wire	B9	⊐	Ignition ON	0 V		
Data link connector (DLC)	A11	◄▷	Ignition OFF	0 V		
	A11	◄▷	Ignition ON	11-14 V		
Engine control relay	A7	←	Ignition OFF	0 V		
	A7	←	Ignition ON	11-14 V		
	A9	⊐▷	Ignition OFF	11-14 V		
	A9	⊐▷	Ignition ON	0-1 V		
	A17	←	Ignition OFF	0 V after 5 seconds		
	A17	←	Ignition ON	11-14 V		
Engine coolant blower motor relay 1	A13	⊐▷	Engine idling – coolant blower motor OFF	11-14 V		
	A13	⊐▷	Engine idling – coolant blower motor ON – low speed	0-1 V		

★ Suggested settings - Voltage/time per division

Component/circuit description	ECM pin	Signal	Condition	Typical value	Oscilloscope setting*	Wave form
Engine coolant blower motor relay 2 – with AC	A4	→▷	Engine idling – coolant blower motor OFF	11-14 V		
	A4	→▷	Engine idling – coolant blower motor ON – high speed	0-1 V		
Engine coolant temperature (ECT) sensor	B1	→⊢	Ignition ON	0 V		
	B5	⟵	Ignition ON – coolant temp. 10°C	3,4 V		
	B5	⟵	Ignition ON – coolant temp. 80°C	0,9 V		
Evaporative emission (EVAP) canister purge valve	B34	→▷	Ignition ON	11-14 V		
	B34	→▷	Engine hot – valve operating		10 V/20 ms	59
Fuel pump relay	A3	→▷	Ignition OFF	0 V		
	A3	→▷	Ignition ON	0-1 V briefly then 11-14 V		
Heated oxygen sensor (HO2S)	B8	→▷	Engine idling	0-1 V		
	B21	→⊢	Engine idling	0-1 V		
	B30	⟵	Engine idling – engine hot	0-1 V fluctuating		
	B30	⟵	Engine idling – engine hot		0,2 V/1 sec.	21
Idle speed control (ISC) actuator	B26	⟹	Engine idling		2 V/50 ms	28
	B35	⟹	Engine idling		2 V/50 ms	28
Idle speed control (ISC) actuator position sensor	B1	→⊢	Ignition ON	0 V		
	B4	⟵	Engine idling	3,1 V		
Ignition coil – cylinder 1/4	B28	→▷	Engine idling		5 V/2 ms	33
	B38	→▷	Engine idling		5 V/2 ms	33
Ignition coil – cylinder 2/3	B10	→▷	Engine idling		5 V/2 ms	33
	B19	→▷	Engine idling		5 V/2 ms	33
Ignition switch	A8	⟵	Ignition OFF	0 V		
	A8	⟵	Ignition ON	11-14 V		
Immobilizer control module	A16		Engine idling	11-14 V		
Injector 1	B6	→▷	Ignition ON	11-14 V		
	B6	→▷	Engine idling – engine hot	2,8 ms		
	B6	→▷	Engine idling		10 V/2 ms	35
Injector 2	B17	→▷	Ignition ON	11-14 V		
	B17	→▷	Engine idling – engine hot	2,8 ms		
	B17	→▷	Engine idling		10 V/2 ms	35
Injector 3	B16	→▷	Ignition ON	11-14 V		
	B16	→▷	Engine idling – engine hot	2,8 ms		
	B16	→▷	Engine idling		10 V/2 ms	35
Injector 4	B7	→▷	Ignition ON	11-14 V		
	B7	→▷	Engine idling – engine hot	2,8 ms		
	B7	→▷	Engine idling		10 V/2 ms	35
Instrumentation control module – vehicle speed signal	A27	⟵	Ignition OFF	0 V		
	A27	⟵	Engine idling	11-14 V		
Intake air temperature (IAT) sensor	B1	→⊢	Ignition ON	0 V		
	B3	⟵	Ignition ON – air temp. 10°C	3,7 V		

* Suggested settings - Voltage/time per division

Component/circuit description	ECM pin	Signal	Condition	Typical value	Oscilloscope setting*	Wave form
Knock sensor (KS)	B2	←	Engine idling – accelerate briefly		0,5 V/0,5 ms	Ⓦ 38
	B11	←	Engine idling – accelerate briefly		0,5 V/0,5 ms	Ⓦ 38
Knock sensor (KS) – shield wire	B9	⊣⊢	Ignition ON	0 V		
Malfunction indicator lamp (MIL)	A12	⊣▷	Ignition ON – MIL ON	0-1 V		
	A12	⊣▷	Ignition ON – MIL OFF	11-14 V		
Manifold absolute pressure (MAP) sensor	B1	⊣⊢	Ignition ON	0 V		
	B12	←	Ignition ON	4 V		
	B12	←	Engine idling	1 V		
	B12	←	Engine idling – accelerate briefly	4 V briefly		
	B29	⇒	Ignition ON	5 V		
Power steering pressure (PSP) switch	A22	←	Engine idling – steering wheel not turned	11-14 V		
	A22	←	Engine idling – steering wheel turned	0 V		
Tachometer	A2	⇒	Engine idling	27 Hz		
	A2	⇒	3000 rpm	100 Hz		
	A2	⇒	Engine idling		2 V/20 ms	Ⓦ 55
Throttle position (TP) sensor	B1	⊣⊢	Ignition ON	0 V		
	B13	←	Ignition ON – throttle closed	1,3 V		
	B13	←	Ignition ON – throttle fully open	4,5 V		
	B29	⇒	Ignition ON	5 V		

*Suggested settings - Voltage/time per division

1 Connected pin - no test data available or random digital signal

Model:	Engine code:	Year:
Brava/Bravo 1,6	182 A4/6 000	1995-98
Marea 1,6	182 A4 000	1996-99

FIAT

Weber-Marelli IAW 1AF

ECM harness multi-plug

Terminal side

19 18 17 16 15 14 13 12 11 10 9 8 7 6 5 4 3 2 1
37 36 35 34 33 32 31 30 29 28 27 26 25 24 23 22 21 20
55 54 53 52 51 50 49 48 47 46 45 44 43 42 41 40 39 38

AD72618

Wire side

1 2 3 4 5 6 7 8 9 10 11 12 13 14 15 16 17 18 19
20 21 22 23 24 25 26 27 28 29 30 31 32 33 34 35 36 37
38 39 40 41 42 43 44 45 46 47 48 49 50 51 52 53 54 55

AD42077

Component/circuit description	ECM pin	Signal	Condition	Typical value	Oscilloscope setting*	Wave form
AC compressor clutch relay – if fitted	26	⊐▷		1		
AC refrigerant pressure switch – if fitted	10			1		
Camshaft position (CMP) sensor	11	◀	Ignition ON – engine turned	4,4-0 V fluctuating		
	11	◀	Engine idling		2 V/50 ms	12
	16	⇨	Ignition ON	5 V		
	53	⊐▷	Engine cranking	0 V		
Crankshaft position (CKP) sensor	30 (49)	◀	Engine idling		5 V/2 ms	2
	49 (30)	◀	Engine idling		5 V/2 ms	Reversed 2
Data link connector (DLC)	12			1		
	17	⊐–	Ignition ON	0 V		
	31			1		
Earth	36		Ignition ON	0 V		
	54		Ignition ON	0 V		
Engine coolant temperature (ECT) sensor	17	⊐–	Ignition ON	0 V		
	47	◀	Ignition ON – coolant temp. 15°C	3 V		
	47	◀	Ignition ON – coolant temp. 80°C	0,5 V		
Evaporative emission (EVAP) canister purge valve	24	⊐▷	Ignition ON	11-14 V briefly then 0 V		
	24	⊐▷	Engine hot – valve operating		10 V/20 ms	20
Heated oxygen sensor (HO2S)	4	⊐–	Ignition ON	0 V		
	22	◀	Engine idling – engine hot	0-1 V fluctuating	0,2 V/1 sec.	21
Idle air control (IAC) valve	3	⇨	Ignition ON	0,2 V or 11-14 V		
	3 (21)	⇨	Engine idling		5 V/0,1 sec.	Intermittent 26
	20	⇨	Ignition ON	0,2 V or 11-14 V		
	20 (40)	⇨	Engine idling		5 V/0,1 sec.	Intermittent 26
	21	⇨	Ignition ON	0,2 V or 11-14 V		
	21 (3)	⇨	Engine idling		5 V/0,1 sec.	Intermittent 26
	40	⇨	Ignition ON	0,2 V or 11-14 V		
	40 (20)	⇨	Engine idling		5 V/0,1 sec.	Intermittent 26

* Suggested settings - Voltage/time per division

Component/circuit description	ECM pin	Signal	Condition	Typical value	Oscilloscope setting*	Wave form
Ignition coil – cylinders 1 & 4	55	⊐⊳	Ignition ON	11-14 V briefly then 0 V		
	55	⊐⊳	Engine cranking	9 V		
	55	⊐⊳	Engine idling		5 V/2 ms	〜〜 33
Ignition coil – cylinders 2 & 3	37	⊐⊳	Ignition ON	11-14 V briefly then 0 V		
	37	⊐⊳	Engine cranking	9 V		
	37	⊐⊳	Engine idling		5 V/2 ms	〜〜 33
Ignition switch	13	⬅	Ignition OFF	0 V		
	13	⬅	Ignition ON	11-14 V		
Immobilizer control module	48	⬅	Ignition ON	11-14 V		
Injector 1	2	⊐⊳	Ignition ON	11-14 V briefly then 0 V		
	2	⊐⊳	Engine idling	3,1 ms	10 V/2 ms	〜〜 35
Injector 2	39	⊐⊳	Ignition ON	11-14 V briefly then 0 V		
	39	⊐⊳	Engine idling	3,1 ms	10 V/2 ms	〜〜 35
Injector 3	1	⊐⊳	Ignition ON	11-14 V briefly then 0 V		
	1	⊐⊳	Engine idling	3,1 ms	10 V/2 ms	〜〜 35
Injector 4	38	⊐⊳	Ignition ON	11-14 V briefly then 0 V		
	38	⊐⊳	Engine idling	3,1 ms	10 V/2 ms	〜〜 35
Intake air temperature (IAT) sensor	17	⊐—	Ignition ON	0 V		
	29	⬅	Ignition ON – air temp. 15°C	3 V		
Malfunction indicator lamp (MIL)	9	⊐⊳	Ignition ON – MIL ON	0-1 V		
	9	⊐⊳	Engine running – MIL OFF	11-14 V		
Manifold absolute pressure (MAP) sensor	14	⇨	Ignition ON	4,5 V		
	14	⇨	Engine idling	1,2 V		
	14	⇨	Engine idling – accelerate briefly	4,5 V briefly		
	17	⊐—	Ignition ON	0 V		
	34	⇨	Ignition ON	5 V		
Relay module	7	⊐⊳	Ignition ON	0-1 V briefly then 11-14 V		
	7	⊐⊳	Engine cranking	0-1 V		
	7	⊐⊳	Engine running	0-1 V		
	35	⬅	Ignition ON	11-14 V		
	52	⊐⊳	Ignition OFF	11-14 V		
	52	⊐⊳	Ignition ON	0-1 V		
	52	⊐⊳	Engine running	0-1 V		
Tachometer	42	⇨	Engine idling	30 Hz		
	42	⇨	3000 rpm	100 Hz		
Throttle position (TP) sensor	16	⇨	Ignition ON	5 V		
	23	⬅	Ignition ON – throttle closed	0,2-0,6 V		
	23	⬅	Ignition ON – throttle fully open	4,2-5 V		
	53	⊐⊳	Ignition ON	0 V		
Transmission control module (TCM) – AT	5			[1]		
	32			[1]		
	44			[1]		
	50			[1]		
Vehicle speed sensor (VSS)	28	⬅	Ignition ON – vehicle pushed	0 V or 11-14 V		

*Suggested settings - Voltage/time per division

[1] Connected pin - no test data available or random digital signal

Model:	Engine code:	Year:
Brava/Bravo 1,9 JTD	182B4.000	1998-02
Marea 1,9 JTD	182B4.000	1998-03
Multipla 1,9 JTD	182B4.000	1999-02

FIAT

Bosch EDC 15C

ECM harness multi-plug

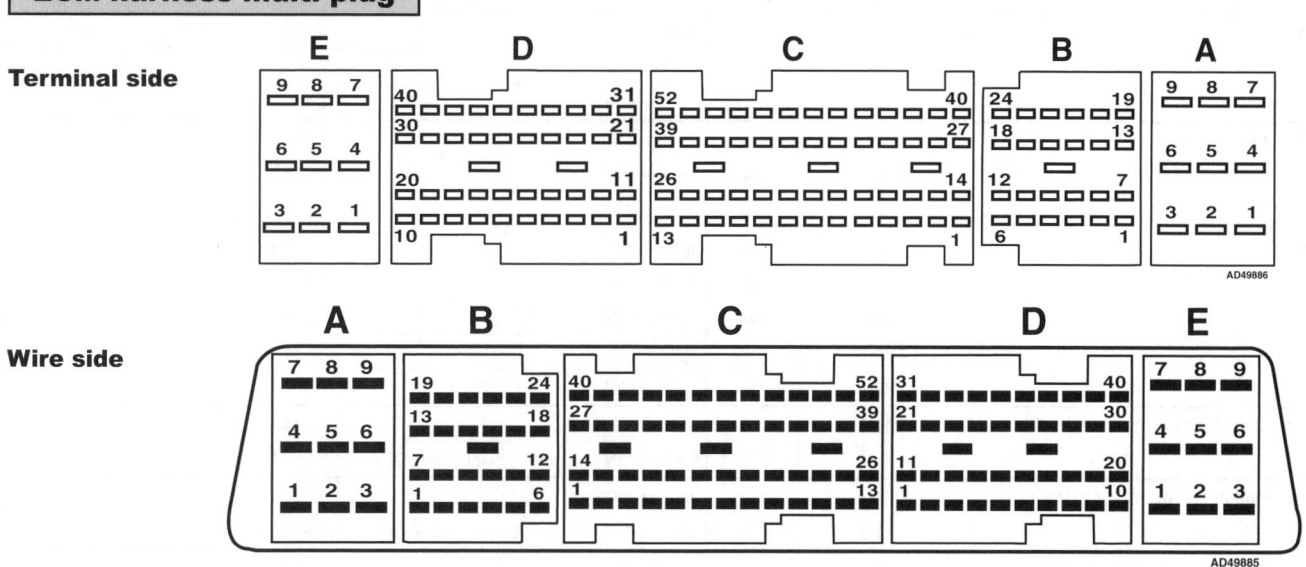

Component/circuit description	ECM pin	Signal	Condition	Typical value
AC compressor clutch relay	D32	⇨	Ignition ON – AC OFF	11-14 V
	D32	⇨	Ignition ON – AC ON	11-14 V
AC refrigerant pressure switch	B3	⬅	Ignition ON – AC OFF	0 V
	B3	⬅	Ignition ON – AC ON	11-14 V
	C20	⬅	Ignition OFF	0 V
	C20	⬅	Ignition ON	11 V
	D15	⬅	Ignition OFF	0 V
	D15	⬅	Ignition ON – AC ON/OFF	11,5 V
Accelerator pedal position (APP) sensor	C5	⇨	Ignition OFF	0 V
	C5	⇨	Ignition ON	5 V
	C8	⌐	Ignition ON	0 V
	C9	⬅	Ignition ON – accelerator pedal released	0,38 V
	C9	⬅	Ignition ON – accelerator pedal depressed	1,88 V
	C10	⬅	Ignition ON – accelerator pedal released	0,74 V
	C10	⬅	Ignition ON – accelerator pedal depressed	3,76 V
	C21	⇨	Ignition OFF	0 V
	C21	⇨	Ignition ON	5 V
	C23	⌐	Ignition ON	0 V
Brake pedal position (BPP) switch	B8	⬅	Ignition ON – brake pedal released	0 V
	B8	⬅	Ignition ON – brake pedal depressed	11-14 V
Camshaft position (CMP) sensor	D2	⌐	Ignition ON	0 V
	D3	⬅	Engine idling	2 V/50 ms per division ⌁ 3
	D3	⬅	Ignition ON	5 V
Clutch pedal position (CPP) switch	B2	⬅	Ignition ON – clutch pedal released	0 V
	B2	⬅	Ignition ON – clutch pedal depressed	11-14 V

Component/circuit description	ECM pin	Signal	Condition	Typical value
Crankshaft position (CKP) sensor – screened lead	D17	⊣⊢	Ignition ON	0 V
	D26	←	Engine idling	7,7 V ac
	D26	←	Engine idling	5 V/2 ms per division ∿∿ **1**
	D37	⊣⊢	Ignition ON	0 V
Data link connector (DLC)	C28	⇄	Ignition ON	11,5 V
Earth	A4		Ignition ON	0 V
	A5		Ignition ON	0 V
	A6		Ignition ON	0 V
Engine control relay	A1	←	Ignition OFF	0 V
	A1	←	Ignition ON	11-14 V
	A7	←	Ignition OFF	0 V
	A7	←	Ignition ON	11-14 V
	A8	←	Ignition OFF	0 V
	A8	←	Ignition ON	11-14 V
	C46	⊓⇨	Ignition OFF	11-14 V
	C46	⊓⇨	Ignition ON	0,9 V
Engine coolant blower motor relay I	B23	⇨	Ignition OFF	11-14 V
	B23	⇨	Ignition ON – coolant blower motor OFF	11-14 V
Engine coolant blower motor relay II	C45	⇨	Ignition OFF	11-14 V
	C45	⇨	Ignition ON – coolant blower motor OFF	11-14 V
Engine coolant temperature (ECT) sensor	D27	⊣⊢	Ignition ON	0 V
	D36	←	Ignition ON – engine cold	3,5 V
	D36	←	Engine idling – engine hot	1,4 V
Engine malfunction indicator lamp (MIL)	C48	⊓⇨	Ignition ON – lamp ON	0 V
	C48	⊓⇨	Ignition ON – lamp OFF	11,3 V
Exhaust gas recirculation (EGR) solenoid	C37	⇨	Ignition OFF	0 V
	C37	⇨	Ignition ON	11-14 V
	C37	⇨	Engine idling	11-14 V
	C50	⊓⇨	Ignition OFF	0 V
	C50	⊓⇨	Ignition ON	11-14 V
	C50	⊓⇨	Engine idling	5 V/2 ms per division ∿∿ **31**
Fuel lift pump – Multipla	C30			[1]
Fuel lift pump relay	C52	⊓⇨	Ignition ON – after 10 seconds approx.	11-14 V
	C52	⊓⇨	Ignition ON	0,85 V
Fuel pressure control solenoid	D21	⊣⊢	Ignition ON	0 V
	D31	←	Engine idling	73%
	D31	←	Engine idling	2 V/1 ms per division ∿∿ **37**
Fuel pressure sensor	D13	⇨	Engine idling	5 V
	D13	⇨	Ignition OFF	0 V
	D13	⇨	Ignition ON	5 V
	D24	←	Engine idling	1,3 V
	D24	←	Engine running – 3000 rpm	2,1 V
	D24	←	Ignition ON	0,5 V
	D34	⊣⊢	Ignition ON	0 V
Fuel temperature sensor	C1	⊣⊢	Ignition ON	0 V
	C24	←	Ignition ON – fuel temp. 15°C	2,6 V

Component/circuit description	ECM pin	Signal	Condition	Typical value
Glow plug control module	B1	⌐—	Ignition OFF	0 V
	B1	⌐—	Ignition ON	0,65 V
	C38	⇨	Engine idling	11-14 V
	C38	⇨	Ignition OFF	0 V
	C38	⇨	Ignition ON	11-14 V
	C51	⇨	Engine idling	11-14 V
	C51	⇨	Ignition ON	0,25 V
Glow plug warning lamp	C43	⇨	Ignition ON – lamp ON	0 V
	C43	⇨	Ignition ON – lamp OFF	11-14 V
Ignition switch	B13	⬅	Ignition OFF	0 V
	B13	⬅	Ignition ON	11-14 V
Immobilizer control module	C13	⬅	Ignition OFF	0 V
	C13	⬅	Ignition ON	11-14 V
Injector 1	E9	⌐⊦⇨	Engine idling	1 ms pilot + 1,2 ms main
	E9	⌐⊦⇨	Engine idling	10 V/0,5 ms per division ⎍⎍ 23
Injector 2	E7	⌐⊦⇨	Engine idling	1 ms pilot + 1,2 ms main
	E7	⌐⊦⇨	Engine idling	10 V/0,5 ms per division ⎍⎍ 23
Injector 3	E5	⌐⊦⇨	Engine idling	1 ms pilot + 1,2 ms main
	E5	⌐⊦⇨	Engine idling	10 V/0,5 ms per division ⎍⎍ 23
Injector 4	E3	⌐⊦⇨	Engine idling	1 ms pilot + 1,2 ms main
	E3	⌐⊦⇨	Engine idling	10 V/0,5 ms per division ⎍⎍ 23
Injectors 1 & 4	E2	⇨	Ignition ON	1,1 V
Injectors 2 & 3	E4	⇨	Ignition ON	1,1 V
Intake air temperature (IAT) sensor	D4	⌐—	Ignition ON	0 V
	D23	⬅	Ignition ON – air temp. 15°C	2,44 V
Manifold absolute pressure (MAP) sensor	D6	⬅	Ignition ON	1,9 V
	D6	⬅	Engine idling	1,88 V
	D6	⬅	Engine idling – accelerate briefly	3,25 V
	D7	⌐—	Ignition ON	0 V
	D8	⇨	Ignition OFF	0 V
	D8	⇨	Ignition ON	5 V
Mass air flow (MAF) sensor	D1	⇨	Engine idling	5 V
	D1	⇨	Ignition OFF	0 V
	D1	⇨	Ignition ON	5 V
	D11	⇨	Engine idling	11-14 V
	D11	⇨	Ignition OFF	0 V
	D11	⇨	Ignition ON	11-14 V
	D14	⬅	Engine idling	2,1 V
	D14	⬅	Engine running – accelerate briefly	4,2 V
	D14	⬅	Ignition ON	1 V
Tachometer	C40	⇨	Engine idling	2 V/20 ms per division ⎍⎍ 21
	C40	⇨	Engine idling	28 Hz
	C40	⇨	Ignition OFF	0 V
	C40	⇨	Ignition ON	11,6 V
Vehicle speedometer	C26			1

1 Connected pin - no test data available

FIAT

Bosch Motronic M2.10.4

Model:	Engine code:	Year:
Bravo 2,0 20V	182 A1 000	1995-99
Marea 2,0 20V	182 A1 000	1996-99

ECM harness multi-plug

Terminal side

19 18 17 16 15 14 13 12 11 10 9 8 7 6 5 4 3 2 1
37 36 35 34 33 32 31 30 29 28 27 26 25 24 23 22 21 20
55 54 53 52 51 50 49 48 47 46 45 44 43 42 41 40 39 38

AD72618

Wire side

1 2 3 4 5 6 7 8 9 10 11 12 13 14 15 16 17 18 19
20 21 22 23 24 25 26 27 28 29 30 31 32 33 34 35 36 37
38 39 40 41 42 43 44 45 46 47 48 49 50 51 52 53 54 55

AD42077

Component/circuit description	ECM pin	Signal	Condition	Typical value	Oscilloscope setting*	Wave form
AC compressor clutch relay – if fitted	32	⊣▷		[1]		
AC condenser blower motor relay – if fitted	41			[1]		
AC refrigerant pressure switch – if fitted	40			[1]		
Battery	18	⟵	Ignition OFF	11-14 V		
Camshaft position (CMP) actuator relay	52	⊣▷	Ignition ON	11-14 V		
	52	⊣▷	Engine idling	11-14 V		
Camshaft position (CMP) sensor	8	⟵	Ignition ON	0 V or 11-14 V		
	8	⟵	Engine idling		5 V/50 ms	∿∿ 12
	12	⇨	Ignition ON	5 V		
Crankshaft position (CKP) sensor	48 (49)	⟵	Engine idling		2 V/2 ms	∿∿ 2
	49 (48)	⟵	Engine idling		2 V/2 ms	Reversed ∿∿ 2
Data link connector (DLC)	55	⟷		[1]		
Earth	2		Ignition ON	0 V		
	14		Ignition ON	0 V		
	19		Ignition ON	0 V		
	24		Ignition ON	0 V		
	42		Ignition ON	0 V		
Engine control relay	36	⊣▷	Ignition OFF	11-14 V		
	36	⊣▷	Ignition ON	0 V		
	37	⟵	Ignition ON	11-14 V		
Engine coolant temperature (ECT) sensor	30	⊣—	Ignition ON	0 V		
	45	⟵	Ignition ON – coolant temp. 10°C	3,5 V		
	45	⟵	Ignition ON – coolant temp. 80°C	0,6 V		
Evaporative emission (EVAP) canister purge valve	5	⊣▷	Ignition ON	11-14 V		
	5	⊣▷	Engine idling	11-14 V		
	5	⊣▷	Engine hot – valve operating		10 V/20 ms	∿∿ 20
Fuel pump relay	3	⊣▷	Ignition ON	0-1 V briefly then 11-14 V		
	3	⊣▷	Engine cranking	0-1 V		
Heated oxygen sensor (HO2S)	10	⊣—	Engine idling	0 V		
	28	⟵	Engine idling – engine hot	0,1-1 V fluctuating	0,2 V/1 sec.	∿∿ 21

* Suggested settings - Voltage/time per division

Autodata

Component/circuit description	ECM pin	Signal	Condition	Typical value	Oscilloscope setting*	Wave form
Idle air control (IAC) valve	4	⅂▷	Engine idling		5 V/5 ms	〰 25
	22	⅂▷	Engine idling		5 V/5 ms	〰 25
Ignition coil – cylinder 1	1	⅂▷	Ignition ON	11-14 V		
	1	⅂▷	Engine cranking	9 V		
	1	⅂▷	Engine idling		5 V/2 ms	〰 33
Ignition coil – cylinder 2	20	⅂▷	Ignition ON	11-14 V		
	20	⅂▷	Engine cranking	9 V		
	20	⅂▷	Engine idling		5 V/2 ms	〰 33
Ignition coil – cylinder 3	39	⅂▷	Ignition ON	11-14 V		
	39	⅂▷	Engine cranking	9 V		
	39	⅂▷	Engine idling		5 V/2 ms	〰 33
Ignition coil – cylinder 4	21	⅂▷	Ignition ON	11-14 V		
	21	⅂▷	Engine cranking	9 V		
	21	⅂▷	Engine idling		5 V/2 ms	〰 33
Ignition coil – cylinder 5	38	⅂▷	Ignition ON	11-14 V		
	38	⅂▷	Engine cranking	9 V		
	38	⅂▷	Engine idling		5 V/2 ms	〰 33
Ignition switch	27	←	Ignition ON	11-14 V		
Immobilizer control module	47			[1]		
Injector 1	17	⅂▷	Ignition ON	11-14 V		
	17	⅂▷	Engine idling – engine hot	2,2-3,2 ms	10 V/2 ms	〰 35
Injector 2	16	⅂▷	Ignition ON	11-14 V		
	16	⅂▷	Engine idling – engine hot	2,2-3,2 ms	10 V/2 ms	〰 35
Injector 3	15	⅂▷	Ignition ON	11-14 V		
	15	⅂▷	Engine idling – engine hot	2,2-3,2 ms	10 V/2 ms	〰 35
Injector 4	35	⅂▷	Ignition ON	11-14 V		
	35	⅂▷	Engine idling – engine hot	2,2-3,2 ms	10 V/2 ms	〰 35
Injector 5	34	⅂▷	Ignition ON	11-14 V		
	34	⅂▷	Engine idling – engine hot	2,2-3,2 ms	10 V/2 ms	〰 35
Intake air temperature (IAT) sensor	30	⅂―	Ignition ON	0 V		
	54	←	Ignition ON – 20°C	3 V		
Knock sensor (KS) 1 – cylinders 1 & 2	11	←	Engine idling – accelerate briefly		50 mV/1 ms	〰 38
	30	⅂―	Engine running	0 V		
Knock sensor (KS) 2 – cylinders 4 & 5	29	←	Engine idling – accelerate briefly		50 mV/1 ms	〰 38
	30	⅂―	Engine running	0 V		
Malfunction indicator lamp (MIL)	51	⅂▷	Ignition ON – MIL ON	0,1 V		
	51	⅂▷	Engine idling – MIL OFF	11-14 V		
Mass air flow (MAF) sensor	7	←	Engine idling – engine hot	0,7-1,5 V		
	30	⅂―	Ignition ON	0 V		
Tachometer – if fitted	6	⇨	Engine idling	30 Hz	2 V/20 ms	〰 55
Throttle position (TP) sensor	12	⇨	Ignition ON	5 V		
	30	⅂―	Ignition ON	0 V		
	53	←	Ignition ON – throttle closed	0,1-0,7 V		
	53	←	Ignition ON – throttle fully open	4-4,8 V		
Vehicle speed sensor (VSS)	9	←	Ignition ON – vehicle pushed	0 V or 11-14 V		

*Suggested settings - Voltage/time per division

[1] Connected pin - no test data available or random digital signal

FIAT

Bosch EDC 15C

Model:	Engine code:	Year:
Stilo 1,9 JTD	192A1.000/192A3.000	2001-06

ECM harness multi-plug

Terminal side

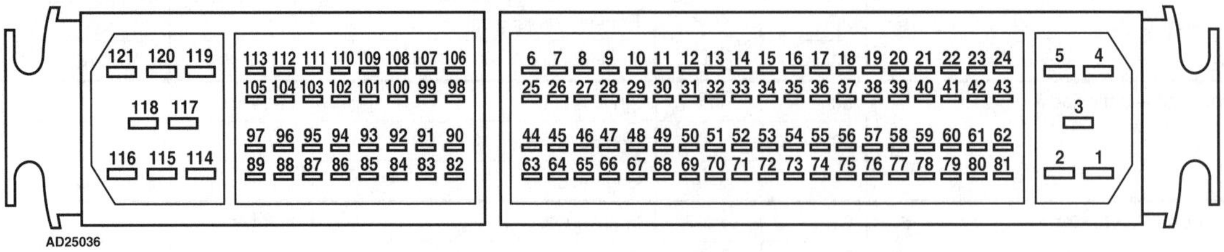

AD25036

Wire side

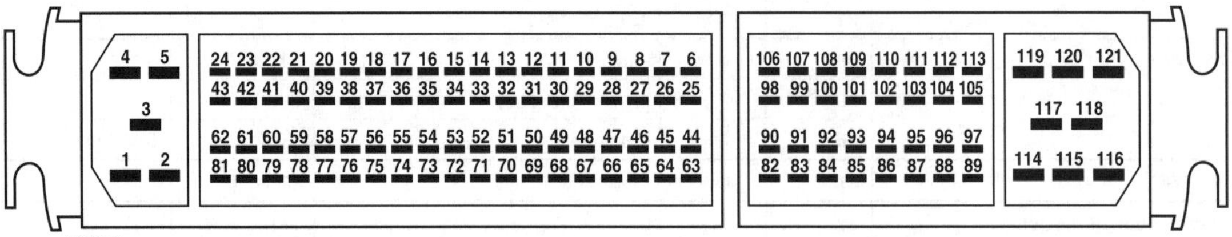

AD25035

Component/circuit description	ECM pin	Signal	Condition	Typical value	Oscilloscope setting*	Wave form
AC refrigerant pressure sensor	40	⇨	Ignition ON	5 V		
	74	⏚	Ignition ON	0 V		
	75	⬅	Ignition ON	0,9 V		
	75	⬅	Engine idling	1,1 V		
Accelerator pedal position (APP) sensor	76	⏚	Ignition ON	0 V		
	77	⬅	Ignition ON – accelerator pedal released	0,7 V		
	77	⬅	Ignition ON – accelerator pedal fully depressed	3,9 V		
	78	⇨	Ignition ON	5 V		
	79	⏚	Ignition ON	0 V		
	80	⬅	Ignition ON – accelerator pedal released	0,3 V		
	80	⬅	Ignition ON – accelerator pedal fully depressed	1,8 V		
	81	⇨	Ignition ON	5 V		
Brake pedal position (BPP) switch	54	⬅	Ignition ON – brake pedal released	11-14 V		
	54	⬅	Ignition ON – brake pedal depressed	0 V		
	59	⬅	Ignition ON – brake pedal released	0 V		
	59	⬅	Ignition ON – brake pedal depressed	11-14 V		
Camshaft position (CMP) sensor	102	⇨	Ignition ON	11-14 V		
	103	⬅	Engine idling		2 V/50 ms	3
	104	⏚	Ignition ON	0 V		
CAN data bus	9	⬌		[1]		
	10	⬌		[1]		
	28	⬌		[1]		
	29	⬌		[1]		

* Suggested settings - Voltage/time per division

Component/circuit description	ECM pin	Signal	Condition	Typical value	Oscilloscope setting*	Wave form
Clutch pedal position (CPP) switch	61	←	Ignition ON – brake pedal released	11-14 V		
	61	←	Ignition ON – brake pedal depressed	0 V		
Crankshaft position (CKP) sensor	99	←	Engine idling		2 V/2 ms	〰 1
	100	←	Engine idling		2 V/2 ms	Reversed 〰 1
Crankshaft position (CKP) sensor – shield wire	101	⌐—	Ignition ON	0 V		
Cruise control selector switch	53	←▷		1		
	55	←▷		1		
	56	←▷		1		
	57	←▷		1		
Earth	1		Ignition ON	0 V		
	2		Ignition ON	0 V		
	3		Ignition ON	0 V		
Engine control relay	4	←	Ignition ON	11-14 V		
	5	←	Ignition ON	11-14 V		
	13	⌐▷	Ignition OFF	11-14 V		
	13	⌐▷	Ignition ON	0-1 V		
Engine coolant blower motor control module	20	←▷		1		
Engine coolant temperature (ECT) sensor	84	←	Ignition ON – coolant temp. 15°C approx.	3,8 V		
	84	←	Ignition ON – coolant temp. 70°C approx.	1,4 V		
	85	⌐—	Ignition ON	0 V		
Engine malfunction indicator lamp (MIL)	21	←▷		1		
Engine oil pressure switch	98	←	Ignition ON	0 V		
	98	←	Engine idling	13 V		
Exhaust gas recirculation (EGR) solenoid	16	▷	Ignition ON		2 V/2 ms	〰 66
	16	▷	Engine idling – valve operating	142 Hz	5 V/2 ms	〰 2
Fuel heater relay	23	⌐▷	Ignition ON – fuel heater OFF	11-14 V		
	23	⌐▷	Ignition ON – fuel heater ON	0-1 V		
Fuel pressure regulator control solenoid	108	▷	Ignition ON	11-14 V		
	109	←	Engine idling		2 V/2 ms	〰 37
Fuel pump (FP) relay	24	⌐▷	Ignition ON	11-14 V		
	24	⌐▷	Engine idling	0-1 V		
Fuel rail pressure (FRP) sensor	90	▷	Ignition ON	5 V		
	91	←	Ignition ON	0,5 V		
	91	←	Engine idling	1,3 V		
	91	←	Engine idling – accelerate briefly	1,7 V briefly		
	92	⌐—	Ignition ON	0 V		
Fuel temperature sensor	82	←	Ignition ON – fuel temp. 15°C approx.	3,5 V		
	82	←	Ignition ON – fuel temp. 20°C approx.	3 V		
	83	⌐—	Ignition ON	0 V		
Fuel/water separator sensor	105	←	Engine idling	11-14 V		

* Suggested settings - Voltage/time per division

Component/circuit description	ECM pin	Signal	Condition	Typical value	Oscilloscope setting*	Wave form
Glow plug control module	22	⬅➡		1		
	62	⬅➡		1		
Ignition switch	58	⬅	Ignition OFF	0 V		
	58	⬅	Ignition ON	11-14 V		
Injector 1	119	➡	Engine idling	1 ms pilot + 1 ms main	10 V/2 ms	71
Injector 1 & 2	117	➡	Engine idling	1 ms pilot + 1 ms main	10 V/2 ms	71
Injector 2	120	➡	Engine idling	1 ms pilot + 1 ms main	10 V/2 ms	71
Injector 3	121	➡	Engine idling	1 ms pilot + 1 ms main	10 V/2 ms	71
Injector 3 & 4	118	➡	Engine idling	1 ms pilot + 1 ms main	10 V/2 ms	71
Injector 4	114	➡	Engine idling	1 ms pilot + 1 ms main	10 V/2 ms	71
Intake air temperature (IAT) sensor	86	⬅	Ignition ON – air temp. 15°C approx.	2,7 V		
Intake manifold air control actuator	15	➡	Engine idling		2 V/2 ms	66
Manifold absolute pressure (MAP) sensor	93	➡	Ignition ON	5 V		
	94	⬅	Engine idling	1,8 V		
	94	⬅	Engine idling – accelerate briefly	3 V briefly		
	95	⌐	Ignition ON	0 V		
Mass air flow (MAF) sensor	88	⌐	Ignition ON	0 V		
	89	⬅	Ignition ON	1 V		
	89	⬅	Engine idling	1,8 V		
	89	⬅	Engine idling – accelerate briefly	3,4 V briefly		
	97	➡	Ignition ON	5 V		
Multifunction control module	48	⬅➡		1		
Turbocharger (TC) wastegate regulating valve	17	➡	Engine idling		2 V/20 ms	66

*Suggested settings - Voltage/time per division

1 Connected pin - no test data available or random digital signal

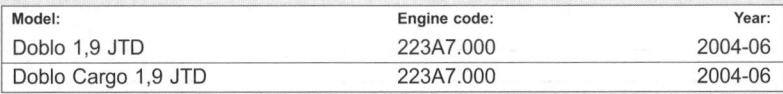
Model:	Engine code:	Year:
Doblo 1,9 JTD	223A7.000	2004-06
Doblo Cargo 1,9 JTD	223A7.000	2004-06

ECM harness multi-plug

Terminal side

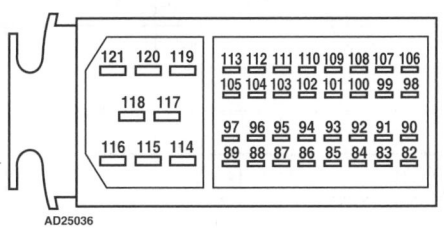 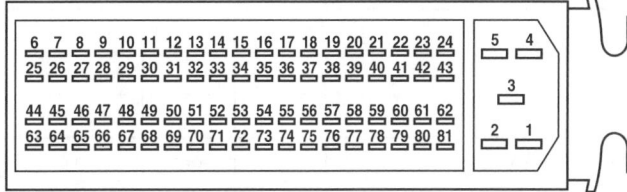

AD25036

Wire side

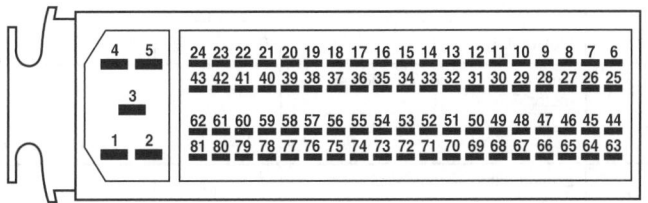

AD25035

Component/circuit description	ECM pin	Signal	Condition	Typical value	Oscilloscope setting*	Wave form
AC compressor clutch relay	18	↗▷	Engine idling – AC OFF	11-14 V		
	18	↗▷	Engine idling – AC ON	0-1 V		
AC refrigerant pressure switch	51	◀▷		1		
	52	◀▷		1		
	60	◀▷		1		
Accelerator pedal position (APP) sensor	76	╤┤	Ignition ON	0 V		
	77	◀	Ignition ON – accelerator pedal released	0,7 V		
	77	◀	Ignition ON – accelerator pedal fully depressed	3,9 V		
	78	▷	Ignition ON	5 V		
	79	╤┤	Ignition ON	0 V		
	80	◀	Ignition ON – accelerator pedal released	0,3 V		
	80	◀	Ignition ON – accelerator pedal fully depressed	1,8 V		
	81	▷	Ignition ON	5 V		
Brake pedal position (BPP) switch	54	◀	Ignition ON – brake pedal released	11-14 V		
	54	◀	Ignition ON – brake pedal depressed	0 V		
	59	◀	Ignition ON – brake pedal released	0 V		
	59	◀	Ignition ON – brake pedal depressed	11-14 V		
Camshaft position (CMP) sensor	102	▷	Ignition ON	11-14 V		
	103	◀	Engine idling		2 V/50 ms	〜〰 3
	104	╤┤	Ignition ON	0 V		
CAN data bus	9	◀▷		1		
	10	◀▷		1		
	28	◀▷		1		
	29	◀▷		1		

* Suggested settings - Voltage/time per division

Component/circuit description	ECM pin	Signal	Condition	Typical value	Oscilloscope setting*	Wave form
Clutch pedal position (CPP) switch	61	←	Ignition ON – brake pedal released	11-14 V		
	61	←	Ignition ON – brake pedal depressed	0 V		
Crankshaft position (CKP) sensor	99	←	Engine idling		2 V/2 ms	
	100	←	Engine idling		2 V/2 ms	Reversed
Crankshaft position (CKP) sensor – shield wire	101	⌐	Ignition ON	0 V		
Earth	1		Ignition ON	0 V		
	2		Ignition ON	0 V		
	3		Ignition ON	0 V		
Engine control relay	4	←	Ignition ON	11-14 V		
	5	←	Ignition ON	11-14 V		
	13	⌐→	Ignition OFF	11-14 V		
	13	⌐→	Ignition ON	0 V		
Engine coolant blower motor relay 1	20	⌐→	Engine idling – coolant blower motor OFF	11-14 V		
	20	⌐→	Engine idling – coolant blower motor ON	0-1 V		
Engine coolant blower motor relay 2	19	⌐→	Engine idling – coolant blower motor OFF	11-14 V		
	19	⌐→	Engine idling – coolant blower motor ON	0-1 V		
Engine coolant temperature (ECT) sensor	84	←	Ignition ON – coolant temp. 15°C approx.	3,8 V		
	84	←	Ignition ON – coolant temp. 70°C approx.	1,4 V		
	85	⌐	Ignition ON	0 V		
Engine oil pressure switch	98	←	Ignition ON	0 V		
	98	←	Engine idling	13 V		
Exhaust gas recirculation (EGR) solenoid	16	⇒	Ignition ON		2 V/2 ms	
	16	⇒	Engine idling – valve operating	142 Hz	5 V/2 ms	
Fuel heater relay	23	⌐→	Ignition ON – fuel heater OFF	11-14 V		
	23	⌐→	Ignition ON – fuel heater ON	0-1 V		
Fuel pressure regulator control solenoid	108	⇒	Ignition ON	11-14 V		
	109	←	Engine idling		2 V/2 ms	
Fuel pump (FP) relay	24	⌐→	Ignition ON	11-14 V		
	24	⌐→	Engine idling	0-1 V		
Fuel rail pressure (FRP) sensor	90	⇒	Ignition ON	5 V		
	91	←	Ignition ON	0,5 V		
	91	←	Engine idling	1,3 V		
	91	←	Engine idling – accelerate briefly	1,7 V briefly		
	92	⌐	Ignition ON	0 V		
Fuel temperature sensor	82	←	Ignition ON – fuel temp. 15°C approx.	3,5 V		
	82	←	Ignition ON – fuel temp. 20°C approx.	3 V		
	83	⌐	Ignition ON	0 V		
Fuel/water separator sensor	105	←	Ignition ON	11 V		
	105	←	Engine idling	13 V		
Glow plug control module	22	←⇒		[1]		
	62	←⇒		[1]		

* Suggested settings - Voltage/time per division

Component/circuit description	ECM pin	Signal	Condition	Typical value	Oscilloscope setting*	Wave form
Ignition switch	58	←	Ignition OFF	0 V		
	58	←	Ignition ON	11-14 V		
Injector 1	119	⇒	Engine idling	1 ms pilot + 1 ms main	10 V/2 ms	71
Injector 1 & 2	117	⇒	Engine idling	1 ms pilot + 1 ms main	10 V/2 ms	71
Injector 2	120	⇒	Engine idling	1 ms pilot + 1 ms main	10 V/2 ms	71
Injector 3	121	⇒	Engine idling	1 ms pilot + 1 ms main	10 V/2 ms	71
Injector 3 & 4	118	⇒	Engine idling	1 ms pilot + 1 ms main	10 V/2 ms	71
Injector 4	114	⇒	Engine idling	1 ms pilot + 1 ms main	10 V/2 ms	71
Intake air temperature (IAT) sensor	86	←	Ignition ON – air temp. 15°C approx.	2,7 V		
Intake manifold air control solenoid	15	⇒	Engine idling		2 V/2 ms	66
Mass air flow (MAF) sensor	88	⌐	Ignition ON	0 V		
	89	←	Ignition ON	1 V		
	89	←	Engine idling	1,8 V		
	89	←	Engine idling – accelerate briefly	3,4 V briefly		
	97	⇒	Ignition ON	5 V		
Multifunction control module	6	←⇒		1		
	7	←⇒		1		
	48	←⇒		1		
Turbocharger (TC) boost pressure sensor	93	⇒	Ignition ON	5 V		
	94	←	Engine idling	1,8 V		
	94	←	Engine idling – accelerate briefly	3 V briefly		
	95	⌐	Ignition ON	0 V		
Turbocharger (TC) wastegate regulating valve	17	⇒	Engine idling		2 V/20 ms	66

*Suggested settings - Voltage/time per division

1 Connected pin - no test data available or random digital signal

FIAT

Weber-Marelli IAW 8P.22

Model:	Engine code:	Year:
Ulysse 2,0	RFU	1994-00

ECM harness multi-plug

Terminal side

35 34 33 32 31 30 29 28 27 26 25 24 23 22 21 20 19

18 17 16 15 14 13 12 11 10 9 8 7 6 5 4 3 2 1

AD78538

Wire side

19 20 21 22 23 24 25 26 27 28 29 30 31 32 33 34 35

1 2 3 4 5 6 7 8 9 10 11 12 13 14 15 16 17 18

AD42096

Component/circuit description	ECM pin	Signal	Condition	Typical value	Oscilloscope setting*	Wave form
AC compressor clutch relay	24	⊐⊳	Ignition ON	11-14 V		
	24	⊐⊳	AC compressor OFF	11-14 V		
	24	⊐⊳	AC compressor ON	0-1 V		
AC refrigerant pressure switch	9	←		1		
Air conditioning	8	←		1		
Crankshaft position (CKP) sensor	11 (28)	←	Engine idling		2 V/2 ms	2
	28 (11)	←	Engine idling		2 V/2 ms	Reversed 2
Data link connector (DLC)	10			1		
	15			1		
Earth	17		Ignition ON	0 V		
	34		Ignition ON	0 V		
Engine coolant temperature (ECT) sensor	13	←	Ignition ON – coolant temp. 10°C	2,7 V		
	13	←	Ignition ON – coolant temp. 80°C	0,4 V		
Evaporative emission (EVAP) canister purge valve	22	⊐⊳	Ignition ON	11-14 V		
	22	⊐⊳	Engine running – valve not operating	0%		
	22	⊐⊳	Engine running – valve operating	1-99%	10 V/20 ms	20
Heated oxygen sensor (HO2S)	12	⊐⊢	Ignition ON	0 V		
	29	←	Engine idling – engine hot	0-1 V fluctuating	0,2 V/1 sec.	21
Idle air control (IAC) valve	2 (20)	⇒	Engine idling		5 V/0,5 sec.	Intermittent 26
	3 (21)	⇒	Engine idling		5 V/0,5 sec.	Intermittent 26
	20 (2)	⇒	Engine idling		5 V/0,5 sec.	Intermittent 26
	21 (3)	⇒	Engine idling		5 V/0,5 sec.	Intermittent 26
Ignition coil – cylinders 1 & 4	1	⊐⊳	Ignition ON	11-14 V briefly then 0 V		
	1	⊐⊳	Engine idling		5 V/2 ms	33
Ignition coil – cylinders 2 & 3	19	⊐⊳	Ignition ON	11-14 V briefly then 0 V		
	19	⊐⊳	Engine idling		5 V/2 ms	33
Immobilizer control module – 1997→	10			1		
	15			1		

* Suggested settings - Voltage/time per division

Component/circuit description	ECM pin	Signal	Condition	Typical value	Oscilloscope setting*	Wave form
Injectors	18	⊐▷	Ignition ON	11-14 V briefly then 0 V		
	18	⊐▷	Engine idling	2,5 ms	10 V/2 ms	〰〰 35
Intake air temperature (IAT) sensor	16	⊐—	Ignition ON	0 V		
	31	⟵	Ignition ON – air temp. 10°C	2,8 V		
Knock sensor (KS)	16	⊐—	Ignition ON	0 V		
	33	⟵	Engine idling – accelerate briefly		50 mV/1 ms	〰〰 38
Malfunction indicator lamp (MIL)	6	⊐▷	Ignition ON – MIL ON	0-1 V		
	6	⊐▷	Engine running – MIL OFF	11-14 V		
Manifold absolute pressure (MAP) sensor	14	⟹	Ignition ON	5 V		
	16	⊐—	Ignition ON	0 V		
	32	⟵	Ignition ON	4,5 V		
	32	⟵	Engine idling	1,2 V		
	32	⟵	Engine idling – accelerate briefly	4,5 V briefly		
Relay module	4	⊐▷	Ignition OFF	11-14 V		
	4	⊐▷	Ignition ON	0-1 V		
	35	⟵	Ignition OFF	0 V		
	35	⟵	Ignition ON	11-14 V		
Relay module – through inertia fuel shut-off (IFS) switch	23	⊐▷	Ignition ON	0-1 V briefly then 11-14 V		
	23	⊐▷	Engine cranking	0-1 V		
	23	⊐▷	Engine idling	0-1 V		
Tachometer	5	⟹	Ignition ON	11-14 V		
	5	⟹	Engine idling	30 Hz		
	5	⟹	3000 rpm	100 Hz		
Throttle position (TP) sensor	14	⟹	Ignition ON	5 V		
	16	⊐—	Ignition ON	0 V		
	30	⟵	Ignition ON – throttle closed	0,4 V		
	30	⟵	Ignition ON – throttle fully open	4,5 V		
Trip computer – if fitted	7	⟹		1		
Vehicle speed sensor (VSS)	27	⟵	Vehicle pushed		5 V/1 sec.	〰〰 43

*Suggested settings - Voltage/time per division

1 Connected pin - no test data available or random digital signal

Model:	Engine code:	Year:
Ka 1,3	J4D	1996-98
Fiesta 1,25	J4C	1995-10/97
Fiesta 1,3	J4C	1995-10/97
Fiesta 1,4	FHA	1995-10/97
Escort 1,3	J4B	1994-98
Escort 1,6/1,8 16V	L1K/RKC	1994-99

ECM harness multi-plug

Terminal side

Wire side

Component/circuit description	ECM pin	Signal	Condition	Typical value	Oscilloscope setting*	Wave form
AC compressor clutch relay	69	⊐⊳	Engine idling – AC OFF	11-14 V		
	69	⊐⊳	Engine idling – AC ON – AC compressor ON	0-1 V		
AC refrigerant pressure switch 1	41			1		
AC refrigerant pressure switch 2	86			1		
Alternator	59	⬅	Engine idling	8-9 V		
Battery	55	⬅	Ignition OFF	11-14 V		
Camshaft position (CMP) sensor	76	⊐⊢	Engine idling	0 V		
	85	⬅	Engine idling		5 V/20 ms	〰 11
Clutch pedal position (CPP) switch	64	⬅	Ignition ON – clutch pedal released – gear lever not in neutral	5 V		
	64	⬅	Ignition ON – clutch pedal depressed	0 V		
	91	⊐⊢	Ignition ON	0 V		
Crankshaft position (CKP) sensor	21	⬅	Engine idling		2 V/1 ms	〰 2
	22	⬅	Engine idling		2 V/1 ms	Reversed 〰 2
Data link connector (DLC)	13	⬅⬄⊳	Engine idling	0,5 V		
	15	⬄⊳	Engine idling	5 V		
	16		Engine idling	0 V		
Data link connector (DLC) – some models	79		Engine idling	11-14 V		
Earth	24		Ignition ON	0 V		
	25		Ignition ON	0 V		
	51		Ignition ON	0 V		
	77		Ignition ON	0 V		
	103		Ignition ON	0 V		
Earth – without PATS	27		Ignition ON	0 V		
Engine control module (ECM) – without PAS	31	⬅	Ignition ON	0 V		
Engine control relay	71	⬅	Ignition OFF	0 V		
	71	⬅	Ignition ON	11-14 V		
	97	⬅	Ignition OFF	0 V		
	97	⬅	Ignition ON	11-14 V		
Engine coolant blower motor relay	68	⊐⊳	Engine idling – coolant blower motor OFF	11-14 V		
Engine coolant blower motor relay – with AC	68	⊐⊳	Engine idling – coolant blower motor ON – low speed	0-1 V		

* Suggested settings - Voltage/time per division

Autodata

Component/circuit description	ECM pin	Signal	Condition	Typical value	Oscilloscope setting*	Wave form
Engine coolant blower motor relay – with AC – except Escort	17	⊐▷	Engine idling – coolant blower motor OFF	11-14 V		
	17	⊐▷	Engine idling – coolant blower motor ON – high speed	0-1 V		
Engine coolant blower motor relay – without AC	68	⊐▷	Engine idling – coolant blower motor ON	0-1 V		
Engine coolant 'hot' warning lamp – some models	98	⊐▷	Ignition ON – lamp OFF	11-14 V		
	98	⊐▷	Ignition ON – lamp ON	0 V		
Engine coolant temperature (ECT) sensor	38	◀	Ignition ON – coolant temp. 10°C	3,5 V		
	38	◀	Ignition ON – coolant temp. 80°C	0,5 V		
	91	⊐–	Ignition ON	0 V		
Evaporative emission (EVAP) canister purge valve	67	⊐▷	Ignition ON	11-14 V		
	67	⊐▷	Engine hot – valve operating		10 V/50 ms	⩊⩊⩊ 20
Exhaust gas pressure sensor – some models	65	◀	Engine idling	0,6 V		
	65	◀	Engine running	0,6-4 V – varies with pressure		
	90	⇨	Ignition ON	5 V		
	91	⊐–	Ignition ON	0 V		
Exhaust gas recirculation (EGR) solenoid – some models	47	⊐▷	Ignition ON	11-14 V		
	47	⊐▷	Engine idling – valve operating	0 V		
Fuel pump relay	40	◀	Ignition ON	11-14 V briefly then 0 V		
	40	◀	Engine idling	11-14 V		
Fuel pump relay – with PATS	54	⊐▷	Ignition ON	0-1 V briefly then 11-14 V		
	54	⊐▷	Engine cranking	0-1 V		
Fuel pump relay – without PATS	80	⊐▷	Ignition ON	0-1 V briefly then 11-14 V		
	80	⊐▷	Engine cranking	0-1 V		
Heated oxygen sensor (HO2S)	60	◀	Engine idling – engine hot	0,1-0,9 V fluctuating	0,2 V/1 sec.	⩊⩊⩊ 21
	91	⊐–	Ignition ON	0 V		
	93	⊐▷	Start engine	11-14 V for 20 seconds		
	93	⊐▷	Start engine	0 V after 20 seconds		
Heated rear window relay – some models	14	◀	Engine idling – heated rear window OFF	0 V		
	14	◀	Engine idling – heated rear window ON	5 V		
Heater function control module	48		Engine idling	6,5 V		
Idle air control (IAC) valve	83	⊐▷	Engine idling – engine hot	40%	2 V/5 ms	⩊⩊⩊ 29
Ignition coil	26	⊐▷	Engine idling		5 V/1 ms	⩊⩊⩊ 33
	52	⊐▷	Engine idling		5 V/1 ms	⩊⩊⩊ 33
Injector 1 – with PATS	70	⊐▷	Ignition ON	11-14 V		
	70	⊐▷	Engine idling	4 ms	10 V/2 ms	⩊⩊⩊ 35
Injector 1 – without PATS	75	⊐▷	Ignition ON	11-14 V		
	75	⊐▷	Engine idling	4 ms	10 V/2 ms	⩊⩊⩊ 35
Injector 2 – with PATS	96	⊐▷	Ignition ON	11-14 V		
	96	⊐▷	Engine idling	4 ms	10 V/2 ms	⩊⩊⩊ 35
Injector 2 – without PATS	101	⊐▷	Ignition ON	11-14 V		
	101	⊐▷	Engine idling	4 ms	10 V/2 ms	⩊⩊⩊ 35
Injector 3 – with PATS	20	⊐▷	Ignition ON	11-14 V		
	20	⊐▷	Engine idling	4 ms	10 V/2 ms	⩊⩊⩊ 35

* Suggested settings - Voltage/time per division

Component/circuit description	ECM pin	Signal	Condition	Typical value	Oscilloscope setting*	Wave form
Injector 3 – without PATS	74	⊣▷	Ignition ON	11-14 V		
	74	⊣▷	Engine idling	4 ms	10 V/2 ms	〰35
Injector 4 – with PATS	95	⊣▷	Ignition ON	11-14 V		
	95	⊣▷	Engine idling	4 ms	10 V/2 ms	〰35
Injector 4 – without PATS	100	⊣▷	Ignition ON	11-14 V		
	100	⊣▷	Engine idling	4 ms	10 V/2 ms	〰35
Intake air temperature (IAT) sensor	39	←	Ignition ON – air temp. 10°C	3,5 V		
	91	⊣—	Ignition ON	0 V		
Mass air flow (MAF) sensor	36	⊣—	Ignition ON	0 V		
	88	←	Engine idling – engine hot	0,7 V		
	88	←	3000 rpm	1,5 V		
Neutral position (NP) switch	91	⊣—	Ignition ON	0 V		
Neutral position (NP) switch – some models	64	←	Ignition ON – gear lever not in neutral	5 V		
	64	←	Ignition ON – gear lever in neutral	0 V		
Octane coding plug	91	⊣—	Ignition ON	0 V		
Octane coding plug – some models	30	←	Ignition ON	0 V		
	30	←		⬚1		
Park/neutral position (PNP) switch	64	←	Ignition ON – AT not in P or N	5 V		
	64	←	Ignition ON – AT in P or N	0 V		
Passive anti-theft system (PATS)	8	←	Engine idling	11-14 V		
	19	←	Engine idling	11-14 V		
	27		Engine idling	0 V		
	42		Engine idling	11-14 V		
	53		Engine idling	11-14 V		
Passive anti-theft system (PATS) – Escort	6	←		⬚1		
Passive anti-theft system (PATS) – Fiesta	11	←	Engine idling	11-14 V		
Power steering pressure (PSP) switch	31	←	Engine idling – steering wheel not turned	0 V		
	31	←	Engine idling – steering wheel turned	9 V		
	91	⊣—	Ignition ON	0 V		
Throttle position (TP) sensor	89	←	Ignition ON – throttle closed	0,9 V		
	89	←	Ignition ON – throttle fully open	4,8 V		
	90	⇨	Ignition ON	5 V		
Throttle position (TP) sensor – 9/97-98	91	⊣—	Ignition ON	0 V		
Vehicle speed sensor (VSS)	58	←	Ignition ON – vehicle pushed	0 V or 11-14 V		
	58	←	Vehicle moving – 10 mph	20 Hz – increases with vehicle speed		
	58	←	Vehicle moving	50%	5 V/50 ms	〰43

*Suggested settings - Voltage/time per division

⬚1 Connected pin - no test data available or random digital signal

Model:	Engine code:	Year:
Ka 1,3	J4D, JJD, J4K, J4M, JJF	1999-02
Fiesta 1,25	DHA, DHB, DHC, DHD	10/97-00
Fiesta 1,3	J4C, JJC, J4L, JJE, J4J,	10/97-02
Fiesta 1,4	FHA, FHE	10/97-02
Fiesta 1,6	L1T	2000-02
Puma 1,4	FHD, FHF	1997-02

ECM harness multi-plug

Terminal side

AD71592

Wire side

AD42072

Component/circuit description	ECM pin	Signal	Condition	Typical value	Oscilloscope setting*	Wave form
AC compressor clutch relay	54	⊐→	Engine idling – AC OFF	11-14 V		
	54	⊐→	Engine idling – AC ON – AC compressor ON	0-1 V		
AC refrigerant pressure switch 1	10			1		
AC refrigerant pressure switch 2	6			1		
Alternator	45	←	Engine idling	8-9 V		
Battery	1	←	Ignition OFF	11-14 V		
Camshaft position (CMP) sensor	24	←	Engine idling		5 V/20 ms	11
	30	⊐	Engine idling	0 V		
Clutch pedal position (CPP) switch – some models	43	←	Ignition ON – clutch pedal released – gear lever not in neutral	5 V		
	43	←	Ignition ON – clutch pedal depressed	0 V		
	46	⊐	Ignition ON	0 V		
Crankshaft position (CKP) sensor	55	←	Engine idling		2 V/1 ms	2
	56	←	Engine idling		2 V/1 ms	Reversed 2
Data link connector (DLC)	17	←→	Engine idling	0,5 V		
	18	⇒	Engine idling	5 V		
	19	←→	Engine idling	0 V		
Data link connector (DLC) – some models	36		Engine idling	11-14 V		
Earth – except Ka	16		Ignition ON	0 V		
Earth	20		Ignition ON	0 V		
	40		Ignition ON	0 V		
	60		Ignition ON	0 V		
Engine control module (ECM), pin 46 – Ka	27	←	Ignition ON	0 V		

★ Suggested settings - Voltage/time per division

Component/circuit description	ECM pin	Signal	Condition	Typical value	Oscilloscope setting*	Wave form
Engine control relay	37	←	Ignition OFF	0 V		
	37	←	Ignition ON	11-14 V		
	57	←	Ignition OFF	0 V		
	57	←	Ignition ON	11-14 V		
Engine coolant blower motor relay – with AC	13	⊐▷	Engine idling – coolant blower motor OFF	11-14 V		
	13	⊐▷	Engine idling – coolant blower motor ON – low speed	0-1 V		
Engine coolant blower motor relay – with AC – →1998	31	⊐▷	Engine idling – coolant blower motor OFF	11-14 V		
	31	⊐▷	Engine idling – coolant blower motor ON – high speed	0-1 V		
Engine coolant blower motor relay – with AC – 1999→	35	⊐▷	Engine idling – coolant blower motor OFF	11-14 V		
	35	⊐▷	Engine idling – coolant blower motor ON – high speed	0-1 V		
Engine coolant blower motor relay – Ka – with AC	29	⊐▷	Engine idling – coolant blower motor OFF	0 V		
	29	⊐▷	Engine idling – coolant blower motor ON – low speed	10-14 V		
Engine coolant blower motor relay – without AC	13	⊐▷	Engine idling – coolant blower motor OFF	11-14 V		
	13	⊐▷	Engine idling – coolant blower motor ON	0-1 V		
Engine coolant temperature (ECT) sensor	7	←	Ignition ON – coolant temp. 10°C	3,5 V		
	7	←	Ignition ON – coolant temp. 80°C	0,5 V		
	46	⊐–	Ignition ON	0 V		
Evaporative emission (EVAP) canister purge valve	11	⊐▷	Ignition ON	11-14 V		
	11	⊐▷	Engine hot – valve operating		10 V/50 ms	⑂ 20
Fuel pump relay	8	←	Ignition ON	11-14 V briefly then 0 V		
	8	←	Engine idling	11-14 V		
Fuel pump relay – with PATS	53	⊐▷	Ignition ON	0-1 V briefly then 11-14 V		
	53	⊐▷	Engine cranking	0-1 V		
Fuel pump relay – without PATS	22	⊐▷	Ignition ON	0-1 V briefly then 11-14 V		
	22	⊐▷	Engine cranking	0-1 V		
Heated oxygen sensor (HO2S)	44	←	Engine idling – engine hot	0,1-0,9 V fluctuating	0,2 V/1 sec.	⑂ 21
	46	⊐–	Ignition ON	0 V		
Heated oxygen sensor (HO2S) – heater control – with PATS	33	⊐▷	Start engine	11-14 V for 20 seconds		
	33	⊐▷	Start engine	0 V after 20 seconds		
Heated oxygen sensor (HO2S) – heater control – without PATS	14	⊐▷	Start engine	11-14 V for 20 seconds		
	14	⊐▷	Start engine	0 V after 20 seconds		
Heater function control module – some models	4		Engine idling	6,5 V		
Idle air control (IAC) valve	21	⊐▷	Engine idling – engine hot	40%		
	21	⊐▷	Engine idling		2 V/5 ms	⑂ 29
Ignition coil – cylinders 1 & 4	58	⊐▷	Engine idling		5 V/1 ms	⑂ 33
Ignition coil – cylinders 2 & 3	59	⊐▷	Engine idling		5 V/1 ms	⑂ 33
Injector 1 – with PATS	12	⊐▷	Ignition ON	11-14 V		
	12	⊐▷	Engine idling	4 ms	10 V/2 ms	⑂ 35

★ Suggested settings - Voltage/time per division

Component/circuit description	ECM pin	Signal	Condition	Typical value	Oscilloscope setting*	Wave form
Injector 1 – without PATS	51	⇥▷	Ignition ON	11-14 V		
	51	⇥▷	Engine idling	4 ms	10 V/2 ms	35
Injector 2 – with PATS	15	⇥▷	Ignition ON	11-14 V		
	15	⇥▷	Engine idling	4 ms	10 V/2 ms	35
Injector 2 – without PATS	52	⇥▷	Ignition ON	11-14 V		
	52	⇥▷	Engine idling	4 ms	10 V/2 ms	35
Injector 3 – with PATS	34	⇥▷	Ignition ON	11-14 V		
	34	⇥▷	Engine idling	4 ms	10 V/2 ms	35
Injector 3 – without PATS	33	⇥▷	Ignition ON	11-14 V		
	33	⇥▷	Engine idling	4 ms	10 V/2 ms	35
Injector 4 – with PATS	14	⇥▷	Ignition ON	11-14 V		
	14	⇥▷	Engine idling	4 ms	10 V/2 ms	35
Injector 4 – without PATS	34	⇥▷	Ignition ON	11-14 V		
	34	⇥▷	Engine idling	4 ms	10 V/2 ms	35
Instrument panel – tachometer – some models	4	⟵		[1]		
Instrument panel – temperature gauge – 2000→	35	⟹		[1]		
Instrument panel – Puma 1999→	31	⟹		[1]		
Intake air temperature (IAT) sensor – in MAF/MAP sensor	25	⟵	Ignition ON – air temp. 10°C	3,5 V		
	46	⟻	Ignition ON	0 V		
Knock sensor (KS)	2	⟵	Engine idling – full throttle briefly		50 mV/1 ms	38
	23	⟵	Engine idling – full throttle briefly		50 mV/1 ms	38
Manifold absolute pressure (MAP) sensor – some models	26	⟹	Ignition ON	5 V		
	46	⟻	Ignition ON	0 V		
	49	⟵	Engine idling	1,5 V		
	49	⟵	Engine under load	4,5 V		
Mass air flow (MAF) sensor – some models	9	⟻	Ignition ON	0 V		
	50	⟵	Engine idling – engine hot	0,7 V		
	50	⟵	3000 rpm	1,5 V		
Neutral position (NP) switch – some models	43	⟵	Ignition ON – gear lever not in neutral	5 V		
	43	⟵	Ignition ON – gear lever in neutral	0 V		
	46	⟻	Ignition ON	0 V		
Octane coding plug – some models	27	⟵	Ignition ON	0 V		
Park/neutral position (PNP) switch – →1999	43	⟵	Ignition ON – AT in P or N	0 V		
	43	⟵	Ignition ON – AT not in P or N	5 V		
	32	⟻	Ignition ON	0 V		
Starter motor relay – through park/neutral position (PNP) switch – 2000→	32	⟹	Engine cranking	0 V		
Passive anti-theft system (PATS)	5	⟵	Engine idling	11-14 V		
	38	⟵	Engine idling	11-14 V		
	39	⟵	Engine idling	11-14 V		
Passive anti-theft system (PATS) – some models	32	⟵	Engine idling	11-14 V		
	41	⟵	Engine idling	0 V		

* Suggested settings - Voltage/time per division

Component/circuit description	ECM pin	Signal	Condition	Typical value	Oscilloscope setting*	Wave form
Power steering pressure (PSP) switch	28	←	Engine idling – steering wheel not turned	0 V		
	28	←	Engine idling – steering wheel turned	9 V		
	46	⌐	Ignition ON	0 V		
Starter motor relay – MT 1999→	32	⌐▷	Engine cranking	0 V		
	32	⌐▷	Ignition switch in start position – cranking inhibited	11-14 V		
Throttle position (TP) sensor	26	⇨	Ignition ON	5 V		
	46	⌐	Ignition ON	0 V		
	47	←	Ignition ON – throttle closed	0,9 V		
	47	←	Ignition ON – throttle fully open	4,8 V		
Vehicle speed sensor (VSS)	3	←	Ignition ON – vehicle pushed	0 V or 11-14 V		
	3	←	Vehicle moving – 10 mph	20 Hz – increases with vehicle speed		
	3	←	Vehicle moving	50%	5 V/50 ms	〰 43

*Suggested settings - Voltage/time per division

1 Connected pin - no test data available or random digital signal

ECM harness multi-plug

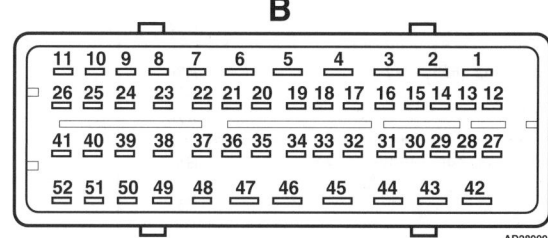

Terminal side

A

```
9  8  7  6  5  4  3  2  1
21 20 19 18 17 16 15 14 13 12 11 10
33 32 31 30 29 28 27 26 25 24 23 22
42 41 40 39 38 37 36 35 34
```

B

```
11 10 9  8  7  6  5  4  3  2  1
26 25 24 23 22 21 20 19 18 17 16 15 14 13 12
41 40 39 38 37 36 35 34 33 32 31 30 29 28 27
52 51 50 49 48 47 46 45 44 43 42
```

AD28909

Wire side

B

```
1  2  3  4  5  6  7  8  9  10 11
12 13 14 15 16 17 18 19 20 21 22 23 24 25 26
27 28 29 30 31 32 33 34 35 36 37 38 39 40 41
42 43 44 45 46 47 48 49 50 51 52
```

AD29011

A

```
1  2  3  4  5  6  7  8  9
10 11 12 13 14 15 16 17 18 19 20 21
22 23 24 25 26 27 28 29 30 31 32 33
34 35 36 37 38 39 40 41 42
```

Component/circuit description	ECM pin	Signal	Condition	Typical value	Oscilloscope setting*	Wave form
AC refrigerant dual pressure switch	A38	←	Engine idling – normal pressure	11-14 V		
	A38	←	Engine idling – high pressure	0 V		
Alternator	B15			1		
Battery	A9	←	Ignition OFF	11-14 V		
Camshaft position (CMP) sensor	B19	←	Engine idling		0,2 V/50 ms	93
	B34	←	Engine idling		0,2 V/50 ms	Reversed 93
Crankshaft position (CKP) sensor	B11	←	Engine idling		2 V/2 ms	Reversed 2
	B26	←	Engine idling		2 V/2 ms	2
Data link connector (DLC)	A19			1		
	A31			1		
Digital clock	A30			1		
Earth	A6		Ignition ON	0 V		
	A7		Ignition ON	0 V		
	B3		Ignition ON	0 V		
	B6		Ignition ON	0 V		
Engine control (EC) relay	A8	←	Ignition OFF	0 V		
	A8	←	Ignition ON	11-14 V		
	A36	⌐▷	Ignition OFF	11-14 V		
	A36	⌐▷	Ignition ON	0-1 V		
Engine coolant blower motor relay 1	A35	⌐▷	Engine idling – coolant blower motor OFF	11-14 V		
	A35	⌐▷	Engine idling – coolant blower motor ON	0-1 V		

* Suggested settings - Voltage/time per division

Component/circuit description	ECM pin	Signal	Condition	Typical value	Oscilloscope setting*	Wave form
Engine coolant blower motor relay 2	A22	⊐▷	Engine idling – coolant blower motor OFF	11-14 V		
	A22	⊐▷	Engine idling – coolant blower motor ON	0-1 V		
Engine coolant temperature (ECT) sensor	B48	◀	Ignition ON – coolant temp. 15°C	3,6 V		
Evaporative emission (EVAP) canister purge valve	B18	⊐▷	Ignition ON	11-14 V		
	B18	⊐▷	Engine idling		5 V/5 ms	Intermittent ⟋⟍ 24
Fuel pump (FP) relay	A24	⊐▷	Ignition ON	0 V briefly then 11-14 V		
	A24	⊐▷	Engine idling	0-1 V		
Heated oxygen sensor (HO2S)	B5	⊐▷	Ignition ON	11-14 V		
	B5	⊐▷	Engine idling	34%	2 V/20 ms	⟋⟍ 72
	B20	⊐⊢	Engine idling	0 V		
	B35	◀	Ignition ON	0,3 V		
	B35	◀	Engine idling		0,2 V/1 sec.	⟋⟍ 21
Idle speed control (ISC) actuator	B12	⇒	Ignition ON		2 V/0,5 sec.	Intermittent ⟋⟍ 61
	B13	⇒	Ignition ON		2 V/0,5 sec.	Intermittent ⟋⟍ 92
	B27	⇒	Ignition ON		2 V/0,5 sec.	Intermittent ⟋⟍ 61
	B28	⇒	Ignition ON		2 V/0,5 sec.	Intermittent ⟋⟍ 61
Ignition coil	B1	⊐▷	Ignition ON	11-14 V briefly then 0 V		
	B1	⊐▷	Engine idling		10 V/2 ms	⟋⟍ 33
	B2	⊐▷	Ignition ON	11-14 V briefly then 0 V		
	B2	⊐▷	Engine idling		10 V/2 ms	⟋⟍ 33
Ignition switch	A21	◀	Ignition OFF	0 V		
	A21	◀	Ignition ON	11-14 V		
Immobilizer control module	A16			1		
	A28			1		
	A29			1		
Injector 1	B41	⊐▷	Ignition ON	11-14 V		
	B41	⊐▷	Engine idling – engine hot		10 V/2 ms	⟋⟍ 35
Injector 2	B52	⊐▷	Ignition ON	11-14 V		
	B52	⊐▷	Engine idling – engine hot		10 V/2 ms	⟋⟍ 35
Injector 3	B40	⊐▷	Ignition ON	11-14 V		
	B40	⊐▷	Engine idling – engine hot		10 V/2 ms	⟋⟍ 35
Injector 4	B51	⊐▷	Ignition ON	11-14 V		
	B51	⊐▷	Engine idling – engine hot		10 V/2 ms	⟋⟍ 35
Instrument panel	A11			1		
	A23			1		
Intake air temperature (IAT) sensor	B22	⊐⊢	Ignition ON	0 V		
	B23	⇒	Ignition ON	5 V		
	B38	◀	Ignition ON – air temp. 15°C	3,2 V		
	B38	◀	Engine idling – engine hot	1,1 V		

* Suggested settings - Voltage/time per division

Component/circuit description	ECM pin	Signal	Condition	Typical value	Oscilloscope setting*	Wave form
Manifold absolute pressure (MAP) sensor	B22	⌐	Ignition ON	0 V		
	B23	⇨	Ignition ON	5 V		
	B37	⇦	Engine idling – accelerate briefly		1 V/2 sec.	〰〰 40
Power steering pressure (PSP) switch	A13			1		
	A25			1		
Starter motor relay – AT	A27			1		
Starter motor relay – MT	A37	⌐⇨	Ignition ON	0 V		
	A37	⌐⇨	Engine cranking	0,2 V		
Throttle position (TP) sensor	B24	⇨	Ignition ON	5 V		
	B39	⌐	Ignition ON	0 V		
	B50	⇦	Ignition ON – throttle closed	1 V		
	B50	⇦	Ignition ON – throttle fully open	4,7 V		
Transmission range (TR) switch	A37	⌐⇨	Ignition ON	0 V		
	A37	⌐⇨	Engine cranking	0,2 V		
Vehicle speed sensor (VSS)	B16	⌐	Ignition ON	0 V		
	B31	⇦	Ignition ON – vehicle pushed	0 or 10,5 V		

*Suggested settings - Voltage/time per division

1 Connected pin - no test data available or random digital signal

FORD
Siemens SIM 22/210

Model:	Engine code:	Year:
Fiesta 1,25	FUJA/FUJB/M7JA/M7JB	2002-06
Fiesta 1,4	FXJA/FXJB	2002-06
Fiesta 1,6	FYJA/FYJB	2002-06

ECM harness multi-plug

Terminal side

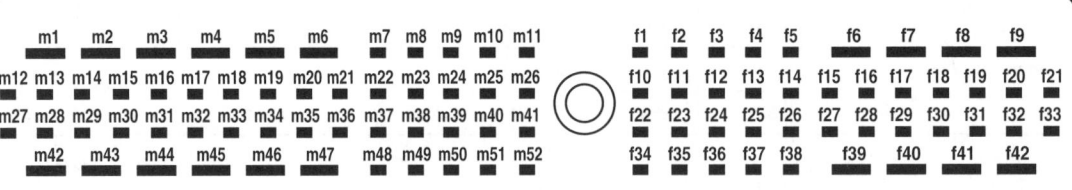

AD106040

Wire side

AD106039

Component/circuit description	ECM pin	Signal	Condition	Typical value	Oscilloscope setting*	Wave form
AC refrigerant dual pressure switch	f22	⬌		1		
	f34	⬌		1		
Accelerator pedal position (APP) sensor	m19	⇨	Ignition ON	5 V		
	m36	⬅	Ignition ON – accelerator pedal released	0,4 V		
	m36	⬅	Ignition ON – accelerator pedal depressed	2,4 V		
	m37	⬅	Ignition ON – accelerator pedal released	0,7 V		
	m37	⬅	Ignition ON – accelerator pedal depressed	4 V		
	m45	⌐	Ignition ON	0 V		
	m46	⌐	Ignition ON	0 V		
	m51	⇨	Ignition ON	5 V		
Alternator	m7		Ignition OFF	0 V		
	m7		Ignition ON		2 V/2 ms	∿ 65
	m7		Engine idling		2 V/5 ms	∿ 55
	m33		Ignition ON	0,7 V		
	m33		Engine idling		2 V/10 ms	∿ 89
Battery	f9	⬅	Ignition OFF	11-14 V		
Brake pedal position (BPP) switch 1	m40	⬅	Ignition ON – brake pedal released	0 V		
	m40	⬅	Ignition ON – brake pedal depressed	11-14 V		
Brake pedal position (BPP) switch 2	m41	⬅	Ignition ON – brake pedal released	0 V		
	m41	⬅	Ignition ON – brake pedal depressed	11-14 V		
Camshaft position (CMP) sensor	f27	⬅	Engine idling		2 V/5 ms	∿ 11
	f38	⬅	Engine idling		2 V/5 ms	Reversed ∿ 11

* Suggested settings - Voltage/time per division

Component/circuit description	ECM pin	Signal	Condition	Typical value	Oscilloscope setting*	Wave form
Clutch pedal position (CPP) switch	m39	←	Ignition ON – clutch pedal released	11-14 V		
	m39	←	Ignition ON – clutch pedal depressed	0 V		
Crankshaft position (CKP) sensor	f26	←	Engine idling		2 V/2 ms	Reversed ⎍ 2
	f37	←	Engine idling		2 V/2 ms	⎍ 2
Earth	f7		Ignition ON	0 V		
	f40		Ignition ON	0 V		
	m5		Ignition ON	0 V		
	m42		Ignition ON	0 V		
Engine control (EC) relay	f8	←	Ignition OFF	0 V		
	f8	←	Ignition ON	11-14 V		
	m8	⊐▷	Ignition OFF	11-14 V		
	m8	⊐▷	Ignition ON	0-1 V		
Engine coolant blower motor relay	m9	⊐▷	Engine running – coolant blower motor OFF	11-14 V		
	m9	⊐▷	Engine running – coolant blower motor ON	0-1 V		
Engine coolant blower motor relay – high speed (if fitted)	m11	⊐▷	Engine running – coolant blower motor OFF	11-14 V		
	m11	⊐▷	Engine running – coolant blower motor ON – high speed	0-1 V		
Engine coolant temperature (ECT) sensor	f13	⊐—	Ignition ON	0 V		
	f36	←	Ignition ON – coolant temp. 15°C	3,6 V		
	f36	←	Ignition ON – coolant temp. 90°C	0,5 V		
Evaporative emission (EVAP) canister purge valve	f16	⊐▷	Ignition ON	11-14 V		
	f16	⊐▷	Engine running – valve operating	0-99%	10 V/50 ms	Intermittent ⎍ 20
Fuel pump (FP) relay	m24	⊐▷	Ignition ON	0-1 V briefly then 11-14 V		
	m24	⊐▷	Engine idling	0-1 V		
Fuel pump (FP) relay – through inertia fuel shut-off (IFS) switch	f35	←	Ignition ON	11-14 V briefly then 0 V		
	f35	←	Engine idling	11-14 V		
Heated oxygen sensor (HO2S) 1	f2	⊐—	Ignition ON	0 V		
	m49	←	Engine idling	0-1 V fluctuating		
Heated oxygen sensor (HO2S) 1 – heater control	f6	⊐▷	Ignition ON	11-14 V		
	f6	⊐▷	Engine idling		2 V/20 ms	⎍ 65
Heated oxygen sensor (HO2S) 2	f1	⊐—	Ignition ON	0 V		
	m38	←	Engine idling – engine hot	0,4-0,6 V		
Heated oxygen sensor (HO2S) 2 – heater control	f39	⊐▷	Ignition ON	11-14 V		
	f39	⊐▷	Engine idling		2 V/20 ms	⎍ 65
Ignition coil	m1	⊐▷	Engine idling		5 V/2 ms	⎍ 33
	m3	⊐▷	Engine idling		5 V/2 ms	⎍ 33
Ignition switch	f21	←	Ignition OFF	0 V		
	f21	←	Ignition ON	11-14 V		
Injector 1	m27	⊐▷	Ignition ON	11-14 V		
	m27	⊐▷	Engine idling	3,2 ms	10 V/2 ms	⎍ 35
Injector 2	m13	⊐▷	Ignition ON	11-14 V		
	m13	⊐▷	Engine idling	3,2 ms	10 V/2 ms	⎍ 35
Injector 3	m28	⊐▷	Ignition ON	11-14 V		
	m28	⊐▷	Engine idling	3,2 ms	10 V/2 ms	⎍ 35
Injector 4	m12	⊐▷	Ignition ON	11-14 V		
	m12	⊐▷	Engine idling	3,2 ms	10 V/2 ms	⎍ 35
Instrumentation control module – CAN-L	f19	←▷		[1]		

* Suggested settings - Voltage/time per division

Component/circuit description	ECM pin	Signal	Condition	Typical value	Oscilloscope setting*	Wave form
Instrumentation control module – CAN-H	f31	⬅⇨		1		
Intake air temperature (IAT) sensor	f3	⬅	Ignition ON – air temp. 15°C	3,4 V		
	f3	⬅	Ignition ON – air temp. 20°C	2,2 V		
	m35	⅃⊢	Ignition ON	0 V		
Knock sensor (KS)	m31	⬅	Engine idling – full throttle briefly		50 mV/1 ms	⩗⩗ 38
	m32	⬅	Engine idling – full throttle briefly		50 mV/1 ms	⩗⩗ 38
Knock sensor (KS) – shield wire	m16	⅃⊢	Ignition ON	0 V		
Manifold absolute pressure (MAP) sensor	m20	⬅	Ignition ON	4 V		
	m20	⬅	Engine idling	1,4 V		
	m20	⬅	Engine idling – accelerate briefly	3,9 V briefly		
	m35	⅃⊢	Ignition ON	0 V		
	m52	⇨	Ignition ON	5 V		
Multifunction control module	m10			1		
	m25			1		
Power steering pressure (PSP) switch	m50	⬅	Engine idling – steering wheel not turned	0 V		
	m50	⬅	Engine idling – steering wheel turned	11-14 V		
Starter motor relay – AT – through transmission range (TR) switch	f30	⅃⊢⇨		1		
Starter motor relay – MT	f30	⅃⊢⇨	Engine cranking	0-1 V		
Throttle motor	f41	⅃⊢	Ignition ON	0 V		
	f42	⇨	Engine idling	3,3 V	2 V/2 ms	⩗⩗ 64
Throttle motor position sensor	m6	⅃⊢	Ignition ON	0 V		
	m21	⬅	Ignition ON – throttle closed	0,7 V		
	m21	⬅	Ignition ON – throttle open	4,1 V		
	m22	⇨	Ignition ON	5 V		
	m48	⬅	Engine running – throttle closed	0,7 V		
	m48	⬅	Engine running – full throttle briefly	3,9 V briefly		
Vehicle speed sensor (VSS) – without ABS	f23			1		
	m18			1		
Wide open throttle (WOT) relay	m26	⅃⊢⇨	Engine idling – AC OFF	11-14 V		
	m26	⅃⊢⇨	Engine idling – AC ON – AC compressor ON	0-1 V		

*Suggested settings - Voltage/time per division

1 Connected pin - no test data available or random digital signal

Model:	Engine code:	Year:
Fiesta 1,4	F4A	1994-95
Fiesta 1,6	L1G	1994-95
Fiesta 1,8	RDB	1994-95
Escort 1,4	F4B	1994-99

ECM harness multi-plug

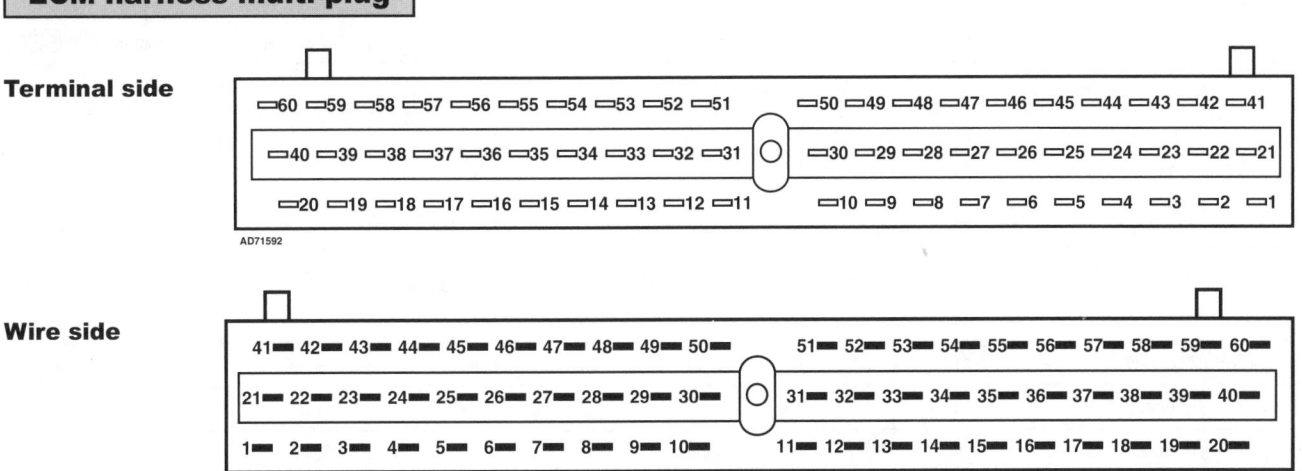

AD71592

AD42072

Component/circuit description	ECM pin	Signal	Condition	Typical value	Oscilloscope setting*	Wave form
AC compressor clutch relay – except Escort with PATS	54	⇥▷	Engine idling – AC OFF	11-14 V		
	54	⇥▷	Engine idling – AC ON – AC compressor ON	0-1 V		
AC refrigerant pressure switch 1	10			1		
Air conditioning – Escort with PATS	35			1		
Battery	1	←	Ignition OFF	11-14 V		
Camshaft position (CMP) sensor	24	←	Engine idling		5 V/20 ms	⋀⋀⋀ 11
	46	⊣⎯	Ignition ON	0 V		
Crankshaft position (CKP) sensor	55	←	Engine idling		2 V/1 ms	⋀⋀⋀ 2
	56	←	Engine idling		2 V/1 ms	⋀⋀⋀ 2
Data link connector (DLC)	17	◄▷	Engine idling	0,5 V		
	18	▷	Engine idling	5 V		
	19	◄▷	Engine idling	0 V		
	48		Engine idling	11-14 V		
Data link connector (DLC) – Escort 1996→	49			1		
Earth	16		Ignition ON	0 V		
	20		Ignition ON	0 V		
	40		Ignition ON	0 V		
	60		Ignition ON	0 V		
Earth – Escort 1994	30		Ignition ON	0 V		
Earth – without PAS	28		Ignition ON	0 V		
Engine control relay	37	←	Ignition OFF	0 V		
	37	←	Ignition ON	11-14 V		
	57	←	Ignition OFF	0 V		
	57	←	Ignition ON	11-14 V		

* Suggested settings - Voltage/time per division

Component/circuit description	ECM pin	Signal	Condition	Typical value	Oscilloscope setting*	Wave form
Engine coolant temperature (ECT) sensor	7	←	Ignition ON – coolant temp. 10°C	3,5 V		
	7	←	Ignition ON – coolant temp. 80°C	0,5 V		
	46	⌐	Ignition ON	0 V		
Evaporative emission (EVAP) canister purge valve	11	⌐▷	Ignition ON	11-14 V		
	11	⌐▷	Engine running		10 V/50 ms	Intermittent ⋀⋁⋀ 20
Fuel pump relay – Escort with PATS	53	⌐▷	Ignition ON	0-1 V briefly then 11-14 V		
	53	⌐▷	Engine cranking	0-1 V		
Fuel pump relay – except Escort with PATS	22	⌐▷	Ignition ON	0-1 V briefly then 11-14 V		
	22	⌐▷	Engine cranking	0-1 V		
Heated oxygen sensor (HO2S)	44	←	Engine idling – engine hot	0,1-0,9 V fluctuating	0,2 V/1 sec.	⋀⋁⋀ 21
	46	⌐	Ignition ON	0 V		
Idle air control (IAC) valve	21	⌐▷	Engine idling – engine hot	40%	2 V/5 ms	⋀⋁⋀ 29
Ignition coil – cylinders 1 & 4	58	⌐▷	Engine idling		5 V/1 ms	⋀⋁⋀ 33
Ignition coil – cylinders 2 & 3	59	⌐▷	Engine idling		5 V/1 ms	⋀⋁⋀ 33
Injector 1 – Escort with PATS	15	⌐▷	Ignition ON	11-14 V		
	15	⌐▷	Engine idling	4 ms	10 V/2 ms	⋀⋁⋀ 35
Injector 1 – except Escort with PATS	51	⌐▷	Ignition ON	11-14 V		
	51	⌐▷	Engine idling	4 ms	10 V/2 ms	⋀⋁⋀ 35
Injector 2 – Escort with PATS	12	⌐▷	Ignition ON	11-14 V		
	12	⌐▷	Engine idling	4 ms	10 V/2 ms	⋀⋁⋀ 35
Injector 2 – except Escort with PATS	52	⌐▷	Ignition ON	11-14 V		
	52	⌐▷	Engine idling	4 ms	10 V/2 ms	⋀⋁⋀ 35
Injector 3 – Escort with PATS	54	⌐▷	Ignition ON	11-14 V		
	54	⌐▷	Engine idling	4 ms	10 V/2 ms	⋀⋁⋀ 35
Injector 3 – except Escort with PATS	39	⌐▷	Ignition ON	11-14 V		
	39	⌐▷	Engine idling	4 ms	10 V/2 ms	⋀⋁⋀ 35
Injector 4 – Escort with PATS	42	⌐▷	Ignition ON	11-14 V		
	42	⌐▷	Engine idling	4 ms	10 V/2 ms	⋀⋁⋀ 35
Injector 4 – except Escort with PATS	35	⌐▷	Ignition ON	11-14 V		
	35	⌐▷	Engine idling	4 ms	10 V/2 ms	⋀⋁⋀ 35
Intake air temperature (IAT) sensor	25	←	Ignition ON – air temp. 10°C	3,5 V		
	46	⌐	Ignition ON	0 V		
Mass air flow (MAF) sensor	9	⌐	Ignition ON	0 V		
	50	←	Engine idling – engine hot	0,7 V		
	50	←	3000 rpm	1,5 V		
Module coding plug – anti-theft system – Escort 1995	49	←		[1]		
Octane coding plug – Escort with PATS	29	←		[1]		
Octane coding plug – except Escort with PATS	42	←		[1]		

* Suggested settings - Voltage/time per division

Component/circuit description	ECM pin	Signal	Condition	Typical value	Oscilloscope setting*	Wave form
Passive anti-theft system (PATS) – Escort	22			1		
	38			1		
	39			1		
	41			1		
	45			1		
Passive anti-theft system (PATS) – Escort 1994-95	5			1		
Power steering pressure (PSP) switch	28	←	Engine idling – steering wheel not turned	0 V		
	28	←	Engine idling – steering wheel turned	9 V		
Secondary air injection (AIR) solenoid – some models	14	⊐⊳	Engine idling – engine cold	0 V		
	14	⊐⊳	Engine idling – engine hot	11-14 V		
Starter motor inhibitor switch relay – Escort 1995 – AT	30	⊐–	Ignition ON – AT in P or N	0 V		
	30	⊐–	Ignition ON – AT not in P or N	11-14 V		
Starter motor inhibitor switch relay – Escort 1996→ – AT	32	⊐–	Ignition ON – AT in P or N	0 V		
	32	⊐–	Ignition ON – AT not in P or N	11-14 V		
Starter motor relay – Escort 1995 – MT with PATS	30	⊐–	Ignition ON	0 V		
Starter motor relay – Escort 1996→ – MT with PATS	32	⊐–	Ignition ON	0 V		
Tachometer	4			1		
Throttle position (TP) sensor	26	⇒	Ignition ON	5 V		
	46	⊐–	Ignition ON	0 V		
	47	←	Ignition ON – throttle closed	0,9 V		
	47	←	Ignition ON – throttle fully open	4,8 V		
Vehicle speed sensor (VSS)	3	←	Ignition ON – vehicle pushed	0 V or 11-14 V switching		
	3	←	Vehicle moving – 10 mph	20 Hz – increases with vehicle speed		
	3	←	Vehicle moving		5 V/50 ms	∿∿ 43

*Suggested settings - Voltage/time per division

1 Connected pin - no test data available or random digital signal

FORD

Siemens SID 802

Model:	Engine code:	Year:
Fiesta 1,4D TDCi	F6JA	2002-06
Fusion 1,4D TDCi	F6JA	2002-06

Autodata

ECM harness multi-plug

Terminal side

```
A
h1 g1 f1 e1 d1 c1 b1 a1
h2 g2 f2 e2 d2 c2 b2 a2
h3 g3 f3 e3 d3 c3 b3 a3
h4 g4 f4 e4 d4 c4 b4 a4

B
m1 l1 k1 j1 h1 g1 f1 e1 d1 c1 b1 a1
m2 l2 k2 j2 h2 g2 f2 e2 d2 c2 b2 a2
m3 l3 k3 j3 h3 g3 f3 e3 d3 c3 b3 a3
m4 l4 k4 j4 h4 g4 f4 e4 d4 c4 b4 a4

C
a4 b4 c4 d4 e4 f4 g4 h4
a3 b3 c3 d3 e3 f3 g3 h3
a2 b2 c2 d2 e2 f2 g2 h2
a1 b1 c1 d1 e1 f1 g1 h1
```

AD106453

Wire side

```
C
h4 g4 f4 e4 d4 c4 b4 a4
h3 g3 f3 e3 d3 c3 b3 a3
h2 g2 f2 e2 d2 c2 b2 a2
h1 g1 f1 e1 d1 c1 b1 a1

B
a1 b1 c1 d1 e1 f1 g1 h1 j1 k1 l1 m1
a2 b2 c2 d2 e2 f2 g2 h2 j2 k2 l2 m2
a3 b3 c3 d3 e3 f3 g3 h3 j3 k3 l3 m3
a4 b4 c4 d4 e4 f4 g4 h4 j4 k4 l4 m4

A
a1 b1 c1 d1 e1 f1 g1 h1
a2 b2 c2 d2 e2 f2 g2 h2
a3 b3 c3 d3 e3 f3 g3 h3
a4 b4 c4 d4 e4 f4 g4 h4
```

AD106452

Component/circuit description	ECM pin	Signal	Condition	Typical value	Oscilloscope setting*	Wave form
AC refrigerant dual pressure switch	Aa2			1		
	Ba1			1		
Accelerator pedal position (APP) sensor	Ac2	←	Ignition ON – accelerator pedal released	0,4 V		
	Ac2	←	Ignition ON – accelerator pedal fully depressed	2,2 V		
	Af2	⇒	Ignition ON	5 V		
	Af4	⌐	Ignition ON	0 V		
	Ag2	⇒	Ignition ON	5 V		
	Ag3	←	Ignition ON – accelerator pedal released	0,7 V		
	Ag3	←	Ignition ON – accelerator pedal fully depressed	4,4 V		
	Ah3	⌐	Ignition ON	0 V		
Alternator	Ce1		Engine idling		2 V/5 ms	〰 19
	Cf1		Engine idling		2 V/5 ms	〰 10
Battery	Bg4	←	Ignition OFF	11-14 V		
Brake pedal position (BPP) switch 1	Bd2	←	Ignition ON – brake pedal released	0 V		
	Bd2	←	Ignition ON – brake pedal depressed	11-14 V		
Brake pedal position (BPP) switch 2	Ae4	←	Ignition ON – brake pedal released	0 V		
	Ae4	←	Ignition ON – brake pedal depressed	11-14 V		
Camshaft position (CMP) sensor	Bc2	⇒	Ignition ON	5 V		
	Be2	⌐	Ignition ON	0 V		
	Cc1	←	Engine idling		5 V/5 ms	〰 4
CAN data bus – high	Aa4	←⇒		1		
CAN data bus – low	Aa3	←⇒		1		

* Suggested settings - Voltage/time per division

Component/circuit description	ECM pin	Signal	Condition	Typical value	Oscilloscope setting*	Wave form
Clutch pedal position (CPP) switch	Ae3	⬅	Ignition ON – clutch pedal released	11-14 V		
	Ae3	⬅	Ignition ON – clutch pedal depressed	0 V		
Crankshaft position (CKP) sensor	Bb3	⇨	Ignition ON	5 V		
	Be3	⬅	Engine idling		2 V/2 ms	⩘ 72
	Be4	⊣⌐	Ignition ON	0 V		
Earth	Ag4		Ignition ON	0 V		
	Ah4		Ignition ON	0 V		
	Bk2		Ignition ON	0 V		
	Cc4		Ignition ON	0 V		
Engine control relay	Cd2	⊣▷	Ignition OFF	11-14 V		
	Cd2	⊣▷	Ignition ON	0-1 V		
	Ce3	⬅	Ignition OFF	0 V		
	Ce3	⬅	Ignition ON	11-14 V		
	Cf2	⬅	Ignition OFF	0 V		
	Cf2	⬅	Ignition ON	11-14 V		
	Cf3	⬅	Ignition OFF	0 V		
	Cf3	⬅	Ignition ON	11-14 V		
Engine coolant blower motor relay 1	Cd3			1️⃣		
Engine coolant blower motor relay 2	Cd1			1️⃣		
Engine coolant temperature (ECT) sensor	Bk1	⊣⌐	Ignition ON	0 V		
	Ca2	⬅	Engine idling – coolant temp. 7°C	4,2 V		
	Ca2	⬅	Engine idling – coolant temp. 60°C	1 V		
Exhaust gas recirculation (EGR) valve actuator	Bm2	⊣▷	Ignition ON	11-14 V		
	Bm2	⊣▷	Engine idling		2 V/1 ms	⩘ 37
Fuel pressure regulator control solenoid	Bl4	⊣▷	Engine idling	13 V	2 V/2 ms	⩘ 37
Fuel quantity adjuster	Bm4	⊣▷	Ignition ON	11-14 V		
	Bm4	⊣▷	Engine idling		2 V/5 ms	⩘ 37
Fuel rail pressure (FRP) sensor	Bd1	⇨	Ignition ON	5 V		
	Cb2	⬅	Ignition ON	0,5 V		
	Cb2	⬅	Engine idling	1 V		
	Cb3	⊣⌐	Ignition ON	0 V		
Fuel temperature sensor	Bh2	⊣⌐	Ignition ON	0 V		
	Ca3	⬅	Engine idling – fuel temp. 7°C approx.	3,5 V		
	Ca3	⬅	Engine idling – fuel temp. 32°C approx.	2 V		
Glow plug control module	Bd4	⇨	Ignition ON – coolant temp. 7°C	10 V for 5 secs then 0 V		
	Ce4			1️⃣		
Ignition switch	Ac3	⬅	Ignition OFF	0 V		
	Ac3	⬅	Ignition ON	11-14 V		
Injector 1	Cg4 (Ch1)	⇨	Engine idling	0,4 ms pilot + 0,7 ms main	20 V/0,5 ms	⩘ 68
	Ch1 (Cg4)	⇨	Engine idling	0,4 ms pilot + 0,7 ms main	20 V/0,5 ms	⩘ 68

* Suggested settings - Voltage/time per division

Component/circuit description	ECM pin	Signal	Condition	Typical value	Oscilloscope setting*	Wave form
Injector 2	Cg1 (Ch2)	⇒	Engine idling	0,4 ms pilot + 0,7 ms main	20 V/0,5 ms	∿∿ 68
	Ch2 (Cg1)	⇒	Engine idling	0,4 ms pilot + 0,7 ms main	20 V/0,5 ms	∿∿ 68
Injector 3	Cg2 (Ch4)	⇒	Engine idling	0,4 ms pilot + 0,7 ms main	20 V/0,5 ms	∿∿ 68
	Ch4 (Cg2)	⇒	Engine idling	0,4 ms pilot + 0,7 ms main	20 V/0,5 ms	∿∿ 68
Injector 4	Cg3 (Ch3)	⇒	Engine idling	0,4 ms pilot + 0,7 ms main	20 V/0,5 ms	∿∿ 68
	Ch3 (Cg3)	⇒	Engine idling	0,4 ms pilot + 0,7 ms main	20 V/0,5 ms	∿∿ 68
Intake air temperature (IAT) sensor	Bh2	⊣	Ignition ON	0 V		
	Cb4	⇐	Ignition ON – air temp. 7°C	3 V		
	Cb4	⇐	Ignition ON – air temp. 22°C	2,7 V		
Mass air flow (MAF) sensor	Bj4	⊣	Ignition ON	0 V		
	Ca1	⇐	Ignition ON	0,6 V		
	Ca1	⇐	Engine idling	2,3 V		
	Ca1	⇐	Engine idling – accelerate briefly	4 V briefly		
Multifunction control module	Cd4	⇔		①		
	Ce2	⇔		①		
Reverse gear position switch	Ca4	⇐	Ignition ON – gear lever in neutral	0 V		
	Ca4	⇐	Ignition ON – gear lever in reverse	11-14 V		
Starter motor relay	Cc3			①		
Vehicle speed sensor (VSS) – without ABS	Cc1	⇐	Ignition ON – vehicle pushed	0 V or 9 V switching		
Wide open throttle (WOT) relay	Ce2			①		

*Suggested settings - Voltage/time per division

① Connected pin - no test data available or random digital signal

Model:	Engine code:	Year:
Focus 1,4 (MT)	FXDA/FXDC	1998-02
Focus 1,6 (MT)	FYDA/FYDC	1998-02
Focus 1,8 (MT)	EYDC	1998-02
Focus 2,0 (MT)	EDDC	1998-02

ECM harness multi-plug

Terminal side

Wire side

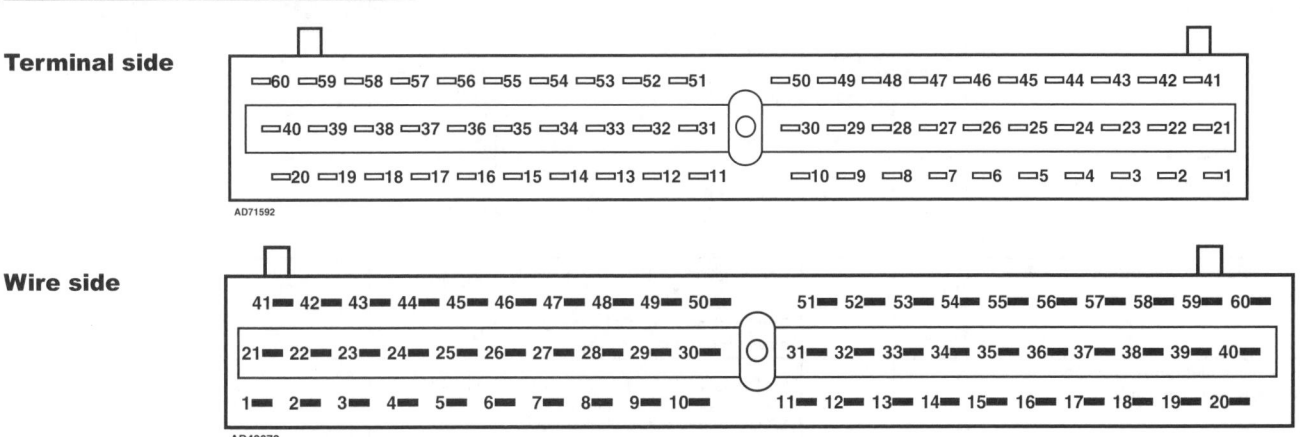

Component/circuit description	ECM pin	Signal	Condition	Typical value	Oscilloscope setting*	Wave form
AC compressor clutch relay	54	⌐▷	Engine idling – AC OFF	11-14 V		
Air conditioning – if fitted	6			1		
	10	←	Engine idling – AC OFF	0-1 V		
	10	←	Engine idling – AC ON	11-14 V		
Alternator	41	←	Ignition ON	11-14 V		
	45	←	Engine idling	8-9 V		
Audio unit	4			1		
Battery	1	←	Ignition OFF	11-14 V		
Camshaft position (CMP) sensor	24	←	Engine idling		1 V/20 ms	⌁ 11
	30	⌐	Ignition ON	0 V		
Clutch pedal position (CPP) switch	43	←	Ignition ON – clutch pedal released	5 V		
	43	←	Ignition ON – clutch pedal depressed	0 V		
	46	⌐	Ignition ON	0 V		
Crankshaft position (CKP) sensor	55	←	Engine idling	1,6 V ac	1 V/2 ms	Reversed ⌁ 2
	56	←	Engine idling	1,6 V ac	1 V/2 ms	⌁ 2
Cruise control module	4			1		
Cylinder head temperature (CHT) sensor	7	←	Ignition ON – coolant temp. 20°C	3-3,2 V		
	46	⌐	Ignition ON	0 V		
Data link connector (DLC)	17	◄▷	Ignition OFF	0 V		
	17	◄▷	Ignition ON	0,4 V		
	18	▷	Ignition OFF	0 V		
	18	▷	Ignition ON	4,75 V		
	19	◄▷	Ignition OFF	0 V		
	19	◄▷	Ignition ON	0,3 V		

* Suggested settings - Voltage/time per division

Component/circuit description	ECM pin	Signal	Condition	Typical value	Oscilloscope setting*	Wave form
Earth	16		Ignition ON	0 V		
	20		Ignition ON	0 V		
	40		Ignition ON	0 V		
	60		Ignition ON	0 V		
Engine control relay	37	←	Ignition OFF	0 V		
	37	←	Ignition ON	11-14 V		
	57	←	Ignition OFF	0 V		
	57	←	Ignition ON	11-14 V		
Engine coolant blower motor relay 1	13	⊐▷	Engine idling – coolant blower motor OFF	11-14 V		
	13	⊐▷	Engine idling – coolant blower motor ON	0-1 V		
Engine coolant blower motor relay 2 – AC	31	⊐▷	Engine idling – AC OFF – coolant blower motor OFF	11-14 V		
	31	⊐▷	Engine idling – AC ON – coolant blower motor ON	0-1 V		
Evaporative emission (EVAP) canister purge valve type 1 – if fitted	11	⊐▷	Ignition ON	11-14 V		
	11	⊐▷	Engine under load – engine hot – valve operating		10 V/10 ms	〰 59
Evaporative emission (EVAP) canister purge valve type 2 – if fitted	22	⊐▷	Ignition ON	11-14 V		
Fuel pump relay	8	←	Ignition ON	11-14 V briefly then 0 V		
	8	←	Engine idling	11-14 V		
	53	⊐▷	Ignition ON	0-1 V briefly then 11-14 V		
	53	⊐▷	Engine cranking	0-1 V		
	53	⊐▷	Engine idling	0-1 V		
Heated oxygen sensor (HO2S) 1	33	⊐▷	Ignition ON	11-14 V		
	33	⊐▷	Engine idling – engine cold	0-1 V		
	44	←	Ignition ON	1 V		
	44	←	Engine idling – engine hot	0,1-0,9 V fluctuating	0,2 V/1 sec.	〰 21
	46	⊐─	Ignition ON	0 V		
Heated oxygen sensor (HO2S) 2 – if fitted	46	⊐─	Ignition ON	0 V		
	48	←		1		
	51	⊐▷	Ignition ON	11-14 V		
	51	⊐▷	Engine idling – engine cold	0-1 V		
Idle air control (IAC) valve	21	⊐▷	Engine idling – engine hot	50-70%	5 V/1ms	〰 39
Ignition auxiliary circuits relay	52	⊐▷		1		
Ignition coil	58	⊐▷	Ignition ON	11-14 V		
	58	⊐▷	Engine idling		10 V/2 ms	〰 33
	59	⊐▷	Ignition ON	11-14 V		
	59	⊐▷	Engine idling		10 V/2 ms	〰 33
Immobilizer control module	5			1		
	5			1		
	38			1		
	38			1		

* Suggested settings - Voltage/time per division

Component/circuit description	ECM pin	Signal	Condition	Typical value	Oscilloscope setting*	Wave form
Immobilizer LED	39	⊐▷	Ignition OFF – immobilizer ON	8,7-11-14 V – fluctuating		
	39	⊐▷	Ignition ON – immobilizer OFF	11-14 V		
Injector 1	12	⊐▷	Ignition ON	11-14 V		
	12	⊐▷	Engine idling – engine hot	3,6 ms	10 V/2 ms	〰 35
Injector 2	15	⊐▷	Ignition ON	11-14 V		
	15	⊐▷	Engine idling – engine hot	3,6 ms	10 V/2 ms	〰 35
Injector 3	34	⊐▷	Ignition ON	11-14 V		
	34	⊐▷	Engine idling – engine hot	3,6 ms	10 V/2 ms	〰 35
Injector 4	14	⊐▷	Ignition ON	11-14 V		
	14	⊐▷	Engine idling – engine hot	3,6 ms	10 V/2 ms	〰 35
Intake air temperature (IAT) sensor	25	⬅	Ignition ON – air temp. 20°C	3-3,2 V		
	46	⊐⎯	Ignition ON	0 V		
Knock sensor (KS) – if fitted	2			1		
	23			1		
Manifold absolute pressure (MAP) sensor – if fitted	26	⇨	Ignition ON	5 V		
	46	⊐⎯	Ignition ON	0 V		
	49	⬅		1		
Mass air flow (MAF) sensor – if fitted	9	⊐⎯	Ignition ON	0 V		
	50	⬅	Engine idling	0,8 V		
	50	⬅	Engine idling – accelerate briefly	4,3 V		
Power steering pressure (PSP) switch – type 1	28	⬅	Engine idling – steering wheel straight ahead	0 V		
	28	⬅	Engine idling – steering wheel being turned	11-14 V		
Power steering pressure (PSP) switch – type 2	28	⬅	Engine idling – steering wheel straight ahead	11-14 V		
	28	⬅	Engine idling – steering wheel being turned	0 V		
Starter motor relay	32	⊐▷	Ignition ON	0-1 V		
Throttle position (TP) sensor	26	⇨	Ignition ON	5 V		
	46	⊐⎯	Ignition ON	0 V		
	47	⬅	Ignition ON – throttle closed	0,8 V		
	47	⬅	Ignition ON – throttle fully open	4,5 V		
Trip computer	4			1		
Vehicle speed sensor (VSS)	3	⬅	Ignition ON – vehicle pushed	0 V or 9 V		
	3	⬅	Vehicle moving		5 V/50 ms	〰 43

*Suggested settings - Voltage/time per division

1 Connected pin - no test data available or random digital signal

FORD

Ford EEC V

Model:	Engine code:	Year:
Focus 1,4 (MT)	FXDB/D	2000-05
Focus 1,6 (MT)	FYDB/D	2000-05

ECM harness multi-plug

Terminal side

60 59 58 57 56 55 54 53 52 51　50 49 48 47 46 45 44 43 42 41
40 39 38 37 36 35 34 33 32 31　30 29 28 27 26 25 24 23 22 21
20 19 18 17 16 15 14 13 12 11　10 9 8 7 6 5 4 3 2 1

AD71592

Wire side

41 42 43 44 45 46 47 48 49 50　51 52 53 54 55 56 57 58 59 60
21 22 23 24 25 26 27 28 29 30　31 32 33 34 35 36 37 38 39 40
1 2 3 4 5 6 7 8 9 10　11 12 13 14 15 16 17 18 19 20

AD42072

Component/circuit description	ECM pin	Signal	Condition	Typical value	Oscilloscope setting*	Wave form
AC refrigerant high pressure switch	6	←		1		
AC refrigerant low pressure switch	10	←	Engine idling – AC OFF	0-1 V		
	10	←	Engine idling – AC ON	11-14 V		
Alternator	41		Ignition ON	11-14 V		
	45		Engine idling	8-9 V		
Audio unit	4	⇒		1		
Battery	1	←	Ignition OFF	11-14 V		
Camshaft position (CMP) sensor	24	←	Engine idling		1 V/20 ms	11
	30	⌐	Ignition ON	0 V		
Clutch pedal position (CPP) switch	43	←	Ignition ON – clutch pedal released	5 V		
	43	←	Ignition ON – clutch pedal depressed	0 V		
	46	⌐	Ignition ON	0 V		
Crankshaft position (CKP) sensor	55	←	Engine idling	1,6 V ac	1 V/2 ms	Reversed 2
	56	←	Engine idling	1,6 V ac	1 V/2 ms	2
Cylinder head temperature (CHT) sensor	7	←	Ignition ON – coolant temp. 20°C	3-3,2 V		
	46	⌐	Ignition ON	0 V		
Data link connector (DLC)	17	⬌	Ignition OFF	0 V		
	17	⬌	Ignition ON	0,4 V		
	18	⇒	Ignition OFF	0 V		
	18	⇒	Ignition ON	4,75 V		
	19	⬌	Ignition OFF	0 V		
	19	⬌	Ignition ON	0,3 V		

* Suggested settings - Voltage/time per division

Component/circuit description	ECM pin	Signal	Condition	Typical value	Oscilloscope setting*	Wave form
Earth	16		Ignition ON	0 V		
	20		Ignition ON	0 V		
	40		Ignition ON	0 V		
	60		Ignition ON	0 V		
Engine control relay	37	←	Ignition OFF	0 V		
	37	←	Ignition ON	11-14 V		
	57	←	Ignition OFF	0 V		
	57	←	Ignition ON	11-14 V		
Engine coolant blower motor relay 1	13	⊐▷	Engine idling – coolant blower motor OFF	11-14 V		
	13	⊐▷	Engine idling – coolant blower motor ON	0-1 V		
Engine coolant blower motor relay 2 – with AC	31	⊐▷	Engine idling – AC OFF – coolant blower motor OFF	11-14 V		
	31	⊐▷	Engine idling – AC ON – coolant blower motor ON	0-1 V		
Evaporative emission (EVAP) canister purge valve	22	⊐▷	Ignition ON	11-14 V		
Fuel pump relay	8	←	Ignition ON	11-14 V briefly then 0 V		
	8	←	Engine idling	11-14 V		
	53	⊐▷	Ignition ON	0-1 V briefly then 11-14 V		
	53	⊐▷	Engine cranking	0-1 V		
	53	⊐▷	Engine idling	0-1 V		
Gas discharge headlamps control module	4	⇨		1		
Heated oxygen sensor (HO2S) 1	33	⊐▷	Ignition ON	11-14 V		
	33	⊐▷	Engine idling	0-1 V		
	44	←	Ignition ON	1 V		
	44	←	Engine idling – engine hot	0,1-0,9 V fluctuating	0,2 V/1 sec.	[waveform] 21
	46	⊐	Ignition ON	0 V		
Heated oxygen sensor (HO2S) 2	46	⊐	Ignition ON	0 V		
	48	←	Engine running	0,6 V		
	51	⊐▷	Ignition ON	11-14 V		
	51	⊐▷	Engine idling	0-1 V		
Idle air control (IAC) valve	21	⊐▷	Engine idling – engine hot	50-70%	5 V/1ms	[waveform] 39
Ignition auxiliary circuits relay	52	⊐▷		1		
Ignition coil	58	⊐▷	Ignition ON	11-14 V		
	58	⊐▷	Engine idling		10 V/2 ms	[waveform] 33
	59	⊐▷	Ignition ON	11-14 V		
	59	⊐▷	Engine idling		10 V/2 ms	[waveform] 33
Immobilizer control module	5	←⇨		1		
	38	←⇨		1		
	38	←⇨		1		
Immobilizer LED	39	⊐▷	Ignition OFF – immobilizer ON	8,7-11-14 V – fluctuating		
	39	⊐▷	Ignition ON – immobilizer OFF	11-14 V		

* Suggested settings - Voltage/time per division

Component/circuit description	ECM pin	Signal	Condition	Typical value	Oscilloscope setting*	Wave form
Injector 1	12	⌐⊢▷	Ignition ON	11-14 V		
	12	⌐⊢▷	Engine idling – engine hot	3,6 ms	10 V/2 ms	⩗⩗ 35
Injector 2	15	⌐⊢▷	Ignition ON	11-14 V		
	15	⌐⊢▷	Engine idling – engine hot	3,6 ms	10 V/2 ms	⩗⩗ 35
Injector 3	34	⌐⊢▷	Ignition ON	11-14 V		
	34	⌐⊢▷	Engine idling – engine hot	3,6 ms	10 V/2 ms	⩗⩗ 35
Injector 4	14	⌐⊢▷	Ignition ON	11-14 V		
	14	⌐⊢▷	Engine idling – engine hot	3,6 ms	10 V/2 ms	⩗⩗ 35
Intake air temperature (IAT) sensor	25	⬅	Ignition ON – air temp. 20°C	3-3,2 V		
	46	⌐⊢	Ignition ON	0 V		
Knock sensor (KS)	2 (23)	⬅	Engine idling – accelerate briefly		50 mV/1 ms	⩗⩗ 38
	23 (2)	⬅	Engine idling – accelerate briefly		50 mV/1 ms	⩗⩗ 38
Manifold absolute pressure (MAP) sensor	26	⇨	Ignition ON	5 V		
	46	⌐⊢	Ignition ON	0 V		
	49	⬅	Ignition ON	4,1 V		
	49	⬅	Engine idling	1,3 V		
	49	⬅	Engine idling – accelerate briefly	4,1 V briefly		
Navigation system control module	4	⇨		1		
Power steering pressure (PSP) switch	28	⬅	Engine idling – steering wheel not turned	0 V		
	28	⬅	Engine idling – steering wheel turned	11-14 V		
Starter motor relay	32	⌐⊢▷	Ignition ON	0-1 V		
Sunroof control module	4	⇨		1		
Throttle position (TP) sensor	26	⇨	Ignition ON	5 V		
	46	⌐⊢	Ignition ON	0 V		
	47	⬅	Ignition ON – accelerator pedal released	0,8 V		
	47	⬅	Ignition ON – accelerator pedal fully depressed	4,5 V		
Trip computer	4	⇨		1		
Vehicle speed sensor (VSS)	3	⬅	Vehicle moving	0 V or 9 V switching	5 V/50 ms	⩗⩗ 43
Wide open throttle (WOT) relay	54	⌐⊢▷	Engine idling – AC ON – AC compressor ON	0-1 V		
	54	⌐⊢▷	Engine idling – AC ON – AC compressor OFF	11-14 V		

*Suggested settings - Voltage/time per division

1 Connected pin - no test data available or random digital signal

ECM harness multi-plug

Terminal side

AD106040

Wire side

AD106039

Component/circuit description	ECM pin	Signal	Condition	Typical value	Oscilloscope setting*	Wave form
AC refrigerant low pressure switch	f22	⬌		1		
	m17	⇨	Ignition ON	5 V		
AC refrigerant pressure sensor	f34	⬅	Engine idling – AC OFF	1 V		
	f34	⬅	Engine idling – AC ON	1,6 V		
	m39	⇥⇨	Ignition ON	0-1 V		
Accelerator pedal position (APP) sensor	m47	⬅	Ignition ON – accelerator pedal released	1,2 V	2 V/5 ms	∿ 64
	m47	⬅	Ignition ON – accelerator pedal fully depressed	8 V	2 V/2 ms	∿ 55
Alternator	m7	⬌	Ignition OFF	11-14 V		
	m7	⬌	Ignition ON		2 V/2 ms	∿ 65
	m7	⬌	Engine idling		2 V/5 ms	∿ 55
	m33	⬌	Ignition ON	0-1 V		
	m33	⬌	Engine idling		2 V/5 ms	∿ 89
Battery	f9	⬅	Ignition OFF	11-14 V		
Brake pedal position (BPP) switch	m40	⬅	Ignition ON – brake pedal released	0 V		
	m40	⬅	Ignition ON – brake pedal depressed	11-14 V		
Camshaft position (CMP) sensor	f27	⬅	Engine idling		0,2 V/20 ms	∿ 11
	f38	⬅	Engine idling		0,2 V/20 ms	Reversed ∿ 11
Crankshaft position (CKP) sensor	f26	⬅	Engine idling		2 V/2 ms	Reversed ∿ 2
	f37	⬅	Engine idling		2 V/2 ms	∿ 2

* Suggested settings - Voltage/time per division

Component/circuit description	ECM pin	Signal	Condition	Typical value	Oscilloscope setting*	Wave form
Earth	f7		Ignition ON	0 V		
	f40		Ignition ON	0 V		
	m5		Ignition ON	0 V		
	m42		Ignition ON	0 V		
Engine control (EC) relay	f8	←	Ignition OFF	0 V		
	f8	←	Ignition ON	11-14 V		
	m8	⊣▷	Ignition OFF	11-14 V		
	m8	⊣▷	Ignition ON	0-1 V		
Engine coolant blower motor control module	m10	←	Ignition ON	11-14 V		
	m10	←	Engine idling – coolant blower motor OFF	11-14 V		
Engine coolant temperature (ECT) sensor	f13	⊣—	Ignition ON	0 V		
	f36	←	Ignition ON – coolant temp. 15°C	3,7 V		
	f36	←	Ignition ON – coolant temp. 80°C	0,7 V		
Engine oil pressure switch	f35	←	Ignition ON	0 V		
	f35	←	Engine idling	11-14 V		
Evaporative emission (EVAP) canister purge valve	f16	⊣▷	Ignition ON	11-14 V		
	f16	⊣▷	Engine running – valve operating	0-99%	5 V/0,2 ms	Intermittent 〰 67
Heated oxygen sensor (HO2S) 1	f2	⊣—	Ignition ON	0 V		
	m49	←	Engine idling – engine hot	0,3-0,7 V fluctuating		
Heated oxygen sensor (HO2S) 1 – heater control	f6	⊣▷	Ignition ON	11-14 V		
	f6	⊣▷	Engine idling		2 V/0,1 ms	〰 64
Heated oxygen sensor (HO2S) 2	f14	⊣—	Ignition ON	0 V		
	m38	←	Engine idling – engine hot	0,3-0,7 V fluctuating		
Heated oxygen sensor (HO2S) 2 – heater control	f39	⊣▷	Engine idling		2 V/0,5 ms	〰 65
Ignition coil	m1	⊣▷	Engine idling		10 V/2 ms	〰 33
	m3	⊣▷	Engine idling		10 V/2 ms	〰 33
Ignition switch	f21	←	Ignition OFF	0 V		
	f21	←	Ignition ON	11-14 V		
Inertia fuel shut-off (IFS) switch	m24	⊣▷	Ignition ON	11-14 V		
	m24	⊣▷	Engine idling	0-1 V		
Injector 1	m27	⊣▷	Ignition ON	11-14 V		
	m27	⊣▷	Engine idling	3,8 ms	10 V/2 ms	〰 35
Injector 2	m13	⊣▷	Ignition ON	11-14 V		
	m13	⊣▷	Engine idling	3,8 ms	10 V/2 ms	〰 35
Injector 3	m28	⊣▷	Ignition ON	11-14 V		
	m28	⊣▷	Engine idling	3,8 ms	10 V/2 ms	〰 35
Injector 4	m12	⊣▷	Ignition ON	11-14 V		
	m12	⊣▷	Engine idling	3,8 ms	10 V/2 ms	〰 35
Instrumentation control module	f19	←▷		1		
	f31	←▷		1		

* Suggested settings - Voltage/time per division

Component/circuit description	ECM pin	Signal	Condition	Typical value	Oscilloscope setting*	Wave form
Intake air temperature (IAT) sensor	f3	←	Ignition ON – air temp. 15°C	3,5 V		
	f3	←	Ignition ON – air temp. 20°C	2,7 V		
	f17	⌐—	Ignition ON	0 V		
Knock sensor (KS)	m16	⌐—	Ignition ON	0 V		
	m31	←	Engine idling – full throttle briefly		50 mV/1 ms	∿∿ 38
	m32	←	Engine idling – full throttle briefly		50 mV/1 ms	∿∿ 38
Manifold absolute pressure (MAP) sensor	m20	←	Ignition ON	4 V		
	m20	←	Engine idling	1,5 V		
	m20	←	Engine idling – accelerate briefly	3,8 V		
	m52	⇒	Ignition ON	5 V		
Power steering pressure (PSP) switch	f29	←	Engine idling – steering wheel not turned	11-14 V		
	f29	←	Engine idling – steering wheel turned	0 V		
Starter motor relay	f30			☐1		
Throttle motor position sensor	f41	⇒	Ignition ON	0 V		
	f41	⇒	Engine idling – full throttle briefly	11-14 V		
	f42	⇒	Engine idling		2 V/2 ms	∿∿ 64
	m6	⌐—	Ignition ON	0 V		
	m21	←	Ignition ON – throttle closed	4,1 V		
	m21	←	Engine idling – throttle closed	4,3 V		
	m21	←	Engine idling – throttle open – briefly	3,8 V		
	m22	⇒	Ignition ON	5 V		
	m48	←	Engine running – throttle closed	0,7 V		
	m48	←	Engine running – full throttle briefly	2 V briefly		
Vehicle speed sensor (VSS) – without ABS	f23			☐1		
	m18			☐1		
Wide open throttle (WOT) relay	m9	⌐▷	Ignition OFF	0-1 V		
	m9	⌐▷	Ignition ON	11-14 V		

*Suggested settings - Voltage/time per division

☐1 Connected pin - no test data available or random digital signal

FORD

Ford EEC V

Model:	Engine code:	Year:
Focus 1,6 (AT)	FYDA/C	1998-02
Galaxy 2,0	NSD/E	1995-02
Galaxy 2,3	Y5B	1996-02
Transit 2,0	NSG/NSF	1994-00

ECM harness multi-plug

Terminal side

AD84086

Wire side

AD42136

Component/circuit description	ECM pin	Signal	Condition	Typical value	Oscilloscope setting*	Wave form
AC compressor clutch relay	69	⊐⊳	Engine idling – AC OFF	11-14 V		
	69	⊐⊳	Engine idling – AC ON – AC compressor ON	0-1 V		
AC refrigerant pressure switch 1	41			1		
AC refrigerant pressure switch 2 – some models	86			1		
Alternator	59			1		
	72			1		
Automatic transmission – some models	1			1		
	33			1		
	34			1		
	37			1		
	44			1		
	46			1		
	73			1		
	81			1		
	82			1		
	99			1		
	102			1		
Auxiliary heater control module – Transit, if fitted	10			1		
Battery	55	←	Ignition OFF	11-14 V		
Camshaft position (CMP) sensor – some models	85	←	Engine idling		5 V/20 ms	11
	86	←	Engine idling		5 V/20 ms	11
Camshaft position (CMP) sensor – some models	76	⊐⌿	Engine idling	0 V		
	91	⌿	Engine idling	0 V		
Clutch pedal position (CPP) switch – Galaxy	64	←	Ignition ON – clutch pedal released – gear lever not in neutral	5 V		
	64	←	Ignition ON – clutch pedal depressed	0 V		
	91	⌿	Ignition ON	0 V		
Crankshaft position (CKP) sensor – 2,3	21	←	Engine idling		2 V/1 ms	2
	22	←	Engine idling		2 V/1 ms	Reversed 2

* Suggested settings - Voltage/time per division

Component/circuit description	ECM pin	Signal	Condition	Typical value	Oscilloscope setting*	Wave form
Data link connector (DLC)	13			1		
	15			1		
	16			1		
	91	⊣—	Ignition ON	0 V		
Earth	24		Ignition ON	0 V		
	25		Ignition ON	0 V		
	51		Ignition ON	0 V		
	77		Ignition ON	0 V		
	103		Ignition ON	0 V		
Earth – some models	76		Ignition ON	0 V		
Engine control relay	71	←	Ignition OFF	0 V		
	71	←	Ignition ON	11-14 V		
	97	←	Ignition OFF	0 V		
	97	←	Ignition ON	11-14 V		
Engine coolant blower motor relay	17	⊣▷	Engine idling – coolant blower motor OFF	11-14 V		
	17	⊣▷	Engine idling – coolant blower motor ON – high speed	0-1 V		
Engine coolant blower motor relay – with AC	68	⊣▷	Engine idling – coolant blower motor ON – low speed	0-1 V		
Engine coolant blower motor relay – without AC	68	⊣▷	Engine idling – coolant blower motor ON	0-1 V		
Engine coolant temperature (ECT) sensor	38	←	Ignition ON – coolant temp. 10°C	3,5 V		
	38	←	Ignition ON – coolant temp. 80°C	0,5 V		
	91	⊣—	Ignition ON	0 V		
Evaporative emission (EVAP) canister purge valve	56	⊣▷	Ignition ON	11-14 V		
	56	⊣▷	Engine running		10 V/50 ms	Intermittent ⋀⋁⋁ 20
Exhaust gas pressure sensor	65	←	Ignition ON	0,5 V		
	65	←	Engine idling	0,6 V		
	65	←	Engine running – 3000 rpm	0,75 V		
	91	⊣—	Ignition ON	0 V		
Exhaust gas pressure sensor – some models	90	⇒	Ignition ON	5 V		
Exhaust gas recirculation (EGR) solenoid – some models	47	⊣▷	Ignition ON	11-14 V		
	47	⊣▷	Engine idling – valve operating	0 V		
Fuel pump relay	40	←	Ignition ON	11-14 V briefly then 0 V		
	40	←	Engine idling	11-14 V		
Fuel pump relay – Transit without PATS	80	⊣▷	Ignition ON	0-1 V briefly then 11-14 V		
	80	⊣▷	Engine cranking	0-1 V		
Fuel pump relay – with PATS	54	⊣▷	Ignition ON	0-1 V briefly then 11-14 V		
	54	⊣▷	Engine cranking	0-1 V		
Heated oxygen sensor (HO2S)	91	⊣—	Ignition ON	0 V		
Heated oxygen sensor (HO2S) – after cat – Transit	35	←	Engine idling – engine hot	0,3-0,7 V	0,2 V/0,5 sec.	⋀⋁⋁ 76
Heated oxygen sensor (HO2S) – after cat – Transit without PATS	95	⊣▷	Start engine	11-14 V for 20 seconds		
	95	⊣▷	Start engine	0 V after 20 seconds		
Heated oxygen sensor (HO2S) – after cat – Transit with PATS	100	⊣▷	Start engine	11-14 V for 20 seconds		
	100	⊣▷	Start engine	0 V after 20 seconds		
Heated oxygen sensor (HO2S) – before cat	60	←	Engine idling – engine hot	0,1-0,9 V fluctuating	0,2 V/1 sec.	⋀⋁⋁ 21

* Suggested settings - Voltage/time per division

Component/circuit description	ECM pin	Signal	Condition	Typical value	Oscilloscope setting*	Wave form
Heated oxygen sensor (HO2S) – before cat – some models	73	⊐▷	Start engine	11-14 V for 20 seconds		
	73	⊐▷	Start engine	0 V after 20 seconds		
	93	⊐▷	Start engine	11-14 V for 20 seconds		
	93	⊐▷	Start engine	0 V after 20 seconds		
Heated windscreen relay – if fitted	14	←	Engine idling – heated windscreen OFF	0 V		
	14	←	Engine idling – heated windscreen ON	11-14 V		
Idle air control (IAC) valve	83	⊐▷	Engine idling – engine hot	40%	2 V/5 ms	〜29
Ignition coil – cylinders 1 & 4 – some models	26	⊐▷	Engine idling		5 V/1 ms	〜33
Ignition coil – cylinders 2 & 3 – some models	52	⊐▷	Engine idling		5 V/1 ms	〜33
Ignition control module (ICM) – some models	23	←	Ignition ON	0 V		
	48	←	Engine idling		2 V/10 ms	〜32
	49	←	Engine idling	30 Hz	5 V/20 ms	〜4
	49	←	3000 rpm	100 Hz		
	50	⇒	Engine idling – engine hot	30 Hz	2 V/10 ms	〜32
	50	⇒	3000 rpm	100 Hz		
Injector 1 – Transit without PATS	75	⊐▷	Ignition ON	11-14 V		
	75	⊐▷	Engine idling – engine hot	3,4 ms	10 V/2 ms	〜35
Injector 1 – with PATS	70	⊐▷	Ignition ON	11-14 V		
	70	⊐▷	Engine idling – engine hot	3,4 ms	10 V/2 ms	〜35
Injector 2 – Transit without PATS	101	⊐▷	Ignition ON	11-14 V		
	101	⊐▷	Engine idling – engine hot	3,4 ms	10 V/2 ms	〜35
Injector 2 – with PATS	96	⊐▷	Ignition ON	11-14 V		
	96	⊐▷	Engine idling – engine hot	3,4 ms	10 V/2 ms	〜35
Injector 3 – Transit without PATS	74	⊐▷	Ignition ON	11-14 V		
	74	⊐▷	Engine idling – engine hot	3,4 ms	10 V/2 ms	〜35
Injector 3 – with PATS	20	⊐▷	Ignition ON	11-14 V		
	20	⊐▷	Engine idling – engine hot	3,4 ms	10 V/2 ms	〜35
Injector 4 – Transit without PATS	100	⊐▷	Ignition ON	11-14 V		
	100	⊐▷	Engine idling – engine hot	3,4 ms	10 V/2 ms	〜35
Injector 4 – with PATS	95	⊐▷	Ignition ON	11-14 V		
	95	⊐▷	Engine idling – engine hot	3,4 ms	10 V/2 ms	〜35
Instrument panel – some models	2			1		
Intake air temperature (IAT) sensor	39	←	Ignition ON – air temp. 10°C	3,5 V		
	91	⊐	Ignition ON	0 V		
Knock sensor (KS)	57	←	Engine idling – full throttle briefly		50 mV/1 ms	〜38
	87	←	Engine idling – full throttle briefly		50 mV/1 ms	〜38
Mass air flow (MAF) sensor	36	⊐	Ignition ON	0 V		
	88	←	Engine idling – engine hot	0,7 V		
	88	←	3000 rpm	1,5 V		
Neutral position (NP) switch – Galaxy 2,0 – MT	91	⊐	Ignition ON	0 V		
Neutral position (NP) switch – some models	64	←	Ignition ON – gear lever not in neutral	5 V		
	64	←	Ignition ON – gear lever in neutral	0 V		
Octane coding plug	30	←	Engine idling	0 V		
	91	⊐	Ignition ON	0 V		
Park/neutral position (PNP) switch – except Focus	64	←	Ignition ON – AT not in P or N	5 V		
	64	←	Ignition ON – AT in P or N	0 V		

* Suggested settings - Voltage/time per division

Component/circuit description	ECM pin	Signal	Condition	Typical value	Oscilloscope setting*	Wave form
Park/neutral position (PNP) switch – Focus	4	←	Ignition ON – AT in R	11-14 V		
	4	←	Ignition ON – AT not in R	0 V		
	7	←	Ignition ON – AT in 1	11-14 V		
	7	←	Ignition ON – AT not in 1	0 V		
	8	←	Ignition ON – AT in 2	11-14 V		
	8	←	Ignition ON – AT not in 2	0 V		
	11	←	Ignition ON – AT in D	11-14 V		
	11	←	Ignition ON – AT not in D	0 V		
	64	←	Ignition ON – AT in P or N	11-14 V		
	64	←	Ignition ON – AT not in P or N	0 V		
Park/neutral position (PNP) switch – Galaxy	91	⌐	Ignition ON	0 V		
Passive anti-theft system (PATS)	19			[1]		
	42			[1]		
	53			[1]		
Power steering pressure (PSP) switch	31	←	Engine idling – steering wheel not turned	0 V		
	31	←	Engine idling – steering wheel turned	9 V		
	91	⌐	Ignition ON	0 V		
Secondary air injection (AIR) pump relay	5	←	Engine idling – engine cold	11-14 V		
	5	←	Engine idling – engine hot	0 V		
Secondary air injection (AIR) pump relay – Transit without PATS	70	⌐▷	Engine idling – engine cold	0 V		
	70	⌐▷	Engine idling – engine hot	11-14 V		
Secondary air injection (AIR) pump relay – with PATS	75	⌐▷	Engine idling – engine cold	0 V		
	75	⌐▷	Engine idling – engine hot	11-14 V		
Secondary air injection (AIR) solenoid – Transit without PATS	70	⌐▷	Engine idling – engine cold	0 V		
	70	⌐▷	Engine idling – engine hot	11-14 V		
Secondary air injection (AIR) solenoid – with PATS	75	⌐▷	Engine idling – engine cold	0 V		
	75	⌐▷	Engine idling – engine hot	11-14 V		
Starter motor relay	27	⌐▷	Ignition ON	11-14 V		
	27	⌐▷	Engine cranking	0 V		
Tachometer – some models	48			[1]		
Throttle position (TP) sensor	89	←	Ignition ON – throttle closed	0,9 V		
	89	←	Ignition ON – throttle fully open	4,8 V		
	90	⇨	Ignition ON	5 V		
	91	⌐	Ignition ON	0 V		
Trip computer – some models	43			[1]		
Vehicle speed sensor (VSS)	58	←	Ignition ON – vehicle pushed	0 V or 11-14 V switching		
	58	←	Vehicle moving	50%		
	58	←	Vehicle moving		5 V/50 ms	〜〜 43

*Suggested settings - Voltage/time per division

[1] Connected pin - no test data available or random digital signal

ECM harness multi-plug

Terminal side

Wire side

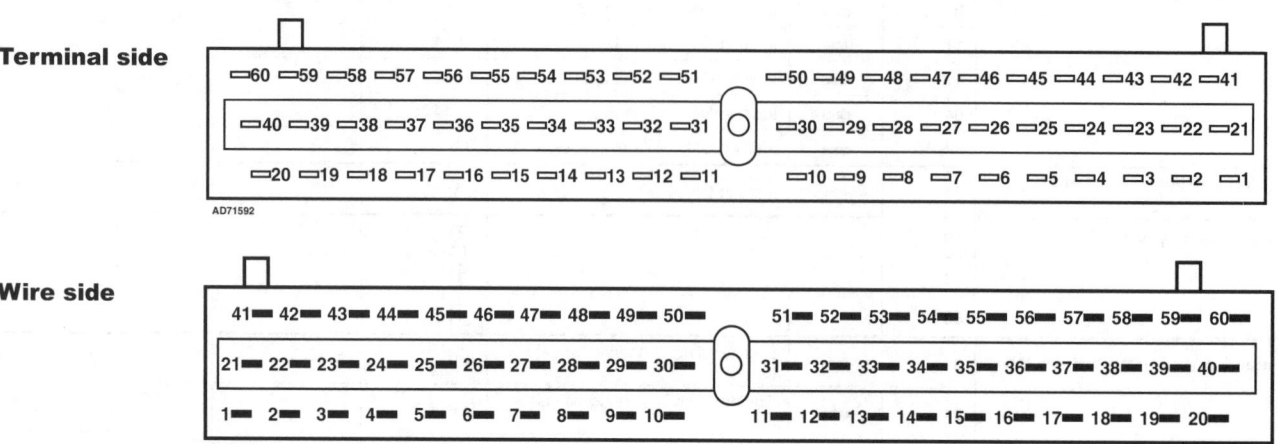

AD71592

AD42072

Component/circuit description	ECM pin	Signal	Condition	Typical value	Oscilloscope setting*	Wave form
AC refrigerant high pressure switch	6	←	Ignition ON	11-14 V		
	6	←	Engine running – AC ON – refrigerant pressure normal	11-14 V		
	6	←	Engine running – AC ON – refrigerant pressure high	0 V		
AC refrigerant low pressure switch – through AC refrigerant dual pressure switch	10	⇒	Ignition ON	11-14 V		
	10	⇒	Engine running – AC ON, AC compressor ON	11-14 V		
	10	⇒	Engine running – AC ON, AC compressor OFF	0 V		
Alarm system LED	39	⇒	Ignition OFF	2-11 V switching		
	39	⇒	Ignition ON	11-14 V		
Alternator	41		Ignition OFF	11-14 V		
	41		Engine idling		2 V/5 ms	Intermittent 55
	45		Ignition OFF	0 V		
	45		Engine idling		5 V/2 ms	51
Audio unit	4	⇒		1		
Battery	1	←	Ignition OFF	11-14 V		
Camshaft position (CMP) sensor	24	←	Engine idling		1 V/20 ms	11
	30	⌐	Ignition ON	0 V		
Clutch pedal position (CPP) switch	43	←	Ignition ON – clutch pedal released	5 V		
	43	←	Ignition ON – clutch pedal depressed	0 V		
	46	⌐	Ignition ON	0 V		
Crankshaft position (CKP) sensor	55	←	Engine idling	1,6 V ac	1 V/2 ms	Reversed 2
	56	←	Engine idling	1,6 V ac	1 V/2 ms	2
Cruise control module	4	⇒		1		
Cylinder head temperature (CHT) sensor	7	←	Ignition ON – coolant temp. 20°C	3,1 V		
	7	←	Ignition ON – coolant temp. 80°C	0,8 V		
	46	⌐	Ignition ON	0 V		

★ Suggested settings - Voltage/time per division

Component/circuit description	ECM pin	Signal	Condition	Typical value	Oscilloscope setting★	Wave form
Data link connector (DLC)	17			1		
	18			1		
	19			1		
Earth	16		Ignition ON	0 V		
	20		Ignition ON	0 V		
	40		Ignition ON	0 V		
	60		Ignition ON	0 V		
Engine control (EC) relay	37	←	Ignition OFF	0 V		
	37	←	Ignition ON	11-14 V		
	37	←	Engine idling	11-14 V		
	57	←	Ignition OFF	0 V		
	57	←	Ignition ON	11-14 V		
	57	←	Engine idling	11-14 V		
Engine coolant blower motor relay 1 – with AC	13	⇥	Engine running – coolant blower motors OFF	11-14 V		
	13	⇥	Engine running – coolant blower motors ON, 1st speed	0-1 V		
Engine coolant blower motor relay 2 – with AC	31	⇥	Engine running – coolant blower motors OFF	11-14 V		
	31	⇥	Engine running – coolant blower motors ON, 2nd speed	0-1 V		
Evaporative emission (EVAP) canister purge valve	22	⇥	Ignition ON	11-14 V		
	22	⇥	Engine running		10 V/50 ms	Intermittent 20
Fuel pump (FP) relay	8	←	Ignition ON	11-14 V briefly then 0 V		
	8	←	Engine idling	11-14 V		
	53	⇥	Ignition ON	0-1 V briefly then 11-14 V		
	53	⇥	Engine cranking	0-1 V		
	53	⇥	Engine idling	0-1 V		
Gas discharge headlamp control module	4	⇨		1		
Heated oxygen sensor (HO2S) 1	44	←	Engine idling – engine hot	0,1-0,9 V fluctuating	0,2 V/1 sec.	21
	46	⊣	Ignition ON	0 V		
Heated oxygen sensor (HO2S) 1 – heater control	33	⇥	Ignition ON	11-14 V		
	33	⇥	Engine idling		5 V/0,1 sec.	24
Heated oxygen sensor (HO2S) 2	46	⊣	Ignition ON	0 V		
	48	←	Engine idling – engine hot	0,3-0,7 V fluctuating	0,2 V/5 sec.	76
Heated oxygen sensor (HO2S) 2 – heater control	51	⇥	Ignition ON	11-14 V		
	51	⇥	Engine idling	0-1 V		
Idle air control (IAC) valve	21	⇥	Engine idling – engine hot		5 V/0,5 ms	24
Ignition auxiliary circuits relay	52	⇥	Ignition ON	11-14 V		
	52	⇥	Engine cranking	11-14 V		
	52	⇥	Engine idling	0-1 V		
Ignition coil – cylinders 1 & 4	58	⇥	Engine idling		5 V/1 ms	33
Ignition coil – cylinders 2 & 3	59	⇥	Engine idling		5 V/1 ms	33
Immobilizer control module (PATS)	5	⬌		1		
	38	⬌		1		
Injector 1	12	⇥	Ignition ON	11-14 V		
	12	⇥	Engine idling	2,8 ms	10 V/2 ms	35
Injector 2	15	⇥	Ignition ON	11-14 V		
	15	⇥	Engine idling	2,8 ms	10 V/2 ms	35

★ Suggested settings - Voltage/time per division

Component/circuit description	ECM pin	Signal	Condition	Typical value	Oscilloscope setting*	Wave form
Injector 3	34	⊐▷	Ignition ON	11-14 V		
	34	⊐▷	Engine idling	2,8 ms	10 V/2 ms	ᴡᴡ 35
Injector 4	14	⊐▷	Ignition ON	11-14 V		
	14	⊐▷	Engine idling	2,8 ms	10 V/2 ms	ᴡᴡ 35
Intake air temperature (IAT) sensor	25	⬅	Ignition ON – air temp. 20°C	3,2 V		
	46	⊐⊢	Ignition ON	0 V		
Mass air flow (MAF) sensor	9	⊐⊢	Ignition ON	0 V		
	50	⬅	Engine idling	0,8 V		
	50	⬅	Engine idling – accelerate briefly	4,3 V		
Navigation control module	4	⟹		[1]		
Power steering pressure (PSP) switch	28	⬅	Engine idling – steering wheel straight ahead	0 V		
	28	⬅	Engine idling – steering wheel being turned	11-14 V		
Starter motor relay	32	⊐▷	Engine cranking	0-1 V		
Sunroof control module	4	⟹		[1]		
Telematics control module	4	⟹		[1]		
Throttle position (TP) sensor	26	⟹	Ignition ON	5 V		
	46	⊐⊢	Ignition ON	0 V		
	47	⬅	Ignition ON – throttle closed	0,8 V		
	47	⬅	Ignition ON – throttle fully open	4,5 V		
Trip computer	4	⟹		[1]		
	35			[1]		
Vehicle speed sensor (VSS)	3	⬅	Ignition ON – vehicle pushed	0 V or 9 V switching		
Wide open throttle (WOT) relay	54	⊐▷	Engine idling – AC OFF	11-14 V		
	54	⊐▷	Engine idling – AC ON – AC compressor ON	0-1 V		

*Suggested settings - Voltage/time per division

[1] Connected pin - no test data available or random digital signal

Model:	Engine code:	Year:	
Focus 1,8 TDdi	C9DA/B/C	1998-01	**FORD**
			Bosch EDC/EEC V

ECM harness multi-plug

Terminal side

AD84086

Wire side

AD42136

Component/circuit description	ECM pin	Signal	Condition	Typical value
AC compressor clutch relay	69	⊐▷	Engine idling – AC OFF	11-14 V
	69	⊐▷	Engine idling – AC ON – AC compressor ON	0-1 V
AC refrigerant pressure switch	41			1
	100			1
Accelerator pedal position (APP) sensor	4	◀	Ignition ON – accelerator pedal released	3,97 V
	4	◀	Ignition ON – accelerator pedal fully depressed	0,85 V
	5	◀	Ignition ON – accelerator pedal released	1,6 V
	5	◀	Ignition ON – accelerator pedal fully depressed	3,92 V
	7	◀	Ignition ON – accelerator pedal released	1 V
	7	◀	Ignition ON – accelerator pedal fully depressed	3,35 V
	39	▷	Ignition ON	5 V
	51	⊣–	Ignition ON	0 V
	90	▷	Ignition ON	5 V
	91	⊣–	Ignition ON	0 V
Alternator	32	◀▷	Engine running – engine hot – electrical loads OFF	9,3 V
	32	◀▷	Engine running – engine hot – electrical loads ON	9 V
	32	◀▷	Ignition ON	0,76 V
	72	◀▷	Engine idling	8,82 V
	72	◀▷	Ignition ON	0 V
Battery	55	◀	Ignition OFF	11-14 V
Brake pedal position (BPP) switch	92	⊣–	Ignition ON – brake pedal released	0 V
	92	⊣–	Ignition ON – brake pedal depressed	11-14 V
Clutch pedal position (CPP) switch	63	◀	Ignition ON – clutch pedal released	11-14 V
	63	◀	Ignition ON – clutch pedal depressed	0 V
	64	◀	Ignition ON – clutch pedal released	11-14 V
	64	◀	Ignition ON – clutch pedal depressed	0 V
	91	⊣–	Ignition ON	0 V

Component/circuit description	ECM pin	Signal	Condition	Typical value
Crankshaft position (CKP) sensor	21	←	Engine idling	1,3 V ac
	21	←	Engine idling	2 V/2 ms per division 40
	21	←	Ignition ON	1,53 V
	22	←	Engine idling	1,3 V ac
	22	←	Engine idling	2 V/2 ms per division 41
	22	←	Ignition ON	1,53 V
Cylinder head temperature (CHT) sensor (dual range)	14	←	Ignition ON – coolant temp. 0°C	4,1 V
	14	←	Ignition ON – coolant temp. 20°C	3,2 V
	14	←	Ignition ON – coolant temp. 60°C	1,3 V
	14	←	Ignition ON – coolant temp. 95°C	0,46 V or 3,5 V
	14	←	Ignition ON – coolant temp. 110°C	3 V
	91	⌐	Ignition ON	0 V
Data link connector (DLC)	13	↔	Ignition ON	0 V
	15	↔	Ignition ON	4,4-5 V fluctuating
	16	↔	Ignition ON	0-0,6 V fluctuating
Earth	25		Ignition ON	0 V
	76		Ignition ON	0 V
	77		Ignition ON	0 V
	103		Ignition ON	0 V
Engine control relay	70	⌐▷	Engine idling	0,15 V
	70	⌐▷	Ignition ON	0,11 V
Engine coolant blower motor relay – MT – with AC	17	⌐▷	Engine idling – coolant blower motor OFF	11-14 V
	17	⌐▷	Engine idling – coolant blower motor ON – high speed	0-1 V
	68	⌐▷	Engine idling – coolant blower motor OFF	11-14 V
	68	⌐▷	Engine idling – coolant blower motor ON – low speed	0-1 V
Engine coolant heater relay I – if fitted	98	⌐▷		1
Engine coolant heater relay II – if fitted	75	⌐▷		1
Exhaust gas recirculation (EGR) solenoid	83	⌐▷	Ignition ON	11-14 V
	83	⌐▷	Engine idling – accelerate briefly	75%
	83	⌐▷	Engine idling	5 V/1 ms per division 39
Exhaust gas recirculation (EGR) valve position sensor	35	←	Ignition ON	1,25 V
	35	←	Engine idling	1,25 V
	90	→	Ignition ON	5 V
	91	⌐	Ignition ON	0 V
Fuel injection pump control module	12	→	Engine idling	0,1 V/10 ms per division 54
	12	→	Ignition ON	10,4 V
	57	→	Engine idling	2 V/20 ms per division 43
	57	→	Ignition ON	4,85 V
Fuel injection pump control module (data bus)	49	↔		1
	50	↔		1
Glow plug relay	1	⌐▷	Ignition ON – glow plugs ON	0 V
	1	⌐▷	Ignition ON – glow plugs OFF	11-14 V

Component/circuit description	ECM pin	Signal	Condition	Typical value
Ignition auxiliary circuits relay	6	⊐▷		☐1
Ignition main circuits relay	96	⊐▷	Ignition OFF	11-14 V
	96	⊐▷	Ignition ON	0 V
	97	⬅	Ignition ON	11-14 V
	97	⬅	Ignition OFF	0 V
Ignition switch	8	⬅	Ignition OFF	0 V
	8	⬅	Ignition ON	11-14 V
Instrument panel	15	⬅▷	Ignition ON	4,4-5 V fluctuating
	16	⬅▷	Ignition ON	0-0,6 V fluctuating
Intake air temperature (IAT) sensor I	3	⬅	Ignition ON – air temp. 20°C	3,95 V
	91	⊐⎯	Ignition ON	0 V
Intake air temperature (IAT) sensor II	65	⬅	Ignition ON – air temp. 20°C	3,2 V
	91	⊐⎯	Ignition ON	0 V
Manifold absolute pressure (MAP) sensor	34	⬅	Ignition ON	1,53 V
	34	⬅	Engine idling	1,57 V
	34	⬅	Engine idling – accelerate briefly	3,1 V
	90	⇨	Ignition ON	5 V
	91	⊐⎯	Ignition ON	0 V
Passive anti-theft system (PATS)	19	⬅	Engine idling	11-14 V
	42		Ignition ON	11-14 V
	53		Engine idling	11-14 V
	53		Ignition ON	0,12 V
Starter motor relay	27	⊐▷		☐1
Trip computer	94		Engine idling	11-14 V
	94		Ignition ON	11-14 V
	95		Engine idling	11-14 V
	95		Ignition ON	11-14 V
Vehicle speed sensor (VSS)	58	⬅	Ignition ON	0,71 V
	58	⬅	Ignition ON – vehicle moving	0 V or 10 V

☐1 Connected pin - no test data available

Model:	Engine code:	Year:
Focus 1,8 TDCi	F9DA/B	2001-07/02

ECM harness multi-plug

Terminal side

AD84086

Wire side

AD42136

Component/circuit description	ECM pin	Signal	Condition	Typical value	Oscilloscope setting*	Wave form
AC refrigerant dual pressure switch	100	←	Ignition ON	11-14 V		
	100	←	Engine running – AC ON – refrigerant pressure normal	11-14 V		
	100	←	Engine running – AC ON – refrigerant pressure high	0 V		
AC refrigerant low pressure switch – through AC refrigerant dual pressure switch	41	⇒	Ignition ON	11-14 V		
	41	⇒	Engine running – AC ON, AC compressor ON	11-14 V		
	41	⇒	Engine running – AC ON, AC compressor OFF	0 V		
Accelerator pedal position (APP) sensor	4	←	Ignition ON – accelerator pedal released	4,2 V		
	4	←	Ignition ON – accelerator pedal depressed	0,8 V		
	5	←	Ignition ON – accelerator pedal released	1,4 V		
	5	←	Ignition ON – accelerator pedal depressed	3,9 V		
	7	←	Ignition ON – accelerator pedal released	0,8 V		
	7	←	Ignition ON – accelerator pedal depressed	3,3 V		
	39	⇒	Ignition ON	5 V		
	51	⌐	Ignition ON	0 V		
	90	⇒	Ignition ON	5 V		
	91	⌐	Ignition ON	0 V		
Alarm system warning lamp	42	⇒	Ignition OFF	2-11 V switching		
	42	⇒	Ignition ON	11-14 V		
Alternator	32		Ignition ON	0,74 V		
	32		Engine running		4 V/2 ms	⎍⎍ 31
	72		Ignition OFF	11-14 V		
	72		Ignition ON	0,25 V		
	72		Engine running	8,2 V	5 V/5 ms	⎍⎍ 39
Battery	55	←	Ignition OFF	11-14 V		
Brake pedal position (BPP) switch	92	←	Ignition ON – brake pedal released	0 V		
	92	←	Ignition ON – brake pedal depressed	11-14 V		
CAN data bus – high	49	⇔		1		

* Suggested settings - Voltage/time per division

Component/circuit description	ECM pin	Signal	Condition	Typical value	Oscilloscope setting*	Wave form
CAN data bus – low	50	⟷		1		
Clutch pedal position (CPP) switch	63	⟹	Ignition ON – clutch pedal released	11-14 V		
	63	⟹	Ignition ON – clutch pedal depressed	0 V		
	91	⌐	Ignition ON	0 V		
Cylinder head temperature (CHT) sensor (dual range)	14	⟸	Ignition ON – coolant temp. 0°C	4,1 V		
	14	⟸	Ignition ON – coolant temp. 20°C	3,2 V		
	14	⟸	Ignition ON – coolant temp. 60°C	1,3 V		
	14	⟸	Ignition ON – coolant temp. 95°C	0,46 V		
	14	⟸	Ignition ON – coolant temp. 110°C	3 V		
	91	⌐	Ignition ON	0 V		
Data link connector (DLC)	13	⟷	Ignition ON	0 V		
	15	⟷	Ignition ON	5 V		
	16	⟷	Ignition ON	0 V		
Earth	25		Ignition ON	0 V		
	76		Ignition ON	0 V		
	77		Ignition ON	0 V		
	103		Ignition ON	0 V		
Engine control (EC) relay	71	⌐⟹	Ignition OFF	11-14 V		
	71	⌐⟹	Ignition ON	0-1 V		
	96	⌐⟹	Ignition OFF	11-14 V		
	96	⌐⟹	Ignition ON	0-1 V		
	97	⟸	Ignition OFF	11-14 V		
	97	⟸	Ignition ON	0-1 V		
Engine coolant blower motor relay – without AC	68	⌐⟹	Engine running – coolant blower motor OFF	11-14 V		
	68	⌐⟹	Engine running – coolant blower motor ON	0-1 V		
Engine coolant blower motor relay 1 – with AC	68	⌐⟹	Engine running – coolant blower motors OFF	11-14 V		
	68	⌐⟹	Engine running – coolant blower motors ON, 1st speed	0-1 V		
Engine coolant blower motor relay 2 – with AC	17	⌐⟹	Engine running – coolant blower motors OFF	11-14 V		
	17	⌐⟹	Engine running – coolant blower motors ON, 2nd speed	0-1 V		
Engine coolant heater relay 1	98	⌐⟹	Ignition ON	11-14 V		
	98	⌐⟹	Engine running – intake air temp. 0°C max.	0-1 V		
Engine coolant heater relay 2	75	⌐⟹	Ignition ON	11-14 V		
	75	⌐⟹	Engine running – intake air temp. below 0°C	0-1 V		
Exhaust gas recirculation (EGR) solenoid	83	⌐⟹	Ignition ON	11-14 V		
	83	⌐⟹	Engine idling		5 V/5 ms	39
Glow plug relay	1	⌐⟹	Ignition ON – glow plugs OFF	11-14 V		
	1	⌐⟹	Ignition ON – glow plugs ON	0-1 V		
Ignition switch	8	⟸	Ignition OFF	0 V		
	8	⟸	Ignition ON	11-14 V		
Immobilizer control module (PATS)	19	⟷	Ignition OFF	0 V		
	19	⟷	Ignition ON	11-14 V		
	53	⟷	Ignition OFF	0 V		
	53	⟷	Ignition ON	11-14 V		
Injector control module – engine RPM signal	57	⟸	Engine idling		2 V/2 ms	65
Injector relay	70	⌐⟹	Ignition OFF	0 V		
	70	⌐⟹	Ignition ON	0-1 V		

* Suggested settings - Voltage/time per division

Component/circuit description	ECM pin	Signal	Condition	Typical value	Oscilloscope setting*	Wave form
Intake air temperature (IAT) sensor	38	←	Ignition ON – air temp. 20°C	3,2 V		
	91	⌐	Ignition ON	0 V		
Intake manifold air control actuator	47	⇥▷	Ignition ON	11-14 V		
	47	⇥▷	Engine running	11-14 V		
	47	⇥▷	Engine idling – switch ignition OFF	0-1 V for 1 sec., 11-14 V for 10 secs then 0 V		
Manifold absolute pressure (MAP) sensor	34	←	Ignition ON	1,5 V		
	34	←	Engine idling	1,6 V		
	34	←	Engine idling – accelerate briefly	3,2 V briefly		
	90	⇨	Ignition ON	5 V		
	91	⌐	Ignition ON	0 V		
Mass air flow (MAF) sensor	36	⌐	Ignition ON	0 V		
	88	←	Ignition ON	0,6 V		
	88	←	Engine idling	1,7 V		
	88	←	3000 rpm	3,4 V		
Reverse gear position switch	66	←	Ignition ON – gear lever in neutral	0 V		
	66	←	Ignition ON – gear lever in reverse	11-14 V		
Starter motor relay	27	⇥▷	Engine cranking	0-1 V		
Trip computer	94	⇨		1		
	95	⇨		1		
Turbocharger (TC) boost air temperature sensor	3	←	Ignition ON – air temp. 20°C	3,8 V		
	91	⌐	Ignition ON	0 V		
Turbocharger (TC) wastegate regulating valve	52	⇥▷	Ignition ON	11-14 V		
	52	⇥▷	Engine idling		2 V/2 ms	⎍⎍ 64
Vehicle speed sensor (VSS)	58	←	Ignition ON – vehicle pushed	0-9 V switching		
Wide open throttle (WOT) relay	69	⇥▷	Engine running – AC compressor OFF	11-14 V		
	69	⇥▷	Engine running – AC compressor ON	0-1 V		

*Suggested settings - Voltage/time per division

1 Connected pin - no test data available or random digital signal

Injector control module harness multi-plug

Terminal side – A – Grey, B – Brown, C – Black

C

h1	g1	f1	e1	d1	c1	b1	a1
h2	g2	f2	e2	d2	c2	b2	a2
h3	g3	f3	e3	d3	c3	b3	a3
h4	g4	f4	e4	d4	c4	b4	a4

B

m1	l1	k1	j1	h1	g1	f1	e1	d1	c1	b1	a1
m2	l2	k2	j2	h2	g2	f2	e2	d2	c2	b2	a2
m3	l3	k3	j3	h3	g3	f3	e3	d3	c3	b3	a3
m4	l4	k4	j4	h4	g4	f4	e4	d4	c4	b4	a4

A

a4	b4	c4	d4	e4	f4	g4	h4
a3	b3	c3	d3	e3	f3	g3	h3
a2	b2	c2	d2	e2	f2	g2	h2
a1	b1	c1	d1	e1	f1	g1	h1

AD22744

Wire side – A – Grey, B – Brown, C – Black

A

h4	g4	f4	e4	d4	c4	b4	a4
h3	g3	f3	e3	d3	c3	b3	a3
h2	g2	f2	e2	d2	c2	b2	a2
h1	g1	f1	e1	d1	c1	b1	a1

B

a1	b1	c1	d1	e1	f1	g1	h1	j1	k1	l1	m1
a2	b2	c2	d2	e2	f2	g2	h2	j2	k2	l2	m2
a3	b3	c3	d3	e3	f3	g3	h3	j3	k3	l3	m3
a4	b4	c4	d4	e4	f4	g4	h4	j4	k4	l4	m4

C

a1	b1	c1	d1	e1	f1	g1	h1
a2	b2	c2	d2	e2	f2	g2	h2
a3	b3	c3	d3	e3	f3	g3	h3
a4	b4	c4	d4	e4	f4	g4	h4

AD22743

Component/circuit description	ECM pin	Signal	Condition	Typical value	Oscilloscope setting*	Wave form
Camshaft position (CMP) sensor	Be1	⟹	Ignition ON	5 V		
	Be2	⟸	Ignition ON	0 V or 5 V		
	Be2	⟸	Engine idling		2 V/50 ms	∿ 3
	Be3	⌐	Ignition ON	0 V		
CAN data bus – high	Aa3	⟺		1		
CAN data bus – low	Aa4	⟺		1		
Crankshaft position (CKP) sensor	Bf2	⟸	Ignition ON	0 V		
	Bf2	⟸	Engine idling	6,8 V ac	5 V/2 ms	∿ 1
	Bf3	⌐	Ignition ON	0 V		
Earth	Ag1		Ignition ON	0 V		
	Ah1		Ignition ON	0 V		
	Cg4		Ignition ON	0 V		
	Ch4		Ignition ON	0 V		
Engine control module (ECM)	Cd4	⟸	Ignition ON	11-14 V		
Fuel pressure regulator control solenoid	Bm4	⌐⟹	Ignition ON		5 V/1 ms	∿ 3
	Bm4	⌐⟹	Engine idling		5 V/2 ms	∿ 39
	Bm4	⌐⟹	3000 rpm		2 V/0,5 ms	∿ 37
Fuel rail pressure (FRP) sensor	Bd1	⟹	Ignition ON	5 V		
	Bd2	⟸	Ignition ON	0,5 V		
	Bd2	⟸	Engine idling	1 V		
	Bd2	⟸	3000 rpm	2 V		
	Bd3	⌐	Ignition ON	0 V		

* Suggested settings - Voltage/time per division

FORD

Component/circuit description	ECM pin	Signal	Condition	Typical value	Oscilloscope setting*	Wave form
Fuel temperature sensor	Bg2	←	Ignition ON – fuel temp. 20°C	3 V		
	Bg2	←	Ignition ON – fuel temp. 40°C	2,2 V		
	Bg2	←	Ignition ON – fuel temp. 55°C	1,6 V		
	Bg3	⌐	Ignition ON	0 V		
Injector 1	Ba4 (Bb4)	⇒	Engine idling	0,3 ms pilot + 0,4 ms main	5 V/0,5 ms	63
	Bb4 (Ba4)	⇒	Engine idling	0,3 ms pilot + 0,4 ms main	5 V/0,5 ms	63
Injector 2	Bc4 (Bd4)	⇒	Engine idling	0,3 ms pilot + 0,4 ms main	5 V/0,5 ms	63
	Bd4 (Bc4)	⇒	Engine idling	0,3 ms pilot + 0,4 ms main	5 V/0,5 ms	63
Injector 3	Be4 (Bf4)	⇒	Engine idling	0,3 ms pilot + 0,4 ms main	5 V/0,5 ms	63
	Bf4 (Be4)	⇒	Engine idling	0,3 ms pilot + 0,4 ms main	5 V/0,5 ms	63
Injector 4	Bg4 (Bh4)	⇒	Engine idling	0,3 ms pilot + 0,4 ms main	5 V/0,5 ms	63
	Bh4 (Bg4)	⇒	Engine idling	0,3 ms pilot + 0,4 ms main	5 V/0,5 ms	63
Injector relay	Ag2	←	Ignition OFF	0 V		
	Ag2	←	Ignition ON	11-14 V		
	Ah2	←	Ignition OFF	0 V		
	Ah2	←	Ignition ON	11-14 V		
	Cg1	←	Ignition OFF	0 V		
	Cg1	←	Ignition ON	11-14 V		
Knock sensor (KS)	Bf1	⌐	Ignition ON	0 V		
	Bg1	←	Ignition ON	0 V		
	Bg1	←	3000 rpm		50 mV/1 ms	62
Knock sensor (KS) – screened lead	Bk1	⌐	Ignition ON	0 V		

*Suggested settings - Voltage/time per division

1 Connected pin - no test data available or random digital signal

Model:	Engine code:	Year:	FORD
Focus 1,8 TDCi	F9DA/B	08/02-05	Delphi

ECM harness multi-plug

Terminal side

AD29502

Wire side

AD29501

Component/circuit description	ECM pin	Signal	Condition	Typical value	Oscilloscope setting*	Wave form
AC refrigerant high pressure switch	76	←	Ignition ON	11-14 V		
	76	←	Engine running – AC ON, refrigerant pressure low	11-14 V		
	76	←	Engine running – AC ON, refrigerant pressure high	0 V		
AC refrigerant low pressure switch	19	←	Ignition ON – AC OFF	0 V		
	19	←	Ignition ON – AC ON	11-14 V		
Accelerator pedal position (APP) sensor	14	⌐−	Ignition ON	0 V		
	32	←	Ignition ON – accelerator pedal released	1,47 V		
	32	←	Ignition ON – accelerator pedal fully depressed	3,98 V		
	33	⇒	Ignition ON	5 V		
	50	←	Ignition ON – accelerator pedal released	0,85 V		
	50	←	Ignition ON – accelerator pedal fully depressed	3,35 V		
	51	⇒	Ignition ON	5 V		
	53	⌐−	Ignition ON	0 V		
	70	⌐−	Ignition ON	0 V		
	71	←	Ignition ON – accelerator pedal released	4,14 V		
	71	←	Ignition ON – accelerator pedal fully depressed	0,78 V		
	72	⇒	Ignition ON	5 V		
Alarm system warning lamp	16	⇒	Ignition ON	0,9 V		
	16	⇒	Engine running	11-14 V		

* Suggested settings - Voltage/time per division

Component/circuit description	ECM pin	Signal	Condition	Typical value	Oscilloscope setting*	Wave form
Alternator	47	⬅⇨	Ignition ON	0,5 V		
	47	⬅⇨	Engine idling		5 V/2 ms	2
	112	⬅	Ignition OFF	11-14 V		
	112	⬅	Ignition ON		2 V/1 ms	49
	112	⬅	Engine idling		2 V/5 ms	39
Audio unit	78	⇨	Ignition ON	0 V		
Brake pedal position (BPP) switch	58	⬅	Ignition ON – brake pedal released	0 V		
	58	⬅	Ignition ON – brake pedal depressed	11-14 V		
Camshaft position (CMP) sensor	103	⬅	Ignition ON	0 or 5 V		
	103	⬅	Engine running		2 V/50 ms	3
	104	⌐	Ignition ON	0 V		
	111	⇨	Ignition ON	5 V		
Clutch pedal position (CPP) switch	38	⬅	Ignition ON – clutch pedal released	11-14 V		
	38	⬅	Ignition ON – clutch pedal depressed	0 V		
Crankshaft position (CKP) sensor	82	⌐	Ignition ON	0 V		
	90	⬅	Ignition ON	0 V		
	90	⬅	Engine idling	6,8 V ac	5 V/2 ms	1
Cylinder head temperature (CHT) sensor (dual range)	101	⬅	Ignition ON – coolant temp. 0°C	4,1 V		
	101	⬅	Ignition ON – coolant temp. 20°C	3,2 V		
	101	⬅	Ignition ON – coolant temp. 60°C	1,3 V		
	101	⬅	Ignition ON – coolant temp. 95°C	0,46 V or 3,5 V		
	101	⬅	Ignition ON – coolant temp. 110°C	3 V		
	102	⌐	Ignition ON	0 V		
Data link connector (DLC)	55	⇨	Ignition ON		2 V/50 μs	38
	74	⬅⇨	Ignition ON		2 V/50 μs	38
Earth	1		Ignition ON	0 V		
	2		Ignition ON	0 V		
	28		Ignition ON	0 V		
	66		Ignition ON	0 V		
	88		Ignition ON	0 V		
Engine control (EC) relay	3	⬅	Ignition ON	11-14 V		
	4	⬅	Ignition ON	11-14 V		
	5	⬅	Ignition ON	11-14 V		
	9	⌐⇨	Ignition OFF	11-14 V		
	9	⌐⇨	Ignition ON	0-1 V		
Engine coolant blower motor relay 1	80	⌐⇨	Ignition ON	11-14 V		
	80	⌐⇨	Engine running – coolant blower motors OFF	11-14 V		
	80	⌐⇨	Engine running – coolant blower motors ON, 1st speed	0-1 V		
Engine coolant blower motor relay 2	81	⌐⇨	Ignition ON	11-14 V		
	81	⌐⇨	Engine running – coolant blower motors OFF	11-14 V		
	81	⌐⇨	Engine running – coolant blower motors ON, 2nd speed	0-1 V		

★ Suggested settings - Voltage/time per division

Component/circuit description	ECM pin	Signal	Condition	Typical value	Oscilloscope setting*	Wave form
Engine coolant heater relay 1 – if fitted	61	⊐▷		1		
Engine coolant heater relay 2 – if fitted	62	⊐▷		1		
Engine running circuits relay	23	⊐▷	Ignition ON	11-14 V		
	23	⊐▷	Engine running	0-1 V		
Exhaust gas recirculation (EGR) solenoid	96	⊐▷	Ignition ON	11-14 V		
	96	⊐▷	Engine idling		5 V/0,1 ms	ᴡᴡ 3
Fuel pressure control solenoid	87	▷	Ignition ON		5 V/1 ms	ᴡᴡ 3
	87	▷	Engine idling		5 V/2 ms	ᴡᴡ 39
	87	▷	3000 rpm		2 V/0,5 ms	ᴡᴡ 37
Fuel rail pressure (FRP) sensor	6	▷	Ignition ON	5 V		
	25	◀	Ignition ON	0,5 V		
	25	◀	Engine idling	1 V		
	25	◀	3000 rpm	2 V		
	26	⊐−	Ignition ON	0 V		
Fuel temperature sensor	109	◀	Ignition ON – fuel temp. 20°C	2,7 V		
	110	⊐−	Ignition ON	0 V		
Glow plug relay	20	⊐▷	Ignition ON – glow plugs OFF	11-14 V		
	20	⊐▷	Ignition ON – glow plugs ON	0-1 V		
Ignition switch	37	◀	Ignition ON	11-14 V		
Immobilizer control module (PATS)	15	◀	Ignition ON	11-14 V		
	34	◀	Ignition ON	10,46 V		
	34	◀	Engine running	11-14 V		
Injector 1	114	⊐▷	Ignition ON	5,3 V		
	114(117)	⊐▷	Engine idling	0,2 ms pilot + 0,4 ms main	5 V/0,5 ms	ᴡᴡ 63
Injectors 1 & 4	117	▷	Ignition ON	5,3 V		
Injector 2	120	⊐▷	Ignition ON	5,3 V		
	120(118)	⊐▷	Engine idling	0,2 ms pilot + 0,4 ms main	5 V/0,5 ms	ᴡᴡ 63
Injectors 2 & 3	118	▷	Ignition ON	5,3 V		
Injector 3	121	⊐▷	Ignition ON	5,3 V		
	121(118)	⊐▷	Engine idling	0,2 ms pilot + 0,4 ms main	5 V/0,5 ms	ᴡᴡ 63
Injector 4	115	⊐▷	Ignition ON	5,3 V		
	115(117)	⊐▷	Engine idling	0,2 ms pilot + 0,4 ms main	5 V/0,5 ms	ᴡᴡ 63
Intake air temperature (IAT) sensor	64	◀	Ignition ON – air temp. 20°C	3,2 V		
Intake manifold air control actuator	113	⊐▷	Ignition ON	11-14 V		
	113	⊐▷	Engine running	11-14 V		
	113	⊐▷	Engine idling – switch ignition OFF	0-1 V for 1 sec., 11-14 V for 10 secs., then 0 V		
Knock sensor (KS)	45	◀	Ignition ON	0 V		
	45	◀	3000 rpm		0,1 V/1 ms	ᴡᴡ 62
	46	◀	Ignition ON	0 V		
Lamps control module	78	▷	Ignition ON	0 V		

* Suggested settings - Voltage/time per division

Component/circuit description	ECM pin	Signal	Condition	Typical value	Oscilloscope setting*	Wave form
Manifold absolute pressure (MAP) sensor	99	←	Ignition ON	1,5 V		
	99	←	Engine idling	1,6 V		
	99	←	Engine idling – accelerate briefly	3,45 V briefly		
	100	⌐—	Ignition ON	0 V		
	108	⇒	Ignition ON	5 V		
Mass air flow (MAF) sensor	65	⌐—	Ignition ON	0 V		
	83	←	Ignition ON	0,6 V		
	83	←	Engine idling	1,9 V		
	83	←	3000 rpm	3,2 V		
	84	⌐—	Ignition ON	0 V		
Navigation control module	78	⇒	Ignition ON	0 V		
Reverse gear position switch	18	←	Ignition ON – gear lever in neutral	0 V		
	18	←	Ignition ON – gear lever in reverse	11-14 V		
Starter motor relay	21	⌐⇒	Ignition ON	0-1 V		
	21	⌐⇒	Engine cranking	0-1 V		
Sunroof control module	78	⇒	Ignition ON	0 V		
Telematics control module	78	⇒	Ignition ON	0 V		
Trip computer	78	⇒	Ignition ON	0 V		
	105	⇒	Ignition ON	2,57 V		
Turbocharger (TC) boost air temperature sensor	98	⌐—	Ignition ON	0 V		
	107	←	Ignition ON – air temp. 20°C	3,2 V		
Turbocharger (TC) wastegate regulating valve	95	⌐⇒	Ignition ON	11-14 V		
	95	⌐⇒	Engine idling		2 V/0,2 ms	〰〰 22
Vehicle speed sensor (VSS)	17	←	Ignition ON – vehicle pushed	0-10,4 V switching		
	75	⌐—	Ignition ON	0 V		
Wide open throttle (WOT) relay	79	⌐⇒	Ignition ON	11-14 V		
	79	⌐⇒	Engine running – AC compressor OFF	11-14 V		
	79	⌐⇒	Engine running – AC compressor ON	0-1 V		

*Suggested settings - Voltage/time per division

1 Connected pin - no test data available or random digital signal

ECM harness multi-plug

Terminal side

A   **B**

Wire side

B   **A**

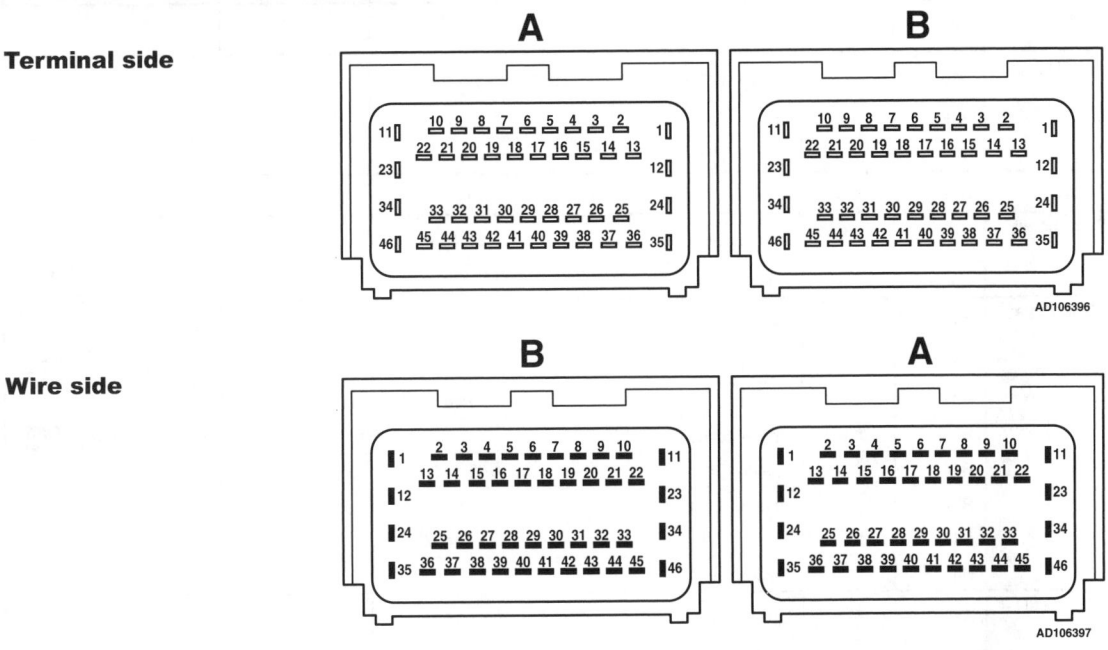

Component/circuit description	ECM pin	Signal	Condition	Typical value	Oscilloscope setting*	Wave form
AC refrigerant low pressure switch – ATC	A14	←		1		
AC refrigerant pressure sensor	A13	←	Engine idling – AC OFF	1,1 V		
	A13	←	Engine idling – AC ON – air temp. 10°C	1,1-2 V		
	A25	⌐	Ignition ON	0 V		
	A28	⇒	Ignition ON	5 V		
Accelerator pedal position (APP) sensor	A32	←	Ignition ON – accelerator pedal released	1,2 V	2 V/5 ms	64
	A32	←	Ignition ON – accelerator pedal fully depressed	8 V	2 V/2 ms	55
	A32	←	Engine idling		5 V/5 ms	94
Alternator	B15	⇒		1		
	B20	⇔		1		
Brake pedal position (BPP) switch	A39	←	Ignition ON – brake pedal released	0 V		
	A39	←	Ignition ON – brake pedal depressed	11-14 V		
Camshaft position (CMP) sensor	B7	⌐	Engine idling	0 V		
	B18	←	Engine idling		2 V/20 ms	11
CAN data bus – high	A41	⇔		1		
CAN data bus – low	A30	⇔		1		
Crankshaft position (CKP) sensor	B6	←	Engine idling		2 V/1 ms	Reversed 2
	B17	←	Engine idling		2 V/1 ms	2
Earth	A10	⌐	Ignition ON	0 V		
	A11	⌐	Ignition ON	0 V		
	A23	⌐	Ignition ON	0 V		

* Suggested settings - Voltage/time per division

Component/circuit description	ECM pin	Signal	Condition	Typical value	Oscilloscope setting*	Wave form
Engine control (EC) relay	A34	←	Ignition ON	11-14 V		
	A35	⅂⊳	Ignition OFF	11-14 V		
	A35	⅂⊳	Ignition ON	0-1 V		
Engine coolant blower motor control module	A12	⇨	Ignition OFF	11-14 V		
	A12	⇨	Engine idling		2 V/10 ms	∿ 71
Engine coolant blower motor relay – without AC	A6	⅂⊳		1		
Engine coolant temperature (ECT) sensor	B16	←	Ignition ON – coolant temp. 10°C	3,5 V		
	B16	←	Ignition ON – coolant temp. 80°C	0,6 V		
	B30	⅂—	Ignition ON	0 V		
Engine oil pressure switch	B31	←		1		
Evaporative emission (EVAP) canister purge valve	A3	⅂⊳	Ignition ON	11-14 V		
	A3	⅂⊳	Engine idling – valve operating		10 V/50 ms	∿ 20
Exhaust gas recirculation (EGR) valve actuator	B32	⅂⊳	Ignition ON	11-14 V		
	B32	⅂⊳	Engine idling		5 V/5 ms	Intermittent ∿ 102
	B33	⅂⊳	Ignition ON	11-14 V		
	B33	⅂⊳	Engine idling		5 V/5 ms	Intermittent ∿ 102
	B44	⅂⊳	Ignition ON	11-14 V		
	B44	⅂⊳	Engine idling		5 V/5 ms	Intermittent ∿ 103
	B45	⅂⊳	Ignition ON	11-14 V		
	B45	⅂⊳	Engine idling		5 V/5 ms	Intermittent ∿ 103
Fuel pump (FP) relay – through inertia fuel shut-off (IFS) switch	A19	⅂⊳	Ignition ON	11-14 V		
	A19	⅂⊳	Engine idling	0-1 V		
Heated oxygen sensor (HO2S) 1	A5	⅂⊳	Ignition ON	11-14 V		
	A5	⅂⊳	Engine idling	0-1 V		
	A25	⅂—	Ignition ON	0 V		
	A26	←	Engine idling – engine hot	0,1-0,9 V fluctuating	0,2 V/1 sec	∿ 21
Heated oxygen sensor (HO2S) 2	A7	⅂⊳	Ignition ON	11-14 V		
	A7	⅂⊳	Engine idling	0-1 V		
	A25	⅂—	Ignition ON	0 V		
	A27	←	Engine idling – engine hot	0,3-0,7 V fluctuating		
Ignition coil – cylinder 1	B11	⅂⊳	Ignition ON	11-14 V		
	B11	⅂⊳	Engine idling		5 V/1 ms	∿ 33
Ignition coil – cylinder 2	B46	⅂⊳	Ignition ON	11-14 V		
	B46	⅂⊳	Engine idling		5 V/1 ms	∿ 33
Ignition coil – cylinder 3	B23	⅂⊳	Ignition ON	11-14 V		
	B23	⅂⊳	Engine idling		5 V/1 ms	∿ 33
Ignition coil – cylinder 4	B34	⅂⊳	Ignition ON	11-14 V		
	B34	⅂⊳	Engine idling		5 V/1 ms	∿ 33
Ignition switch	A46	←	Ignition ON	11-14 V		
Injector 1	B2	⅂⊳	Ignition ON	11-14 V		
	B2	⅂⊳	Engine idling	2,8 ms	10 V/2 ms	∿ 35
Injector 2	B3	⅂⊳	Ignition ON	11-14 V		
	B3	⅂⊳	Engine idling	2,8 ms	10 V/2 ms	∿ 35
Injector 3	B13	⅂⊳	Ignition ON	11-14 V		
	B13	⅂⊳	Engine idling	2,8 ms	10 V/2 ms	∿ 35
Injector 4	B14	⅂⊳	Ignition ON	11-14 V		
	B14	⅂⊳	Engine idling	2,8 ms	10 V/2 ms	∿ 35

* Suggested settings - Voltage/time per division

Component/circuit description	ECM pin	Signal	Condition	Typical value	Oscilloscope setting*	Wave form
Intake air temperature (IAT) sensor	B27	←	Ignition ON – air temp. 10°C	3,8 V		
	B27	←	Ignition ON – air temp. 15°C	2,8 V		
Intake manifold air control solenoid 1	B9	⌐⊳	Ignition ON	0-1 V		
	B9	⌐⊳	Engine running	0 or 11-14 V switching		
Intake manifold air control solenoid 2	B8	⌐⊳	Ignition ON	0-1 V		
	B8	⌐⊳	Engine running	0 or 11-14 V switching		
Knock sensor (KS) 1	B29	←	Ignition ON	0 V		
	B41	←	Engine idling – full throttle briefly		50 mV/1 ms	∿∿ 38
Knock sensor (KS) 2	B28	←	Ignition ON	0 V		
	B40	←	Engine idling – full throttle briefly		50 mV/1 ms	∿∿ 38
Manifold absolute pressure (MAP) sensor	B30	⌐–	Ignition ON	0 V		
	B36	⇨	Ignition ON	5 V		
	B39	←	Ignition ON	4,1 V		
	B39	←	Engine idling	1,2 V		
	B39	←	Engine idling – accelerate briefly	4,1 V briefly		
Starter motor relay	A4	⌐⊳		☐1		
Throttle motor	B10	⇨	Ignition ON	11-14 V		
	B22	⌐⊳	Ignition ON		2 V/2 ms	∿∿ 71
	B22	⌐⊳	Engine idling		2 V/2 ms	∿∿ 71
Throttle motor position sensor	B25	⇨	Ignition ON	5 V		
	B26	←	Ignition ON – accelerator pedal released	0,8 V		
	B26	←	Ignition ON – accelerator pedal fully depressed	4,4 V		
	B37	←	Ignition ON – accelerator pedal released	4,3 V		
	B37	←	Ignition ON – accelerator pedal fully depressed	1,2 V		
	B38	⌐–	Ignition ON	0 V		
Vehicle speed sensor (VSS)	A29	←		☐1		
Wide open throttle (WOT) relay – ATC	A1	⌐⊳		☐1		

*Suggested settings - Voltage/time per division

☐1 Connected pin - no test data available or random digital signal

FORD

Siemens SID 803

Model:	Engine code:	Year:
Focus C-MAX 2,0 TDCi	G6DA	2003-06

ECM harness multi-plug

Terminal side

B

h1	g1	f1	e1	d1	c1	b1	a1
h2	g2	f2	e2	d2	c2	b2	a2
h3	g3	f3	e3	d3	c3	b3	a3
h4	g4	f4	e4	d4	c4	b4	a4

A

m1	l1	k1	j1	h1	g1	f1	e1	d1	c1	b1	a1
m2	l2	k2	j2	h2	g2	f2	e2	d2	c2	b2	a2
m3	l3	k3	j3	h3	g3	f3	e3	d3	c3	b3	a3
m4	l4	k4	j4	h4	g4	f4	e4	d4	c4	b4	a4

C

a4	b4	c4	d4	e4	f4	g4	h4	j4	k4	l4	m4
a3	b3	c3	d3	e3	f3	g3	h3	j3	k3	l3	m3
a2	b2	c2	d2	e2	f2	g2	h2	j2	k2	l2	m2
a1	b1	c1	d1	e1	f1	g1	h1	j1	k1	l1	m1

AD106434

Wire side

C

m4	l4	k4	j4	h4	g4	f4	e4	d4	c4	b4	a4
m3	l3	k3	j3	h3	g3	f3	e3	d3	c3	b3	a3
m2	l2	k2	j2	h2	g2	f2	e2	d2	c2	b2	a2
m1	l1	k1	j1	h1	g1	f1	e1	d1	c1	b1	a1

A

a1	b1	c1	d1	e1	f1	g1	h1	j1	k1	l1	m1
a2	b2	c2	d2	e2	f2	g2	h2	j2	k2	l2	m2
a3	b3	c3	d3	e3	f3	g3	h3	j3	k3	l3	m3
a4	b4	c4	d4	e4	f4	g4	h4	j4	k4	l4	m4

B

a1	b1	c1	d1	e1	f1	g1	h1
a2	b2	c2	d2	e2	f2	g2	h2
a3	b3	c3	d3	e3	f3	g3	h3
a4	b4	c4	d4	e4	f4	g4	h4

AD106435

Component/circuit description	ECM pin	Signal	Condition	Typical value	Oscilloscope setting*	Wave form
AC refrigerant high pressure switch	Bd2	←	Ignition ON	11-14 V		
	Bd2	←	Engine idling – AC ON, AC compressor ON	11-14 V		
	Bd2	←	Engine idling – AC ON, AC compressor OFF	0-1 V		
AC refrigerant low pressure switch	Bh2			1		
Accelerator pedal position (APP) sensor	Bf3	←	Ignition ON – accelerator pedal released	1,2 V	2 V/5 ms	⎍ 64
	Bf3	←	Ignition ON – accelerator pedal fully depressed	8 V	2 V/2 ms	⎍ 10
Alternator	Ah4	←	Ignition ON	0-1 V		
	Ah4	←	Engine idling	1		
	Ba1	←	Ignition OFF	11-14 V		
	Ba1	←	Ignition ON	0 V		
	Ba1	←	Engine idling		5 V/2 ms	⎍ 2
Battery	Ag4	←	Ignition OFF	11-14 V		
Brake pedal position (BPP) switch	Be4	←	Ignition ON – brake pedal released	0 V		
	Be4	←	Ignition ON – brake pedal depressed	11-14 V		
Camshaft position (CMP) sensor	Cc1	←	Engine idling		2 V/50 ms	⎍ 64
	Cd4	⌐	Ignition ON	0 V		
	Ce3	⇒	Ignition ON	5 V		
CAN data bus – high	Ba4	←⇒		1		
CAN data bus – low	Ba3	←⇒		1		
Crankshaft position (CKP) sensor	Cb4	←	Engine idling		2 V/2 ms	⎍ 72
	Cf1	⌐	Engine idling	0 V		
	Cf4	⇒	Ignition ON	5 V		

* Suggested settings - Voltage/time per division

Autodata

Component/circuit description	ECM pin	Signal	Condition	Typical value	Oscilloscope setting*	Wave form
Earth	Ak2		Ignition ON	0 V		
	Bg4		Ignition ON	0 V		
	Bh4		Ignition ON	0 V		
	Ch4		Ignition ON	0 V		
	Cj4		Ignition ON	0 V		
	Ck4		Ignition ON	0 V		
Engine control relay	Ah3	⊐▷	Ignition OFF	11-14 V		
	Ah3	⊐▷	Ignition ON	0-1 V		
	Cj3	⟵	Ignition ON	11-14 V		
	Ck2	⟵	Ignition ON	11-14 V		
	Ck3	⟵	Ignition ON	11-14 V		
Engine coolant blower motor control module	Bb2	⟺	Ignition OFF	11-14 V		
	Bb2	⟺	Ignition ON	11-14 V		
	Bb2	⟺	Engine idling	11-14 V		
	Bd4	⊐▷	Ignition ON	11-14 V		
	Bd4	⊐▷	Engine idling – coolant blower motor OFF	11-14 V		
	Bd4	⊐▷	Engine idling – coolant blower motor ON	0-1 V		
Engine coolant pump bypass solenoid	Aj1	⊐▷		[1]		
Engine coolant shut-off valve	Ag1	⊐▷		[1]		
Engine coolant temperature (ECT) sensor	Ca2	⟵	Engine idling – coolant temp. 16°C	2,6 V		
	Ca2	⟵	Engine idling – coolant temp. 65°C	1,2 V		
	Cg1	⊐─	Ignition ON	0 V		
Engine oil pressure switch	Cf3	⟵	Ignition ON	0 V		
	Cf3	⟵	Engine idling	11-14 V		
Exhaust gas pressure sensor	Ab2			[1]		
	Ac2			[1]		
	Ad3			[1]		
Exhaust gas recirculation (EGR) valve actuator	Ac3	▷	Ignition ON	5 V		
	Ad2	⟵	Ignition ON	0,8 V		
	Ad2	⟵	Engine idling	2 V		
	Ad2	⟵	Engine idling – accelerate briefly	0,8 V briefly		
	Ae2	⊐▷	Ignition ON	0-1 V		
	Al2	⟵	Engine idling	11-14 V		
	Am2	⟵	Ignition ON	11-14 V		
	Am2	⟵	Engine idling		2 V/1 ms	⋀⋀ᴡ 37
Exhaust gas temperature sensor 1	Aa3			[1]		
	Ah2	⟺		[1]		
Exhaust gas temperature sensor 2	Ab4			[1]		
	Aj2			[1]		
Fuel flow control valve	Am4	⊐▷	Ignition ON	11-14 V		
	Am4	⊐▷	Engine idling		2 V/5 ms	⋀⋀ᴡ 37
Fuel pressure regulator control solenoid	Al4	⊐▷	Engine idling	12,5 V	2 V/2 ms	⋀⋀ᴡ 37
Fuel rail pressure (FRP) sensor	Ca4	▷	Ignition ON	5 V		
	Cb2	⟵	Ignition ON	5 V		
	Cb2	⟵	Engine idling	1,1 V		
	Cb2	⟵	Engine running – 3000 rpm	1,7 V		
	Cb3	⊐─	Engine idling	0 V		

* Suggested settings - Voltage/time per division

Component/circuit description	ECM pin	Signal	Condition	Typical value	Oscilloscope setting*	Wave form
Fuel temperature sensor	Ca3	←	Engine idling – fuel temp. 20°C approx.	2,5 V		
	Cj1	⌐⌐	Engine idling	0 V		
Fuel/water separator sensor	Ch2	←		1		
Glow plug control module	Ad4			1		
	Ae1			1		
Ignition switch	Bc3	←	Ignition ON	11-14 V		
Injector 1	Cl3 (Cm3)	⇒	Engine idling	0,4 ms pilot + 0,7 ms main	20 V/0,5 ms	68
	Cm3 (Cl3)	⇒	Engine idling	0,4 ms pilot + 0,7 ms main	20 V/0,5 ms	68
Injector 2	Cl2 (Cm4)	⇒	Engine idling	0,4 ms pilot + 0,7 ms main	20 V/0,5 ms	68
	Cm4 (Cl2)	⇒	Engine idling	0,4 ms pilot + 0,7 ms main	20 V/0,5 ms	68
Injector 3	Cl1 (Cm2)	⇒	Engine idling	0,4 ms pilot + 0,7 ms main	20 V/0,5 ms	68
	Cm2 (Cl1)	⇒	Engine idling	0,4 ms pilot + 0,7 ms main	20 V/0,5 ms	68
Injector 4	Cl4 (Cm1)	⇒	Engine idling	0,4 ms pilot + 0,7 ms main	20 V/0,5 ms	68
	Cm1 (Cl4)	⇒	Engine idling	0,4 ms pilot + 0,7 ms main	20 V/0,5 ms	68
Intake air shut-off solenoid	Am3	⌐⇒	Ignition ON	11-14 V		
	Am3	⌐⇒	Engine idling		2 V/2 ms	43
Intake air temperature (IAT) sensor	Ac1	←	Ignition ON	2,7 V		
Knock sensor (KS)	Cc2			1		
	Cc3	⌐⌐		1		
	Cd2			1		
Mass air flow (MAF) sensor	Ag2	⌐⇒	Ignition ON	0-1 V		
	Ch3	←	Ignition ON	2,3 V		
	Ch3	←	Engine idling	4 V		
	Ch3	←	Engine running – 3000 rpm	4,4 V		
Starter motor relay	Bd1	⌐⇒	Engine cranking	0-1 V		
Turbocharger (TC) boost pressure sensor	Cb1	←	Engine idling	2,4 V		
	Cb1	←	Engine idling – accelerate briefly	3,1 V briefly		
	Cd1	⌐⌐	Ignition ON	0 V		
	Ce2	⇒	Ignition ON	5 V		
Turbocharger (TC) control solenoid	Am1	⌐⇒	Ignition ON	11-14 V		
	Am1	⌐⇒	Engine idling		2 V/2 ms	64
Turbocharger (TC) intercooler bypass solenoid	Al3	⌐⇒		1		
Turbocharger (TC) vane position sensor	Ac4	←	Engine idling	4 V		
	Ac4	←	Engine running – 3000 rpm	2 V		
	Ad1	⇒	Ignition ON	5 V		
	Ae4	⌐⇒	Ignition ON	0-1 V		
Turbocharger/Supercharger (TC/SC) boost air temperature sensor	Aa2	←	Ignition ON – air temp. 13°C	3,7 V		
	Aa2	←	Ignition ON – air temp. 18°C	3,4 V		
	Ag3	⌐⇒	Ignition ON	0-1 V		

*Suggested settings - Voltage/time per division

1 Connected pin - no test data available or random digital signal

Model:	Engine code:	Year:
Mondeo 1,6	L1J, L1L, L1N, L1Q	1996-01
Mondeo 1,8	RKB, RKF, RKJ, RKH	1996-01
Mondeo 2,0	NGA, NGB, NGC	1996-01
Puma 1,7 16V	MHA	1997-02
Cougar 2,0	EDBA/C	1998-02

Ford EEC V

ECM harness multi-plug

Terminal side

AD84086

Wire side

AD42136

Component/circuit description	ECM pin	Signal	Condition	Typical value	Oscilloscope setting*	Wave form
AC compressor clutch relay	69	⊐▷	Engine idling – AC OFF	11-14 V		
	69	⊐▷	Engine idling – AC ON – AC compressor ON	0-1 V		
AC refrigerant pressure switch 1	41			1		
AC refrigerant pressure switch 2	86			1		
Alternator – Puma/Cougar	59			1		
Automatic transmission	1			1		
	27			1		
	29			1		
	34			1		
	37			1		
	76	⊐—	Engine idling	0 V		
	81			1		
	84			1		
	102			1		
Automatic transmission – Mondeo – with PATS	80			1		
Automatic transmission – Mondeo – without PATS	54			1		
Automatic transmission – Cougar	11			1		
	73			1		
	99			1		
Battery	55	←	Ignition OFF	11-14 V		
Brake pedal position (BPP) switch – Mondeo/Cougar	92	⊐—	Ignition ON – brake pedal depressed	11-14 V		
	92	⊐—	Ignition ON – brake pedal released	0 V		
Camshaft position (CMP) actuator – Puma	45	⊐▷	Ignition ON	11-14 V		
	45	⊐▷	Engine idling – accelerate briefly	0-1 V briefly		
Camshaft position (CMP) sensor	76	⊐—	Engine idling	0 V		
	85	←	Engine idling		5 V/20 ms	ᐧᐧᐧ 11
Clutch pedal position (CPP) switch	64	←	Ignition ON – clutch pedal released – gear lever not in neutral	5 V		
	64	←	Ignition ON – clutch pedal depressed	0 V		
	91	⊐—	Ignition ON	0 V		

* Suggested settings - Voltage/time per division

Component/circuit description	ECM pin	Signal	Condition	Typical value	Oscilloscope setting*	Wave form
Crankshaft position (CKP) sensor	21	←	Engine idling		2 V/1 ms	〰 2
	22	←	Engine idling		2 V/1 ms	Reversed 〰 2
Data link connector (DLC)	13	←→	Engine idling	0,5 V		
	16		Engine idling	0 V		
Data link connector (DLC) – some models	15	→	Engine idling	5 V		
Earth	24		Ignition ON	0 V		
	25		Ignition ON	0 V		
	51		Ignition ON	0 V		
	77		Ignition ON	0 V		
	103		Ignition ON	0 V		
Engine control module (ECM) – pin 91 – some models	30	⊣	Ignition ON	0 V		
Engine control relay	71	←	Ignition OFF	0 V		
	71	←	Ignition ON	11-14 V		
	97	←	Ignition OFF	0 V		
	97	←	Ignition ON	11-14 V		
Engine coolant blower motor relay – AT – with AC	19	⊣▷	Engine idling – coolant blower motor OFF	11-14 V		
	19	⊣▷	Engine idling – coolant blower motor ON – high speed	0-1 V		
Engine coolant blower motor relay – Mondeo – AT	45	⊣▷	Engine idling – coolant blower motor OFF	11-14 V		
Engine coolant blower motor relay – Mondeo – AT – without AC	45	⊣▷	Engine idling – coolant blower motor ON	0-1 V		
Engine coolant blower motor relay – Mondeo – AT – with AC	45	⊣▷	Engine idling – coolant blower motor ON – low speed	0-1 V		
Engine coolant blower motor relay – MT	68	⊣▷	Engine idling – coolant blower motor OFF	11-14 V		
Engine coolant blower motor relay – MT – with AC	17	⊣▷	Engine idling – coolant blower motor OFF	11-14 V		
	17	⊣▷	Engine idling – coolant blower motor ON – high speed	0-1 V		
	68	⊣▷	Engine idling – coolant blower motor ON – low speed	0-1 V		
Engine coolant blower motor relay – MT – without AC	68	⊣▷	Engine idling – coolant blower motor ON	0-1 V		
Engine coolant temperature (ECT) sensor	38	←	Ignition ON – coolant temp. 10°C	3,5 V		
	38	←	Ignition ON – coolant temp. 80°C	0,5 V		
	91	⊣	Ignition ON	0 V		
Evaporative emission (EVAP) canister purge valve – Cougar 1999→	56	⊣▷	Ignition ON	11-14 V		
	56	⊣▷	Engine running – valve operating		10 V/50 ms	〰 20
Evaporative emission (EVAP) canister purge valve – except Cougar 1999→	67	⊣▷	Ignition ON	11-14 V		
	67	⊣▷	Engine running – valve operating		10 V/50 ms	〰 20
Exhaust gas pressure sensor – some models	65	←	Engine idling	0,6 V		
	65	←	Engine running	0,6-4 V varies with pressure		
	90	→	Ignition ON	5 V		
	91	⊣	Ignition ON	0 V		
Exhaust gas recirculation (EGR) solenoid – some models	47	⊣▷	Ignition ON	11-14 V		
	47	⊣▷	Engine idling – valve operating	0 V		
Fuel pump relay	40	←	Ignition ON	11-14 V briefly then 0 V		
	40	←	Engine idling	11-14 V		
Fuel pump relay – MT – with PATS	54	⊣▷	Ignition ON	0-1 V briefly then 11-14 V		
	54	⊣▷	Engine cranking	0-1 V		

★ Suggested settings - Voltage/time per division

Component/circuit description	ECM pin	Signal	Condition	Typical value	Oscilloscope setting*	Wave form
Fuel pump relay – MT – without PATS	80	⊐▷	Ignition ON	0-1 V briefly then 11-14 V		
	80	⊐▷	Engine cranking	0-1 V		
Heated oxygen sensor (HO2S)	60	←	Engine idling – engine hot	0,1-0,9 V fluctuating	0,2 V/1 sec.	
	91	⊐—	Ignition ON	0 V		
	93	⊐▷	Start engine	11-14 V for 20 seconds		
	93	⊐▷	Start engine	0 V after 20 seconds		
Heated oxygen sensor (HO2S) – AT – with PATS	73	⊐▷	Start engine	11-14 V for 20 seconds		
	73	⊐▷	Start engine	0 V after 20 seconds		
Heated windscreen relay – if fitted	14	←	Engine idling – heated windscreen OFF	0 V		
	14	←	Engine idling – heated windscreen ON	5 V		
Idle air control (IAC) valve	83	⊐▷	Engine idling – engine hot	40%	2 V/5 ms	
Ignition coil – cylinders 1 & 4	52	⊐▷	Engine idling		5 V/1 ms	
Ignition coil – cylinders 2 & 3	26	⊐▷	Engine idling		5 V/1 ms	
Injector 1 – with PATS	70	⊐▷	Ignition ON	11-14 V		
	70	⊐▷	Engine idling	4 ms	10 V/2 ms	
Injector 1 – without PATS	75	⊐▷	Ignition ON	11-14 V		
	75	⊐▷	Engine idling	4 ms	10 V/2 ms	
Injector 2 – with PATS	96	⊐▷	Ignition ON	11-14 V		
	96	⊐▷	Engine idling	4 ms	10 V/2 ms	
Injector 2 – without PATS	101	⊐▷	Ignition ON	11-14 V		
	101	⊐▷	Engine idling	4 ms	10 V/2 ms	
Injector 3 – with PATS	20	⊐▷	Ignition ON	11-14 V		
	20	⊐▷	Engine idling	4 ms	10 V/2 ms	
Injector 3 – without PATS	74	⊐▷	Ignition ON	11-14 V		
	74	⊐▷	Engine idling	4 ms	10 V/2 ms	
Injector 4 – with PATS	95	⊐▷	Ignition ON	11-14 V		
	95	⊐▷	Engine idling	4 ms	10 V/2 ms	
Injector 4 – without PATS	100	⊐▷	Ignition ON	11-14 V		
	100	⊐▷	Engine idling	4 ms	10 V/2 ms	
Instrument panel – Puma	75			[1]		
Instrument panel – Cougar	28			[1]		
Instrument panel – Cougar with AT	74			[1]		
Instrumentation control module – Mondeo – AT	10			[1]		
	79			[1]		
Intake air temperature (IAT) sensor	39	←	Ignition ON – air temp. 10°C	3,5 V		
	91	⊐—	Ignition ON	0 V		
Malfunction indicator lamp (MIL) – Cougar 1999→	2	⊐▷	Ignition ON – MIL ON	0 V		
	2	⊐▷	Ignition ON – MIL OFF	11-14 V		
Mass air flow (MAF) sensor	36	⊐—	Ignition ON	0 V		
	88	←	Engine idling – engine hot	0,7 V		
	88	←	3000 rpm	1,5 V		
Neutral position (NP) switch – Puma →1999	64	←	Ignition ON – gear lever in neutral	5 V		
	64	←	Ignition ON – gear lever not in neutral	0 V		
	91	⊐—	Ignition ON	0 V		
Octane coding plug	91	⊐—	Ignition ON	0 V		

* Suggested settings - Voltage/time per division

Component/circuit description	ECM pin	Signal	Condition	Typical value	Oscilloscope setting*	Wave form
Octane coding plug – some models	30	←	Ignition ON	0 V		
	30	←		1		
Park/neutral position (PNP) switch	64	←	Ignition ON – AT not in P or N	5 V		
	64	←	Ignition ON – AT in P or N	0 V		
	91	⌐	Ignition ON	0 V		
Passive anti-theft system (PATS)	42		Engine idling	11-14 V		
	53		Engine idling	11-14 V		
Passive anti-theft system (PATS) – Mondeo	8	←	Engine idling	11-14 V		
Passive anti-theft system (PATS) – Mondeo – MT	79			1		
Passive anti-theft system (PATS) – MT	19	←	Engine idling	11-14 V		
Power steering pressure (PSP) switch	31	←	Engine idling – steering wheel not turned	0 V		
	31	←	Engine idling – steering wheel turned	9 V		
	91	⌐	Ignition ON	0 V		
Secondary air injection (AIR) solenoid – some models	98	⌐▷	Engine idling – engine cold	0 V		
	98	⌐▷	Engine idling – engine hot	11-14 V		
Spare cable – Cougar 1999→	47					
	65					
	75					
Starter motor relay – MT	27			1		
Tachometer – some models	48			1		
Throttle position (TP) sensor	89	←	Ignition ON – throttle closed	0,9 V		
	89	←	Ignition ON – throttle fully open	4,8 V		
	90	⇒	Ignition ON	5 V		
	91	⌐	Ignition ON	0 V		
Trip computer – some models	43			1		
Vehicle speed sensor (VSS) – Cougar with AT	33	⌐	Vehicle moving		1 V/5 ms	〰 42
	58	←	Vehicle moving		1 V/5 ms	〰 42
Vehicle speed sensor (VSS) – except Cougar with AT	58	←	Ignition ON – vehicle pushed	0 V or 11-14 V		
	58	←	Vehicle moving – 10 mph	20 Hz – increases with vehicle speed		
	58	←	Vehicle moving	50%	5 V/50 ms	〰 43

*Suggested settings - Voltage/time per division

1 Connected pin - no test data available or random digital signal

Model:	Engine code:		Year:
Mondeo 1,8	CDBB, CGBA/B, CHBA/B, CHBB		2000-06
Mondeo 2,0	CJBA/B		2000-06

ECM harness multi-plug

Terminal side

Terminal side diagram: pins 1-104, AD84086

Wire side

Wire side diagram: pins 26-1, AD42136

Component/circuit description	ECM pin	Signal	Condition	Typical value	Oscilloscope setting*	Wave form
AC refrigerant dual pressure switch	86	←	Ignition ON	11-14 V		
	86	←	Engine running – AC ON – refrigerant pressure normal	11-14 V		
	86	←	Engine running – AC ON – refrigerant pressure high	0 V		
AC refrigerant low pressure switch – through AC refrigerant dual pressure switch	41	⇨	Ignition ON	11-14 V		
	41	⇨	Engine running – AC ON, AC compressor ON	11-14 V		
	41	⇨	Engine running – AC ON, AC compressor OFF	0 V		
Alarm system warning lamp	42	⇨	Ignition OFF	2-11 V switching		
	42	⇨	Ignition ON	11-14 V		
Alternator	59		Ignition OFF	0 V		
	59		Ignition ON	0,68 V		
	59		Engine idling		5 V/2 ms	51
	72		Ignition OFF	11-14 V		
	72		Engine idling		2 V/5 ms	55
Audio unit	28	⇨		1		
Battery	55	←	Ignition OFF	11-14 V		
Camshaft position (CMP) sensor	76	⌐⌐	Engine idling	0 V		
	85	←	Engine idling		1 V/20 ms	11
CAN data bus – high	50	◄⇨	Ignition ON	2,5 V		
CAN data bus – low	49	◄⇨	Ignition ON	2,5 V		
Clutch pedal position (CPP) switch	64	←	Ignition ON – clutch pedal released	5 V		
	64	←	Ignition ON – clutch pedal depressed	0 V		
	91	⌐⌐	Ignition ON	0 V		
Crankshaft position (CKP) sensor	21	←	Engine idling	2,1 V ac	2 V/1 ms	2
	22	←	Engine idling	2,1 V ac	2 V/1 ms	Reversed 2
Cruise control module	28	⇨		1		
Data link connector (DLC)	13	◄⇨	Engine idling	0 V		
	15	⇨	Engine idling	5 V		
	16	◄⇨	Engine idling	0,15 V		

* Suggested settings - Voltage/time per division

Component/circuit description	ECM pin	Signal	Condition	Typical value	Oscilloscope setting*	Wave form
Earth	24		Ignition ON	0 V		
	25		Ignition ON	0 V		
	51		Ignition ON	0 V		
	77		Ignition ON	0 V		
	103		Ignition ON	0 V		
Engine control (EC) relay	71	←	Ignition OFF	0 V		
	71	←	Ignition ON	11-14 V		
	71	←	Engine idling	11-14 V		
	97	←	Ignition OFF	0 V		
	97	←	Ignition ON	11-14 V		
	97	←	Engine idling	11-14 V		
Engine coolant blower motor relay 1	68	⊐▷	Engine running – coolant blower motors OFF	11-14 V		
	68	⊐▷	Engine running – coolant blower motors ON, 1st speed	0-1 V		
Engine coolant blower motor relay 2	17	⊐▷	Engine running – coolant blower motors OFF	11-14 V		
	17	⊐▷	Engine running – coolant blower motors ON, 2nd speed	0-1 V		
Engine coolant temperature (ECT) sensor	38	←	Ignition ON – coolant temp. 20°C	3 V		
	38	←	Ignition ON – coolant temp. 80°C	0,5 V		
	91	⊐—	Ignition ON	0 V		
Engine coolant thermostat	10	←	Ignition ON	11-14 V		
	10	←	Engine idling – engine cold	11-14 V		
Evaporative emission (EVAP) canister purge valve	67	⊐▷	Ignition ON	11-14 V		
	67	⊐▷	Engine running – engine hot – valve operating		10 V/50 ms	Intermittent ⩗⩗ 20
Exhaust gas recirculation (EGR) valve actuator	43	⊐▷	Ignition ON	11-14 V		
	43	⊐▷	Engine idling		5 V/5 ms	Intermittent ⩗⩗ 102
	79	⊐▷	Ignition ON	11-14 V		
	79	⊐▷	Engine idling		5 V/5 ms	Intermittent ⩗⩗ 103
	80	⊐▷	Ignition ON	11-14 V		
	80	⊐▷	Engine idling		5 V/5 ms	Intermittent ⩗⩗ 102
	82	⊐▷	Ignition ON	11-14 V		
	82	⊐▷	Engine idling		5 V/5 ms	Intermittent ⩗⩗ 103
Fuel pump (FP) relay	54	⊐▷	Ignition ON	0-1 V briefly then 11-14 V		
	54	⊐▷	Engine idling	0-1 V		
Fuel pump (FP) relay – through inertia fuel shut-off (IFS) switch	40	←	Ignition ON	11-14 V briefly then 0 V		
	40	←	Engine idling	11-14 V		
Gas discharge headlamp control module	28	⇒		[1]		
Heated oxygen sensor (HO2S) 1	60	←	Engine idling – engine hot	0,1-0,9 V fluctuating	0,2 V/1 sec.	⩗⩗ 21
	91	⊐—	Ignition ON	0 V		
Heated oxygen sensor (HO2S) 1 – heater control	93	⊐▷	Ignition ON	11-14 V		
	93	⊐▷	Engine idling		5 V/0,1 sec.	⩗⩗ 24
Heated oxygen sensor (HO2S) 2	35	←	Engine idling – engine hot	0,3-0,7 V fluctuating	0,2 V/5 sec.	⩗⩗ 76
	91	⊐—	Ignition ON	0 V		
Heated oxygen sensor (HO2S) 2 – heater control	100	⊐▷	Ignition ON	11-14 V		
	100	⊐▷	Engine idling	0-1 V		
Idle air control (IAC) valve	83	⊐▷	Engine idling – engine hot		5 V/0,5 ms	⩗⩗ 24

* Suggested settings - Voltage/time per division

Component/circuit description	ECM pin	Signal	Condition	Typical value	Oscilloscope setting*	Wave form
Ignition coil	26	⊐▷	Ignition ON	11-14 V		
	26	⊐▷	Engine idling		5 V/1 ms	∿∿ 33
	52	⊐▷	Ignition ON	11-14 V		
	52	⊐▷	Engine idling		5 V/1 ms	∿∿ 33
Immobilizer control module (PATS)	19	◆▷		1		
	53	◆▷	Ignition OFF	0 V		
	53	◆▷	Ignition ON	11-14 V		
Injector 1	70	⊐▷	Ignition ON	11-14 V		
	70	⊐▷	Engine idling	3 ms	10 V/2 ms	∿∿ 35
Injector 2	96	⊐▷	Ignition ON	11-14 V		
	96	⊐▷	Engine idling	3 ms	10 V/2 ms	∿∿ 35
Injector 3	20	⊐▷	Ignition ON	11-14 V		
	20	⊐▷	Engine idling	3 ms	10 V/2 ms	∿∿ 35
Injector 4	95	⊐▷	Ignition ON	11-14 V		
	95	⊐▷	Engine idling	3 ms	10 V/2 ms	∿∿ 35
Intake air temperature (IAT) sensor	39	◀	Ignition ON – air temp. 20°C	3,2 V		
	91	⊐—	Ignition ON	0 V		
Intake manifold air control solenoid	12	⊐▷	Ignition ON	0-1 V		
	12	⊐▷	Engine idling	0-1 V		
	12	⊐▷	Engine under load	11-14 V		
Knock sensor (KS)	32	◀	Engine idling – full throttle briefly		50 mV/1 ms	∿∿ 38
	57	◀	Engine idling – full throttle briefly		50 mV/1 ms	∿∿ 38
Manifold absolute pressure (MAP) sensor	9	◀	Ignition ON	4,1 V		
	9	◀	Engine idling	1,3 V		
	9	◀	Engine idling – accelerate briefly	4,6 V briefly		
	90	▷	Ignition ON	5 V		
	91	⊐—	Ignition ON	0 V		
Navigation control module	28	▷		1		
Outside air temperature sensor	8	◀	Ignition ON – air temp. 20°C	1,8 V		
	91	⊐—	Ignition ON	0 V		
Power steering pressure (PSP) switch	31	◀	Engine idling – steering wheel not turned	0 V		
	31	◀	Engine idling – steering wheel turned	11-14 V		
	91	⊐—	Ignition ON	0 V		
Starter motor relay – AT – through transmission range (TR) sensor	27	⊐▷	Engine cranking – AT in P or N	0-1 V		
	27	⊐▷	Engine cranking – AT not in P or N	0-1 V		
Starter motor relay – MT	27	⊐▷	Engine cranking	0-1 V		
Sunroof control module	28	▷		1		
Throttle position (TP) sensor	89	◀	Ignition ON – throttle closed	0,9 V		
	89	◀	Ignition ON – throttle fully open	4,5 V		
	90	▷	Ignition ON	5 V		
	91	⊐—	Ignition ON	0 V		
Vehicle speed sensor (VSS)	58	◀	Ignition ON – vehicle pushed	0 V or 9 V switching		
Wide open throttle (WOT) relay	69	⊐▷	Engine running – AC compressor OFF	11-14 V		
	69	⊐▷	Engine running – AC compressor ON	0-1 V		

*Suggested settings - Voltage/time per division

1 Connected pin - no test data available or random digital signal

Model:	Engine code:	Year:
Mondeo 2,0 TDCi 130 hp (MT)	FMBA/B	2001-01/02

ECM harness multi-plug

Terminal side

```
  1  2  3  4  5  6  7  8  9  10 11 12 13        14 15 16 17 18 19 20 21 22 23 24 25 26
 27 28 29 30 31 32 33 34 35 36 37 38 39         40 41 42 43 44 45 46 47 48 49 50 51 52
    53 54 55 56 57 58 59 60 61 62 63 64 65      66 67 68 69 70 71 72 73 74 75 76 77 78
 79 80 81 82 83 84 85 86 87 88 89 90 91         92 93 94 95 96 97 98 99 100 101 102 103 104
AD84086
```

Wire side

```
 26 25 24 23 22 21 20 19 18 17 16 15 14        13 12 11 10  9  8  7  6  5  4  3  2  1
 52 51 50 49 48 47 46 45 44 43 42 41 40         39 38 37 36 35 34 33 32 31 30 29 28 27
 78 77 76 75 74 73 72 71 70 69 68 67 66         65 64 63 62 61 60 59 58 57 56 55 54 53
104 103 102 101 100 99 98 97 96 95 94 93 92     91 90 89 88 87 86 85 84 83 82 81 80 79
AD42136
```

Component/circuit description	ECM pin	Signal	Condition	Typical value	Oscilloscope setting*	Wave form
AC refrigerant dual pressure switch	100	←	Ignition ON	11-14 V		
	100	←	Engine running – AC ON – refrigerant pressure normal	11-14 V		
	100	←	Engine running – AC ON – refrigerant pressure high	0 V		
AC refrigerant low pressure switch – through AC refrigerant dual pressure switch	41	⇒	Ignition ON	11-14 V		
	41	⇒	Engine running – AC ON, AC compressor ON	11-14 V		
	41	⇒	Engine running – AC ON, AC compressor OFF	0 V		
Accelerator pedal position (APP) sensor	4	←	Ignition ON – accelerator pedal released	4,23 V		
	4	←	Ignition ON – accelerator pedal depressed	0,88 V		
	5	←	Ignition ON – accelerator pedal released	1,46 V		
	5	←	Ignition ON – accelerator pedal depressed	3,9 V		
	7	←	Ignition ON – accelerator pedal released	0,89 V		
	7	←	Ignition ON – accelerator pedal depressed	3,36 V		
	39	⇒	Ignition ON	5 V		
	51	⊶	Ignition ON	0 V		
	90	⇒	Ignition ON	5 V		
	91	⊶	Ignition ON	0 V		
Alarm system warning lamp	42	⇒	Ignition OFF	2-11 V switching		
	42	⇒	Ignition ON	11-14 V		
Alternator	32		Ignition ON	0,74 V		
	32		Engine running		4 V/2 ms	〰️〰️ 31
	72		Ignition OFF	11-14 V		
	72		Ignition ON	0,25 V		
	72		Engine running	8,2 V	5 V/5 ms	〰️〰️ 39
Audio unit	94	⇒		1		
Battery	55	←	Ignition OFF	11-14 V		
Brake pedal position (BPP) switch	92	←	Ignition ON – brake pedal released	0 V		
	92	←	Ignition ON – brake pedal depressed	11-14 V		
CAN data bus – high	50	⇄	Ignition ON	2,5 V		

* Suggested settings - Voltage/time per division

Component/circuit description	ECM pin	Signal	Condition	Typical value	Oscilloscope setting*	Wave form
CAN data bus – low	49	⬅⇨	Ignition ON	2,5 V		
Clutch pedal position (CPP) switch	63	⇨	Ignition ON – clutch pedal released	11-14 V		
	63	⇨	Ignition ON – clutch pedal depressed	0 V		
Clutch pedal position (CPP) switch – cruise control	78	⬅	Ignition ON – brake pedal depressed, clutch pedal released	11-14 V		
	78	⬅	Ignition ON – brake pedal depressed, clutch pedal depressed	0 V		
Cruise control brake pedal switch	59	⬅	Ignition ON – brake pedal released	11-14 V		
	59	⬅	Ignition ON – brake pedal depressed forcibly	0 V		
Cruise control selector switch	26	⇨		☐1		
	30	⇨		☐1		
Cylinder head temperature (CHT) sensor (dual range)	14	⬅	Ignition ON – coolant temp. 0°C	4,1 V		
	14	⬅	Ignition ON – coolant temp. 20°C	3,2 V		
	14	⬅	Ignition ON – coolant temp. 60°C	1,3 V		
	14	⬅	Ignition ON – coolant temp. 95°C	0,46 V		
	14	⬅	Ignition ON – coolant temp. 110°C	3 V		
	91	⊣⊢	Ignition ON	0 V		
Data link connector (DLC)	13	⬅⇨	Ignition ON	0 V		
	15	⬅⇨	Ignition ON	5 V		
	16	⬅⇨	Ignition ON	0 V		
Earth	25		Ignition ON	0 V		
	76		Ignition ON	0 V		
	77		Ignition ON	0 V		
	103		Ignition ON	0 V		
Engine control (EC) relay	71	⬅	Ignition OFF	0 V		
	71	⬅	Ignition ON	11-14 V		
	96	⊣⇨	Ignition OFF	11-14 V		
	96	⊣⇨	Ignition ON	0-1 V		
	97	⬅	Ignition OFF	0 V		
	97	⬅	Ignition ON	11-14 V		
Engine coolant blower motor relay 1	68	⊣⇨	Engine running – coolant blower motors OFF	11-14 V		
	68	⊣⇨	Engine running – coolant blower motors ON, 1st speed	0-1 V		
Engine coolant blower motor relay 2	17	⊣⇨	Engine running – coolant blower motors OFF	11-14 V		
	17	⊣⇨	Engine running – coolant blower motors ON, 2nd speed	0-1 V		
Engine coolant heater relay 1	98	⊣⇨	Ignition ON	11-14 V		
	98	⊣⇨	Engine running – intake air temp. 0°C max.	0-1 V		
Engine coolant heater relay 2	75	⊣⇨	Ignition ON	11-14 V		
	75	⊣⇨	Engine running – intake air temp. below 0°C	0-1 V		
Exhaust gas recirculation (EGR) solenoid	83	⊣⇨	Ignition ON	11-14 V		
	83	⊣⇨	Engine idling		5 V/5 ms	⎍⎍ 39
Gas discharge headlamp control module	94	⇨		☐1		
Glow plug relay	1	⊣⇨	Ignition ON – glow plugs OFF	11-14 V		
	1	⊣⇨	Ignition ON – glow plugs ON	0-1 V		
Ignition switch	8	⬅	Ignition OFF	0 V		
	8	⬅	Ignition ON	11-14 V		

* Suggested settings - Voltage/time per division

Component/circuit description	ECM pin	Signal	Condition	Typical value	Oscilloscope setting*	Wave form
Immobilizer control module (PATS)	19	⬌	Ignition OFF	0 V		
	19	⬌	Ignition ON	11-14 V		
	53	⬌	Ignition OFF	0 V		
	53	⬌	Ignition ON	11-14 V		
Injector control module – engine RPM signal	57	⇨	Engine idling		2 V/2 ms	〰 65
Injector relay	70	⇥▷	Ignition OFF	0 V		
	70	⇥▷	Ignition ON	0-1 V		
Instrument panel	79	⇨		1		
Intake air temperature (IAT) sensor	3	⬅	Ignition ON – air temp. 20°C	3,2 V		
	91	⇥	Ignition ON	0 V		
Manifold absolute pressure (MAP) sensor	34	⬅	Ignition ON	1,5 V		
	34	⬅	Engine idling	1,5 V		
	34	⬅	Engine idling – accelerate briefly	3,9 V briefly		
	90	⇨	Ignition ON	5 V		
	91	⇥	Ignition ON	0 V		
Mass air flow (MAF) sensor	36	⇥	Ignition ON	0 V		
	88	⬅	Ignition ON	0,5 V		
	88	⬅	Engine idling	1,5 V		
	88	⬅	3000 rpm	3,6 V		
Navigation control module	94	⇨		1		
Outside air temperature sensor	38	⬅	Ignition ON – air temp. 20°C	1,8 V		
	91	⇥	Ignition ON	0 V		
Reverse gear position switch	66	⬅	Ignition ON – gear lever in neutral	0 V		
	66	⬅	Ignition ON – gear lever in reverse	11-14 V		
Starter motor relay	27	⇥▷	Engine cranking	0-1 V		
Sunroof control module	94	⇨		1		
Telematics control module	94	⇨		1		
Turbocharger (TC) wastegate regulating valve	52	⇥▷	Ignition ON	11-14 V		
	52	⇥▷	Engine idling		2 V/2 ms	〰 64
Vehicle speed sensor (VSS)	58	⬅	Ignition ON – vehicle pushed	0-9 V switching		
Wide open throttle (WOT) relay	69	⇥▷	Engine running – AC compressor OFF	11-14 V		
	69	⇥▷	Engine running – AC compressor ON	0-1 V		

*Suggested settings - Voltage/time per division

1 Connected pin - no test data available or random digital signal

ECM harness multi-plug

Terminal side

```
  1  2  3  4  5  6  7  8  9  10 11 12 13          14 15 16 17 18 19 20 21 22 23 24 25 26
 27 28 29 30 31 32 33 34 35 36 37 38 39          40 41 42 43 44 45 46 47 48 49 50 51 52
 53 54 55 56 57 58 59 60 61 62 63 64 65          66 67 68 69 70 71 72 73 74 75 76 77 78
 79 80 81 82 83 84 85 86 87 88 89 90 91          92 93 94 95 96 97 98 99 100 101 102 103 104
```
AD84086

Wire side

```
 26 25 24 23 22 21 20 19 18 17 16 15 14          13 12 11 10 9 8 7 6 5 4 3 2 1
 52 51 50 49 48 47 46 45 44 43 42 41 40          39 38 37 36 35 34 33 32 31 30 29 28 27
 78 77 76 75 74 73 72 71 70 69 68 67 66          65 64 63 62 61 60 59 58 57 56 55 54 53
 104 103 102 101 100 99 98 97 96 95 94 93 92      91 90 89 88 87 86 85 84 83 82 81 80 79
```
AD42136

Component/circuit description	ECM pin	Signal	Condition	Typical value	Oscilloscope setting*	Wave form
AC refrigerant low pressure switch – through AC refrigerant dual pressure switch	41	⇨	Ignition ON	11-14 V		
	41	⇨	Engine running – AC ON, AC compressor ON	11-14 V		
	41	⇨	Engine running – AC ON, AC compressor OFF	0 V		
AC refrigerant dual pressure switch	100	⇐	Ignition ON	11-14 V		
	100	⇐	Engine running – AC ON – refrigerant pressure normal	11-14 V		
	100	⇐	Engine running – AC ON – refrigerant pressure high	0 V		
Accelerator pedal position (APP) sensor	4	⇐	Ignition ON – accelerator pedal released	4,23 V		
	4	⇐	Ignition ON – accelerator pedal depressed	0,88 V		
	5	⇐	Ignition ON – accelerator pedal released	1,46 V		
	5	⇐	Ignition ON – accelerator pedal depressed	3,9 V		
	7	⇐	Ignition ON – accelerator pedal released	0,89 V		
	7	⇐	Ignition ON – accelerator pedal depressed	3,36 V		
	39	⇨	Ignition ON	5 V		
	51	⊣	Ignition ON	0 V		
	90	⇨	Ignition ON	5 V		
	91	⊣	Ignition ON	0 V		
Alarm system warning lamp	42	⇨	Ignition OFF	2-11 V switching		
	42	⇨	Ignition ON	11-14 V		
Alternator	32		Ignition ON	0,74 V		
	32		Engine running		4 V/2 ms	⎍ 31
	72		Ignition OFF	11-14 V		
	72		Ignition ON	0,25 V		
	72		Engine running	8,2 V	5 V/5 ms	⎍ 39
Audio unit	94	⇨	Ignition ON	11-14 V		
Battery	55	⇐	Ignition OFF	11-14 V		
Brake pedal position (BPP) switch	92	⇐	Ignition ON – brake pedal released	0 V		
	92	⇐	Ignition ON – brake pedal depressed	11-14 V		

★ Suggested settings - Voltage/time per division

Component/circuit description	ECM pin	Signal	Condition	Typical value	Oscilloscope setting*	Wave form
Brake pedal position (BPP) switch – cruise control	59	←	Ignition ON – brake pedal released	11-14 V		
	59	←	Ignition ON – brake pedal depressed	0 V		
CAN data bus, high	50	←⇒	Ignition ON	2,5 V		
CAN data bus, low	49	←⇒	Ignition ON	2,5 V		
Clutch pedal position (CPP) switch	63	←	Ignition ON – clutch pedal released	11-14 V		
	63	←	Ignition ON – clutch pedal depressed	0 V		
Clutch pedal position (CPP) switch – cruise control	78	⇒	Ignition ON – brake pedal depressed, clutch pedal released	11-14 V		
	78	←	Ignition ON – brake pedal depressed, clutch pedal depressed	0 V		
Cruise control selector switch	26	⇒		1		
	30	⇒		1		
Cylinder head temperature (CHT) sensor (dual range)	14	←	Ignition ON – coolant temp. 0°C	4,1 V		
	14	←	Ignition ON – coolant temp. 20°C	3,2 V		
	14	←	Ignition ON – coolant temp. 60°C	1,3 V		
	14	←	Ignition ON – coolant temp. 95°C	0,46 or 3,5 V		
	14	←	Ignition ON – coolant temp. 110°C	3 V		
Data link connector (DLC)	13	←⇒	Ignition ON	0 V		
	15	←⇒	Ignition ON	5 V		
	16	←⇒	Ignition ON	0 V		
Earth	25		Ignition ON	0 V		
	76		Ignition ON	0 V		
	77		Ignition ON	0 V		
	103		Ignition ON	0 V		
Engine control relay	71	←	Ignition ON	11-14 V		
	96	⊣⊳	Ignition OFF	11-14 V		
	96	⊣⊳	Ignition ON	0-1 V		
	97	←	Ignition ON	11-14 V		
Engine coolant blower motor	95	⇒		1		
Engine coolant heater relay 1	98	⊣⊳	Ignition ON	11-14 V		
	98	⊣⊳	Engine running – intake air temp. 0°C max.	0-1 V		
Engine coolant heater relay 2	75	⊣⊳	Ignition ON	11-14 V		
	75	⊣⊳	Engine running – intake air temp. below 0°C	0-1 V		
Exhaust gas recirculation (EGR) solenoid	83	⊣⊳	Ignition ON	11-14 V		
	83	⊣⊳	Engine idling		5 V/5 ms	〰 39
Glow plug relay	20	⊣⊳	Ignition ON – glow plugs OFF	11-14 V		
	20	⊣⊳	Ignition ON – glow plugs ON	0-1 V		
Ignition switch	8	←	Ignition OFF	0 V		
	8	←	Ignition ON	11-14 V		
Immobilizer control module (PATS)	53	←⇒	Ignition OFF	0 V		
	53	←⇒	Ignition ON	11-14 V		
	19	←⇒	Ignition OFF	0 V		
	19	←⇒	Ignition ON	11-14 V		
Injector control module – engine RPM signal	57	⇒	Engine idling		2 V/2 ms	〰 65
Injector relay	70	⊣⊳	Ignition OFF	0 V		
	70	⊣⊳	Ignition ON	0-1 V		
Instrument panel	79	⇒		1		
Intake air temperature (IAT) sensor	3	←	Ignition ON – air temp. 20°C	3,2 V		
Lamps control module, LH (Xenon)	94	⇒	Ignition ON	11-14 V		

* Suggested settings - Voltage/time per division

Component/circuit description	ECM pin	Signal	Condition	Typical value	Oscilloscope setting*	Wave form
Manifold absolute pressure (MAP) sensor	34	←	Ignition ON	1,53 V		
	34	←	Engine idling	1,53 V		
	34	←	Engine idling – accelerate briefly	3,9 V briefly		
Mass air flow (MAF) sensor	36	⅂–	Ignition ON	0 V		
	88	←	Ignition ON	0,05 V		
	88	←	Engine idling	1,5 V		
	88	←	3000 rpm	3,6 V		
Outside air temperature sensor	38	←	Ignition ON – air temp. 20°C	1,8 V		
Reverse gear position switch – MT	66	←	Ignition ON – gear lever in reverse	11-14 V		
	66	←	Ignition ON – gear lever in neutral	0 V		
Starter motor relay	27	⅂▷	Ignition OFF	0 V		
	27	⅂▷	Ignition ON	0-1 V		
	27	⅂▷	Ignition ON – starter motor operating	0-1 V		
Sunroof control module	94	⇒	Ignition ON	11-14 V		
Telematics control module	94	⇒	Ignition ON	11-14 V		
Turbocharger (TC) wastegate regulating valve	52	⅂▷	Ignition ON	11-14 V		
	52	⅂▷	Engine idling		2 V/2 ms	∿∿ 64
Vehicle speed sensor (VSS)	58	←	Ignition ON – vehicle pushed	0-9 V switching		
Wide open throttle (WOT) relay	69	⅂▷	Ignition ON	11-14 V		
	69	⅂▷	Engine running – AC ON	0-1 V		

*Suggested settings - Voltage/time per division

1 Connected pin - no test data available or random digital signal

Model:	Engine code:	Year:
Mondeo 2,0 TDCi 115 hp (MT)	HJBA/B	2002-01/03

ECM harness multi-plug

Terminal side

AD84086

Wire side

AD42136

Component/circuit description	ECM pin	Signal	Condition	Typical value	Oscilloscope setting*	Wave form
AC refrigerant dual pressure switch	100	←	Ignition ON	11-14 V		
	100	←	Engine running – AC ON – refrigerant pressure normal	11-14 V		
	100	←	Engine running – AC ON – refrigerant pressure high	0 V		
AC refrigerant low pressure switch – through AC refrigerant dual pressure switch	41	⇒	Ignition ON	11-14 V		
	41	⇒	Engine running – AC ON, AC compressor ON	11-14 V		
	41	⇒	Engine running – AC ON, AC compressor OFF	0 V		
Accelerator pedal position (APP) sensor	4	←	Ignition ON – accelerator pedal released	4,23 V		
	4	←	Ignition ON – accelerator pedal depressed	0,88 V		
	5	←	Ignition ON – accelerator pedal released	1,46 V		
	5	←	Ignition ON – accelerator pedal depressed	3,9 V		
	7	←	Ignition ON – accelerator pedal released	0,89 V		
	7	←	Ignition ON – accelerator pedal depressed	3,36 V		
	39	⇒	Ignition ON	5 V		
	51	⌐	Ignition ON	0 V		
	90	⇒	Ignition ON	5 V		
	91	⌐	Ignition ON	0 V		
Alarm system warning lamp	42	⇒	Ignition OFF	2-11 V switching		
	42	⇒	Ignition ON	11-14 V		
Alternator	32		Ignition ON	0,74 V		
	32		Engine running		4 V/2 ms	〰 31
	72		Ignition OFF	11-14 V		
	72		Ignition ON	0,25 V		
	72		Engine running	8,2 V	5 V/5 ms	〰 39
Audio unit	94	⇒		1		
Battery	55	←	Ignition OFF	11-14 V		
Brake pedal position (BPP) switch	92	←	Ignition ON – brake pedal released	0 V		
	92	←	Ignition ON – brake pedal depressed	11-14 V		

* Suggested settings - Voltage/time per division

/Autodata

Component/circuit description	ECM pin	Signal	Condition	Typical value	Oscilloscope setting*	Wave form
CAN data bus – high	50	←▷	Ignition ON	2,5 V		
CAN data bus – low	49	←▷	Ignition ON	2,5 V		
Clutch pedal position (CPP) switch	63	▷	Ignition ON – clutch pedal released	11-14 V		
	63	▷	Ignition ON – clutch pedal depressed	0 V		
Clutch pedal position (CPP) switch – cruise control	78	←	Ignition ON – brake pedal depressed, clutch pedal released	11-14 V		
	78	←	Ignition ON – brake pedal depressed, clutch pedal depressed	0 V		
Cruise control brake pedal switch	59	←	Ignition ON – brake pedal released	11-14 V		
	59	←	Ignition ON – brake pedal depressed forcibly	0 V		
Cruise control selector switch	26	▷		1		
	30	▷		1		
Cylinder head temperature (CHT) sensor (dual range)	14	←	Ignition ON – coolant temp. 0°C	4,1 V		
	14	←	Ignition ON – coolant temp. 20°C	3,2 V		
	14	←	Ignition ON – coolant temp. 60°C	1,3 V		
	14	←	Ignition ON – coolant temp. 95°C	0,46 V		
	14	←	Ignition ON – coolant temp. 110°C	3 V		
	91	⅂─	Ignition ON	0 V		
Data link connector (DLC)	13	←▷	Ignition ON	0 V		
	15	←▷	Ignition ON	5 V		
	16	←▷	Ignition ON	0 V		
Earth	25		Ignition ON	0 V		
	76		Ignition ON	0 V		
	77		Ignition ON	0 V		
	103		Ignition ON	0 V		
Engine control (EC) relay	71	←	Ignition OFF	0 V		
	71	←	Ignition ON	11-14 V		
	96	⅂▷	Ignition OFF	11-14 V		
	96	⅂▷	Ignition ON	0-1 V		
	97	←	Ignition OFF	0 V		
	97	←	Ignition ON	11-14 V		
Engine coolant blower motor	95	▷		1		
Engine coolant heater relay 1	98	⅂▷	Ignition ON	11-14 V		
	98	⅂▷	Engine running – intake air temp. 0°C max.	0-1 V		
Engine coolant heater relay 2	75	⅂▷	Ignition ON	11-14 V		
	75	⅂▷	Engine running – intake air temp. below 0°C	0-1 V		
Exhaust gas recirculation (EGR) solenoid	83	⅂▷	Ignition ON	11-14 V		
	83	⅂▷	Engine idling		5 V/5 ms	∿ 39
Exhaust gas recirculation (EGR) valve position sensor	35	←		1		
	90	▷	Ignition ON	5 V		
	91	⅂─	Ignition ON	0 V		
Gas discharge headlamp control module	94	▷		1		
Glow plug relay	1	⅂▷	Ignition ON – glow plugs OFF	11-14 V		
	1	⅂▷	Ignition ON – glow plugs ON	0-1 V		
Ignition switch	8	←	Ignition OFF	0 V		
	8	←	Ignition ON	11-14 V		

* Suggested settings - Voltage/time per division

Component/circuit description	ECM pin	Signal	Condition	Typical value	Oscilloscope setting*	Wave form
Immobilizer control module (PATS)	19	←▷	Ignition OFF	0 V		
	19	←▷	Ignition ON	11-14 V		
	53	←▷	Ignition OFF	0 V		
	53	←▷	Ignition ON	11-14 V		
Injector control module – engine RPM signal	57	▷	Engine idling		2 V/2 ms	〰 65
Injector relay	70	⊐▷	Ignition OFF	0 V		
	70	⊐▷	Ignition ON	0-1 V		
Instrument panel	79	▷		[1]		
Intake air temperature (IAT) sensor	3	←	Ignition ON – air temp. 20°C	3,2 V		
	91	⊣	Ignition ON	0 V		
Manifold absolute pressure (MAP) sensor	34	←	Ignition ON	1,5 V		
	34	←	Engine idling	1,5 V		
	34	←	Engine idling – accelerate briefly	3,9 V briefly		
	90	▷	Ignition ON	5 V		
	91	⊣	Ignition ON	0 V		
Navigation control module	94	▷		[1]		
Outside air temperature sensor	38	←	Ignition ON – air temp. 20°C	1,8 V		
	91	⊣	Ignition ON	0 V		
Reverse gear position switch	66	←	Ignition ON – gear lever in neutral	0 V		
	66	←	Ignition ON – gear lever in reverse	11-14 V		
Starter motor relay	27	⊐▷	Engine cranking	0-1 V		
Sunroof control module	94	▷		[1]		
Telematics control module	94	▷		[1]		
Vehicle speed sensor (VSS)	58	←	Ignition ON – vehicle pushed	0-9 V switching		
Wide open throttle (WOT) relay	69	⊐▷	Engine running – AC compressor OFF	11-14 V		
	69	⊐▷	Engine running – AC compressor ON	0-1 V		

*Suggested settings - Voltage/time per division

[1] Connected pin - no test data available or random digital signal

Model:	Engine code:	Year:
Mondeo 2,0 TDCi 115 hp (MT)	HJBA/B/C	02/03-04
Mondeo 2,0 TDCi 130 hp (MT)	N7BA	2003-04

FORD
Delphi/EEC V
(Engine control module)

ECM harness multi-plug

Terminal side

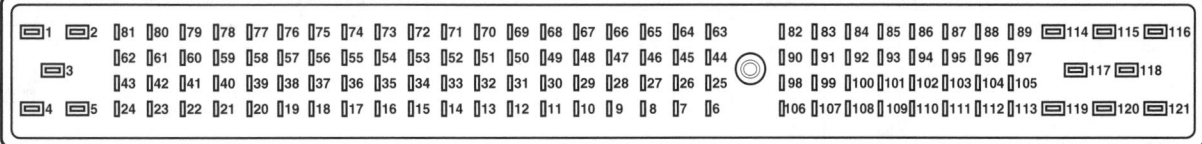

AD29502

Wire side

AD29501

Component/circuit description	ECM pin	Signal	Condition	Typical value	Oscilloscope setting*	Wave form
AC refrigerant dual pressure switch	76	←	Ignition ON	11-14 V		
	76	←	Engine running – AC ON – refrigerant pressure normal	11-14 V		
	76	←	Engine running – AC ON – refrigerant pressure high	0 V		
AC refrigerant low pressure switch – through AC refrigerant dual pressure switch	19	⇒	Ignition ON	11-14 V		
	19	⇒	Engine running – AC ON, AC compressor ON	11-14 V		
	19	⇒	Engine running – AC ON, AC compressor OFF	0 V		
Accelerator pedal position (APP) sensor	14	⌐├	Ignition ON	0 V		
	32	←	Ignition ON – accelerator pedal released	1,46 V		
	32	←	Ignition ON – accelerator pedal fully depressed	3,9 V		
	33	⇒	Ignition ON	5 V		
	50	←	Ignition ON – accelerator pedal released	0,89 V		
	50	←	Ignition ON – accelerator pedal fully depressed	3,36 V		
	51	⇒	Ignition ON	5 V		
	53	⌐├	Ignition ON	0 V		
	70	⌐├	Ignition ON	0 V		
	71	←	Ignition ON – accelerator pedal released	4,23 V		
	71	←	Ignition ON – accelerator pedal fully depressed	0,88 V		
	72	⇒	Ignition ON	5 V		
Alarm system warning lamp	16	⇒	Engine running	11-14 V		

* Suggested settings - Voltage/time per division

FORD

Component/circuit description	ECM pin	Signal	Condition	Typical value	Oscilloscope setting*	Wave form
Alternator	47	←⇒	Ignition ON	0,5 V		
	47	←⇒	Engine idling		5 V/2 ms	2
	112	←	Ignition OFF	11-14 V		
	112	←	Engine idling		2 V/5 ms	39
Audio unit	78	⇒		☐1		
Brake pedal position (BPP) switch	58	←	Ignition ON – brake pedal released	0 V		
	58	←	Ignition ON – brake pedal depressed	11-14 V		
Camshaft position (CMP) sensor	103	←	Ignition ON	0 V or 5 V		
	103	←	Engine idling		2 V/0,1 s	3
	104	⌐	Ignition ON	0 V		
	111	⇒	Ignition ON	5 V		
CAN data bus – high	73	←⇒		☐1		
CAN data bus – low	54	←⇒		☐1		
Clutch pedal position (CPP) switch	12	⇒	Ignition ON – clutch pedal released	0 V		
	12	⇒	Ignition ON – clutch pedal depressed	11-14 V		
	38	⇒	Ignition ON – clutch pedal released	11-14 V		
	38	⇒	Ignition ON – clutch pedal depressed	0 V		
Crankshaft position (CKP) sensor	82	⌐	Ignition ON	0 V		
	90	←	Ignition ON	0 V		
	90	←	Engine idling	8,8 V ac	5 V/2 ms	1
Cruise control brake pedal switch	77	←	Ignition ON – brake pedal released	11-14 V		
	77	←	Ignition ON – brake pedal depressed forcibly	0 V		
Cruise control selector switch	13	←		☐1		
	57	←		☐1		
Cylinder head temperature (CHT) sensor (dual range)	101	←	Ignition ON – coolant temp. 0°C	4,1 V		
	101	←	Ignition ON – coolant temp. 20°C	3,2 V		
	101	←	Ignition ON – coolant temp. 60°C	1,3 V		
	101	←	Ignition ON – coolant temp. 95°C	0,46 V		
	101	←	Ignition ON – coolant temp. 110°C	3 V		
	102	⌐	Ignition ON	0 V		
Data link connector (DLC)	55			☐1		
	74			☐1		
Earth	1		Ignition ON	0 V		
	2		Ignition ON	0 V		
	28		Ignition ON	0 V		
	66		Ignition ON	0 V		
	88		Ignition ON	0 V		

★ Suggested settings - Voltage/time per division

Component/circuit description	ECM pin	Signal	Condition	Typical value	Oscilloscope setting*	Wave form
Engine control (EC) relay	3	←	Ignition OFF	0 V		
	3	←	Ignition ON	11-14 V		
	4	←	Ignition OFF	0 V		
	4	←	Ignition ON	11-14 V		
	5	←	Ignition OFF	0 V		
	5	←	Ignition ON	11-14 V		
	9	⊐▷	Ignition OFF	11-14 V		
	9	⊐▷	Ignition ON	0-1 V		
Engine coolant blower motor	105	⇒		①		
Engine coolant heater relay 1	61	⊐▷	Ignition ON	11-14 V		
	61	⊐▷	Engine running – intake air temp. 0°C max.	0-1 V		
Engine coolant heater relay 2	62	⊐▷	Ignition ON	11-14 V		
	62	⊐▷	Engine running – intake air temp. 0°C max.	0-1 V		
Exhaust gas recirculation (EGR) solenoid	96	⊐▷	Ignition ON	11-14 V		
	96	⊐▷	Engine idling		5 V/0,5 ms	∿∿ 39
Exhaust gas recirculation (EGR) valve position sensor	7			①		
	8	←		①		
	27			①		
Fuel pressure control solenoid	87	⊐▷	Ignition ON		5 V/1 ms	∿∿ 3
	87	⊐▷	Engine idling		5 V/2 ms	∿∿ 39
	87	⊐▷	3000 rpm		2 V/0,5 ms	∿∿ 37
Fuel rail pressure (FRP) sensor	6	⇒	Ignition ON	5 V		
	25	←	Ignition ON	0,5 V		
	25	←	Engine idling	1 V		
	25	←	3000 rpm	2 V		
	26	⊐—	Ignition ON	0 V		
Fuel temperature sensor	109	←	Ignition ON – fuel temp. 20°C	3 V		
	109	←	Ignition ON – fuel temp. 40°C	2,2 V		
	110	⊐—	Ignition ON	0 V		
Gas discharge headlamp control module	78	⇒		①		
Glow plug relay	20	⊐▷	Ignition ON – glow plugs OFF	11-14 V		
	20	⊐▷	Ignition ON – glow plugs ON	0-1 V		
Ignition switch	37	←	Ignition OFF	0 V		
	37	←	Ignition ON	11-14 V		
Immobilizer control module (PATS)	15	←⇒		①		
	34	←⇒		①		
Injector 1	114	⊐▷	Ignition ON	5,3 V		
	114 (117)	⊐▷	Engine idling	0,3 ms pilot + 0,4 ms main	5 V/0,5 ms	∿∿ 63
Injector 2	120	⊐▷	Ignition ON	5,3 V		
	120 (118)	⊐▷	Engine idling	0,3 ms pilot + 0,4 ms main	5 V/0,5 ms	∿∿ 63

* Suggested settings - Voltage/time per division

FORD

Component/circuit description	ECM pin	Signal	Condition	Typical value	Oscilloscope setting*	Wave form
Injector 3	121		Ignition ON	5,3 V		
	121 (118)		Engine idling	0,3 ms pilot + 0,4 ms main	5 V/0,5 ms	63
Injector 4	115		Ignition ON	5,3 V		
	115 (117)		Engine idling	0,3 ms pilot + 0,4 ms main	5 V/0,5 ms	63
Injectors 1 & 4	117		Ignition ON	5,3 V		
Injectors 2 & 3	118		Ignition ON	5,3 V		
Instrument panel	60			1		
Intake air temperature (IAT) sensor	107		Ignition ON – air temp. 20°C	3,2 V		
Knock sensor (KS)	45		Ignition ON	0 V		
	45		3000 rpm		0,1 V/1 ms	62
	46		Ignition ON	0 V		
Manifold absolute pressure (MAP) sensor	99		Ignition ON	1,5 V		
	99		Engine idling	1,5 V		
	99		Engine idling – accelerate briefly	3,9 V		
	100		Ignition ON	0 V		
	108		Ignition ON	5 V		
Mass air flow (MAF) sensor – 130 hp	83		Ignition ON	0,05 V		
	83		Engine idling	1,7 V		
	83		3000 rpm	3,4 V		
	84		Ignition ON	0 V		
Navigation control module	78			1		
Outside air temperature sensor	64		Ignition ON – air temp. 20°C	2 V		
	65		Ignition ON	0 V		
Reverse gear position switch	18		Ignition ON – gear lever in neutral	0 V		
	18		Ignition ON – gear lever in reverse	11-14 V		
Starter motor relay	21		Engine cranking	0-1 V		
Sunroof control module	78			1		
Telematics control module	78			1		
Turbocharger (TC) wastegate regulating valve – 130 hp	95		Ignition ON	11-14 V		
	95		Engine idling		2 V/2 ms	64
Wide open throttle (WOT) relay	79		Ignition ON	11-14 V		
	79		Engine running – AC compressor OFF	11-14 V		
	79		Engine running – AC compressor ON	0-1 V		

*Suggested settings - Voltage/time per division

1 Connected pin - no test data available or random digital signal

Model:	Engine code:	Year:
Mondeo 2,0 TDCi 115 hp (AT)	HJBA/B/C	2002-04
Mondeo 2,0 TDCi 130 hp (AT)	FMBA/B	2002-04
Mondeo 2,0 TDCi 130 hp (AT)	N7BA	2003-04

FORD
Delphi/EEC V
(Engine control module)

ECM harness multi-plug

Terminal side

AD84086

Wire side

AD42136

Component/circuit description	ECM pin	Signal	Condition	Typical value	Oscilloscope setting*	Wave form
AC refrigerant dual pressure switch	100	←	Ignition ON	11-14 V		
	100	←	Engine running – AC ON – refrigerant pressure normal	11-14 V		
	100	←	Engine running – AC ON – refrigerant pressure high	0 V		
AC refrigerant low pressure switch – through AC refrigerant dual pressure switch	41	⇨	Ignition ON	11-14 V		
	41	⇨	Engine running – AC ON, AC compressor ON	11-14 V		
	41	⇨	Engine running – AC ON, AC compressor OFF	0 V		
Accelerator pedal position (APP) sensor	4	←	Ignition ON – accelerator pedal released	4,23 V		
	4	←	Ignition ON – accelerator pedal depressed	0,88 V		
	5	←	Ignition ON – accelerator pedal released	1,46 V		
	5	←	Ignition ON – accelerator pedal depressed	3,9 V		
	7	←	Ignition ON – accelerator pedal released	0,89 V		
	7	←	Ignition ON – accelerator pedal depressed	3,36 V		
	39	⇨	Ignition ON	5 V		
	51	⌐	Ignition ON	0 V		
	90	⇨	Ignition ON	5 V		
	91	⌐	Ignition ON	0 V		
Alarm system warning lamp	42	⇨	Ignition OFF	2-11 V switching		
	42	⇨	Ignition ON	11-14 V		
Alternator	32		Ignition ON	0,74 V		
	32		Engine running		4 V/2 ms	⩗ 31
	72		Ignition OFF	11-14 V		
	72		Ignition ON	0,25 V		
	72		Engine running	8,2 V	5 V/5 ms	⩗ 39
Audio unit	94	⇨		1		
Battery	55	←	Ignition OFF	11-14 V		
Brake pedal position (BPP) switch	92	←	Ignition ON – brake pedal released	0 V		
	92	←	Ignition ON – brake pedal depressed	11-14 V		

* Suggested settings - Voltage/time per division

Component/circuit description	ECM pin	Signal	Condition	Typical value	Oscilloscope setting*	Wave form
CAN data bus – high	50	⟺	Ignition ON	2,5 V		
CAN data bus – low	49	⟺	Ignition ON	2,5 V		
Cruise control brake pedal switch	59	⟵	Ignition ON – brake pedal released	11-14 V		
	59	⟵	Ignition ON – brake pedal depressed forcibly	0 V		
Cruise control selector switch	26	⟹		1		
	30	⟹		1		
Cylinder head temperature (CHT) sensor (dual range)	14	⟵	Ignition ON – coolant temp. 0°C	4,1 V		
	14	⟵	Ignition ON – coolant temp. 20°C	3,2 V		
	14	⟵	Ignition ON – coolant temp. 60°C	1,3 V		
	14	⟵	Ignition ON – coolant temp. 95°C	0,46 V		
	14	⟵	Ignition ON – coolant temp. 110°C	3 V		
	91	⌐	Ignition ON	0 V		
Data link connector (DLC)	13	⟺	Ignition ON	0 V		
	15	⟺	Ignition ON	5 V		
	16	⟺	Ignition ON	0 V		
Earth	25		Ignition ON	0 V		
	76		Ignition ON	0 V		
	77		Ignition ON	0 V		
	103		Ignition ON	0 V		
Engine control (EC) relay	71	⟵	Ignition OFF	0 V		
	71	⟵	Ignition ON	11-14 V		
	96	⌐⟹	Ignition OFF	11-14 V		
	96	⌐⟹	Ignition ON	0-1 V		
	97	⟵	Ignition OFF	0 V		
	97	⟵	Ignition ON	11-14 V		
Engine coolant blower motor	95	⟹		1		
Engine coolant heater relay 1	98	⌐⟹	Ignition ON	11-14 V		
	98	⌐⟹	Engine running – intake air temp. 0°C max.	0-1 V		
Engine coolant heater relay 2	75	⌐⟹	Ignition ON	11-14 V		
	75	⌐⟹	Engine running – intake air temp. below 0°C	0-1 V		
Exhaust gas recirculation (EGR) solenoid	83	⌐⟹	Ignition ON	11-14 V		
	83	⌐⟹	Engine idling		5 V/5 ms	∿ 39
Exhaust gas recirculation (EGR) valve position sensor – 115 hp	35	⟵		1		
	90	⟹	Ignition ON	5 V		
	91	⌐	Ignition ON	0 V		
Gas discharge headlamp control module	94	⟹		1		
Glow plug relay	1	⌐⟹	Ignition ON – glow plugs OFF	11-14 V		
	1	⌐⟹	Ignition ON – glow plugs ON	0-1 V		
Ignition switch	8	⟵	Ignition OFF	0 V		
	8	⟵	Ignition ON	11-14 V		
Immobilizer control module (PATS)	19	⟺	Ignition OFF	0 V		
	19	⟺	Ignition ON	11-14 V		
	53	⟺	Ignition OFF	0 V		
	53	⟺	Ignition ON	11-14 V		
Injector control module – engine RPM signal	57	⟹	Engine idling		2 V/2 ms	∿ 65
Injector relay	70	⌐⟹	Ignition OFF	0 V		
	70	⌐⟹	Ignition ON	0-1 V		
Instrument panel	79	⟹		1		

* Suggested settings - Voltage/time per division

Component/circuit description	ECM pin	Signal	Condition	Typical value	Oscilloscope setting*	Wave form
Intake air temperature (IAT) sensor	**3**	⬅	Ignition ON – air temp. 20°C	3,2 V		
	91	⏚	Ignition ON	0 V		
Manifold absolute pressure (MAP) sensor	**34**	⬅	Ignition ON	1,5 V		
	34	⬅	Engine idling	1,5 V		
	34	⬅	Engine idling – accelerate briefly	3,9 V briefly		
	90	⇨	Ignition ON	5 V		
	91	⏚	Ignition ON	0 V		
Mass air flow (MAF) sensor – 130 hp	**88**	⬅	Ignition ON	0,5 V		
	36	⏚	Ignition ON	0 V		
	88	⬅	Engine idling	1,5 V		
	88	⬅	3000 rpm	3,6 V		
Navigation control module	**94**	⇨		1		
Outside air temperature sensor	**38**	⬅	Ignition ON – air temp. 20°C	1,8 V		
	91	⏚	Ignition ON	0 V		
Reversing lamp relay	**66**	⬅	Ignition ON – AT not in reverse	0 V		
	66	⬅	Ignition ON – AT in reverse	11-14 V		
Starter motor relay – through transmission range (TR) sensor	**27**	⊣▷	Engine cranking – AT in P or N	0-1 V		
	27	⊣▷	Engine cranking – AT not in P or N	0 V		
Sunroof control module	**94**	⇨		1		
Telematics control module	**94**	⇨		1		
Turbocharger (TC) wastegate regulating valve – 130 hp	**52**	⊣▷	Ignition ON	11-14 V		
	52	⊣▷	Engine idling		2 V/2 ms	64
Wide open throttle (WOT) relay	**69**	⊣▷	Engine running – AC compressor OFF	11-14 V		
	69	⊣▷	Engine running – AC compressor ON	0-1 V		

*Suggested settings - Voltage/time per division

1 Connected pin - no test data available or random digital signal

Model:	Engine code:	Year:
Mondeo 2,0 TDCi 115 hp (MT)	HJBA/B	2002-01/03
Mondeo 2,0 TDCi 115 hp (AT)	HJBA/B/C	2002-04
Mondeo 2,0 TDCi 130 hp (MT)	FMBA/B	2001-03
Mondeo 2,0 TDCi 130 hp (AT)	FMBA/B	2002-04
Mondeo 2,0 TDCi 130 hp (AT)	N7BA	2003-04

Injector control module harness multi-plug

Terminal side – A – Grey, B – Brown, C – Black

C

h1	g1	f1	e1	d1	c1	b1	a1
h2	g2	f2	e2	d2	c2	b2	a2
h3	g3	f3	e3	d3	c3	b3	a3
h4	g4	f4	e4	d4	c4	b4	a4

B

m1	l1	k1	j1	h1	g1	f1	e1	d1	c1	b1	a1
m2	l2	k2	j2	h2	g2	f2	e2	d2	c2	b2	a2
m3	l3	k3	j3	h3	g3	f3	e3	d3	c3	b3	a3
m4	l4	k4	j4	h4	g4	f4	e4	d4	c4	b4	a4

A

a4	b4	c4	d4	e4	f4	g4	h4
a3	b3	c3	d3	e3	f3	g3	h3
a2	b2	c2	d2	e2	f2	g2	h2
a1	b1	c1	d1	e1	f1	g1	h1

AD22744

Wire side – A – Grey, B – Brown, C – Black

A

h4	g4	f4	e4	d4	c4	b4	a4
h3	g3	f3	e3	d3	c3	b3	a3
h2	g2	f2	e2	d2	c2	b2	a2
h1	g1	f1	e1	d1	c1	b1	a1

B

a1	b1	c1	d1	e1	f1	g1	h1	j1	k1	l1	m1
a2	b2	c2	d2	e2	f2	g2	h2	j2	k2	l2	m2
a3	b3	c3	d3	e3	f3	g3	h3	j3	k3	l3	m3
a4	b4	c4	d4	e4	f4	g4	h4	j4	k4	l4	m4

C

a1	b1	c1	d1	e1	f1	g1	h1
a2	b2	c2	d2	e2	f2	g2	h2
a3	b3	c3	d3	e3	f3	g3	h3
a4	b4	c4	d4	e4	f4	g4	h4

AD22743

Component/circuit description	ECM pin	Signal	Condition	Typical value	Oscilloscope setting*	Wave form
Camshaft position (CMP) sensor	Be1	→	Ignition ON	5 V		
	Be2	←	Ignition ON	0 V or 5 V		
	Be2	←	Engine idling		2 V/0,1 s	∿ 3
	Be3	⊣	Ignition ON	0 V		
CAN data bus – high	Aa4	←→	Ignition ON	2,5 V		
CAN data bus – low	Aa3	←→	Ignition ON	2,5 V		
Crankshaft position (CKP) sensor	Bf2	→	Ignition ON	0 V		
	Bf2	→	Engine idling	8,8 V ac	5 V/2 ms	∿ 1
	Bf3	⊣	Ignition ON	0 V		
Earth	Ag1		Ignition ON	0 V		
	Ah1		Ignition ON	0 V		
	Cg4		Ignition ON	0 V		
	Ch4		Ignition ON	0 V		
Engine control module (ECM) – →01/02	Cd4	←	Ignition ON	11-14 V		
Engine control module (ECM) – 02/02→	Bm2	←	Ignition ON	11-14 V		
Fuel pressure regulator control solenoid	Bm4	⊣▷	Ignition ON		5 V/1 ms	∿ 3
	Bm4	⊣▷	Engine idling		5 V/2 ms	∿ 39
	Bm4	⊣▷	3000 rpm		2 V/0,5 ms	∿ 37
Fuel rail pressure (FRP) sensor	Bd1	→	Ignition ON	5 V		
	Bd2	←	Ignition ON	0,5 V		
	Bd2	←	Engine idling	1 V		
	Bd2	←	3000 rpm	1,9 V		
	Bd3	⊣	Ignition ON	0 V		
Fuel temperature sensor	Bg2	←	Ignition ON – fuel temp. 20°C	3,3 V		
	Bg2	←	Ignition ON – fuel temp. 40°C	2,2 V		
	Bg2	←	Ignition ON – fuel temp. 55°C	1,6 V		
	Bg3	⊣	Ignition ON	0 V		

* Suggested settings - Voltage/time per division

Component/circuit description	ECM pin	Signal	Condition	Typical value	Oscilloscope setting*	Wave form
Injector 1	Ba4	⇒	Ignition ON	2,7 V		
	Ba4 (Bb4)	⇒	Engine idling	0,5 ms pilot + 0,5 ms main	5 V/1 ms	〰 63
	Bb4	⇒	Ignition ON	2,7 V		
	Bb4 (Ba4)	⇒	Engine idling	0,5 ms pilot + 0,5 ms main	5 V/1 ms	〰 63
Injector 2	Bg4	⇒	Ignition ON	2,7 V		
	Bg4 (Bh4)	⇒	Engine idling	0,5 ms pilot + 0,5 ms main	5 V/1 ms	〰 63
	Bh4	⇒	Ignition ON	2,7 V		
	Bh4 (Bg4)	⇒	Engine idling	0,5 ms pilot + 0,5 ms main	5 V/1 ms	〰 63
Injector 3	Bc4	⇒	Ignition ON	2,7 V		
	Bc4 (Bd4)	⇒	Engine idling	0,5 ms pilot + 0,5 ms main	5 V/1 ms	〰 63
	Bd4	⇒	Ignition ON	2,7 V		
	Bd4 (Bc4)	⇒	Engine idling	0,5 ms pilot + 0,5 ms main	5 V/1 ms	〰 63
Injector 4	Be4	⇒	Ignition ON	2,7 V		
	Be4 (Bf4)	⇒	Engine idling	0,5 ms pilot + 0,5 ms main	5 V/1 ms	〰 63
	Bf4	⇒	Ignition ON	2,7 V		
	Bf4 (Be4)	⇒	Engine idling	0,5 ms pilot + 0,5 ms main	5 V/1 ms	〰 63
Injector relay	Ag2	⇥	Ignition ON	11-14 V		
	Ah2	←	Ignition ON	11-14 V		
	Cg1	←	Ignition OFF	0 V		
	Cg1	←	Ignition ON	11-14 V		
Knock sensor (KS)	Bf1	⊣	Ignition ON	0 V		
	Bg1	←	Ignition ON	0 V		
	Bg1	←	3000 rpm		50 mV/1 ms	〰 62
Knock sensor (KS) – screened lead	Bk1	⊣	Ignition ON	0 V		

*Suggested settings - Voltage/time per division

1 Connected pin - no test data available or random digital signal

Model:	Engine code:	Year:
Mondeo 2,5	SEA, SEB, SGA	1996-01
Scorpio 2,9	BOB	1994-98
Cougar 2,5	LCBA/C	1998-02

ECM harness multi-plug

Terminal side

```
  1  2  3  4  5  6  7  8  9  10 11 12 13          14 15 16 17 18 19 20 21 22 23 24 25 26
 27 28 29 30 31 32 33 34 35 36 37 38 39          40 41 42 43 44 45 46 47 48 49 50 51 52
 53 54 55 56 57 58 59 60 61 62 63 64 65   O      66 67 68 69 70 71 72 73 74 75 76 77 78
 79 80 81 82 83 84 85 86 87 88 89 90 91          92 93 94 95 96 97 98 99 100 101 102 103 104
AD84086
```

Wire side

```
 26 25 24 23 22 21 20 19 18 17 16 15 14          13 12 11 10 9  8  7  6  5  4  3  2  1
 52 51 50 49 48 47 46 45 44 43 42 41 40          39 38 37 36 35 34 33 32 31 30 29 28 27
 78 77 76 75 74 73 72 71 70 69 68 67 66   O      65 64 63 62 61 60 59 58 57 56 55 54 53
104 103 102 101 100 99 98 97 96 95 94 93 92      91 90 89 88 87 86 85 84 83 82 81 80 79
AD42136
```

Component/circuit description	ECM pin	Signal	Condition	Typical value	Oscilloscope setting*	Wave form
ABS control module	4			1		
AC compressor clutch relay	69	⊐▷	Engine idling – AC OFF	11-14 V		
	69	⊐▷	Engine idling – AC ON – AC compressor ON	0-1 V		
AC refrigerant pressure switch – Scorpio	41			1		
AC refrigerant pressure switch – Mondeo/Cougar	86			1		
Air conditioning – Scorpio	66			1		
Automatic transmission	76			1		
	81			1		
	84			1		
	91			1		
Automatic transmission – some models	1			1		
	6			1		
	11			1		
	27			1		
	74			1		
	80			1		
	102			1		
Automatic transmission – Scorpio	53			1		
	72			1		
Automatic transmission – with PATS	80			1		
Automatic transmission – without PATS	54			1		
Battery	55	⟵	Ignition OFF	11-14 V		
Brake pedal position (BPP) switch	92	⟵	Ignition ON – brake pedal depressed	11-14 V		
	92	⟵	Ignition ON – brake pedal released	0 V		
Camshaft position (CMP) sensor	76	⌐	Engine idling	0 V		
	85	⟵	Engine idling		5 V/20 ms	⩗⩗⩗ 11
Clutch pedal position (CPP) switch	64	⟵	Ignition ON – clutch pedal released	5 V		
	64	⟵	Ignition ON – clutch pedal depressed	0 V		
	91	⌐	Ignition ON	0 V		

★ Suggested settings - Voltage/time per division

Autodata

Component/circuit description	ECM pin	Signal	Condition	Typical value	Oscilloscope setting*	Wave form
Crankshaft position (CKP) sensor – Mondeo/Cougar	21	←	Engine idling		2 V/1 ms	[2]
	22	←	Engine idling		2 V/1 ms	[2]
Data link connector (DLC)	13			[1]		
	15			[1]		
	16			[1]		
Earth	24		Ignition ON	0 V		
	25		Ignition ON	0 V		
	51		Ignition ON	0 V		
	77		Ignition ON	0 V		
	103		Ignition ON	0 V		
Earth – through ignition control module (ICM) – Scorpio	23		Ignition ON	0 V		
Engine control module (ECM) – pin 91 – some models	30	⊣	Ignition ON	0 V		
Engine control relay	71	←	Ignition OFF	0 V		
	71	←	Ignition ON	11-14 V		
	97	←	Ignition OFF	0 V		
	97	←	Ignition ON	11-14 V		
Engine coolant blower motor relay – some models	17	⊣▷	Engine idling – coolant blower motor OFF	11-14 V		
	17	⊣▷	Engine idling – coolant blower motor ON – high speed	0-1 V		
	68	←	Engine idling – coolant blower motor OFF	0-1 V		
	68	←	Engine idling – coolant blower motor ON – low speed	11-14 V		
Engine coolant blower motor relay – some models	19	⊣▷	Engine idling – coolant blower motor OFF	11-14 V		
	19	⊣▷	Engine idling – coolant blower motor ON – high speed	0-1 V		
	45	←	Engine idling – coolant blower motor OFF	0-1 V		
	45	←	Engine idling – coolant blower motor ON – low speed	11-14 V		
Engine coolant temperature (ECT) sensor	38	←	Ignition ON – coolant temp. 0°C	3,8-3,9 V		
	38	←	Ignition ON – coolant temp. 20°C	3-3,2 V		
	38	←	Ignition ON – coolant temp. 80°C	0,6-0,9 V		
	91	⊣	Ignition ON	0 V		
Evaporative emission (EVAP) canister purge valve	56	⊣▷	Engine idling	11-14 V		
	56	⊣▷	Engine running		10 V/50 ms	Intermittent [20]
Exhaust gas pressure sensor – some models	65	←	Ignition ON	0,5 V		
	65	←	Engine idling	0,6 V		
	65	←	Engine running – 3000 rpm	0,75 V		
	90	⇒	Ignition ON	5 V		
	91	⊣	Ignition ON	0 V		
Exhaust gas recirculation (EGR) solenoid – some models	47	⊣▷	Ignition ON	11-14 V		
	47	⊣▷	Engine running		2 V/5 ms	Intermittent [29]
Fuel pump relay	40	←	Ignition ON	11-14 V briefly then 0 V		
	40	←	Engine idling	11-14 V		
Fuel pump relay – AT – with PATS	54	⊣▷	Ignition ON	0-1 V briefly then 11-14 V		
	54	⊣▷	Engine cranking	0-1 V		
Fuel pump relay – AT – without PATS	80	⊣▷	Ignition ON	0-1 V briefly then 11-14 V		
	80	⊣▷	Engine cranking	0-1 V		

* Suggested settings - Voltage/time per division

Component/circuit description	ECM pin	Signal	Condition	Typical value	Oscilloscope setting*	Wave form
Heated oxygen sensor (HO2S) 2 – bank 2 – Scorpio	61	←	Engine idling – engine hot	0,3-0,6 V	0,2 V/0,5 sec.	76
	91		Ignition ON	0 V		
Heated oxygen sensor (HO2S) 2 – bank 2 – Scorpio – heater control, without PATS	96	⇒	Start engine	11-14 V for 20 seconds		
	96	⇒	Start engine	0 V after 20 seconds		
Heated oxygen sensor (HO2S) 2 – bank 2 – Scorpio – heater control, with PATS	101	⇒	Start engine	11-14 V for 20 seconds		
	101	⇒	Start engine	0 V after 20 seconds		
Heated oxygen sensor (HO2S) 1 – bank 2	87	←	Engine idling – engine hot	0,1-0,9 V	0,2 V/1 sec.	21
	91		Ignition ON	0 V		
Heated oxygen sensor (HO2S) 1 – bank 2 – heater control, without PATS	94	⇒	Start engine	11-14 V for 20 seconds		
	94	⇒	Start engine	0 V after 20 seconds		
Heated oxygen sensor (HO2S) 1 – bank 2 – heater control, with PATS	99	⇒	Start engine	11-14 V for 20 seconds		
	99	⇒	Start engine	0 V after 20 seconds		
Heated oxygen sensor (HO2S) 2 – bank 1 – Scorpio	35	←	Engine idling – engine hot	0,3-0,7 V	0,2 V/0,5 sec.	76
	91		Ignition ON	0 V		
Heated oxygen sensor (HO2S) 2 – bank 1 – Scorpio – heater control, without PATS	95	⇒	Start engine	11-14 V for 20 seconds		
	95	⇒	Start engine	0 V after 20 seconds		
Heated oxygen sensor (HO2S) 2 – bank 1 – Scorpio – heater control, with PATS	100	⇒	Start engine	11-14 V for 20 seconds		
	100	⇒	Start engine	0 V after 20 seconds		
Heated oxygen sensor (HO2S) 1 – bank 1	60	←	Engine idling – engine hot	0,1-0,9 V	0,2 V/1 sec.	21
	91		Ignition ON	0 V		
Heated oxygen sensor (HO2S) 1 – bank 1 – heater control, with PATS	73	⇒	Start engine	11-14 V for 20 seconds		
	73	⇒	Start engine	0 V after 20 seconds		
Heated oxygen sensor (HO2S) 1 – bank 1 – heater control, without PATS	93	⇒	Start engine	11-14 V for 20 seconds		
	93	⇒	Start engine	0 V after 20 seconds		
Heated windscreen relay – if fitted	14	←	Engine idling – heated windscreen OFF	0 V		
	14	←	Engine idling – heated windscreen ON	5 V		
Idle air control (IAC) valve	83	⇒	Engine idling	33%	2 V/5 ms	29
Ignition coil 1 & 5 – Mondeo/Cougar	26	⇒	Engine idling		5 V/1 ms	33
Ignition coil 2 & 6 – Mondeo/Cougar	78	⇒	Engine idling		5 V/1 ms	33
Ignition coil 3 & 4 – Mondeo/Cougar	52	⇒	Engine idling		5 V/1 ms	33
Ignition control module (ICM) – Scorpio	48	←	Engine idling		2 V/10 ms	32
	49	←	Engine idling		5 V/20 ms	4
	50	⇒	Engine idling		2 V/10 ms	32
Injector 1 – with PATS	70	⇒	Ignition ON	11-14 V		
	70	⇒	Engine idling	3,4 ms	10 V/2 ms	35
Injector 1 – without PATS	75	⇒	Ignition ON	11-14 V		
	75	⇒	Engine idling	3,4 ms	10 V/2 ms	35
Injector 2 – with PATS	96	⇒	Ignition ON	11-14 V		
	96	⇒	Engine idling	3,4 ms	10 V/2 ms	35
Injector 2 – without PATS	101	⇒	Ignition ON	11-14 V		
	101	⇒	Engine idling	3,4 ms	10 V/2 ms	35

* Suggested settings - Voltage/time per division

Component/circuit description	ECM pin	Signal	Condition	Typical value	Oscilloscope setting*	Wave form
Injector 3 – with PATS	20	→▷	Ignition ON	11-14 V		
	20	→▷	Engine idling	3,4 ms	10 V/2 ms	〰 35
Injector 3 – without PATS	74	→▷	Ignition ON	11-14 V		
	74	→▷	Engine idling	3,4 ms	10 V/2 ms	〰 35
Injector 4 – with PATS	95	→▷	Ignition ON	11-14 V		
	95	→▷	Engine idling	3,4 ms	10 V/2 ms	〰 35
Injector 4 – without PATS	100	→▷	Ignition ON	11-14 V		
	100	→▷	Engine idling	3,4 ms	10 V/2 ms	〰 35
Injector 5 – with PATS	93	→▷	Ignition ON	11-14 V		
	93	→▷	Engine idling	3,4 ms	10 V/2 ms	〰 35
Injector 5 – without PATS	73	→▷	Ignition ON	11-14 V		
	73	→▷	Engine idling	3,4 ms	10 V/2 ms	〰 35
Injector 6 – with PATS	94	→▷	Ignition ON	11-14 V		
	94	→▷	Engine idling	3,4 ms	10 V/2 ms	〰 35
Injector 6 – without PATS	99	→▷	Ignition ON	11-14 V		
	99	→▷	Engine idling	3,4 ms	10 V/2 ms	〰 35
Instrumentation control module – AT – →07/99	79			☐1		
Instrumentation control module – AT – 08/99→	12			☐1		
Instrumentation control module – Scorpio	86			☐1		
Instrument panel – Mondeo 08/99→	28			☐1		
Intake air temperature (IAT) sensor	39	←	Ignition ON – air temp. 0°C	3,8-3,9 V		
	39	←	Ignition ON – air temp. 20°C	3-3,2 V		
	39	←	Ignition ON – air temp. 60°C	1,2-1,4 V		
	91	⊐—	Ignition ON	0 V		
Intake manifold air control module – Mondeo	8			☐1		
	42			☐1		
	91	⊐—	Ignition ON	0 V		
Intake manifold air control solenoid – Scorpio	44		Engine idling	11-14 V		
	44		Engine idling – accelerate briefly	11-14 V		
Knock sensor (KS) – 08/99→	57	←	Engine idling – full throttle briefly		50 mV/1 ms	〰 38
	32	←	Engine idling – full throttle briefly		50 mV/1 ms	〰 38
Malfunction indicator lamp (MIL) – 12/99→	2	→▷	Ignition ON – MIL ON	0,1 V		
	2	→▷	Engine idling – MIL OFF	11-14 V		
Mass air flow (MAF) sensor	36	⊐—	Ignition ON	0 V		
	88	←	Engine cranking	0,7 V		
	88	←	Engine idling – engine hot	0,9 V		
	88	←	3000 rpm	1,7 V		
	88	←	Engine running – accelerate briefly	3,3 V		
Octane coding plug	91	⊐—	Ignition ON	0 V		
Overdrive selection switch	29	←	Ignition ON – overdrive selected	0 V		
	29	←	Ignition ON – overdrive not selected	11-14 V		
Park/neutral position (PNP) switch	64	←	Ignition ON – AT not in P or N	5 V		
	64	←	Ignition ON – AT in P or N	0 V		
	91	⊐—	Ignition ON	0 V		
Passive anti-theft system (PATS) – Mondeo →02/97	2			☐1		
Passive anti-theft system (PATS) – Mondeo →07/99	17			☐1		
	34			☐1		
	82			☐1		

* Suggested settings - Voltage/time per division

Component/circuit description	ECM pin	Signal	Condition	Typical value	Oscilloscope setting*	Wave form
Passive anti-theft system (PATS) – Mondeo 08/99→	19			1		
	44			1		
	104			1		
Power steering pressure (PSP) switch	31	←	Engine idling – steering wheel not turned	0 V		
	31	←	Engine idling – steering wheel turned	9 V		
	91	⅂—	Ignition ON	0 V		
Starter motor relay – Mondeo/Cougar →07/99	18	⅂▷	Ignition ON	11-14 V		
	18	⅂▷	Engine cranking	0 V		
Spare cable – Cougar 12/99→	18					
	34					
	45					
Starter motor relay – Mondeo/Cougar 08/99→	82	⅂▷	Ignition ON	11-14 V		
	82	⅂▷	Engine cranking	0 V		
Tachometer	48			1		
Throttle position (TP) sensor	89	←	Ignition ON – throttle closed	0,5-1 V		
	89	←	Ignition ON – throttle fully open	4,3-4,8 V		
	90	⇒	Ignition ON	5 V		
	91	⅂—	Ignition ON	0 V		
Transmission fluid temperature sensor	37	←		1		
	91	⅂—	Ignition ON	0 V		
Transmission mode selection switch/instrumentation control module – →07/99	10	←	Engine idling – economy mode selected	11-14 V		
	10	←	Engine idling – sport mode selected	0 V		
Transmission mode selection switch/instrumentation control module – →08/99	23	←	Engine idling – economy mode selected	11-14 V		
	23	←	Engine idling – sport mode selected	0 V		
Trip computer – some models	43			1		
Vehicle speed sensor (VSS) – some models	33	⅂—	Vehicle moving		1 V/5 ms	∿ 42
	58	←	Vehicle moving		1 V/5 ms	∿ 42
Vehicle speed sensor (VSS) – some models	58	←	Ignition ON – vehicle pushed	0 V or 10-14 V switching		
	58	←	Vehicle moving		5 V/50 ms	∿ 43

*Suggested settings - Voltage/time per division

1 Connected pin - no test data available or random digital signal

ECM harness multi-plug

Terminal side

2 3 4 5 6 7 8 9 10 11 12 13 14 15 16 17 18 19 20 21 22
1   23
24 25 26 27 28 29 30 31 32 33 34 35 36 37 38 39 40 41 42 43 44 45

46 47 48 49 50 51 52 53 54 55 56 57 58 59 60 61 62 63 64 65 66 67 68

AD81718

Wire side

22 21 20 19 18 17 16 15 14 13 12 11 10 9 8 7 6 5 4 3 2
23   1
45 44 43 42 41 40 39 38 37 36 35 34 33 32 31 30 29 28 27 26 25 24

68 67 66 65 64 63 62 61 60 59 58 57 56 55 54 53 52 51 50 49 48 47 46

AD42119

Component/circuit description	ECM pin	Signal	Condition	Typical value
Accelerator pedal position (APP) sensor	15	←	Ignition ON – accelerator pedal released	0,4 V
	15	←	Ignition ON – accelerator pedal depressed	3,4 V
	33	⌐	Ignition ON	0 V
	55	⌐	Ignition ON	0 V
	57	⇒	Ignition ON	5 V
	62	←	Ignition ON – accelerator pedal released	8,32 V
	62	←	Ignition ON – accelerator pedal depressed	0,06 V
	65	←	Ignition ON – accelerator pedal released	0,06 V
	65	←	Ignition ON – accelerator pedal depressed	2,75 V
Air conditioning	3			[1]
	28			[1]
	37			[1]
Brake pedal position (BPP) switch	33	⌐	Ignition ON	0 V
Brake pedal position (BPP) switch – →1998	20	←	Ignition ON – brake pedal released	11-14 V
	20	←	Ignition ON – brake pedal depressed	0 V
Brake pedal position (BPP) switch – 1998→	20	←	Ignition ON – brake pedal released	0 V
	20	←	Ignition ON – brake pedal depressed	11-14 V
	44	←	Ignition ON – brake pedal released	0 V
	44	←	Ignition ON – brake pedal depressed	11-14 V
Clutch pedal position (CPP) switch	33	⌐	Ignition ON	0 V
Clutch pedal position (CPP) switch – →1998	17	←	Ignition ON – clutch pedal released	11-14 V
	17	←	Ignition ON – clutch pedal depressed	0 V
Clutch pedal position (CPP) switch – 1998→	17	←	Ignition ON – clutch pedal released	0 V
	17	←	Ignition ON – clutch pedal depressed	11-14 V
Crankshaft position (CKP) sensor	8	←	Engine idling	4,5 V ac
	8	←	Engine idling	5 V/5 ms per division ∿ 6
	33	⌐	Ignition ON	0 V

Component/circuit description	ECM pin	Signal	Condition	Typical value
Cruise control master switch – if fitted	34			1️⃣
	35			1️⃣
	58			1️⃣
	66			1️⃣
Earth	1		Ignition ON	0 V
	24		Ignition ON	0 V
	39		Ignition ON	0 V
	46		Ignition ON	0 V
Engine control relay	23	⬅	Ignition ON	11-14 V
	42	⇉▷	Ignition OFF	11-14 V
	42	⇉▷	Ignition ON	0-1 V
	45	⬅	Ignition ON	11-14 V
	68	⬅	Ignition OFF	0 V
	68	⬅	Ignition ON	11-14 V
Engine coolant heater relay I – if fitted	26	⇉▷		1️⃣
Engine coolant heater relay II – if fitted	6	⇉▷		1️⃣
Engine coolant temperature (ECT) sensor	14	⬅	Ignition ON – coolant temp. 20°C	3,5 V
	14	⬅	Ignition ON – coolant temp. 80°C	1,3 V
	33	⊣–	Ignition ON	0 V
Exhaust gas recirculation (EGR) solenoid	25	⇉▷	Ignition ON	11-14 V
	25	⇉▷	Engine idling	60%
	25	⇉▷	Engine idling	5 V/5 ms per division 〰39
Fuel injection timing solenoid	51	⇉▷	Engine idling	2 V/10 ms per division 〰10
	51	⇉▷	Ignition ON	0 V briefly then 11-14 V
Fuel quantity adjuster	4	⇉▷	Engine idling	2 V/2 ms per division 〰5
	4	⇉▷	Ignition ON	9 V briefly then 11-14 V
	5	⇉▷	Engine idling	2 V/2 ms per division 〰5
	5	⇉▷	Ignition ON	9 V briefly then 11-14 V
	49	⇉▷	Engine idling	2 V/2 ms per division 〰5
	49	⇉▷	Ignition ON	9 V briefly then 11-14 V
Fuel quantity adjuster position sensor	7	⇨	Ignition ON	2,5 V
	29	⬅	Engine idling	2,5 V
	29	⬅	Engine idling	0,5 V/0,1 ms per division 〰8
	52	⬅	Engine idling	2,5 V
	52	⬅	Engine idling	0,5 V/0,1 ms per division 〰8
Fuel shut-off solenoid	53	⇨	Engine idling	11-14 V
Fuel temperature sensor	33	⊣–	Ignition ON	0 V
	63	⬅	Ignition ON – fuel temp. 20°C	2,5 V
Glow plug relay	50	⇉▷	Ignition ON – glow plugs ON	0 V
	50	⇉▷	Ignition ON – glow plugs OFF	11-14 V

Component/circuit description	ECM pin	Signal	Condition	Typical value
Glow plug warning lamp	48	⊐⊳	Ignition ON – lamp ON	0 V
	48	⊐⊳	Ignition ON – lamp OFF	11-14 V
Ignition switch	38	⬅	Ignition ON	11-14 V
Immobilizer control module	61			1
Injector needle lift sensor	11	⊐⊢	Ignition ON	0 V
	12	⬅	Engine idling	0,2 V/2 ms per division 〰〰 7
	12	⬅	Ignition ON	3,5 V
Instrumentation control module	2			1
	9			1
	43			1
Intake air temperature (IAT) sensor	33	⊐⊢	Ignition ON	0 V
	64	⬅	Ignition ON – air temp. 20°C	3,5 V
Mass air flow (MAF) sensor	13	⬅	Engine idling	1,3 V
	13	⬅	Engine idling – accelerate briefly	3,7 V
	13	⬅	Ignition ON	0,3 V
	19	⇨	Ignition ON	4,96 V
	21	⊐⊢	Ignition ON	0 V
Mass air flow (MAF) sensor – →1997	33	⊐⊢	Ignition ON	0 V
Transmission control module (TCM)	18			1
	31			1
	32			1
Turbocharger (TC) wastegate regulating valve	47	⊐⊳	Ignition ON	11-14 V

1 Connected pin - no test data available

Model:	Engine code:	Year:
Galaxy 1,9 TDI	ANU, AUY	1999-02

ECM harness multi-plug

Terminal side

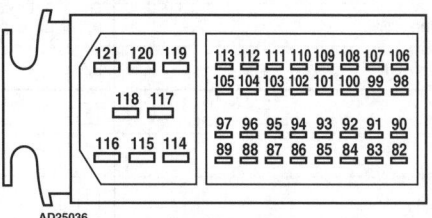
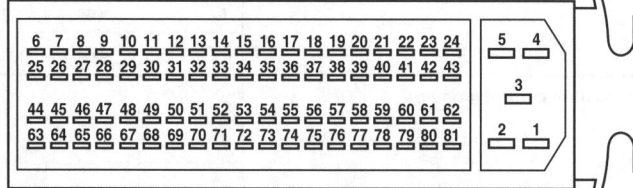

AD25036

Wire side

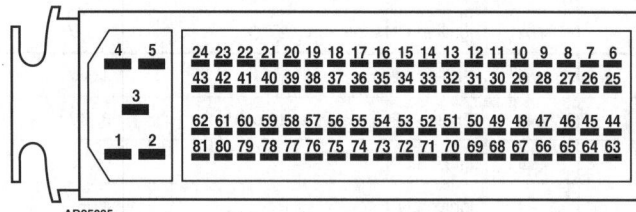
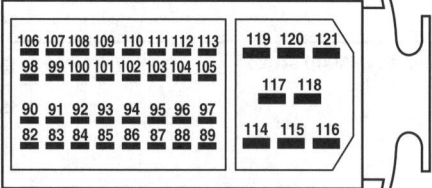

AD25035

Component/circuit description	ECM pin	Signal	Condition	Typical value
AC compressor clutch cut-off relay – with MTC →2000	29	⊐▷	Engine idling – AC OFF	0 V
	29	⊐▷	Engine idling – AC ON – compressor ON	11-14 V
AC compressor control module – 2000→	11			1
AC compressor control module, compressor cut-off signal – with MTC 2000→	29			1
AC control module – with ATC	34	←	Engine idling – AC OFF	0 V
	34	←	Engine idling – AC ON	11-14 V
AC control module, compressor cut-off signal – with ATC →2000	29	⇨		1
AC master switch – with MTC →2000	34	←	Engine idling – AC OFF	0 V
	34	←	Engine idling – AC ON	11-14 V
AC/heater function control panel – with MTC 2000→	34	←	Engine idling – AC OFF	0 V
	34	←	Engine idling – AC ON	11-14 V
Accelerator pedal position (APP) sensor	12	⇨	Ignition ON	5 V
	50	⊐	Ignition ON	0 V
	69	←	Ignition ON – accelerator pedal released	0,4 V
	69	←	Ignition ON – accelerator pedal fully depressed	4,4 V
Accelerator pedal position (APP) switch	51	⊐	Ignition ON	0 V
	70	←	Ignition ON – accelerator pedal released	0,2 V
	70	←	Ignition ON – accelerator pedal depressed	5 V
Alternator, charging signal – 2000→	38	⇨	Ignition ON	2 V/20 ms per division 〰43
Brake pedal position (BPP) switch 1	32	←	Ignition OFF – brake pedal released	0 V
	32	←	Ignition OFF – brake pedal depressed	11-14 V
Brake pedal position (BPP) switch 2	65	←	Ignition ON – brake pedal released	11-14 V
	65	←	Ignition ON – brake pedal depressed	0 V
Camshaft position (CMP) sensor	101	⊐	Ignition ON	0 V
	109	←	Engine idling	2 V/0,5 ms per division 〰58
CAN data bus, high – 2000→	7	◄⇨		1
CAN data bus, low – 2000→	6	◄⇨		1

Autodata

Component/circuit description	ECM pin	Signal	Condition	Typical value
Clutch pedal position (CPP) switch	66	←	Ignition ON – clutch pedal released	11-14 V
	66	←	Ignition ON – clutch pedal depressed	0 V
Crankshaft position (CKP) sensor	102	←	Ignition ON	2,5 V
	102	←	Engine idling	1,9 V ac
	102	←	Engine idling	2 V/1 ms per division 〰〰 25
	102	←	3000 rpm	3,1 V
	110	←	Ignition ON	2,5 V
	110	←	Engine idling	1,9 V ac
	110	←	Engine idling	2 V/1 ms per division – wave form reversed 〰〰 25
	110	←	3000 rpm	3,1 V
Cruise control master switch	14	←	Ignition ON – selector switch set to 'OFF'	0 V
	14	←	Ignition ON – selector switch set to 'ON'	11-14 V
	44	←	Ignition ON – master switch released	0 V
	44	←	Ignition ON – master switch depressed	11-14 V
Cruise control selector switch	14	←	Ignition ON – selector switch set to 'OFF'	0 V
	14	←	Ignition ON – selector switch set to 'ON'	11-14 V
	45	←	Ignition ON – selector switch set to 'ON'	0 V
	45	←	Ignition ON – selector switch set to 'RES'	11-14 V
	46	←	Ignition ON – selector switch set to 'OFF'	0 V
	46	←	Ignition ON – selector switch set to 'ON'	11-14 V
Data link connector (DLC)	6			1
	7			1
Earth	4		Ignition ON	0 V
	5		Ignition ON	0 V
Engine control relay	1	←	Ignition OFF	0 V
	1	←	Ignition ON	11-14 V
	2	←	Ignition OFF	0 V
	2	←	Ignition ON	11-14 V
	18	⊣▷	Ignition OFF	11-14 V
	18	⊣▷	Ignition ON	0-1 V
Engine coolant temperature (ECT) sensor	104	⊣	Ignition ON	0 V
	112	←	Ignition ON – coolant temp. 10°C	4 V
	112	←	Ignition ON – coolant temp. 80°C	1,2 V
Exhaust gas recirculation (EGR) solenoid	61	⊣▷	Ignition ON	11-14 V
	61	⊣▷	Engine idling	5 V/1 ms per division 〰〰 2
Fuel lift pump relay – 2000→	80	⊣▷	Ignition ON	0-1 V briefly then 11-14 V
	80	⊣▷	Engine idling	0-1 V
Fuel temperature sensor	103	⊣	Ignition ON	0 V
	111	←	Ignition ON – fuel temperature 5°C	4,6 V
Glow plug relay	42	⊣▷	Ignition ON – glow plugs ON	0-1 V
	42	⊣▷	Ignition ON – glow plugs OFF	11-14 V
Glow plug warning lamp – →2000	40	⊣▷	Ignition ON – warning lamp ON	0-1 V
	40	⊣▷	Ignition ON – warning lamp OFF	11-14 V
Ignition auxiliary circuits relay – 2000→	88	←	Ignition OFF	0 V
	88	←	Ignition ON	11-14 V
	88	←	Engine cranking	0 V
	88	←	Engine idling	11-14 V
Ignition switch	37	←	Engine cranking	11-14 V
	37	←	Engine idling	11-14 V
	37	←	Ignition OFF	0 V
	37	←	Ignition ON	11-14 V

Component/circuit description	ECM pin	Signal	Condition	Typical value
Immobilizer control module, immobilization/ diagnosis signal	16	⬅⇨		1
Injector 1	114	⇨	Ignition ON	0,3 V
	116	⇨	Ignition ON	0,3 V
	116 (114)	⇨	Engine idling	2,2 ms
	116 (114)	⇨	Engine idling	10 V/0,5 ms per division 〰 57
Injector 2	114	⇨	Ignition ON	0,3 V
	117	⇨	Ignition ON	0,3 V
	117 (114)	⇨	Engine idling	2,2 ms
	117 (114)	⇨	Engine idling	10 V/0,5 ms per division 〰 57
Injector 3	114	⇨	Ignition ON	0,3 V
	118	⇨	Ignition ON	0,3 V
	118 (114)	⇨	Engine idling	2,2 ms
	118 (114)	⇨	Engine idling	10 V/0,5 ms per division 〰 57
Injector 4	114	⇨	Ignition ON	0,3 V
	121	⇨	Ignition ON	0,3 V
	121 (114)	⇨	Engine idling	2,2 ms
	121 (114)	⇨	Engine idling	10 V/0,5 ms per division 〰 57
Instrumentation control module, engine RPM signal – →2000	27	⇨	Engine idling	30 Hz
	27	⇨	Engine idling	5 V/10 ms per division 〰 2
	27	⇨	3000 rpm	100 Hz
Instrumentation control module, fuel consumption signal – some models →2000	28	⇨		1
Instrumentation control module, vehicle speed signal – →2000	20	⬅	Ignition ON – vehicle pushed	0 V or 10 V min. (switching)
Intake air temperature (IAT) sensor	52	⌐	Ignition ON	0 V
	73	⬅	Ignition ON – air temp. 10°C	3 V
Intake manifold air control solenoid	81	⌐⇨	Ignition ON	11-14 V
	81	⌐⇨	Engine idling	11-14 V
	81	⌐⇨	Engine idling – switch ignition OFF	0-1 V for 2,5 secs., 11-14 V for 0,5 secs. then 0 V
Manifold absolute pressure (MAP) sensor, TC system	31	⇨	Ignition ON	5 V
	52	⌐	Ignition ON	0 V
	71	⬅	Ignition ON	1,6 V
	71	⬅	Engine idling	1,7 V
Mass air flow (MAF) sensor	30	⇨	Ignition ON	5 V
	49	⌐	Ignition ON	0 V
	68	⬅	Ignition ON	1 V
	68	⬅	Engine idling	1,5-2,1 V
	68	⬅	3000 rpm	3,2 V
Transmission control module (TCM) – 2000→	20			1
Transmission kick-down switch	51	⌐	Ignition ON	0 V
	63	⬅	Ignition ON – accelerator pedal released	5 V
	63	⬅	Ignition ON – accelerator pedal fully depressed	0 V
Turbocharger (TC) wastegate regulating valve	62	⌐⇨	Ignition ON	11-14 V
	62	⌐⇨	Engine idling	11-14 V
	62	⌐⇨	Engine idling – accelerator pedal briefly fully depressed	0-1 V briefly
	62	⌐⇨	Engine running – valve not operating	11-14 V
	62	⌐⇨	Engine running – valve operating	0-1 V

1 Connected pin - no test data available

ECM harness multi-plug

Terminal side

```
 2  3  4  5  6  7  8  9  10 11 12 13 14 15 16 17 18 19 20 21 22
1                                                               23
 24 25 26 27 28 29 30 31 32 33 34 35 36 37 38 39 40 41 42 43 44 45
 46 47 48 49 50 51 52 53 54 55 56 57 58 59 60 61 62 63 64 65 66 67 68
```
AD81718

Wire side

```
    22 21 20 19 18 17 16 15 14 13 12 11 10 9 8 7 6 5 4 3 2
23                                                            1
    45 44 43 42 41 40 39 38 37 36 35 34 33 32 31 30 29 28 27 26 25 24
    68 67 66 65 64 63 62 61 60 59 58 57 56 55 54 53 52 51 50 49 48 47 46
```
AD42119

Component/circuit description	ECM pin	Signal	Condition	Typical value	Oscilloscope setting*	Wave form
Air conditioning	37			[1]		
	39			[1]		
Automatic transmission	7			[1]		
	11			[1]		
	18			[1]		
Battery	54	←	Ignition OFF	11-14 V		
Camshaft position (CMP) sensor	7		Ignition ON	0 V		
	44	←	Engine idling		5 V/20 ms	[12]
	56		Ignition ON	0 V		
Closed throttle position (CTP) switch	10	←	Ignition ON – throttle closed	0 V		
	10	←	Ignition ON – throttle open	11-14 V		
	33		Ignition ON	0 V		
Crankshaft position (CKP) sensor	7		Ignition ON	0 V		
	56		Ignition ON	0 V		
	67	←	Engine idling		2 V/1 ms	[2]
	68	←	Engine idling		2 V/1 ms	[2]
Earth	1		Ignition ON	0 V		
Engine coolant temperature (ECT) sensor	14	←	Ignition ON – coolant temp. 10°C	2,8 V		
	14	←	Ignition ON – coolant temp. 80°C	0,4 V		
	33		Ignition ON	0 V		
Evaporative emission (EVAP) canister purge valve	31		Engine hot – valve operating		10 V/50 ms	[20]
Exhaust gas recirculation (EGR) solenoid	30			[1]		
Exhaust gas recirculation temperature (EGRT) sensor	15	←		[1]		
	33		Ignition ON	0 V		
Fuel pump relay – 1995-97	6		Engine cranking	0-1 V		
Fuel pump relay – through fuel pump shut-off control module – 1998-01	6		Engine cranking	0-1 V		
Heated oxygen sensor (HO2S)	12		Engine idling – engine cold	0 V		
	20	←	Engine idling – engine hot	0-1 V fluctuating	0,2 V/1 sec.	[21]
	42		Engine idling	0 V		

* Suggested settings - Voltage/time per division

Component/circuit description	ECM pin	Signal	Condition	Typical value	Oscilloscope setting*	Wave form
Heated oxygen sensor (HO2S) – shield wire	56	⌐⌐	Ignition ON	0 V		
Idle speed control (ISC) actuator	27 (53)	⇨	Engine idling		5 V/2 ms	⩘⩘ 28
	53 (27)	⇨	Engine idling		5 V/2 ms	⩘⩘ 28
Idle speed control (ISC) actuator position sensor	33	⌐⌐	Ignition ON	0 V		
	41	⇨	Ignition ON	5 V		
	62	⬅	Engine idling – engine hot	3,7 V		
Ignition amplifier	8	⇨	Engine idling		2 V/10 ms	⩘⩘ 32
	52	⇨	Engine idling		2 V/10 ms	⩘⩘ 32
	60	⇨	Engine idling		2 V/10 ms	⩘⩘ 32
Ignition switch	23	⬅	Ignition OFF	0 V		
	23	⬅	Ignition ON	11-14 V		
Injector 1	24	⌐⊳	Engine idling – engine hot	3,3 ms	10 V/2 ms	⩘⩘ 35
Injector 2	25	⌐⊳	Engine idling – engine hot	3,3 ms	10 V/2 ms	⩘⩘ 35
Injector 3	26	⌐⊳	Engine idling – engine hot	3,3 ms	10 V/2 ms	⩘⩘ 35
Injector 4	2	⌐⊳	Engine idling – engine hot	3,3 ms	10 V/2 ms	⩘⩘ 35
Injector 5	3	⌐⊳	Engine idling – engine hot	3,3 ms	10 V/2 ms	⩘⩘ 35
Injector 6	4	⌐⊳	Engine idling – engine hot	3,3 ms	10 V/2 ms	⩘⩘ 35
Instrument panel	22			1		
	51			1		
Intake air temperature (IAT) sensor	33	⌐⌐	Ignition ON	0 V		
	36	⬅	Ignition ON – air temp. 10°C	2,8 V		
Knock sensor (KS) 1	7	⌐⌐	Ignition ON	0 V		
	33	⌐⌐	Engine idling	0 V		
	34	⬅	Engine idling – accelerate briefly		50 mV/1 ms	⩘⩘ 38
	56	⌐⌐	Ignition ON	0 V		
Knock sensor (KS) 2	7	⌐⌐	Ignition ON	0 V		
	33	⌐⌐	Engine idling	0 V		
	56	⌐⌐	Ignition ON	0 V		
	57	⬅	Engine idling – accelerate briefly		50 mV/1 ms	⩘⩘ 38
Mass air flow (MAF) sensor	16	⌐⌐	Engine idling	0 V		
	17	⬅	Engine idling – engine hot	0,8 V		
	17	⬅	3000 rpm	1,6 V		
Passive anti-theft system (PATS)	43		Engine idling	11-14 V		
Secondary air injection (AIR) pump relay	49	⌐⊳	Engine idling – engine cold	0-1 V		
	49	⌐⊳	Engine idling – engine hot	11-14 V		
Secondary air injection (AIR) solenoid	50	⌐⊳	Engine idling – engine cold	0-1 V		
	50	⌐⊳	Engine idling – engine hot	11-14 V		
Throttle position (TP) sensor	33	⌐⌐	Ignition ON	0 V		
	40	⬅	Ignition ON – throttle closed	3,9 V for 20 seconds		
	40	⬅	Ignition ON – throttle closed	4,3 V after 20 seconds		
	40	⬅	Ignition ON – throttle fully open	0,7 V		
	41	⇨	Ignition ON	5 V		
Vehicle speed sensor (VSS)	65	⬅	Ignition ON – vehicle pushed	0 V or 11-14 V switching		

*Suggested settings - Voltage/time per division

1 Connected pin - no test data available or random digital signal

Model:	Engine code:	Year:
Transit 2,0D Di	ABFA/D3FA/F3FA	2000-06

ECM harness multi-plug

Terminal side

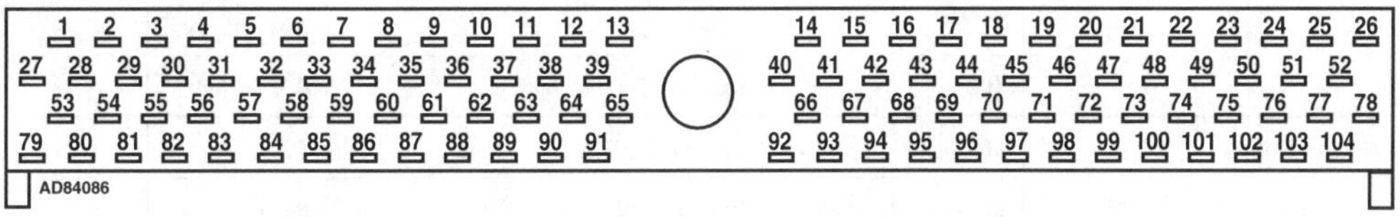

Wire side

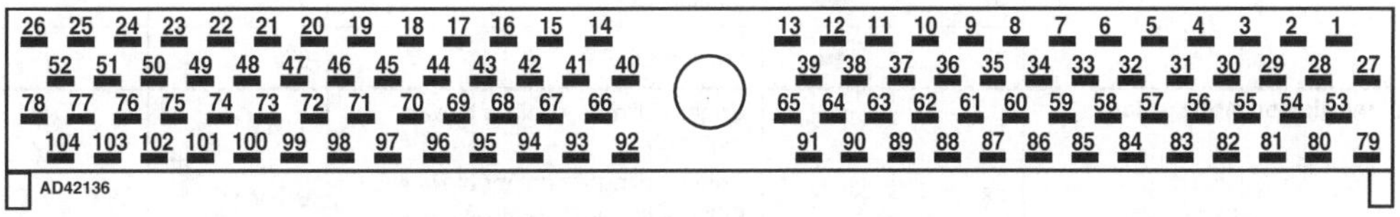

Component/circuit description	ECM pin	Signal	Condition	Typical value	Oscilloscope setting*	Wave form
Accelerator pedal position (APP) sensor	**4**	⬅	Ignition ON – accelerator pedal released	4,11 V		
	4	⬅	Ignition ON – accelerator pedal fully depressed	1,04 V		
	5	⬅	Ignition ON – accelerator pedal released	1,49 V		
	5	⬅	Ignition ON – accelerator pedal fully depressed	3,83 V		
	7	⬅	Ignition ON – accelerator pedal released	0,93 V		
	7	⬅	Ignition ON – accelerator pedal fully depressed	3,27 V		
	9	⇨	Ignition ON	5 V		
	24	⏚	Ignition ON	0 V		
	39	⇨	Ignition ON	5 V		
	51	⏚	Ignition ON	0 V		
	90	⇨	Ignition ON	5 V		
	91	⏚	Ignition ON	0 V		
Battery	**55**	⬅	Ignition OFF	11-14 V		
Brake pedal position (BPP) switch	**92**	⬅	Ignition ON – brake pedal released	0 V		
	92	⬅	Ignition ON – brake pedal depressed	11-14 V		
Crankshaft position (CKP) sensor	**21**	⬅	Engine idling	1,8 V ac		
	21	⬅	Engine idling		2 V/2 ms	40
	21	⬅	Ignition ON	1,53 V		
	22	⬅	Engine idling	1,8 V ac		
	22	⬅	Engine idling		2 V/2 ms	41
	22	⬅	Ignition ON	1,53 V		
Cylinder head temperature (CHT) sensor	**14**	⬅	Ignition ON – coolant temp. 20°C	3 V		
	14	⬅	Ignition ON – coolant temp. 80°C	3,7 V		
	91	⏚	Ignition ON	0 V		

* Suggested settings - Voltage/time per division

Component/circuit description	ECM pin	Signal	Condition	Typical value	Oscilloscope setting*	Wave form
Data link connector (DLC)	13	⬌	Ignition ON	0,1 V		
	15	⬌	Ignition ON	5 V		
	16	⬌	Ignition ON	0 V		
Earth	25		Ignition ON	0 V		
	76		Ignition ON	0 V		
	77		Ignition ON	0 V		
	103		Ignition ON	0 V		
Engine control (EC) relay	96	⊐⇥▷	Ignition OFF	11-14 V		
	96	⊐⇥▷	Ignition ON	0-1 V		
	97	⬅	Ignition ON	11-14 V		
	97	⬅	Ignition OFF	0 V		
Engine coolant blower motor relay →07/03	68	⊐⇥▷	Engine idling – coolant blower motor OFF	11-14 V		
	68	⊐⇥▷	Engine idling – coolant blower motor ON – low speed	0-1 V		
Engine coolant blower motor relay →07/00 with AC	68	⊐⇥▷	Engine idling – coolant blower motor OFF	11-14 V		
	68	⊐⇥▷	Engine idling – coolant blower motor ON – low speed	0-1 V		
Engine coolant blower motor relay 1 – 08/00→ with AC	68	⊐⇥▷	Engine idling – coolant blower motor OFF	11-14 V		
	68	⊐⇥▷	Engine idling – coolant blower motor ON – low speed	0-1 V		
Engine coolant blower motor relay 2 – 08/00→	17	⊐⇥▷	Engine idling – coolant blower motor OFF	11-14 V		
	17	⊐⇥▷	Engine idling – coolant blower motor ON – high speed	0-1 V		
Engine coolant temperature gauge	46			1		
Exhaust gas recirculation (EGR) solenoid	83	⊐⇥▷	Ignition ON	11-14 V		
	83	⊐⇥▷	Engine idling	50% intermittent		
	83	⊐⇥▷	Engine idling		5 V/0,5 ms	〜〜 39
Exhaust gas recirculation (EGR) valve position sensor	35	⬅	Ignition ON	1,2 V		
	35	⬅	Engine idling	1,2 V		
	90	⇨	Ignition ON	5 V		
	91	⊐⇥	Ignition ON	0 V		
Fuel injection pump control module	12	⬌	Ignition OFF	0 V		
	12	⬌	Ignition ON	10,38 V		
	23		Engine idling	0 V		
	49	⬌	Engine idling	2,5 V		
	49	⬌	Ignition ON	2,5 V		
	50	⬌	Engine idling	2,5 V		
	50	⬌	Ignition ON	2,5 V		
	57	⬌	Engine idling	7,3-14 V		
	57	⬌	Engine idling		2 V/20 ms	〜〜 43
	57	⬌	Ignition ON	4,85 V		
Fuel pump relay	70	⊐⇥▷	Engine idling	0-1 V		
	70	⊐⇥▷	Ignition ON	0-1 V		
Glow plug relay	1	⊐⇥▷	Ignition ON – glow plugs ON	0-1 V		
	1	⊐⇥▷	Ignition ON – glow plugs OFF	11-14 V		

* Suggested settings - Voltage/time per division

Component/circuit description	ECM pin	Signal	Condition	Typical value	Oscilloscope setting*	Wave form
Glow plug warning lamp	80	⇥▷	Ignition ON – lamp ON	0-1 V		
	80	⇥▷	Ignition ON – lamp OFF	11-14 V		
Ignition auxiliary circuits relay	6	⇥▷		1		
Ignition switch	8	⬅	Ignition OFF	0 V		
	8	⬅	Ignition ON	11-14 V		
Instrument panel	31			1		
Intake air temperature (IAT) sensor	3			1		
	90			1		
Passive anti-theft system (PATS)	19	⬅	Ignition ON	10,35 V		
	42		Engine idling	11-14 V		
	53			1		
Service indicator	2	⇥▷	Engine running – lamp ON	0-1 V		
	2	⇥▷	Engine running – lamp OFF	11-14 V		
Starter motor relay	27	⇥▷		1		
Tachometer	18			1		
Turbocharger (TC) boost pressure sensor	34			1		
	91			1		
Vehicle speed sensor (VSS)	58	⬅	Ignition ON	0 V		
	58	⬅	Ignition ON – vehicle pushed		0,2 V/20 ms	⋀⋁⋀ 28
	91	⇥⎯	Ignition ON	0 V		
Vehicle speedometer	94			1		

*Suggested settings - Voltage/time per division

1 Connected pin - no test data available

Model:	Engine code:	Year:
Transit 2,0 TDCi	FIFA	2000-07/03

ECM harness multi-plug

Terminal side

```
 1  2  3  4  5  6  7  8  9 10 11 12 13          14 15 16 17 18 19 20 21 22 23 24 25 26
27 28 29 30 31 32 33 34 35 36 37 38 39          40 41 42 43 44 45 46 47 48 49 50 51 52
53 54 55 56 57 58 59 60 61 62 63 64 65          66 67 68 69 70 71 72 73 74 75 76 77 78
79 80 81 82 83 84 85 86 87 88 89 90 91          92 93 94 95 96 97 98 99 100 101 102 103 104
AD84086
```

Wire side

```
26 25 24 23 22 21 20 19 18 17 16 15 14          13 12 11 10  9  8  7  6  5  4  3  2  1
52 51 50 49 48 47 46 45 44 43 42 41 40          39 38 37 36 35 34 33 32 31 30 29 28 27
78 77 76 75 74 73 72 71 70 69 68 67 66          65 64 63 62 61 60 59 58 57 56 55 54 53
104 103 102 101 100 99 98 97 96 95 94 93 92      91 90 89 88 87 86 85 84 83 82 81 80 79
AD42136
```

Component/circuit description	ECM pin	Signal	Condition	Typical value	Oscilloscope setting*	Wave form
AC refrigerant low pressure switch – through AC refrigerant dual pressure switch	41	⇒	Ignition ON	11-14 V		
	41	⇒	Engine running – AC ON, AC compressor ON	11-14 V		
	41	⇒	Engine running – AC ON, AC compressor OFF	0 V		
Accelerator pedal position (APP) sensor	4	←	Ignition ON – accelerator pedal released	4,2 V		
	4	←	Ignition ON – accelerator pedal depressed	0,9 V		
	5	←	Ignition ON – accelerator pedal released	1,4 V		
	5	←	Ignition ON – accelerator pedal depressed	3,9 V		
	7	←	Ignition ON – accelerator pedal released	0,9 V		
	7	←	Ignition ON – accelerator pedal depressed	3,4 V		
	9	⇒	Ignition ON	5 V		
	24	⊣⊢	Ignition ON	0 V		
	39	⇒	Ignition ON	5 V		
	51	⊣⊢	Ignition ON	0 V		
	90	⇒	Ignition ON	5 V		
	91	⊣⊢	Ignition ON	0 V		
Alarm system warning lamp	42	⇒	Ignition OFF	2-11 V switching		
	42	⇒	Ignition ON	11-14 V		
Battery	55	←	Ignition OFF	11-14 V		
Brake pedal position (BPP) switch 1	92	←	Ignition ON – brake pedal released	0 V		
	92	←	Ignition ON – brake pedal depressed	11-14 V		
Brake pedal position (BPP) switch 2 – Durashift	59	←	Ignition ON – brake pedal released	0 V		
	59	←	Ignition ON – brake pedal depressed	11-14 V		
CAN data bus, high	50	⟷		1		
CAN data bus, low	49	⟷		1		

* Suggested settings - Voltage/time per division

Component/circuit description	ECM pin	Signal	Condition	Typical value	Oscilloscope setting*	Wave form
Cylinder head temperature (CHT) sensor (dual range)	14	←	Ignition ON – coolant temp. 0°C	4,1 V		
	14	←	Ignition ON – coolant temp. 20°C	3,2 V		
	14	←	Ignition ON – coolant temp. 60°C	1,3 V		
	14	←	Ignition ON – coolant temp. 95°C	0,46 V or 3,5 V		
	14	←	Ignition ON – coolant temp. 110°C	3 V		
	91	⊣⊢	Ignition ON	0 V		
Data link connector (DLC)	13	⇄	Ignition ON	0 V		
	15	⇄	Ignition ON	5 V		
	16	⇄	Ignition ON	0 V		
Earth	25		Ignition ON	0 V		
	76		Ignition ON	0 V		
	77		Ignition ON	0 V		
	103		Ignition ON	0 V		
Engine control (EC) relay	96	⊣→	Ignition OFF	11-14 V		
	96	⊣→	Ignition ON	0-1 V		
	97	←	Ignition ON	11-14 V		
	97	←	Ignition OFF	0-1 V		
Engine coolant blower motor relay 1 – with AC	68	⊣→	Engine running – coolant blower motors OFF	11-14 V		
	68	⊣→	Engine running – coolant blower motors ON, 1st speed	0-1 V		
Engine coolant blower motor relay 2	17	⊣→	Engine running – coolant blower motors OFF	11-14 V		
	17	⊣→	Engine running – coolant blower motors ON, 2nd speed	0-1 V		
Exhaust gas recirculation (EGR) solenoid	83	⊣→	Ignition ON	11-14 V		
	83	⊣→	Engine idling		5 V/5 ms	〜〜 39
Fuel 'low' warning lamp	31	⊣→	Ignition ON – warning lamp ON	0-1 V		
	31	⊣→	Ignition ON – warning lamp OFF	11-14 V		
Glow plug relay	1	⊣→	Ignition ON – glow plugs OFF	11-14 V		
	1	⊣→	Ignition ON – glow plugs ON	0-1 V		
Glow plug warning lamp	80	⊣→	Ignition ON – warning lamp ON	0-1 V		
	80	⊣→	Ignition ON – warning lamp OFF	11-14 V		
Ignition switch	8	←	Ignition OFF	0 V		
	8	←	Ignition ON	11-14 V		
Immobilizer control module (PATS)	19	⇄	Ignition OFF	0 V		
	19	⇄	Ignition ON	11-14 V		
	53	⇄	Ignition OFF	0 V		
	53	⇄	Ignition ON	11-14 V		
Injector control module – engine RPM signal	57	←	Engine idling		2 V/2 ms	〜〜 65
Injector relay	70	⊣→	Ignition OFF	0-1 V		
	70	⊣→	Ignition ON	0-1 V		
Instrument panel – tachometer signal	18	→		[1]		
Instrument panel – temperature gauge	46	→		[1]		
Instrument panel – vehicle speedometer	94	→		[1]		

★ Suggested settings - Voltage/time per division

Component/circuit description	ECM pin	Signal	Condition	Typical value	Oscilloscope setting*	Wave form
Intake air temperature (IAT) sensor	3	←	Ignition ON – air temp. 20°C	3,2 V		
Manifold absolute pressure (MAP) sensor	34	←	Ignition ON	1,48 V		
	34	←	Engine idling	1,54 V		
	34	←	Engine idling – accelerate briefly	2,75 V		
	90	⇨	Ignition ON	5 V		
	91	⊣⊢	Ignition ON	0 V		
Mass air flow (MAF) sensor	36	⊣⊢	Ignition ON	0 V		
	88	←	Ignition ON	0,6 V		
	88	←	Engine idling	1,7 V		
	88	←	3000 rpm	3,4 V		
Service indicator	2	⊣⊢⇨	Ignition ON – service indicator ON	0-1 V		
	2	⊣⊢⇨	Ignition ON – service indicator OFF	11-14 V		
Spare cable, fuse box/relay plate	44			1		
	66			1		
Starter motor relay	27	⊣⊢⇨	Engine cranking	0-1 V		
Transmission control module (TCM) – Durashift – tachometer signal	18	⇨		1		
Turbocharger (TC) wastegate regulating valve	52	⊣⊢⇨	Ignition ON	11-14 V		
	52	⊣⊢⇨	Engine idling		2 V/2 ms	64
Vehicle speed sensor (VSS)	58	←	Ignition ON – vehicle pushed		0,2 V/20 ms	28
	91	⊣⊢	Ignition ON	0 V		
Wide open throttle (WOT) relay	69	⊣⊢⇨	Engine running – AC compressor OFF	11-14 V		
	69	⊣⊢⇨	Engine running – AC compressor ON	0-1 V		

*Suggested settings - Voltage/time per division

1 Connected pin - no test data available or random digital signal

Injector control module harness multi-plug

Terminal side – A – Black , B – Brown, C – Grey

A

h1	g1	f1	e1	d1	c1	b1	a1
h2	g2	f2	e2	d2	c2	b2	a2
h3	g3	f3	e3	d3	c3	b3	a3
h4	g4	f4	e4	d4	c4	b4	a4

B

m1	l1	k1	j1	h1	g1	f1	e1	d1	c1	b1	a1
m2	l2	k2	j2	h2	g2	f2	e2	d2	c2	b2	a2
m3	l3	k3	j3	h3	g3	f3	e3	d3	c3	b3	a3
m4	l4	k4	j4	h4	g4	f4	e4	d4	c4	b4	a4

C

a4	b4	c4	d4	e4	f4	g4	h4
a3	b3	c3	d3	e3	f3	g3	h3
a2	b2	c2	d2	e2	f2	g2	h2
a1	b1	c1	d1	e1	f1	g1	h1

AD105372

Wire side – A – Black , B – Brown, C – Grey

C

h4	g4	f4	e4	d4	c4	b4	a4
h3	g3	f3	e3	d3	c3	b3	a3
h2	g2	f2	e2	d2	c2	b2	a2
h1	g1	f1	e1	d1	c1	b1	a1

B

a1	b1	c1	d1	e1	f1	g1	h1	j1	k1	l1	m1
a2	b2	c2	d2	e2	f2	g2	h2	j2	k2	l2	m2
a3	b3	c3	d3	e3	f3	g3	h3	j3	k3	l3	m3
a4	b4	c4	d4	e4	f4	g4	h4	j4	k4	l4	m4

A

a1	b1	c1	d1	e1	f1	g1	h1
a2	b2	c2	d2	e2	f2	g2	h2
a3	b3	c3	d3	e3	f3	g3	h3
a4	b4	c4	d4	e4	f4	g4	h4

AD105371

Component/circuit description	ECM pin	Signal	Condition	Typical value	Oscilloscope setting*	Wave form
Camshaft position (CMP) sensor	Be1	⇒	Ignition ON	5 V		
	Be2	⬅	Ignition ON	0 V or 5 V		
	Be2	⬅	Engine idling		2 V/0,1 s	〰 3
	Be3	⌐	Ignition ON	0 V		
CAN data bus – high	Ca4	⬌		1		
CAN data bus – low	Ca3	⬌		1		
Crankshaft position (CKP) sensor	Bf2	⇒	Ignition ON	0 V		
	Bf2	⇒	Engine idling	8,8 V ac	5 V/2 ms	〰 1
	Bf3	⌐	Ignition ON	0 V		
Earth	Ag4		Ignition ON	0 V		
	Ah4		Ignition ON	0 V		
	Cg1		Ignition ON	0 V		
	Ch1		Ignition ON	0 V		
Engine control module (ECM)	Bm2	⬅	Ignition ON	11-14 V		
Fuel pressure regulator control solenoid	Bm4	⌐⊳	Ignition ON		5 V/1 ms	〰 3
	Bm4	⌐⊳	Engine idling		5 V/2 ms	〰 39
	Bm4	⌐⊳	3000 rpm		2 V/0,5 ms	〰 37
Fuel rail pressure (FRP) sensor	Bd1	⇒	Ignition ON	5 V		
	Bd2	⬅	Ignition ON	0,5 V		
	Bd2	⬅	Engine idling	1 V		
	Bd2	⬅	3000 rpm	1,9 V		
	Bd3	⌐	Ignition ON	0 V		

* Suggested settings - Voltage/time per division

Component/circuit description	ECM pin	Signal	Condition	Typical value	Oscilloscope setting*	Wave form
Fuel temperature sensor	**Bg2**	⬅	Ignition ON – fuel temp. 20°C	3,2 V		
	Bg2	⬅	Ignition ON – fuel temp. 40°C	2,2 V		
	Bg2	⬅	Ignition ON – fuel temp. 55°C	1,6 V		
	Bg3	⏚	Ignition ON	0 V		
Injector 1	**Ba4 (Bb4)**	⇨	Engine idling	0,5 ms pilot + 0,5 ms main	5 V/1 ms	63
	Bb4 (Ba4)	⇨	Engine idling	0,5 ms pilot + 0,5 ms main	5 V/1 ms	63
Injector 2	**Bc4 (Bd4)**	⇨	Engine idling	0,5 ms pilot + 0,5 ms main	5 V/1 ms	63
	Bd4 (Bc4)	⇨	Engine idling	0,5 ms pilot + 0,5 ms main	5 V/1 ms	63
Injector 3	**Be4 (Bf4)**	⇨	Engine idling	0,5 ms pilot + 0,5 ms main	5 V/1 ms	63
	Bf4 (Be4)	⇨	Engine idling	0,5 ms pilot + 0,5 ms main	5 V/1 ms	63
Injector 4	**Bg4 (Bh4)**	⇨	Engine idling	0,5 ms pilot + 0,5 ms main	5 V/1 ms	63
	Bh4 (Bg4)	⇨	Engine idling	0,5 ms pilot + 0,5 ms main	5 V/1 ms	63
Injector relay	**Ag1**	⬅	Ignition OFF	0 V		
	Ag1	⬅	Ignition ON	11-14 V		
	Cg2	⬅	Ignition OFF	0 V		
	Cg2	⬅	Ignition ON	11-14 V		
	Ch2	⬅	Ignition OFF	0 V		
	Ch2	⬅	Ignition ON	11-14 V		
Knock sensor (KS)	**Bf1**	⏚	Ignition ON	0 V		
	Bg1	⬅	Ignition ON	0 V		
	Bg1	⬅	3000 rpm		50 mV/1 ms	62
Knock sensor (KS) – screened lead	**Bk1**	⏚	Ignition ON	0 V		

*Suggested settings - Voltage/time per division

[1] Connected pin - no test data available or random digital signal

Model:	Engine code:	Year:
Transit 2,0 TDCi	FIFA	08/03-06
Transit 2,4 TDCi	FXFA/H9FA	2003-06

ECM harness multi-plug

Terminal side

Wire side

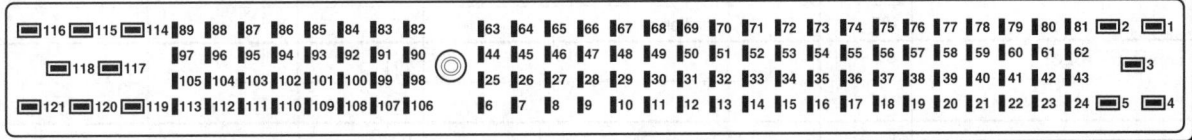

AD29502

AD29501

Component/circuit description	ECM pin	Signal	Condition	Typical value	Oscilloscope setting*	Wave form
AC refrigerant high pressure switch	76	←	Ignition ON	11-14 V		
	76	←	Engine running – AC ON, refrigerant pressure low	11-14 V		
	76	←	Engine running – AC ON, refrigerant pressure high	0 V		
AC refrigerant low pressure switch – through AC refrigerant high pressure switch	19	←	Ignition ON	11-14 V		
	19	⇒	Engine running – AC ON, AC compressor ON	11-14 V		
	19	⇒	Engine running – AC ON, AC compressor OFF	0 V		
Accelerator pedal position (APP) sensor	14	⌐	Ignition ON	0 V		
	32	←	Ignition ON – accelerator pedal released	1,46 V		
	32	←	Ignition ON – accelerator pedal fully depressed	3,9 V		
	33	⇒	Ignition ON	5 V		
	50	←	Ignition ON – accelerator pedal released	0,89 V		
	50	←	Ignition ON – accelerator pedal fully depressed	3,36 V		
	51	⇒	Ignition ON	5 V		
	53	⌐	Ignition ON	0 V		
	70	⌐	Ignition ON	0 V		
	71	←	Ignition ON – accelerator pedal released	4,23 V		
	71	←	Ignition ON – accelerator pedal fully depressed	0,88 V		
	72	⇒	Ignition ON	5 V		
Alarm system warning lamp	16	⇒	Engine running	11-14 V		
Brake pedal position (BPP) switch 1	58	←	Ignition ON – brake pedal released	0 V		
	58	←	Ignition ON – brake pedal depressed	11-14 V		
Brake pedal position (BPP) switch 2	59	←	Ignition ON – brake pedal released	11-14 V		
	59	←	Ignition ON – brake pedal depressed	0 V		

* Suggested settings - Voltage/time per division

Component/circuit description	ECM pin	Signal	Condition	Typical value	Oscilloscope setting★	Wave form
Camshaft position (CMP) sensor	103	←	Ignition ON	0 V or 5 V		
	103	←	Engine idling		2 V/0,1 s	[waveform] 3
	104	⊣	Ignition ON	0 V		
Camshaft position (CMP) sensor – 2,4	111	⇨	Ignition ON	5 V		
Clutch pedal position (CPP) switch	38	←	Ignition ON – clutch pedal released	0 V		
	38	←	Ignition ON – clutch pedal depressed	11-14 V		
Crankshaft position (CKP) sensor	82	⊣	Ignition ON	0 V		
	90	←	Ignition ON	0 V		
	90	←	Engine idling	6 V ac	5 V/2 ms	[waveform] 1
Cylinder head temperature (CHT) sensor (dual range)	101	←	Ignition ON – coolant temp. 0°C	4,1 V		
	101	←	Ignition ON – coolant temp. 20°C	3,2 V		
	101	←	Ignition ON – coolant temp. 60°C	1,3 V		
	101	←	Ignition ON – coolant temp. 95°C	0,46 V		
	101	←	Ignition ON – coolant temp. 110°C	3 V		
	102	⊣	Ignition ON	0 V		
Data link connector (DLC)	55			[1]		
	74			[1]		
Earth	1		Ignition ON	0 V		
	2		Ignition ON	0 V		
	28		Ignition ON	0 V		
	66		Ignition ON	0 V		
	88		Ignition ON	0 V		
Engine control (EC) relay	3	←	Ignition OFF	0 V		
	3	←	Ignition ON	11-14 V		
	4	←	Ignition OFF	0 V		
	4	←	Ignition ON	11-14 V		
	5	←	Ignition OFF	0 V		
	5	←	Ignition ON	11-14 V		
	9	⊣▷	Ignition OFF	11-14 V		
	9	⊣▷	Ignition ON	0-1 V		
Engine coolant blower motor relay 1	80	⊣▷	Ignition ON	11-14 V		
	80	⊣▷	Engine running – coolant blower motors OFF	11-14 V		
	80	⊣▷	Engine running – coolant blower motors ON, 1st speed	0-1 V		
Engine coolant blower motor relay 2	81	⊣▷	Ignition ON	11-14 V		
	81	⊣▷	Engine running – coolant blower motors OFF	11-14 V		
	81	⊣▷	Engine running – coolant blower motors ON, 2nd speed	0-1 V		
Exhaust gas recirculation (EGR) solenoid	96	⊣▷	Ignition ON	11-14 V		
	96	⊣▷	Engine idling		5 V/0,1 ms	[waveform] 39
Fuel pressure control solenoid	87	⊣▷	Ignition ON		5 V/1 ms	[waveform] 3
	87	⊣▷	Engine idling		5 V/2 ms	[waveform] 39
	87	⊣▷	3000 rpm		2 V/0,5 ms	[waveform] 37
Fuel rail pressure (FRP) sensor	6	⇨	Ignition ON	5 V		
	25	←	Ignition ON	0,5 V		
	25	←	Engine idling	1 V		
	25	←	3000 rpm	2 V		
	26	⊣	Ignition ON	0 V		
Fuel temperature sensor	109	←	Ignition ON – fuel temp. 20°C	3 V		
	109	←	Ignition ON – fuel temp. 40°C	2,2 V		
	110	⊣	Ignition ON	0 V		

★ Suggested settings - Voltage/time per division

Component/circuit description	ECM pin	Signal	Condition	Typical value	Oscilloscope setting*	Wave form
Glow plug relay	20	⊐⊳	Ignition ON – glow plugs OFF	11-14 V		
	20	⊐⊳	Ignition ON – glow plugs ON	0-1 V		
Ignition auxiliary circuits relay	23	⊐⊳	Ignition ON	11-14 V		
Ignition switch	37	⟵	Ignition OFF	0 V		
	37	⟵	Ignition ON	11-14 V		
Immobilizer control module (PATS)	15	⟷		[1]		
	34	⟷		[1]		
Injector 1	114	⊐⊳	Ignition ON	5,3 V		
	114 (117)	⊐⊳	Engine idling	0,3 ms pilot + 0,4 ms main	5 V/0,5 ms	〰63
Injector 2	120	⊐⊳	Ignition ON	5,3 V		
	120 (118)	⊐⊳	Engine idling	0,3 ms pilot + 0,4 ms main	5 V/0,5 ms	〰63
Injector 3	121	⊐⊳	Ignition ON	5,3 V		
	121 (118)	⊐⊳	Engine idling	0,3 ms pilot + 0,4 ms main	5 V/0,5 ms	〰63
Injector 4	115	⊐⊳	Ignition ON	5,3 V		
	115 (117)	⊐⊳	Engine idling	0,3 ms pilot + 0,4 ms main	5 V/0,5 ms	〰63
Injectors 1 & 4	117	⟹	Ignition ON	5,3 V		
Injectors 2 & 3	118	⟹	Ignition ON	5,3 V		
Intake air temperature (IAT) sensor	100	⊐⊢	Ignition ON	0 V		
	107	⟵	Ignition ON – air temp. 20°C	3,2 V		
Knock sensor (KS)	45	⟵	Ignition ON	0 V		
	45	⟵	3000 rpm		0,1 V/1 ms	〰62
	46	⊐⊢	Ignition ON	0 V		
Manifold absolute pressure (MAP) sensor	99	⟵	Ignition ON	1,5 V		
	99	⟵	Engine idling	1,5 V		
	99	⟵	Engine idling – accelerate briefly	3,9 V		
	100	⊐⊢	Ignition ON	0 V		
	108	⟹	Ignition ON	5 V		
Mass air flow (MAF) sensor	83	⟵	Ignition ON	0,05 V		
	83	⟵	Engine idling	1,7 V		
	83	⟵	3000 rpm	3,4 V		
	84	⊐⊢	Ignition ON	0 V		
Reverse gear position switch	18	⟵	Ignition ON – gear lever in neutral	0 V		
	18	⟵	Ignition ON – gear lever in reverse	11-14 V		
Starter motor relay	21	⊐⊳	Engine cranking	0-1 V		
Transmission control module (TCM)/ clutch control module	18			[1]		
	49			[1]		
	50			[1]		
Turbocharger (TC) wastegate regulating valve	95	⊐⊳	Ignition ON	11-14 V		
	95	⊐⊳	Engine idling		2 V/2 ms	〰64
Vehicle speed sensor (VSS)	17	⟵	Ignition ON – vehicle pushed	0-11 V switching		
	75	⊐⊢	Ignition ON	0 V		
Wide open throttle (WOT) relay	79	⊐⊳	Ignition ON	11-14 V		
	79	⊐⊳	Engine running – AC compressor OFF	11-14 V		
	79	⊐⊳	Engine running – AC compressor ON	0-1 V		

*Suggested settings - Voltage/time per division

[1] Connected pin - no test data available or random digital signal

HONDA

Honda PGM-FI

Model:	Engine code:	Year:
Civic 1,4	D14A2	1996-99
Civic 1,6 VTEC	D16Y2	1996-98
Civic 1,6	D16Y3	1996-99

ECM harness multi-plug

Terminal side

Wire side

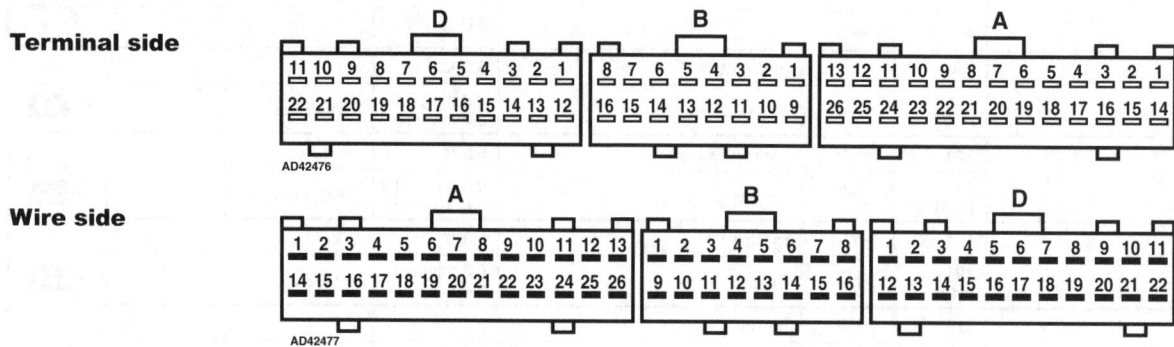

Component/circuit description	ECM pin	Signal	Condition	Typical value	Oscilloscope setting*	Wave form
AC compressor clutch relay – if fitted	A8	⇥▷	Ignition ON – AC OFF	11-14 V		
	A8	⇥▷	Ignition ON – AC ON	0 V		
AC master switch – if fitted	B3	⬅	Ignition ON – AC OFF	11-14 V		
	B3	⬅	Ignition ON – AC ON	0 V		
Alternator	D5	⬅	Engine idling	0-5 V		
Battery	D1	⬅	Ignition OFF	11-14 V		
Camshaft position (CMP) actuator – VTEC	A15	⇨	Engine idling	0 V		
	A15	⇨	Engine idling – full throttle briefly	11-14 V		
Camshaft position (CMP) sensor	B6	⬅	Engine cranking	0,2 V ac		
	B6	⬅	Engine idling	0,7 V ac	5 V/20 ms	〰 11
	B14	⌐	Engine cranking	0 V		
	B14	⌐	Engine idling	0 V		
Crankshaft position (CKP) sensor	B7	⬅	Engine cranking	0,4 V ac		
	B7	⬅	Engine idling	1,5 V ac	2 V/20 ms	〰 1
	B15	⌐	Engine cranking	0 V		
	B15	⌐	Engine idling	0 V		
Data link connector (DLC)	D4	⇨	Ignition ON	5 V		
Earth	A12		Ignition ON	0 V		
	A25		Ignition ON	0 V		
	A26		Ignition ON	0 V		
	B9		Ignition ON	0 V		
Engine coolant temperature (ECT) sensor	D7	⬅	Ignition ON – 20°C	3,3 V		
	D7	⬅	Ignition ON – 80°C	0,6 V		
	D22	⌐	Ignition ON	0 V		
Engine diagnostic link	D13	⇨		①		
Engine speed (RPM) sensor	B8	⬅	Engine cranking	1 V ac		
	B8	⬅	Engine idling	2,8 V ac	2 V/5 ms	〰 17
	B16	⌐	Engine cranking	0 V		
	B16	⌐	Engine idling	0 V		
Evaporative emission (EVAP) cut-off valve	A23	⇥▷	Engine running – coolant temp. 75°C max.	11-14 V		
	A23	⇥▷	Engine running – coolant temp. 75°C min.	0 V		

* Suggested settings - Voltage/time per division

Component/circuit description	ECM pin	Signal	Condition	Typical value	Oscilloscope setting*	Wave form
Heated oxygen sensor (HO2S)	A16	⊣▷	Engine idling	0-1 V		
	A16	⊣▷	Ignition ON	11-14 V		
	D18	◀	Engine running – engine hot	0,1-0,9 V fluctuating		
	D22	⊣—	Ignition ON	0 V		
Idle air control (IAC) valve	A5	⊣▷	Ignition ON	11-14 V		
	A5	⊣▷	Engine idling		5 V/5 ms	〜〜 24
Ignition amplifier	A11	⇨	Ignition ON	10 V		
	A11	⇨	Engine cranking	10 Hz		
	A11	⇨	Engine idling	25 Hz	5 V/5 ms	〜〜 32
	A11	⇨	3000 rpm	100 Hz		
Ignition switch	B5	◀	Engine cranking	9 V		
Immobilizer control module – if fitted	D2	◀		1		
Injector 1	A1	⊣▷	Ignition ON	11-14 V		
	A1	⊣▷	Engine idling	2 ms	10 V/2 ms	〜〜 35
Injector 2	A2	⊣▷	Ignition ON	11-14 V		
	A2	⊣▷	Engine idling	2 ms	10 V/2 ms	〜〜 35
Injector 3	A3	⊣▷	Ignition ON	11-14 V		
	A3	⊣▷	Engine idling	2 ms	10 V/2 ms	〜〜 35
Injector 4	A14	⊣▷	Ignition ON	11-14 V		
	A14	⊣▷	Engine idling	2 ms	10 V/2 ms	〜〜 35
Intake air temperature (IAT) sensor	D8	◀	Ignition ON – 15°C	3,5 V		
	D22	⊣—	Ignition ON	0 V		
Malfunction indicator lamp (MIL)	A7	⊣▷	Ignition ON – MIL ON	0-1 V		
	A7	⊣▷	Ignition ON – MIL OFF	11-14 V		
Manifold absolute pressure (MAP) sensor	D9	◀	Ignition ON	3 V		
	D9	◀	Engine idling	0,8-1,5 V		
	D9	◀	Engine idling – full throttle briefly	2,8 V		
	D10	⇨	Ignition ON	5 V		
	D11	⊣▷	Ignition ON	0 V		
Relay module	A4	⊣▷	Ignition ON	0-1 V briefly then 11-14 V		
	A4	⊣▷	Engine idling	0-1 V		
	A13	◀	Ignition OFF	0 V		
	A13	◀	Ignition ON	11-14 V		
	B1	◀	Ignition OFF	0 V		
	B1	◀	Ignition ON	11-14 V		
Throttle position (TP) sensor	D6	◀	Ignition ON – throttle closed	0,5 V		
	D6	◀	Ignition ON – throttle fully open	4,5 V		
	D21	⇨	Ignition ON	5 V		
	D22	⊣—	Ignition ON	0 V		
Transmission lockup control valve A – AT	A10	⇨		1		
Transmission lockup control valve B – AT	A9	⇨		1		
Transmission range (TR) switch – AT	B2	⊣▷	Ignition ON – AT in D3	0-1 V		
	B2	⊣▷	Ignition ON – AT not in D3	11-14 V		
	B4	⊣▷	Ignition ON – AT in P or N	0-1 V		
	B4	⊣▷	Ignition ON – AT not in P or N	11-14 V		
	B10	⊣▷	Ignition ON – AT in D4	0-1 V		
	B10	⊣▷	Ignition ON – AT not in D4	11-14 V		
Vehicle speed sensor (VSS)	B13	◀	Ignition ON – vehicle pushed	0-5 V fluctuating		

*Suggested settings - Voltage/time per division

1 Connected pin - no test data available or random digital signal

HONDA

Honda PGM-FI

Model:	Engine code:	Year:
Civic 1,4	D14A3	1996-99
Civic 1,4	D14A4	1996-99

ECM harness multi-plug

Terminal side

D

11	10	9	8	7	6	5	4	3	2	1
22	21	20	19	18	17	16	15	14	13	12

AD42282

A

13	12	11	10	9	8	7	6	5	4	3	2	1
26	25	24	23	22	21	20	19	18	17	16	15	14

Wire side

A

1	2	3	4	5	6	7	8	9	10	11	12	13
14	15	16	17	18	19	20	21	22	23	24	25	26

AD42283

D

1	2	3	4	5	6	7	8	9	10	11
12	13	14	15	16	17	18	19	20	21	22

Component/circuit description	ECM pin	Signal	Condition	Typical value	Oscilloscope setting★	Wave form
AC compressor clutch relay – if fitted	A20	→▷	AC compressor OFF	11-14 V		
	A20	→▷	AC compressor ON	0-1 V		
AC refrigerant pressure switch	A23	→▷	AC OFF	11-14 V		
	A23	→▷	AC ON	0-1 V		
Alternator	D18	←	Engine running – engine hot	0-14 V varies with engine load		
Battery	D1	←	Ignition OFF	11-14 V		
Brake pedal position (BPP) switch	A16	←	Brake pedal released	0 V		
	A16	←	Brake pedal depressed	11-14 V		
Crankshaft position (CKP) sensor	D4	←	Engine idling		2 V/20 ms	〰 18
Data link connector (DLC)	A24	⟷	Ignition ON	5 V		
Earth	A14		Ignition ON	0 V		
	A15		Ignition ON	0 V		
	A25		Ignition ON	0 V		
	A26		Ignition ON	0 V		
Engine coolant temperature (ECT) sensor	D9	←	Ignition ON – 20°C	3,3 V		
	D9	←	Ignition ON – 80°C	0,6 V		
	D21	⅂	Ignition ON	0 V		
Engine diagnostic link	D13	←		1		
Evaporative emission (EVAP) cut-off valve	A5	→▷	Engine running – coolant temp. 75°C max.	0 V		
	A5	→▷	Engine running – coolant temp. 75°C min.	11-14 V		
Idle air control (IAC) valve	A6	→▷	Ignition ON	11-14 V		
	A6	→▷	Engine idling		5 V/5 ms	〰 25
	A7	→▷	Ignition ON	11-14 V		
	A7	→▷	Engine idling		5 V/5 ms	〰 25
Ignition amplifier	A21	⟹	Ignition ON	11-14 V		
	A21	⟹	Engine cranking	10 Hz		
	A21	⟹	Engine idling	25 Hz	5 V/5 ms	〰 32
	A21	⟹	3000 rpm	100 Hz		

★ Suggested settings - Voltage/time per division

Component/circuit description	ECM pin	Signal	Condition	Typical value	Oscilloscope setting*	Wave form
Ignition coil	D15	←	Ignition ON	11-14 V		
	D15	←	Engine idling		5 V/2 ms	∿ 33
Ignition switch	A10	←	Engine cranking	11-14 V		
Immobilizer control module	D3	←		1		
Injectors 1 & 4	A1	⊣▷	Ignition ON	11-14 V		
	A1	⊣▷	Engine idling	2 ms	10 V/2 ms	∿ 35
Injectors 2 & 3	A2	⊣▷	Ignition ON	11-14 V		
	A2	⊣▷	Engine idling	2 ms	10 V/2 ms	∿ 35
Intake air temperature (IAT) sensor	D8	←	Ignition ON – 15°C	3,5 V		
	D21	⊣−	Ignition ON	0 V		
Malfunction indicator lamp (MIL)	A19	⊣▷	Ignition ON – MIL ON	0-1 V		
	A19	⊣▷	Ignition ON – MIL OFF	11-14 V		
Manifold absolute pressure (MAP) sensor	D7	←	Ignition ON	3 V		
	D7	←	Engine idling	0,85 V		
	D7	←	Engine idling – full throttle briefly	2,8 V		
	D10	⊣−	Ignition ON	0 V		
	D11	⇨	Ignition ON	5 V		
Oxygen sensor (O2S)	D20	←	Engine running – engine hot	0,1-0,9 V		
Power steering pressure (PSP) switch	A11	←	Engine running – steering wheel not turned	0 V		
	A11	←	Engine running – steering wheel turned	0 V		
Relay module	A4	⊣▷	Ignition ON	0-1 V briefly then 11-14 V		
	A4	⊣▷	Engine idling	0-1 V		
	A12	←	Ignition OFF	0 V		
	A12	←	Ignition ON	11-14 V		
	A13	←	Ignition OFF	0 V		
	A13	←	Ignition ON	11-14 V		
Throttle position (TP) sensor	D6	←	Ignition ON – throttle closed	0,5 V		
	D6	←	Ignition ON – throttle fully open	4,8 V		
	D21	⊣−	Ignition ON	0 V		
	D22	⇨	Ignition ON	5 V		
Transmission lockup control valve A – AT	A9	⇨		1		
Transmission lockup control valve B – AT	A8	⇨		1		
Transmission range (TR) switch – AT	A22	←	Ignition ON – AT in P or N	0 V		
	A22	←	Ignition ON – AT not in P or N	11-14 V		
	D5	←	Ignition ON – AT in D3	0 V		
	D5	←	Ignition ON – AT not in D3	11-14 V		
	D16	←	Ignition ON – AT in D4	0 V		
	D16	←	Ignition ON – AT not in D4	11-14 V		
Vehicle speed sensor (VSS)	D2	←	Ignition ON – vehicle pushed	0 or 5 V fluctuating		

*Suggested settings - Voltage/time per division

1 Connected pin - no test data available or random digital signal

HONDA

Honda PGM-FI

Model:	Engine code:	Year:
Civic 1,4	D14Z1, D14Z2	1999-01
Civic 1,5	D15Z6	1999-01
Civic 1,6	B16A2, D16Y5	1999-01

ECM harness multi-plug

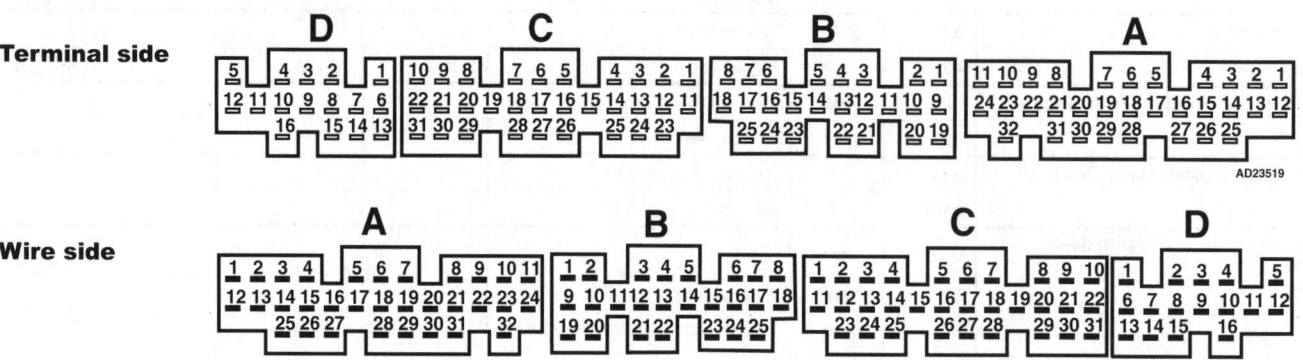

Component/circuit description	ECM pin	Signal	Condition	Typical value	Oscilloscope setting*	Wave form
AC compressor clutch relay – if fitted	A17	⇥▷	AC compressor OFF	11-14 V		
	A17	⇥▷	AC compressor ON	0-1 V		
AC refrigerant pressure switch	A27	⬅	Ignition ON – AC OFF	11-14 V		
	A27	⬅	Ignition ON – AC ON	0-1 V		
Alternator	C5	⬅	Engine running	0-14 V varies with electrical load		
Alternator – D15Z6/D16Y5	C2	⇨	Engine running – electrical load OFF	11-14 V		
	C2	⇨	Engine running – electrical load ON	0 V		
Battery	B21	⬅	Ignition OFF	11-14 V		
Brake pedal position (BPP) switch	A32	⬅	Ignition ON – brake pedal released	0 V		
	A32	⬅	Ignition ON – brake pedal depressed	11-14 V		
Camshaft position (CMP) actuator – 1,5/1,6	B12	⇨	Engine idling	0 V		
	B12	⇨	Engine running – high RPM	11-14 V		
Camshaft position (CMP) sensor	C20	⬅	Engine cranking	0,2 V ac		
	C20	⬅	Engine idling		5 V/20 ms	⎍⏦⏦ 11
	C21	⌐	Engine idling	0 V		
Crankshaft position (CKP) sensor	C8	⬅	Engine cranking	0,4 V ac		
	C8	⬅	Engine idling		2 V/20 ms	⎍⏦⏦ 1
	C9	⌐	Engine idling	0 V		
Data link connector (DLC)	A21	⬄		1		
Earth	B2		Ignition ON	0 V		
	B10		Ignition ON	0 V		
	B20		Ignition ON	0 V		
	B22		Ignition ON	0 V		
Econolight – D15Z6/D16Y5	A4	⇥▷	Ignition ON – econolight ON	0 V		
	A4	⇥▷	Ignition ON – econolight OFF	11-14 V		
Electrical load control module – D15Z6/D16Y5	A30	⬅	Engine idling – side lights ON	2,5-3,5 V		
	A30	⬅	Engine idling – head lights ON	1,5-2,5 V		

* Suggested settings - Voltage/time per division

Component/circuit description	ECM pin	Signal	Condition	Typical value	Oscilloscope setting*	Wave form
Engine coolant blower motor relay	A20	⊣▷	Engine idling – coolant blower motor OFF	11-14 V		
	A20	⊣▷	Engine idling – coolant blower motor ON	0 V		
Engine coolant temperature (ECT) sensor	C18	⊣–	Ignition ON	0 V		
	C26	⟵	Ignition ON – 20°C	3,3 V		
	C26	⟵	Ignition ON – 80°C	0,6 V		
Engine diagnostic link	A10	⟹		[1]		
Engine speed (RPM) sensor	C29	⟵	Engine cranking	1 V ac		
	C29	⟵	Engine idling		2 V/5 ms	∿ 17
	C30	⊣–	Engine idling	0 V		
Engine speed fluctuation sensor	C22	⟵		[1]		
	C31	⊣–	Engine idling	0 V		
Evaporative emission (EVAP) canister purge valve	A6	⊣▷	Engine running – coolant temp. above 68°C		10 V/50 ms	Intermittent ∿ 20
	A6	⊣▷	Engine running – coolant temp. below 68°C	11-14 V		
Exhaust gas recirculation (EGR) solenoid – 1,5/1,6	B7	⟹	Ignition ON	0 V		
Exhaust gas recirculation (EGR) valve position sensor	C18	⊣–	Ignition ON	0 V		
Exhaust gas recirculation (EGR) valve position sensor – D15Z6/D16Y5	C6	⟵	Engine idling	1,2 V		
Heated oxygen sensor (HO2S) 1	C1	⊣▷	Ignition ON	11-14 V		
	C1	⊣▷	Engine running		2 V/1 sec.	∿ 72
	C16	⟵	Engine running – engine hot	0,1-0,9 V	0,2 V/1 sec.	∿ 21
	C18	⊣–	Ignition ON	0 V		
Heated oxygen sensor (HO2S) 2 – if fitted	A8	⊣▷	Ignition ON	11-14 V		
	A8	⊣▷	Engine idling	0-1 V		
	A23	⟵	Engine running – engine hot	0,3-0,7 V	0,2 V/0,5 sec.	∿ 76
	C18	⊣–	Ignition ON	0 V		
Idle air control (IAC) valve – 1,5/1,6 MT	B23	⊣▷	Ignition ON	11-14 V		
	B23	⊣▷	Engine idling		5 V/5 ms	∿ 24
Idle air control (IAC) valve – except 1,5/1,6 MT	B6	⊣▷	Ignition ON	11-14 V		
	B6	⊣▷	Engine idling		10 V/5 ms	∿ 25
	B15	⊣▷	Ignition ON	11-14 V		
	B15	⊣▷	Engine idling		10 V/5 ms	∿ 25
Ignition control module (ICM)	B13	⟹	Ignition ON	11-14 V		
	B13	⟹	Engine cranking	10 Hz		
	B13	⟹	Engine idling	30 Hz	5 V/5 ms	∿ 32
	B13	⟹	3000 rpm	100 Hz		
Ignition switch – starter signal	A24	⟵	Engine cranking	10-14 V		
Immobilizer control module	A13	⟵		[1]		
	A25	⟵		[1]		
Immobilizer warning lamp	A12		Ignition ON – immobilizer warning lamp ON	0 V		
	A12		Ignition ON – immobilizer warning lamp OFF	11-14 V		
Injector 1	B11	⊣▷	Ignition ON	11-14 V		
	B11	⊣▷	Engine idling	3 ms	10 V/2 ms	∿ 35
Injector 2	B3	⊣▷	Ignition ON	11-14 V		
	B3	⊣▷	Engine idling	3 ms	10 V/2 ms	∿ 35
Injector 3	B4	⊣▷	Ignition ON	11-14 V		
	B4	⊣▷	Engine idling	3 ms	10 V/2 ms	∿ 35

* Suggested settings - Voltage/time per division

Component/circuit description	ECM pin	Signal	Condition	Typical value	Oscilloscope setting*	Wave form
Injector 4	B5	⇥▷	Ignition ON	11-14 V		
	B5	⇥▷	Engine idling	3 ms	10 V/2 ms	∿ 35
Intake air temperature (IAT) sensor	C18	⊣—	Ignition ON	0 V		
	C25	⬅	Ignition ON – 15°C	3,5 V		
Knock sensor (KS) – 1,6	C3	⬅	Engine idling – full throttle briefly		50 mV/1 ms	∿ 38
Malfunction indicator lamp (MIL)	A18	⇥▷	Ignition ON – MIL ON	0-1 V		
	A18	⇥▷	Ignition ON – MIL OFF	11-14 V		
Manifold absolute pressure (MAP) sensor	C7	⊣Y	Ignition ON	0 V		
	C17	⬅	Ignition ON	3 V		
	C17	⬅	Engine idling	0,9 V		
	C17	⬅	Engine idling – full throttle briefly	2,8 V		
	C19	⇨	Ignition ON	5 V		
Power steering pressure (PSP) switch – D15Z6/D16Y5	A26	⬅	Engine idling – steering wheel not turned	0-1 V		
	A26	⬅	Engine idling – steering wheel turned	11-14 V		
Relay module	B1	⬅	Ignition OFF	0 V		
	B1	⬅	Ignition ON	11-14 V		
	B9	⬅	Ignition OFF	0 V briefly		
	B9	⬅	Ignition ON	11-14 V		
Relay module – fuel pump	A15	⇥▷	Ignition ON	0 V briefly then 11-14 V		
	A15	⇥▷	Engine idling	0-1 V		
Tachometer	A19	⇨		1		
Throttle position (TP) sensor	C18	⊣—	Ignition ON	0 V		
	C27	⬅	Ignition ON – throttle closed	0,5 V		
	C27	⬅	Ignition ON – throttle fully open	4,8 V		
	C28	⇨	Ignition ON	5 V		
Transmission lockup control valve 1	B17	⇨	Vehicle moving – AT lock-up ON	11-14 V		
	B17	⇨	Vehicle moving – AT lock-up OFF	0 V		
Transmission lockup control valve 2	B25	⇨	Vehicle moving – AT lock-up ON	11-14 V		
	B25	⇨	Vehicle moving – AT lock-up OFF	0 V		
Transmission range (TR) switch	A7	⬅	Ignition ON – AT in D4	0 V		
	A7	⬅	Ignition ON – AT not in D4	11-14 V		
	A9	⬅	Ignition ON – AT in P or N	0 V		
	A9	⬅	Ignition ON – AT not in P or N	11-14 V		
	A22	⬅	Ignition ON – AT in D3	0 V		
	A22	⬅	Ignition ON – AT not in D3	11-14 V		
Vehicle speed sensor (VSS)	C23	⬅	Ignition ON – vehicle pushed	0 or 5 V fluctuating	2 V/50 ms	∿ 43

*Suggested settings - Voltage/time per division

1 Connected pin - no test data available or random digital signal

ECM harness multi-plug

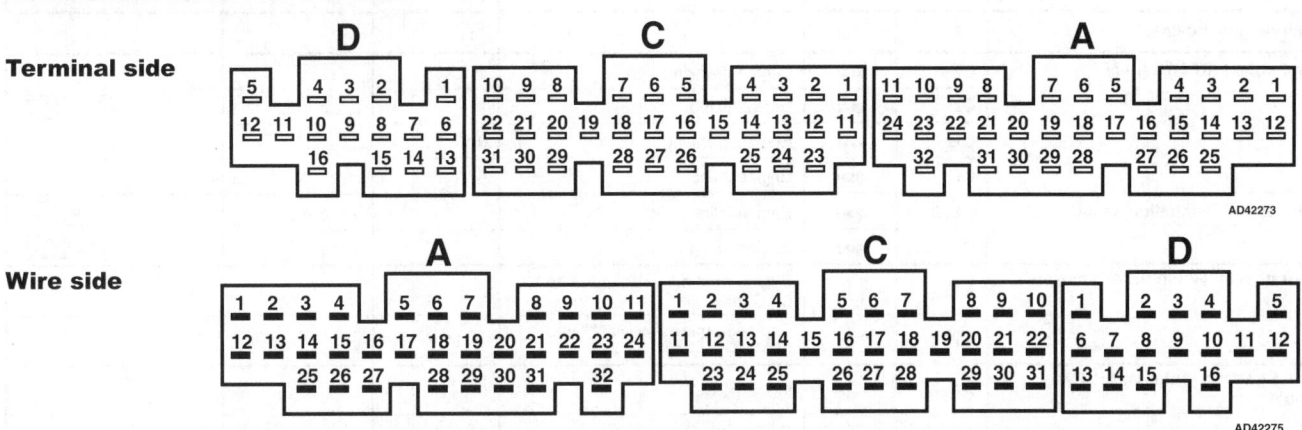

AD42273

AD42275

Component/circuit description	ECM pin	Signal	Condition	Typical value	Oscilloscope setting*	Wave form
AC compressor clutch relay – if fitted	A17	⇥▷	AC compressor OFF	11-14 V		
	A17	⇥▷	AC compressor ON	0-1 V		
AC refrigerant pressure switch – if fitted	C5	⬅	Ignition ON – AC OFF	11-14 V		
	C5	⬅	Ignition ON – AC ON	0-1 V		
Alternator	A19	⬅	Engine running – engine hot – electrical loads OFF	11-14 V		
	A19	⬅	Engine running – engine hot – electrical loads ON	0 V		
	C17	⬅	Engine running – engine hot	0-14 V varies with electrical load		
Battery	C10	⬅	Ignition OFF	11-14 V		
Brake pedal position (BPP) switch	D5	⬅	Brake pedal released	0 V		
	D5	⬅	Brake pedal depressed	11-14 V		
Camshaft position (CMP) actuator	A8	⇨	Ignition ON	0 V		
	A8	⇨	Engine running – low RPM	0 V		
	A8	⇨	Engine running – high RPM	11-14 V		
Camshaft position (CMP) sensor	C4	⬅	Engine cranking	0,2 V ac		
	C4	⬅	Engine idling		5 V/20 ms	⩘ww **11**
	C14	⬅	Engine cranking	0 V		
	C14	⬅	Engine idling	0 V		
Crankshaft position (CKP) sensor	C3	⬅	Engine cranking	0,4 V ac		
	C3	⬅	Engine idling		2 V/20 ms	⩘ww **1**
	C13	⬅	Engine cranking	0 V		
	C13	⬅	Engine idling	0 V		
Data link connector (DLC)	C8	⬄	Ignition ON	5 V		
Earth	A9		Ignition ON	0 V		
	A10		Ignition ON	0 V		
	A22		Ignition ON	0 V		
	A23		Ignition ON	0 V		
Econolight	A30	⇥▷	Ignition ON – lamp ON	0-1 V		
	A30	⇥▷	Ignition ON – lamp OFF	11-14 V		
Electrical load control module	D16	⬅	Engine idling	0-5 V varies with electrical load		

* Suggested settings - Voltage/time per division

Component/circuit description	ECM pin	Signal	Condition	Typical value	Oscilloscope setting*	Wave form
Engine coolant blower motor relay	A27	⊐▷	Coolant blower motor OFF	11-14 V		
	A27	⊐▷	Coolant blower motor ON	0-1 V		
Engine coolant temperature (ECT) sensor	D2	◀	Ignition ON – 20°C	3,3 V		
	D2	◀	Ignition ON – 80°C	0,6 V		
	D11	⊐	Ignition ON	0 V		
Engine diagnostic link	C7	▷		1		
Engine speed (RPM) sensor	C2	◀	Engine cranking	1 V ac		
	C2	◀	Engine idling		2 V/5 ms	⌇⌇ 17
	C12	◀	Engine cranking	0 V		
	C12	◀	Engine idling	0 V		
Engine speed fluctuation sensor	C1 (C11)	◀	Engine idling		2 V/5 ms	⌇⌇ 17
	C11 (C1)	◀	Engine idling		2 V/5 ms	⌇⌇ 17
Evaporative emission (EVAP) cut-off valve	A15	⊐▷	Engine running – coolant temp. 68°C max.	0 V		
	A15	⊐▷	Engine running – coolant temp. 68°C min.	11-14 V		
Exhaust gas recirculation (EGR) solenoid	A7	▷	Ignition ON	0 V		
	A7	▷	Engine running – valve operating	11-14 V		
	A7	▷	Engine running – valve operating		5 V/0,1 sec.	⌇⌇ 19
Exhaust gas recirculation (EGR) valve position sensor	D9	◀	Ignition ON	1,2 V		
	D9	◀	Engine idling – vacuum 0,27 bar	4,3 V		
	D10	▷	Ignition ON	5 V		
	D11	⊐	Ignition ON	0 V		
Heated oxygen sensor (HO2S)	A6	⊐▷	Ignition ON	11-14 V		
	A6	⊐▷	Engine idling	0-1 V		
	D7	◀	Engine running – engine hot	0,1-0,9 V		
Idle air control (IAC) valve – AT	A13	⊐▷	Ignition ON	11-14 V		
	A13	⊐▷	Engine idling		5 V/5 ms	⌇⌇ 25
	A14	⊐▷	Ignition ON	11-14 V		
	A14	⊐▷	Engine idling		5 V/5 ms	⌇⌇ 25
Idle air control (IAC) valve – MT	A12	⊐▷	Ignition ON	11-14 V		
	A12	⊐▷	Engine idling		5 V/5 ms	⌇⌇ 24
Ignition control module (ICM)	A20	▷	Ignition ON	11-14 V		
	A20	▷	Engine cranking	10 Hz		
	A20	▷	Engine idling	30 Hz	5 V/5 ms	⌇⌇ 32
	A20	▷	3000 rpm	100 Hz		
Ignition switch	C6	◀	Engine cranking	11-14 V		
Immobilizer control module	C22	◀		1		
Injector 1	A4	⊐▷	Ignition ON	11-14 V		
	A4	⊐▷	Engine idling	2 ms	10 V/2 ms	⌇⌇ 35
Injector 2	A3	⊐▷	Ignition ON	11-14 V		
	A3	⊐▷	Engine idling	2 ms	10 V/2 ms	⌇⌇ 35
Injector 3	A2	⊐▷	Ignition ON	11-14 V		
	A2	⊐▷	Engine idling	2 ms	10 V/2 ms	⌇⌇ 35
Injector 4	A1	⊐▷	Ignition ON	11-14 V		
	A1	⊐▷	Engine idling	2 ms	10 V/2 ms	⌇⌇ 35
Intake air temperature (IAT) sensor	D8	◀	Ignition ON – 15°C	3,5 V		
	D11	⊐	Ignition ON	0 V		
Knock sensor (KS)	D6	◀	Engine idling – accelerate briefly		50 mV/1 ms	⌇⌇ 38
Malfunction indicator lamp (MIL)	A18	⊐▷	Ignition ON – MIL ON	0-1 V		
	A18	⊐▷	Ignition ON – MIL OFF	11-14 V		

★ Suggested settings - Voltage/time per division

Component/circuit description	ECM pin	Signal	Condition	Typical value	Oscilloscope setting*	Wave form
Manifold absolute pressure (MAP) sensor	D3	←	Ignition ON	3 V		
	D3	←	Engine idling	0,9 V		
	D3	←	Engine idling – full throttle briefly	2,8 V		
	D4	⇒	Ignition ON	5 V		
	D12	⊣⊢	Ignition ON	0 V		
Power steering pressure (PSP) switch	C16	⇒	Engine idling – steering wheel not turned	0 V		
	C16	⇒	Engine idling – steering wheel turned	11-14 V		
Relay module	A11	←	Ignition OFF	0 V		
	A11	←	Ignition ON	11-14 V		
	A16	⊣⊳	Ignition ON	0-1 V briefly then 11-14 V		
	A16	⊣⊳	Engine idling	0-1 V		
	A24	←	Ignition OFF	0 V		
	A24	←	Ignition ON	11-14 V		
Throttle position (TP) sensor	D1	←	Ignition ON – throttle closed	0,1 V		
	D1	←	Ignition ON – throttle fully open	4,8 V		
	D10	⇒	Ignition ON	5 V		
	D11	⊣⊢	Ignition ON	0 V		
Transmission control module (TCM)	A25	⇒	Ignition ON	5 V		
	C9	⬌		1		
	C30	⬌		1		
Transmission range (TR) switch – AT	C29	←	Ignition ON – AT in P or N	0 V		
	C29	←	Ignition ON – AT not in P or N	11-14 V		
Vehicle speed sensor (VSS)	C18	←	Ignition ON – vehicle pushed	0 or 5 V fluctuating		

*Suggested settings - Voltage/time per division

1 Connected pin - no test data available or random digital signal

Model:	Engine code:	Year:
Accord 1,8	F18B2	1998-03
Accord 2,0	F20B6	1998-03
Accord 2,2	H22A7	1998-03

ECM harness multi-plug

Terminal side

AD23519

Wire side

AD23520

Component/circuit description	ECM pin	Signal	Condition	Typical value	Oscilloscope setting*	Wave form
AC compressor clutch relay – if fitted	A17	⊐▷	AC compressor OFF	11-14 V		
	A17	⊐▷	AC compressor ON	0-1 V		
AC refrigerant pressure switch	A27	◀	Ignition ON – AC OFF	5 V		
	A27	◀	Ignition ON – AC ON	0-1 V		
Alternator	C5	◀	Engine running – engine hot	0-14 V varies with electrical load		
Battery	B21	◀	Ignition OFF	11-14 V		
Brake pedal position (BPP) switch	A32	◀	Ignition ON – brake pedal released	0 V		
	A32	◀	Ignition ON – brake pedal depressed	11-14 V		
Camshaft position (CMP) actuator	B12	▷	Engine idling	0 V		
	B12	▷	Engine running – high RPM	11-14 V		
Camshaft position (CMP) sensor	C20	◀	Engine cranking	0,2 V ac		
	C20	◀	Engine idling		5 V/20 ms	Ⱳ 11
	C21	⊐⊢	Engine idling	0 V		
Crankshaft position (CKP) sensor	C8	◀	Engine cranking	0,4 V ac		
	C8	◀	Engine idling		2 V/20 ms	Ⱳ 1
	C9	⊐⊢	Engine idling	0 V		
Cruise control module – AT	A5			1		
Data link connector (DLC)	A21	◀▷		1		
Earth	B2		Ignition ON	0 V		
	B10		Ignition ON	0 V		
	B20		Ignition ON	0 V		
	B22		Ignition ON	0 V		
Engine coolant temperature (ECT) sensor	C18	⊐⊢	Ignition ON	0 V		
	C26	◀	Ignition ON – 20°C	3,3 V		
	C26	◀	Ignition ON – 80°C	0,6 V		
Engine diagnostic link	A10	▷		1		
Engine mounting control solenoid – AT	C11	⊐▷	Engine idling	0 V		
	C11	⊐▷	Engine idling – full throttle briefly	11-14 V		

★ Suggested settings - Voltage/time per division

Autodata

Component/circuit description	ECM pin	Signal	Condition	Typical value	Oscilloscope setting*	Wave form
Engine oil pressure switch – valve timing – 2,0/2,2	C10	←	Engine idling	0 V		
	C10	←	Engine idling – full throttle briefly	11-14 V		
Engine speed (RPM) sensor	C29	←	Engine cranking	1 V ac		
	C29	←	Engine idling		2 V/5 ms	17
	C30	⊣	Engine idling	0 V		
Evaporative emission (EVAP) canister purge valve	C22	⊣▷	Engine running – coolant temp. above 70°C	0 V intermittent		
	C22	⊣▷	Engine running – coolant temp. below 70°C	11-14 V		
Exhaust gas recirculation (EGR) solenoid	B7	⊣▷	Ignition ON	0 V		
Exhaust gas recirculation (EGR) valve position sensor	C6	←	Engine idling – vacuum OFF	1,2 V		
	C6	←	Engine idling – vacuum 0,27 bar	4,3 V		
	C18	⊣	Ignition ON	0 V		
	C28	⇒	Ignition ON	5 V		
Heated oxygen sensor (HO2S) 1 – 1,8	A20	⊣▷	Ignition ON	11-14 V		
	A20	⊣▷	Engine running	0-100%	2 V/20 ms	65
	C16	←	Engine running – engine hot	0,1-0,9 V	0,2 V/1 sec.	21
	C18	⊣	Ignition ON	0 V		
Heated oxygen sensor (HO2S) 1 – 2,0	B19	⊣▷	Ignition ON	11-14 V		
	B19	⊣▷	Engine running	0-100%	2 V/20 ms	65
	C14	←	Engine running – engine hot	0,1-0,9 V	0,2 V/1 sec.	21
	C15	⊣	Ignition ON	0 V		
Heated oxygen sensor (HO2S) 1 – 2,2	A20	⊣▷	Ignition ON	11-14 V		
	A20	⊣▷	Engine running – engine hot	0 V		
	C16	←	Engine running – engine hot	0,1-0,9 V	0,2 V/1 sec.	21
	C18	⊣	Ignition ON	0 V		
Heated oxygen sensor (HO2S) 2 – 1,8 AT	A8	⊣▷	Ignition ON	11-14 V		
	A8	⊣▷	Engine running	0-100%	2 V/20 ms	65
	A23	←	Engine running – engine hot	0,4-0,6 V	0,2 V/0,5 sec.	76
	C18	⊣	Ignition ON	0 V		
Heated oxygen sensor (HO2S) 2 – 2,0/2,2	A8	⊣▷	Ignition ON	11-14 V		
	A8	⊣▷	Engine running – engine hot	0 V		
	A23	←	Engine running – engine hot	0,4-0,6 V	0,2 V/0,5 sec.	76
	C18	⊣	Ignition ON	0 V		
Heated oxygen sensor (HO2S) relay 1, heater control – 2,0	A20	⊣▷	Ignition ON	0 V		
	A20	⊣▷	Engine running	0 V		
	C13	←	Ignition ON	11-14 V		
	C13	←	Engine running	11-14 V		
Idle air control (IAC) valve	B23	⊣▷	Ignition ON	11-14 V		
	B23	⊣▷	Engine idling		5 V/5 ms	24
Ignition control module (ICM)	B13	⊣▷	Ignition ON	11-14 V		
	B13	⊣▷	Engine cranking	10 Hz		
	B13	⊣▷	Engine idling	30 Hz	5 V/5 ms	32
	B13	⊣▷	3000 rpm	100 Hz		
Ignition switch	D5	←	Ignition OFF	0 V		
	D5	←	Ignition ON	11-14 V		
Ignition switch – starter signal	A24	←	Engine cranking	10-14 V		
Immobilizer control module	A13	←		1️⃣		
	A25	←		1️⃣		

* Suggested settings - Voltage/time per division

Component/circuit description	ECM pin	Signal	Condition	Typical value	Oscilloscope setting*	Wave form
Immobilizer warning lamp	A12		Ignition ON – immobilizer warning lamp ON	0 V		
	A12		Ignition ON – immobilizer warning lamp OFF	11-14 V		
Injector 1	B11	⇥▷	Ignition ON	11-14 V		
	B11	⇥▷	Engine idling	3 ms	10 V/2 ms	〰35
Injector 2	B3	⇥▷	Ignition ON	11-14 V		
	B3	⇥▷	Engine idling	3 ms	10 V/2 ms	〰35
Injector 3	B4	⇥▷	Ignition ON	11-14 V		
	B4	⇥▷	Engine idling	3 ms	10 V/2 ms	〰35
Injector 4	B5	⇥▷	Ignition ON	11-14 V		
	B5	⇥▷	Engine idling	3 ms	10 V/2 ms	〰35
Instrument panel – AT	A6	⇨		1		
	A7	⇨		1		
	A11			1		
Instrument panel – AT – VSS signal	A9	⇨		1		
Intake air temperature (IAT) sensor	C18	⊣	Ignition ON	0 V		
	C25	⇐	Ignition ON – 15°C	3,5 V		
Intake air valve control valve – 1,8/2,2	B16	⇥▷	Below 4200 rpm	11-14 V		
	B16	⇥▷	Above 4200 rpm	0-1 V		
Intake manifold air control solenoid – 2,0	B15	⇥▷	Below 4000 rpm	11-14 V		
	B15	⇥▷	Above 4000 rpm	0-1 V		
Knock sensor (KS)	C3	⇐	Engine idling – full throttle briefly		50 mV/1 ms	〰38
Malfunction indicator lamp (MIL)	A18	⇥▷	Ignition ON – MIL ON	0-1 V		
	A18	⇥▷	Ignition ON – MIL OFF	11-14 V		
Manifold absolute pressure (MAP) sensor	C7	⊣	Ignition ON	0 V		
	C17	⇐	Ignition ON	3 V		
	C17	⇐	Engine idling	0,9 V		
	C17	⇐	Full throttle briefly	2,8 V		
	C19	⇨	Ignition ON	5 V		
Park/neutral position (PNP) switch	D13	⇐	Ignition ON – AT in P or N	0 V		
	D13	⇐	Ignition ON – AT not in P or N	5 V		
Power steering pressure (PSP) switch	C31	⇐	Engine idling – steering wheel not turned	0-1 V		
	C31	⇐	Engine idling – steering wheel turned	11-14 V		
Relay module	B1	⇐	Ignition OFF	0 V		
	B1	⇐	Ignition ON	11-14 V		
	B9	⇐	Ignition OFF	0 V briefly		
	B9	⇐	Ignition ON	11-14 V		
Relay module – fuel pump	A15	⇥▷	Ignition ON	0 V briefly then 11-14 V		
	A15	⇥▷	Engine idling	0-1 V		
Tachometer	A19	⇨		1		
Throttle position (TP) sensor	C18	⊣	Ignition ON	0 V		
	C27	⇐	Ignition ON – throttle closed	0,1 V		
	C27	⇐	Ignition ON – throttle fully open	4,8 V		
	C28	⇨	Ignition ON	5 V		
Transmission clutch pressure control valve 1 – AT	B8	⇨		1		
	B17	⇨		1		
Transmission clutch pressure control valve 2 – AT	B18	⇨		1		
	B25	⇨		1		

* Suggested settings - Voltage/time per division

Component/circuit description	ECM pin	Signal	Condition	Typical value	Oscilloscope setting*	Wave form
Transmission fluid pressure switch 1 – AT	B14	⬅	Ignition ON	11-14 V		
Transmission fluid pressure switch 2 – AT	B24	⬅	Ignition ON	11-14 V		
Transmission interlock control module	A28	⮕	Ignition ON – brake pedal depressed	11-14 V		
	A28	⮕	Ignition ON – brake pedal released	0-1 V		
Transmission lockup control valve	D1	⮕	Vehicle moving – AT lock-up ON	11-14 V		
	D1	⮕	Vehicle moving – AT lock-up OFF	0 V		
Transmission mode selection switch – AT	A31	⬅	Ignition ON – selector lever not in manual mode	11-14 V		
	A31	⬅	Vehicle moving – selector lever in manual mode	0 V		
Transmission range (TR) switch	D4	⬅	Ignition ON – AT in N	0 V		
	D4	⬅	Ignition ON – AT not in N	5 V		
	D6	⬅	Ignition ON – AT in R	0 V		
	D6	⬅	Ignition ON – AT not in R	5 V		
	D8	⬅	Ignition ON – AT in D3	0 V		
	D8	⬅	Ignition ON – AT not in D3	5 V		
	D9	⬅	Ignition ON – AT in D4	0 V		
	D9	⬅	Ignition ON – AT not in D4	5 V		
	D14	⬅	Ignition ON – AT in 2	0 V		
	D14	⬅	Ignition ON – AT not in 2	5 V		
	D15	⬅	Ignition ON – AT in 1	0 V		
	D15	⬅	Ignition ON – AT not in 1	5 V		
Transmission secondary shaft speed sensor	C19	⮕	Ignition ON	5 V		
	D10	⬅		1		
	D16	⌐	Ignition ON	0 V		
Transmission selector position lamp – D4	A14	⬅	Ignition ON – AT position selector D4 lamp ON	0 V		
	A14	⬅	Ignition ON – AT position selector D4 lamp OFF	11-14 V		
Transmission shift control switch – AT	A22	⬅	Vehicle moving – selector lever in neutral	11-14 V		
	A22	⬅	Vehicle moving – selector lever in manual down-shift	0 V		
	A26	⬅	Vehicle moving – selector lever in neutral	11-14 V		
	A26	⬅	Vehicle moving – selector lever in manual up-shift	0 V		
Transmission shift control valve 1	D7	⮕	Vehicle moving – AT in 2nd or 3rd	11-14 V		
	D7	⮕	Vehicle moving – AT in 1st or 4th	0 V		
Transmission shift control valve 2	D2	⮕	Vehicle moving – AT not in 3rd or 4th	11-14 V		
	D2	⮕	Vehicle moving – AT in 3rd or 4th	0 V		
Transmission shift control valve 3	D3	⮕	Vehicle moving – AT in 1st or 3rd	11-14 V		
	D3	⮕	Vehicle moving – AT not in 1st or 3rd	0 V		
Transmission turbine shaft speed (TSS) sensor	C28	⮕	Ignition ON	5 V		
	D11	⬅		1		
	D12	⌐	Ignition ON	0 V		
Vehicle speed sensor (VSS) – MT	C23	⬅	Ignition ON – vehicle pushed	0 or 5-12 V fluctuating	5 V/50 ms	⟋⟍⟋ 43

*Suggested settings - Voltage/time per division

1 Connected pin - no test data available or random digital signal

HONDA

Honda PGM-FI

Model:	Engine code:	Year:
Accord 2,0	F20Z1	1996-97
Accord 2,2	F22Z2	1996-99

ECM harness multi-plug

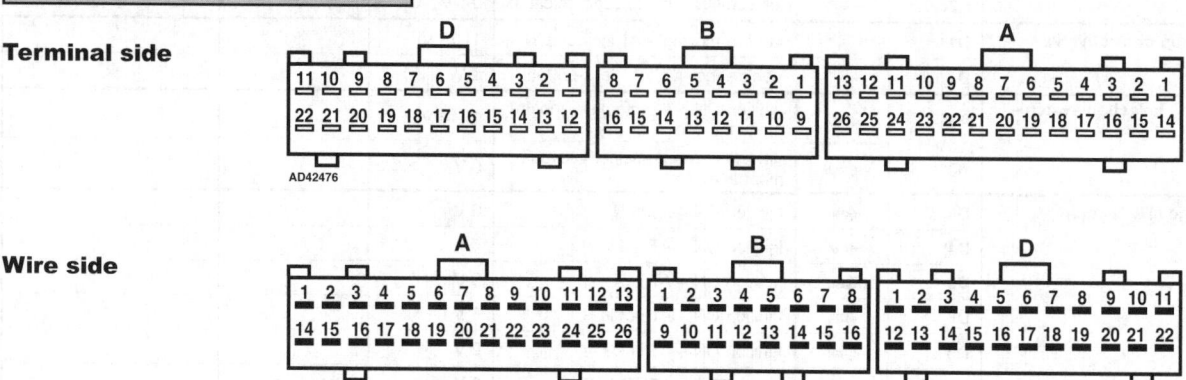

Component/circuit description	ECM pin	Signal	Condition	Typical value	Oscilloscope setting*	Wave form
AC compressor clutch relay	A8	⊐➤	AC ON	0-1 V		
	A8	⊐➤	AC OFF	11-14 V		
AC master switch	B3	←	AC OFF	11-14 V		
	B3	←	AC ON	0 V		
Alternator	D5	←	Engine idling – engine hot	0-5 V varies with electrical load		
Battery	D1	←	Ignition OFF	11-14 V		
Camshaft position (CMP) actuator – F22Z2	A15	⇨	Engine idling	0 V		
	A15	⇨	Engine running – high RPM	11-14 V		
Camshaft position (CMP) sensor	B6	←	Engine cranking	0,3 V ac		
	B6	←	Engine idling	1 V ac	5 V/20 ms	〰11
	B6	←	3000 rpm	3,5 V ac		
	B14	⊐-	Ignition ON	0 V		
	B14	⊐-	Engine idling	0 V		
Crankshaft position (CKP) sensor	B7	←	Engine cranking	0,5 V ac		
	B7	←	Engine idling	2,5 V ac	2 V/20 ms	〰1
	B7	←	3000 rpm	7 V ac		
	B15	⊐-	Ignition ON	0 V		
	B15	⊐-	Engine idling	0 V		
Data link connector (DLC)	D4	←⇨	Ignition ON	5 V		
Earth	A12		Ignition ON	0 V		
	A25		Ignition ON	0 V		
	A26		Ignition ON	0 V		
	B9		Ignition ON	0 V		

* Suggested settings - Voltage/time per division

Component/circuit description	ECM pin	Signal	Condition	Typical value	Oscilloscope setting*	Wave form
Engine coolant temperature (ECT) sensor	D7	←	Ignition ON – 20°C	3,3 V		
	D7	←	Ignition ON – 80°C	0,6 V		
	D22	⅂―	Ignition ON	0 V		
Engine diagnostic link	D13	⇒	Ignition ON	5 V		
Engine mounting control solenoid – AT	A18	⅂⇒	Engine idling	0-1 V		
	A18	⅂⇒	2000 rpm	11-14 V		
Engine speed (RPM) sensor	B8	←	Engine cranking	1 V ac		
	B8	←	Engine idling	2,7 V ac	2 V/5 ms	∿∿ 17
	B8	←	3000 rpm	8 V ac		
	B16	⅂―	Ignition ON	0 V		
	B16	⅂―	Engine idling	0 V		
Evaporative emission (EVAP) cut-off valve	A23	⅂⇒	Engine idling – coolant temp. 75°C max.	11-14 V		
	A23	⅂⇒	Engine idling – coolant temp. 75°C min.	0-1 V		
Exhaust gas recirculation (EGR) solenoid	A16	⅂⇒	Ignition ON	11-14 V		
Exhaust gas recirculation (EGR) valve position sensor	D17	←	Engine idling – vacuum OFF	1,2 V		
	D17	←	Engine idling – vacuum 0,27 bar	4,3 V		
	D21	⇒	Ignition ON	5 V		
	D22	⅂―	Ignition ON	0 V		
Heated oxygen sensor (HO2S)	A6	⅂⇒	Ignition ON	11-14 V		
	A6	⅂⇒	Engine idling	0-1 V		
	D18	←	Engine idling – engine hot	0,1-0,9 V fluctuating		
	D22	⅂―	Ignition ON	0 V		
Idle air control (IAC) valve	A5	⅂⇒	Ignition ON	11-14 V		
	A5	⅂⇒	Engine idling	6-10 V		
	A5	⅂⇒	Engine idling	30%	5 V/5 ms	∿∿ 24
Ignition amplifier	A11	⇒	Ignition ON	11-14 V		
	A11	⇒	Engine cranking	10 V/9 Hz		
	A11	⇒	Engine idling	12 V/25 Hz	5 V/5 ms	∿∿ 32
	A11	⇒	3000 rpm	7-10 V/100 Hz		
Ignition switch – start signal	B5	←	Engine cranking	9 V		
Immobilizer control module	D2			①		
Injector 1	A1	⅂⇒	Ignition ON	11-14 V		
	A1	⅂⇒	Engine idling	3 ms	10 V/2 ms	∿∿ 35
Injector 2	A2	⅂⇒	Ignition ON	11-14 V		
	A2	⅂⇒	Engine idling	3 ms	10 V/2 ms	∿∿ 35
Injector 3	A3	⅂⇒	Ignition ON	11-14 V		
	A3	⅂⇒	Engine idling	3 ms	10 V/2 ms	∿∿ 35
Injector 4	A14	⅂⇒	Ignition ON	11-14 V		
	A14	⅂⇒	Engine idling	3 ms	10 V/2 ms	∿∿ 35
Intake air temperature (IAT) sensor	D8	←	Ignition ON – 10°C	4 V		
	D22	⅂―	Ignition ON	0 V		

* Suggested settings - Voltage/time per division

Component/circuit description	ECM pin	Signal	Condition	Typical value	Oscilloscope setting*	Wave form
Intake air valve control valve – F22Z2	A10	⊐↦	Ignition ON	11-14 V		
	A10	⊐↦	Engine idling	0-1 V		
	A10	⊐↦	Above 3500 rpm	11-14 V		
Malfunction indicator lamp (MIL)	A7	⊐↦	Ignition ON – MIL ON	0-1 V		
	A7	⊐↦	Ignition ON – MIL OFF	11-14 V		
Manifold absolute pressure (MAP) sensor	D9	⟵	Ignition ON	3 V		
	D9	⟵	Engine idling	1,5 V		
	D10	⟹	Ignition ON	5 V		
	D11	⊐⊢	Ignition ON	0 V		
Relay module	A4	⊐↦	Ignition ON	0-1 V briefly then 11-14 V		
	A4	⊐↦	Engine idling	0-1 V		
	A13	⟵	Ignition OFF	0 V		
	A13	⟵	Ignition ON	11-14 V		
	B1	⟵	Ignition OFF	0 V		
	B1	⟵	Ignition ON	11-14 V		
Throttle position (TP) sensor	D6	⟵	Ignition ON – throttle closed	0,5 V		
	D6	⟵	Ignition ON – throttle fully open	4,5 V		
	D21	⟹	Ignition ON	5 V		
	D22	⊐⊢	Ignition ON	0 V		
Transmission control module (TCM) – AT	A22	⟹	Engine idling	5 V		
	B2	⟵	Engine idling	5 V		
	B10	⟵	Engine idling	5 V		
	D20	⟹	Ignition ON	5 V		
Transmission range (TR) switch – AT	B4	⟹	Ignition ON – AT not in P or N	11-14 V		
	B4	⟹	Ignition ON – AT in P or N	0 V		
Vehicle speed sensor (VSS)	B13	⟵	Ignition ON – vehicle pushed	0 V or 5-12 V		

*Suggested settings - Voltage/time per division

1 Connected pin - no test data available or random digital signal

ECM harness multi-plug

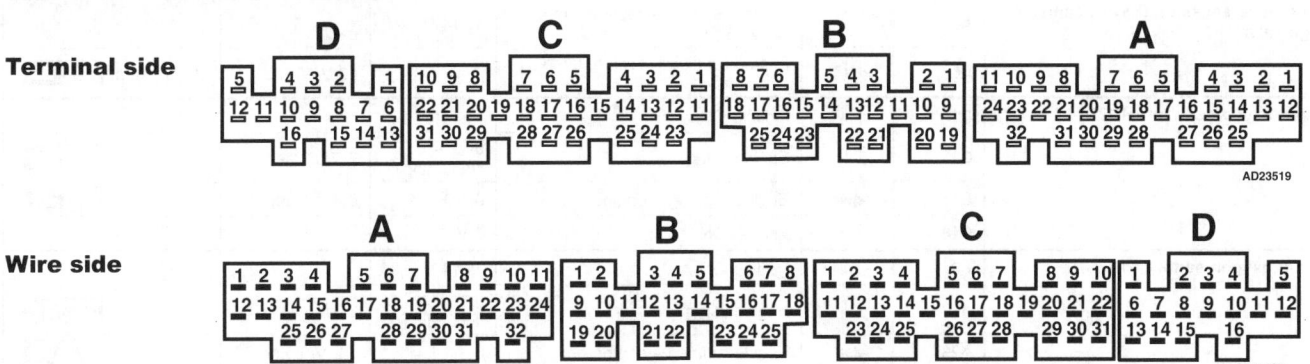

Terminal side

D C B A

Wire side

A B C D

AD23519

AD23520

Component/circuit description	ECM pin	Signal	Condition	Typical value	Oscilloscope setting*	Wave form
AC compressor clutch relay – if fitted	A17	⌐▷	AC compressor OFF	11-14 V		
	A17	⌐▷	AC compressor ON	0-1 V		
AC refrigerant pressure switch	A27	⬅	Ignition ON – AC OFF	11-14 V		
	A27	⬅	Ignition ON – AC ON	0-1 V		
Alternator	C5	⬅	Engine running – engine hot	0-14 V varies with electrical load		
Alternator – some models	C2	⇨	Engine running – electrical load OFF	11-14 V		
	C2	⇨	Engine running – electrical load ON	0 V		
Battery	B21	⬅	Ignition OFF	11-14 V		
Brake pedal position (BPP) switch	A32	⬅	Ignition ON – brake pedal released	0 V		
	A32	⬅	Ignition ON – brake pedal depressed	11-14 V		
Camshaft position (CMP) sensor	C20	⬅	Engine cranking	0,2 V ac		
	C20	⬅	Engine idling		5 V/20 ms	∿∿ 11
	C21	⌐	Engine idling	0 V		
Crankshaft position (CKP) sensor	C8	⬅	Engine cranking	0,4 V ac		
	C8	⬅	Engine idling		2 V/20 ms	∿∿ 1
	C9	⌐	Engine idling	0 V		
Cruise control module – some models	A5			1		
Data link connector (DLC)	A21	⬌		1		
Earth	B2		Ignition ON	0 V		
	B10		Ignition ON	0 V		
	B20		Ignition ON	0 V		
	B22		Ignition ON	0 V		
Engine coolant blower motor relay	A20	⌐▷	Engine idling – coolant blower motor OFF	11-14 V		
	A20	⌐▷	Engine idling – coolant blower motor ON	0 V		
Engine coolant temperature (ECT) sensor	C18	⌐	Ignition ON	0 V		
	C26	⬅	Ignition ON – 20°C	3,3 V		
	C26	⬅	Ignition ON – 80°C	0,6 V		
Engine diagnostic link	A10	⬌		1		

★ Suggested settings - Voltage/time per division

Component/circuit description	ECM pin	Signal	Condition	Typical value	Oscilloscope setting*	Wave form
Engine speed (RPM) sensor	C29	←	Engine cranking	1 V ac		
	C29	←	Engine idling		2 V/5 ms	⌁ 17
	C30	⊣─	Engine idling	0 V		
Engine speed fluctuation sensor	C22	←		[1]		
	C31	⊣─	Engine idling	0 V		
Evaporative emission (EVAP) canister purge valve	A6	⊣▷	Engine running – coolant temp. above 66°C	11-14 V		
	A6	⊣▷	Engine running – coolant temp. below 66°C		10 V/50 ms	Intermittent ⌁ 20
Heated oxygen sensor (HO2S) 1	C1	⊣▷	Ignition ON	11-14 V		
	C1	⊣▷	Engine idling	0-12 V fluctuating	2 V/0,2 sec.	⌁ 65
	C16	←	Engine running – engine hot	0,1-0,9 V	0,2 V/1 sec.	⌁ 21
	C18	⊣─	Ignition ON	0 V		
Heated oxygen sensor (HO2S) 2	A8	⊣▷	Ignition ON	11-14 V		
	A8	⊣▷	Engine idling	0-12 V fluctuating	2 V/1 sec.	⌁ 72
	A23	←	Engine running – engine hot	0,3-0,7 V	0,2 V/0,5 sec.	⌁ 76
Heated oxygen sensor (HO2S) 2 – some models	C18	⊣─	Ignition ON	0 V		
Idle air control (IAC) valve	B23	⊣▷	Ignition ON	11-14 V		
	B23	⊣▷	Engine idling		5 V/5 ms	⌁ 24
Ignition control module (ICM)	B13	⇒	Ignition ON	11-14 V		
	B13	⇒	Engine cranking	10 Hz		
	B13	⇒	Engine idling	30 Hz	5 V/5 ms	⌁ 32
	B13	⇒	3000 rpm	100 Hz		
Ignition switch	D5	←	Ignition OFF	0 V		
	D5	←	Ignition ON	11-14 V		
Ignition switch – starter signal	A24	←	Engine cranking	10-14 V		
Immobilizer control module	A13	←		[1]		
	A25	←		[1]		
Immobilizer warning lamp	A12	⊣▷	Ignition ON – immobilizer warning lamp ON	0 V		
	A12	⊣▷	Ignition ON – immobilizer warning lamp OFF	11-14 V		
Injector 1	B11	⊣▷	Ignition ON	11-14 V		
	B11	⊣▷	Engine idling	3 ms	10 V/2 ms	⌁ 35
Injector 2	B3	⊣▷	Ignition ON	11-14 V		
	B3	⊣▷	Engine idling	3 ms	10 V/2 ms	⌁ 35
Injector 3	B4	⊣▷	Ignition ON	11-14 V		
	B4	⊣▷	Engine idling	3 ms	10 V/2 ms	⌁ 35
Injector 4	B5	⊣▷	Ignition ON	11-14 V		
	B5	⊣▷	Engine idling	3 ms	10 V/2 ms	⌁ 35
Intake air temperature (IAT) sensor	C18	⊣─	Ignition ON	0 V		
	C25	←	Ignition ON – 15°C	3,5 V		
Knock sensor (KS)	C3	←	Engine idling – full throttle briefly		50 mV/1 ms	⌁ 38
Malfunction indicator lamp (MIL)	A18	⊣▷	Ignition ON – MIL ON	0-1 V		
	A18	⊣▷	Ignition ON – MIL OFF	11-14 V		
Manifold absolute pressure (MAP) sensor	C7	⊣─	Ignition ON	0 V		
	C17	←	Ignition ON	3 V		
	C17	←	Engine idling	1 V		
	C17	←	Engine idling – full throttle briefly	2,8 V		
	C19	⇒	Ignition ON	5 V		
Overdrive indicator lamp	B19	⊣▷	Engine idling – overdrive indicator lamp OFF	11-14 V		
	B19	⊣▷	Engine idling – overdrive indicator lamp ON	0 V		

★ Suggested settings - Voltage/time per division

Component/circuit description	ECM pin	Signal	Condition	Typical value	Oscilloscope setting*	Wave form
Overdrive selection switch	D8	⬅	Ignition ON – overdrive ON	5 V		
	D8	⬅	Ignition ON – overdrive OFF	0 V		
Park/neutral position (PNP) switch	D13	⬅	Ignition ON – AT in P or N	0 V		
	D13	⬅	Ignition ON – AT not in P or N	5 V		
Power steering pressure (PSP) switch	A26	⬅	Engine idling – steering wheel not turned	0-1 V		
	A26	⬅	Engine idling – steering wheel turned	11-14 V		
Relay module	B1	⬅	Ignition OFF	0 V		
	B1	⬅	Ignition ON	11-14 V		
	B9	⬅	Ignition OFF	0 V briefly		
	B9	⬅	Ignition ON	11-14 V		
Relay module – fuel pump – with immobilizer	A15	⼂▷	Ignition ON	0 V briefly then 11-14 V		
	A15	⼂▷	Engine idling	0-1 V		
Relay module – fuel pump – without immobilizer	A16	⼂▷	Ignition ON	0 V briefly then 11-14 V		
	A16	⼂▷	Engine idling	0-1 V		
Tachometer	A19	⇨		1		
Throttle position (TP) sensor	C18	⼂—	Ignition ON	0 V		
	C27	⬅	Ignition ON – throttle closed	0,1 V		
	C27	⬅	Ignition ON – throttle fully open	4,8 V		
	C28	⇨	Ignition ON	5 V		
Transmission interlock control module – some models	A28	⇨	Ignition ON – brake pedal depressed	11-14 V		
	A28	⇨	Ignition ON – brake pedal released	0-1 V		
Transmission linear control valve 1 – AT	B8	⇨		1		
	B17	⇨		1		
Transmission lockup control valve 1	D1	⇨	Vehicle moving – AT lock-up ON	11-14 V		
	D1	⇨	Vehicle moving – AT lock-up OFF	0 V		
Transmission range (TR) switch	D6	⬅	Ignition ON – AT in R	0 V		
	D6	⬅	Ignition ON – AT not in R	11-14 V		
	D9	⬅	Ignition ON – AT in D4	0 V		
	D9	⬅	Ignition ON – AT not in D4	11-14 V		
	D14	⬅	Ignition ON – AT in 2	0 V		
	D14	⬅	Ignition ON – AT not in 2	11-14 V		
	D15	⬅	Ignition ON – AT in 1	0 V		
	D15	⬅	Ignition ON – AT not in 1	11-14 V		
Transmission secondary shaft speed sensor	D10	⬅		1		
	D16	⼂—	Ignition ON	0 V		
Transmission selector position lamp – D4	A14	⬅	Ignition ON – AT position selector D4 lamp ON	0 V		
	A14	⬅	Ignition ON – AT position selector D4 lamp OFF	11-14 V		
Transmission shift control valve 1	D7	⇨	Vehicle moving – AT in 2nd or 3rd	11-14 V		
	D7	⇨	Vehicle moving – AT in 1st or 4th	0 V		
Transmission shift control valve 2	D2	⇨	Vehicle moving – AT not in 3rd or 4th	11-14 V		
	D2	⇨	Vehicle moving – AT in 3rd or 4th	0 V		
Transmission shift control valve 3	D3	⇨	Vehicle moving – AT lock-up ON	11-14 V		
	D3	⇨	Vehicle moving – AT lock-up OFF	0 V		
Transmission turbine shaft speed (TSS) sensor	D11	⬅		1		
	D12	⼂—	Ignition ON	0 V		
Vehicle speed sensor (VSS) – MT	C23	⬅	Ignition ON – vehicle pushed	0-5 V–11-14 V fluctuating	2 V/50 ms	〰〰 43

*Suggested settings - Voltage/time per division

1 Connected pin - no test data available or random digital signal

Model:	Engine code:	Year:
Accent 1,5	G4K – SOHC	1995-00
Accent 1,5	G4K – DOHC	1996-00

ECM harness multi-plug

Terminal side

```
19 18 17 16 15 14 13 12 11 10 9 8 7 6 5 4 3 2 1
37 36 35 34 33 32 31 30 29 28 27 26 25 24 23 22 21 20
55 54 53 52 51 50 49 48 47 46 45 44 43 42 41 40 39 38
```
AD72618

Wire side

```
1 2 3 4 5 6 7 8 9 10 11 12 13 14 15 16 17 18 19
20 21 22 23 24 25 26 27 28 29 30 31 32 33 34 35 36 37
38 39 40 41 42 43 44 45 46 47 48 49 50 51 52 53 54 55
```
AD42077

Component/circuit description	ECM pin	Signal	Condition	Typical value	Oscilloscope setting*	Wave form
AC compressor clutch relay	25	⊐⊢▷	Engine idling – AC OFF	11-14 V		
	25	⊐⊢▷	Engine idling – AC ON – AC compressor ON	0-1 V		
AC condenser blower motor relay	34	⊐⊢▷	Engine idling – condenser blower motor OFF	11-14 V		
	34	⊐⊢▷	Engine idling – condenser blower motor ON	0-1 V		
AC master switch	52	←	Engine idling – heater motor switch ON – AC OFF	0 V		
	52	←	Engine idling – heater motor switch ON – AC ON	11-14 V		
AC refrigerant pressure switch	53	←		[1]		
Battery	2	←	Ignition OFF	11-14 V		
Camshaft position (CMP) sensor	12	←	Ignition ON – engine turned	0 V or 11-14 V		
	12	←	Engine idling		2 V/20 ms	⟋⟍⟋⟍ 12
CO adjustment resistor – SOHC without cat	8	⇨	Ignition ON	5 V		
	29	←	Engine idling	0,3-1 V – varies with CO level		
Crankshaft position (CKP) sensor	44	←	Engine idling		2 V/1 ms	⟋⟍⟋⟍ 2
	45	←	Engine idling	0 V		
Data link connector (DLC)	7		Ignition ON	11-14 V		
	38		Ignition ON	11-14 V		
Earth	6		Ignition ON	0 V		
	18		Ignition ON	0 V		
	33		Ignition ON	0 V		
Earth – DOHC	1		Ignition ON	0 V		
Earth – SOHC	10		Ignition ON	0 V		
Engine control relay	20	←	Ignition OFF	0 V		
	20	←	Ignition ON	11-14 V		
	21	⊐⊢▷	Ignition OFF	11-14 V		
	21	⊐⊢▷	Ignition ON	0-1 V		
Engine control relay – MT	51	←	Ignition OFF	0 V		
	51	←	Ignition ON	11-14 V		
Engine coolant temperature (ECT) sensor	48	←	Ignition ON – coolant temp. 0°C	4 V		
	48	←	Ignition ON – coolant temp. 20°C	3,4 V		
	48	←	Ignition ON – coolant temp. 80°C	1,2 V		

* Suggested settings - Voltage/time per division

/Autodata

Component/circuit description	ECM pin	Signal	Condition	Typical value	Oscilloscope setting*	Wave form
Engine coolant temperature (ECT) sensor – DOHC	9	⊣—	Ignition ON	0 V		
Engine coolant temperature (ECT) sensor – SOHC	27	⊣—	Ignition ON	0 V		
Evaporative emission (EVAP) canister purge valve	15	⊣▷	Ignition ON	11-14 V		
	15	⊣▷	Engine hot – valve operating		10 V/50 ms	⩗⩘ 20
Fuel pump relay	17	⊣▷	Engine cranking	0-1 V		
Heated oxygen sensor (HO2S) – DOHC	10	⊣—	Engine idling	0 V		
Heated oxygen sensor (HO2S)	29	⬅	Engine idling – engine hot	0-1 V fluctuating	0,2 V/1 sec.	⩗⩘ 21
Idle air control (IAC) valve	16	⊣▷	Engine idling – engine hot	30%	10 V/5 ms	⩗⩘ 25
	35	⊣▷	Engine idling – engine hot	70%	10 V/5 ms	⩗⩘ 25
Ignition coil	19	⇨	Engine idling		5 V/2 ms	⩗⩘ 33
	37	⇨	Engine idling		5 V/2 ms	⩗⩘ 33
Ignition switch	30	⬅	Ignition OFF	0 V		
	30	⬅	Ignition ON	11-14 V		
Injector 1	3	⊣▷	Ignition ON	11-14 V		
	3	⊣▷	Engine idling – engine hot	1,5-4,5 ms	10 V/2 ms	⩗⩘ 35
Injector 2	23	⊣▷	Ignition ON	11-14 V		
	23	⊣▷	Engine idling – engine hot	1,5-4,5 ms	10 V/2 ms	⩗⩘ 35
Injector 3	4	⊣▷	Ignition ON	11-14 V		
	4	⊣▷	Engine idling – engine hot	1,5-4,5 ms	10 V/2 ms	⩗⩘ 35
Injector 4	22	⊣▷	Ignition ON	11-14 V		
	22	⊣▷	Engine idling – engine hot	1,5-4,5 ms	10 V/2 ms	⩗⩘ 35
Intake air temperature (IAT) sensor – if fitted	27	⊣—	Ignition ON	0 V		
	46	⬅	Ignition ON – air temp. 0°C	3,3-3,7 V		
	46	⬅	Ignition ON – air temp. 20°C	2,4-2,8 V		
Knock sensor (KS) – SOHC	9	⬅	Engine idling – accelerate briefly		50 mV/1 ms	⩗⩘ 38
	27	⊣—	Engine idling	0 V		
Malfunction indicator lamp (MIL)	36	⊣▷	Ignition ON – MIL ON	0-1 V		
	36	⊣▷	Engine idling – MIL OFF	11-14 V		
Mass air flow (MAF) sensor	13	⬅	Engine idling – engine hot	0,7-1,1 V		
	13	⬅	3000 rpm	1,3-2 V		
	31	⊣—	Ignition ON	0 V		
Tachometer – MT	14	⇨	Ignition ON	11-14 V		
Throttle position (TP) sensor	8	⇨	Ignition ON	5 V		
	40	⬅	Ignition ON – throttle closed	0,2-0,8 V		
	40	⬅	Ignition ON – throttle fully open	4,2-4,8 V		
Throttle position (TP) sensor – DOHC	9	⊣—	Ignition ON	0 V		
Throttle position (TP) sensor – SOHC	27	⊣—	Ignition ON	0 V		
Transmission control module (TCM)	14	⇨	Ignition ON	11-14 V		
	41	⇨		1		
Transmission range (TR) switch	51	⬅	Ignition ON – AT in P or N	11-14 V		
	51	⬅	Ignition ON – AT not in P or N	0 V		
Vehicle speed sensor (VSS)	11	⬅	Ignition ON – vehicle pushed	0 V or 11-14 V		

*Suggested settings - Voltage/time per division

1 Connected pin - no test data available or random digital signal

JAGUAR (DAIMLER)

Denso

Model:	Engine code:	Year:
X-Type 2,0	YB	2001-02/04

ECM harness multi-plug

Terminal side

```
104 103 102 101 100  99 98  97 96  95 94  93 92          91 90 89 88 87  86 85  84 83  82 81  80 79
 78 77 76 75  74 73 72  71 70  69 68  67 66              65 64 63 62  61  60 59  58 57  56 55  54 53
 52 51 50 49  48 47 46  45 44  43 42  41 40              39 38 37 36  35  34 33  32 31  30 29  28 27
 26 25 24 23 22  21 20  19 18  17 16  15 14              13 12 11 10  9   8  7   6  5   4  3   2  1
```

AD105303

Wire side

```
 79 80 81 82 83 84 85 86 87 88 89 90 91               92 93 94 95 96 97 98 99 100 101 102 103 104
 53 54 55 56 57 58 59 60 61 62 63 64 65                  66 67 68 69 70 71 72 73 74 75 76 77 78
 27 28 29 30 31 32 33 34 35 36 37 38 39                  40 41 42 43 44 45 46 47 48 49 50 51 52
  1  2  3  4  5  6  7  8  9 10 11 12 13                     14 15 16 17 18 19 20 21 22 23 24 25 26
```

AD105301

Component/circuit description	ECM pin	Signal	Condition	Typical value	Oscilloscope setting*	Wave form
AC compressor clutch relay	20	⊐▷	Engine idling – AC ON – compressor ON	0-1 V		
	20	⊐▷	Engine idling – AC ON – compressor OFF	11-14 V		
AC refrigerant pressure sensor	2	←	Ignition ON	1 V		
	3	⅂—	Ignition ON	0 V		
	11	⇒	Ignition ON	5 V		
Alternator	8	⇒	Engine idling		3 V/10 ms	
	35	←	Engine idling	11-14 V		
	43	←	Ignition ON	7,2 V		
Battery	21	←	Ignition OFF	11-14 V		
	21	←	Ignition ON	11-14 V		
Brake pedal position (BPP) switch	34	←	Ignition ON – brake pedal released	0 V		
	34	←	Ignition ON – brake pedal depressed	11-14 V		
Camshaft position (CMP) actuator 1	96	⇒	Engine running	0-99%	2 V/5 ms	∿ 64
Camshaft position (CMP) actuator 2	95	⇒	Engine running	0-99%	2 V/5 ms	∿ 64
Camshaft position (CMP) sensor 1, bank 1	59	←	Engine idling		0,5 V/50 ms	
	60	⅂—	Ignition ON	0 V		
Camshaft position (CMP) sensor 1, bank 1 – shield wire	38	⅂—	Ignition ON	0 V		
Camshaft position (CMP) sensor 2, bank 2	86	←	Engine idling		0,5 V/50 ms	∿ 109
	87	⅂—	Ignition ON	0 V		
Camshaft position (CMP) sensor 2, bank 2 – shield wire	38	⅂—	Ignition ON	0 V		
CAN data bus – high	89	◄⇒		1		

★ Suggested settings - Voltage/time per division

Component/circuit description	ECM pin	Signal	Condition	Typical value	Oscilloscope setting*	Wave form
CAN data bus – low	88	⇔		1		
Clutch pedal position (CPP) switch – MT	84	←	Ignition ON – clutch pedal released	11-14 V		
	84	←	Ignition ON – clutch pedal depressed	0 V		
Crankshaft position (CKP) sensor	61	←	Ignition ON	0 V		
	61	←	Engine idling	2,9 V ac	2 V/2 ms	2
	62	⌐	Ignition ON	0 V		
Crankshaft position (CKP) sensor – shield wire	38	⌐	Ignition ON	0 V		
Cruise control brake pedal switch – if fitted	7	←	Ignition ON – cruise control ON – brake pedal released	11-14 V		
	7	←	Ignition ON – cruise control ON – brake pedal depressed	0 V		
Cruise control module – if fitted	17	⇒		1		
	56	←		1		
	57	←		1		
Data link connector (DLC)	39	⇔		1		
Earth	4		Ignition ON	0 V		
	5		Ignition ON	0 V		
	18		Ignition ON	0 V		
	19		Ignition ON	0 V		
	48		Ignition ON	0 V		
	52		Ignition ON	0 V		
	64		Ignition ON	0 V		
	75		Ignition ON	0 V		
	78		Ignition ON	0 V		
	91		Ignition ON	0 V		
	102		Ignition ON	0 V		
Engine control (EC) relay	22	←	Ignition OFF	0 V		
	22	←	Ignition ON	11-14 V		
	23	←	Ignition OFF	0 V		
	23	←	Ignition ON	11-14 V		
	69	←	Ignition OFF	11-14 V		
	69	←	Ignition ON	0 V		
Engine coolant blower motor control module	44	⇒	Engine running – coolant blower motor OFF		2 V/1 ms	65
	44	⇒	Engine running – coolant blower motor ON		4 V/2 ms	24
Engine coolant temperature (ECT) sensor	3	⌐	Ignition ON	0 V		
	80	←	Ignition ON – coolant temp. 10°C	2,5 V		
	80	←	Engine running – engine hot	0,3 V		
Evaporative emission (EVAP) canister purge valve	74	⌐▷	Ignition ON	11-14 V		
	74	⌐▷	Engine running – engine hot – valve operating		10 V/50 ms	Intermittent 20
Engine oil temperature sensor	3	⌐	Ignition ON	0 V		
	79	←	Ignition ON – oil temp low	3,2 V		
	79	←	Ignition ON – oil temp high	0,5 V		
Fuel pump (FP) relay	99	⌐▷	Ignition ON	0-1 V briefly then 11-14 V		
	99	⌐▷	Engine idling	0-1 V		

* Suggested settings - Voltage/time per division

Component/circuit description	ECM pin	Signal	Condition	Typical value	Oscilloscope setting*	Wave form
Heated oxygen sensor (HO2S) 1, bank 1 – planar sensor	50	←	Ignition ON	3,8 V		
	50	←	Engine idling	3,8 V		
	51	←	Ignition ON	3,8 V		
	51	←	Engine idling	3,8 V		
	77	⊐▷	Ignition ON	11-14 V		
	77	⊐▷	Engine idling		2 V/0,2 sec.	72
	104	⊐▷	Ignition ON	11-14 V		
	104	⊐▷	Engine idling		2 V/0,2 sec.	72
Heated oxygen sensor (HO2S) 1, bank 1 – shield wire	55	⊣‒	Ignition ON	0 V		
Heated oxygen sensor (HO2S) 1, bank 2 – planar sensor	25	←	Ignition ON	3,8 V		
	25	←	Engine idling	3,8 V		
	26	←	Ignition ON	3,8 V		
	26	←	Engine idling	3,8 V		
	76	⊐▷	Ignition ON	11-14 V		
	76	⊐▷	Engine idling		2 V/0,2 sec.	72
	103	⊐▷	Ignition ON	11-14 V		
	103	⊐▷	Engine idling		2 V/0,2 sec.	72
Heated oxygen sensor (HO2S) 1, bank 2 – shield wire	55	⊣‒	Ignition ON	0 V		
Heated oxygen sensor (HO2S) 2, bank 1	47	⊐▷	Ignition ON	11-14 V		
	47	⊐▷	Engine idling		2 V/0,2 sec.	72
	53	←	Engine idling	0,1-0,9 V		
	55	⊣‒	Ignition ON	0 V		
Heated oxygen sensor (HO2S) 2, bank 1 – shield wire	55	⊣‒	Ignition ON	0 V		
Heated oxygen sensor (HO2S) 2, bank 2	46	⊐▷	Ignition ON	11-14 V		
	46	⊐▷	Engine idling		2 V/0,2 sec.	72
	54	←	Engine idling	0,1-0,9 V		
	55	⊣‒	Ignition ON	0 V		
Heated oxygen sensor (HO2S) 2, bank 2 – shield wire	55	⊣‒	Ignition ON	0 V		
Idle air control (IAC) valve	97	⇒	Engine idling	50%	5 V/0,5 ms	66
	98	⇒	Ignition ON	11-14 V		
Ignition switch	63	←	Ignition ON	11-14 V		
Ignition switch – MT	85	←	Ignition ON	11-14 V		
Ignition switch – start signal	6	←	Engine cranking	9 V min.		
Ignition coil 1	12	←	Ignition ON	5 V		
	12	←	Engine idling		2 V/10 ms	53
	14	⊐▷	Engine idling		1 V/50 ms	65
Ignition coil 2	13	←	Ignition ON	5 V		
	13	←	Engine idling		2 V/10 ms	53
	40	⊐▷	Engine idling		1 V/50 ms	65
Ignition coil 3	12	←	Ignition ON	5 V		
	12	←	Engine idling		2 V/10 ms	53
	15	⊐▷	Engine idling		1 V/50 ms	65
Ignition coil 4	13	←	Ignition ON	5 V		
	13	←	Engine idling		2 V/10 ms	53
	41	⊐▷	Engine idling		1 V/50 ms	65
Ignition coil 5	12	←	Ignition ON	5 V		
	12	←	Engine idling		2 V/10 ms	53
	16	⊐▷	Engine idling		1 V/50 ms	65

* Suggested settings - Voltage/time per division

Component/circuit description	ECM pin	Signal	Condition	Typical value	Oscilloscope setting*	Wave form
Ignition coil 6	13	←	Ignition ON	5 V		
	13	←	Engine idling		2 V/10 ms	〜 53
	42	⊣▷	Engine idling		1 V/50 ms	〜 65
Inertia fuel shut-off (IFS) switch	36	←	Ignition ON – switch depressed	11-14 V		
	36	←	Ignition ON – switch activated	0 V		
Injector 1	65	⊣▷	Ignition ON	11-14 V		
	65	⊣▷	Engine idling	3,2 ms	10 V/2 ms	〜 35
Injector 2	92	⊣▷	Ignition ON	11-14 V		
	92	⊣▷	Engine idling	3,2 ms	10 V/2 ms	〜 35
Injector 3	66	⊣▷	Ignition ON	11-14 V		
	66	⊣▷	Engine idling	3,2 ms	10 V/2 ms	〜 35
Injector 4	93	⊣▷	Ignition ON	11-14 V		
	93	⊣▷	Engine idling	3,2 ms	10 V/2 ms	〜 35
Injector 5	67	⊣▷	Ignition ON	11-14 V		
	67	⊣▷	Engine idling	3,2 ms	10 V/2 ms	〜 35
Injector 6	94	⊣▷	Ignition ON	11-14 V		
	94	⊣▷	Engine idling	3,2 ms	10 V/2 ms	〜 35
Intake air temperature (IAT) sensor – in MAF sensor	3	⊣─	Ignition ON	0 V		
	81	←	Ignition ON – air temp. 10°C	2,4 V		
Intake manifold air control solenoid 1	70	⊣▷	Engine running – valve not operating	11-14 V		
	70	⊣▷	Engine running – valve operating	0-1 V		
Intake manifold air control solenoid 2	71	⊣▷	Engine running – valve not operating	11-14 V		
	71	⊣▷	Engine running – valve operating	0-1 V		
Knock sensor (KS)	37	←	Ignition ON	2,2 V		
	37	←	Engine idling – full throttle briefly		50 mV/1 ms	〜 38
	38	⊣─	Ignition ON	0 V		
Knock sensor (KS) – shield wire	38	⊣─	Ignition ON	0 V		
Manifold absolute pressure (MAP) sensor	1	←	Ignition ON	2,4 V		
	1	←	Engine idling	1 V		
	1	←	Engine idling – accelerate briefly	2,2 V		
	3	⊣─	Ignition ON	0 V		
	11	⇒	Ignition ON	5 V		
Mass air flow (MAF) sensor	29	⊣─	Ignition ON	0 V		
	30	←	Ignition ON	0,6 V		
	30	←	Engine idling	1,5 V		
	30	←	Engine idling – accelerate briefly	4 V		
	31	⊣─	Ignition ON	0 V		
Starter motor relay	6	⊣▷	Engine cranking	11-14 V		
	68	⊣▷	Engine cranking	0-1 V		
Throttle position (TP) sensor	3	⊣─	Ignition ON	0 V		
	11	⇒	Ignition ON	5 V		
	27	←	Ignition ON – throttle closed	0,8 V		
	27	←	Ignition ON – throttle fully open	4,4 V		
Throttle position (TP) sensor – shield wire	28	⊣─	Ignition ON	0 V		
Transmission range (TR) switch	85	←	Ignition ON – AT in P or N	12-14 V		
	85	←	Ignition ON – AT not in P or N	0 V		

*Suggested settings - Voltage/time per division

1 Connected pin - no test data available or random digital signal

JAGUAR (DAIMLER)

Denso

Model:	Engine code:	Year:
XJ8/Sovereign 3,2/Sport	AC/KC	1999-03
XJ8/Sovereign 4,0	BC/LC/DC/MA	1999-03
XK8 4,0	CE/CC/NC	1999-02
XKR 4,0	EC/PA	2000-02

ECM harness multi-plug

Terminal side

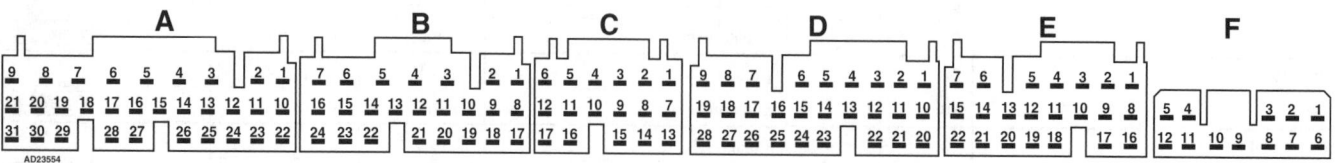

Wire side

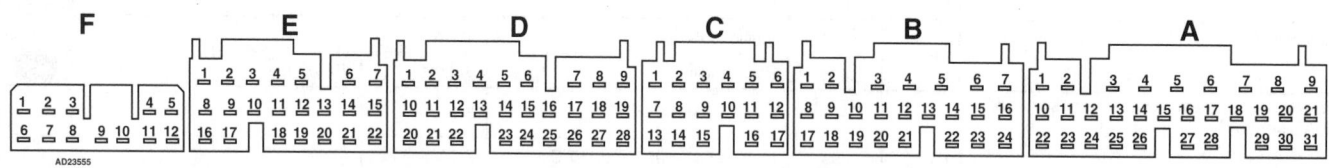

Component/circuit description	ECM pin	Signal	Condition	Typical value	Oscilloscope setting*	Wave form
AC compressor clutch relay	A25	⌐⊳	Engine running – compressor OFF	11-14 V		
	A25	⌐⊳	Engine running – compressor ON	0 V		
AC control module	A11	←	Ignition ON – AC OFF	0 V		
	A11	←	Ignition ON – AC ON	11-14 V		
	A11	←	Engine running – AC OFF	0 V		
	A11	←	Engine running – AC ON	11-14 V		
	A23	←	Ignition ON – heated rear window OFF	11-14 V		
	A23	←	Ignition ON – heated rear window ON	0,4 V		
AC control module – electrical load signal	A12	←	Ignition ON	0 V		
	A12	←	Engine running	11-14 V		
AC refrigerant quadruple pressure switch	A10	←	Ignition ON	11-14 V		
	A10	←	Engine running – AC refrigerant pressure 20 bar min.	0 V		
	A10	←	Engine running – AC refrigerant pressure 20 bar max.	11-14 V		
	A22	←	Ignition ON	11-14 V		
	A22	←	Engine running – AC refrigerant pressure 12 bar min.	0 V		
	A22	←	Engine running – AC refrigerant pressure 12 bar max.	11-14 V		
Accelerator pedal position (APP) sensor – in throttle control unit	B9	←	Ignition ON – accelerator pedal released	0,5 V		
	B9	←	Ignition ON – accelerator pedal fully depressed	4,75 V		
	B18	←	Ignition ON – accelerator pedal released	0,5 V		
	B18	←	Ignition ON – accelerator pedal fully depressed	4,75 V		
	C1	⇨	Ignition ON	5 V		
	C7	⌐—	Ignition ON	0 V		
	D13	⌐—	Ignition ON	0 V		
	D5	⇨	Ignition ON	5 V		
Accelerator pedal position (APP) sensor – shield wire	B24	⌐—	Ignition ON	0 V		

* Suggested settings - Voltage/time per division

Component/circuit description	ECM pin	Signal	Condition	Typical value	Oscilloscope setting*	Wave form
Air assisted injector air control valve – except DC/MA/PA	D3	⇨	Engine idling	78%		
Battery	D20	⬅	Ignition OFF	11-14 V		
Brake pedal position (BPP) switch	C8	⬅	Ignition ON – brake pedal released	11-14 V		
	C8	⬅	Ignition ON – brake pedal depressed	0 V		
Camshaft position (CMP) actuator A – BC/LC	B1	⇨	Ignition ON		2 V/2 ms	
	B1	⇨	Engine idling	12%	2 V/2 ms	
	B2	⌐	Ignition ON	0 V		
Camshaft position (CMP) actuator B – BC/LC	B6	⇨	Ignition ON		2 V/2 ms	
	B6	⇨	Engine idling	12%	2 V/2 ms	
	B7	⌐	Ignition ON	0 V		
Camshaft position (CMP) sensor A	D9	⌐	Ignition ON	0 V		
	D19	⬅	Engine idling	0,77 V ~	0,5 V/50 ms	
Camshaft position (CMP) sensor A – shield wire	D6	⌐	Ignition ON	0 V		
Camshaft position (CMP) sensor B	D17	⌐	Ignition ON	0 V		
	D18	⬅	Engine idling	0,77 V ~	0,5 V/50 ms	
Camshaft position (CMP) sensor B – shield wire	D6	⌐	Ignition ON	0 V		
CAN databus	D15	⬅⇨		1		
	D16	⬅⇨		1		
	D24	⬅⇨		1		
	D25	⬅⇨		1		
Crankshaft position (CKP) sensor	D7	⌐	Ignition ON	0 V		
	D8	⬅	Ignition ON	0 V		
	D8	⬅	Engine idling	2,2 V ~	2 V/10 ms	
Crankshaft position (CKP) sensor – shield wire	D6	⌐	Ignition ON	0 V		
Cruise control brake pedal switch	A20	⬅	Ignition ON – cruise control ON – brake pedal released	11-14 V		
	A20	⬅	Ignition ON – cruise control ON – brake pedal depressed	0 V		
Cruise control indicator lamp	A16	⬅	Ignition ON – lamp OFF	11-14 V		
	A16	⬅	Cruise control ON – lamp ON	0-1 V		
Cruise control master switch	B13	⬅	Ignition ON – cruise control OFF	0 V		
	B13	⬅	Ignition ON – cruise control ON	11-14 V		
Cruise control selector switch – cancel/resume	B15	⬅	Ignition ON	11-14 V		
	B15	⬅	Ignition ON – cancel switch operated	8,8 V briefly then 11-14 V		
	B15	⬅	Ignition ON – resume switch operated	7,3 V briefly then 11-14 V		
Cruise control selector switch – set +/-	B14	⬅	Ignition ON	11-14 V		
	B14	⬅	Ignition ON – set + switch operated	7,3 V briefly then 11-14 V		
	B14	⬅	Ignition ON – set - switch operated	8,8 V briefly then 11-14 V		
Data link connector (DLC)	A17	⬅⇨	Ignition ON	0 V		
	A18	⬅⇨	Ignition ON	0 V		
	A19	⬅⇨	Ignition ON	0 V		
	A27	⬅⇨	Ignition ON	11-14 V		

* Suggested settings - Voltage/time per division

Component/circuit description	ECM pin	Signal	Condition	Typical value	Oscilloscope setting*	Wave form
Earth	A3		Ignition ON	0 V		
	A21		Ignition ON	0 V		
	A29		Ignition ON	0 V		
	A31		Ignition ON	0 V		
	B8		Ignition ON	0 V		
	B21		Ignition ON	0 V		
	E1		Ignition ON	0 V		
	E16		Ignition ON	0 V		
	E22		Ignition ON	0 V		
	F6		Ignition ON	0 V		
	F7		Ignition ON	0 V		
Engine control relay	B3	⇥▷	Ignition OFF	11-14V		
	B3	⇥▷	Ignition ON	0 V		
	B17	⬅	Ignition OFF	0 V		
	B17	⬅	Ignition ON	11-14 V		
	C13	⬅	Ignition ON	11-14 V		
Engine coolant blower motor relay module	B4	⇥▷	Engine running – coolant blower motors OFF	11-14 V		
	B4	⇥▷	Engine running – coolant blower motors ON – low speed	11-14 V		
	B4	⇥▷	Engine running – coolant blower motors ON – high speed	0 V		
	B5	⇥▷	Engine running – coolant blower motors OFF	11-14 V		
	B5	⇥▷	Engine running – coolant blower motors ON – high speed	11-14 V		
	B5	⇥▷	Engine running – coolant blower motors ON – low speed	0 V		
Engine coolant pump relay – DC/MA/PA	A14	⇨	Engine running – coolant pump ON	11-14 V		
Engine coolant temperature (ECT) sensor	C7	⊐—	Ignition ON	0 V		
	C14	⬅	Ignition ON – coolant temp. 20°C	2 V		
	C14	⬅	Ignition ON – coolant temp. 90°C	0,4 V		
	D13	⊐—	Ignition ON	0 V		
Engine oil temperature (EOT) sensor	A15	⬅	Ignition ON – oil temp. 34°C	2,5 V		
	A15	⬅	Ignition ON – oil temp. 90°C	0,5 V		
	C7	⊐—	Ignition ON	0 V		
	D13	⊐—	Ignition ON	0 V		
Evaporative emission (EVAP) canister purge valve	A1	⇥▷	Ignition ON	11-14 V		
	A1	⇥▷	Engine running	1-99%	10 V/5 ms	Intermittent ⋀⋀⋀ 20
Exhaust gas recirculation (EGR) solenoid – DC/MA/PA 2001→	F3	⇥▷	Ignition ON	11-14 V		
	F3	⇥▷	Engine running	[1]		
	F4	⇥▷	Ignition ON	11-14 V		
	F4	⇥▷	Engine running	[1]		
	F9	⇥▷	Ignition ON	11-14 V		
	F9	⇥▷	Engine running	[1]		
	F10	⇥▷	Ignition ON	11-14 V		
	F10	⇥▷	Engine running	[1]		
Fuel pump relay 1	D4	⇥▷	Ignition ON	0 V briefly then 11-14 V		
	D4	⇥▷	Engine running	0 V		
Fuel pump relay 2 – DC/MA/PA	C3	⇥▷	Ignition ON	0 V briefly then 11-14 V		
	C3	⇥▷	Engine running	0 V		
Handbrake switch	B22	⬅	Ignition ON – handbrake OFF	11-14 V		
	B22	⬅	Ignition ON – handbrake ON	0,15 V		

★ Suggested settings - Voltage/time per division

Component/circuit description	ECM pin	Signal	Condition	Typical value	Oscilloscope setting*	Wave form
Heated oxygen sensor (HO2S) front, bank A	C4	←	Ignition ON	3,8 V		
	C4	←	Engine idling	3,5 V		
	C10	⇒	Ignition ON	3,8 V		
	F1	⅂▷	Ignition ON	11-14 V		
	F1	⅂▷	Engine idling	85-90%		
Heated oxygen sensor (HO2S) front, bank A – shield wire	D12	⅂—	Ignition ON	0 V		
Heated oxygen sensor (HO2S) front, bank B	C5	←	Ignition ON	3,8 V		
	C5	←	Engine idling	3,5 V		
	C11	⇒	Ignition ON	3,8 V		
	F2	⅂▷	Ignition ON	11-14 V		
	F2	⅂▷	Engine idling	85-90%		
Heated oxygen sensor (HO2S) front, bank B – shield wire	D12	⅂—	Ignition ON	0 V		
Heated oxygen sensor (HO2S) rear, bank A	D12	⅂—	Ignition ON	0 V		
	D21	←	Ignition ON	0 V		
	D21	←	Engine idling	0,4-0,6 V		
	E7	⅂▷	Ignition ON	11-14 V		
	E7	⅂▷	Engine idling	20-60%	2 V/0,2 sec.	MM 72
Heated oxygen sensor (HO2S) rear, bank A – shield wire	D12	⅂—	Ignition ON	0 V		
Heated oxygen sensor (HO2S) rear, bank B	D12	⅂—	Ignition ON	0 V		
	D22	←	Ignition ON	0 V		
	D22	←	Engine idling	0,4-0,6 V		
	E15	⅂▷	Ignition ON	11-14 V		
	E15	⅂▷	Engine idling	20-60%	2 V/0,2 sec.	MM 72
Heated oxygen sensor (HO2S) rear, bank B – shield wire	D12	⅂—	Ignition ON	0 V		
Ignition coil 1A	D10	←	Ignition ON	4 V		
	D10	←	Engine idling	23 Hz	1 V/10 ms	MM 53
	E12	⇒	Engine idling		0,5 V/50 ms	MM 65
Ignition coil 1B	D11	←	Ignition ON	4 V		
	D11	←	Engine idling	23 Hz	1 V/10 ms	MM 53
	E20	⇒	Engine idling		0,5 V/50 ms	MM 65
Ignition coil 2A	D11	←	Ignition ON	4 V		
	D11	←	Engine idling	23 Hz	1 V/10 ms	MM 53
	E11	⇒	Engine idling		0,5 V/50 ms	MM 65
Ignition coil 2B	D10	←	Ignition ON	4 V		
	D10	←	Engine idling	23 Hz	1 V/10 ms	MM 53
	E19	⇒	Engine idling		0,5 V/50 ms	MM 65
Ignition coil 3A	D11	←	Ignition ON	4 V		
	D11	←	Engine idling	23 Hz	1 V/10 ms	MM 53
	E10	⇒	Engine idling		0,5 V/50 ms	MM 65
Ignition coil 3B	D10	←	Ignition ON	4 V		
	D10	←	Engine idling	23 Hz	1 V/10 ms	MM 53
	E18	⇒	Engine idling		0,5 V/50 ms	MM 65
Ignition coil 4A	D10	←	Ignition ON	4 V		
	D10	←	Engine idling	23 Hz	1 V/10 ms	MM 53
	E9	⇒	Engine idling		0,5 V/50 ms	MM 65
Ignition coil 4B	D11	←	Ignition ON	4 V		
	D11	←	Engine idling	23 Hz	1 V/10 ms	MM 53
	E17	⇒	Engine idling		0,5 V/50 ms	MM 65

* Suggested settings - Voltage/time per division

Component/circuit description	ECM pin	Signal	Condition	Typical value	Oscilloscope setting*	Wave form
Ignition main circuits relay	C9	←	Ignition ON	11-14 V		
Immobilizer control module	C15	←	Ignition ON	11-14 V briefly then 0 V		
	C16	←	Ignition ON	11-14 V briefly then 0 V		
Inertia fuel shut-off (IFS) switch	C12	←	Ignition ON – switch depressed	11-14 V		
	C12	←	Ignition ON – switch activated	0 V		
Injector 1A	E2	⇥▷	Ignition ON	11-14 V		
	E2	⇥▷	Engine idling	2,8 ms	10 V/2 ms	ᴡᴡᴡ 35
Injector 1B	E6	⇥▷	Ignition ON	11-14 V		
	E6	⇥▷	Engine idling	2,8 ms	10 V/2 ms	ᴡᴡᴡ 35
Injector 2A	E21	⇥▷	Ignition ON	11-14 V		
	E21	⇥▷	Engine idling	2,8 ms	10 V/2 ms	ᴡᴡᴡ 35
Injector 2B	E4	⇥▷	Ignition ON	11-14 V		
	E4	⇥▷	Engine idling	2,8 ms	10 V/2 ms	ᴡᴡᴡ 35
Injector 3A	E14	⇥▷	Ignition ON	11-14 V		
	E14	⇥▷	Engine idling	2,8 ms	10 V/2 ms	ᴡᴡᴡ 35
Injector 3B	E3	⇥▷	Ignition ON	11-14 V		
	E3	⇥▷	Engine idling	2,8 ms	10 V/2 ms	ᴡᴡᴡ 35
Injector 4A	E5	⇥▷	Ignition ON	11-14 V		
	E5	⇥▷	Engine idling	2,8 ms	10 V/2 ms	ᴡᴡᴡ 35
Injector 4B	E13	⇥▷	Ignition ON	11-14 V		
	E13	⇥▷	Engine idling	2,8 ms	10 V/2 ms	ᴡᴡᴡ 35
Intake air temperature (IAT) sensor – DC/MA/PA	B23	←	Ignition ON – air temp. 20°C	2,3 V		
	C7	⇥	Ignition ON	0 V		
	D13	⇥	Ignition ON	0 V		
Knock sensor (KS) A	D14	←	Ignition ON	2,2 V		
	D14	←	Engine idling – NO knocking	0 Hz		
	D14	←	Engine idling – knocking	2-20 kHz		
	D14	←	Engine idling – accelerate briefly		50 mV/1 ms	ᴡᴡᴡ 38
Knock sensor (KS) A – shield wire	D6	⇥	Ignition ON	0 V		
Knock sensor (KS) B	D23	←	Ignition ON	2,2 V		
	D23	←	Engine idling – NO knocking	0 Hz		
	D23	←	Engine idling – knocking	2-20 kHz		
	D23	←	Engine idling – accelerate briefly		50 mV/1 ms	ᴡᴡᴡ 38
Knock sensor (KS) B – shield wire	D6	⇥	Ignition ON	0 V		
Manifold absolute pressure (MAP) sensor – DC/MA/PA 2001	A28	←	Ignition ON	3,6 V		
	A28	←	Engine idling	1,2 V		
	C1	⇨	Ignition ON	5 V		
	C7	⇥	Ignition ON	0 V		
	D5	⇨	Ignition ON	5 V		
	D13	⇥	Ignition ON	0 V		
Mass air flow (MAF) sensor	C7	⇥	Ignition ON	0 V		
	C17	←	Ignition ON – air temp. 18°C	2 V		
	D13	⇥	Ignition ON	0 V		
	D26	⇥	Ignition ON	0 V		
	D27	⇥	Ignition ON	0 V		
	D28	←	Ignition ON	0,75 V		
	D28	←	Engine idling	1,2 V		
	D28	←	Engine idling – accelerate briefly	3,75 V briefly	1 V/2 secs.	ᴡᴡᴡ 41
Module cooling fan	F5	⇥▷	Ignition ON	0 V		

* Suggested settings - Voltage/time per division

Component/circuit description	ECM pin	Signal	Condition	Typical value	Oscilloscope setting*	Wave form
Multifunction control module	C16	⬅	Ignition ON	11-14 V briefly then 0 V		
Oxygen sensor heater relay	F8	⬅	Ignition ON	11-14 V		
Park/neutral position (PNP) switch	B12	⬅	Ignition ON – AT in P or N	0 V		
	B12	⬅	Ignition ON – AT not in P or N	11-14 V		
Starter motor relay	C2	⬅	Ignition ON	11-14 V		
	C2	⬅	Engine cranking	0,5 V		
Throttle actuator	A4	⮕	Ignition ON		2 V/2 ms	71
	A4	⮕	Engine idling		2 V/2 ms	71
	A5	⮕	Ignition ON		2 V/2 ms	71
	A5	⮕	Engine idling		2 V/2 ms	71
	A6	⮕	Ignition ON	11-14 V		
	A6	⮕	Engine idling	11-14 V		
	A7	⮕	Ignition ON	11-14 V		
	A7	⮕	Engine idling	11-14 V		
Throttle actuator relay	A8	⬅	Ignition ON	11-14 V		
	A9	⬅	Ignition ON	11-14 V		
	C6	⇥▷	Ignition ON	11-14 V briefly then 0 V		
	C6	⇥▷	Engine idling	0 V		
Throttle position (TP) sensor	B10	⬅	Ignition ON – throttle closed	0,5 V		
	B10	⬅	Ignition ON – throttle fully open	4,75 V		
	B19	⬅	Ignition ON – throttle closed	0,9 V		
	B19	⬅	Ignition ON – throttle fully open	4,75 V		
	C1	⮕	Ignition ON	5 V		
	C7	⇥―	Ignition ON	0 V		
	D5	⮕	Ignition ON	5 V		
	D13	⇥―	Ignition ON	0 V		
Throttle position (TP) sensor – shield wire	B24	⇥―	Ignition ON	0 V		

*Suggested settings - Voltage/time per division

[1] Connected pin - no test data available or random digital signal

ECM harness multi-plug

Terminal side

19 18 17 16 15 14 13 12 11 10 9 8 7 6 5 4 3 2 1
37 36 35 34 33 32 31 30 29 28 27 26 25 24 23 22 21 20
55 54 53 52 51 50 49 48 47 46 45 44 43 42 41 40 39 38

AD72618

Wire side

1 2 3 4 5 6 7 8 9 10 11 12 13 14 15 16 17 18 19
20 21 22 23 24 25 26 27 28 29 30 31 32 33 34 35 36 37
38 39 40 41 42 43 44 45 46 47 48 49 50 51 52 53 54 55

AD42077

Component/circuit description	ECM pin	Signal	Condition	Typical value
ABS control module	40	⇒	Ignition ON	10 V
AC refrigerant triple pressure switch	24	⇐	Ignition ON	10 V
	44	⇐	Ignition ON	10,3 V
	44	⇐	Engine idling – AC OFF	11-14 V
	44	⇐	Engine idling – AC ON	0,01 V
Accelerator pedal position (APP) sensor	33	⇒	Ignition ON	5 V
	37	⇐	Ignition ON – accelerator pedal released	0,4 V
	37	⇐	Ignition ON – accelerator pedal fully depressed	3,5 V
	25	⇐	Ignition ON	0,4 V
Brake pedal position (BPP) switch	26	⇐	Ignition ON – brake pedal released	0 V
	26	⇐	Ignition ON – brake pedal depressed	11-14 V
Combination control module – immobilizer	45	⇐	Ignition ON	10 V
Crankshaft position (CKP) sensor	47	⇐	Engine idling	4,5 V ac
	47	⇐	Engine idling	10 V/5 ms per division 〰6
	47	⇐	Ignition ON	0,02 V
Data link connector (DLC)	27	⇐	Ignition ON	6,8 V
	42	⇒	Ignition ON	6,8 V
Earth	18	⊣	Ignition ON	0 V
	19	⊣	Ignition ON	0 V
Engine control relay	15	⊣⇒	Ignition OFF	11-14 V
	15	⊣⇒	Ignition ON	0,2 V
	16	⇐	Engine idling	11-14 V
	16	⇐	Ignition ON	11-14 V
	17	⇐	Engine idling	11-14 V
	17	⇐	Ignition ON	11-14 V
Engine coolant temperature (ECT) sensor	53	⇐	Ignition ON – coolant temp. 17°C	3,8 V
	53	⇐	Engine idling – coolant temp. 80°C	1,4 V
Exhaust gas recirculation (EGR) solenoid	6	⇒	Ignition ON	11-14 V
	6	⇒	Engine idling	5 V/2 ms per division 〰31
Fuel injection timing solenoid	10	⇒	Ignition ON	8,5-9,5 V (fluctuating)
	10	⇒	Ignition ON	5 V/2 ms per division 〰31

Autodata

Component/circuit description	ECM pin	Signal	Condition	Typical value	
Fuel quantity adjuster	1	⇨	Engine idling	2 V/2 ms per division	〰〰 5
	1	⇨	Ignition ON	11-14 V after 30 seconds	
	2	⇨	Engine idling	2 V/2 ms per division	〰〰 5
	2	⇨	Ignition ON	11-14 V after 30 seconds	
Fuel quantity adjuster position sensor	14	⇦	Ignition ON	2,5 V	
	14	⇦	Engine idling	2,5 V	
	21	⇨	Ignition ON	2,5 V	
	21	⇨	Engine idling	2,5 V	
	21	⇨	Engine idling	0,5 V/0,5 ms per division	〰〰 8
	39	⇨	Ignition ON	2,5 V	
	39	⇨	Engine idling	0,5 V/0,5 ms per division	〰〰 8
Fuel shut-off solenoid	3	⇨	Ignition ON	11-14 V	
Fuel temperature sensor	35	⇦	Engine idling	3,5 V	
	35	⇦	Ignition ON	3,9 V	
Glow plug relay	8	⇨	Ignition ON – glow plugs ON	0 V	
	8	⇨	Ignition ON – glow plugs OFF	11-14 V	
Glow plug warning lamp	11	⇨	Ignition ON	11-14 V	
Ignition switch	55	⇦	Ignition ON	11-14 V	
Injector needle lift sensor	5	⇨	Engine idling	0,5 V/1 ms per division	〰〰 7
	5	⇦	Ignition ON	3,47 V	
	12	⇥⇨	Ignition ON	0 V	
Intake air temperature (IAT) sensor	36	⇦	Ignition ON – air temp. 17°C	3,9 V	
Malfunction indicator lamp (MIL)	4	⇨	Ignition ON – MIL ON	0 V	
	4	⇨	Ignition ON – MIL OFF	11-14 V	
Manifold absolute pressure (MAP) sensor	51	⇨	Ignition ON	5 V	
	51	⇨	Engine idling	5 V	
	54	⇦	Ignition ON	1,9 V	
	54	⇦	Engine idling	1,9 V	
	54	⇦	Accelerate briefly	3,4 V	
Mass air flow (MAF) sensor	34	⇨	Ignition ON	5 V	
	38	⇦	Engine idling	2,0 V	
	38	⇦	Engine idling – accelerate briefly	3,9 V	
	38	⇦	Ignition ON	1,1 V	
Relay module	7	⇨	Ignition ON	11-14 V after 10 seconds	
	9	⇨	Engine idling – AC OFF	11-14 V	
	9	⇨	Engine idling – AC ON	0,14 V	
	9	⇨	Ignition ON	11-14 V	
	46	⇨	Ignition ON	11-14 V	
Sensor earth	13	⇥⇨	Ignition ON	0 V	
Tachometer	50	⇨	3000 rpm	98 Hz	
	50	⇨	Engine idling	26 Hz	
	50	⇨	Ignition ON	10,6 V	
Vehicle speed sensor (VSS)	29	⇦	Drive vehicle at 10 mph min.	0 to 11-14 V (fluctuating)	
	29	⇦	Drive vehicle at 10 mph min.	5 V/50 ms per division	〰〰 2
	29	⇦	Ignition ON	10,6 V	

1 Connected pin - no test data available

LAND ROVER

Siemens EMS 2000

Model:	Engine code:	Year:
Freelander 2,5	KV6	2000-06

ECM harness multi-plug

Terminal side

```
61 62 63 64 65 66 67 68 69 70 71 72 73 74 75      76 77 78 79 80 81 82 83 84 85 86 87 88 89 90
31 32 33 34 35 36 37 38 39 40 41 42 43 44 45      46 47 48 49 50 51 52 53 54 55 56 57 58 59 60
 1  2  3  4  5  6  7  8  9 10 11 12 13 14 15      16 17 18 19 20 21 22 23 24 25 26 27 28 29 30
```

AD22771

Wire side

```
90 89 88 87 86 85 84 83 82 81 80 79 78 77 76      75 74 73 72 71 70 69 68 67 66 65 64 63 62 61
60 59 58 57 56 55 54 53 52 51 50 49 48 47 46      45 44 43 42 41 40 39 38 37 36 35 34 33 32 31
30 29 28 27 26 25 24 23 22 21 20 19 18 17 16      15 14 13 12 11 10  9  8  7  6  5  4  3  2  1
```

AD22770

Component/circuit description	ECM pin	Signal	Condition	Typical value	Oscilloscope setting*	Wave form
ABS control module, vehicle speed signal	21	←		1		
AC compressor clutch relay	64	⇥▷	Engine idling – AC OFF	11-14 V		
	64	⇥▷	Engine idling – AC ON – AC compressor ON	0-1 V		
AC evaporator temperature sensor	46	←		1		
	53	⊣—	Ignition ON	0 V		
AC refrigerant pressure sensor	17	←		1		
	53	⊣—	Ignition ON	0 V		
	81	⇨	Ignition ON	5 V		
Accelerator pedal position (APP) sensor	49	←		1		
Alternator	51	←		1		
Battery	30	←	Ignition OFF	11-14 V		
Camshaft position (CMP) sensor	19	⊣—	Ignition ON	0 V		
	82	←	Engine idling		2 V/0,2 sec.	〜 18
CAN data bus – "high" signal line	27	⟷		1		
CAN data bus – "low" signal line	57	⟷		1		
Crankshaft position (CKP) sensor	18	⊣—	Ignition ON	0 V		
	54	←	Engine idling		2 V/1 ms	〜 49
Cruise control amplifier – if fitted	10			1		
Data link connector (DLC)	56	⟷		1		
Earth	3		Ignition ON	0 V		
	28		Ignition ON	0 V		
	33		Ignition ON	0 V		
	63		Ignition ON	0 V		
	67		Ignition ON	0 V		
Engine control relay	7	⇥▷	Ignition OFF	11-14 V after 5 minutes		
	7	⇥▷	Ignition ON	0-1 V		
	66	←	Ignition OFF	0 V after 5 minutes		
	66	←	Ignition ON	11-14 V		

★ Suggested settings - Voltage/time per division

Autodata

Component/circuit description	ECM pin	Signal	Condition	Typical value	Oscilloscope setting*	Wave form
Engine coolant blower control module	69	⇨		□1		
Engine coolant temperature (ECT) sensor	15	⊣−	Ignition ON	0 V		
	45	←	Ignition ON – coolant temp. 15°C	3 V		
	45	←	Ignition ON – coolant temp. 85°C	0,5 V		
Evaporative emission (EVAP) canister purge valve 1	4	⊣▷	Ignition ON	11-14 V		
	4	⊣▷	Engine running – valve operating		10 V/20 ms	〜 59
Evaporative emission (EVAP) canister purge valve 2	85	⊣▷		□1		
Fuel pump relay	9	⊣▷	Ignition ON	0-1 V briefly then 11-14 V		
	9	⊣▷	Engine cranking	0-1 V		
Heated oxygen sensor (HO2S) 1, bank 1	13	←	Engine idling – engine hot	0-1 V fluctuating	0,2 V/1 sec.	〜 21
	77	⊣−	Engine idling	0 V		
Heated oxygen sensor (HO2S) 1, bank 1 – heater control	36	⊣▷	Ignition ON	11-14 V		
	36	⊣▷	Engine idling – engine hot	97%	2 V/20 ms	〜 65
Heated oxygen sensor (HO2S) 1, bank 2	14	←	Engine idling – engine hot	0-1 V fluctuating	0,2 V/1 sec.	〜 21
	77	⊣−	Engine idling	0 V		
Heated oxygen sensor (HO2S) 1, bank 2 – heater control	34	⊣▷	Engine idling – engine hot	97%	2 V/20 ms	〜 65
Heated oxygen sensor (HO2S) 2	16	←	Engine idling – engine hot	0,3-0,7 V	0,2 V/0,5 sec.	〜 76
	76	⊣−	Engine idling	0 V		
Heated oxygen sensor (HO2S) 2 – heater control	35	⊣▷	Ignition ON	3,9 V		
	35	⊣▷	Engine idling – engine hot	98%	1 V/20 ms	〜 62
Idle air control (IAC) valve	42	⇨	Engine idling	0 V or 11-14 V	5 V/0,1 sec.	〜 14
	70	⇨	Engine idling	0 V or 11-14 V	5 V/0,1 sec.	〜 14
	71	⇨	Engine idling	0 V or 11-14 V	5 V/0,1 sec.	〜 14
	72	⇨	Engine idling	0 V or 11-14 V	5 V/0,1 sec.	〜 14
Ignition coil – cylinder 1	61	⊣▷	Ignition ON	11-14 V		
	61	⊣▷	Engine idling	11-14 V	5 V/2 ms	〜 33
Ignition coil – cylinder 2	62	⊣▷	Ignition ON	11-14 V		
	62	⊣▷	Engine idling	11-14 V	5 V/2 ms	〜 33
Ignition coil – cylinder 3	2	⊣▷	Ignition ON	11-14 V		
	2	⊣▷	Engine idling	11-14 V	5 V/2 ms	〜 33
Ignition coil – cylinder 4	1	⊣▷	Ignition ON	11-14 V		
	1	⊣▷	Engine idling	11-14 V	5 V/2 ms	〜 33
Ignition coil – cylinder 5	32	⊣▷	Ignition ON	11-14 V		
	32	⊣▷	Engine idling	11-14 V	5 V/2 ms	〜 33
Ignition coil – cylinder 6	31	⊣▷	Ignition ON	11-14 V		
	31	⊣▷	Engine idling	11-14 V	5 V/2 ms	〜 33
Ignition switch	29	←	Ignition ON	11-14 V		
Immobilizer control module	52	←		□1		
Injector 1	60	⊣▷	Ignition ON	11-14 V		
	60	⊣▷	Engine idling	3,3 ms	10 V/2 ms	〜 35
Injector 2	59	⊣▷	Ignition ON	11-14 V		
	59	⊣▷	Engine idling	3,3 ms	10 V/2 ms	〜 35
Injector 3	88	⊣▷	Ignition ON	11-14 V		
	88	⊣▷	Engine idling	3,3 ms	10 V/2 ms	〜 35
Injector 4	58	⊣▷	Ignition ON	11-14 V		
	58	⊣▷	Engine idling	3,3 ms	10 V/2 ms	〜 35

* Suggested settings - Voltage/time per division

Component/circuit description	ECM pin	Signal	Condition	Typical value	Oscilloscope setting*	Wave form
Injector 5	89	⊐⊳	Ignition ON	11-14 V		
	89	⊐⊳	Engine idling	3,3 ms	10 V/2 ms	Ⓜ35
Injector 6	90	⊐⊳	Ignition ON	11-14 V		
	90	⊐⊳	Engine idling	3,3 ms	10 V/2 ms	Ⓜ35
Intake air flap control actuator 1	8	⇨	Ignition ON	11-14 V		
	8	⇨	Engine idling	11-14 V		
	8	⇨	Engine idling – throttle fully open briefly	0 V – briefly		
	84	⬅	Ignition ON	0 V		
	84	⬅	Engine idling	0 V		
Intake air flap control actuator 2	23	⬅	Ignition ON	0 V		
	23	⬅	Engine idling	0 V		
	38	⇨	Ignition ON	11-14 V		
	38	⇨	Engine idling	11-14 V		
	38	⇨	Engine idling – throttle fully open briefly	0 V – briefly		
Intake air temperature (IAT) sensor	12	⌐	Ignition ON	0 V		
	47	⬅	Ignition ON – air temp. 10°C	3,2 V		
Knock sensor (KS) 1	20	⬅	Engine idling – accelerate briefly		0,1 V/0,5 ms	Ⓜ38
	80	⌐	Ignition ON	0 V		
Knock sensor (KS) 2	50	⬅	Engine idling – accelerate briefly		0,1 V/0,5 ms	Ⓜ38
	80	⌐	Ignition ON	0 V		
Manifold absolute pressure (MAP) sensor	12	⌐	Ignition ON	0 V		
	73	⬅	Ignition ON	5 V		
	73	⬅	Engine idling	1,6 V		
	73	⬅	Engine idling – accelerate briefly	4,3 V		
	78	⇨	Ignition ON	5 V		
Throttle position (TP) sensor	44	⬅	Ignition ON – throttle closed	0,6 V		
	44	⬅	Ignition ON – throttle fully open	4,3 V		
	74	⇨	Ignition ON	5 V		
	75	⌐	Ignition ON	0 V		

*Suggested settings - Voltage/time per division

1 Connected pin - no test data available or random digital signal

Model:	Engine code:	Year:
Discovery 2,5D TD5	VIN No. digit 8 = 8 or 9	1998-02
Defender 2,5D TD5	VIN No. digit 8 = 8	1999-06

LAND ROVER

Lucas

ECM harness multi-plug

Terminal side – A – Red, B – Black

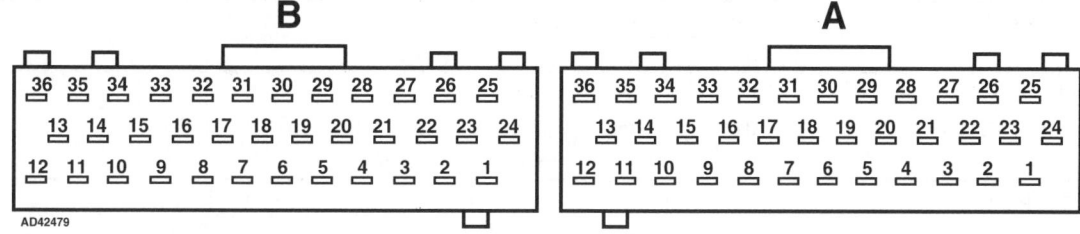

Wire side – A – Red, B – Black

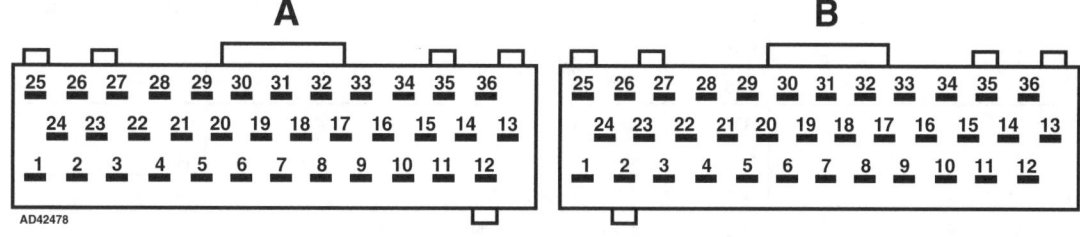

Component/circuit description	ECM pin	Signal	Condition	Typical value
ABS control module	B13	⬅	Ignition OFF	0 V or 9,5 V
	B13	⬅	Ignition ON	0 V or 11-14 V
	B32	⇨	Ignition OFF	11-14 V after 10 seconds
	B32	⇨	Ignition ON	1,5 V approx.
AC compressor clutch relay	B29	⌐⤏	Ignition OFF	0 V
	B29	⌐⤏	Ignition ON	11-14 V
	B29	⌐⤏	Engine idling – AC OFF	11-14 V
	B29	⌐⤏	Engine idling – AC ON	0,1 V
AC master switch	B9	⬅	Ignition ON – AC ON	0 V
	B9	⬅	Ignition ON – AC OFF	11,6 V
Accelerator pedal position (APP) sensor	B12	⬅	Ignition ON – accelerator pedal released	0,7 V
	B12	⬅	Ignition ON – accelerator pedal fully depressed	3,9 V
	B14	⇨	Ignition OFF	0 V
	B14	⇨	Ignition ON	5 V
	B26	⌐–	Ignition ON	0 V
	B36	⬅	Ignition ON – accelerator pedal released	4,3 V
	B36	⬅	Ignition ON – accelerator pedal depressed	1,2 V
Barometric pressure (BARO) sensor	A8	⇨	Ignition ON	5 V
	A8	⇨	Engine idling	5 V
	A10	⬅	Ignition ON	4,6 V
	A10	⬅	Engine idling	4,6 V
	A30	⌐–	Ignition ON	0 V
Brake pedal position (BPP) switch	B10	⬅	Ignition ON – brake pedal released	11-14 V
	B10	⬅	Ignition ON – brake pedal depressed	0 V
	B16	⬅	Ignition ON – brake pedal released	0 V
	B16	⬅	Ignition ON – brake pedal depressed	11-14 V

Component/circuit description	ECM pin	Signal	Condition	Typical value
Clutch pedal position (CPP) switch – MT	B35	←	Ignition ON – clutch pedal released	11-14 V
	B35	←	Ignition ON – clutch pedal depressed	0 V
Crankshaft position (CKP) sensor	A13	←	Ignition ON	0 V
	A13	←	Engine idling	2 V ac
	A13	←	Engine idling	2 V/2 ms per division ⎍ 36
	A16	⊣—	Ignition ON	0 V
	A36	⊣—	Ignition ON	0 V
Cruise control master switch	B15	←	Ignition OFF	0 V
	B15	←	Ignition ON – switch ON	11-14 V
Cruise control selector switch	B11	←	Ignition ON	0 V
	B17	←	Ignition ON – switch released	0 V
	B17	←	Ignition ON – switch depressed	11-14 V
Data link connector (DLC)	B18	←▷	Ignition OFF	0 V
	B18	←▷	Ignition ON	6,8 V
Earth	B1	⊣—	Ignition ON	0 V
	B2	⊣—	Ignition ON	0 V
	B24	⊣—	Ignition ON	0 V
	B25	⊣—	Ignition ON	0 V
Engine control relay	B3	←	Ignition OFF	0 V
	B3	←	Ignition ON	11-14 V
	B21	⊣▷	Ignition OFF	11-14 V
	B21	⊣▷	Ignition ON	1,1 V
	B21	⊣▷	Engine idling	1,2 V
	B22	←	Ignition OFF	0 V
	B22	←	Ignition ON	11-14 V
	B27	←	Ignition OFF	0 V
	B27	←	Ignition ON	11-14 V
Engine coolant blower motor relay	B4	⊣▷	Ignition ON	11-14 V
	B4	⊣▷	Engine idling – coolant blower motor OFF	11-14 V
	B4	⊣▷	Engine idling – coolant blower motor ON	0 V
Engine coolant temperature (ECT) sensor	A7	←	Ignition ON – coolant temp. 20°C	2,7 V
	A7	←	Engine idling – coolant temp. 80°C	0,7 V
	A18	⊣—	Ignition ON	0 V
Exhaust gas recirculation (EGR) solenoid	A3	⊣▷	Ignition ON	11-14 V
	A3	⊣▷	Engine idling – valve not operating	11-14 V
Fuel pump relay	B5	⊣▷	Ignition ON	0,1 V
	B5	⊣▷	Engine idling	0,1 V
Fuel temperature sensor	A5	⊣—	Ignition ON	0 V
	A19	←	Engine idling	0,9 V
	A19	←	Ignition ON – fuel temp. 20°C	2,7 V
Glow plug relay	A29	⊣▷	Ignition ON – glow plugs ON	0 V
	A29	⊣▷	Ignition ON – glow plugs OFF	11-14 V
Ignition switch	B33	←	Ignition OFF	0 V
	B33	←	Ignition ON	11-14 V
Injector 1	A22	▷	Ignition ON	0,28 V
	A25	⊣▷	Ignition ON	0,28 V
	A25(A22)	⊣▷	Engine idling	20 V/1 ms per division ⎍ 35
Injector 2	A23	▷	Ignition ON	0,28 V
	A26	⊣▷	Ignition ON	0,28 V
	A26(A23)	⊣▷	Engine idling	20 V/1 ms per division ⎍ 35

Component/circuit description	ECM pin	Signal	Condition	Typical value	
Injector 3	A22	⇒	Ignition ON	0,28 V	
	A27	⌐⊦▷	Ignition ON	0,28 V	
	A27(A22)	⌐⊦▷	Engine idling	20 V/1 ms per division	〰〰 **35**
Injector 4	A22	⇒	Ignition ON	0,28 V	
	A24	⌐⊦▷	Ignition ON	0,28 V	
	A24(A22)	⌐⊦▷	Engine idling	20 V/1 ms per division	〰〰 **35**
Injector 5	A1	⌐⊦▷	Ignition ON	0,28 V	
	A23	⇒	Ignition ON	0,28 V	
	A1(A23)	⌐⊦▷	Engine idling	20 V/1 ms per division	〰〰 **35**
Instrument panel	B7	⇒	Ignition ON	3,9 V	
	B30	⇒	Ignition OFF	0 V	
	B30	⇒	Ignition ON	11 V after 5 seconds	
	B30	⇒	Engine idling	11-14 V	
Intake air temperature (IAT) sensor	A17	⌐⊢	Ignition ON	0 V	
	A34	⟵	Ignition ON – air temp. 20°C	2,8 V	
Manifold absolute pressure (MAP) sensor	A6	⟵	Engine idling	1,9 V	
	A8	⇒	Ignition ON	5 V	
	A17	⌐⊢	Ignition ON	0 V	
Mass air flow (MAF) sensor	A11	⟵	Ignition ON	0,03 V	
	A11	⟵	Engine idling	2 V	
	A11	⟵	Engine idling – accelerate briefly	4,4 V briefly	
	A20	⌐⊢	Ignition ON	0 V	
Suspension control module	B34	⟵		[1]	
Tachometer	B19	⇒	Engine idling	22 Hz	
	B19	⇒	3000 rpm	100 Hz	
Transmission control module (TCM)	A32	⟵⇒	Ignition ON	2,48 V	
	A32	⟵⇒	Engine idling	0,5 V/10 ms per division	〰〰 **38**
	A35	⟵⇒	Ignition ON	0 V	
Transmission mode selector switch	A33	⟵	Engine idling – in HIGH ratio	11-14 V	
	A33	⟵	Ignition ON – in HIGH ratio	10 V	
Transmission range (TR) switch – AT	B35	⟵	Ignition ON – AT in N or P	0 V	
Turbocharger (TC) wastegate regulating valve	A21	⌐⊦▷	Ignition ON	11-14 V	
	A21	⌐⊦▷	Engine idling – valve not operating	11-14 V	

[1] Connected pin - no test data available

LAND ROVER

Bosch Motronic M5.2.1

Model:	Engine code:	Year:
Discovery 4,0	36D	1998-02

ECM harness multi-plug

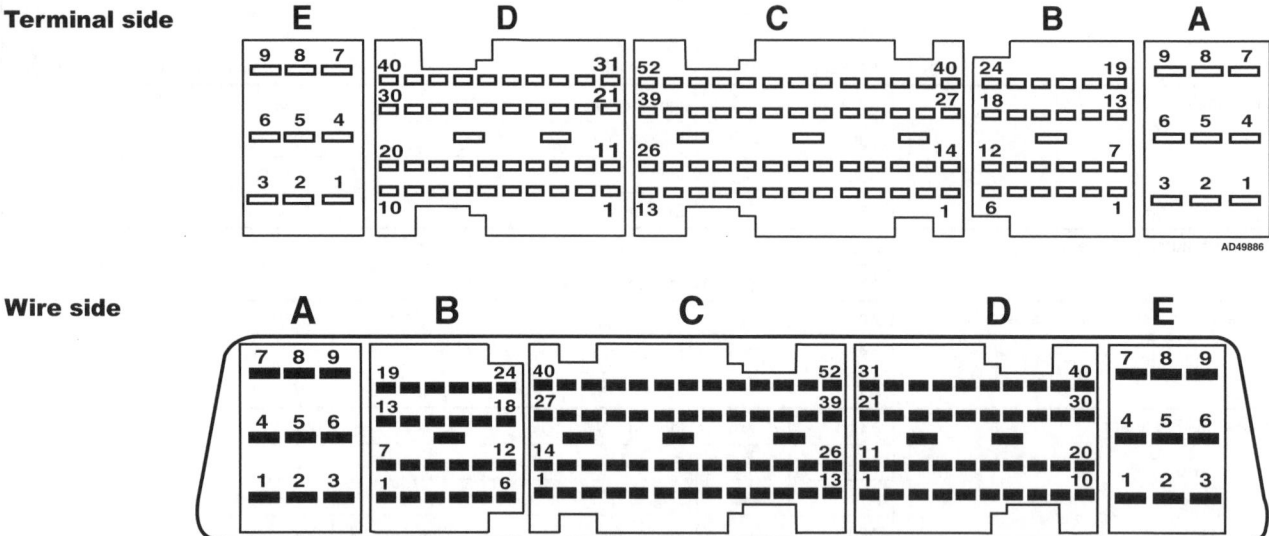

AD49886

AD49885

Component/circuit description	ECM pin	Signal	Condition	Typical value	Oscilloscope setting*	Wave form
ABS control module	C29	⇨	Ignition OFF	11,3 V		
	C29	⇨	Ignition ON	1,5 V approx.		
ABS control module – rough road signal	D34			①1		
ABS control module – VSS signal	D22	⬅	Ignition ON – vehicle pushed	0 V or 11 V		
AC compressor clutch relay	D29	⊐⊳	Ignition ON	11-14 V		
	D29	⊐⊳	Engine idling – AC OFF	11-14 V		
	D29	⊐⊳	Engine idling – AC ON	0 V		
AC control module	D38	⬅	Ignition ON	11 V		
	D38	⬅	Engine idling	11-14 V		
AC refrigerant pressure switch	D16	⬅	Ignition ON	11 V		
	D16	⬅	Engine idling – AC OFF	11-14 V		
	D16	⬅	Engine idling – AC ON	0 V		
Battery	A7	⬅	Ignition OFF	11-14 V		
Camshaft position (CMP) sensor	C20	⬅	Engine idling	0-14 V switching	5 V/50 ms	∿∿ 14
CAN data bus – AT	D36	⬌		①1		
	D37	⬌		①1		
Crankshaft position (CKP) sensor	C32	⬅	Engine idling		0,2 V/2 ms	Reversed ∿∿ 2
	C45	⊐	Ignition ON	0 V		
	C46	⬅	Engine idling		0,2 V/2 ms	∿∿ 2
Data link connector (DLC)	D32	⬌		①1		
Earth	A5		Ignition ON	0 V		
	A6		Ignition ON	0 V		
	C17		Ignition ON	0 V		
	E5		Ignition ON	0 V		
Earth – 2000→	A4		Ignition ON	0 V		

* Suggested settings - Voltage/time per division

Autodata

Component/circuit description	ECM pin	Signal	Condition	Typical value	Oscilloscope setting*	Wave form
Engine control relay	A8	←	Ignition OFF	0 V		
	A8	←	Ignition ON	11-14 V		
	B23	⊐⊳	Ignition OFF	11-14 V		
	B23	⊐⊳	Ignition ON	0-1 V		
Engine coolant blower motor relay	C31	⊐⊳	Ignition ON	11-14 V		
	C31	⊐⊳	Engine idling	11-14 V		
Engine coolant temperature (ECT) sensor	C21	⊐—	Ignition ON	0 V		
	C22	←	Ignition ON – coolant temp. 25-30°C	3 V		
	C22	←	Engine idling – engine hot	0,7 V approx.		
Evaporative emission (EVAP) canister purge valve	C3	⊐⊳	Ignition ON	11-14 V		
	C3	⊐⊳	Engine idling		10 V/20 ms	59
Fuel pump relay	B18	⊐⊳	Ignition ON	0 V briefly then 11-14 V		
	B18	⊐⊳	Engine idling	0 V		
Heated oxygen sensor (HO2S) 1, bank 1	B9	⊐—	Ignition ON	0 V		
	B15	←	Engine idling	0,1-0,9 V fluctuating	0,2 V/1 sec.	21
Heated oxygen sensor (HO2S) 1, bank 1 – heater control	B19	⊐⊳	Ignition ON	11-14 V		
	B19	⊐⊳	Engine idling – engine cold		5 V/0,1 sec.	66
Heated oxygen sensor (HO2S) 1, bank 2	B10	⊐—	Ignition ON	0 V		
	B16	←	Engine idling	0,1-0,9 V fluctuating	0,2 V/1 sec.	21
Heated oxygen sensor (HO2S) 1, bank 2 – heater control	B13	⊐⊳	Ignition ON	11-14 V		
	B13	⊐⊳	Engine idling – engine cold		5 V/0,1 sec.	66
Idle air control (IAC) valve	C42	⊐⊳	Ignition ON	6 V		
	C42	⊐⊳	Engine idling	27%	2 V/5 ms	45
	C43	⊐⊳	Ignition ON	6 V		
	C43	⊐⊳	Engine idling	63%	2 V/5 ms	45
Ignition coil 1, cyl. 1 & 6	E6	⊐⊳	Ignition ON	11-14 V		
	E6	⊐⊳	Engine idling		5 V/1 ms	33
Ignition coil 1, cyl. 4 & 7	E7	⊐⊳	Ignition ON	11-14 V		
	E7	⊐⊳	Engine idling		5 V/1 ms	33
Ignition coil 2, cyl. 2 & 3	E2	⊐⊳	Ignition ON	11-14 V		
	E2	⊐⊳	Engine idling		5 V/1 ms	33
Ignition coil 2, cyl. 5 & 8	E8	⊐⊳	Ignition ON	11-14 V		
	E8	⊐⊳	Engine idling		5 V/1 ms	33
Ignition switch relay	A1	←	Ignition OFF	0 V		
	A1	←	Ignition ON	11-14 V		
Injector 1	C41	⊐⊳	Ignition ON	11-14 V		
	C41	⊐⊳	Engine idling	3,7 ms	10 V/2 ms	35
Injector 2	C1	⊐⊳	Ignition ON	11-14 V		
	C1	⊐⊳	Engine idling	3,7 ms	10 V/2 ms	35
Injector 3	C27	⊐⊳	Ignition ON	11-14 V		
	C27	⊐⊳	Engine idling	3,7 ms	10 V/2 ms	35
Injector 4	C40	⊐⊳	Ignition ON	11-14 V		
	C40	⊐⊳	Engine idling	3,7 ms	10 V/2 ms	35
Injector 5	C2	⊐⊳	Ignition ON	11-14 V		
	C2	⊐⊳	Engine idling	3,7 ms	10 V/2 ms	35
Injector 6	C15	⊐⊳	Ignition ON	11-14 V		
	C15	⊐⊳	Engine idling	3,7 ms	10 V/2 ms	35

* Suggested settings - Voltage/time per division

LAND ROVER

Component/circuit description	ECM pin	Signal	Condition	Typical value	Oscilloscope setting*	Wave form
Injector 7	C14	→▷	Ignition ON	11-14 V		
	C14	→▷	Engine idling	3,7 ms	10 V/2 ms	35
Injector 8	C28	→▷	Ignition ON	11-14 V		
	C28	→▷	Engine idling	3,7 ms	10 V/2 ms	35
Instrument panel – ECT sensor signal	C44	⇨	Ignition OFF	9 V		
	C44	⇨	Ignition ON	4,1 V		
	C44	⇨	Engine idling		2 V/5 ms	39
Instrument panel – engine speed signal	D17	⇨	Engine idling	22 Hz	5 V/20 ms	45
	D17	⇨	3000 rpm	100 Hz		
Instrument panel – fuel level	D8			1		
Intake air temperature (IAT) sensor	C34	⇐	Ignition ON	2,4 V		
	C34	⇐	Engine idling – engine hot	2,2 V		
Knock sensor (KS) – signal, bank 1	C49	⇐	Engine idling – accelerate briefly		50 mV/1 ms	58
Knock sensor (KS) – signal, bank 2	C36	⇐	Engine idling – accelerate briefly		50 mV/1 ms	58
Knock sensor (KS), bank 1 – shield wire	C48	�	Ignition ON	0 V		
Knock sensor (KS), bank 2 – shield wire	C35	⥁	Ignition ON	0 V		
Malfunction indicator lamp (MIL)	D20	→▷	Ignition ON – MIL ON	0-1 V		
	D20	→▷	Engine idling – MIL OFF	11-14 V		
Mass air flow (MAF) sensor	C7	⇨	Ignition ON	5 V		
	C9	⥁	Ignition ON	0 V		
	C23	⇐	Ignition ON	1 V		
	C23	⇐	Engine idling	1,5 V		
	C23	⇐	Engine idling – full throttle briefly	4,1 V		
Multifunction control module	D33			1		
Throttle position (TP) sensor	C10	⇨	Ignition ON	5 V		
	C24	⇐	Ignition ON – throttle closed	0,7 V		
	C24	⇐	Ignition ON – throttle fully open	4,3 V		
	C25	⥁	Ignition ON	0 V		
Transmission low range switch	C18			1		
Transmission range (TR) switch	D6			1		

*Suggested settings - Voltage/time per division

1 Connected pin - no test data available or random digital signal

ECM harness multi-plug

Terminal side – A – Black, B – Red

A

36 35 34 33 32 31 30 29 28 27 26 25
13 14 15 16 17 18 19 20 21 22 23 24
12 11 10 9 8 7 6 5 4 3 2 1

B

1 2 3 4 5 6 7 8 9 10 11 12
24 23 22 21 20 19 18 17 16 15 14 13
25 26 27 28 29 30 31 32 33 34 35 36

C

18 17 16 15 14 13
7 8 9 10 11 12
6 5 4 3 2 1

AD23552

Wire side – A – Black, B – Red

C

13 14 15 16 17 18
12 11 10 9 8 7
1 2 3 4 5 6

B

12 11 10 9 8 7 6 5 4 3 2 1
13 14 15 16 17 18 19 20 21 22 23 24
36 35 34 33 32 31 30 29 28 27 26 25

A

25 26 27 28 29 30 31 32 33 34 35 36
24 23 22 21 20 19 18 17 16 15 14 13
1 2 3 4 5 6 7 8 9 10 11 12

AD23553

Component/circuit description	ECM pin	Signal	Condition	Typical value	Oscilloscope setting*	Wave form
ABS control module – rough road signal	B1	←		1		
AC condenser blower motor relay	A3	⊐▷	Engine running – AC OFF	11-14 V		
	A3	⊐▷	Engine running – AC ON – condenser blower motor ON	0 V		
AC control module	A1	⇨	Engine running – AC OFF	11-14 V		
	A1	⇨	Engine running – AC ON	0 V		
	B21	←	Engine running – heated windscreen ON	11-14 V		
	B28	←	Engine running – AC OFF	11-14 V		
	B28	←	Engine running – AC ON	0 V		
AC refrigerant pressure switch	B29	←	Engine running – AC ON – refrigerant pressure 13 bar max.	11-14 V		
	B29	←	Engine running – AC ON – refrigerant pressure 17 bar min.	0 V		
Camshaft position (CMP) sensor	B2	←	Engine idling	23 Hz	5 V/20 ms	∿〰 90
	B36	⊐⊢	Ignition ON	0 V		
Crankshaft position (CKP) sensor	C11	⊐⊢	Ignition ON	0 V		
	C12	←	Engine idling		0,2 V/2 ms	∿〰 2
Data link connector (DLC)	B20	←▷		1		
	B23	←▷		1		
Earth	C5		Ignition ON	0 V		
	C9		Ignition ON	0 V		
	C10		Ignition ON	0 V		
	C16		Ignition ON	0 V		
Earth – MT	B18		Ignition ON	0 V		
Engine control relay	C7	←	Ignition ON	11-14 V		
	C17	⊐▷	Ignition OFF	11-14 V		
	C17	⊐▷	Ignition ON	0 V		

* Suggested settings - Voltage/time per division

Component/circuit description	ECM pin	Signal	Condition	Typical value	Oscilloscope setting*	Wave form
Engine coolant temperature (ECT) sensor	B14	←	Ignition ON – coolant temp. -30°C	4,7 V		
	B14	←	Ignition ON – coolant temp. 40°C	2 V		
	B14	←	Ignition ON – coolant temp. 130°C	0,25 V		
	B36	⌐	Ignition ON	0 V		
Evaporative emission (EVAP) canister purge valve	A19	⇥	Ignition ON	11-14 V		
	A19	⇥	Engine running	100 Hz	10 V/50 ms	Intermittent 〰 20
Four wheel drive control module – low range signal – 1997→	B4	←		[1]		
Fuel pump relay	A24	⇥	Ignition OFF	0 V		
	A24	⇥	Ignition ON	0 V briefly then 11-14 V		
	A24	⇥	Engine running	0 V		
Fuel temperature sensor	B35	←	Ignition ON – fuel temp. 40°C	2 V		
	B36	⌐	Ignition ON	0 V		
Heated oxygen sensor (HO2S) 1, bank 1	B34	←	Engine idling	0-5 V fluctuating	1 V/1 sec.	〰 21
	B32	⌐	Ignition ON	0 V		
	A21	⇥	Ignition ON	11-14 V		
	A21	⇥	Engine idling		2 V/0,2 ms	〰 72
Heated oxygen sensor (HO2S) 1, bank 2	B33	←	Engine idling	0-5 V fluctuating	1 V/1 sec.	〰 21
	B32	⌐	Ignition ON	0 V		
	A21	⇥	Ignition ON	11-14 V		
	A21	⇥	Engine idling		2 V/0,2 ms	〰 72
Idle air control (IAC) valve	A15 (A16)	⇨	Engine idling		5 V/0,5 sec.	Intermittent 〰 26
	A34 (A35)	⇨	Engine idling		5 V/0,5 sec.	Intermittent 〰 26
Ignition coil – cylinders 1 & 6	C14	⇥	Ignition ON	11-14 V		
	C14	⇥	Engine idling		5 V/1 ms	〰 33
Ignition coil – cylinders 2 & 3	C13	⇥	Ignition ON	11-14 V		
	C13	⇥	Engine idling		5 V/1 ms	〰 33
Ignition coil – cylinders 4 & 7	C15	⇥	Ignition ON	11-14 V		
	C15	⇥	Engine idling		5 V/1 ms	〰 33
Ignition coil – cylinders 5 & 8	C1	⇥	Ignition ON	11-14 V		
	C1	⇥	Engine idling		5 V/1 ms	〰 33
Ignition switch	C8	←	Ignition ON	11-14 V		
Injector 1	A13	⇥	Ignition ON	11-14 V		
	A13	⇥	Engine idling	3 ms	10 V/2 ms	〰 35
Injector 2	A36	⇥	Ignition ON	11-14 V		
	A36	⇥	Engine idling	3 ms	10 V/2 ms	〰 35
Injector 3	A11	⇥	Ignition ON	11-14 V		
	A11	⇥	Engine idling	3 ms	10 V/2 ms	〰 35
Injector 4	A30	⇥	Ignition ON	11-14 V		
	A30	⇥	Engine idling	3 ms	10 V/2 ms	〰 35
Injector 5	A33	⇥	Ignition ON	11-14 V		
	A33	⇥	Engine idling	3 ms	10 V/2 ms	〰 35
Injector 6	A17	⇥	Ignition ON	11-14 V		
	A17	⇥	Engine idling	3 ms	10 V/2 ms	〰 35
Injector 7	A32	⇥	Ignition ON	11-14 V		
	A32	⇥	Engine idling	3 ms	10 V/2 ms	〰 35
Injector 8	A18	⇥	Ignition ON	11-14 V		
	A18	⇥	Engine idling	3 ms	10 V/2 ms	〰 35
Instrument panel – fuel consumption signal	A2	⇨		[1]		

* Suggested settings - Voltage/time per division

Component/circuit description	ECM pin	Signal	Condition	Typical value	Oscilloscope setting*	Wave form
Intake air temperature (IAT) sensor	B13	⬅	Ignition ON – air temp. 40°C	2 V		
	B36	⌐—	Ignition ON	0 V		
Knock sensor (KS), bank 1	B10	⌐—	Ignition ON	0 V		
	B11	⬅	Engine idling – accelerate briefly		50 mV/1 ms	∿∿ 38
Knock sensor (KS), bank 2	B10	⌐—	Ignition ON	0 V		
	B12	⬅	Engine idling – accelerate briefly		50 mV/1 ms	∿∿ 38
Mass air flow (MAF) sensor	B16	⬅	Engine idling	1,4 V		
	B16	⬅	Engine idling – accelerate briefly	4,8 V briefly		
	B36	⌐—	Ignition ON	0 V		
Multifunction control module – fuel level signal	B7	⬅		1		
Multifunction control module – immobilizer signal	B26	⬅		1		
Multifunction control module – MIL signal	A22	⌐⊳	Ignition ON – MIL ON	0 V		
	A22	⌐⊳	Engine running – MIL OFF	11-14 V		
Multifunction control module – engine RPM signal	A23	⇨	Engine idling	46 Hz		
	A23	⇨	3000 rpm	200 Hz		
Multifunction control module – vehicle speed signal	B27	⬅	Vehicle moving – 10 mph	22 Hz		
Park/neutral position (PNP) switch – AT	B18	⬅	Ignition ON – AT in P or N	0 V		
	B18	⬅	Ignition ON – AT not in P or N	11-14 V		
Suspension control module – vehicle speed signal	B27	⬅	Vehicle moving – 10 mph	22 Hz		
Throttle position (TP) sensor	B15	⬅	Ignition ON – throttle closed	0,6 V		
	B15	⬅	Ignition ON – throttle fully open	4,5 V		
	B36	⌐—	Ignition ON	0 V		
	C4	⇨	Ignition ON	5 V		
Transmission control module (TCM) – throttle position signal	A27	⬅	Engine idling	1,4 V		
Transmission control module (TCM) – engine torque signal	A29	⇨		1		
Transmission control module (TCM) – ignition retard signal	B31	⬅		1		

*Suggested settings - Voltage/time per division

1 Connected pin - no test data available or random digital signal

MAZDA

Mazda EGI

Model:	Engine code:	Year:
6 1,8	L8	2002-06
6 2,0	LF	2002-05
6 2,3 (2WD)	L3	2002-06

ECM harness multi-plug

Terminal side

AD105225

Wire side

AD105224

Component/circuit description	ECM pin	Signal	Condition	Typical value	Oscilloscope setting*	Wave form
AC compressor clutch relay	4O	⊐▷	Engine idling – AC ON – compressor ON	0-1 V		
	4O	⊐▷	Engine idling – AC ON – compressor OFF	11-14 V		
AC refrigerant pressure switch	1AC	⬅	Engine idling – AC ON	0 V		
	1AC	⬅	Engine idling – AC OFF	11-14 V		
AC refrigerant dual pressure switch – 2,3	1Q	⬅	Engine running – AC ON – refrigerant pressure 15 bar min.	0 V		
	1Q	⬅	Engine running – AC ON – refrigerant pressure 12 bar max.	11-14 V		
Alternator	1AA		Ignition ON	0 V		
	1AA		Engine idling		5 V/2 ms	〜〰 51
	1AD		Ignition ON	0 V		
	1AD		Engine idling		2 V/10 ms	〜〰 55
Barometric pressure (BARO) sensor	1G	⬅	Ignition ON – at sea level	4 V		
	2H	⊐−	Ignition ON	0 V		
	2K	⇨	Ignition ON	5 V		
Battery	2Z	⬅	Ignition OFF	11-14 V		
	2Z	⬅	Ignition ON	11-14 V		
Brake pedal position (BPP) switch	1K	⬅	Ignition ON – brake pedal released	0 V		
	1K	⬅	Ignition ON – brake pedal depressed	11-14 V		
Camshaft position (CMP) actuator – 2,3	4M	⊐▷	Engine idling – actuator not operating	11-14 V		
	4M	⊐▷	Engine running at high RPM – actuator operating	0-1 V		
Camshaft position (CMP) sensor	2J	⬅	Engine idling		1 V/20 ms	Reversed 〜〰 11
	2M	⬅	Engine idling		1 V/20 ms	〜〰 11
Camshaft position (CMP) sensor – 2,3	2J	⬅	Engine idling		1 V/20 ms	〜〰 108
	2M	⬅	Engine idling		1 V/20 ms	Reversed 〜〰 108
CAN data bus – high	2U	⬄		1		
CAN data bus – low	2R	⬄		1		
Clutch pedal position (CPP) switch	1R	⬅	Ignition ON – clutch pedal released	11-14 V		
	1R	⬅	Ignition ON – clutch pedal depressed	0 V		
Crankshaft position (CKP) sensor	2D	⬅	Engine idling	2,1 V ac	2 V/5 ms	〜〰 2
	2G	⬅	Engine idling	3,2 V ac	2 V/5 ms	Reversed 〜〰 2

* Suggested settings - Voltage/time per division

Autodata

Component/circuit description	ECM pin	Signal	Condition	Typical value	Oscilloscope setting*	Wave form
Cruise control motor/actuator	1L			1		
Data link connector (DLC) – through CAN data bus	2R	↔		1		
	2U	↔		1		
Earth	1C		Ignition ON	0 V		
	1D		Ignition ON	0 V		
	2AB		Ignition ON	0 V		
	2AC		Ignition ON	0 V		
	4X		Ignition ON	0 V		
Engine control (EC) relay	2X	←	Ignition OFF	11-14 V		
	2X	←	Ignition ON	0 V		
	2Y	←	Ignition OFF	0 V		
	2Y	←	Ignition ON	11-14 V		
Engine control (EC) relay – AT	4V	←	Ignition OFF	0 V		
	4V	←	Ignition ON	11-14 V		
Engine coolant blower motor relay 1 – 1,8/2,0	4B	⊐▷	Engine running – coolant blower motor OFF	11-14 V		
	4B	⊐▷	Engine running – coolant blower motor ON	0-1 V		
Engine coolant blower motor relay 2 – 1,8/2,0	4L	⊐▷	Engine running – coolant blower motor OFF	11-14 V		
	4L	⊐▷	Engine running – coolant blower motor ON	0-1 V		
Engine coolant blower motor relay 1/4 – 2,3	4F	⊐▷	Engine running – coolant blower motors OFF	11-14 V		
	4F	⊐▷	Engine running – coolant blower motors ON	0-1 V		
Engine coolant blower motor relay 2 – 2,3	4L	⊐▷	Engine running – coolant blower motors OFF	11-14 V		
	4L	⊐▷	Engine running – coolant blower motors ON	0-1 V		
Engine coolant blower motor relay 3 – 2,3	4B	⊐▷	Engine running – coolant blower motors OFF	11-14 V		
	4B	⊐▷	Engine running – coolant blower motors ON	0-1 V		
Engine coolant temperature (ECT) sensor	1M	←	Ignition ON – coolant temp. 20°C	3 V		
	1M	←	Ignition ON – coolant temp. 60°C	1,3 V		
	2H	⊐⊢	Ignition ON	0 V		
Evaporative emission (EVAP) canister purge valve	4U	⊐▷	Ignition ON	11-14 V		
	4U	⊐▷	Engine running – engine hot – valve operating		10 V/50 ms	Intermittent 〰〰 20
Exhaust gas recirculation (EGR) valve actuator	4E	⊐▷	Ignition ON	0-1 V		
	4H	⊐▷	Ignition ON	11-14 V		
	4K	⊐▷	Ignition ON	11-14 V		
	4N	⊐▷	Ignition ON	0-1 V		
Fuel pump (FP) relay	4Q	⊐▷	Ignition ON	0-1 V briefly then 11-14 V		
	4Q	⊐▷	Engine idling	0-1 V		
Heated oxygen sensor (HO2S) 1	1AB	←	Engine idling – engine hot	0,1-0,9 V fluctuating	0,2 V/1 sec.	〰〰 21
	2H	⊐⊢	Ignition ON	0 V		
Heated oxygen sensor (HO2S) 1 – heater control	4A	⊐▷	Ignition ON	11-14 V		
	4A	⊐▷	Engine idling		5 V/0,5 sec.	〰〰 24
Heated oxygen sensor (HO2S) 2	1Y	←	Engine idling – engine hot	0,4 V		
	2H	⊐⊢	Ignition ON	0 V		
Heated oxygen sensor (HO2S) 2 – heater control	4D	⊐▷	Ignition ON	11-14 V		
	4D	⊐▷	Engine running – below 4000 rpm	11-14 V		
	4D	⊐▷	Engine running – above 4000 rpm	0-1 V		

★ Suggested settings - Voltage/time per division

Component/circuit description	ECM pin	Signal	Condition	Typical value	Oscilloscope setting*	Wave form
Idle air control (IAC) valve	4G	⇨	Engine idling	7-12 V switching	2 V/2 ms	107
	4J	⏚⇨	Engine idling	0-9 V switching	5 V/1 ms	24
Ignition coil	1A	⏚⇨	Ignition ON	11-14 V		
	1A	⏚⇨	Engine idling		5 V/2 ms	110
	1B	⏚⇨	Ignition ON	11-14 V		
	1B	⏚⇨	Engine idling		5 V/2 ms	110
Immobilizer read coil	2Q	⬅⇨		1		
	2T	⬅⇨		1		
Injector 1	4Z	⏚⇨	Ignition ON	11-14 V		
	4Z	⏚⇨	Engine idling	2,6 ms	10 V/2 ms	35
Injector 2	4W	⏚⇨	Ignition ON	11-14 V		
	4W	⏚⇨	Engine idling	2,6 ms	10 V/2 ms	35
Injector 3	4AD	⏚⇨	Ignition ON	11-14 V		
	4AD	⏚⇨	Engine idling	2,6 ms	10 V/2 ms	35
Injector 4	4AA	⏚⇨	Ignition ON	11-14 V		
	4AA	⏚⇨	Engine idling	2,6 ms	10 V/2 ms	35
Instrument panel – alarm system warning lamp	2W	⇨	Ignition OFF – warning lamp flashing	2-11 V switching		
	2W	⇨	Ignition ON – lamp OFF	11-14 V		
Intake air temperature (IAT) sensor – in MAF sensor	2E	⬅	Ignition ON – air temp. 20°C	2,4-2,6 V		
	2E	⬅	Ignition ON – air temp. 30°C	1,7-1,9 V		
	2H	⏚	Ignition ON	0 V		
Intake air valve control valve – 2,3	4C	⏚⇨	Engine speed below 5800 rpm	11-14 V		
	4C	⏚⇨	Engine speed above 5800 rpm	0-1 V		
Intake manifold air control solenoid 1	4T	⏚⇨	Engine idling – coolant temp. above 63°C	11-14 V		
	4T	⏚⇨	Below 3750 rpm – coolant temp. below 63°C	0-1 V		
Intake manifold air control solenoid 2 – 2,3	4R	⏚⇨	Engine running – below 4500 rpm	0-1 V		
	4R	⏚⇨	Engine running – above 4500 rpm	11-14 V		
Knock sensor (KS)	2P	⏚	Ignition ON	0 V		
	2S	⬅	Ignition ON	2,9 V		
	2S	⬅	Engine idling – full throttle briefly		50 mV/1 ms	38
Manifold absolute pressure (MAP) sensor	1J	⬅	Ignition ON – at sea level	4 V		
	1J	⬅	Engine idling – at sea level	1,5 V		
	1J	⬅	Engine idling – accelerate briefly	4,1 V		
	2H	⏚	Ignition ON	0 V		
	2K	⇨	Ignition ON	5 V		
Mass air flow (MAF) sensor	1P	⬅	Ignition ON	0,7 V		
	1P	⬅	Engine idling – engine hot	1,2 V		
	1P	⬅	Engine idling – accelerate briefly	3,8 V		
	2H	⏚	Ignition ON	0 V		
Neutral position (NP) switch – MT	1W	⬅	MT in neutral	0 V		
	1W	⬅	All other positions	11-14 V		
Power steering pressure (PSP) switch	1Z	⬅	Engine idling – steering wheel straight ahead	11-14 V		
	1Z	⬅	Engine idling – steering wheel being turned	0 V		
Starter motor relay – AT – through transmission range (TR) sensor	4I	⏚⇨	Engine cranking – AT in P or N	0-1 V		
Starter motor relay – MT	4I	⏚⇨	Engine cranking	0-1 V		

* Suggested settings - Voltage/time per division

Component/circuit description	ECM pin	Signal	Condition	Typical value	Oscilloscope setting*	Wave form
Throttle position (TP) sensor	2A	←	Ignition ON – throttle closed	0,65-1,15 V		
	2A	←	Ignition ON – throttle fully open	4,3-4,8 V		
	2H	⌐—	Ignition ON	0 V		
	2K	⇒	Ignition ON	5 V		
Transmission fluid pressure (TFP) solenoid	3V			1		
	3Y			1		
Transmission fluid pressure (TFP) switch	3T	←	Switch ON	0 V		
	3T	←	Switch OFF	11-14 V		
Transmission fluid temperature sensor	2H	⌐—	Ignition ON	0 V		
	3D	←	Ignition ON – fluid temp. 20°C	3,3 V		
	3D	←	Ignition ON – fluid temp. 40°C	2,4 V		
	3D	←	Ignition ON – fluid temp. 60°C	1,5 V		
Transmission shift hold switch	3Q	←	Ignition ON – switch depressed	0 V		
	3Q	←	Ignition ON – switch released	11-14 V		
Transmission range (TR) switch	1W	←	Ignition ON – AT in P	4,6 V		
	1W	←	AT in R	3,9 V		
	1W	←	AT in N	3,2 V		
	1W	←	AT in D	2,5 V		
	1W	←	AT in S	1,7 V		
	1W	←	AT in L	0,94 V		
	2H	⌐—	Ignition ON	0 V		
Transmission shift solenoid (SS) – A	4AB			1		
Transmission shift solenoid (SS) – B	4AC			1		
Transmission shift solenoid (SS) – C	4Y			1		
Transmission shift solenoid (SS) – D	3S			1		
Transmission shift solenoid (SS) – E	3P			1		
Transmission turbine shaft speed (TSS) sensor	3G	←		1		
	3J	←		1		
Vehicle speed sensor (VSS) – AT	3C	←	Drive vehicle at 20 mph min.	0-5 V switching		

*Suggested settings - Voltage/time per division

1 Connected pin - no test data available or random digital signal

MERCEDES-BENZ

Siemens MSM 1.4

Model:	Engine code:	Year:
A140	166.940	1998-08/01
A160	166.960	1998-08/01
A190	166.990	1999-08/01

ECM harness multi-plug

Terminal side

AD29103

Wire side

AD29102

Component/circuit description	ECM pin	Signal	Condition	Typical value	Oscilloscope setting*	Wave form
Accelerator pedal position (APP) sensor	42	⅂—	Ignition ON	0 V		
	45	←	Ignition ON – accelerator pedal released	0,3 V		
	45	←	Ignition ON – accelerator pedal depressed	4,5 V		
	50	⅂—	Ignition ON	0 V		
	55	←	Ignition ON – accelerator pedal released	0,2 V		
	55	←	Ignition ON – accelerator pedal depressed	2,1 V		
	65	⇒	Ignition ON	4,9 V		
Battery	57	←	Ignition OFF	11-14 V		
Camshaft position (CMP) sensor	18	⇒	Ignition ON	11-14 V		
	25	⅂—	Ignition ON	0 V		
	35	←	Engine idling		5 V/50 ms	⎍⎍⎍ 68
CAN data bus – high	76	⬌	Ignition ON	1		
CAN data bus – low	75	⬌	Ignition ON	1		
Clutch pedal position (CPP) switch	61	←	Ignition ON – clutch pedal released	0 V		
	61	←	Ignition ON – clutch pedal depressed	10,4 V		
Crankshaft position (CKP) sensor	9 (10)	←	Engine idling	8,5 V ac		
	9 (10)	←	Engine idling		10 V/2 ms	⎍⎍⎍ 2
	10 (9)	←	Engine idling	8,5 V ac		
	10 (9)	←	Engine idling		10 V/2 ms	Reversed ⎍⎍⎍ 2
Cruise control – if fitted	43			1		
	44			1		
	51			1		
	52			1		
	53			1		
	54			1		

* Suggested settings - Voltage/time per division

Component/circuit description	ECM pin	Signal	Condition	Typical value	Oscilloscope setting*	Wave form
Data link connector (DLC)	64	⇨	Ignition ON	0 V		
	66	⬥⇨	Ignition ON	10,5 V		
Earth	40		Ignition ON	0 V		
	41		Ignition ON	0 V		
	47		Ignition ON	0 V		
Engine control (EC) relay	48	⬅	Ignition OFF	0 V		
	48	⬅	Ignition ON	11-14 V		
	68	⬅	Ignition OFF	0 V		
	68	⬅	Ignition ON	11-14 V		
	69	⬅	Ignition OFF	0 V		
	69	⬅	Ignition ON	11-14 V		
Engine coolant blower motor control module – AC – if fitted	74	⊐▷	AC OFF – coolant blower motor OFF	11-14 V		
	74	⊐▷	AC ON – coolant blower motor ON	0-1 V		
Engine coolant blower motor relay	74	⊐▷	Engine idling – coolant blower motor OFF	11-14 V		
	74	⊐▷	Engine idling – coolant blower motor ON	0-1 V		
Engine coolant temperature (ECT) sensor	26	⊐—	Ignition ON	0 V		
	22	⬅	Ignition ON – coolant temp. 20°C	3,1 V		
	22	⬅	Ignition ON – coolant temp. 90°C	0,5 V		
Engine oil level/temperature sensor	26	⊐—	Ignition ON	0 V		
	29	⇨	Ignition ON	5 V		
	30	⬅	Ignition ON	0,6-1,5 V fluctuating		
Evaporative emission (EVAP) canister purge valve	18	⇨	Ignition ON	11-14 V		
	31	⊐▷	Ignition ON	11-14 V		
	31	⊐▷	Engine running – valve operating		10 V/50 ms	〰〰 **59**
Fuel pump (FP) relay	73	⊐▷	Ignition ON	0-1 V briefly then 11-14 V		
	73	⊐▷	Engine cranking	0-1 V		
	73	⊐▷	Engine idling	0-1 V		
Heated oxygen sensor (HO2S) 1	5	⊐▷	Ignition ON	11-14 V		
	5	⊐▷	Engine idling – engine cold	0-1 V		
	18	⇨	Ignition ON	11-14 V		
	23	⬅	Ignition ON	0,5 V		
	23	⬅	Engine idling	0,1-0,9 V fluctuating		
	24	⊐—	Ignition ON	0 V		
Heated oxygen sensor (HO2S) 2 – if fitted	6			1		
	18	⇨	Ignition ON	11-14 V		
	36			1		
	37			1		

* Suggested settings - Voltage/time per division

Component/circuit description	ECM pin	Signal	Condition	Typical value	Oscilloscope setting*	Wave form
Ignition coil	7	⊐▷	Ignition ON	11-14 V		
	7	⊐▷	Engine idling		5 V/2 ms	〰 33
	8	⊐▷	Ignition ON	11-14 V		
	8	⊐▷	Engine idling		5 V/2 ms	〰 33
	39	⇨	Ignition ON	11-14 V		
Ignition switch	58	⬅	Ignition start position	9 V min		
Injector 1	1	⊐▷	Ignition ON	11-14 V		
	1	⊐▷	Engine idling – engine hot	4 ms	10 V/2 ms	〰 35
	38	⇨	Ignition ON	11-14 V		
Injector 2	2	⊐▷	Ignition ON	11-14 V		
	2	⊐▷	Engine idling – engine hot	4 ms	10 V/2 ms	〰 35
	38	⇨	Ignition ON	11-14 V		
Injector 3	3	⊐▷	Ignition ON	11-14 V		
	3	⊐▷	Engine idling – engine hot	4 ms	10 V/2 ms	〰 35
	38	⇨	Ignition ON	11-14 V		
Injector 4	4	⊐▷	Ignition ON	11-14 V		
	4	⊐▷	Engine idling – engine hot	4 ms	10 V/2 ms	〰 35
	38	⇨	Ignition ON	11-14 V		
Knock sensor (KS)	19 (20)	⬅	Engine idling		50 mV/1 ms	〰 38
	20 (19)	⬅	Engine idling		50 mV/1 ms	〰 38
Secondary air injection (AIR) pump relay – if fitted	60	⊐▷	Ignition ON	11-14 V		
	60	⊐▷	Engine running – pump operating	0 V		
Secondary air injection (AIR) solenoid – if fitted	18	⇨	Ignition ON	11-14 V		
	32			1		
SRS control module	59	⬅	Ignition ON	0 V		
Starter motor relay	72	⊐▷	Ignition ON	11-14 V		
	72	⊐▷	Engine cranking	0-1 V		
	72	⊐▷	Engine idling	11-14 V		
Throttle motor position sensor	12	⊐—	Ignition ON	0 V		
	13	⇨	Ignition ON	5 V		
	14	⬅	Ignition ON	0,7 V		
	14	⬅	Engine idling	0,6 V		
	15	⬅	Ignition ON	4,19 V		
	15	⬅	Engine idling	4,25 V		
Throttle motor	33	⊐▷	Engine idling		5 V/2 ms	〰 39
	34	⇨	Ignition ON	11-14 V		
Transmission kick-down switch – AT	63			1		

*Suggested settings - Voltage/time per division

1 Connected pin - no test data available or random digital signal

Model:	Engine code:	Year:
C180 (202)	111.920	1993-01
C200 (202)	111.941	1993-01
E200/200E/CE/TE (124)	111.940	1992-95

MERCEDES-BENZ

Mercedes-Benz PMS

ECM harness multi-plug

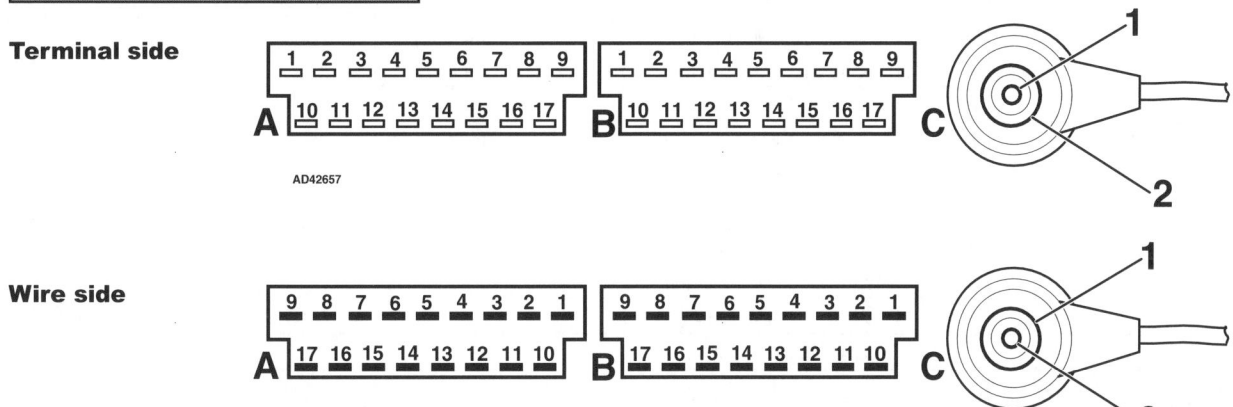

Terminal side

AD42657

Wire side

AD42656

Component/circuit description	ECM pin	Signal	Condition	Typical value	Oscilloscope setting*	Wave form
ABS control module – if fitted	A14	←		1		
AC control module – if fitted	A12			1		
Battery	A10	←	Ignition OFF	11-14 V		
Closed throttle position (CTP) switch	B17	←	Ignition ON – throttle closed	0,4 V		
	B17	←	Ignition ON – throttle fully open	5 V		
Crankshaft position (CKP) sensor	C1 (C2)	←	Engine cranking	0,7 V ac		
	C1 (C2)	←	Engine idling	4,5 V ac	10 V/10 ms	8
	C1 (C2)	←	3000 rpm	8 V ac		
Cruise control module – if fitted	A4			1		
Data link connector (DLC)	A13	⇒	Ignition ON	11-14 V		
	A13	⇒	Engine idling	25 Hz		
	A15	◄⇒	Ignition ON	11-14 V		
	A15	◄⇒	Engine idling	11-14 V		
Earth	A1		Ignition ON	0 V		
	A9		Ignition ON	0 V		
Earth – MT	A5		Ignition ON	0 V		
Engine coolant temperature (ECT) sensor	B7	←	Ignition ON – coolant temp. 20°C	3 V		
	B7	←	Ignition ON – coolant temp. 80°C	1 V		
	B9	⅂—	Ignition ON	0 V		
Evaporative emission (EVAP) canister purge valve – 202 series	A17	⇒	Ignition ON	0 V		
	A17	⇒	Engine idling	11-14 V		
	A17	⇒	Throttle slightly open		10 V/20 ms	20
Fuel pump relay	A8	⇒	Ignition ON	10 V briefly then 0 V		
Heated oxygen sensor (HO2S)	A6	←	Engine idling – engine hot	0,1-0,9 V fluctuating	0,2 V/1 sec.	21
	A7	⅂—	Ignition ON	0 V		
	A16	⇒	Ignition ON	0 V		
	A16	⇒	Engine idling	11-14 V		

* Suggested settings - Voltage/time per division

Component/circuit description	ECM pin	Signal	Condition	Typical value	Oscilloscope setting*	Wave form
Idle speed control (ISC) actuator	B5 (B14)	←⇨	Engine idling	1,5-3,2 V fluctuating		
	B5 (B14)	←⇨	Engine idling – electrical loads OFF	10 Hz	10 V/10 ms	〰35
	B5 (B14)	←⇨	Engine idling – electrical loads ON	10 Hz	10 V/5 ms	〰35
Idle speed control (ISC) actuator position sensor	B6	⇨	Ignition ON	5 V		
	B8	←	Ignition ON	3,6 V		
	B8	←	Engine idling	3-4,2 V		
	B9	⊣⊢	Ignition ON	0 V		
Ignition coil – cylinders 1 & 4	B10	⊣⊳	Ignition ON	11-14 V		
	B10	⊣⊳	Engine cranking	9 V		
	B10	⊣⊳	Engine idling		5 V/2 ms	〰33
Ignition coil – cylinders 2 & 3	B11	⊣⊳	Ignition ON	11-14 V		
	B11	⊣⊳	Engine cranking	9 V		
	B11	⊣⊳	Engine idling		5 V/2 ms	〰33
Ignition switch	A2	←	Ignition ON	11-14 V		
Ignition switch – AT – except 202 series with anti-theft system	A5	←	Engine cranking	9 V		
Injectors 1 & 4	B4	⊣⊳	Ignition ON	11-14 V		
	B4	⊣⊳	Engine idling – engine hot	2,1 ms	10 V/2 ms	〰35
Injectors 2 & 3	B13	⊣⊳	Ignition ON	11-14 V		
	B13	⊣⊳	Engine idling – engine hot	2,1 ms	10 V/2 ms	〰35
Instrument panel	A13	⇨	Ignition ON	11-14 V		
	A13	⇨	Engine idling	25 Hz		
Intake air temperature (IAT) sensor	B9	⊣⊢	Ignition ON	0 V		
	B16	←	Ignition ON – 20°C	2,5 V		
Intake manifold heater relay – 124 series	A17	⇨	Ignition ON	0 V		
	A17	⇨	Engine idling – engine cold	11-14 V		
Starter motor relay – AT – 202 series with anti-theft system	A5	←	Engine cranking	9 V		
Throttle position (TP) sensor	B6	⇨	Ignition ON	5 V		
	B9	⊣⊢	Ignition ON	0 V		
	B15	←	Ignition ON – throttle closed	4,3 V		
	B15	←	Ignition ON – throttle fully open	0,47 V		
Transmission kick-down relay – AT	A13	⇨	Ignition ON	11-14 V		
	A13	⇨	Engine idling	25 Hz		
Transmission range (TR) switch – AT	A11	←	Ignition ON – AT not in 2 or 3	5 V		
	A11	←	Ignition ON – AT in 2 or 3	0 V		
Transmission shift control valve – AT	A3	⇨		1		

*Suggested settings - Voltage/time per division

1 Connected pin - no test data available or random digital signal

Model:	Engine code:	Year:
C180K (203)	271.946	2002-06
C200K (203)	271.940	2002-06
C230K (203)	271.948	2002-06
CLK 200K (209)	271.940	2002-06

ECM harness multi-plug

Terminal side

M

| 96 | 95 | 94 | 93 | 92 | 91 | 90 | 89 | 88 | 87 | 86 | 85 | 84 | 83 | 82 | 81 | 80 | 79 | 78 | 77 | 76 | 75 | 74 | 73 |
| 72 | 71 | 70 | 69 | 68 | 67 | 66 | 65 | 64 | 63 | 62 | 61 | 60 | 59 | 58 | 57 | 56 | 55 | 54 | 53 | 52 | 51 | 50 | 49 |

| 48 | 47 | 46 | 45 | 44 | 43 | 42 | 41 | 40 | 39 | 38 | 37 | 36 | 35 | 34 | 33 | 32 | 31 | 30 | 29 | 28 | 27 | 26 | 25 |
| 24 | 23 | 22 | 21 | 20 | 19 | 18 | 17 | 16 | 15 | 14 | 13 | 12 | 11 | 10 | 9 | 8 | 7 | 6 | 5 | 4 | 3 | 2 | 1 |

F

| 58 | 57 | 56 | 55 | 54 | 53 | 52 | 51 | 50 | 49 | 48 | 47 | 46 | 6 | 5 |
| 45 | 44 | 43 | 42 | 41 | 40 | 39 | 38 | 37 | 36 | 35 | 34 | 33 | 4 | 3 |

| 32 | 31 | 30 | 29 | 28 | 27 | 26 | 25 | 24 | 23 | 22 | 21 | 20 | 2 | 1 |
| 19 | 18 | 17 | 16 | 15 | 14 | 13 | 12 | 11 | 10 | 9 | 8 | 7 | | |

AD106492

Wire side

F

5	6	46	47	48	49	50	51	52	53	54	55	56	57	58
		33	34	35	36	37	38	39	40	41	42	43	44	45
3	4													
1	2	20	21	22	23	24	25	26	27	28	29	30	31	32
		7	8	9	10	11	12	13	14	15	16	17	18	19

AD29429

M

| 73 | 74 | 75 | 76 | 77 | 78 | 79 | 80 | 81 | 82 | 83 | 84 | 85 | 86 | 87 | 88 | 89 | 90 | 91 | 92 | 93 | 94 | 95 | 96 |
| 49 | 50 | 51 | 52 | 53 | 54 | 55 | 56 | 57 | 58 | 59 | 60 | 61 | 62 | 63 | 64 | 65 | 66 | 67 | 68 | 69 | 70 | 71 | 72 |

| 25 | 26 | 27 | 28 | 29 | 30 | 31 | 32 | 33 | 34 | 35 | 36 | 37 | 38 | 39 | 40 | 41 | 42 | 43 | 44 | 45 | 46 | 47 | 48 |
| 1 | 2 | 3 | 4 | 5 | 6 | 7 | 8 | 9 | 10 | 11 | 12 | 13 | 14 | 15 | 16 | 17 | 18 | 19 | 20 | 21 | 22 | 23 | 24 |

Component/circuit description	ECM pin	Signal	Condition	Typical value	Oscilloscope setting*	Wave form
Accelerator pedal position (APP) sensor	F21	⇨	Ignition ON	5 V		
	F27	⌐	Ignition ON	0 V		
	F34	⌐	Ignition ON	0 V		
	F49	⟵	Ignition ON – accelerator pedal released	0,2 V		
	F49	⟵	Ignition ON – accelerator pedal fully depressed	2,3 V		
	F53	⟵	Ignition ON – accelerator pedal released	0 V		
	F53	⟵	Ignition ON – accelerator pedal fully depressed	4,5 V		
Alternator	M47	⟵	Ignition ON		2 V/1 ms	〜 83
Barometric pressure (BARO) sensor	M57	⌐	Ignition ON	0 V		
	M68	⇨	Ignition ON	5 V		
	M85	⟵	Ignition ON – 100 m above sea level	1,9 V		
Camshaft position (CMP) actuator – exhaust	M26	⌐▷	Ignition ON	2 V		
Camshaft position (CMP) actuator – intake	M73	⌐▷	Engine idling		5 V/2 ms	〜 68
Camshaft position (CMP) sensor – exhaust	M30	⟵	Engine idling		2 V/0,1 sec.	〜 89
	M53	⌐	Ignition ON	0 V		
Camshaft position (CMP) sensor – intake	M32	⟵	Engine idling		2 V/0,1 sec.	〜 89
	M53	⌐	Ignition ON	0 V		
CAN data bus	F41	⟷		1		
	F42	⟷		1		
Clutch pedal position (CPP) switch	F58	⟵		1		
Crankshaft position (CKP) sensor	M13	⟵	Engine idling	0,8 V ac	5 V/2 ms	〜 2
	M14	⟵	Engine idling	0,4 V ac	5 V/2 ms	Reversed 〜 2
Data link connector (DLC)	F51	⟷		1		

* Suggested settings - Voltage/time per division

Component/circuit description	ECM pin	Signal	Condition	Typical value	Oscilloscope setting*	Wave form
Earth	F2		Ignition ON	0 V		
	F4		Ignition ON	0 V		
	F6		Ignition ON	0 V		
Engine coolant blower motor	F16	←		[1]		
Engine coolant temperature (ECT) sensor	M33	⊣⊢	Ignition ON	0 V		
	M80	←	Ignition ON – coolant temp. 40°C	3,1 V		
Engine oil sensor module	M33	⊣⊢	Ignition ON	0 V		
	M68	⇒	Ignition ON	5 V		
	M90	←	Ignition ON		2 V/0,5 sec.	77
Evaporative emission (EVAP) canister purge valve	F46	⊣▷	Ignition ON	11-14 V		
	F46	⊣▷	Engine idling – throttle slightly open		10 V/20 ms	20
Heated oxygen sensor (HO2S) 1	M25	←	Ignition ON	0,4 V		
	M25	←	Engine idling – engine hot		10 V/20 ms	11
	M39	←	Ignition ON	5 V		
	M39	←	Engine running – 3000 rpm	2,2 V		
	M43	←	Engine idling	2,8 V		
	M44	←	Ignition ON	2,6 V		
	M44	←	Engine idling	2,9 V		
	M56	⬌		[1]		
Heated oxygen sensor (HO2S) 2	M7	←	Ignition ON	0,4 V		
	M7	←	Engine idling – engine hot	0,6 V		
	M83	⊣⊢	Ignition ON	0 V		
Heated oxygen sensor (HO2S) 2 – heater control	M29	⊣▷	Ignition ON	11-14 V		
	M29	⊣▷	Engine idling		2 V/0,1 sec.	64
Ignition coil 1	M1	⊣▷	Ignition ON	11-14 V		
	M1	⊣▷	Engine idling		5 V/2 ms	33
Ignition coil 2	M2	⊣▷	Ignition ON	11-14 V		
	M2	⊣▷	Engine idling		5 V/2 ms	33
Ignition coil 3	M3	⊣▷	Ignition ON	11-14 V		
	M3	⊣▷	Engine idling		5 V/2 ms	33
Ignition coil 4	M4	⊣▷	Ignition ON	11-14 V		
	M4	⊣▷	Engine idling		5 V/2 ms	33
Injector 1	M22	⊣▷	Ignition ON	11-14 V		
	M22	⊣▷	Engine idling	2,7 ms	10 V/2 ms	35
Injector 2	M21	⊣▷	Ignition ON	11-14 V		
	M21	⊣▷	Engine idling	2,7 ms	10 V/2 ms	35
Injector 3	M20	⊣▷	Ignition ON	11-14 V		
	M20	⊣▷	Engine idling	2,7 ms	10 V/2 ms	35
Injector 4	M23	⊣▷	Ignition ON	11-14 V		
	M23	⊣▷	Engine idling	2,7 ms	10 V/2 ms	35
Knock sensor (KS)	M50	⊣⊢	Ignition ON	0 V		
	M18	←	Engine idling – accelerate briefly		50 mV/1 ms	58
Manifold absolute pressure (MAP) sensor	M27	←	Engine idling		10 V/20 ms	11
	M57	⊣⊢	Ignition ON	0 V		
	M68	⇒	Ignition ON	5 V		
Mass air flow (MAF) sensor	M10	⊣⊢	Ignition ON	0 V		
	M28	←	Engine idling – accelerate briefly	0,7 V		
	M28	←	Engine running – 3000 rpm		1 V/2 sec.	44
	M37	⊣⊢	Ignition ON	0 V		

* Suggested settings - Voltage/time per division

Component/circuit description	ECM pin	Signal	Condition	Typical value	Oscilloscope setting*	Wave form
Multifunction control module 1	F1	←	Ignition ON	11-14 V		
	F3	←	Ignition ON	11-14 V		
	F5	←	Ignition ON	11-14 V		
	F11	←	Ignition ON	11-14 V		
	F12	←→		1		
	F23	←	Ignition ON	11-14 V		
	F50	⊣▷	Ignition OFF	11-14 V		
	F50	⊣▷	Ignition ON	0-1 V		
	F52	←	Ignition ON	11-14 V		
	F55	←	Ignition ON	11-14 V		
	M24	←	Ignition ON	11-14 V		
	M48	←	Ignition ON	11-14 V		
	M72	←	Ignition ON	11-14 V		
Secondary air injection (AIR) solenoid	M82	⊣▷	Ignition ON	11-14 V		
Supercharger (SC) boost air temperature sensor	M33	⊣—	Ignition ON	0 V		
	M78	←	Ignition ON – air temp. 12°C	3,7 V		
Supercharger (SC) bypass valve motor	M11	⇒	Ignition ON	11-14 V		
	M12	←	Engine idling		2 V/2 ms	∿ 71
Supercharger (SC) bypass valve motor position sensor	M36	←	Ignition ON	0,7 V		
	M42	←	Ignition ON	4,3 V		
	M62	⊣—	Ignition ON	0 V		
	M68	⇒	Ignition ON	5 V		
Throttle motor	M45	⇒	Ignition ON		2 V/2 ms	∿ 64
	M46	⊣—	Ignition ON	0 V		
Throttle motor position sensor	M51	⊣—	Ignition ON	0 V		
	M66	⇒	Ignition ON	5 V		
	M76	←	Ignition ON	0,9 V		
	M77	←	Ignition ON	4,1 V		

*Suggested settings - Voltage/time per division

1 Connected pin - no test data available or random digital signal

MERCEDES-BENZ

Bosch EDC 15C0

Model:	Engine code:	Year:
C200/C220 CDI (202)	611.960	1998-01
E200/E220 CDI (210)	611.961	1998-03

ECM harness multi-plug

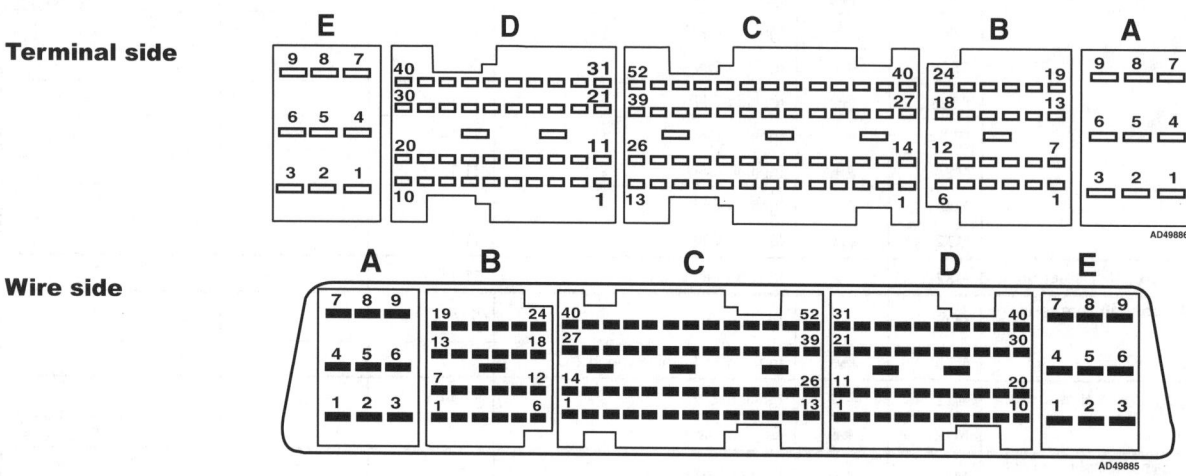

Terminal side

Wire side

AD49886

AD49885

Component/circuit description	ECM pin	Signal	Condition	Typical value
Airbag control module	B17			1
AC control module – →05/99	C47			1
AC control module – 06/99→	C41			1
Accelerator pedal position (APP) sensor	C5	⇨	Ignition OFF	0 V
	C5	⇨	Ignition ON	5 V
	C8	⌐‒	Ignition ON	0 V
	C9	⬅	Ignition ON – accelerator pedal released	0,14 V
	C9	⬅	Ignition ON – accelerator pedal depressed	2,3 V
	C10	⬅	Ignition ON – accelerator pedal released	0,3 V
	C10	⬅	Ignition ON – accelerator pedal depressed	4,6 V
	C23	⌐‒	Ignition ON	0 V
Camshaft position (CMP) sensor	D2	⌐‒	Ignition ON	0 V
	D3	⬅	Engine idling	2 V/50 ms per division ⌁ 3
	D3	⬅	Ignition ON	4,9 V
	D12	⇨	Ignition OFF	0 V
	D12	⇨	Ignition ON	11-14 V
CAN data bus connection	B11			1
	B12			1
Clutch pedal position (CPP) switch	B2	⬅	Ignition ON – clutch pedal released	0 V
	B2	⬅	Ignition ON – clutch pedal depressed	11-14 V
Crankshaft position (CKP) sensor	D26	⬅	Engine idling	8,6 V ac
	D26	⬅	Engine idling	5 V/2 ms per division ⌁ 1
	D37	⌐‒	Ignition ON	0 V
Data link connector (DLC)	C28	⬅⇨	Ignition OFF	0 V
	C28	⬅⇨	Ignition ON	11 V
	C40	⬅⇨	Ignition ON	1,0 V
Earth	A4		Ignition ON	0 V
	A5		Ignition ON	0 V
	A6		Ignition ON	0 V
Engine coolant blower motor control module	C45	⌐⇨	Ignition OFF	0 V
	C45	⌐⇨	Ignition ON	0-14 V fluctuating

Component/circuit description	ECM pin	Signal	Condition	Typical value
Engine coolant blower motor control module – →05/99	C31	⇨	Ignition OFF	0 V
	C31	⇨	Ignition ON	11-14 V
Engine coolant heater control module	C49			1
Engine coolant temperature (ECT) sensor	D27	⊣	Ignition ON	0 V
	D36	⬅	Ignition ON – engine cold	4 V
	D36	⬅	Engine idling – engine hot	1,5 V
Engine coolant temperature (ECT) switch – 06/99→	B23			1
Engine oil temperature sensor/engine oil level sensor	D5	⊣	Ignition ON	0 V
	D15	⬅		2 V/0,5 s per division ⎍ 11
	D16	⇨	Ignition OFF	0 V
	D16	⇨	Ignition ON	5 V
Exhaust gas recirculation (EGR) solenoid	C37	⇨	Ignition OFF	0 V
	C37	⇨	Ignition ON	11-14 V
	C37	⇨	Engine idling	11-14 V
	C50	⊣⬎	Ignition OFF	0 V
	C50	⊣⬎	Ignition ON	11-14 V
	C50	⊣⬎	Engine idling	5 V/2 ms per division ⎍ 31
Fuel pressure control solenoid	D21	⊣	Ignition ON	0 V
	D31	⇨	Engine idling	82%
	D31	⇨	Engine idling	5 V/1 ms per division ⎍ 12
	D31	⇨	Ignition ON	1,6 V – 0 V after 5 secs.
Fuel pressure sensor	D4	⊣	Ignition ON	0 V
	D13	⇨	Ignition OFF	0 V
	D13	⇨	Ignition ON	5 V
	D14	⬅	Engine idling	1,1 V
	D14	⬅	Engine running – 3000 rpm	2,1 V
	D14	⬅	Ignition ON	0,51 V
Fuel shut-off solenoid	D25	⇨	Engine idling	11-14 V
	D25	⇨	Ignition OFF	0 V
	D25	⇨	Ignition ON	11-14 V
	D35	⊣⬎	Engine idling	11-14 V
	D35	⊣⬎	Ignition OFF	0 V
	D35	⊣⬎	Ignition ON	1,6-10,3 V
Glow plug control module – →05/99	C13	⇨	Ignition OFF	0 V
	C13	⇨	Ignition ON	5-10 V fluctuating
Glow plug control module – 06/99→	C25	⇨	Ignition OFF	0 V
	C25	⇨	Ignition ON	5-10 V fluctuating
Ignition switch	B13	⬅	Ignition OFF	0 V
	B13	⬅	Ignition ON	11-14 V
Ignition switch – start signal	C20	⬅	Engine cranking	11-14 V
Injector 1	E5	⊣⬎	Engine idling	1 ms pilot + 1,5 ms main
	E5	⊣⬎	Engine idling	10 V/0,5 ms per division ⎍ 23
Injector 2	E3	⊣⬎	Engine idling	1 ms pilot + 1,5 ms main
	E3	⊣⬎	Engine idling	10 V/0,5 ms per division ⎍ 23
Injector 3	E9	⊣⬎	Engine idling	1 ms pilot + 1,5 ms main
	E9	⊣⬎	Engine idling	10 V/0,5 ms per division ⎍ 23
Injector 4	E7	⊣⬎	Engine idling	1 ms pilot + 1,5 ms main
	E7	⊣⬎	Engine idling	10 V/0,5 ms per division ⎍ 23
Injectors 1 & 4 – except 01/99-06/99	E4	⇨	Ignition ON	1,1 V
Injectors 1, 2, 3 & 4 – 01/99-05/99	E2	⇨	Ignition ON	1,1 V
Injectors 2 & 3 – →12/98	E1	⇨	Ignition ON	1,1 V
	E2	⇨	Ignition ON	1,1 V

Component/circuit description	ECM pin	Signal	Condition	Typical value
Intake air temperature (IAT) sensor	C12	←	Ignition ON – air temp. 15°C	4,1 V
Intake air temperature (IAT) sensor – →05/99	C11	⅂─	Ignition ON	0 V
Intake air temperature (IAT) sensor – 06/99→	C1	⅂─	Ignition ON	0 V
Intake manifold air control solenoid – →05/99	C39			1
	C52			1
Intake manifold air control solenoid – 06/99→	D22			1
	D33			1
Manifold absolute pressure (MAP) sensor	C6	←	Ignition ON	1,88 V
	C6	←	Engine idling	1,88 V
	C6	←	Engine running – accelerate briefly	3,4 V
	C17	⇒	Ignition OFF	0 V
	C17	⇒	Ignition ON	5 V
	C22	⅂─	Ignition ON	0 V
Mass air flow (MAF) sensor – →05/99	C7	⅂─	Ignition ON	0 V
	C18	←	Ignition ON	1 V
	C18	←	Engine idling	2,2 V
	C18	←	Engine idling – accelerate briefly	4,2 V
	C19	⇒	Ignition OFF	0 V
	C19	⇒	Ignition ON	5 V
	C33	⇒	Ignition OFF	0 V
	C33	⇒	Ignition ON	11-14 V
Mass air flow (MAF) sensor – 06/99→	D1	⇒	Ignition OFF	0 V
	D1	⇒	Ignition ON	5 V
	D11	⇒	Ignition OFF	0 V
	D11	⇒	Ignition ON	11-14 V
	D24	←	Ignition ON	1 V
	D24	←	Engine idling	2,2 V
	D24	←	Engine idling – accelerate briefly	4,2 V
	D34	⅂─	Ignition ON	0 V
Relay module	A1	←	Ignition OFF	0 V
	A1	←	Ignition ON	11-14 V
	A7	←	Ignition OFF	0 V
	A7	←	Ignition ON	11-14 V
	A8	←	Ignition OFF	0 V
	A8	←	Ignition ON	11-14 V
	C46	⅂⇒	Ignition OFF	11-14 V
	C46	⅂⇒	Ignition ON	0,8 V
Relay module – starter relay	C30	⇒	Ignition OFF	0 V
	C30	⇒	Ignition ON	11-14 V
	C43	⅂⇒	Engine cranking	0 V
	C43	⅂⇒	Ignition ON	11-14 V
Transmission control module (TCM)	B2	←	Ignition ON – AT in N or P	0 V
	B2	←	Ignition ON – AT in other positions	10,7 V
Transmission kick-down switch – 06/99→	B7			1
Turbocharger (TC) wastegate regulating valve	C35	⇒	Ignition OFF	0 V
	C35	⇒	Ignition ON	11-14 V
	C48	⅂⇒	Ignition ON	11-14 V
	C48	⅂⇒	Engine idling	5,3 V
	C48	⅂⇒	Engine idling	5 V/2 ms per division 〰️ 29

1 Connected pin - no test data available

Model:	Engine code:	Year:
C200 CDI (203)	646.962/646.963	2003-06
C220 CDI (203)	646.962/646.963	2003-06
CLK 220 CDI (209)	646.963	2005-06

ECM harness multi-plug

Terminal side

M

AD106492

F

Wire side

F

M

AD29429

Component/circuit description	ECM pin	Signal	Condition	Typical value	Oscilloscope setting*	Wave form
Accelerator pedal position (APP) sensor	F13	←	Ignition ON – accelerator pedal released	0,1 V		
	F13	←	Ignition ON – accelerator pedal fully depressed	2,3 V		
	F14	⌐	Ignition ON	0 V		
	F24	⇒	Ignition ON	5 V		
	F25	←	Ignition ON – accelerator pedal released	0,3 V		
	F25	←	Ignition ON – accelerator pedal fully depressed	4,6 V		
	F26	⌐	Ignition ON	0 V		
Alternator	M66			1		
Barometric pressure (BARO) sensor	M12	⌐	Ignition ON	0 V		
	M13	←	Ignition ON – 100 m above sea level	3,8 V		
	M36	⇒	Ignition ON	5 V		
Camshaft position (CMP) sensor	M14	⌐	Ignition ON	0 V		
	M37	⇒	Ignition ON	5 V		
	M38	←	Engine idling		2 V/0,1 sec.	∿ 4
CAN data bus connection – high	F53	←⇒		1		
CAN data bus connection – low	F54	←⇒		1		
Crankcase breather heater	M21	⇒	Ignition ON	11-14 V		
	M91	⇒	Ignition ON	11-14 V		
Crankshaft position (CKP) sensor	M87	←	Engine idling	4,9 V ac		
	M87	←	Engine idling		5 V/2 ms	∿ 1
	M88	←	Engine idling	4,9 V ac		
	M88	←	Engine idling		5 V/2 ms	Reversed ∿ 11
Data link connector (DLC)	F31	←⇒		1		
Earth	F2		Ignition ON	0 V		
	F4		Ignition ON	0 V		
	F6		Ignition ON	0 V		

∗ Suggested settings - Voltage/time per division

Component/circuit description	ECM pin	Signal	Condition	Typical value	Oscilloscope setting*	Wave form
Engine coolant blower motor control module	F57	⇒	Ignition OFF	11-14 V		
	F57	⇒	Engine idling – AC ON		2 V/50 ms	⍊⍊ 22
Engine coolant heater regulator valve	M71			1		
Engine coolant temperature (ECT) sensor	M56	⌐—	Ignition ON	0 V		
	M57	⬅	Ignition ON – coolant temp. 60°C	2,3 V		
	M57	⬅	Engine idling – coolant temp. 95°C	1 V		
Engine oil sensor module	M10	⇒	Ignition ON	5 V		
	M11	⬅	Ignition ON		2 V/1 sec.	⍊⍊ 11
	M35	⌐—	Ignition ON	0 V		
Exhaust gas pressure sensor – with Euro stage IV emissions	M9			1		
	M33			1		
	M82			1		
Exhaust gas recirculation (EGR) valve actuator	M90	⇒	Ignition ON		1 V/10 ms	⍊⍊ 5
	M90	⇒	Engine idling		2 V/5 ms	Intermittent ⍊⍊ 22
Exhaust gas temperature sensor 1 – with Euro stage IV emissions	M29			1		
	M78			1		
Exhaust gas temperature sensor 2 – with Euro stage IV emissions	M6			1		
	M30			1		
Exhaust particulate filter pressure differential sensor – with Euro stage IV emissions	M5			1		
	M53			1		
	M58			1		
Fuel quantity adjuster	M28	⇒	Ignition ON	11-14 V		
	M76	⇒	Ignition ON		2 V/5 ms	⍊⍊ 22
	M76	⇒	Engine idling		2 V/5 ms	⍊⍊ 22
	M76	⇒	3000 rpm		2 V/5 ms	⍊⍊ 22
Fuel rail pressure (FRP) control valve	M4	⇒	Ignition ON	11-14 V		
	M52	⌐⇒	Ignition ON	Wave pattern for 20 secs.	2 V/4 ms	⍊⍊ 37
Fuel rail pressure (FRP) sensor	M59	⬅	Ignition ON	0,5 V		
	M59	⬅	Engine idling	1,2 V		
	M59	⬅	3000 rpm	2 V		
	M84	⌐—	Ignition ON	0 V		
	M86	⇒	Ignition ON	5 V		
Fuel temperature sensor	M8	⬅	Ignition ON	2,4 V		
	M32	⌐—	Ignition ON	0 V		
Glow plug control module	F43	⇒	Ignition ON		2 V/50 ms	⍊⍊ 14
Heated oxygen sensor (HO2S) 1 – with Euro stage IV emissions	M15			1		
	M39			1		
	M40			1		
	M62			1		
	M72			1		
Heated oxygen sensor (HO2S) 2 – with Euro stage IV emissions	M16			1		
	M41			1		
	M43			1		
	M89			1		
	M96			1		

* Suggested settings - Voltage/time per division

Component/circuit description	ECM pin	Signal	Condition	Typical value	Oscilloscope setting*	Wave form
Heater function control module	M45			1		
Injector 1	M25 (M74)	⇒	Engine idling – engine hot	0,3 ms	10 V/0,1 ms	61
	M74 (M25)	⇒	Engine idling – engine hot	0,3 ms	10 V/0,1 ms	61
Injector 2	M2 (M49)	⇒	Engine idling – engine hot	0,3 ms	10 V/0,1 ms	61
	M49 (M2)	⇒	Engine idling – engine hot	0,3 ms	10 V/0,1 ms	61
Injector 3	M1 (M73)	⇒	Engine idling – engine hot	0,3 ms	10 V/0,1 ms	61
	M73 (M1)	⇒	Engine idling – engine hot	0,3 ms	10 V/0,1 ms	61
Injector 4	M26 (M51)	⇒	Engine idling – engine hot	0,3 ms	10 V/0,1 ms	61
	M51 (M26)	⇒	Engine idling – engine hot	0,3 ms	10 V/0,1 ms	61
Intake air temperature (IAT) sensor – in MAF sensor	M31	⇐	Ignition ON – air temp. 25°C	1,6 V		
	M61	⌐	Ignition ON	0 V		
Intake manifold air control actuator	M92	⇒	Ignition ON		4 V/10 ms	12
	M92	⇒	Engine idling		4 V/10 ms	12
Mass air flow (MAF) sensor	M17	⇒	Ignition ON	11-14 V		
	M64	⌐	Ignition ON	0 V		
	M85	⇐	Ignition ON	1 V		
	M85	⇐	Engine idling	1,9 V		
	M85	⇐	3000 rpm	3,5 V		
Multifunction control module 1	F1	⇐	Ignition ON	11-14 V		
	F3	⇐	Ignition ON	11-14 V		
	F5	⇐	Ignition ON	11-14 V		
	F18	⇐	Ignition OFF	0 V		
	F18	⇐	Ignition ON	11-14 V		
	F19	⇐	Ignition ON	11-14 V		
	F27			1		
	F44			1		
	F58	⇐	Ignition ON	11-14 V		
	M67			1		
Multifunction control module 2	F55	⌐⇒	Ignition OFF	11-14 V		
	F55	⌐⇒	Ignition ON	0-1 V		
Power steering pressure (PSP) valve	M95			1		
Throttle control unit – with Euro stage IV emissions	M68			1		
Turbocharger (TC) boost air temperature sensor	M34	⇐	Engine idling	3 V		
	M65	⌐	Ignition ON	0 V		
Turbocharger (TC) boost pressure actuator	M93	⇒	Ignition ON	0 V		
	M93	⇒	Engine idling		1 V/10 ms	37
	M93	⇒	3000 rpm		2 V/5 ms	22
Turbocharger (TC) boost pressure sensor	M60	⇒	Ignition ON	5 V		
	M63	⇐	Ignition ON	1,9 V		
	M63	⇐	Engine idling	1,9 V		
	M63	⇐	3000 rpm	2,2 V		
	M83	⌐	Ignition ON	0 V		

*Suggested settings - Voltage/time per division

1 Connected pin - no test data available or random digital signal

MERCEDES-BENZ

Bosch ME 2.1

Model:	Engine code:	Year:
C230K (202)	111.975	1997-01
CLK 230K (208)	111.975	1997-03
S280 (220)	104.944	1996-98
S320 (220)	104.994	1996-98

ECM harness multi-plug

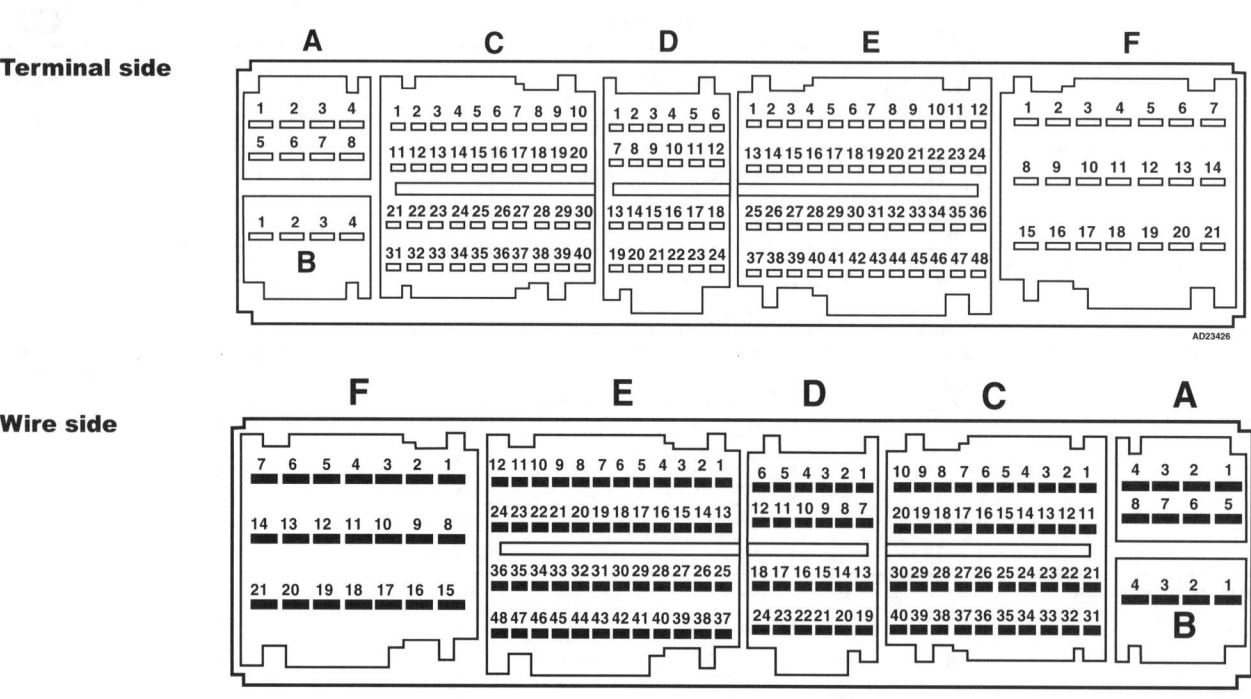

AD23426

AD23425

Component/circuit description	ECM pin	Signal	Condition	Typical value	Oscilloscope setting*	Wave form
Accelerator pedal position (APP) sensor	C22	⟹	Ignition ON	5 V		
	C23	⌐	Ignition ON	0 V		
	C24	⟵	Ignition ON – accelerator pedal released	0,3 V		
	C24	⟵	Ignition ON – accelerator pedal fully depressed	4,7 V		
	C25	⟵	Ignition ON – accelerator pedal released	0,2 V		
	C25	⟵	Ignition ON – accelerator pedal fully depressed	2,3 V		
	C26	⌐	Ignition OFF	0 V		
Accelerator pedal position (APP) sensor – some models	C27	⟹	Ignition ON	5 V		
Airbag control module – 4 cyl.	D16			[1]		
Battery – 4 cyl.	B4	⟵	Ignition OFF	11-14 V		
Camshaft position (CMP) actuator	E4	⌐▷	Engine idling	11-14 V		
	E4	⌐▷	Engine idling – full throttle briefly	0 V		
Camshaft position (CMP) sensor	E39	⌐	Ignition ON	0 V		
	E40	⟵	Ignition ON – engine turned	0 V or 12 V		
	E40	⟵	Engine idling		5 V/0,2 sec.	∿∿ 68
CAN data bus	D11	⟷		[1]		
	D12	⟷		[1]		
Clutch pedal position (CPP) switch	D19	⟵	Ignition ON – clutch pedal released	0 V		
	D19	⟵	Ignition ON – clutch pedal depressed	11-14 V		

★ Suggested settings - Voltage/time per division

Component/circuit description	ECM pin	Signal	Condition	Typical value	Oscilloscope setting*	Wave form
Crankshaft position (CKP) sensor	E37	←	Engine idling	4,2 V ac	2 V/2 ms	Reversed 〜 2
	E38	←	Engine idling	3,9 V ac	2 V/2 ms	〜 2
Cruise control master switch	D20			1		
	D21			1		
	D22			1		
	D23			1		
	D24			1		
Data link connector (DLC)	B3			1		
Data link connector (DLC) – engine RPM signal	C38	⇒	Engine idling	25 Hz		
	C38	⇒	3000 rpm	100 Hz		
Data link connector (DLC) – supply voltage	C39	⇒	Ignition ON	11-14 V		
Earth	A3		Ignition ON	0 V		
	A7		Ignition ON	0 V		
	A8		Ignition ON	0 V		
	F8		Ignition ON	0 V		
	F15		Ignition ON	0 V		
Engine coolant temperature (ECT) sensor	E28	⊣	Ignition ON	0 V		
	E29	←	Ignition ON – coolant temp. 15°C	3,5 V		
	E29	←	Engine idling – engine hot	0,8 V		
Engine oil level switch – some models	E17	←		1		
Evaporative emission (EVAP) canister purge valve	C21	⊣▷	Ignition ON	11-14 V		
	C21	⊣▷	Engine idling	11%	10 V/0,2 sec.	〜 20
Fuel pump relay	C29	⊣▷	Ignition ON	11-14 V		
	C29	⊣▷	Engine idling	0 V		
Heated oxygen sensor (HO2S) 1	C31	⊣	Ignition ON	0 V		
	C32	←	Engine idling	0,1-0,9 V fluctuating	0,2 V/1 sec.	〜 21
Heated oxygen sensor (HO2S) 1 – heater control	A5	⊣▷	Ignition ON	11-14 V		
	A5	⊣▷	Engine idling	0 V		
Ignition coil – cylinders 1 & 4 – 4 cyl.	F20	⊣▷	Ignition ON	11-14 V		
	F20	⊣▷	Engine idling		5 V/2 ms	〜 33
Ignition coil – cylinders 2 & 3 – 4 cyl.	F13	⊣▷	Ignition ON	11-14 V		
	F13	⊣▷	Engine idling		5 V/2 ms	〜 33
Ignition coil – cylinders 1 & 6 – 6 cyl.	F20	⊣▷	Ignition ON	11-14 V		
	F20	⊣▷	Engine idling		5 V/2 ms	〜 33
Ignition coil – cylinders 2 & 5 – 6 cyl.	F13	⊣▷	Ignition ON	11-14 V		
	F13	⊣▷	Engine idling		5 V/2 ms	〜 33
Ignition coil – cylinders 3 & 4 – 6 cyl.	F6	⊣▷	Ignition ON	11-14 V		
	F6	⊣▷	Engine idling		5 V/2 ms	〜 33
Ignition switch control module – through multifunction control module 1 – 4 cyl.	C40			1		
Injector 1 – 4 cyl.	E25	⊣▷	Ignition ON	11-14 V		
	E25	⊣▷	Engine idling	2,8 ms	10 V/2 ms	〜 35
Injector 2 – 4 cyl.	E14	⊣▷	Ignition ON	11-14 V		
	E14	⊣▷	Engine idling	2,8 ms	10 V/2 ms	〜 35
Injector 3 – 4 cyl.	E26	⊣▷	Ignition ON	11-14 V		
	E26	⊣▷	Engine idling	2,8 ms	10 V/2 ms	〜 35
Injector 4 – 4 cyl.	E13	⊣▷	Ignition ON	11-14 V		
	E13	⊣▷	Engine idling	2,8 ms	10 V/2 ms	〜 35
Injector 1 – 6 cyl.	E25	⊣▷	Ignition ON	11-14 V		
	E25	⊣▷	Engine idling	2,8 ms	10 V/2 ms	〜 35

* Suggested settings - Voltage/time per division

Component/circuit description	ECM pin	Signal	Condition	Typical value	Oscilloscope setting*	Wave form
Injector 2 – 6 cyl.	E26	⊐▷	Ignition ON	11-14 V		
	E26	⊐▷	Engine idling	2,8 ms	10 V/2 ms	35
Injector 3 – 6 cyl.	E13	⊐▷	Ignition ON	11-14 V		
	E13	⊐▷	Engine idling	2,8 ms	10 V/2 ms	35
Injector 4 – 6 cyl.	E14	⊐▷	Ignition ON	11-14 V		
	E14	⊐▷	Engine idling	2,8 ms	10 V/2 ms	35
Injector 5 – 6 cyl.	E1	⊐▷	Ignition ON	11-14 V		
	E1	⊐▷	Engine idling	2,8 ms	10 V/2 ms	35
Injector 6 – 6 cyl.	E2	⊐▷	Ignition ON	11-14 V		
	E2	⊐▷	Engine idling	2,8 ms	10 V/2 ms	35
Ignition switch – 6 cyl.	C40	←	Engine cranking	10 V		
Intake air temperature (IAT) sensor – in MAF sensor	E45	←	Ignition ON – air temp. 15°C	2,7 V		
Intake manifold air control solenoid – 6 cyl.	E12			☐1		
Knock sensor (KS) – signal 1 – 4 cyl.	E41	←	Engine idling – accelerate briefly		50 mV/1 ms	58
Knock sensor (KS) – signal 2 – 4 cyl.	E42	←	Engine idling – accelerate briefly		50 mV/1 ms	58
Knock sensor (KS) 1 – signal 1 – 6 cyl.	E41	←	Engine idling – accelerate briefly		50 mV/1 ms	58
Knock sensor (KS) 1 – signal 2 – 6 cyl.	E42	←	Engine idling – accelerate briefly		50 mV/1 ms	58
Knock sensor (KS) 2 – signal 1 – 6 cyl.	E43	←	Engine idling – accelerate briefly		50 mV/1 ms	58
Knock sensor (KS) 2 – signal 2 – 6 cyl.	E44	←	Engine idling – accelerate briefly		50 mV/1 ms	58
Lights control module	D14			☐1		
Mass air flow (MAF) sensor	E46	⇒	Ignition ON	5 V		
	E47	←	Ignition ON	1 V		
	E47	←	Engine idling	1,4 V		
	E47	←	Engine idling – full throttle briefly	4,4 V		
	E48	⊐─	Ignition ON	0 V		
Multifunction control module – 6 cyl.	A2	←	Ignition ON	11-14 V		
	B4			☐1		
Secondary air injection (AIR) relay – if fitted	C28			☐1		
Secondary air injection (AIR) solenoid – if fitted	E12			☐1		
Starter motor relay – 4 cyl.	D3	⊐▷	Ignition ON	11-14 V		
	D3	⊐▷	Engine cranking	0 V		
Supercharger (SC) bypass valve – 4 cyl.	E3	⊐▷	Ignition ON	11-14 V		
	E3	⊐▷	Engine idling	88%	2 V/20 ms	64
Supercharger (SC) clutch – 4 cyl.	F21	⊐▷	Engine idling – SC clutch disengaged	11-14 V		
	F21	⊐▷	Engine running – SC clutch engaged	0 V		
Throttle motor position sensor 1	E31	←	Ignition ON – throttle closed	4,1 V		
	E31	←	Ignition ON – throttle fully open	3,4 V		
	E31	←	Engine idling	4,4 V		
Throttle motor position sensor 1 & 2	E32	⊐─	Ignition ON	0 V		
	E33	⇒	Ignition ON	5 V		
Throttle motor position sensor 2	E34	←	Ignition ON – throttle closed	0,9 V		
	E34	←	Ignition ON – throttle fully open	1,7 V		
	E34	←	Engine idling	0,7 V		
Throttle position motor	F1	⇒	Engine idling		5 V/1 ms	Intermittent 81
	F2	⇒	Engine idling		5 V/1 ms	68
Transmission control module (TCM) – AT	D19			☐1		
Voltage polarity protection relay	A2	←	Ignition ON	11-14 V		

*Suggested settings - Voltage/time per division

☐1 Connected pin - no test data available or random digital signal

Model:	Engine code:	Year:
C240/C280 (202)	112.910, 112.920	1997-01
CLK 320 (208)	112.940	1997-03
E240/E280/E320 (210)	112.911, 112.921, 112.941	1997-03

ECM harness multi-plug

Terminal side

Wire side

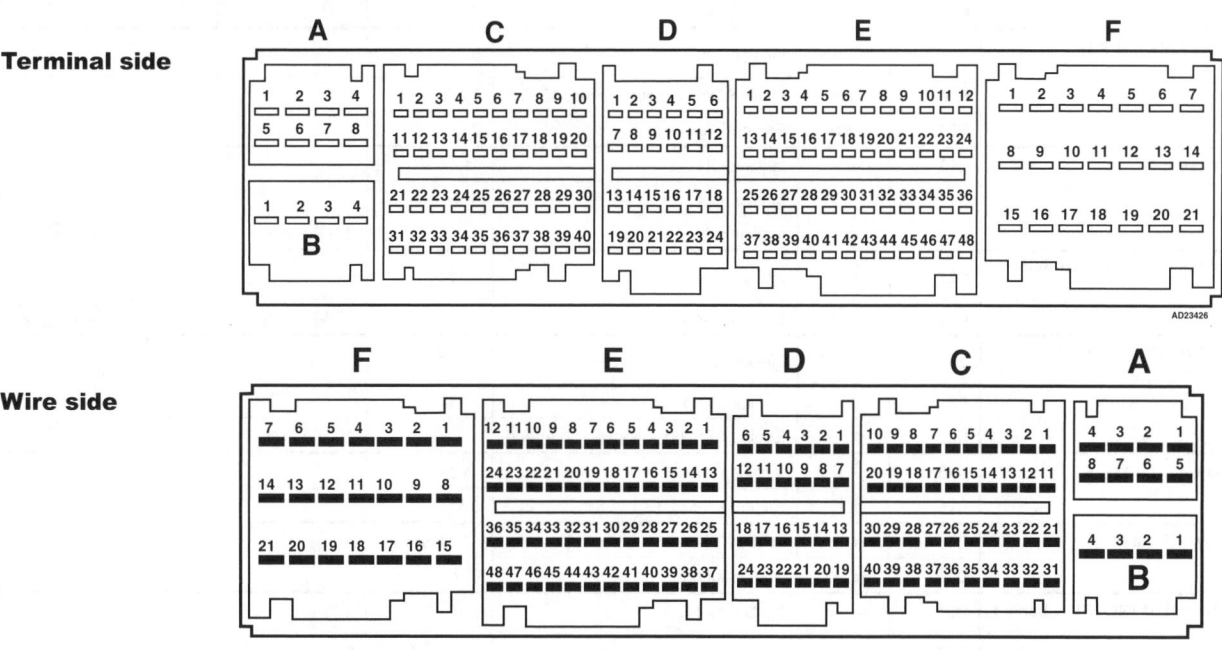

AD23426

AD23425

Component/circuit description	ECM pin	Signal	Condition	Typical value	Oscilloscope setting*	Wave form
AC control module	A6			1		
Accelerator pedal position (APP) sensor	C22	⇒	Ignition ON	5 V		
	C23	⅃—	Ignition ON	0 V		
	C24	⟵	Ignition ON – accelerator pedal released	0,8 V		
	C24	⟵	Ignition ON – accelerator pedal fully depressed	4,7 V		
	C25	⟵	Ignition ON – accelerator pedal released	0,4 V		
	C25	⟵	Ignition ON – accelerator pedal fully depressed	2,3 V		
	C26	⅃—		0 V		
Accelerator pedal position (APP) sensor – some models	C27	⇒	Ignition ON	5 V		
Airbag control module	D16			1		
Battery	B4	⟵	Ignition OFF	11-14 V		
Camshaft position (CMP) sensor	E39	⅃—	Ignition ON	0 V		
	E40	⟵	Ignition ON – engine turned	0 V or 12 V		
	E40	⟵	Engine idling		5 V/0,2 sec.	〰 68
CAN data bus	D11	⟷		1		
	D12	⟷		1		
Clutch pedal position (CPP) switch	D19	⟵	Ignition ON – clutch pedal released	11-14 V		
	D19	⟵	Ignition ON – clutch pedal depressed	0 V		
Crankshaft position (CKP) sensor	E38	⟵	Engine idling	3,9 V ac	2 V/2 ms	〰 2
	E37	⟵	Engine idling	3,9 V ac	2 V/2 ms	Reversed 〰 2
Data link connector (DLC)	B3	⟷		1		
Data link connector (DLC) – engine RPM signal	C38	⇒	Engine idling	34 Hz		

* Suggested settings - Voltage/time per division

Component/circuit description	ECM pin	Signal	Condition	Typical value	Oscilloscope setting*	Wave form
Data link connector (DLC) – supply voltage	C39	⇨	Ignition ON	11-14 V		
Earth	A3		Ignition ON	0 V		
	A7		Ignition ON	0 V		
	A8		Ignition ON	0 V		
	F8		Ignition ON	0 V		
	F15		Ignition ON	0 V		
Engine coolant temperature (ECT) sensor	E28		Ignition ON	0 V		
	E29	⬅	Ignition ON – coolant temp. 15°C	3,6 V		
	E29	⬅	Engine idling – engine hot	0,6 V		
Engine oil level sensor	E15	⇨	Ignition ON	11-14 V		
	E16		Ignition ON	0 V		
	E17	⬅	Ignition ON		2 V/0,1 ms	77
Evaporative emission (EVAP) canister purge valve	C21		Ignition ON	11-14 V		
	C21		Engine idling		10 V/50 ms	20
Exhaust gas recirculation (EGR) solenoid	E5		Ignition ON	11-14 V		
	E5		Engine idling	11-14 V		
	E5		Engine running – above idle speed		10 V/50 ms	20
Fuel pump relay – C-class	C29		Ignition ON	11-14 V		
	C29		Engine idling	0 V		
Fuel pump relay – E-class	D1		Ignition ON	11-14 V		
	D1		Engine idling	0 V		
Heated oxygen sensor (HO2S) 1, bank 1	C31		Ignition ON	0 V		
	C32	⬅	Engine idling	0,1-0,9 V fluctuating	0,2 V/1 sec.	21
Heated oxygen sensor (HO2S) 1, bank 1 – heater control	A5		Ignition ON	11-14 V		
	A5		Start engine – constant heating after 1 minute	0 V after 1 minute		
	A5		Start engine – intermittent heating for 1 minute		5 V/0,1 sec.	68
Heated oxygen sensor (HO2S) 1, bank 2	C33	⬅	Engine idling	0,1-0,9 V fluctuating	0,2 V/1 sec.	21
	C34		Ignition ON	0 V		
Heated oxygen sensor (HO2S) 1, bank 2 – heater control	A1		Ignition ON	11-14 V		
	A1		Start engine – constant heating after 1 minute	0 V after 1 minute		
	A1		Start engine – intermittent heating for 1 minute		5 V/0,1 sec.	68
Ignition coil 1 – signal a	F20		Ignition ON	11-14 V		
	F20		Engine idling		5 V/2 ms	33
Ignition coil 1 – signal b	F21		Ignition ON	11-14 V		
	F21		Engine idling		5 V/2 ms	33
Ignition coil 2 – signal a	F17		Ignition ON	11-14 V		
	F17		Engine idling		5 V/2 ms	33
Ignition coil 2 – signal b	F16		Ignition ON	11-14 V		
	F16		Engine idling		5 V/2 ms	33
Ignition coil 3 – signal a	F6		Ignition ON	11-14 V		
	F6		Engine idling		5 V/2 ms	33
Ignition coil 3 – signal b	F7		Ignition ON	11-14 V		
	F7		Engine idling		5 V/2 ms	33
Ignition coil 4 – signal a	F13		Ignition ON	11-14 V		
	F13		Engine idling		5 V/2 ms	33
Ignition coil 4 – signal b	F14		Ignition ON	11-14 V		
	F14		Engine idling		5 V/2 ms	33

* Suggested settings - Voltage/time per division

Component/circuit description	ECM pin	Signal	Condition	Typical value	Oscilloscope setting*	Wave form
Ignition coil 5 – signal a	F5	⊐▷	Ignition ON	11-14 V		
	F5	⊐▷	Engine idling		5 V/2 ms	⌇⌇ 33
Ignition coil 5 – signal b	F4	⊐▷	Ignition ON	11-14 V		
	F4	⊐▷	Engine idling		5 V/2 ms	⌇⌇ 33
Ignition coil 6 – signal a	F19	⊐▷	Ignition ON	11-14 V		
	F19	⊐▷	Engine idling		5 V/2 ms	⌇⌇ 33
Ignition coil 6 – signal b	F18	⊐▷	Ignition ON	11-14 V		
	F18	⊐▷	Engine idling		5 V/2 ms	⌇⌇ 33
Ignition switch control module – through multifunction control module 1	C40			1		
Injector 1	E25	⊐▷	Ignition ON	11-14 V		
	E25	⊐▷	Engine idling	3,5 ms	10 V/2 ms	⌇⌇ 35
Injector 2	E1	⊐▷	Ignition ON	11-14 V		
	E1	⊐▷	Engine idling	3,5 ms	10 V/2 ms	⌇⌇ 35
Injector 3	E13	⊐▷	Ignition ON	11-14 V		
	E13	⊐▷	Engine idling	3,5 ms	10 V/2 ms	⌇⌇ 35
Injector 4	E26	⊐▷	Ignition ON	11-14 V		
	E26	⊐▷	Engine idling	3,5 ms	10 V/2 ms	⌇⌇ 35
Injector 5	E2	⊐▷	Ignition ON	11-14 V		
	E2	⊐▷	Engine idling	3,5 ms	10 V/2 ms	⌇⌇ 35
Injector 6	E14	⊐▷	Ignition ON	11-14 V		
	E14	⊐▷	Engine idling	3,5 ms	10 V/2 ms	⌇⌇ 35
Intake air temperature (IAT) sensor – in MAF sensor	E45	⬅	Ignition ON – air temp. 15°C	2,7 V		
Intake manifold air control valve	E12	⊐▷	Ignition ON	11-14 V		
	E12	⊐▷	Engine idling – full throttle briefly	0 V		
Knock sensor (KS) 1	E41	⬅	Engine idling – accelerate briefly		50 mV/1 ms	⌇⌇ 58
	E42	⬅	Engine idling – accelerate briefly		50 mV/1 ms	⌇⌇ 58
Knock sensor (KS) 2	E43	⬅	Engine idling – accelerate briefly		50 mV/1 ms	⌇⌇ 58
	E44	⬅	Engine idling – accelerate briefly		50 mV/1 ms	⌇⌇ 58
Lights control module	D14			1		
Mass air flow (MAF) sensor	E46	⇨	Ignition ON	5 V		
	E47	⬅	Ignition ON	1 V		
	E47	⬅	Engine idling	1,3 V		
	E47	⬅	Engine idling – full throttle briefly	4,2 V		
	E48	⊐─	Ignition ON	0 V		
Starter motor relay	D3	⊐▷	Ignition ON	11-14 V		
	D3	⊐▷	Engine cranking	0 V		
Throttle motor position sensor 1	E31	⬅	Ignition ON – throttle closed	4,2 V		
	E31	⬅	Ignition ON – throttle fully open	3,5 V		
	E31	⬅	Engine idling	4,4 V		
Throttle motor position sensor 1 & 2	E32	⊐─	Ignition ON	0 V		
	E33	⇨	Ignition ON	5 V		
Throttle motor position sensor 2	E34	⬅	Ignition ON – throttle closed	0,8 V		
	E34	⬅	Ignition ON – throttle fully open	1,6 V		
	E34	⬅	Engine idling	0,5 V		
Throttle position motor	F1	⇨	Engine idling – intermittent signal		5 V/1 ms	⌇⌇ 67
	F2	⇨	Engine idling		5 V/1 ms	⌇⌇ 68
Transmission control module (TCM) – AT	D19			1		
Voltage polarity protection relay	A2	⬅	Ignition ON	11-14 V		

*Suggested settings - Voltage/time per division

1 Connected pin - no test data available or random digital signal

MERCEDES-BENZ
Siemens ME-SIM4

Model:	Engine code:	Year:
E200K (211)	271.941	2002-06

ECM harness multi-plug

Terminal side

M

96 95 94 93 92 91 90 89 88 87 86 85 84 83 82 81 80 79 78 77 76 75 74 73
72 71 70 69 68 67 66 65 64 63 62 61 60 59 58 57 56 55 54 53 52 51 50 49

48 47 46 45 44 43 42 41 40 39 38 37 36 35 34 33 32 31 30 29 28 27 26 25
24 23 22 21 20 19 18 17 16 15 14 13 12 11 10 9 8 7 6 5 4 3 2 1

AD106492

F

58 57 56 55 54 53 52 51 50 49 48 47 46   6   5
45 44 43 42 41 40 39 38 37 36 35 34 33   4   3

32 31 30 29 28 27 26 25 24 23 22 21 20   2   1
19 18 17 16 15 14 13 12 11 10 9 8 7

Wire side

F

5   6   46 47 48 49 50 51 52 53 54 55 56 57 58
          33 34 35 36 37 38 39 40 41 42 43 44 45
3   4
          20 21 22 23 24 25 26 27 28 29 30 31 32
1   2   7 8 9 10 11 12 13 14 15 16 17 18 19

AD29429

M

73 74 75 76 77 78 79 80 81 82 83 84 85 86 87 88 89 90 91 92 93 94 95 96
49 50 51 52 53 54 55 56 57 58 59 60 61 62 63 64 65 66 67 68 69 70 71 72

25 26 27 28 29 30 31 32 33 34 35 36 37 38 39 40 41 42 43 44 45 46 47 48
1 2 3 4 5 6 7 8 9 10 11 12 13 14 15 16 17 18 19 20 21 22 23 24

Component/circuit description	ECM pin	Signal	Condition	Typical value	Oscilloscope setting*	Wave form
Accelerator pedal position (APP) sensor	F21	⇨	Ignition ON	5 V		
	F27	⌐	Ignition ON	0 V		
	F34	⌐	Ignition ON	0 V		
	F49	⟵	Ignition ON – accelerator pedal released	0,2 V		
	F49	⟵	Ignition ON – accelerator pedal fully depressed	2,3 V		
	F53	⟵	Ignition ON – accelerator pedal released	0 V		
	F53	⟵	Ignition ON – accelerator pedal fully depressed	4,5 V		
Alternator	M47	⟵	Ignition ON		2 V/1 ms	〰 83
Barometric pressure (BARO) sensor	M57	⌐	Ignition ON	0 V		
	M68	⇨	Ignition ON	5 V		
	M85	⟵	Ignition ON – 100 m above sea level	1,9 V		
Camshaft position (CMP) actuator – exhaust	M26	⌐▷	Ignition ON	2 V		
Camshaft position (CMP) actuator – intake	M73	⌐▷	Engine idling		5 V/2 ms	〰 68
Camshaft position (CMP) sensor – exhaust	M30	⟵	Engine idling		2 V/0,1 sec.	〰 89
	M53	⌐	Ignition ON	0 V		
	M72	⇨	Ignition ON	11-14 V		
Camshaft position (CMP) sensor – intake	M24	⇨	Ignition ON	11-14 V		
	M32	⟵	Engine idling		2 V/0,1 sec.	〰 89
	M53	⌐	Ignition ON	0 V		
CAN data bus	F41	⟷		1		
	F42	⟷		1		
Clutch pedal position (CPP) switch	F58	⟵		1		
Crankshaft position (CKP) sensor	M13	⟵	Engine idling	0,8 V ac	5 V/2 ms	〰 2
	M14	⟵	Engine idling	0,4 V ac	5 V/2 ms	Reversed 〰 2

* Suggested settings - Voltage/time per division

Autodata

Component/circuit description	ECM pin	Signal	Condition	Typical value	Oscilloscope setting*	Wave form
Data link connector (DLC)	F51	⬅⇨		[1]		
Earth	F2		Ignition ON	0 V		
	F4		Ignition ON	0 V		
	F6		Ignition ON	0 V		
Engine coolant blower motor	F16	⬅		[1]		
Engine coolant temperature (ECT) sensor	M33	⌐	Ignition ON	0 V		
	M80	⬅	Ignition ON – coolant temp. 40°C	3,1 V		
Engine oil sensor module	M33	⌐	Ignition ON	0 V		
	M68	⇨	Ignition ON	5 V		
	M90	⬅	Ignition ON		2 V/0,5 sec.	[77]
Evaporative emission (EVAP) canister purge valve	F46	⌐⇨	Ignition ON	11-14 V		
	F46	⌐⇨	Engine idling – throttle slightly open		10 V/20 ms	[20]
Heated oxygen sensor (HO2S) 1	M25	⬅	Ignition ON	0,4 V		
	M25	⬅	Engine idling – engine hot		10 V/20 ms	[11]
	M39	⬅	Ignition ON	5 V		
	M39	⬅	Engine running – 3000 rpm	2,2 V		
	M43	⬅	Engine idling	2,8 V		
	M44	⬅	Ignition ON	2,6 V		
	M44	⬅	Engine idling	2,9 V		
	M56	⬅⇨		[1]		
Heated oxygen sensor (HO2S) 2	M7	⬅	Ignition ON	0,4 V		
	M7	⬅	Engine idling – engine hot	0,6 V		
	M72	⇨	Ignition ON	11-14 V		
	M83	⌐	Ignition ON	0 V		
Heated oxygen sensor (HO2S) 2 – heater control	M29	⌐⇨	Ignition ON	11-14 V		
	M29	⌐⇨	Engine idling		2 V/0,1 sec.	[64]
Ignition coil 1	M1	⌐⇨	Ignition ON	11-14 V		
	M1	⌐⇨	Engine idling		5 V/2 ms	[33]
Ignition coil 2	M2	⌐⇨	Ignition ON	11-14 V		
	M2	⌐⇨	Engine idling		5 V/2 ms	[33]
Ignition coil 3	M3	⌐⇨	Ignition ON	11-14 V		
	M3	⌐⇨	Engine idling		5 V/2 ms	[33]
Ignition coil 4	M4	⌐⇨	Ignition ON	11-14 V		
	M4	⌐⇨	Engine idling		5 V/2 ms	[33]
Ignition switch	F52	⬅	Ignition OFF	0 V		
	F52	⬅	Ignition ON	11-14 V		
Injector 1	M22	⌐⇨	Ignition ON	11-14 V		
	M22	⌐⇨	Engine idling	2,7 ms	10 V/2 ms	[35]
Injector 2	M21	⌐⇨	Ignition ON	11-14 V		
	M21	⌐⇨	Engine idling	2,7 ms	10 V/2 ms	[35]
Injector 3	M20	⌐⇨	Ignition ON	11-14 V		
	M20	⌐⇨	Engine idling	2,7 ms	10 V/2 ms	[35]
Injector 4	M23	⌐⇨	Ignition ON	11-14 V		
	M23	⌐⇨	Engine idling	2,7 ms	10 V/2 ms	[35]
Knock sensor (KS)	M50	⌐	Ignition ON	0 V		
	M18	⬅	Engine idling – accelerate briefly		50 mV/1 ms	[58]
Manifold absolute pressure (MAP) sensor	M27	⬅	Engine idling		10 V/20 ms	[11]
	M57	⌐	Ignition ON	0 V		
	M68	⇨	Ignition ON	5 V		

* Suggested settings - Voltage/time per division

Component/circuit description	ECM pin	Signal	Condition	Typical value	Oscilloscope setting*	Wave form
Mass air flow (MAF) sensor	M10	⌐—	Ignition ON	0 V		
	M28	⟵	Engine idling – accelerate briefly	0,7 V briefly		
	M28	⟵	Engine running – 3000 rpm		1 V/2 sec.	〰 44
	M37	⌐—	Ignition ON	0 V		
	M72	⟹	Ignition ON	11-14 V		
Multifunction control module 1	F1	⟵	Ignition ON	11-14 V		
	F3	⟵	Ignition ON	11-14 V		
	F5	⟵	Ignition ON	11-14 V		
	F11	⟵	Ignition ON	11-14 V		
	F12	⟺		①1		
	F23	⟵	Ignition ON	11-14 V		
	F50	⌐⟹	Ignition OFF	11-14 V		
	F50	⌐⟹	Ignition ON	0-1 V		
	F55	⟵	Ignition ON	11-14 V		
	M24	⟵	Ignition ON	11-14 V		
	M48	⟵	Ignition ON	11-14 V		
	M72	⟵	Ignition ON	11-14 V		
Secondary air injection (AIR) solenoid	M82	⌐⟹	Ignition ON	11-14 V		
Supercharger (SC) boost air temperature sensor	M33	⌐—	Ignition ON	0 V		
	M78	⟵	Ignition ON – air temp. 12°C	3,7 V		
Supercharger (SC) bypass valve motor	M11	⟹	Ignition ON	11-14 V		
	M12	⟵	Engine idling		2 V/2 ms	〰 71
Supercharger (SC) bypass valve motor position sensor	M36	⟵	Ignition ON	0,7 V		
	M42	⟵	Ignition ON	4,3 V		
	M62	⌐—	Ignition ON	0 V		
	M68	⟹	Ignition ON	5 V		
Throttle motor	M45	⟹	Ignition ON		2 V/2 ms	〰 64
	M46	⌐—	Ignition ON	0 V		
Throttle motor position sensor	M51	⌐—	Ignition ON	0 V		
	M66	⟹	Ignition ON	5 V		
	M76	⟵	Ignition ON	0,9 V		
	M77	⟵	Ignition ON	4,1 V		

*Suggested settings - Voltage/time per division

1 Connected pin - no test data available or random digital signal

Model:	Engine code:	Year:
E200 CDI (211)	646.951	2002-06
E220 CDI (211)	646.951/961	2002-06

ECM harness multi-plug

Terminal side

M

```
96 95 94 93 92 91 90 89 88 87 86 85 84 83 82 81 80 79 78 77 76 75 74 73
72 71 70 69 68 67 66 65 64 63 62 61 60 59 58 57 56 55 54 53 52 51 50 49

48 47 46 45 44 43 42 41 40 39 38 37 36 35 34 33 32 31 30 29 28 27 26 25
24 23 22 21 20 19 18 17 16 15 14 13 12 11 10 9 8 7 6 5 4 3 2 1
```

F

```
58 57 56 55 54 53 52 51 50 49 48 47 46      6  5
45 44 43 42 41 40 39 38 37 36 35 34 33
                                            4  3
32 31 30 29 28 27 26 25 24 23 22 21 20
19 18 17 16 15 14 13 12 11 10 9 8 7         2  1
```

AD29036

Wire side

F

```
5  6   46 47 48 49 50 51 52 53 54 55 56 57 58
       33 34 35 36 37 38 39 40 41 42 43 44 45
3  4
1  2   20 21 22 23 24 25 26 27 28 29 30 31 32
       7  8  9  10 11 12 13 14 15 16 17 18 19
```

M

```
73 74 75 76 77 78 79 80 81 82 83 84 85 86 87 88 89 90 91 92 93 94 95 96
49 50 51 52 53 54 55 56 57 58 59 60 61 62 63 64 65 66 67 68 69 70 71 72

25 26 27 28 29 30 31 32 33 34 35 36 37 38 39 40 41 42 43 44 45 46 47 48
1  2  3  4  5  6  7  8  9  10 11 12 13 14 15 16 17 18 19 20 21 22 23 24
```

AD29429

Component/circuit description	ECM pin	Signal	Condition	Typical value	Oscilloscope setting*	Wave form
Accelerator pedal position (APP) sensor	F13	←	Ignition ON – accelerator pedal released	0,1 V		
	F13	←	Ignition ON – accelerator pedal fully depressed	2,3 V		
	F14	⌐—	Ignition ON	0 V		
	F24	⇒	Ignition ON	5 V		
	F25	←	Ignition ON – accelerator pedal released	0,3 V		
	F25	←	Ignition ON – accelerator pedal fully depressed	4,6 V		
	F26	⌐—	Ignition ON	0 V		
Barometric pressure (BARO) sensor	M12	⌐—	Ignition ON	0 V		
	M13	←	Ignition ON	3,8 V		
	M13	←	Engine idling	3,8 V		
	M36	⇒	Ignition ON	5 V		
Camshaft position (CMP) sensor	M14	⌐—	Ignition ON	0 V		
	M37	⇒	Ignition ON	5 V		
	M38	←	Engine idling		2 V/0,1 sec.	⎍⎍ 4
CAN data bus connection – high	F53	←⇒		1		
CAN data bus connection – low	F54	←⇒		1		
Clutch pedal position (CPP) switch	F27	←		1		
Crankcase breather heater	M21	⇒	Ignition ON	11-14 V		
	M91	⇒	Ignition ON	11-14 V		
Crankshaft position (CKP) sensor	M87	←	Engine idling	4,9 V ac		
	M87	←	Engine idling		5 V/2 ms	⎍⎍ 1
	M88	←	Engine idling	4,9 V ac		
	M88	←	Engine idling		5 V/2 ms	Reversed ⎍⎍ 11
Data link connector (DLC)	F31	←⇒		1		

★ Suggested settings - Voltage/time per division

Component/circuit description	ECM pin	Signal	Condition	Typical value	Oscilloscope setting*	Wave form
Earth	F2		Ignition ON	0 V		
	F4		Ignition ON	0 V		
	F6		Ignition ON	0 V		
Engine coolant blower motor control module	F57	⇒	Ignition OFF	11-14 V		
	F57	⇒	Engine idling – AC ON		2 V/50 ms	[waveform 22]
Engine coolant temperature (ECT) sensor	M56	⊣—	Ignition ON	0 V		
	M57	←	Ignition ON – coolant temp. 60°C	2,3 V		
	M57	←	Engine idling – coolant temp. 95°C	1 V		
Engine oil sensor module	M10	⇒	Ignition ON	5 V		
	M11	←	Ignition ON		2 V/1 sec.	[waveform 11]
	M35	⊣—	Ignition ON	0 V		
Exhaust gas recirculation (EGR) valve actuator	M47	⊣—	Ignition ON	0 V		
	M90	⇒	Ignition ON		1 V/10 ms	[waveform 5]
	M90	⇒	Engine idling		2 V/5 ms	Intermittent [waveform 22]
Fuel quantity adjuster	M28	⇒	Ignition ON	11-14 V		
	M76	⇒	Ignition ON		2 V/5 ms	[waveform 22]
	M76	⇒	Engine idling		2 V/5 ms	[waveform 22]
	M76	⇒	3000 rpm		2 V/5 ms	[waveform 22]
Fuel rail pressure (FRP) control valve	M4	⇒	Ignition ON	11-14 V		
	M52	←	Ignition ON	Wave pattern for 20 secs.	2 V/4 ms	[waveform 37]
Fuel rail pressure (FRP) sensor	M59	←	Ignition ON	0,5 V		
	M59	←	Engine idling	1,2 V		
	M59	←	3000 rpm	2 V		
	M84	⊣—	Ignition ON	0 V		
	M86	⇒	Ignition ON	5 V		
Fuel temperature sensor	M8	←	Ignition ON – coolant temp. 60°C	2,4 V		
	M8	←	Ignition ON – coolant temp. 90°C	2,2 V		
	M32	⊣—	Ignition ON	0 V		
Glow plug control module	F43	⇒	Ignition ON		2 V/50 ms	[waveform 14]
Injector 1	M25 (M74)	⇒	Engine idling – engine hot	0,3 ms	10 V/0,1 ms	[waveform 61]
	M74 (M25)	⇒	Engine idling – engine hot	0,3 ms	10 V/0,1 ms	[waveform 61]
Injector 2	M2 (M49)	⇒	Engine idling – engine hot	0,3 ms	10 V/0,1 ms	[waveform 61]
	M49 (M2)	⇒	Engine idling – engine hot	0,3 ms	10 V/0,1 ms	[waveform 61]
Injector 3	M1 (M73)	⇒	Engine idling – engine hot	0,3 ms	10 V/0,1 ms	[waveform 61]
	M73 (M1)	⇒	Engine idling – engine hot	0,3 ms	10 V/0,1 ms	[waveform 61]
Injector 4	M26 (M51)	⇒	Engine idling – engine hot	0,3 ms	10 V/0,1 ms	[waveform 61]
	M51 (M26)	⇒	Engine idling – engine hot	0,3 ms	10 V/0,1 ms	[waveform 61]
Intake air temperature (IAT) sensor – in MAF sensor	M31	←	Ignition ON – air temp. 25°C	1,6 V		
	M31	←	Engine idling – air temp. 25°C	2,1 V		
	M61	⊣—	Ignition ON	0 V		
Intake manifold air control actuator	M69	⊣—	Ignition ON	0 V		
	M92	⇒	Ignition ON		4 V/10 ms	[waveform 12]
	M92	⇒	Engine idling		4 V/10 ms	[waveform 12]

★ Suggested settings - Voltage/time per division

Component/circuit description	ECM pin	Signal	Condition	Typical value	Oscilloscope setting*	Wave form
Mass air flow (MAF) sensor	M17	⟹	Ignition ON	11-14 V		
	M64	⌐—	Ignition ON	0 V		
	M85	⟸	Ignition ON	1 V		
	M85	⟸	Engine idling	1,9 V		
	M85	⟸	3000 rpm	3,5 V		
Multifunction control module 1	F1	⟸	Ignition ON	11-14 V		
	F3	⟸	Ignition ON	11-14 V		
	F5	⟸	Ignition ON	11-14 V		
	F18	⟸	Ignition OFF	0 V		
	F18	⟸	Ignition ON	11-14 V		
	F19	⟸	Ignition ON	11-14 V		
	F44			1		
	F58	⟸	Ignition ON	11-14 V		
Multifunction control module 2	F55	⌐⟹	Ignition OFF	11-14 V		
	F55	⌐⟹	Ignition ON	0-1 V		
Transmission kick-down switch	F17			1		
Turbocharger (TC) boost air temperature sensor	M34	⟸	Engine idling – coolant temp. 50°C	3 V		
	M65	⌐—	Ignition ON	0 V		
	M83	⌐—	Ignition ON	0 V		
Turbocharger (TC) boost pressure actuator	M44	⌐—	Ignition ON	0 V		
	M70	⟹	Ignition ON	11-14 V		
	M93	⟹	Ignition ON	0 V		
	M93	⟹	Engine idling		1 V/10 ms	∿∿ 37
	M93	⟹	3000 rpm		2 V/5 ms	∿∿ 22
Turbocharger (TC) boost pressure sensor	M60	⟹	Ignition ON	5 V		
	M63	⟸	Ignition ON	1,9 V		
	M63	⟸	Engine idling	1,9 V		
	M63	⟸	3000 rpm	2,2 V		

*Suggested settings - Voltage/time per division

1 Connected pin - no test data available or random digital signal

MERCEDES-BENZ

Bosch EDC

Model:	Engine code:	Year:
E270 CDI (211)	647.961	2002-05

ECM harness multi-plug

Terminal side

M

F

AD29036

Wire side

F

M

AD29429

Component/circuit description	ECM pin	Signal	Condition	Typical value	Oscilloscope setting*	Wave form
Accelerator pedal position (APP) sensor	F13	⬅	Ignition ON – accelerator pedal released	0,1 V		
	F13	⬅	Ignition ON – accelerator pedal fully depressed	2,3 V		
	F14	⌐⎯	Ignition ON	0 V		
	F24	⇒	Ignition ON	5 V		
	F25	⬅	Ignition ON – accelerator pedal released	0,3 V		
	F25	⬅	Ignition ON – accelerator pedal fully depressed	4,6 V		
	F26	⌐⎯	Ignition ON	0 V		
Barometric pressure (BARO) sensor	M12	⌐⎯	Ignition ON	0 V		
	M13	⬅	Ignition ON	3,8 V		
	M13	⬅	Engine idling	3,8 V		
	M36	⇒	Ignition ON	5 V		
Camshaft position (CMP) sensor	M14	⌐⎯	Ignition ON	0 V		
	M37	⇒	Ignition ON	5 V		
	M38	⬅	Engine idling		2 V/0,1 sec.	[wave] 4
CAN data bus connection – high	F53	⬅⇒		[1]		
CAN data bus connection – low	F54	⬅⇒		[1]		
Clutch pedal position (CPP) switch	F27	⬅		[1]		
Crankcase breather heater	M21	⇒	Ignition ON	11-14 V		
	M91	⇒	Ignition ON	11-14 V		
Crankshaft position (CKP) sensor	M87	⬅	Engine idling	4,9 V ac		
	M87	⬅	Engine idling		5 V/2 ms	[wave] 1
	M88	⬅	Engine idling	4,9 V ac		
	M88	⬅	Engine idling		5 V/2 ms	Reversed [wave] 11
Data link connector (DLC)	F18	⬅	Ignition OFF	0 V		
	F18	⬅	Ignition ON	11-14 V		
	F31	⬅⇒		[1]		

* Suggested settings - Voltage/time per division

Component/circuit description	ECM pin	Signal	Condition	Typical value	Oscilloscope setting*	Wave form
Earth	F2		Ignition ON	0 V		
	F4		Ignition ON	0 V		
	F6		Ignition ON	0 V		
Engine coolant blower motor control module	F57	⇒	Ignition OFF	11-14 V		
	F57	⇒	Engine idling – AC ON		2 V/50 ms	〜 22
Engine coolant temperature (ECT) sensor	M56	⏚	Ignition ON	0 V		
	M57	←	Ignition ON – coolant temp. 60°C	2,3 V		
	M57	←	Engine idling – coolant temp. 95°C	1 V		
Engine oil sensor module	M10	⇒	Ignition ON	5 V		
	M11	←	Ignition ON		2 V/1 sec.	〜 11
	M35	⏚	Ignition ON	0 V		
Exhaust gas recirculation (EGR) valve actuator	M47	⏚	Ignition ON	0 V		
	M90	⇒	Ignition ON		1 V/10 ms	〜 5
	M90	⇒	Engine idling		2 V/5 ms	Intermittent 〜 22
Fuel quantity adjuster	M28	⇒	Ignition ON	11-14 V		
	M76	⇒	Ignition ON		2 V/5 ms	〜 22
	M76	⇒	Engine idling		2 V/5 ms	〜 22
	M76	⇒	3000 rpm		2 V/5 ms	〜 22
Fuel rail pressure (FRP) control valve	M4	⇒	Ignition ON	11-14 V		
	M52	←	Ignition ON	Wave pattern for 20 secs.	2 V/4 ms	〜 37
Fuel rail pressure (FRP) sensor	M59	←	Ignition ON	0,5 V		
	M59	←	Engine idling	1,2 V		
	M59	←	3000 rpm	2 V		
	M84	⏚	Ignition ON	0 V		
	M86	⇒	Ignition ON	5 V		
Fuel temperature sensor	M8	←	Ignition ON – coolant temp. 60°C	2,4 V		
	M8	←	Ignition ON – coolant temp. 90°C	2,2 V		
	M32	⏚	Ignition ON	0 V		
Glow plug control module	F43	⇒	Ignition ON		2 V/50 ms	〜 14
Injector 1	M2 (M49)	⇒	Engine idling – engine hot	0,3 ms	10 V/0,1 ms	〜 61
	M49 (M2)	⇒	Engine idling – engine hot	0,3 ms	10 V/0,1 ms	〜 61
Injector 2	M25 (M74)	⇒	Engine idling – engine hot	0,3 ms	10 V/0,1 ms	〜 61
	M74 (M25)	⇒	Engine idling – engine hot	0,3 ms	10 V/0,1 ms	〜 61
Injector 3	M3 (M50)	⇒	Engine idling – engine hot	0,3 ms	10 V/0,1 ms	〜 61
	M50 (M3)	⇒	Engine idling – engine hot	0,3 ms	10 V/0,1 ms	〜 61
Injector 4	M1 (M73)	⇒	Engine idling – engine hot	0,3 ms	10 V/0,1 ms	〜 61
	M73 (M1)	⇒	Engine idling – engine hot	0,3 ms	10 V/0,1 ms	〜 61
Injector 5	M26 (M51)	⇒	Engine idling – engine hot	0,3 ms	10 V/0,1 ms	〜 61
	M51 (M26)	⇒	Engine idling – engine hot	0,3 ms	10 V/0,1 ms	〜 61
Intake air temperature (IAT) sensor – in MAF sensor	M31	←	Ignition ON – air temp. 25°C	1,6 V		
	M31	←	Engine idling – air temp. 25°C	2,1 V		
	M61	⏚	Ignition ON	0 V		
Intake manifold air control actuator	M69	⏚	Ignition ON	0 V		
	M92	⇒	Ignition ON		4 V/10 ms	〜 12
	M92	⇒	Engine idling		4 V/10 ms	〜 12

* Suggested settings - Voltage/time per division

Component/circuit description	ECM pin	Signal	Condition	Typical value	Oscilloscope setting*	Wave form
Mass air flow (MAF) sensor	M17	⇨	Ignition ON	11-14 V		
	M64	⌐	Ignition ON	0 V		
	M85	⇦	Ignition ON	1 V		
	M85	⇦	Engine idling	1,9 V		
	M85	⇦	3000 rpm	3,5 V		
Multifunction control module 1	F1	⇦	Ignition ON	11-14 V		
	F3	⇦	Ignition ON	11-14 V		
	F5	⇦	Ignition ON	11-14 V		
	F18	⇦	Ignition OFF	0 V		
	F18	⇦	Ignition ON	11-14 V		
	F19	⇦	Ignition ON	11-14 V		
	F44			1		
	F58	⇦	Ignition ON	11-14 V		
Multifunction control module 2	F55	⌐⇨	Ignition OFF	11-14 V		
	F55	⌐⇨	Ignition ON	0-1 V		
Transmission kick-down switch	F17			1		
Turbocharger (TC) boost air temperature sensor	M34	⇦	Engine idling – coolant temp. 50°C	3 V		
	M65	⌐	Ignition ON	0 V		
	M83	⌐	Ignition ON	0 V		
Turbocharger (TC) boost pressure actuator	M44	⌐	Ignition ON	0 V		
	M70	⇨	Ignition ON	11-14 V		
	M93	⇨	Ignition ON	0 V		
	M93	⇨	Engine idling		1 V/10 ms	〰 37
	M93	⇨	3000 rpm		2 V/5 ms	〰 22
Turbocharger (TC) boost pressure sensor	M60	⇨	Ignition ON	5 V		
	M63	⇦	Ignition ON	1,9 V		
	M63	⇦	Engine idling	1,9 V		
	M63	⇦	3000 rpm	2,2 V		

*Suggested settings - Voltage/time per division

1 Connected pin - no test data available or random digital signal

ECM harness multi-plug

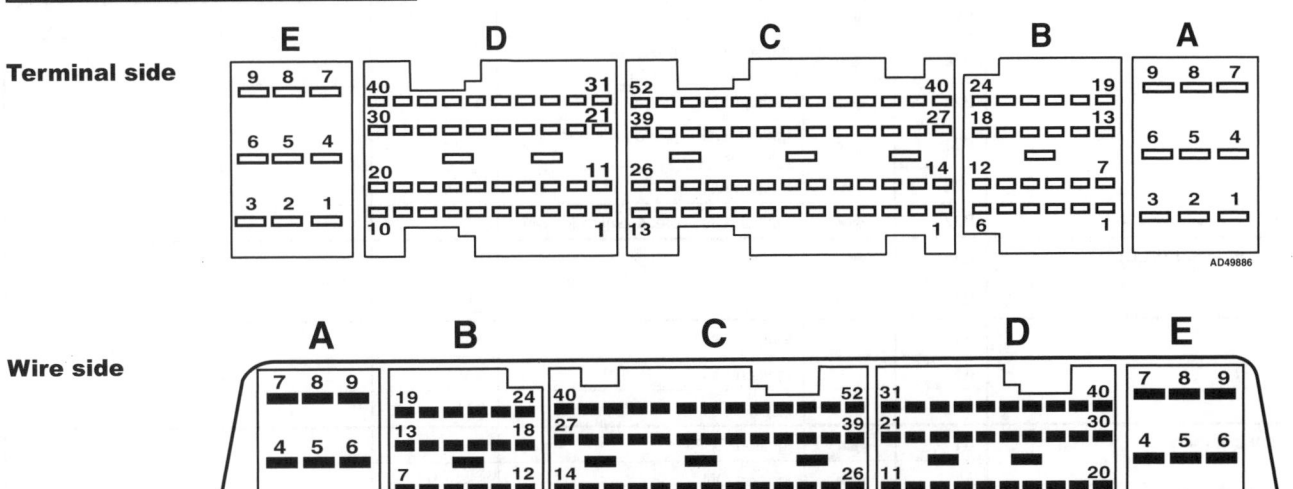

Component/circuit description	ECM pin	Signal	Condition	Typical value	Oscilloscope setting★	Wave form
3rd piston cut-off solenoid	D22	⇨	Ignition ON	11-14 V		
	D32	⇥▷	Engine idling – piston cut-off solenoid operating	0-1 V		
Accelerator pedal position (APP) sensor	C5	⇨	Ignition ON	5 V		
	C8	⇤	Ignition ON	0 V		
	C9	⇐	Ignition ON – accelerator pedal released	0,1 V		
	C9	⇐	Ignition ON – accelerator pedal fully depressed	2,2 V		
	C10	⇐	Ignition ON – accelerator pedal released	0,3 V		
	C10	⇐	Ignition ON – accelerator pedal fully depressed	4,5 V		
	C23	⇤	Ignition ON	0 V		
Airbag control module	B17			☐1		
Camshaft position (CMP) sensor	D2	⇤	Ignition ON	0 V		
	D3	⇐	Ignition ON	0 or 5 V		
	D3	⇐	Engine idling		2 V/50 ms	∿∿ ▊3
	D12	⇨	Ignition ON	11-14 V		
CAN data bus	B11	⬅⇨		☐1		
	B12	⬅⇨		☐1		
Clutch pedal position (CPP) switch	B2	⇐	Ignition ON – clutch pedal released	0 V		
	B2	⇐	Ignition ON – clutch pedal depressed	11-14 V		
	B9	⇤	Ignition ON	0 V		
Crankshaft position (CKP) sensor	D26	⇐	Engine idling		5 V/2 ms	∿∿ ▊1

★ Suggested settings - Voltage/time per division

Component/circuit description	ECM pin	Signal	Condition	Typical value	Oscilloscope setting*	Wave form
Cruise control actuator switch	B14	←	Ignition ON	0 V		
	B14	←	Ignition ON – press switch upwards	11-14 V		
	B16	←	Ignition ON	0 V		
	B16	←	Ignition ON – press switch downwards	11-14 V		
	B19	⇨	Ignition ON	11-14 V		
	B20	←	Ignition ON	0 V		
	B20	←	Ignition ON – press switch backwards	11-14 V		
	B21	←	Ignition ON	0 V		
	B21	←	Ignition ON – press switch in all positions	11-14 V		
	B22	←	Ignition ON	11-14 V		
	B22	←	Ignition ON – press switch forwards	0 V		
Data link connector (DLC)	C28	⬅⇨		☐1		
	C40	⬅⇨		☐1		
Earth	A4		Ignition ON	0 V		
	A5		Ignition ON	0 V		
	A6		Ignition ON	0 V		
Engine control relay	A1	←	Ignition OFF	0 V		
	A1	←	Ignition ON	11-14 V		
	A7	←	Ignition OFF	0 V		
	A7	←	Ignition ON	11-14 V		
	A8	←	Ignition OFF	0 V		
	A8	←	Ignition ON	11-14 V		
Engine coolant temperature (ECT) sensor	D27	⊣—	Ignition ON	0 V		
	D36	←	Ignition ON – engine cold	4 V		
	D36	←	Engine idling – engine hot	1,6 V		
Engine oil sensor module	D15	←		☐1		
	D17	⊣—		☐1		
	D18	⇨	Ignition ON	5 V		
Exhaust gas recirculation (EGR) solenoid	C37	⇨	Ignition ON	11-14 V		
	C50	⊣▷	Ignition ON	11-14 V		
	C50	⊣▷	Engine idling		2 V/2 ms	〰20
Fuel pressure regulator control solenoid	D21	⊣—	Ignition ON	0 V		
	D31	⇨	Ignition ON	1,6 V – 0 V after 5 secs.		
	D31	⇨	Engine idling		5 V/1 ms	〰12
Fuel rail pressure (FRP) sensor	D4	⊣—	Ignition ON	0 V		
	D13	⇨	Ignition ON	5 V		
Fuel shut-off solenoid	D25	⇨	Ignition ON	11-14 V		
Fuel system pressure sensor	D7			☐1		
	D8			☐1		
	D14	←	Ignition ON	0,5 V		
	D14	←	Engine idling	1,2 V		
Fuel temperature sensor	D30	⊣—	Ignition ON	0 V		
	D39	←	Ignition ON	3,6 V		
	D39	←	Engine idling	2 V		
Glow plug control module	C25	⇨	Ignition ON	5-10 V fluctuating		
Ignition switch	B13	←	Ignition OFF	0 V		
	B13	←	Ignition ON	11-14 V		
	C20	←	Engine cranking	9 V min.		

* Suggested settings - Voltage/time per division

Component/circuit description	ECM pin	Signal	Condition	Typical value	Oscilloscope setting*	Wave form
Injector 1	E4	⇨	Ignition ON	1,1 V		
	E5	⇨ (pulsed)	Engine idling	1 ms pilot + 1,5 ms main	10 V/0,5 ms	23
Injector 2	E2	⇨	Ignition ON	1,1 V		
	E3	⇨ (pulsed)	Engine idling	1 ms pilot + 1,5 ms main	10 V/0,5 ms	23
Injector 3	E2	⇨	Ignition ON	1,1 V		
	E9	⇨ (pulsed)	Engine idling	1 ms pilot + 1,5 ms main	10 V/0,5 ms	23
Injector 4	E4	⇨	Ignition ON	1,1 V		
	E7	⇨ (pulsed)	Engine idling	1 ms pilot + 1,5 ms main	10 V/0,5 ms	23
Intake manifold air control solenoid	C36 (C52)	⇨	Engine idling	8,5 V min.		
	C36 (C52)	⇨	Engine running – 2400 rpm min.	0,5 V max.		
	C52 (C36)	⇨	Engine idling	8,5 V min.		
	C52 (C36)	⇨	Engine running – 2400 rpm min.	0,5 V max.		
Mass air flow (MAF) sensor	C7	⏚	Ignition ON	0 V		
	C18	⬅	Engine idling	2 V		
	C19	⇨	Ignition ON	5 V		
Neutral position (NP) switch	B8	⬅		[1]		
Reverse gear position switch	B8	⬅		[1]		
Starter motor relay	C30	⇨	Ignition ON	11-14 V		
	C43	⇨ (pulsed)	Ignition ON	11-14 V		
	C43	⇨ (pulsed)	Engine cranking	0-1 V		
Turbocharger (TC) boost air temperature sensor	C1	⏚	Ignition ON	0 V		
	C12	⬅	Ignition ON – air temp. 15°C	4,1 V		
Turbocharger (TC) boost pressure sensor	C6	⬅	Engine idling	1,8 V		
	C6	⬅	Engine idling – accelerate briefly	3,2 V briefly		
	C17	⇨	Ignition ON	5 V		
	C22	⏚	Ignition ON	0 V		
Turbocharger (TC) wastegate regulating valve	C35	⇨	Ignition ON	11-14 V		
	C48	⇨ (pulsed)	Ignition ON	11-14 V		
	C48	⇨ (pulsed)	Engine idling	5,3 V	5 V/2 ms	29

*Suggested settings - Voltage/time per division

[1] Connected pin - no test data available or random digital signal

MITSUBISHI

Mitsubishi MFI

Model:	Engine code:	Year:
Colt 1,3 12V	4G13	1996-03
Lancer 1,3 12V	4G13	1996-99

ECM harness multi-plug

Terminal side

```
81 80 79 78 77 76 75 74 73 72 71   56 55 54 53 52 51   38 37 36 35 34 33 32 31   13 12 11 10 9 8 7 6 5 4 3 2 1
92 91 90 89 88 87 86 85 84 83 82   62 61 60 59 58 57   46 45 44 43 42 41 40 39   26 25 24 23 22 21 20 19 18 17 16 15 14
```

AD42230

Wire side

```
1 2 3 4 5 6 7 8 9 10 11 12 13   31 32 33 34 35 36 37 38   51 52 53 54 55 56   71 72 73 74 75 76 77 78 79 80 81
14 15 16 17 18 19 20 21 22 23 24 25 26   39 40 41 42 43 44 45 46   57 58 59 60 61 62   82 83 84 85 86 87 88 89 90 91 92
```

AD42063

Component/circuit description	ECM pin	Signal	Condition	Typical value	Oscilloscope setting*	Wave form
AC condenser blower motor relay	20	⊐⊳	Engine idling – condenser blower motor OFF	11-14 V		
	20	⊐⊳	Engine idling – condenser blower motor ON	0-3 V		
AC refrigerant pressure switch	45	⬅	Engine idling – AC OFF	0-3 V		
	45	⬅	Engine idling – AC ON	11-14 V		
AC relay – with immobilizer	8	⊐⊳	Engine idling – AC OFF	11-14 V		
	8	⊐⊳	Engine idling – AC ON	0-3 V		
AC relay – without immobilizer	22	⊐⊳	Engine idling – AC OFF	11-14 V		
	22	⊐⊳	Engine idling – AC ON	0-3 V		
Alternator	33	⬅	Engine idling – engine hot – headlamps OFF	0,4-0,8 V		
	33	⬅	Engine idling – engine hot – headlamps ON	0,8-1,2 V		
	33	⬅	Engine idling – engine hot – heated rear window OFF	0,4-0,8 V		
	33	⬅	Engine idling – engine hot – heated rear window ON	0,8-1,2 V		
	41	⬅	Engine idling – engine hot – headlamps OFF	1,8-2,4 V		
	41	⬅	Engine idling – engine hot – headlamps ON	1-1,6 V		
	41	⬅	Engine idling – engine hot – heated rear window OFF	1,8-2,4 V		
	41	⬅	Engine idling – engine hot – heated rear window ON	1-1,6 V		
Automatic transmission	7			1		
	59			1		
Battery	80	⬅	Ignition OFF	11-14 V		
Closed throttle position (CTP) switch	87	⬅	Ignition ON – throttle closed	0-1 V		
	87	⬅	Ignition ON – throttle slightly open	4 V min.		
	92	⊐	Ignition ON	0 V		
Crankshaft position (CKP) sensor	89	⬅	Engine cranking	0,4-4 V		
	89	⬅	Engine idling	1,5-2,5 V	2 V/20 ms	ᴡᴡ 45
Data link connector (DLC)	56			1		
Data link connector (DLC) – 1998	79			1		
Data link connector (DLC) – without immobilizer	62			1		
Earth	13		Ignition ON	0 V		
	26		Ignition ON	0 V		

* Suggested settings - Voltage/time per division

Component/circuit description	ECM pin	Signal	Condition	Typical value	Oscilloscope setting*	Wave form
Earth – MT	91		Ignition ON	0 V		
Engine control relay	12	←	Ignition OFF	0 V		
	12	←	Ignition ON	11-14 V		
	25	←	Ignition OFF	0 V		
	25	←	Ignition ON	11-14 V		
	38	⇥▷	Ignition OFF	11-14 V		
	38	⇥▷	Ignition ON	0-3 V		
Engine coolant blower motor relay	21	⇥▷	Engine idling – coolant blower motor OFF	11-14 V		
	21	⇥▷	Engine idling – coolant blower motor OFF	0-3 V		
Engine coolant temperature (ECT) sensor	83	←	Ignition ON – coolant temp. 0°C	3,2-3,8 V		
	83	←	Ignition ON – coolant temp. 20°C	2,3-2,9 V		
	83	←	Ignition ON – coolant temp. 40°C	1,3-1,9 V		
	83	←	Ignition ON – coolant temp. 80°C	0,3-0,9 V		
	92	⇥—	Ignition ON	0 V		
Evaporative emission (EVAP) canister purge valve	9	⇥▷	Ignition ON	11-14 V		
	9	⇥▷	Engine running – 3000 rpm – engine cold	0 V		
Exhaust gas recirculation (EGR) solenoid	6	⇥▷	Ignition ON	11-14 V		
	6	⇥▷	Engine idling	11-14 V		
Fuel pump relay – with immobilizer	22	⇥▷	Ignition ON	0 V briefly then 11-14 V		
	22	⇥▷	Engine idling	0 V		
Fuel pump relay – without immobilizer	8	⇥▷	Ignition ON	0 V briefly then 11-14 V		
	8	⇥▷	Engine idling	11-14 V		
Heated oxygen sensor (HO2S) – front	60	⇥▷	Engine idling – engine hot	0-3 V		
	60	⇥▷	Engine running – engine hot – 5000 rpm	11-14 V		
	76	←	RPM decreasing	0,5-0,2 V		
	76	←	RPM increasing	0,6-1 V		
	76	←	Engine running – 2500 rpm	0-0,8 V fluctuating	0,2 V/1 sec.	
	92	⇥—	Ignition ON	0 V		
Heated oxygen sensor (HO2S) – rear	54	⇥▷	Engine idling – engine hot	0-3 V		
	54	⇥▷	Engine running – engine hot – 5000 rpm	11-14 V		
	75	←	Vehicle moving – engine under load	0,6-1 V		
	92	⇥—	Ignition ON	0 V		
Idle air control (IAC) valve	4	⇥▷	Engine idling – engine hot	0 V or 11-14 V switching	10 V/2 ms	Intermittent
	5	⇥▷	Engine idling – engine hot	0 V or 11-14 V switching	10 V/2 ms	Intermittent
	17	⇥▷	Engine idling – engine hot	0 V or 11-14 V switching	10 V/2 ms	Intermittent
	18	⇥▷	Engine idling – engine hot	0 V or 11-14 V switching	10 V/2 ms	Intermittent
Ignition adjustment connector	52	←	Ignition ON – connected to earth	0-1 V		
	52	←	Ignition ON – not connected to earth	4-5,5 V		
Ignition amplifier	10	⇨	Engine running – 3000 rpm	0,3-3 V	1 V/5 ms	
	10	⇨	Engine running – 1200 rpm		2 V/20 ms	
Ignition switch	82	←	Ignition OFF	0 V		
	82	←	Ignition ON	11-14 V		
Immobilizer control module	62	←		1		

* Suggested settings - Voltage/time per division

Component/circuit description	ECM pin	Signal	Condition	Typical value	Oscilloscope setting*	Wave form
Injector 1	1	⇥▷	Ignition ON	11-14 V		
	1	⇥▷	Engine idling – engine hot	1,7-2,9 ms	10 V/2 ms	∿∿ 35
Injector 2	14	⇥▷	Ignition ON	11-14 V		
	14	⇥▷	Engine idling – engine hot	1,7-2,9 ms	10 V/2 ms	∿∿ 35
Injector 3	2	⇥▷	Ignition ON	11-14 V		
	2	⇥▷	Engine idling – engine hot	1,7-2,9 ms	10 V/2 ms	∿∿ 35
Injector 4	15	⇥▷	Ignition ON	11-14 V		
	15	⇥▷	Engine idling – engine hot	1,7-2,9 ms	10 V/2 ms	∿∿ 35
Intake air temperature (IAT) sensor	72	⬅	Ignition ON – air temp. 0°C	3,2-3,8 V		
	72	⬅	Ignition ON – air temp. 20°C	2,3-2,9 V		
	72	⬅	Ignition ON – air temp. 40°C	1,5-2,1 V		
	72	⬅	Ignition ON – air temp. 80°C	0,4-1 V		
	92	⇥–	Ignition ON	0 V		
Malfunction indicator lamp (MIL)	36	⇥▷	Ignition ON – MIL ON	0-3 V		
	36	⇥▷	Ignition ON – MIL OFF	11-14 V		
Manifold absolute pressure (MAP) sensor	81	⇨	Ignition ON	5 V		
	85	⬅	Ignition ON – at sea level	3,7-4,3 V		
	85	⬅	Ignition ON – 1200 m above sea level	3,2-3,8 V		
	85	⬅	Engine idling	0,9-1,5 V		
	85	⬅	Engine running – accelerate briefly	0,9-1,5 V		
	92	⇥–	Ignition ON	0 V		
Park/neutral position (PNP) switch	91	⬅	Ignition ON – AT in P or N	0-3 V		
	91	⬅	Ignition ON – AT not in P or N	8-14 V		
Power steering pressure (PSP) switch	37	⬅	Engine idling – steering wheel not turned	11-14 V		
	37	⬅	Engine idling – steering wheel turned	0-3 V		
Starter motor	71	⬅	Engine cranking	9 V		
Throttle position (TP) sensor	81	⇨	Ignition ON	5 V		
	84	⬅	Ignition ON – throttle closed	0,3-1 V		
	84	⬅	Ignition ON – throttle fully open	5 V		
	92	⇥–	Ignition ON	0 V		
Vehicle speed sensor (VSS)	86	⬅	Ignition ON – vehicle pushed	0 V or 5 V switching		

*Suggested settings - Voltage/time per division

1 Connected pin - no test data available or random digital signal

Model:	Engine code:	Year:
Colt 1,6 16V	4G92 – SOHC	1996-03
Lancer 1,6 16V	4G92 – SOHC	1996-01

ECM harness multi-plug

Terminal side

```
81 80 79 78 77 76 75 74 73 72 71    56 55 54 53 52 51    38 37 36 35 34 33 32 31    13 12 11 10 9 8 7 6 5 4 3 2 1
92 91 90 89 88 87 86 85 84 83 82    62 61 60 59 58 57    46 45 44 43 42 41 40 39    26 25 24 23 22 21 20 19 18 17 16 15 14
```
AD42230

Wire side

```
1 2 3 4 5 6 7 8 9 10 11 12 13    31 32 33 34 35 36 37 38    51 52 53 54 55 56    71 72 73 74 75 76 77 78 79 80 81
14 15 16 17 18 19 20 21 22 23 24 25 26    39 40 41 42 43 44 45 46    57 58 59 60 61 62    82 83 84 85 86 87 88 89 90 91 92
```
AD42231

Component/circuit description	ECM pin	Signal	Condition	Typical value	Oscilloscope setting*	Wave form
AC condenser blower motor relay	20	⊐▷	Engine idling – condenser blower motor OFF	11-14 V		
	20	⊐▷	Engine idling – condenser blower motor ON	0-3 V		
AC refrigerant pressure switch	45	←	Engine idling – AC OFF	0-3 V		
	45	←	Engine idling – AC ON	11-14 V		
AC relay – with immobilizer	8	⊐▷	Engine idling – AC OFF	11-14 V		
	8	⊐▷	Engine idling – AC ON	0-3 V		
AC relay – without immobilizer	22	⊐▷	Engine idling – AC OFF	11-14 V		
	22	⊐▷	Engine idling – AC ON	6 V or 0-3 V		
Additional idle air control valve	39	⊐▷	Engine idling – engine hot	0-3 V		
	39	⊐▷	Engine running – 1000 rpm	11-14 V		
Alternator	33	←	Engine idling – engine hot – headlamps OFF	0,4-0,8 V		
	33	←	Engine idling – engine hot – headlamps ON	0,8-1,2 V		
	33	←	Engine idling – engine hot – heated rear window OFF	0,4-0,8 V		
	33	←	Engine idling – engine hot – heated rear window ON	0,8-1,2 V		
	41	←	Engine idling – engine hot – headlamps OFF	1,8-2,4 V		
	41	←	Engine idling – engine hot – headlamps ON	1-1,6 V		
	41	←	Engine idling – engine hot – heated rear window OFF	1,8-2,4 V		
	41	←	Engine idling – engine hot – heated rear window ON	1-1,6 V		
Automatic transmission	7			①￼		
	59			①￼		
Barometric pressure (BARO) sensor	81	⇨	Ignition ON	5 V		
	85	←	Ignition ON – at sea level	3,7-4,3 V		
	85	←	Ignition ON – 1200 m above sea level	3,2-3,8 V		
	92	⊐−	Ignition ON	0 V		
Battery	80	←	Ignition OFF	11-14 V		
Camshaft position (CMP) sensor	88	←	Engine cranking	0,4-3 V		
	88	←	Engine idling	0,5-2 V	5 V/50 ms	∿∿ 16
Closed throttle position (CTP) switch	87	←	Ignition ON – throttle closed	0-1 V		
	87	←	Ignition ON – throttle slightly open	4 V min.		
	92	⊐−	Ignition ON	0 V		

* Suggested settings - Voltage/time per division

Component/circuit description	ECM pin	Signal	Condition	Typical value	Oscilloscope setting★	Wave form
Crankshaft position (CKP) sensor	89	←	Engine cranking	0,4-4 V		
	89	←	Engine idling	1,5-2,5 V	2 V/20 ms	⎍ 45
Data link connector (DLC)	56	↔		1		
Data link connector (DLC) – some models	79	↔		1		
Data link connector (DLC) – without immobilizer	62	↔		1		
Earth	13		Ignition ON	0 V		
	26		Ignition ON	0 V		
Earth – MT	91		Ignition ON	0 V		
Engine control relay	12	←	Ignition OFF	0 V		
	12	←	Ignition ON	11-14 V		
	25	←	Ignition OFF	0 V		
	25	←	Ignition ON	11-14 V		
	38	⇒	Ignition OFF	11-14 V		
	38	⇒	Ignition ON	0-3 V		
Engine coolant blower motor relay	21	⇒	Engine idling – coolant blower motor OFF	11-14 V		
	21	⇒	Engine idling – coolant blower motor ON	0-3 V		
Engine coolant temperature (ECT) sensor	83	←	Ignition ON – coolant temp. 0°C	3,2-3,8 V		
	83	←	Ignition ON – coolant temp. 20°C	2,3-2,9 V		
	83	←	Ignition ON – coolant temp. 40°C	1,3-1,9 V		
	83	←	Ignition ON – coolant temp. 80°C	0,3-0,9 V		
	92	⌐	Ignition ON	0 V		
Evaporative emission (EVAP) canister purge valve	9	⇒	Ignition ON	11-14 V		
	9	⇒	Engine running – 3000 rpm – engine cold	0 V		
Exhaust gas recirculation (EGR) solenoid	6	⇒	Ignition ON	11-14 V		
	6	⇒	Engine idling	11-14 V		
Fuel pump relay – with immobilizer	22	⇒	Ignition ON	0 V briefly then 11-14 V		
	22	⇒	Engine idling	0 V		
Fuel pump relay – without immobilizer	8	⇒	Ignition ON	0 V briefly then 11-14 V		
	8	⇒	Engine idling	0 V		
Heated oxygen sensor (HO2S)	60	⇒	Engine idling – engine hot	0-3 V		
	60	⇒	Engine running – engine hot – 5000 rpm	11-14 V		
	76	←	RPM decreasing	0,5-0,2 V		
	76	←	RPM increasing	0,6-1 V		
	76	←	Engine running – 2500 rpm	0-0,8 V fluctuating	0,2 V/1 sec.	⎍ 21
	92	⌐	Ignition ON	0 V		
Idle air control (IAC) valve	4	⇒	Engine idling – engine hot	0 V or 11-14 V switching	10 V/2 ms	Intermittent ⎍ 25
	5	⇒	Engine idling – engine hot	0 V or 11-14 V switching	10 V/2 ms	Intermittent ⎍ 25
	17	⇒	Engine idling – engine hot	0 V or 11-14 V switching	10 V/2 ms	Intermittent ⎍ 25
	18	⇒	Engine idling – engine hot	0 V or 11-14 V switching	10 V/2 ms	Intermittent ⎍ 25
Ignition amplifier – cylinders 1 & 4	10	⇒	Engine running – 3000 rpm	0,3-3 V		
	10	⇒	Engine running – 1200 rpm		2 V/20 ms	⎍ 82
Ignition amplifier – cylinders 2 & 3	23	⇒	Engine running – 3000 rpm	0,3-3 V		
	23	⇒	Engine running – 1200 rpm		2 V/20 ms	⎍ 82

★ Suggested settings - Voltage/time per division

Component/circuit description	ECM pin	Signal	Condition	Typical value	Oscilloscope setting*	Wave form
Ignition switch	**82**	←	Ignition OFF	0 V		
	82	←	Ignition ON	11-14 V		
Immobilizer control module	**62**	←		1		
Injector 1	**1**	⊣▷	Ignition ON	11-14 V		
	1	⊣▷	Engine idling – engine hot	1,7-2,9 ms	10 V/2 ms	35
Injector 2	**14**	⊣▷	Ignition ON	11-14 V		
	14	⊣▷	Engine idling – engine hot	1,7-2,9 ms	10 V/2 ms	35
Injector 3	**2**	⊣▷	Ignition ON	11-14 V		
	2	⊣▷	Engine idling – engine hot	1,7-2,9 ms	10 V/2 ms	35
Injector 4	**15**	⊣▷	Ignition ON	11-14 V		
	15	⊣▷	Engine idling – engine hot	1,7-2,9 ms	10 V/2 ms	35
Intake air temperature (IAT) sensor	**72**	←	Ignition ON – air temp. 0°C	3,2-3,8 V		
	72	←	Ignition ON – air temp. 20°C	2,3-2,9 V		
	72	←	Ignition ON – air temp. 40°C	1,5-2,1 V		
	72	←	Ignition ON – air temp. 80°C	0,4-1 V		
	92	⊣—	Ignition ON	0 V		
Knock sensor (KS)	**78**	←	Engine idling – accelerate briefly		50 mV/1 ms	38
Malfunction indicator lamp (MIL)	**36**	⊣▷	Ignition ON – MIL OFF	0-3 V		
	36	⊣▷	Ignition ON – MIL ON	11-14 V		
Park/neutral position (PNP) switch	**91**	←	Ignition ON – AT in P or N	0-3 V		
	91	←	Ignition ON – AT not in P or N	8-14 V		
Power steering pressure (PSP) switch	**37**	←	Engine idling – steering wheel not turned	11-14 V		
	37	←	Engine idling – steering wheel turned	0-3 V		
Starter motor	**71**	←	Engine cranking	9 V		
Tachometer	**58**	⇨	Engine running – 3000 rpm	0,3-3 V		
Throttle position (TP) sensor	**81**	⇨	Ignition ON	5 V		
	84	←	Ignition ON – throttle closed	0,3-1 V		
	84	←	Ignition ON – throttle fully open	5 V		
	92	⊣—	Ignition ON	0 V		
Vehicle speed sensor (VSS)	**86**	←	Ignition ON – vehicle pushed	0 V or 5 V switching		
Volume air flow (VAF) sensor	**19**	←	Engine idling	0-1 V		
	19	←	Engine running – 3000 rpm	6-9 V		
	90	←	Engine idling	2,2-3,2 V	2 V/20 ms	45
	90	←	Engine running – 2500 rpm	2,2-3,2 V		
	92	⊣—	Ignition ON	0 V		

*Suggested settings - Voltage/time per division

1 Connected pin - no test data available or random digital signal

MITSUBISHI
Mitsubishi MFI (Engine control module)

Model:	Engine code:	Year:
Carisma 1,8 GDI	4G93	1997-99

ECM harness multi-plug

Terminal side

81 80 79 78 77 76 75 74 73 72 71	56 55 54 53 52 51	38 37 36 35 34 33 32 31	13 12 11 10 9 8 7 6 5 4 3 2 1
92 91 90 89 88 87 86 85 84 83 82	62 61 60 59 58 57	46 45 44 43 42 41 40 39	26 25 24 23 22 21 20 19 18 17 16 15 14

AD42230

Wire side

1 2 3 4 5 6 7 8 9 10 11 12 13	31 32 33 34 35 36 37 38	51 52 53 54 55 56	71 72 73 74 75 76 77 78 79 80 81
14 15 16 17 18 19 20 21 22 23 24 25 26	39 40 41 42 43 44 45 46	57 58 59 60 61 62	82 83 84 85 86 87 88 89 90 91 92

AD42063

Component/circuit description	ECM pin	Signal	Condition	Typical value	Oscilloscope setting*	Wave form
AC compressor clutch relay	8	⊣▷	Engine idling – AC OFF	0 V		
	8	⊣▷	Engine idling – AC ON	6-12 V briefly then 0 V		
AC condenser blower motor	21	⊣▷	Engine idling – AC condenser blower motor OFF	11-14 V		
	21	⊣▷	Engine idling – AC condenser blower motor ON	0 V		
AC refrigerant pressure switch	45	⟵	Engine idling – AC OFF	0-1 V		
	45	⟵	Engine idling – AC ON	11-14 V		
Alternator	33	⟵	Engine idling – electrical load OFF	25 Hz		
	33	⟵	Engine idling – electrical load ON	6,5-7,5 V		
	41	⟵	Engine idling – electrical load OFF	2-3 V		
	41	⟵	Engine idling – electrical load ON	1-2 V		
Auxiliary air valve 1	3	⊣▷	Engine idling – engine cold, valve operating	0 V		
	3	⊣▷	Engine idling – engine hot	11-14 V		
Auxiliary air valve 2	16	⊣▷	Engine idling – valve operating	203 Hz		
Barometric pressure (BARO) sensor	85	⟵	Ignition ON – at sea level	3,9-4,1 V		
	85	⟵	Ignition ON – 1200 m above sea level	3,3-3,6 V		
Battery	80	⟵	Ignition OFF	11-14 V		
Brake booster vacuum sensor	42	⟵	Ignition ON – brake booster discharged	4 V		
	42	⟵	Engine idling	0,8 V		
	81	⟹	Ignition ON	5 V		
	92	⊣⟍	Ignition ON	0 V		
Brake pedal position (BPP) switch	35	⟵	Ignition ON – brake pedal released	0-1 V		
	35	⟵	Ignition ON – brake pedal depressed	11-14 V		
Camshaft position (CMP) sensor	88	⟵	Ignition ON – engine turned	0 or 5 V switching		
	88	⟵	Engine idling		1 V/0,1 sec.	∿〰 89
Closed throttle position (CTP) switch	87	⟵	Ignition ON – throttle closed	0 V		
	87	⟵	Ignition ON – throttle slightly open	4,6 V		
Crankshaft position (CKP) sensor	89	⟵	Ignition ON – engine turned	0 or 5 V switching		
	89	⟵	Engine idling		2 V/20 ms	∿〰 4
Data link connector (DLC)	79	⟸		☐1		
	56			☐1		
Earth	13		Ignition ON	0 V		
	26		Ignition ON	0 V		

* Suggested settings - Voltage/time per division

Component/circuit description	ECM pin	Signal	Condition	Typical value	Oscilloscope setting*	Wave form
Earth – MT	91		Ignition ON	0 V		
Engine control relay	12	⬅	Ignition OFF	0 V		
	12	⬅	Ignition ON	11-14 V		
	25	⬅	Ignition OFF	0 V		
	25	⬅	Ignition ON	11-14 V		
	38	⟶	Ignition OFF	11-14 V		
	38	⟶	Ignition ON	0 V		
Engine coolant blower motor relay	54	⬅	Ignition ON – coolant temp. below 90°C	11-14 V		
	54	⬅	Ignition ON – coolant temp. above 105°C	0-1 V		
	54	⟶	Engine idling – coolant blower motor OFF	11-14 V		
	54	⟶	Engine idling – coolant blower motor ON	0-1 V		
Engine coolant temperature (ECT) sensor	83	⬅	Ignition ON – coolant temp. 0°C	3,2-3,8 V		
	83	⬅	Ignition ON – coolant temp. 20°C	2,3-2,9 V		
	83	⬅	Ignition ON – coolant temp. 50°C	1-1,6 V		
	83	⬅	Ignition ON – coolant temp. 80°C	0,3-0,9 V		
	92	⊣	Ignition ON	0 V		
Evaporative emission (EVAP) canister purge valve	57	⟶	Ignition ON	11-14 V		
	57	⟶	Engine idling – engine hot	9%	10 V/20 ms	〰 20
Exhaust gas recirculation (EGR) solenoid	31	⟶	Ignition ON	11-14 V		
	31	⟶	Engine idling	11-14 V		
	32	⟶	Ignition ON	0 V		
	32	⟶	Engine idling	0 V		
	39	⟶	Ignition ON	11-14 V		
	39	⟶	Engine idling	11-14 V		
	40	⟶	Ignition ON	0 V		
	40	⟶	Engine idling	0 V		
Fuel pump relay	22	⟶	Ignition ON	0 V briefly then 11-14 V		
	22	⟶	Engine idling	0 V		
Fuel rail pressure (FRP) sensor	74	⬅	Ignition ON	0-0,5 V		
	74	⬅	Engine idling	2,85 V		
	77	⟹	Ignition ON	5 V		
	92	⊣	Ignition ON	0 V		
Headlamp switch	52	⬅	Engine idling – headlamp switch OFF	0-1 V		
	52	⬅	Engine idling – headlamp switch ON	11-14 V		
Heated oxygen sensor (HO2S)	60	⬅	Ignition ON	11-14 V		
	60	⬅	Engine idling	0-1 V		
	76	⬅	Engine running – 2000 rpm	0,1-0,9 V fluctuating	0,2 V/1 sec.	〰 21
	92	⊣	Ignition ON	0 V		
Idle air control (IAC) valve	4	⟹	Engine idling		5 V/50 ms	Intermittent 〰 87
	5	⟹	Engine idling		5 V/50 ms	Intermittent 〰 86
	17		Engine idling		5 V/50 ms	Intermittent 〰 87
	18		Engine idling		5 V/50 ms	Intermittent 〰 86
Ignition coil 1	10	⟹	Ignition ON	0,4 V		
	10	⟹	Engine idling		1 V/10 ms	〰 32
Ignition coil 2	11	⟹	Ignition ON	0,4 V		
	11	⟹	Engine idling		1 V/10 ms	〰 32

* Suggested settings - Voltage/time per division

Component/circuit description	ECM pin	Signal	Condition	Typical value	Oscilloscope setting*	Wave form
Ignition coil 3	23	⇨	Ignition ON	0,4 V		
	23	⇨	Engine idling		1 V/50 ms	∿ 32
Ignition coil 4	24	⇨	Ignition ON	0,4 V		
	24	⇨	Engine idling		1 V/50 ms	∿ 32
Ignition coil relay	20	⊐⇨	Ignition OFF	0 V		
	20	⊐⇨	Ignition ON	11-14 V		
Ignition switch	82	⇐	Ignition OFF	0 V		
	82	⇐	Ignition ON	11-14 V		
Immobilizer control module – diagnostic signal	62			1		
Injector control module – diagnostic signal	51			1		
Injector control module – injector 1	1	⊐⇨	Engine idling – engine hot		2 V/10 ms	∿ 88
Injector control module – injector 2	14	⊐⇨	Engine idling – engine hot		2 V/10 ms	∿ 88
Injector control module – injector 3	2	⊐⇨	Engine idling – engine hot		2 V/10 ms	∿ 88
Injector control module – injector 4	15	⊐⇨	Engine idling – engine hot		2 V/10 ms	∿ 88
Injector relay	20	⊐⇨	Ignition OFF	0 V		
	20	⊐⇨	Ignition ON	11-14 V		
Instrument panel	43	⇨		1		
Instrument panel – tachometer signal	58	⇨	Engine idling	26 Hz		
	58	⇨	3000 rpm	100 Hz		
Intake air temperature (IAT) sensor	72	⇐	Ignition ON – air temp. 0°C	3,2-3,8 V		
	72	⇐	Ignition ON – air temp. 20°C	2,3-2,9 V		
	72	⇐	Ignition ON – air temp. 40°C	1,5-2 V		
	92	⊐⊢	Ignition ON	0 V		
Knock sensor (KS)	78	⇐	Engine idling – accelerate briefly		50 mV/1 ms	∿ 38
Malfunction indicator lamp (MIL)	36	⊐⇨	Ignition ON – MIL ON	0-1 V		
	36	⊐⇨	Ignition ON – MIL OFF	11-14 V		
Power steering pressure (PSP) switch	37	⇐	Engine idling – steering wheel not turned	11-14 V		
	37	⇐	Engine idling – steering wheel turned	0-1 V		
Starter motor	71	⇐	Engine cranking	9-12 V		
Starter motor – AT	91	⇐	Engine cranking	9-12 V		
Throttle position (TP) sensor	81	⇨	Ignition ON	5 V		
	84	⇐	Ignition ON – throttle closed	0,6 V		
	84	⇐	Ignition ON – throttle fully open	4,8 V		
	92	⊐⊢	Ignition ON	0 V		
Transmission control module (TCM)	7	⇐		1		
	59	⇐		1		
Transmission fluid temperature sensor	75	⇐	Ignition ON – fluid temp. 80°C	0,5-0,8 V		
	92	⊐⊢	Ignition ON	0 V		
Transmission fluid temperature sensor – MT	75	⇐	Ignition ON – fluid temp. 25°C	2,4-2,7 V		
Vehicle speed sensor (VSS)	86	⇐	Ignition ON – vehicle pushed	0 V or 5 V switching		
Volume air flow (VAF) sensor	19	⇐	Ignition ON	7,5 V		
	19	⇐	Engine idling	0-1 V		
	19	⇐	Engine running – above idle speed	7,5 V		
	81	⇨	Ignition ON	5 V		
	90	⇐	Engine idling	2,2-3,2 V	2 V/20 ms	∿ 39
	92	⊐⊢	Ignition ON	0 V		

*Suggested settings - Voltage/time per division

1 Connected pin - no test data available or random digital signal

Injector control module harness multi-plug

Terminal side

AD23629

Wire side

AD23627

Component/circuit description	ECM pin	Signal	Condition	Typical value	Oscilloscope setting*	Wave form
Earth	14		Ignition ON	0 V		
	22		Ignition ON	0 V		
ECM pin 1	20	←	Engine idling		2 V/10 ms	∿∿ 88
ECM pin 2	11	←	Engine idling		2 V/10 ms	∿∿ 88
ECM pin 14	19	←	Engine idling		2 V/10 ms	∿∿ 88
ECM pin 17	10	←	Engine idling		2 V/10 ms	∿∿ 88
ECM pin 51	1	←▷	Engine idling	0 or 5 V		
Ignition relay	12	←	Ignition ON	11-14 V		
	21	←	Ignition ON	11-14 V		
Injector 1	17	⅂▷	Engine idling	0,5 ms	10 V/2 ms	∿∿ 35
	26	▷	Ignition ON	100 V		
Injector 2	16	⅂▷	Engine idling	0,5 ms	10 V/2 ms	∿∿ 35
	25	▷	Ignition ON	100 V		
Injector 3	15	⅂▷	Engine idling	0,5 ms	10 V/2 ms	∿∿ 35
	24	▷	Ignition ON	100 V		
Injector 4	14	⅂▷	Engine idling	0,5 ms	10 V/2 ms	∿∿ 35
	23	▷	Ignition ON	100 V		

*Suggested settings - Voltage/time per division

1 Connected pin - no test data available or random digital signal

MITSUBISHI

Mitsubishi MFI

Model:	Engine code:	Year:
Space Wagon 2,0	4G63	1994-99

ECM harness multi-plug

Terminal side

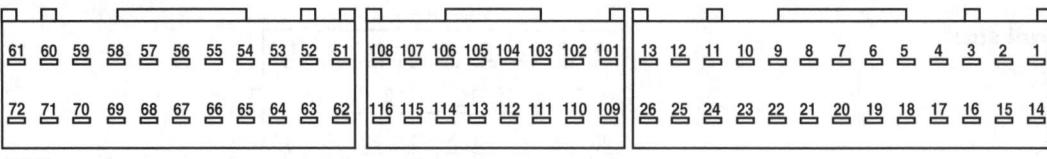

AD41770

Wire side

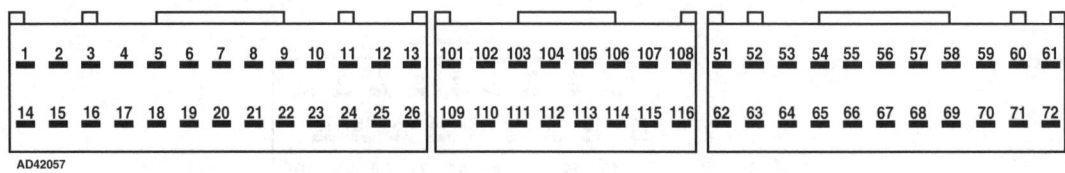

AD42057

Component/circuit description	ECM pin	Signal	Condition	Typical value	Oscilloscope setting*	Wave form
ABS control module – some models	114			1		
AC refrigerant pressure switch	115	←	Engine idling – AC OFF	0-3 V		
	115	←	Engine idling – AC ON	11-14 V		
AC relay – with immobilizer	8	⊐▷	Engine idling – AC OFF	11-14 V		
	8	⊐▷	Engine idling – AC ON	0-3 V		
AC relay – without immobilizer	22	⊐▷	Engine idling – AC OFF	11-14 V		
	22	⊐▷	Engine idling – AC ON	0-3 V		
Air conditioning	11			1		
Barometric pressure (BARO) sensor	61	⇨	Ignition ON	5 V		
	65	←	Ignition ON – at sea level	3,7-4,3 V		
	65	←	Ignition ON – 1200 m above sea level	3,2-3,8 V		
	72	⊣‾	Ignition ON	0 V		
Battery	60	←	Ignition OFF	11-14 V		
Camshaft position (CMP) sensor	68	←	Engine cranking	0,4-3 V		
	68	←	Engine idling	0,5-2 V	2 V/0,1 sec.	∿∿ 18
Closed throttle position (CTP) switch	67	←	Ignition ON – throttle closed	0-1 V		
	67	←	Ignition ON – throttle slightly open	4 V min.		
Crankshaft position (CKP) sensor	69	←	Engine cranking	0,4-4 V		
	69	←	Engine idling	1,5-2,5 V	2 V/10 ms	∿∿ 45
Data link connector (DLC)	113	◄▷		1		
Data link connector (DLC) – without immobilizer	112	◄▷		1		
Earth	13		Ignition ON	0 V		
	26		Ignition ON	0 V		
Earth – MT	71		Ignition ON	0 V		
Engine coolant blower motor relay – some models	3			1		
	16			1		

★ Suggested settings - Voltage/time per division

Component/circuit description	ECM pin	Signal	Condition	Typical value	Oscilloscope setting*	Wave form
Engine coolant temperature (ECT) sensor	63	←	Ignition ON – coolant temp. 0°C	3,2-3,8 V		
	63	←	Ignition ON – coolant temp. 20°C	2,3-2,9 V		
	63	←	Ignition ON – coolant temp. 40°C	1,3-1,9 V		
	63	←	Ignition ON – coolant temp. 80°C	0,3-0,9 V		
	72	⌐	Ignition ON	0 V		
Evaporative emission (EVAP) canister purge valve	9	⊐▷	Ignition ON	11-14 V		
	9	⊐▷	Engine running – 3000 rpm – engine hot	0-3 V	10 V/20 ms	20
Exhaust gas recirculation (EGR) solenoid	6	⊐▷	Ignition ON	11-14 V		
	6	⊐▷	Engine idling – coolant temp. 40°C max.	0-3 V	10 V/20 ms	20
Heated oxygen sensor (HO2S)	56	←	RPM decreasing	0,5-0,2 V		
	56	←	RPM increasing	0,6-1 V		
	56	←	Engine running – 2000 rpm	0-0,8 V fluctuating	0,2 V/1 sec.	21
	72	⌐	Ignition ON	0 V		
	105	⊐▷	Engine idling – engine hot	0-3 V		
	105	⊐▷	Engine running – engine hot – 5000 rpm	11-14 V		
Idle air control (IAC) valve	4	⇨	Ignition ON	2 V briefly then 0-1 V		
	4	⇨	Engine idling		5 V/2 ms	Intermittent 27
	17	⇨	Ignition ON	4 V min. briefly then 0-1 V		
	17	⇨	Engine idling		5 V/2 ms	Intermittent 27
Idle air control (IAC) valve position sensor	5	←	Ignition ON	1,5-4 V briefly then 0-1 V or 5 V		
	5	←	Engine idling		5 V/2 ms	Intermittent 31
	18	←	Ignition ON	1,5-4 V briefly then 0-1 V or 5 V		
	18	←	Engine idling		5 V/2 ms	Intermittent 31
	61	⇨	Ignition ON	5 V		
	72	⌐	Ignition ON	0 V		
Ignition adjustment connector	104	←	Ignition ON – connected to earth	0-1 V		
	104	←	Ignition ON – not connected to earth	4-5,5 V		
Ignition amplifier	10	⇨	Engine idling	25 Hz		
	10	⇨	Engine running – 1200 rpm		2 V/20 ms	82
	10	⇨	Engine running – 3000 rpm	0,3-3 V/96 Hz		
Ignition switch – with immobilizer	62	←	Ignition OFF	0 V		
	62	←	Ignition ON	11-14 V		
Immobilizer control module	112	←		[1]		
Injector 1	1	⊐▷	Engine idling – engine hot	2-3,2 ms	10 V/2 ms	35
	1	⊐▷	Engine running – engine hot – 2000 rpm	1,8-3 ms		
Injector 2	14	⊐▷	Engine idling – engine hot	2-3,2 ms	10 V/2 ms	35
	14	⊐▷	Engine running – engine hot – 2000 rpm	1,8-3 ms		
Injector 3	2	⊐▷	Engine idling – engine hot	2-3,2 ms	10 V/2 ms	35
	2	⊐▷	Engine running – engine hot – 2000 rpm	1,8-3 ms		
Injector 4	15	⊐▷	Engine idling – engine hot	2-3,2 ms	10 V/2 ms	35
	15	⊐▷	Engine running – engine hot – 2000 rpm	1,8-3 ms		

* Suggested settings - Voltage/time per division

Component/circuit description	ECM pin	Signal	Condition	Typical value	Oscilloscope setting*	Wave form
Intake air temperature (IAT) sensor	52	←	Ignition ON – air temp. 0°C	3,2-3,8 V		
	52	←	Ignition ON – air temp. 20°C	2,3-2,9 V		
	52	←	Ignition ON – air temp. 40°C	1,5-2,1 V		
	52	←	Ignition ON – air temp. 80°C	0,4-1 V		
	72	⌐—	Ignition ON	0 V		
Knock sensor (KS)	58	←	Engine idling – accelerate briefly		50 mV/1 ms	〰 38
Malfunction indicator lamp (MIL)	106	⌐▷	Ignition ON – MIL ON	0-3 V		
	106	⌐▷	Ignition ON – MIL OFF	11-14 V		
Octane coding plug – connected to earth – some models	53	⌐—	Ignition ON	0 V		
Octane coding plug – some models	53			1		
Park/neutral position (PNP) switch	71	←	Ignition ON – AT in P or N	0-3 V		
	71	←	Ignition ON – AT not in P or N	8-14 V		
Power steering pressure (PSP) switch	107	←	Engine idling – steering wheel not turned	11-14 V		
	107	←	Engine idling – steering wheel turned	0-3 V		
Relay module	12	←	Ignition OFF	0 V		
	12	←	Ignition ON	11-14 V		
	25	←	Ignition OFF	0 V		
	25	←	Ignition ON	11-14 V		
Relay module – 1996-99	108	⌐▷	Ignition OFF	11-14 V		
	108	⌐▷	Ignition ON	0-3 V		
Relay module – with immobilizer	22	⌐▷	Ignition ON	11-14 V		
	22	⌐▷	Engine idling	0-3 V		
Relay module – without immobilizer	8	⌐▷	Ignition ON	11-14 V		
	8	⌐▷	Engine idling	0-3 V		
Starter motor	51	←	Engine cranking	9 V		
Throttle position (TP) sensor	61	▷	Ignition ON	5 V		
	64	←	Ignition ON – throttle closed	0,3-1 V		
	64	←	Ignition ON – throttle fully open	5 V		
	72	⌐—	Ignition ON	0 V		
Transmission control module (TCM)	7			1		
	59			1		
	116			1		
Vehicle speed sensor (VSS)	66	←	Ignition ON – vehicle pushed	0 V or 5 V switching		
Volume air flow (VAF) sensor	19	←	Engine idling	0-1 V		
	19	←	Engine running – 3000 rpm	6-9 V		
	70	←	Engine idling	2,2-3,2 V		
	70	←	Engine idling	30 Hz		
	70	←	Engine running – 3000 rpm	98 Hz		
	70	←	Engine idling		2 V/20 ms	〰 45
	72	⌐—	Ignition ON	0 V		

*Suggested settings - Voltage/time per division

1 Connected pin - no test data available or random digital signal

ECM harness multi-plug

Terminal side

39 38 37 36 35 34 33 32 31　　22 21 20 19 18 17 16 15　　7 6 5 4 3 2 1　　108 107 106 105 104 103 102 101
48 47 46 45 44 43 42 41 40　　30 29 28 27 26 25 24 23　　14 13 12 11 10 9 8　　116 115 114 113 112 111 110 109

AD74784

Wire side

101 102 103 104 105 106 107 108　　1 2 3 4 5 6 7　　15 16 17 18 19 20 21 22　　31 32 33 34 35 36 37 38 39
109 110 111 112 113 114 115 116　　8 9 10 11 12 13 14　　23 24 25 26 27 28 29 30　　40 41 42 43 44 45 46 47 48

AD42095

Component/circuit description	ECM pin	Signal	Condition	Typical value	Oscilloscope setting*	Wave form
ABS control module – if fitted	27			1		
AC refrigerant pressure switch	41	←	Engine running – AC ON	0 V		
	41	←	Engine running – AC OFF	11-14 V		
AC relay	11	⊐▷	Engine running – AC ON	0-1 V		
	11	⊐▷	Engine running – AC OFF	11-14 V		
Battery	46	←	Ignition OFF	11-14 V		
Camshaft position (CMP) sensor/ crankshaft position (CKP) sensor	31	←	Engine running	2-3 V	5 V/10 ms	47
	40	←	Engine running	2-3 V	5 V/10 ms	47
Data link connector (DLC)	7	←▷		1		
	14	←▷		1		
	15	←▷		1		
	23	←▷		1		
Earth	6		Ignition ON	0 V		
	13		Ignition ON	0 V		
	39		Ignition ON	0 V		
	48		Ignition ON	0 V		
	107		Ignition ON	0 V		
	108		Ignition ON	0 V		
Engine control relay	4	⊐▷	Engine running	0-1 V		
	4	⊐▷	Ignition OFF – for 5 seconds	0-1 V		
	4	⊐▷	Ignition OFF – after 5 seconds	11-14 V		
	38	←	Ignition OFF	0 V		
	38	←	Ignition ON	11-14 V		
	47	←	Ignition OFF	0 V		
	47	←	Ignition ON	11-14 V		

★ Suggested settings - Voltage/time per division

Component/circuit description	ECM pin	Signal	Condition	Typical value	Oscilloscope setting*	Wave form
Engine coolant blower motor relay	9	→▷	Engine running – coolant blower motor OFF	11-14 V		
	9	→▷	Engine running – coolant blower motor ON	0-1 V		
Engine coolant temperature (ECT) sensor	18	←	Ignition ON – coolant temp. 10°C	4 V		
	18	←	Ignition ON – coolant temp. 80°C	1 V		
	21	⅂—	Ignition ON	0 V		
	29	⅂—	Ignition ON	0 V		
Fuel pump relay	106	→▷	Ignition ON – for 5 seconds	0-1 V		
	106	→▷	Ignition ON – after 5 seconds	11-14 V		
	106	→▷	Engine running	0-1 V		
Headlamp switch	33	←	Engine idling – headlamps ON	11-14 V		
	33	←	Engine idling – headlamps OFF	0 V		
Heated oxygen sensor (HO2S)	19	←	Engine running – engine hot	0-1 V fluctuating	0,2 V/1 sec.	
	105	→▷	Ignition ON	11-14 V		
	105	→▷	Engine idling	0-1 V		
Heated rear window switch	33	←	Engine idling – heated rear window ON	11-14 V		
	33	←	Engine idling – heated rear window OFF	0 V		
Heater motor switch – without AC	45	←		[1]		
Heater/AC motor switch – with AC	45	←		[1]		
Idle air control (IAC) valve	111	→▷	Engine idling	40%	5 V/5 ms	
	113	→▷	Engine idling	40%	5 V/5 ms	
Ignition amplifier	1	⇨	Engine idling	0,2-0,4 V		
	1	⇨	Engine idling	30 Hz	2 V/10 ms	
	1	⇨	2000 rpm	0,6-0,8 V		
Ignition coil – through ignition signal resistor	3	←	Engine idling	11-14 V	5 V/2 ms	
Ignition switch	12	←	Ignition OFF	0 V		
	12	←	Ignition ON	11-14 V		
Ignition switch – start signal	34		Ignition ON	0 V		
	34		Engine cranking	11-14 V		
Immobilizer control module	26			[1]		
Immobilizer control module – some models	8			[1]		
Injector 1	101	→▷	Ignition ON	11-14 V		
	101	→▷	Engine idling – engine hot	2,3 ms	10 V/2 ms	
Injector 2	110	→▷	Ignition ON	11-14 V		
	110	→▷	Engine idling – engine hot	2,3 ms	10 V/2 ms	
Injector 3	103	→▷	Ignition ON	11-14 V		
	103	→▷	Engine idling – engine hot	2,3 ms	10 V/2 ms	
Injector 4	112	→▷	Ignition ON	11-14 V		
	112	→▷	Engine idling – engine hot	2,3 ms	10 V/2 ms	
Malfunction indicator lamp (MIL)	24	→▷	Ignition ON – MIL ON	0-1 V		
	24	→▷	Engine running – MIL ON	0-1 V		
	24	→▷	Engine running – MIL OFF	11-14 V		

* Suggested settings - Voltage/time per division

Component/circuit description	ECM pin	Signal	Condition	Typical value	Oscilloscope setting*	Wave form
Mass air flow (MAF) sensor	16	←	Ignition ON	0,4 V		
	16	←	Engine idling	1-1,8 V		
	16	←	2000 rpm	1,6-2,1 V		
	16	←	Engine idling – accelerate briefly	3,8 V briefly		
	21	⌐	Ignition ON	0 V		
	29	⌐	Ignition ON	0 V		
Neutral position (NP) switch – MT	35	←	Ignition ON – gear lever in neutral	0 V		
	35	←	Ignition ON – gear lever not in neutral	5 V		
Power steering pressure (PSP) switch	43	←	Engine running – steering wheel not turned	5 V		
	43	←	Engine running – steering wheel turned	0 V		
Tachometer – if fitted	2	⇒	Engine idling	30 Hz		
Throttle position (TP) sensor	20	←	Ignition ON – accelerator pedal released	0,6-0,7 V		
	20	←	Ignition ON – accelerator pedal fully depressed	4 V		
	21	⌐	Ignition ON	0 V		
	29	⌐	Ignition ON	0 V		
	37	⇒	Ignition ON	5 V		
Transmission control module (TCM) – AT	25			☐1		
	35	←	Ignition ON – AT in P or N	0 V		
	35	←	Ignition ON – AT not in P or N	5 V		
	42			☐1		
Vehicle speed sensor (VSS)	32	←	Ignition ON – vehicle pushed	0-5 V fluctuating		

*Suggested settings - Voltage/time per division

☐1 Connected pin - no test data available or random digital signal

Model:	Engine code:	Year:
Micra 1,2	CR12DE	2003-06

ECM harness multi-plug

Terminal side

AD106111

Wire side

AD106110

Component/circuit description	ECM pin	Signal	Condition	Typical value	Oscilloscope setting*	Wave form
AC refrigerant pressure sensor	46	⇨	Ignition ON	5 V		
	57	⌐⌐	Ignition ON	0 V		
	69	⬅		[1]		
Accelerator pedal position (APP) sensor	82	⌐⌐	Ignition ON	0 V		
	83	⌐⌐	Ignition ON	0 V		
	90	⇨	Ignition ON	5 V		
	91	⇨	Ignition ON	5 V		
	98	⬅	Ignition ON – accelerator pedal released	0,3 V		
	98	⬅	Ignition ON – accelerator pedal fully depressed	1,9 V		
	106	⬅	Ignition ON – accelerator pedal released	0,7 V		
	106	⬅	Ignition ON – accelerator pedal fully depressed	3,9 V		
Battery	121	⬅	Ignition OFF	11-14 V		
Brake pedal position (BPP) switch	101	⬅	Ignition ON – brake pedal released	0 V		
	101	⬅	Ignition ON – brake pedal depressed	11-14 V		
Camshaft position (CMP) actuator, intake	62	⌐⇨	Ignition ON	11-14 V		
	62	⌐⇨	Engine idling	11-14 V		
Camshaft position (CMP) sensor	14	⬅	Engine idling		5 V/20 ms	⌁⌁ 84
	29	⌐⌐	Ignition ON	0 V		
CAN data bus – high	94	⬅⇨		[1]		

⭑ Suggested settings - Voltage/time per division

Component/circuit description	ECM pin	Signal	Condition	Typical value	Oscilloscope setting*	Wave form
CAN data bus – low	86	◄▷		1		
Crankshaft position (CKP) sensor	13	◄━	Engine idling		5 V/2 ms	9
	30	┤─	Ignition ON	0 V		
Data link connector (DLC)	85	◄▷	Ignition ON	10 V		
	85	◄▷	Engine idling	12 V		
Earth	1		Ignition ON	0 V		
	115		Ignition ON	0 V		
	116		Ignition ON	0 V		
Engine control (EC) relay	111	┤▷	Ignition OFF	11-14 V		
	111	┤▷	Ignition ON	0-1 V		
	119	◄━	Ignition ON	11-14 V		
	120	◄━	Ignition ON	11-14 V		
Engine coolant temperature (ECT) sensor	72	◄━	Ignition ON – coolant temp. 20°C	3,4 V		
	72	◄━	Ignition ON – coolant temp. 80°C	0,9 V		
	73	┤─	Ignition ON	0 V		
Evaporative emission (EVAP) canister purge valve	19	┤▷	Ignition ON	11-14 V		
Fuel pump (FP) relay	113	┤▷	Ignition ON	0-1 V briefly then 11-14 V		
	113	┤▷	Engine idling	0-1 V		
Heated oxygen sensor (HO2S) 1	24	┤▷	Ignition ON		11-14 V	
	24	┤▷	Engine idling		0-1 V	
	35	◄━	Engine idling	0-1 V (fluctuating)	0,2 V/1 sec.	21
	74	┤─	Ignition ON	0 V		
Heated oxygen sensor (HO2S) 2	2	┤▷	Ignition ON	11-14 V		
	2	┤▷	Engine idling		2 V/50 ms	71
	16	◄━	Engine idling	0,3 V		
	74	┤─	Ignition ON	0 V		
Ignition amplifier 1	61	▷	Engine idling		2 V/50 ms	32
Ignition amplifier 2	80	▷	Engine idling		2 V/50 ms	32
Ignition amplifier 3	60	▷	Engine idling		2 V/50 ms	32
Ignition amplifier 4	79	▷	Engine idling		2 V/50 ms	32
Ignition switch	109	◄━	Ignition ON	11-14 V		
Injector 1	23	┤▷	Ignition ON	11-14 V		
	23	┤▷	Engine idling	1,9 ms	10 V/2 ms	35
Injector 2	42	┤▷	Ignition ON	11-14 V		
	42	┤▷	Engine idling	1,9 ms	10 V/2 ms	35
Injector 3	22	┤▷	Ignition ON	11-14 V		
	22	┤▷	Engine idling	1,9 ms	10 V/2 ms	35
Injector 4	41	┤▷	Ignition ON	11-14 V		
	41	┤▷	Engine idling	1,9 ms	10 V/2 ms	35

* Suggested settings - Voltage/time per division

Component/circuit description	ECM pin	Signal	Condition	Typical value	Oscilloscope setting*	Wave form
Intake air temperature (IAT) sensor	34	←	Ignition ON – air temp. 15°C	3,5 V		
	34	←	Ignition ON – air temp. 25°C	3,3 V		
	34	←	Ignition ON – air temp. 80°C	1,2 V		
	56	⊣⏄	Ignition ON	0 V		
Knock sensor (KS)	15	←	Engine idling – accelerate briefly		50 mV/1 ms	⎍⎍ 38
	54	⊣⏄	Ignition ON	0 V		
Manifold absolute pressure (MAP) sensor	45	⇨	Ignition ON	5 V		
	51	←	Ignition ON	4,5 V		
	51	←	Engine idling	1,3 V		
	51	←	Engine idling – full throttle briefly	4 V briefly		
	56	⊣⏄	Ignition ON	0 V		
Multifunction control module	102	⊣⏄	Ignition ON	0 V		
Throttle control unit relay	3	←	Ignition ON	11-14 V		
	104	⊣⏄▷	Ignition OFF	11-14 V		
	104	⊣⏄▷	Ignition ON	0-1 V		
Throttle motor	4	⇨	Engine idling		2 V/20 ms	⎍⎍ 28
	5	⇨	Engine idling	0,2 V		
Throttle motor position sensor	47	⇨	Ignition ON	5 V		
	49	←	Ignition ON	0,9 V		
	49	←	Engine idling	0,6 V		
	66	⊣⏄	Ignition ON	0 V		
	68	←	Ignition ON	4,2 V		
	68	←	Engine idling	4,5 V		
Transmission control module (TCM) – AT	92			[1]		
	103			[1]		

*Suggested settings - Voltage/time per division

[1] Connected pin - no test data available or random digital signal

Model:	Engine code:	Year:
Almera 1,4	GA14DE	1995-00
Almera 1,6	GA16DE	1995-00
Primera 1,6	GA16DE	1996-00

ECM harness multi-plug

Terminal side

39 38 37 36 35 34 33 32 31 22 21 20 19 18 17 16 15   7 6 5 4 3 2 1 108 107 106 105 104 103 102 101
48 47 46 45 44 43 42 41 40   30 29 28 27 26 25 24 23   14 13 12 11 10 9 8 116 115 114 113 112 111 110 109

AD74784

Wire side

101 102 103 104 105 106 107 108   1 2 3 4 5 6 7   15 16 17 18 19 20 21 22   31 32 33 34 35 36 37 38 39
109 110 111 112 113 114 115 116   8 9 10 11 12 13 14   23 24 25 26 27 28 29 30   40 41 42 43 44 45 46 47 48

AD42095

Component/circuit description	ECM pin	Signal	Condition	Typical value	Oscilloscope setting*	Wave form
AC refrigerant pressure switch	41	←	Engine running – AC ON	0 V		
	41	←	Engine running – AC OFF	11-14 V		
AC relay	11	⇥▷	Engine running – AC ON	0-1 V		
	11	⇥▷	Engine running – AC OFF	11-14 V		
Battery	46	←	Ignition OFF	11-14 V		
Camshaft position (CMP) sensor/ crankshaft position (CKP) sensor	31	←	Engine running	1,5-3 V	5 V/10 ms	⊲⋀⋀ 47
	40	←	Engine running	1,5-3 V	5 V/10 ms	⊲⋀⋀ 47
Data link connector (DLC)	7	◄⟶		1		
	14	◄⟶		1		
	15	◄⟶		1		
	23	◄⟶		1		
Earth	6		Ignition ON	0 V		
	13		Ignition ON	0 V		
	39		Ignition ON	0 V		
	48		Ignition ON	0 V		
	107		Ignition ON	0 V		
	108		Ignition ON	0 V		
	116		Ignition ON	0 V		
Engine control relay	4	⇥▷	Engine running	0-1 V		
	4	⇥▷	Ignition OFF – for 5 seconds	0-1 V		
	4	⇥▷	Ignition OFF – after 5 seconds	11-14 V		
	38	←	Ignition OFF	0 V		
	38	←	Ignition ON	11-14 V		
	47	←	Ignition OFF	0 V		
	47	←	Ignition ON	11-14 V		
	109	←	Ignition OFF	0 V		
	109	←	Ignition ON	11-14 V		
Engine coolant blower motor relay	9	⇥▷	Engine running – coolant blower motor OFF	11-14 V		
	9	⇥▷	Engine running – coolant blower motor ON	0-1 V		

* Suggested settings - Voltage/time per division

Component/circuit description	ECM pin	Signal	Condition	Typical value	Oscilloscope setting*	Wave form
Engine coolant temperature (ECT) sensor	18	←	Ignition ON – coolant temp. 10°C	4 V		
	18	←	Ignition ON – coolant temp. 80°C	1 V		
	21	⌐—	Ignition ON	0 V		
	29	⌐—	Ignition ON	0 V		
Exhaust gas recirculation (EGR) solenoid/evaporative emission (EVAP) canister purge valve	105		Engine idling – engine hot	0-1 V		
	105		Driven/RPM increasing – engine hot	11-14 V		
Fuel pump relay	106	⊐▷	Ignition ON – for 5 seconds	0-1 V		
	106	⊐▷	Ignition ON – after 5 seconds	11-14 V		
	106	⊐▷	Engine running	0-1 V		
Headlamp switch	33	←	Engine idling – headlamps ON	11-14 V		
	33	←	Engine idling – headlamps OFF	0 V		
Heated oxygen sensor (HO2S)	19	←	Engine running – engine hot	0-1 V fluctuating	0,2 V/1 sec.	⩗⩗ 21
	102	⊐▷	Ignition ON	11-14 V		
	102	⊐▷	Engine idling	0-1 V		
Heated rear window relay – Primera	33	←	Engine idling – heated rear window ON	11-14 V		
	33	←	Engine idling – heated rear window OFF	0 V		
Heated rear window switch – Almera	33	←	Engine idling – heated rear window ON	11-14 V		
	33	←	Engine idling – heated rear window OFF	0 V		
Heater motor switch – without AC	45	←		1		
Heater/AC motor switch – with AC	45	←		1		
Idle air control (IAC) valve	113	⊐▷	Engine idling		5 V/5 ms	⩗⩗ 24
Ignition amplifier	1	⇒	Engine idling	0,2-0,3 V		
	1	⇒	Engine idling	30 Hz	2 V/10 ms	⩗⩗ 32
	1	⇒	2000 rpm	0,6-0,8 V		
Ignition coil – through ignition signal resistor	3	←	Engine idling	11-14 V	5 V/2 ms	⩗⩗ 33
Ignition switch	44		Ignition OFF	0 V		
	44		Ignition ON	11-14 V		
Ignition switch – start signal	34		Ignition ON	0 V		
	34		Engine cranking	11-14 V		
Immobilizer control module	26			1		
Immobilizer control module – some models	25			1		
Injector 1	101	⊐▷	Ignition ON	11-14 V		
	101	⊐▷	Engine idling – engine hot	2,4-3,2 ms	10 V/2 ms	⩗⩗ 35
Injector 2	110	⊐▷	Ignition ON	11-14 V		
	110	⊐▷	Engine idling – engine hot	2,4-3,2 ms	10 V/2 ms	⩗⩗ 35
Injector 3	103	⊐▷	Ignition ON	11-14 V		
	103	⊐▷	Engine idling – engine hot	2,4-3,2 ms	10 V/2 ms	⩗⩗ 35
Injector 4	112	⊐▷	Ignition ON	11-14 V		
	112	⊐▷	Engine idling – engine hot	2,4-3,2 ms	10 V/2 ms	⩗⩗ 35
Malfunction indicator lamp (MIL)	24	⊐▷	Ignition ON – MIL ON	0-1 V		
	24	⊐▷	Engine running – MIL ON	0-1 V		
	24	⊐▷	Engine running – MIL OFF	11-14 V		

* Suggested settings - Voltage/time per division

Component/circuit description	ECM pin	Signal	Condition	Typical value	Oscilloscope setting*	Wave form
Mass air flow (MAF) sensor	16	⬅	Ignition ON	1 V max.		
	16	⬅	Engine idling	1-1,8 V		
	16	⬅	2000 rpm	1,5-2,3 V		
	21	⌐—	Ignition ON	0 V		
	29	⌐—	Ignition ON	0 V		
Neutral position (NP) switch – MT	35	⬅	Ignition ON – gear lever in neutral	0 V		
	35	⬅	Ignition ON – gear lever not in neutral	5 V		
Park/neutral position (PNP) switch – AT	35	⬅	Ignition ON – AT in P or N	0 V		
	35	⬅	Ignition ON – AT not in P or N	5 V		
Power steering pressure (PSP) switch	43	⬅	Engine running – steering wheel not turned	5 V		
	43	⬅	Engine running – steering wheel turned	0 V		
Tachometer – if fitted	2	⇨	Engine idling	0,7-1,3 V		
	2	⇨	Engine idling	30 Hz		
Throttle position (TP) sensor	20	⬅	Ignition ON – accelerator pedal released	0,4-0,7 V		
	20	⬅	Ignition ON – accelerator pedal fully depressed	4 V		
	21	⌐—	Ignition ON	0 V		
	29	⌐—	Ignition ON	0 V		
	37	⇨	Ignition ON	5 V		
Transmission lockup control valve – AT – some models	115	⌐⇨		1		
Vehicle speed sensor (VSS)	32	⬅	Ignition ON – vehicle pushed	0-5 V fluctuating	2 V/50 ms	

*Suggested settings - Voltage/time per division

1 Connected pin - no test data available or random digital signal

Model:	Engine code:	Year:
Almera 1,5	QG15DE	2000-06
Almera/Almera Tino 1,8	QG18DE	2000-06
Primera 1,6	QG16DE	2000-02
Primera 1,8	QG18DE	1999-02

ECM harness multi-plug

Terminal side

110 109 | 67 66 65 64 63 62 61 60 59 58 | 10 9 8 7 6 5 4 3 2 1 | 102 101
112 111 | 76 75 74 73 72 71 70 69 68 | 48 47 46 45 44 43 42 41 40 39 | 19 18 17 16 15 14 13 12 11 | 104 103
114 113 | 86 85 84 83 82 81 80 79 78 77 | 57 56 55 54 53 52 51 50 49 | 29 28 27 26 25 24 23 22 21 20 | 106 105
116 115 | 95 94 93 92 91 90 89 88 87 | 38 37 36 35 34 33 32 31 30 | 108 107

AD23522

Wire side

101 102 | 1 2 3 4 5 6 7 8 9 10 | 58 59 60 61 62 63 64 65 66 67 | 109 110
103 104 | 11 12 13 14 15 16 17 18 19 | 39 40 41 42 43 44 45 46 47 48 | 68 69 70 71 72 73 74 75 76 | 111 112
105 106 | 20 21 22 23 24 25 26 27 28 29 | 49 50 51 52 53 54 55 56 57 | 77 78 79 80 81 82 83 84 85 86 | 113 114
107 108 | 30 31 32 33 34 35 36 37 38 | 87 88 89 90 91 92 93 94 95 | 115 116

AD23521

Component/circuit description	ECM pin	Signal	Condition	Typical value	Oscilloscope setting*	Wave form
AC compressor clutch relay	23	⊐▷	Engine idling – AC OFF	11-14 V		
	23	⊐▷	Engine idling – AC ON – AC compressor ON	0-1 V		
AC master switch	44	◀━	Engine idling – AC OFF	5 V		
	44	◀━	Engine idling – AC ON – AC compressor ON	0 V		
AC refrigerant pressure sensor	58	⊐─	Engine idling	0 V		
	74	◀━		[1]		
	111	⇨	Ignition ON	5 V		
AC/heater blower motor switch	51	◀━	Ignition ON – blower motor switch OFF	5 V		
	51	◀━	Ignition ON – blower motor switch ON	0 V		
Battery	67	◀━	Ignition OFF	11-14 V		
Camshaft position (CMP) actuator – 1,8	1	⊐▷	Ignition ON	11-14 V		
	1	⊐▷	Engine idling	11-14 V		
	1	⊐▷	Engine running – valve operating	0-1 V		
Camshaft position (CMP) sensor	75	◀━	Engine idling		5 V/40 ms	〜〜 84
Camshaft position (CMP) sensor – some models	66	◀━	Engine idling		5 V/40 ms	〜〜 84
Closed throttle position (CTP) switch – some models	40	◀━	Ignition ON – throttle closed	11-14 V		
	40	◀━	Ignition ON – throttle open	0-1 V		
Crankshaft position (CKP) sensor	85	◀━	Engine idling		5 V/2 ms	〜〜 18
Data link connector (DLC)	115	◀⇨		[1]		
Data link connector (DLC) – some models	93	◀⇨		[1]		
	114	◀⇨		[1]		
Earth	48		Ignition ON	0 V		
	57		Ignition ON	0 V		
	106		Ignition ON	0 V		
	108		Ignition ON	0 V		

✱ Suggested settings - Voltage/time per division

Autodata

Component/circuit description	ECM pin	Signal	Condition	Typical value	Oscilloscope setting*	Wave form
Engine control relay	31	⊃▷	Ignition OFF – for 9 secs.	0-1 V		
	31	⊃▷	Ignition OFF – after 9 secs.	11-14 V		
	31	⊃▷	Ignition ON	0-1 V		
	110	◄—	Ignition OFF	0 V		
	110	◄—	Ignition ON	11-14 V		
	112	◄—	Ignition OFF	0 V		
	112	◄—	Ignition ON	11-14 V		
Engine coolant blower motor relay	13	⊃▷	Engine idling – coolant blower motor OFF	11-14 V		
	13	⊃▷	Engine idling – coolant blower motor ON	0-1 V		
Engine coolant temperature (ECT) sensor	58	⊃—	Engine idling	0 V		
	70	◄—	Ignition ON – coolant temp. 20°C	3,5 V		
	70	◄—	Ignition ON – coolant temp. 90°C	0,9 V		
Evaporative emission (EVAP) canister purge valve	14	⊃▷	Ignition ON	11-14 V		
	14	⊃▷	Engine running – valve operating		10 V/20 ms	〰 20
Exhaust gas recirculation (EGR) temperature sensor – some models	8	⇨		1		
	9	⇨		1		
	17	⇨		1		
	18	⇨		1		
	58	⊃—	Engine idling	0 V		
	72	◄—	Ignition ON – EGR temp. 0°C	4,5 V		
	72	◄—	Engine running – EGR temp. 100°C	0,6 V		
Fuel pump relay	21	⊃▷	Ignition ON	0-1 V briefly then 11-14 V		
	21	⊃▷	Engine cranking	0-1 V		
Fuel temperature sensor – some models	82	◄—	Ignition ON – fuel temp. 20°C	3,5 V		
Headlamp switch	50	◄—	Engine idling – headlamps ON	11-14 V		
	50	◄—	Engine idling – headlamps OFF	0 V		
Heated oxygen sensor (HO2S) 1	62	◄—	Engine running – engine hot	0-1 V fluctuating	0,2 V/1 sec.	〰 21
Heated oxygen sensor (HO2S) 1 – heater control	4	⊃▷	Ignition ON	11-14 V		
	4	⊃▷	Engine running above 3200 rpm	11-14 V		
	4	⊃▷	Engine running below 3200 rpm	0-1 V		
Heated oxygen sensor (HO2S) 2	63	◄—	Engine idling	0,3-0,7 V	0,2 V/0,5 sec.	〰 76
Heated oxygen sensor (HO2S) 2 – heater control	3	⊃▷	Ignition ON	11-14 V		
	3	⊃▷	Engine running below 3600 rpm – engine hot	0-1 V		
Heated rear window switch	50	◄—	Engine idling – heated rear window ON	11-14 V		
	50	◄—	Engine idling – heated rear window OFF	0 V		
Idle air control (IAC) valve	6	⇨	Engine idling		5 V/5 ms	Intermittent 〰 25
	7	⇨	Engine idling		5 V/5 ms	Intermittent 〰 25
	15	⇨	Engine idling		5 V/5 ms	Intermittent 〰 25
	16	⇨	Engine idling		5 V/5 ms	Intermittent 〰 25
Ignition amplifier/coil 1	35	⇨	Engine idling		2 V/50 ms	〰 32
Ignition amplifier/coil 2	36	⇨	Engine idling		2 V/50 ms	〰 32
Ignition amplifier/coil 3	37	⇨	Engine idling		2 V/50 ms	〰 32
Ignition amplifier/coil 4	38	⇨	Engine idling		2 V/50 ms	〰 32
Ignition switch	43	◄—	Ignition OFF	0 V		
	43	◄—	Ignition ON	11-14 V		

* Suggested settings - Voltage/time per division

Component/circuit description	ECM pin	Signal	Condition	Typical value	Oscilloscope setting*	Wave form
Ignition switch – start signal	41	←	Ignition ON	0 V		
	41	←	Engine cranking	9-12 V		
Immobilizer control module	116			[1]		
Injector 1	101	⊣▷	Engine idling – engine hot	2-3,5 ms	10 V/2 ms	∿ 35
Injector 2	103	⊣▷	Engine idling – engine hot	2-3,5 ms	10 V/2 ms	∿ 35
Injector 3	105	⊣▷	Engine idling – engine hot	2-3,5 ms	10 V/2 ms	∿ 35
Injector 4	107	⊣▷	Engine idling – engine hot	2-3,5 ms	10 V/2 ms	∿ 35
Instrument panel – some models	34			[1]		
Intake air temperature (IAT) sensor	64	←	Ignition ON – air temp. 25°C	3,5 V		
Intake air temperature (IAT) sensor – some models	58	⊣	Engine idling	0 V		
	73	⊣	Ignition ON	0 V		
Intake manifold air control solenoid – some models	104	⊣▷	Engine idling – coolant temp. 15-40°C	0-1 V		
	104	⊣▷	Engine idling – coolant temp. above 40°C	11-14 V		
Knock sensor (KS)	81	←	Engine idling – accelerate briefly		50 mV/1 ms	∿ 38
Malfunction indicator lamp (MIL)	22	⊣▷	Ignition ON – MIL ON	0-1 V		
	22	⊣▷	Engine running – MIL ON	0-1 V		
	22	⊣▷	Engine running – MIL OFF	11-14 V		
Mass air flow (MAF) sensor	61	←	Engine idling	1-1,7 V		
	61	←	2500 rpm	1,5-2,1 V		
	73	⊣	Ignition ON	0 V		
	111	⇨	Ignition ON	5 V		
Neutral position (NP) switch – MT	42	←	Ignition ON – gear lever in neutral	0 V		
	42	←	Ignition ON – gear lever not in neutral	5 V		
Park/neutral position (PNP) switch – AT	42	←	Ignition ON – AT in P or N	0 V		
	42	←	Ignition ON – AT not in P or N	11-14 V		
Power steering pressure (PSP) switch	46	←	Engine running – steering wheel not turned	5 V		
	46	←	Engine running – steering wheel fully turned	0 V		
Tachometer	32	⇨	Engine idling	28 Hz	2 V/20 ms	∿ 55
Throttle position (TP) sensor	58	⊣	Engine idling	0 V		
	92	←	Ignition ON – accelerator pedal released	0,2-0,9 V		
	92	←	Ignition ON – accelerator pedal fully depressed	3,5-4,7 V		
	111	⇨	Ignition ON	5 V		
Transmission control module (TCM)	10		Engine idling	0 V		
	19		Engine idling	8 V		
	54		Engine idling	0 V		
	55		Engine idling	0 V		
	56		Engine idling	0 V		
	58	⊣	Engine idling	0 V		
	71	⇨	Engine running – accelerator pedal released	0,4 V		
	71	⇨	Ignition ON – accelerator pedal fully depressed	4 V		
	91		Engine idling	0-5 V		
	111	⇨	Ignition ON	5 V		
Vehicle speed sensor (VSS)	86	←	Vehicle speed 25 mph		2 V/50 ms	∿ 43

*Suggested settings - Voltage/time per division

[1] Connected pin - no test data available or random digital signal

Model:	Engine code:	Year:
Almera Tino 2,0	SR20DE	2000-03
Primera 2,0	SR20DE	1999-02

NISSAN

Nissan ECCS

ECM harness multi-plug

Terminal side

```
110 109   67 66 65 64 63 62 61 60 59 58              10 9 8 7 6 5 4 3 2 1  102 101
112 111   76 75 74 73 72 71 70 69 68   48 47 46 45 44 43 42 41 40 39   19 18 17 16 15 14 13 12 11  104 103
114 113   86 85 84 83 82 81 80 79 78 77   57 56 55 54 53 52 51 50 49   29 28 27 26 25 24 23 22 21 20  106 105
116 115   95 94 93 92 91 90 89 88 87              38 37 36 35 34 33 32 31 30  108 107
```
AD23522

Wire side

```
101 102   1 2 3 4 5 6 7 8 9 10              58 59 60 61 62 63 64 65 66 67  109 110
103 104   11 12 13 14 15 16 17 18 19   39 40 41 42 43 44 45 46 47 48   68 69 70 71 72 73 74 75 76  111 112
105 106   20 21 22 23 24 25 26 27 28 29   49 50 51 52 53 54 55 56 57   77 78 79 80 81 82 83 84 85 86  113 114
107 108   30 31 32 33 34 35 36 37 38              87 88 89 90 91 92 93 94 95  115 116
```
AD23521

Component/circuit description	ECM pin	Signal	Condition	Typical value	Oscilloscope setting*	Wave form
AC compressor clutch relay	23	⊐⊳	Engine idling – AC OFF	11-14 V		
	23	⊐⊳	Engine idling – AC ON – AC compressor ON	0-1 V		
AC master switch	44	⬅	Engine idling – AC OFF	5 V		
	44	⬅	Engine idling – AC ON – AC compressor ON	0 V		
AC refrigerant pressure sensor	58	⊐⊢	Engine idling	0 V		
	74	⬅		[1]		
	111	⟹	Ignition ON	5 V		
AC/heater blower motor switch	51	⬅	Ignition ON – blower motor switch OFF	5 V		
	51	⬅	Ignition ON – blower motor switch ON	0 V		
Battery	67	⬅	Ignition OFF	11-14 V		
Camshaft position (CMP) sensor	66	⬅	Engine idling		2 V/10 ms	∿∿ 46
	75	⬅	Engine idling		2 V/10 ms	∿∿ 46
Closed throttle position (CTP) switch – some models	40	⬅	Ignition ON – throttle closed	11-14 V		
	40	⬅	Ignition ON – throttle open	0-1 V		
Crankshaft position (CKP) sensor	58	⊐⊢	Engine idling	0 V		
	65	⬅	Engine idling		1 V/0,5 ms	∿∿ 17
Data link connector (DLC)	114	⬅⟹		[1]		
	115	⬅⟹		[1]		
Data link connector (DLC) – Almera Tino	113	⬅⟹		[1]		
Data link connector (DLC) – Primera	93	⬅⟹		[1]		
Earth	48		Ignition ON	0 V		
	57		Ignition ON	0 V		
	106		Ignition ON	0 V		
	108		Ignition ON	0 V		

★ Suggested settings - Voltage/time per division

NISSAN

Component/circuit description	ECM pin	Signal	Condition	Typical value	Oscilloscope setting*	Wave form
Engine control relay	31	→▷	Ignition OFF – for 9 secs.	0-1 V		
	31	→▷	Ignition OFF – after 9 secs.	11-14 V		
	31	→▷	Ignition ON	0-1 V		
	110	←	Ignition OFF	0 V		
	110	←	Ignition ON	11-14 V		
	112	←	Ignition OFF	0 V		
	112	←	Ignition ON	11-14 V		
Engine coolant blower motor relay 1	13	→▷	Engine idling – coolant blower motor OFF	11-14 V		
	13	→▷	Engine idling – coolant blower motor ON	0-1 V		
Engine coolant blower motor relay 2 & 3 – Almera Tino	12	→▷	Engine idling – coolant blower motor OFF	11-14 V		
	12	→▷	Engine idling – coolant blower motor ON, low speed	11-14 V		
	12	→▷	Engine idling – coolant blower motor ON, high speed	0-1 V		
Engine coolant temperature (ECT) sensor	58	→—	Engine idling	0 V		
	70	←	Ignition ON – coolant temp. 20°C	3,5 V		
	70	←	Ignition ON – coolant temp. 90°C	0,9 V		
Engine speed (RPM) sensor	85	←	Engine idling		2 V/0,2 ms	〰 45
Evaporative emission (EVAP) canister purge valve	14	→▷	Ignition ON	11-14 V		
	14	→▷	Engine running – valve operating		10 V/20 ms	〰 20
Exhaust gas recirculation (EGR) temperature sensor – some models	58	→—	Engine idling	0 V		
	72	←	Ignition ON – EGR temp. 0°C	4,5 V		
	72	←	Engine running – EGR temp. 100°C	0,6 V		
Exhaust gas recirculation (EGR) valve actuator – some models	8	⇨		[1]		
	9	⇨		[1]		
	17	⇨		[1]		
	18	⇨		[1]		
Fuel pump relay	21	→▷	Ignition ON	0-1 V briefly then 11-14 V		
	21	→▷	Engine cranking	0-1 V		
Fuel temperature sensor – some models	82	←	Ignition ON – fuel temp. 20°C	3,5 V		
Headlamp switch	50	←	Engine idling – headlamps ON	11-14 V		
	50	←	Engine idling – headlamps OFF	0 V		
Heated oxygen sensor (HO2S) 1	62	←	Engine running – engine hot	0-1 V fluctuating	0,2 V/1 sec.	〰 21
Heated oxygen sensor (HO2S) 1 – heater control	4	→▷	Ignition ON	11-14 V		
	4	→▷	Engine running above 3200 rpm	11-14 V		
	4	→▷	Engine running below 3200 rpm	0-1 V		
Heated oxygen sensor (HO2S) 2	63	←	Engine idling	0,3-0,7 V	0,2 V/0,5 sec.	〰 76
Heated oxygen sensor (HO2S) 2 – heater control	3	→▷	Ignition ON	11-14 V		
	3	→▷	Engine running below 3600 rpm – engine hot	0-1 V		
Heated rear window switch	50	←	Engine idling – heated rear window ON	11-14 V		
	50	←	Engine idling – heated rear window OFF	0 V		
Idle air control (IAC) valve	6	⇨	Engine idling		5 V/5 ms	Intermittent 〰 25
	7	⇨	Engine idling		5 V/5 ms	Intermittent 〰 25
	15	⇨	Engine idling		5 V/5 ms	Intermittent 〰 25
	16	⇨	Engine idling		5 V/5 ms	Intermittent 〰 25
Ignition amplifier	35	⇨	Engine idling		2 V/10 ms	〰 32
Ignition coil	36	←	Engine idling		5 V/2 ms	〰 33

* Suggested settings - Voltage/time per division

Component/circuit description	ECM pin	Signal	Condition	Typical value	Oscilloscope setting*	Wave form
Ignition switch	43	←	Ignition OFF	0 V		
	43	←	Ignition ON	11-14 V		
Ignition switch – start signal	41	←	Ignition ON	0 V		
	41	←	Engine cranking	9-12 V		
Immobilizer control module	116			☐1		
Injector 1	101	⊐▷	Engine idling – engine hot	2,4-3,2 ms	10 V/2 ms	⎍⎍ 35
Injector 2	103	⊐▷	Engine idling – engine hot	2,4-3,2 ms	10 V/2 ms	⎍⎍ 35
Injector 3	105	⊐▷	Engine idling – engine hot	2,4-3,2 ms	10 V/2 ms	⎍⎍ 35
Injector 4	107	⊐▷	Engine idling – engine hot	2,4-3,2 ms	10 V/2 ms	⎍⎍ 35
Instrument panel – some models	34			☐1		
Intake air temperature (IAT) sensor	58	⊐—	Engine idling	0 V		
	64	←	Ignition ON – air temp. 20°C	3,5 V		
Knock sensor (KS)	81	←	Engine idling – accelerate briefly		50 mV/1 ms	⎍⎍ 38
Malfunction indicator lamp (MIL)	22	⊐▷	Ignition ON – MIL ON	0-1 V		
	22	⊐▷	Engine running – MIL ON	0-1 V		
	22	⊐▷	Engine running – MIL OFF	11-14 V		
Mass air flow (MAF) sensor	61	←	Engine idling	1,3-1,7 V		
	61	←	2500 rpm	1,8-2,4 V		
	73	⊐—	Ignition ON	0 V		
	111	⇨	Ignition ON	5 V		
Neutral position (NP) switch – Primera MT	42	←	Ignition ON – gear lever in neutral	0 V		
	42	←	Ignition ON – gear lever not in neutral	5 V		
Park/neutral position (PNP) switch	42	←	Ignition ON – AT in P or N	0 V		
	42	←	Ignition ON – AT not in P or N	11-14 V		
Power steering pressure (PSP) switch	46	←	Engine running – steering wheel not turned	5 V		
	46	←	Engine running – steering wheel fully turned	0 V		
Tachometer	32	⇨	Engine idling	28 Hz	2 V/20 ms	⎍⎍ 55
Throttle position (TP) sensor	58	⊐—	Engine idling	0 V		
	92	←	Ignition ON – accelerator pedal released	0,3-0,9 V		
	92	←	Ignition ON – accelerator pedal fully depressed	3,5-4,7 V		
	111	⇨	Ignition ON	5 V		
Transmission control module (TCM)	10		Engine idling	0 V		
	19		Engine idling	8 V		
	54		Engine idling	0-3,5 V		
	55		Engine idling	0-3,5 V		
	58	⊐—	Engine idling	0 V		
	71	⇨	Engine running – accelerator pedal released	0,2-0,8 V		
	71	⇨	Ignition ON – accelerator pedal fully depressed	3,5-4,7 V		
	91		Engine idling	0-5 V		
	111	⇨	Ignition ON	5 V		
	56		Engine idling – AT in R	0-3,5 V		
Vehicle speed sensor (VSS)	86	←	Vehicle speed 25 mph		2 V/50 ms	⎍⎍ 43

*Suggested settings - Voltage/time per division

☐1 Connected pin - no test data available or random digital signal

PEUGEOT
Bosch Mono-Motronic MA3.1

Model:	Engine code:	Year:
106 1,0i	CDY (TU9M)	1996-03
106 1,0i	CDZ (TU9M)	1996-03
106 1,1i	HDY (TU1M)	1997-02
106 1,1i	HDZ (TU1M)	1997-03
Partner 1,1i	HDZ (TU1M)	1996-02

ECM harness multi-plug

Terminal side

19 18 17 16 15 14 13 12 11 10 9 8 7 6 5 4 3 2 1
37 36 35 34 33 32 31 30 29 28 27 26 25 24 23 22 21 20
55 54 53 52 51 50 49 48 47 46 45 44 43 42 41 40 39 38

AD72618

Wire side

1 2 3 4 5 6 7 8 9 10 11 12 13 14 15 16 17 18 19
20 21 22 23 24 25 26 27 28 29 30 31 32 33 34 35 36 37
38 39 40 41 42 43 44 45 46 47 48 49 50 51 52 53 54 55

AD42077

Component/circuit description	ECM pin	Signal	Condition	Typical value	Oscilloscope setting*	Wave form
Battery	18	←	Ignition OFF	11-14 V		
Closed throttle position (CTP) switch	31	←	Ignition ON – throttle closed	0 V		
	31	←	Ignition ON – throttle slightly open	11-14 V		
Crankshaft position (CKP) sensor	11	⊣	Ignition ON	0 V		
	30	←	Engine idling	9 V ac	2 V/1 ms	◈ 2
Data link connector (DLC)	13			1		
	16			1		
Data link connector (DLC) – some models	6			1		
Earth	2		Ignition ON	0 V		
	14		Ignition ON	0 V		
	19		Ignition ON	0 V		
Engine coolant temperature (ECT) sensor	25	←	Ignition ON – coolant temp. 20°C	2,5 V		
	25	←	Ignition ON – coolant temp. 80°C	0,4 V		
	26	⊣	Ignition ON	0 V		
Evaporative emission (EVAP) canister purge valve	5	⊣▷	Ignition OFF	11-14 V		
	5	⊣▷	Engine idling	1-99%	10 V/50 ms	◈ 20
Heated oxygen sensor (HO2S)	10	⊣	Ignition ON	0 V		
	28	←	Engine idling – accelerate briefly	0,1-1,0 V fluctuating	0,2 V/1 sec.	◈ 21
Idle speed control (ISC) actuator	15 (33)	⇨	Engine idling		5 V/5 ms	Intermittent ◈ 25
	33 (15)	⇨	Engine idling		5 V/5 ms	Intermittent ◈ 25
Idle speed control (ISC) actuator position sensor – HDY/HDZ	24	←	Engine idling		2 V/20 ms	Intermittent ◈ 31
Ignition coil – cylinders 1 & 4	1	⊣▷	Engine idling		5 V/2 ms	◈ 33
Ignition coil – cylinders 2 & 3	20	⊣▷	Engine idling		5 V/2 ms	◈ 33
Immobilizer control module	22	←		1		
	34			1		
Injector	17	⊣▷	Engine idling	1,9 ms	10 V/2 ms	◈ 35
	17	⊣▷	3000 rpm	2,2 ms	10 V/2 ms	◈ 35

* Suggested settings - Voltage/time per division

Component/circuit description	ECM pin	Signal	Condition	Typical value	Oscilloscope setting*	Wave form
Intake air temperature (IAT) sensor	26	⅃—	Ignition ON	0 V		
	27	◄—	Ignition ON – air temp. 20°C	2,8 V		
Intake manifold heater relay – HDY/HDZ	36	⅃▷	Ignition ON	11-14 V		
	36	⅃▷	Engine running – engine cold	0-1 V		
	36	⅃▷	Engine running – engine hot	11-14 V		
Malfunction indicator lamp (MIL)	22	⅃▷	Ignition ON – MIL ON	0-1 V		
	22	⅃▷	Engine running – MIL OFF	11-14 V		
Relay module – HDY/HDZ	3	⅃▷	Ignition ON	0-1 V briefly then 11-14 V		
	3	⅃▷	Engine cranking	0-1 V		
	3	⅃▷	Engine running	0-1 V		
Relay module – through inertia fuel shut-off (IFS) switch – CDY/CDZ	3	⅃▷	Ignition ON	0-1 V briefly then 11-14 V		
	3	⅃▷	Engine cranking	0-1 V		
	3	⅃▷	Engine running	0-1 V		
Relay module	37	◄—	Ignition ON	11-14 V		
Tachometer – some models	6	⇨	Engine idling	30 Hz		
	6	⇨	3000 rpm	100 Hz		
Throttle position (TP) sensor	7	◄—	Ignition ON – throttle closed	1,8 V		
	7	◄—	Ignition ON – throttle fully open	4,9 V		
	12	⇨	Ignition ON	5 V		
	26	⅃—	Ignition ON	0 V		
	29	◄—	Ignition ON – throttle closed	0 V		
	29	◄—	Ignition ON – throttle fully open	4 V		
Vehicle speed sensor (VSS)	9	◄—	Vehicle moving	Voltage varies with vehicle speed		

*Suggested settings - Voltage/time per division

1 Connected pin - no test data available or random digital signal

Model:	Engine code:	Year:
106 1,3 Rallye	MFZ (TU2J2L/Z)	1994-97
306 1,8i/2,0i	XU7JP/L3/Z/XU10J2CL/Z	1993-03
405 1,8i/2,0i	XU7JP/Z/XU10J2C	1992-97
406 1,6i	BFZ (XU5JP)	1995-97
806 2,0	RFU (XU10J2C/Z)	1994-02
Boxer 2,0i	RFW (XU10J2U/X3)	1994-02

ECM harness multi-plug

Terminal side

AD71594

Wire side

AD42073

Component/circuit description	ECM pin	Signal	Condition	Typical value	Oscilloscope setting*	Wave form
Air conditioning	8		Engine running – AC ON	11-14 V		
	9		Engine running – AC compressor ON	11-14 V		
	24		Engine running – AC compressor ON	11-14 V		
Crankshaft position (CKP) sensor	11	←	Engine idling	3 V ac	2 V/1 ms	WW 2
	11	←	3000 rpm	8,5 V	2 V/1 ms	WW 2
	28	←	Engine idling	3 V ac	2 V/1 ms	WW 2
	28	←	3000 rpm	8,5 V ac	2 V/1 ms	WW 2
Crankshaft position (CKP) sensor – shield wire	17	⊣	Ignition ON	0 V		
Data link connector (DLC)	10		Ignition ON	11-14 V		
	15	⇨	Ignition OFF	0 V		
	15	⇨	Ignition ON	11-14 V		
Data link connector (DLC) – some models	5	⇨		1		
Earth	34		Ignition ON	0 V		
Engine coolant temperature (ECT) sensor	13	←	Ignition ON – coolant temp. 13°C	3 V		
	13	←	Ignition ON – coolant temp. 80°C	0,5 V		
	17	⊣	Ignition ON	0 V		
	34	⊣	Ignition ON	0 V		
Evaporative emission (EVAP) canister purge valve	22	⇨	Ignition ON	0 V		
	22	⇨	Engine idling	1-99%	10 V/50 ms	WW 20
Heated oxygen sensor (HO2S)	12	⊣	Ignition ON	0 V		
	29	←	Engine idling – accelerate briefly	0-1 V fluctuating		
Heated oxygen sensor (HO2S) – shield wire	16	⊣	Ignition ON	0 V		
Idle air control (IAC) valve	2 (20)	⇨	Engine idling		5 V/0,5 sec.	Intermittent WW 26
	3 (21)	⇨	Engine idling		5 V/0,5 sec.	Intermittent WW 26
	2	⇨	Ignition ON	1 V		
	3	⇨	Ignition ON	11-14 V		
	20 (2)	⇨	Engine idling		5 V/0,5 sec.	Intermittent WW 26
	21 (3)	⇨	Engine idling		5 V/0,5 sec.	Intermittent WW 26
	20	⇨	Ignition ON	11-14 V		
	21	⇨	Ignition ON	1 V		

* Suggested settings - Voltage/time per division

Component/circuit description	ECM pin	Signal	Condition	Typical value	Oscilloscope setting*	Wave form
Ignition coil	1	⊐⊳	Ignition ON	11-14 V briefly then 0 V		
	1	⊐⊳	Engine idling		5 V/2 ms	⋀⋀ 33
	19	⊐⊳	Ignition ON	11-14 V briefly then 0 V		
	19	⊐⊳	Engine idling		5 V/2 ms	⋀⋀ 33
Immobilizer control module – some models	10		Ignition ON	11-14 V		
	15		Ignition ON	0 V		
	15		Ignition OFF	11-14 V		
Inertia fuel shut-off (IFS) switch – some models	23	⊐⊳	Ignition ON	0-1 V briefly then 11-14 V		
	23	⊐⊳	Engine cranking	0-1 V		
	23	⊐⊳	Engine idling	0-1 V		
Injectors	18	⊐⊳	Ignition ON	11-14 V briefly then 0 V		
	18	⊐⊳	Engine idling	2,4 ms	10 V/2 ms	⋀⋀ 35
Intake air temperature (IAT) sensor	16	⊐⊢	Ignition ON	0 V		
	31	⟵	Ignition ON – air temp. 13°C	3 V		
Knock sensor (KS) – some models	16	⊐⊢	Ignition ON	0 V		
	17	⊐⊢	Ignition ON	0 V		
	33	⟵	Engine idling – accelerate briefly		50 mV/1 ms	⋀⋀ 38
	34	⊐⊢	Ignition ON	0 V		
Malfunction indicator lamp (MIL)	6	⊐⊳	Ignition ON – MIL ON	0-1 V		
	6	⊐⊳	Engine running – MIL OFF	11-14 V		
Manifold absolute pressure (MAP) sensor	14	⟹	Ignition ON	5 V		
	16	⊐⊢	Ignition ON	0 V		
	32	⟵	Ignition ON	4,6 V		
	32	⟵	Engine idling	1,5 V		
	32	⟵	Engine idling – accelerate briefly	4,5 V briefly		
Relay module	4	⊐⊳	Ignition ON	0-1 V		
	4	⊐⊳	Engine cranking	0-1 V		
	4	⊐⊳	Engine idling	0-1 V		
	35	⟵	Ignition ON	11-14 V		
	35	⟵	Engine cranking	11-14 V		
	35	⟵	Engine idling	11-14 V		
Relay module – some models	23	⊐⊳	Ignition ON	0-1 V briefly then 11-14 V		
	23	⊐⊳	Engine cranking	0-1 V		
	23	⊐⊳	Engine idling	0-1 V		
Starter motor inhibitor switch relay – AT	26	⟵		1		
Tachometer – some models	5	⟹	Engine idling	30 Hz		
	5	⟹	3000 rpm	100 Hz		
Throttle position (TP) sensor	14	⟹	Ignition ON	5 V		
	16	⊐⊢	Ignition ON	0 V		
	30	⟵	Ignition ON – throttle closed	0,3 V		
	30	⟵	Ignition ON – throttle fully open	4,5 V		
Trip computer – some models	7			1		
Vehicle speed sensor (VSS)	27	⟵	Vehicle moving	1,5 V or 11-14 V fluctuating		

*Suggested settings - Voltage/time per division

1 Connected pin - no test data available or random digital signal

Model:	Engine code:	Year:
106 1,4i	KFX (TU3JP)	1997-03
106 1,6 GTI	NFX (TU5J4/L3)	1997-03
206 1,1i	HFZ/HFY (TU1JP)	1998-06
206 1,4i	KFX (TU3JP)	1998-06
306 1,4i	KFX (TU3JP/L3)	1997-02
Partner 1,4i	KFX (TU3JP)	1996-02

ECM harness multi-plug

Terminal side

AD72618

Wire side

AD42077

Component/circuit description	ECM pin	Signal	Condition	Typical value	Oscilloscope setting*	Wave form
Air conditioning	26			1		
	50			1		
Alternator – 206	46			1		
Crankshaft position (CKP) sensor	30	←	Engine cranking	2 V ac	2 V/1 ms	2
	30	←	Engine idling	5 V ac	2 V/1 ms	2
	30	←	3000 rpm	12 V ac	5 V/1 ms	2
	49	←	Engine cranking	2 V ac	2 V/1 ms	Reversed 2
	49	←	Engine idling	5 V ac	2 V/1 ms	Reversed 2
	49	←	3000 rpm	12 V ac	5 V/1 ms	Reversed 2
Data link connector (DLC)	12	←		1		
	31			1		
Data link connector (DLC) – some models	42	⇒		1		
Earth	36		Ignition ON	0 V		
	54		Ignition ON	0 V		
Earth – some models	19		Ignition ON	0 V		
Engine coolant temperature (ECT) sensor	47	←	Ignition ON – coolant temp. 20°C	1,7 V		
	47	←	Ignition ON – coolant temp. 80°C	0,4 V		
	53	⌐	Ignition ON	0 V		
Evaporative emission (EVAP) canister purge valve	24	⇒	Engine running	1-99%	10 V/50 ms	20
Heated oxygen sensor (HO2S)	4	⌐	Ignition ON	0 V		
	22	←	Engine idling – accelerate briefly	0-1 V fluctuating	0,2 V/1 sec.	21
Heated oxygen sensor (HO2S) – shield wire – some models	19	⌐	Ignition ON	0 V		
Idle air control (IAC) valve	3 (20)	⇒	Engine idling		5 V/0,5 sec.	Intermittent 26
	21 (40)	⇒	Engine idling		5 V/0,5 sec.	Intermittent 26
	20 (3)	⇒	Engine idling		5 V/0,5 sec.	Intermittent 26
	40 (21)	⇒	Engine idling		5 V/0,5 sec.	Intermittent 26
Ignition coil – cylinders 1 & 4	55	⌐▷	Engine idling		5 V/2 ms	33
Ignition coil – cylinders 2 & 3	37	⌐▷	Engine idling		5 V/2 ms	33

* Suggested settings - Voltage/time per division

Component/circuit description	ECM pin	Signal	Condition	Typical value	Oscilloscope setting*	Wave form
Immobilizer control module – some models	13	←	Ignition ON	11-14 V		
	27			1		
	48			1		
Injectors 1 & 4	2	⊐▷	Engine idling	4,2 ms	10 V/2 ms	〰35
Injectors 2 & 3	1	⊐▷	Engine idling	4,2 ms	10 V/2 ms	〰35
Intake air temperature (IAT) sensor	17	⊐—	Ignition ON	0 V		
	29	←	Ignition ON – air temp. 20°C	2,5 V		
Knock sensor (KS)	15	←	Engine idling – accelerate briefly		50 mV/1 ms	〰38
Knock sensor (KS) – some models	18	⊐—	Ignition ON	0 V		
Knock sensor (KS) – shield wire – some models	19	⊐—	Ignition ON	0 V		
Malfunction indicator lamp (MIL)	9	⊐▷	Ignition ON	0-1 V		
Manifold absolute pressure (MAP) sensor	17	⊐—	Ignition ON	0 V		
	34	⇒	Ignition ON	5 V		
	41	←	Ignition ON	4,5 V		
	41	←	Engine idling	1,3 V		
Multifunction control module – 206	13	←	Ignition ON	11-14 V		
	27			1		
	48			1		
Power steering pressure (PSP) switch – some models	14	←	Engine running – steering wheel not turned	0 V		
	14	←	Engine running – steering wheel turned	11-14 V		
	17	⊐—	Ignition ON	0 V		
Relay module – through inertia fuel shut-off (IFS) switch – Partner	7	⊐▷	Ignition ON	0-1 V briefly then 11-14 V		
Relay module – except Partner	7	⊐▷	Ignition ON	0-1 V briefly then 11-14 V		
Relay module	13	←	Ignition ON	11-14 V		
	35	←	Ignition ON	11-14 V		
	35	←	Engine running	11-14 V		
	52	⊐▷	Ignition ON	0-1 V		
	52	⊐▷	Engine running	0-1 V		
Tachometer – some models	42	⇒	Engine idling	28 Hz		
	42	⇒	3000 rpm	100 Hz		
Throttle position (TP) sensor	16	⇒	Ignition ON	5 V		
	23	←	Ignition ON – throttle closed	0,7 V		
	23	←	Ignition ON – throttle fully open	4,7 V		
	53	⊐—	Ignition ON	0 V		
Vehicle speed sensor (VSS)	28	←	Ignition ON – vehicle moving	0-12 V fluctuating		

*Suggested settings - Voltage/time per division

1 Connected pin - no test data available or random digital signal

PEUGEOT

Bosch MP 7.2/7.3

Model:	Engine code:	Year:
106 1,4	KFX (TU3JP/IFL4)	1998-03
206 1,4	KFX (TU3JP)	1998-06
206 1,6	NFZ (TU5JP/L3/D3)	1998-02
306 1,6	NFZ (TU5JP/L3/D3)	1998-03
806 2,0 16V	RFV (XU10J4R)	1998-02

ECM harness multi-plug

Terminal side

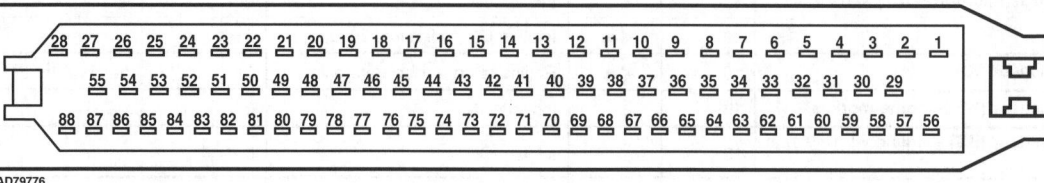

AD79776

Wire side

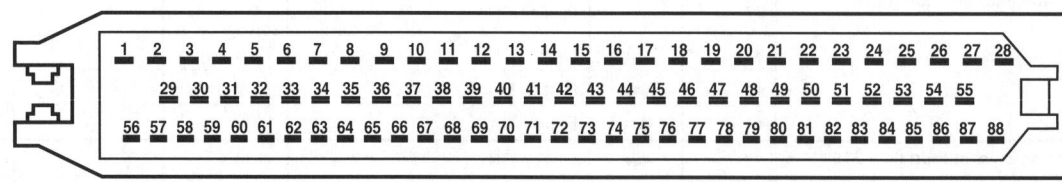

AD42101

Component/circuit description	ECM pin	Signal	Condition	Typical value	Oscilloscope setting*	Wave form
AC compressor clutch cut-off relay – 306/806	24		Ignition ON	0-1 V		
AC compressor clutch cut-off relay – 806	36			☐1		
AC control module – 106/206	24			☐1		
	36			☐1		
Acceleration sensor – 106/206 1,4/806	72	⬅		☐1		
	37	⅃⎺	Ignition ON	0 V		
	42	⇨	Ignition ON	5 V		
Battery	49	⬅	Ignition OFF	11-14 V		
Camshaft position (CMP) sensor – 106/206 1,4/806	45	⬅	Engine idling		2 V/20 ms	〰〰 12
Camshaft position (CMP) sensor – 106/206 1,4	37	⅃⎺	Ignition ON	0 V		
Camshaft position (CMP) sensor – 806	75	⅃⎺	Ignition ON	0 V		
Crankshaft position (CKP) sensor	18	⬅	Engine idling	2,6 V ac	2 V/1 ms	〰〰 2
	46	⬅	Engine idling	2,6 V ac	2 V/1 ms	Reversed 〰〰 2
Data link connector (DLC)	19	⬅⇨	Ignition ON	0 V		
	20	⬅⇨	Ignition ON	0 V		
Data link connector (DLC) – engine speed signal	44	⇨	Engine running		5 V/50 ms	〰〰 4
Earth	1		Ignition ON	0 V		
	6		Ignition ON	0 V		
	23		Ignition ON	0 V		
	28		Ignition ON	0 V		
Engine coolant blower motor control module – 306	24		Ignition ON	0-1 V		
Engine coolant blower motor control module – 106/306	36	⬅	Engine idling – AC OFF	0 V		
	36	⬅	Engine idling – AC ON	11-14 V		
Engine coolant temperature (ECT) sensor	37	⅃⎺	Ignition ON	0 V		
	39	⬅	Ignition ON – coolant temp. 20°C	3,3 V		
	39	⬅	Ignition ON – coolant temp. 80°C	0,9 V		
Evaporative emission (EVAP) canister purge valve	51	⅃⇨	Engine idling	10-15%		

* Suggested settings - Voltage/time per division

Component/circuit description	ECM pin	Signal	Condition	Typical value	Oscilloscope setting*	Wave form
Heated oxygen sensor (HO2S) front	13	←	Engine idling – accelerate briefly	0,1-0,9 V fluctuating	0,2 V/1 sec.	21
	40	⊣—	Ignition ON	0 V		
	55	⊣▷	Engine idling	90%		
Heated oxygen sensor (HO2S) rear – 106	71	←	Engine idling – accelerate briefly	0,6 V	0,2 V/0,5 sec.	76
	70	⊣—	Ignition ON	0 V		
	86	⊣▷	Engine idling	90%		
Idle air control (IAC) valve	3 (32)	⇒	Engine idling		5 V/0,5 sec.	Intermittent 26
	4 (31)	⇒	Engine idling		5 V/0,5 sec.	Intermittent 26
	31 (4)	⇒	Engine idling		5 V/0,5 sec.	Intermittent 26
	32 (3)	⇒	Engine idling		5 V/0,5 sec.	Intermittent 26
Ignition coil – cylinder 1 & 4	30	⊣▷	Engine idling		5 V/2 ms	33
Ignition coil – cylinder 2 & 3	29	⊣▷	Engine idling		5 V/2 ms	33
Ignition switch	21	←	Ignition OFF	0 V		
	21	←	Ignition ON	11-14 V		
Immobilizer control module – 106/306/806	22		Engine idling	11-14 V		
	48		Ignition ON	11-14 V		
Injectors 1 & 4 – 206 1,6/306	26	⊣▷	Ignition ON	11-14 V		
	26	⊣▷	Engine idling – engine hot	3,1 ms	10 V/2 ms	35
	27	⊣▷	Ignition ON	11-14 V		
	27	⊣▷	Engine idling – engine hot	3,1 ms	10 V/2 ms	35
Injectors 2 & 3 – 206 1,6/306	53	⊣▷	Ignition ON	11-14 V		
	53	⊣▷	Engine idling – engine hot	3,1 ms	10 V/2 ms	35
	54	⊣▷	Ignition ON	11-14 V		
	54	⊣▷	Engine idling – engine hot	3,1 ms	10 V/2 ms	35
Injector 1 – 106/206 1,4/806	27	⊣▷	Ignition ON	11-14 V		
	27	⊣▷	Engine idling – engine hot	3,1 ms	10 V/2 ms	35
Injector 2 – 106/206 1,4/806	53	⊣▷	Ignition ON	11-14 V		
	53	⊣▷	Engine idling – engine hot	3,1 ms	10 V/2 ms	35
Injector 3 – 106/206 1,4/806	54	⊣▷	Ignition ON	11-14 V		
	54	⊣▷	Engine idling – engine hot	3,1 ms	10 V/2 ms	35
Injector 4 – 106/206 1,4/806	26	⊣▷	Ignition ON	11-14 V		
	26	⊣▷	Engine idling – engine hot	3,1 ms	10 V/2 ms	35
Instrumentation control module – engine speed signal – 206 1,6/306	44	⇒	Engine running	5 V/50 ms		4
Instrumentation control module – 806	47			1		
Intake air temperature (IAT) sensor	12	←	Ignition ON – air temp. 22°C	3,3 V		
Intake air temperature (IAT) sensor – except 806	37	⊣—	Ignition ON	0 V		
Intake air temperature (IAT) sensor – 806	68	⊣—	Ignition ON	0 V		
Knock sensor (KS)	10	←	Engine idling – accelerate briefly		50 mV/1 ms	38
	38	←	Engine idling – accelerate briefly		50 mV/1 ms	38
Malfunction indicator lamp (MIL)	43	⊣▷	Ignition ON – MIL ON	0-1 V		
	43	⊣▷	Engine idling – MIL OFF	11-14 V		
Manifold absolute pressure (MAP) sensor	14	←	Ignition ON	4,5 V		
	14	←	Engine idling	1,2 V		
	14	←	Engine idling – accelerate briefly	4,7 V briefly		
	37	⊣—	Ignition ON	0 V		
	42	⇒	Ignition ON	5 V		
Multifunction control module – 206	22			1		
	48			1		

* Suggested settings - Voltage/time per division

Component/circuit description	ECM pin	Signal	Condition	Typical value	Oscilloscope setting*	Wave form
Power steering pressure (PSP) switch – except 106	9	←	Engine running – steering wheel not turned	0 V		
	9	←	Engine running – steering wheel turned	11-14 V		
Power steering pressure (PSP) switch – except 106 – some models	37	⌐	Ignition ON	0 V		
Relay module	33	←	Ignition ON	11-14 V		
	50	⌐▷	Ignition OFF	11-14 V		
	50	⌐▷	Ignition ON	0-1 V		
Relay module – 206/306	15	⌐▷	Ignition ON	11-14 V		
	15	⌐▷	Engine cranking	0-1 V		
	15	⌐▷	Engine running	0-1 V		
Relay module – through inertia fuel shut-off (IFS) switch – 106/806	15	⌐▷	Ignition ON	11-14 V		
	15	⌐▷	Engine cranking	0-1 V		
	15	⌐▷	Engine running	0-1 V		
Secondary air injection (AIR) pump relay – 106/206 1,4/806	84	⌐▷	Ignition ON	11-14 V		
	84	⌐▷	Engine running – pump operating	0 V		
Throttle position (TP) sensor	41	←	Ignition ON – throttle closed	0,6 V		
	41	←	Ignition ON – throttle fully open	4,7 V		
Throttle position (TP) sensor – 806	68	⌐	Ignition ON	0 V		
Throttle position (TP) sensor – except 806	37	⌐	Ignition ON	0 V		
Throttle position (TP) sensor – 106/206 1,4/806	74	⇒	Ignition ON	5 V		
Throttle position (TP) sensor – 206 1,6/306	42	⇒	Ignition ON	5 V		
Transmission control module (TCM)	7		Ignition ON	10,8 V		
	7		Engine idling	11-14 V		
	16		Ignition ON	9,5 V		
	16		Engine idling	50 Hz		
	19	⇔	Ignition ON	0 V		
	20	⇔	Ignition ON	0 V		
	25		Ignition ON	5-8 V fluctuating		
	25		Engine idling	100 Hz		
	35		Ignition ON	10,6 V		
	35		Engine idling	11-14 V		
Transmission control module (TCM) – 306	24		Ignition ON	0-1 V		
Transmission control module (TCM) – engine speed signal	44	⇒	Engine running		5 V/50 ms	∿⟋ 4
Vehicle speed sensor (VSS)	17	←	Ignition ON – vehicle pushed	0 V or 11-14 V fluctuating		
	17	←	Engine running – vehicle moving		5 V/1 sec.	∿⟋ 43

*Suggested settings - Voltage/time per division

1 Connected pin - no test data available or random digital signal

Model:	Engine code:	Year:
106 1,6i	NFZ (TU5JP)	1997-02
306 1,6i	NFZ (TU5JP/L3)	1997-02
306 2,0 16V	RFV (XU10J4R/L3)	1997-03

ECM harness multi-plug

Terminal side

19 18 17 16 15 14 13 12 11 10 9 8 7 6 5 4 3 2 1
37 36 35 34 33 32 31 30 29 28 27 26 25 24 23 22 21 20
55 54 53 52 51 50 49 48 47 46 45 44 43 42 41 40 39 38

AD72618

Wire side

1 2 3 4 5 6 7 8 9 10 11 12 13 14 15 16 17 18 19
20 21 22 23 24 25 26 27 28 29 30 31 32 33 34 35 36 37
38 39 40 41 42 43 44 45 46 47 48 49 50 51 52 53 54 55

AD42077

Component/circuit description	ECM pin	Signal	Condition	Typical value	Oscilloscope setting*	Wave form
AC compressor cut-off relay – RFY	23	⊐→	Engine running – AC compressor ON	11-14 V		
AC refrigerant triple pressure switch	32	←	Engine running – AC ON	11-14 V		
Battery	18	←	Ignition OFF	11-14 V		
Crankshaft position (CKP) sensor	11	←	Engine idling	2,2 V ac	2 V/1 ms	2
	11	←	3000 rpm	3,5 V ac	2 V/1 ms	2
	30	←	Engine idling	2,2 V ac	2 V/1 ms	Reversed 2
	30	←	3000 rpm	3,5 V ac	2 V/1 ms	Reversed 2
Data link connector (DLC)	6			[1]		
	13	⇨	Engine idling	11-14 V		
	16		Ignition ON	11-14 V		
Earth	2		Ignition ON	0 V		
	14		Ignition ON	0 V		
	19		Ignition ON	0 V		
Engine coolant blower control module – RFY	23	⊐→	Engine running – AC compressor ON	11-14 V		
	32	←	Engine running – AC ON	11-14 V		
Engine coolant temperature (ECT) sensor	25	←	Ignition ON – coolant temp. 20°C	3,5 V		
	25	←	Ignition ON – coolant temp. 80°C	1 V		
	26	⊐—	Ignition ON	0 V		
Evaporative emission (EVAP) canister purge valve	5	⊐→	Ignition OFF	11-14 V		
	5	⊐→	Engine running	1-99%	10 V/50 ms	20
Heated oxygen sensor (HO2S)	10	⊐—	Ignition ON	0 V		
	28	←	Engine idling – accelerate briefly	0-1 V fluctuating	0,2 V/1 sec.	21
Idle air control (IAC) valve – NFZ	15	⊐→	Ignition ON	9 V		
	15	⊐→	Engine idling	40%	5 V/5 ms	25
	33	⊐→	Ignition ON	4 V		
	33	⊐→	Engine idling	57%	5 V/5 ms	25
Idle air control (IAC) valve – RFY	15 (33)	⊐→	Engine idling		5 V/0,5 sec.	26
	24 (21)	⊐→	Engine idling		5 V/0,5 sec.	26
	33 (15)	⊐→	Engine idling		5 V/0,5 sec.	26
	21 (24)	⊐→	Engine idling		5 V/0,5 sec.	26
Ignition coil – cylinders 1 & 4	1	⊐→	Engine idling		5 V/2 ms	33
Ignition coil – cylinders 2 & 3	20	⊐→	Engine idling		5 V/2 ms	33

* Suggested settings - Voltage/time per division

Component/circuit description	ECM pin	Signal	Condition	Typical value	Oscilloscope setting*	Wave form
Ignition switch – through relay module – RFY	34	←	Ignition ON	11-14 V		
Immobilizer control module	22			[1]		
	35		Ignition ON	11-14 V		
Injectors	17	⇥▷	Ignition ON	11-14 V		
	17	⇥▷	Engine idling	2,4 ms	10 V/2 ms	⌁ 35
Intake air temperature (IAT) sensor	26	⊣⊢	Ignition ON	0 V		
	27	←	Ignition ON – air temp. 20°C	3,5 V		
Knock sensor (KS) – RFY	8 (26)	←	Engine idling – accelerate briefly		50 mV/1 ms	⌁ 58
Malfunction indicator lamp (MIL)	22	⇥▷	Ignition ON – MIL ON	0-1 V		
	22	⇥▷	Engine idling – MIL OFF	11-14 V		
Manifold absolute pressure (MAP) sensor	7	←	Ignition ON	4,5 V		
	7	←	Engine idling	1,2 V		
	7	←	Accelerate briefly	4,4 V briefly		
	12	⇨	Ignition ON	5 V		
	26	⊣⊢	Ignition ON	0 V		
Relay module	3	⇥▷	Ignition ON	0-1 V briefly then 11-14 V		
	3	⇥▷	Engine cranking	0-1 V		
	37	←	Ignition ON	11-14 V		
Relay module – RFY	36	⇥▷	Ignition OFF	11-14 V		
	36	⇥▷	Ignition ON	0-1 V		
Tachometer	6	⇨	Engine idling	30 Hz		
	6	⇨	3000 rpm	100 Hz		
Throttle position (TP) sensor	12	⇨	Ignition ON	5 V		
	26	⊣⊢	Ignition ON	0 V		
	29	←	Ignition ON – throttle closed	0,6 V		
	29	←	Ignition ON – throttle fully open	4,6 V		
Transmission control module (TCM)	31	←	Ignition ON – AT in P or N	11-14 V		
	31	←	Ignition ON – AT not in P or N	0 V		
Vehicle speed sensor (VSS)	9	←	Ignition ON – vehicle moving	0 V or 11-14 V – fluctuating		

*Suggested settings - Voltage/time per division

[1] Connected pin - no test data available or random digital signal

Model:	Engine code:	Year:
206 2,0	RFR (EW10J4)	1998-06
406 2,0	RFR (EW10J4)	1999-04

PEUGEOT

Magneti Marelli 4.8P

ECM harness multi-plug

Terminal side – A – Grey, B – Brown, C – Black

AD22744

Wire side – A – Grey, B – Brown, C – Black

AD22743

Component/circuit description	ECM pin	Signal	Condition	Typical value	Oscilloscope setting*	Wave form
AC control module – 206	Bc3	⇒	Engine running – AC OFF	0 V		
	Bc3	⇒	Engine running – AC ON	10,85 V		
	Bd3	←	Engine running – AC OFF	0,4 V		
	Bd3	←	Engine running – AC ON	9,45 V		
AC refrigerant triple pressure switch	Be2	←		1		
Camshaft position (CMP) sensor	Aa2	⌐	Ignition ON	0 V		
	Ae1	⇒	Ignition ON	5 V		
	Cf3	←	Ignition ON – engine turned	0,6-11 V fluctuating		
	Cf3	←	Engine idling		5 V/20 ms	51
Crankshaft position (CKP) sensor	Ab1	←	Engine idling	1,9 V ac	2 V/2 ms	2
	Ab2	←	Engine idling	1,9 V ac	2 V/2 ms	Reversed 2
Crankshaft position (CKP) sensor – shield wire	Aa2	⌐	Ignition ON	0 V		
Cruise control module – 406	Bb2		Ignition OFF	0 V		
	Bb2		Engine running	0 V		
Data link connector (DLC)	Bb3	←⇒	Ignition ON	0 V		
	Bh2	←⇒	Ignition ON	0 V		
	Bj2	←⇒	Ignition OFF	10 V		
	Bj2	←⇒	Ignition ON	10 V		
Earth	Ah1	⌐	Ignition ON	0 V		
	Bl4	⌐	Ignition ON	0 V		
	Bm4	⌐	Ignition ON	0 V		
	Ch4	⌐	Ignition ON	0 V		

* Suggested settings - Voltage/time per division

Component/circuit description	ECM pin	Signal	Condition	Typical value	Oscilloscope setting*	Wave form
Engine coolant blower motor	Bf2	⇒	Coolant blower motor OFF	0 V		
	Bf2	⇒	Ccoolant blower motor ON	11-14 V		
Engine coolant blower motor relay – high speed	Bj4	←	Engine running – coolant blower motor OFF	11-14 V		
	Bj4	←	Engine running – coolant blower motor ON	0 V		
Engine coolant blower motor relay – low speed	Bk4	⊐▷	Ignition OFF	0 V		
	Bk4	⊐▷	Ignition ON – coolant blower motor OFF	11-14 V		
	Bk4	⊐▷	Engine running – coolant blower motor ON	0 V		
Engine coolant temperature (ECT) sensor	Cd4	⊐—	Ignition ON	0 V		
	Ce4	←	Ignition ON – coolant temp. 10°C	4,12 V		
	Ce4	←	Ignition ON – coolant temp. 80°C	1 V		
Evaporative emission (EVAP) canister purge valve	Af2	⊐▷	Ignition ON	11-14 V briefly then 0 V		
Exhaust gas recirculation (EGR) solenoid	Cg4	⊐▷	Ignition ON	11-14 V briefly then 0 V		
	Cg4	⊐▷	Engine idling	11-14 V		
Exhaust gas recirculation (EGR) valve position sensor	Aa2	⊐—	Ignition ON	0 V		
	Ae1	⇒	Ignition ON	5 V		
	Cf4	←	Ignition ON	0,7 V		
	Cf4	←	Engine idling	0,7 V		
Heated oxygen sensor (HO2S) – front	Aa3	←	Ignition ON	0,1 V		
	Aa3	←	Engine running	0,1-0,9 V fluctuating	0,2 V/1 sec.	WᴡW 21
	Ab3	⊐—	Ignition ON	0 V		
	Ce2	⊐▷	Ignition ON	11-14 V briefly then 0 V		
	Ce2	⊐▷	Engine idling	0 V		
Heated oxygen sensor (HO2S) – front – shield wire	Aa2	⊐—	Ignition ON	0 V		
Heated oxygen sensor (HO2S) – rear – some models	Cd2	⊐▷	Engine idling	1		
	Cd3		Engine idling	1		
	Ce3		Engine idling	1		
Idle air control (IAC) valve	Ad1	⇒	Ignition ON	0,18 V		
	Ad1 (Ae3)	⇒	Engine idling		4 V/0,1 sec.	Intermittent WᴡW 26
	Ad2	⇒	Ignition ON	11-14 V		
	Ad2 (Ad3)	⇒	Engine idling		4 V/0,1 sec.	Intermittent WᴡW 26
	Ad3	⇒	Ignition ON	0,18 V		
	Ad3 (Ad2)	⇒	Engine idling		4 V/0,1 sec.	Intermittent WᴡW 26
	Ae3	⇒	Ignition ON	11-14 V		
	Ae3 (Ad1)	⇒	Engine idling		4 V/0,1 sec.	Intermittent WᴡW 26
Ignition coil – cylinders 1 & 4	Cg3	⊐▷	Ignition ON	11-14 V		
	Cg3	⊐▷	Engine running		5 V/1 ms	WᴡW 33
Ignition coil – cylinders 2 & 3	Ch3	⊐▷	Ignition ON	11-14 V		
	Ch3	⊐▷	Engine running		5 V/1 ms	WᴡW 33

* Suggested settings - Voltage/time per division

Component/circuit description	ECM pin	Signal	Condition	Typical value	Oscilloscope setting*	Wave form
Ignition switch	Bb4	←	Ignition ON	11-14 V		
Inertia fuel shut-off (IFS) switch – 406	Af3	⊣▷	Ignition ON	0,1 V briefly then 11-14 V		
	Af3	⊣▷	Engine cranking	0,1 V		
	Af3	⊣▷	Engine running	0,1 V		
Injector 1	Ah2	⊣▷	Ignition ON	11-14 V briefly then 0 V		
	Ah2	⊣▷	Engine idling	3,8 ms	10 V/2 ms	⟋⟍ 35
Injector 2	Ag3	⊣▷	Ignition ON	11-14 V briefly then 0 V		
	Ag3	⊣▷	Engine idling	3,8 ms	10 V/2 ms	⟋⟍ 35
Injector 3	Ag2	⊣▷	Ignition ON	11-14 V briefly then 0 V		
	Ag2	⊣▷	Engine idling	3,8 ms	10 V/2 ms	⟋⟍ 35
Injector 4	Ah3	⊣▷	Ignition ON	11-14 V briefly then 0 V		
	Ah3	⊣▷	Engine idling	3,8 ms	10 V/2 ms	⟋⟍ 35
Instrument panel – 206	Bj3		Ignition OFF	0 V		
	Bj3		Ignition ON	4,8-6,9 V		
	Bj3		Engine idling	100 Hz		
	Bk3		Ignition OFF	0 V		
	Bk3		Ignition ON	10,9 V		
	Bk3		Engine idling	11-14 V		
Intake air temperature (IAT) sensor	Ca2	←	Ignition ON – air temp. 10°C	3,13 V		
	Ca3	⊢	Ignition ON	0 V		
Knock sensor (KS)	Cb3	←	Ignition ON	2,46 V		
	Cb3	←	Engine idling – accelerate briefly		50 mV/0,5 ms	⟋⟍ 38
	Cc3	←	Ignition ON	2,46 V		
	Cc3	←	Engine idling – accelerate briefly		50 mV/0,5 ms	⟋⟍ 38
Malfunction indicator lamp (MIL) – 206	Bc4	⊣▷	Ignition ON – MIL ON	0 V		
	Bc4	⊣▷	Engine running – MIL OFF	11-14 V		
Manifold absolute pressure (MAP) sensor	Ac1	←	Ignition ON	4,4 V		
	Ac1	←	Engine idling	1,3 V		
	Ac1	←	Engine idling – accelerate briefly	4,4 V briefly		
	Ac3	⇒	Ignition ON	5 V		
	Ca3	⊢	Ignition ON	0 V		
Multifunction control module	Bf3	↔	Ignition OFF	7,7 V		
	Bf3	↔	Ignition ON	11-14 V		
	Bf4	↔	Ignition OFF	0 V		
	Bf4	↔	Ignition ON	0 V		

* Suggested settings - Voltage/time per division

Component/circuit description	ECM pin	Signal	Condition	Typical value	Oscilloscope setting*	Wave form
Multifunction control module – 406	Bc2	⇔	Ignition ON	11-14 V		
	Bc2	⇔	Engine running	11-14 V		
	Bc3	⇔	Ignition ON	0 V		
	Bc3	⇔	Engine running	11-14 V		
	Bc4	⇔	Ignition ON	0 V		
	Bc4	⇔	Engine running	11-14 V		
	Bd3	⇔	Ignition ON	0,5 V		
	Bd3	⇔	Engine running	11-14 V		
	Bj3	⇔	Ignition OFF	11-14 V		
	Bj3	⇔	Engine idling	100 Hz		
	Bk3	⇔	Ignition ON	11-14 V		
	Bm3	⇔	Ignition OFF	0,8 V		
	Bm3	⇔	Ignition ON	11-14 V briefly then 0,2 V		
Power steering pressure (PSP) switch	Be3	⟵	Engine running – steering wheel not turned	0 V		
	Be3	⟵	Engine running – steering wheel turned	11-14 V		
Pulsed secondary air injection (PAIR) relay – 406 AT	Bm2	⊐▷	Engine running – PAIR OFF	11-14 V		
	Bm2	⊐▷	Engine running – PAIR ON	0 V		
Relay module	Ca4	⟵	Ignition OFF	0 V		
	Ca4	⟵	Ignition ON	11-14 V		
	Cf2	⊐▷	Ignition OFF	11-14 V		
	Cf2	⊐▷	Ignition ON	0,1 V		
Relay module – 206	Af3	⊐▷	Ignition ON	0,1 V briefly then 11-14 V		
	Af3	⊐▷	Engine cranking	0,1 V		
	Af3	⊐▷	Engine running	0,1 V		
Throttle position (TP) sensor	Aa2	⊐—	Ignition ON	0 V		
	Ae1	⇨	Ignition ON	5 V		
	Cb4	⟵	Ignition ON – throttle closed	0,68 V		
	Cb4	⟵	Ignition ON – throttle fully open	4,07 V		
Transmission control module (TCM) – 406 AT	Bb3			[1]		
	Bh2			[1]		
	Bh3			[1]		
	Bh4			[1]		
Vehicle speed sensor (VSS)	Bg2	⟵	Ignition ON – vehicle pushed	0,5-13 V fluctuating		

*Suggested settings - Voltage/time per division

[1] Connected pin - no test data available or random digital signal

Model:	Engine code:	Year:
306 1,4	KFX (TU3JP/L3)	1998-02
306 1,8 16V	LFY (XU7JP4/Z/L/L3)	1997-03
406 1,8 16V	LFY (XU7JP4/L3)	1997-02

PEUGEOT

Sagem SL96

ECM harness multi-plug

Terminal side

⊐19 ⊐18 ⊐17 ⊐16 ⊐15 ⊐14 ⊐13 ⊐12 ⊐11 ⊐10 ⊐9 ⊐8 ⊐7 ⊐6 ⊐5 ⊐4 ⊐3 ⊐2 ⊐1
⊐37 ⊐36 ⊐35 ⊐34 ⊐33 ⊐32 ⊐31 ⊐30 ⊐29 ⊐28 ⊐27 ⊐26 ⊐25 ⊐24 ⊐23 ⊐22 ⊐21 ⊐20
⊐55 ⊐54 ⊐53 ⊐52 ⊐51 ⊐50 ⊐49 ⊐48 ⊐47 ⊐46 ⊐45 ⊐44 ⊐43 ⊐42 ⊐41 ⊐40 ⊐39 ⊐38

AD72618

Wire side

1■ 2■ 3■ 4■ 5■ 6■ 7■ 8■ 9■ 10■ 11■ 12■ 13■ 14■ 15■ 16■ 17■ 18■ 19■
20■ 21■ 22■ 23■ 24■ 25■ 26■ 27■ 28■ 29■ 30■ 31■ 32■ 33■ 34■ 35■ 36■ 37■
38■ 39■ 40■ 41■ 42■ 43■ 44■ 45■ 46■ 47■ 48■ 49■ 50■ 51■ 52■ 53■ 54■ 55■

AD42077

Component/circuit description	ECM pin	Signal	Condition	Typical value	Oscilloscope setting★	Wave form
Air conditioning – 406 →1999/306	26	⊣⊢▷	Engine idling – AC OFF	0-1 V		
	26	⊣⊢▷	Engine idling – AC ON	11-14 V		
	50	⇨	Engine idling – AC OFF	0-1 V		
	50	⇨	Engine idling – AC ON	11-14 V		
Alarm system signal sensor – 406 06/98-99/306	27		Ignition ON	10,6 V		
	48		Engine idling	11-14 V		
Coded keypad – 406 →05/98	27		Ignition ON	10,6 V		
	48		Engine idling	11-14 V		
Crankshaft position (CKP) sensor	30	◄	Engine idling	2,5 V ac	2 V/1 ms	Reversed ⋀⋁⋀ 2
	49	◄	Engine idling	2,5 V ac	2 V/1 ms	⋀⋁⋀ 2
Crankshaft position (CKP) sensor – 406/306 1,8	19	⊣⊢	Ignition ON	0 V		
Crankshaft position (CKP) sensor – shield wire	19	⊣⊢	Ignition ON	0 V		
Data link connector (DLC)	12		Ignition ON	9,5 V		
	31		Ignition ON	9,6 V		
	31		Engine idling	0 V		
Data link connector (DLC) – engine speed signal	42	⇨	Ignition ON	11-14 V		
	42	⇨	Engine idling	29 Hz		
Earth	36		Ignition ON	0 V		
	54		Ignition ON	0 V		
Engine coolant temperature (ECT) sensor	47	◄	Ignition ON – coolant temp. 15°C	2,6 V		
	47	◄	Ignition ON – coolant temp. 80-85°C	0,5 V		
	53	⊣⊢	Ignition ON	0 V		
Evaporative emission (EVAP) canister purge valve	24	⊣⊢▷	Ignition ON	11-14 V		
Heated oxygen sensor (HO2S)	4	⊣⊢	Ignition ON	0 V		
	22	◄	Engine running	0,1-0,9 V fluctuating	0,2 V/1 sec.	⋀⋁⋀ 21
Heated oxygen sensor (HO2S) – shield wire	19	⊣⊢	Ignition ON	0 V		
Idle air control (IAC) valve	3	⇨	Engine idling		5 V/0,2 sec.	⋀⋁⋀ 51
	20	⇨	Engine idling		5 V/0,2 sec.	⋀⋁⋀ 51
	21	⇨	Engine idling		5 V/0,2 sec.	⋀⋁⋀ 51
	40	⇨	Engine idling		5 V/0,2 sec.	⋀⋁⋀ 51
Ignition coil – cylinders 1 & 4	55	⊣⊢▷	Engine idling		5 V/1 ms	⋀⋁⋀ 33

★ Suggested settings - Voltage/time per division

Component/circuit description	ECM pin	Signal	Condition	Typical value	Oscilloscope setting*	Wave form
Ignition coil – cylinders 2 & 3	37	⇥▷	Engine idling		5 V/1 ms	∿ 33
Injector 1	2	⇥▷	Ignition ON	11-14 V		
	2	⇥▷	Engine idling – engine hot	2,1 ms	10 V/2 ms	∿ 35
Injector 2	1	⇥▷	Ignition ON	11-14 V		
	1	⇥▷	Engine idling – engine hot	2,1 ms	10 V/2 ms	∿ 35
Injector 3	1	⇥▷	Ignition ON	11-14 V		
	1	⇥▷	Engine idling – engine hot	2,1 ms	10 V/2 ms	∿ 35
Injector 4	2	⇥▷	Ignition ON	11-14 V		
	2	⇥▷	Engine idling – engine hot	2,1 ms	10 V/2 ms	∿ 35
Instrument panel – 406 →1999/306 – engine speed signal	42	⇨	Ignition ON	11-14 V		
	42	⇨	Engine idling	29 Hz		
Intake air temperature (IAT) sensor	17	⊣	Ignition ON	0 V		
	29	⬅	Ignition ON – air temp. 15°C	2,79 V		
Knock sensor (KS)	15	⬅	Engine idling – accelerate briefly		50 mV/1 ms	∿ 58
	18	⊣	Ignition ON	0 V		
Knock sensor (KS) – shield wire – 306 1,4	19	⊣	Ignition ON	0 V		
Knock sensor (KS) – shield wire – 406/306 1,8	18	⊣	Ignition ON	0 V		
Malfunction indicator lamp (MIL)	9	⇥▷	Ignition ON – MIL ON	0-1 V		
	9	⇥▷	Ignition ON – MIL OFF	11-14 V		
Manifold absolute pressure (MAP) sensor	17	⊣	Ignition ON	0 V		
	34	⇨	Ignition ON	5 V		
	41	⬅	Ignition ON	4,5 V		
	41	⬅	Engine idling	1,2 V		
	41	⬅	Engine idling – accelerate briefly	4,5 V briefly		
Multifunction control module – 406 1999→	5	⇨	Ignition ON	11-14 V		
	9	⇥▷	Ignition ON – MIL ON	0-1 V		
	9	⇥▷	Ignition ON – MIL OFF	11-14 V		
	26	⇥▷	Engine idling – AC OFF	0-1 V		
	26	⇥▷	Engine idling – AC ON	11-14 V		
	27		Ignition ON	10,6 V		
	48		Engine idling	11-14 V		
	50	⇨	Engine idling – AC OFF	0-1 V		
	50	⇨	Engine idling – AC ON	11-14 V		
Multifunction control module – 406 1999→ – engine speed signal	42	⇨	Ignition ON	11-14 V		
	42	⇨	Engine idling	29 Hz		
Power steering pressure (PSP) switch – 306 1,4	14	⬅		1		
Relay module	7	⇥▷	Ignition ON	0-1 V briefly then 11-14 V		
	13	⬅	Ignition ON	11-14 V		
	35	⬅	Ignition ON	11-14 V		
	52	⇥▷	Ignition OFF	11-14 V		
	52	⇥▷	Ignition ON	0-1 V		
Throttle position (TP) sensor	16	⇨	Ignition ON	5 V		
	23	⬅	Ignition ON – throttle closed	0,6 V		
	23	⬅	Ignition ON – throttle fully open	4,7 V		
	53	⊣	Ignition ON	0 V		
Trip computer – 406 →1999	5	⇨	Ignition ON	11-14 V		
Vehicle speed sensor (VSS)	28	⬅	Ignition ON – vehicle moving	0 V or 9-12 V fluctuating		

*Suggested settings - Voltage/time per division

1 Connected pin - no test data available or random digital signal

ECM harness multi-plug

Terminal side – A – Grey, B – Brown, C – Black

C

```
h1 g1 f1 e1 d1 c1 b1 a1
h2 g2 f2 e2 d2 c2 b2 a2
h3 g3 f3 e3 d3 c3 b3 a3
h4 g4 f4 e4 d4 c4 b4 a4
```

B

```
m1 l1 k1 j1 h1 g1 f1 e1 d1 c1 b1 a1
m2 l2 k2 j2 h2 g2 f2 e2 d2 c2 b2 a2
m3 l3 k3 j3 h3 g3 f3 e3 d3 c3 b3 a3
m4 l4 k4 j4 h4 g4 f4 e4 d4 c4 b4 a4
```

A

```
a4 b4 c4 d4 e4 f4 g4 h4
a3 b3 c3 d3 e3 f3 g3 h3
a2 b2 c2 d2 e2 f2 g2 h2
a1 b1 c1 d1 e1 f1 g1 h1
```

AD22744

Wire side – A – Grey, B – Brown, C – Black

A

```
h4 g4 f4 e4 d4 c4 b4 a4
h3 g3 f3 e3 d3 c3 b3 a3
h2 g2 f2 e2 d2 c2 b2 a2
h1 g1 f1 e1 d1 c1 b1 a1
```

B

```
a1 b1 c1 d1 e1 f1 g1 h1 j1 k1 l1 m1
a2 b2 c2 d2 e2 f2 g2 h2 j2 k2 l2 m2
a3 b3 c3 d3 e3 f3 g3 h3 j3 k3 l3 m3
a4 b4 c4 d4 e4 f4 g4 h4 j4 k4 l4 m4
```

C

```
a1 b1 c1 d1 e1 f1 g1 h1
a2 b2 c2 d2 e2 f2 g2 h2
a3 b3 c3 d3 e3 f3 g3 h3
a4 b4 c4 d4 e4 f4 g4 h4
```

AD22743

Component/circuit description	ECM pin	Signal	Condition	Typical value	Oscilloscope setting*	Wave form
AC refrigerant triple pressure switch	Be2			[1]		
Air conditioning	Bc3			[1]		
	Bd3			[1]		
Crankshaft position (CKP) sensor	Ab1	←	Engine idling	2,3 V ac	2 V/1 ms	2
	Ab2	←	Engine idling	2,3 V ac	2 V/1 ms	Reversed 2
Data link connector (DLC)	Bb3	←→	Ignition ON	0 V		
	Bh2			[1]		
	Bj2	←→	Ignition ON	0 V		
	Bj2	←→	Engine idling	25 Hz		
	Bj2	←→	3000 rpm	100 Hz		
Earth	Ah1		Ignition ON	0 V		
	Bl4		Ignition ON	0 V		
	Bm4		Ignition ON	0 V		
Engine coolant blower motor	Bf2	→	Coolant blower motor OFF	0 V		
	Bf2	→	Coolant blower motor ON	11-14 V		
Engine coolant blower motor relay I (with AC 2001→)	Bj4	←	Engine running – coolant blower motor OFF	11-14 V		
	Bj4	←	Engine running – coolant blower motor ON	0 V		
Engine coolant blower motor relay II – low speed (with AC 2001→)	Bk4	⊐→	Ignition OFF	0-1 V		
	Bk4	⊐→	Ignition ON – engine coolant blower motor OFF	11-14 V		
	Bk4	⊐→	Ignition ON – engine coolant blower motor ON	0-1 V		
Engine coolant temperature (ECT) sensor	Cd4	⊐	Ignition ON	0 V		
	Ce4	←	Engine idling – coolant temp. 10°C	3-3,5 V switching	2 V/0,1 sec.	101
	Ce4	←	Engine idling – coolant temp. 80°C	3-3,5 V switching	2 V/0,2 sec.	18

* Suggested settings - Voltage/time per division

Component/circuit description	ECM pin	Signal	Condition	Typical value	Oscilloscope setting*	Wave form
Evaporative emission (EVAP) canister purge valve	Af2	→	Ignition ON	11-14 V briefly then 0-1 V		
	Af2	→	Engine running		10 V/50 ms	∿ 20
Heated oxygen sensor (HO2S) 1 – before cat	Aa3	←	Engine idling	0,1-0,8 V		
	Ab3	—	Engine idling	0 V		
	Ce2	→	Engine idling	0,1-0,9 V	4 V/0,2 sec.	∿ 4
Heated oxygen sensor (HO2S) 2 – after cat	Cd2	→	Ignition ON	11-14 V briefly then 0-1 V		
	Cd2	→	Engine idling	0-1 V		
	Cd3	—	Engine idling	0 V		
	Ce3	←	Engine idling	0,1-0,8 V		
Idle air control (IAC) valve	Ad1	⇒	Engine idling		5 V/0,5 sec.	Intermittent ∿ 26
	Ad2	⇒	Engine idling		5 V/0,5 sec.	Intermittent ∿ 26
	Ad3	⇒	Engine idling		5 V/0,5 sec.	Intermittent ∿ 26
	Ae3	⇒	Engine idling		5 V/0,5 sec.	Intermittent ∿ 26
Ignition coil	Cf3	←	Ignition ON	11-14 V briefly then 0-1 V		
	Cf3	←	Engine running		5 V/50 µs	∿ 100
	Cg3	→	Ignition ON	11-14 V briefly then 0-1 V		
	Cg3	→	Engine idling		5 V/2 ms	∿ 33
	Ch3	→	Ignition ON	11-14 V briefly then 0-1 V		
	Ch3	→	Engine idling		5 V/2 ms	∿ 33
Ignition switch	Bb4	←	Ignition ON	9 V min.		
Immobiliser	Bf3			[1]		
	Bf4			[1]		
Inertia fuel shut-off (IFS) switch	Af3	→	Ignition ON	0-1 V briefly then 11-14 V		
	Af3	→	Engine idling	0-1 V		
Injector 1	Ah2	→	Ignition ON	11-14 V briefly then 0-1 V		
	Ah2	→	Engine idling	4 ms	10 V/2 ms	∿ 35
Injector 2	Ag3	→	Ignition ON	11-14 V briefly then 0-1 V		
	Ag3	→	Engine idling	4 ms	10 V/2 ms	∿ 35
Injector 3	Ag2	→	Ignition ON	11-14 V briefly then 0-1 V		
	Ag2	→	Engine idling	4 ms	10 V/2 ms	∿ 35
Injector 4	Ah3	→	Ignition ON	11-14 V briefly then 0-1 V		
	Ah3	→	Engine idling	4 ms	10 V/2 ms	∿ 35
Instrument panel	Bk3		Ignition OFF	0 V		
	Bk3		Ignition ON	0-1 V briefly then 11-14 V		
	Bk3		Engine idling	11-14 V		
	Bm3		Ignition OFF	0 V		
	Bm3		Ignition ON	0-1 V briefly then 11-14 V		
	Bm3		Engine idling	11-14 V		
Intake air temperature (IAT) sensor	Aa2	—	Ignition ON	0 V		
	Ca2	←	Ignition ON – air temp. 20°C	2,35 V		

* Suggested settings - Voltage/time per division

Component/circuit description	ECM pin	Signal	Condition	Typical value	Oscilloscope setting*	Wave form
Knock sensor (KS)	Cb3	←	Ignition ON	2,5 V		
	Cb3	←	Engine idling – accelerate briefly		50 mV/1 ms	〰〰 38
	Cc3	←	Ignition ON	2,5 V		
	Cc3	←	Engine idling – accelerate briefly		50 mV/1 ms	〰〰 38
Malfunction indicator lamp (MIL)	Bc4	⊐▷	Engine running – MIL OFF	11-14 V		
	Bc4	⊐▷	Ignition ON – MIL ON	0-1 V		
Manifold absolute pressure (MAP) sensor	Aa2	⊐─	Ignition ON	0 V		
	Ac1	←	Ignition ON	4,2 V		
	Ac1	←	Engine idling	1,8 V		
	Ac1	←	Engine idling – accelerate briefly	4,4 V		
	Ae1	⇨	Ignition ON	5 V		
Power steering pressure (PSP) switch	Be3	←	Engine running – steering wheel not turned	0 V		
	Be3	←	Engine running – steering wheel turned	11-14 V		
Relay module (RM)	Ca4	←	Ignition ON	11-14 V		
	Cf2	⊐▷	Ignition OFF	11-14 V		
	Cf2	⊐▷	Ignition ON	0-1 V		
Throttle position (TP) sensor	Ac3	⇨	Ignition ON	5 V		
	Ca3	⊐─	Ignition ON	0 V		
	Cb4	←	Ignition ON – throttle closed	0,5 V		
	Cb4	←	Ignition ON – throttle fully open	4 V		
Vehicle speed sensor (VSS)	Bg2	←	Ignition OFF	10,8 V		
	Bg2	←	Ignition ON – vehicle pushed	0 V or 11-14 V switching		
	Ch4	⊐─		0 V		

*Suggested settings - Voltage/time per division

1 Connected pin - no test data available or random digital signal

PEUGEOT

Magneti Marelli 1AP.10

Model:	Engine code:	Year:
306 2,0i 16V	RFS (XU10J4RS/L3)	1997-01

ECM harness multi-plug

Terminal side

19 18 17 16 15 14 13 12 11 10 9 8 7 6 5 4 3 2 1
37 36 35 34 33 32 31 30 29 28 27 26 25 24 23 22 21 20
55 54 53 52 51 50 49 48 47 46 45 44 43 42 41 40 39 38

AD72618

Wire side

1 2 3 4 5 6 7 8 9 10 11 12 13 14 15 16 17 18 19
20 21 22 23 24 25 26 27 28 29 30 31 32 33 34 35 36 37
38 39 40 41 42 43 44 45 46 47 48 49 50 51 52 53 54 55

AD42077

Component/circuit description	ECM pin	Signal	Condition	Typical value	Oscilloscope setting*	Wave form
Air conditioning	26	←	AC compressor ON	11-14 V		
	50	←	AC ON	11-14 V		
Camshaft position (CMP) sensor	11	←	Ignition ON – engine turned	4,4-0 V fluctuating		
	11	←	Engine idling		2 V/20 ms	⋀⋁⋀ 12
	32	⌐	Ignition ON	0 V		
	34	⇨	Ignition ON	5 V		
Coded keypad	13	←	Ignition ON	11-14 V		
	27		Ignition ON	11-14 V		
	48		Ignition ON	11-14 V		
Crankshaft position (CKP) sensor	30 (49)	←	Engine idling		2 V/1 ms	⋀⋁⋀ 2
	49 (30)	←	Engine idling		2 V/1 ms	Reversed ⋀⋁⋀ 2
Crankshaft position (CKP) sensor – shield wire	32	⌐	Ignition ON	0 V		
Data link connector (DLC)	12		Ignition ON	11-14 V		
	31		Ignition ON	11-14 V		
Earth	17		Ignition ON	0 V		
	36		Ignition ON	0 V		
Earth – some models	54		Ignition ON	0 V		
Engine coolant temperature (ECT) sensor	47	←	Ignition ON – coolant temp. 15°C	3 V		
	47	←	Ignition ON – coolant temp. 80°C	0,5 V		
	53	⌐	Ignition ON	0 V		
Evaporative emission (EVAP) canister purge valve	24	⌐⇨	Ignition ON	11-14 V		
	24	⌐⇨	Engine running		10 V/50 ms	⋀⋁⋀ 20
Heated oxygen sensor (HO2S)	4	⌐	Ignition ON	0 V		
	22	←	Engine idling – accelerate briefly	0-1 V fluctuating	0,2 V/1 sec.	⋀⋁⋀ 21
Idle air control (IAC) valve	3	⇨	Ignition ON	11-14 V		
	3 (20)	⇨	Engine idling		5 V/0,5 sec.	Intermittent ⋀⋁⋀ 26
	20	⇨	Ignition ON	11-14 V		
	20 (3)	⇨	Engine idling		5 V/0,5 sec.	Intermittent ⋀⋁⋀ 26
	21	⇨	Ignition ON	0,1 V		
	21 (40)	⇨	Engine idling		5 V/0,5 sec.	Intermittent ⋀⋁⋀ 26
	40	⇨	Ignition ON	0,1 V		
	40 (21)	⇨	Engine idling		5 V/0,5 sec.	Intermittent ⋀⋁⋀ 26

* Suggested settings - Voltage/time per division

Autodata

Component/circuit description	ECM pin	Signal	Condition	Typical value	Oscilloscope setting*	Wave form
Ignition coil – cylinder 1	55	⇥▷	Engine idling		5 V/2 ms	33
Ignition coil – cylinder 2	18	⇥▷	Engine idling		5 V/2 ms	33
Ignition coil – cylinder 3	19	⇥▷	Engine idling		5 V/2 ms	33
Ignition coil – cylinder 4	37	⇥▷	Engine idling		5 V/2 ms	33
Injector 1	2	⇥▷	Engine idling	3,4 ms	10 V/2 ms	35
Injector 2	39	⇥▷	Engine idling	3,4 ms	10 V/2 ms	35
Injector 3	1	⇥▷	Engine idling	3,4 ms	10 V/2 ms	35
Injector 4	38	⇥▷	Engine idling	3,4 ms	10 V/2 ms	35
Intake air temperature (IAT) sensor	17	⇥—	Ignition ON	0 V		
	29	⟵	Ignition ON – air temp. 15°C	3 V		
Knock sensor (KS)	15	⟵	Engine running – accelerate briefly		50 mV/1 ms	38
	51	⇥—	Ignition ON	0 V		
Malfunction indicator lamp (MIL)	9	⇥▷	Ignition ON – MIL ON	0 V		
	9	⇥▷	Engine running – MIL OFF	11-14 V		
Manifold absolute pressure (MAP) sensor	17	⇥—	Ignition ON	0 V		
	34	⇨	Ignition ON	5 V		
	41	⟵	Ignition ON	4,6 V		
	41	⟵	Engine idling	1,75 V		
	41	⟵	Engine idling – accelerate briefly	4,6 V briefly		
Power steering pressure (PSP) switch	14	⇥▷	Ignition ON – steering wheel not turned	0 V		
	14	⇥▷	Ignition ON – steering wheel turned	11-14 V		
Relay module	7	⇥▷	Ignition ON	0-1 V briefly then 11-14 V		
	7	⇥▷	Engine cranking	0-1 V		
	7	⇥▷	Engine running	0-1 V		
	13	⟵	Ignition ON	11-14 V		
	35	⟵	Ignition ON	11-14 V		
	52	⇥▷	Ignition ON	0-1 V		
	52	⇥▷	Engine running	0-1 V		
Speedometer	28	⟵	Engine running – vehicle pushed	0-12 V fluctuating		
Tachometer	42	⇨	Engine idling	30 Hz		
	42	⇨	3000 rpm	100 Hz		
Throttle position (TP) sensor	16	⇨	Ignition ON	5 V		
	23	⟵	Ignition ON – throttle closed	0 V		
	23	⟵	Ignition ON – throttle fully open	4,6 V		
	53	⇥—	Ignition ON	0 V		
Vehicle speed sensor (VSS)	28	⟵	Engine running – vehicle pushed	0-12 V fluctuating		

*Suggested settings - Voltage/time per division

1 Connected pin - no test data available or random digital signal

ECM harness multi-plug

Terminal side – A – Grey, B – Brown, C – Black

```
        C                              B                                    A
h1 g1 f1 e1 d1 c1 b1 a1    m1 l1 k1 j1 h1 g1 f1 e1 d1 c1 b1 a1    a4 b4 c4 d4 e4 f4 g4 h4
h2 g2 f2 e2 d2 c2 b2 a2    m2 l2 k2 j2 h2 g2 f2 e2 d2 c2 b2 a2    a3 b3 c3 d3 e3 f3 g3 h3
h3 g3 f3 e3 d3 c3 b3 a3    m3 l3 k3 j3 h3 g3 f3 e3 d3 c3 b3 a3    a2 b2 c2 d2 e2 f2 g2 h2
h4 g4 f4 e4 d4 c4 b4 a4    m4 l4 k4 j4 h4 g4 f4 e4 d4 c4 b4 a4    a1 b1 c1 d1 e1 f1 g1 h1
```
AD22744

Wire side – A – Grey, B – Brown, C – Black

```
        A                              B                                    C
h4 g4 f4 e4 d4 c4 b4 a4    a1 b1 c1 d1 e1 f1 g1 h1 j1 k1 l1 m1    a1 b1 c1 d1 e1 f1 g1 h1
h3 g3 f3 e3 d3 c3 b3 a3    a2 b2 c2 d2 e2 f2 g2 h2 j2 k2 l2 m2    a2 b2 c2 d2 e2 f2 g2 h2
h2 g2 f2 e2 d2 c2 b2 a2    a3 b3 c3 d3 e3 f3 g3 h3 j3 k3 l3 m3    a3 b3 c3 d3 e3 f3 g3 h3
h1 g1 f1 e1 d1 c1 b1 a1    a4 b4 c4 d4 e4 f4 g4 h4 j4 k4 l4 m4    a4 b4 c4 d4 e4 f4 g4 h4
```
AD22743

Component/circuit description	ECM pin	Signal	Condition	Typical value	Oscilloscope setting*	Wave form
AC refrigerant triple pressure switch	Af2	⇒	Ignition ON	5 V		
	Af4	⌐	Ignition ON	0 V		
	Ah2	←	Ignition OFF	0 V		
	Ah2	←	Engine idling	1,1 V		
Accelerator pedal position (APP) sensor	Ac2	←	Ignition ON – accelerator pedal released	0,2 V		
	Ac2	←	Ignition ON – accelerator pedal depressed	1,85 V		
	Ag2	⇒	Ignition ON	5 V		
	Ag3	←	Ignition ON – accelerator pedal released	0,4 V		
	Ag3	←	Ignition ON – accelerator pedal depressed	3,7 V		
	Ah3	⌐	Ignition ON	0 V		
Brake pedal position (BPP) switch	Ae4	←	Ignition ON – brake pedal released	11-14 V		
	Ae4	←	Ignition ON – brake pedal depressed	0 V		
Camshaft position (CMP) sensor	Bf2	⌐	Ignition ON	0 V		
	Bg2	←	Engine idling		2 V/50 ms per division	〰 64
	Bh2	⇒	Ignition ON	5 V		
CAN data bus – high	Aa3	←⇒		[1]		
CAN data bus – low	Aa4	←⇒		[1]		
Clutch pedal position (CPP) switch	Ae3	←	Ignition ON – clutch pedal released	11-14 V		
	Ae3	←	Ignition ON – clutch pedal depressed	0 V		
Crankshaft position (CKP) sensor	Bj1	←	Engine idling	1,5 V ac	1 V/2 ms per division	〰 1
	Bk1	←	Engine idling	1,5 V ac	1 V/2 ms per division	Reversed 〰 1
Data link connector (DLC)	Ab4	←⇒	Ignition ON	0 V		

* Suggested settings - Voltage/time per division

Autodata

Component/circuit description	ECM pin	Signal	Condition	Typical value	Oscilloscope setting*	Wave form
Earth	Ag1		Ignition ON	0 V		
	Ah1		Ignition ON	0 V		
	Bl4		Ignition ON	0 V		
	Bm4		Ignition ON	0 V		
Engine coolant blower motor relay	Ab2	⊐▷	Ignition ON	0-1 V		
	Ab2	⊐▷	Engine idling	11-14 V		
	Ac4	◀	Ignition ON	0 V		
	Ad4	⊐▷	Ignition ON	11-14 V		
Engine coolant temperature (ECT) sensor	Bd1	⊐—	Ignition ON	0 V		
	Be1	◀	Coolant temp. 20°C	3 V		
	Be1	◀	Coolant temp. 85°C	0,6 V		
Exhaust gas recirculation (EGR) solenoid 1	Ba3	⊐▷	Ignition ON	Wave pattern for 5 secs then 0-1 V	2 V/2 ms per division	〰️ 66
	Ba3	⊐▷	Engine idling	61%	2 V/5 ms per division	〰️ 64
Exhaust gas recirculation (EGR) solenoid 2	Ca4	⊐▷	Ignition ON	Wave pattern for 5 secs then 0-1 V	2 V/2 ms per division	〰️ 66
	Ca4	⊐▷	Engine idling		2 V/5 ms per division	〰️ 37
Fuel pressure control solenoid	Bl2	⊐▷	Ignition ON		2 V/0,5 ms per division	〰️ 43
	Bl2	⊐▷	Engine idling		2 V/1 ms per division	〰️ 37
Fuel pressure sensor	Bf1	⊐—	Ignition ON	0 V		
	Bg1	◀	Ignition ON	0,5 V		
	Bg1	◀	Engine idling	1,3 V		
	Bg1	◀	3000 rpm	1,8 V		
	Bh1	▷	Ignition ON	5 V		
Fuel temperature sensor	Bd2	⊐—	Ignition ON	0 V		
	Be2	◀	Engine idling	2,2 V		
Glow plug timer relay	Cb1	⊐▷	Engine idling	140 Hz	5 V/5 ms per division	〰️ 12
	Cf1	⊐▷	Ignition ON	1,1 V		
Injector 1	Cg1	▷	Ignition ON	1 V		
	Cg1 (Ch2)	▷	Engine idling	0,25 ms pilot + 0,5 ms main		
	Cg1 (Ch2)	▷	Engine idling		20 V/0,5 ms per division	〰️ 67
	Ch2	▷	Ignition ON	1 V		
	Ch2 (Cg1)	▷	Engine idling	0,25 ms pilot + 0,5 ms main		
	Ch2 (Cg1)	▷	Engine idling		20 V/0,5 ms per division	〰️ 67
Injector 2	Ch3	▷	Ignition ON	1 V		
	Ch3 (Ch4)	▷	Engine idling	0,25 ms pilot + 0,5 ms main		
	Ch3 (Ch4)	▷	Engine idling		20 V/0,5 ms per division	〰️ 67
	Ch4	▷	Ignition ON	1 V		
	Ch4 (Ch3)	▷	Engine idling	0,25 ms pilot + 0,5 ms main		
	Ch4 (Ch3)	▷	Engine idling		20 V/0,5 ms per division	〰️ 67

* Suggested settings - Voltage/time per division

Component/circuit description	ECM pin	Signal	Condition	Typical value	Oscilloscope setting*	Wave form
Injector 3	Cg3	⇨	Ignition ON	1 V		
	Cg3 (Cg4)	⇨	Engine idling	0,25 ms pilot + 0,5 ms main		
	Cg3 (Cg4)	⇨	Engine idling		20 V/0,5 ms per division	〜〜 67
	Cg4	⇨	Ignition ON	1 V		
	Cg4 (Cg3)	⇨	Engine idling	0,25 ms pilot + 0,5 ms main		
	Cg4 (Cg3)	⇨	Engine idling		20 V/0,5 ms per division	〜〜 67
Injector 4	Cg2	⇨	Ignition ON	1 V		
	Cg2 (Ch1)	⇨	Engine idling	0,25 ms pilot + 0,5 ms main		
	Cg2 (Ch1)	⇨	Engine idling		20 V/0,5 ms per division	〜〜 67
	Ch1	⇨	Ignition ON	1 V		
	Ch1 (Cg2)	⇨	Engine idling	0,25 ms pilot + 0,5 ms main		
	Ch1 (Cg2)	⇨	Engine idling		20 V/0,5 ms per division	〜〜 67
Intake air temperature (IAT) sensor	Bj3	⬅	Ignition ON – air temp. 18°C	2,3 V		
Mass air flow (MAF) sensor	Bg3	⌐	Ignition ON	0 V		
	Bh3	⬅	Ignition ON	0,5 V		
	Bh3	⬅	Engine idling	2,1 V		
	Bh3	⬅	Engine idling – accelerate briefly	4 V		
Multifunction control module 1 – CAN data bus	Aa3	⬌		1		
	Aa4	⬌		1		
Multifunction control module 2	Ac3	⬅	Ignition OFF	0 V		
	Ac3	⬅	Ignition ON	11-14 V		
	Ba2	⇥	Ignition OFF	11-14 V		
	Ba2	⇥	Ignition ON	0-1 V		
	Ba4	⇥	Ignition ON	0-1 V for 5 secs then 10,6 V		
	Bl1	⬅	Ignition ON	11-14 V		
	Bm1	⬅	Ignition ON	11-14 V		
3rd piston cut-off solenoid	Bc3	⇥	Ignition ON	11-14 V for 5 secs then 0-1 V		
	Bc3	⇥	Engine idling	11-14 V		
	Bc3	⇥	Engine under full load	0-1 V		

*Suggested settings - Voltage/time per division

1 Connected pin - no test data available or random digital signal

ECM harness multi-plug

Terminal side – A – Grey, B – Brown, C – Black

C

h1	g1	f1	e1	d1	c1	b1	a1
h2	g2	f2	e2	d2	c2	b2	a2
h3	g3	f3	e3	d3	c3	b3	a3
h4	g4	f4	e4	d4	c4	b4	a4

B

m1	l1	k1	j1	h1	g1	f1	e1	d1	c1	b1	a1
m2	l2	k2	j2	h2	g2	f2	e2	d2	c2	b2	a2
m3	l3	k3	j3	h3	g3	f3	e3	d3	c3	b3	a3
m4	l4	k4	j4	h4	g4	f4	e4	d4	c4	b4	a4

A

a4	b4	c4	d4	e4	f4	g4	h4
a3	b3	c3	d3	e3	f3	g3	h3
a2	b2	c2	d2	e2	f2	g2	h2
a1	b1	c1	d1	e1	f1	g1	h1

AD22744

Wire side – A – Grey, B – Brown, C – Black

A

h4	g4	f4	e4	d4	c4	b4	a4
h3	g3	f3	e3	d3	c3	b3	a3
h2	g2	f2	e2	d2	c2	b2	a2
h1	g1	f1	e1	d1	c1	b1	a1

B

a1	b1	c1	d1	e1	f1	g1	h1	j1	k1	l1	m1
a2	b2	c2	d2	e2	f2	g2	h2	j2	k2	l2	m2
a3	b3	c3	d3	e3	f3	g3	h3	j3	k3	l3	m3
a4	b4	c4	d4	e4	f4	g4	h4	j4	k4	l4	m4

C

a1	b1	c1	d1	e1	f1	g1	h1
a2	b2	c2	d2	e2	f2	g2	h2
a3	b3	c3	d3	e3	f3	g3	h3
a4	b4	c4	d4	e4	f4	g4	h4

AD22743

Component/circuit description	ECM pin	Signal	Condition	Typical value	Oscilloscope setting*	Wave form
AC refrigerant triple pressure switch	Cf2	⇨	Ignition ON	5 V		
	Cf4	⌐—	Ignition ON	0 V		
	Ch2	⬅	Ignition OFF	0 V		
	Ch2	⬅	Ignition ON	0,8 V		
Accelerator pedal position (APP) sensor	Cc2	⬅	Ignition ON – accelerator pedal released	0,2 V		
	Cc2	⬅	Ignition ON – accelerator pedal depressed	1,85 V		
	Cg2	⇨	Ignition ON	5 V		
	Cg3	⬅	Ignition ON – accelerator pedal released	0,4 V		
	Cg3	⬅	Ignition ON – accelerator pedal depressed	3,7 V		
	Ch3	⌐—	Ignition ON	0 V		
Battery	Bg4	⬅	Ignition OFF	11-14 V		
Brake pedal position (BPP) switch – if fitted	Ce4	⬅	Ignition ON – brake pedal released	11-14 V		
	Ce4	⬅	Ignition ON – brake pedal depressed	0 V		
Camshaft position (CMP) sensor	Aa1	⌐—	Ignition ON	0 V		
	Ad1	⬅	Engine idling		2 V/50 ms per division	⟋⟍⟋⟍ 64
	Bc3	⇨	Ignition ON	5 V		
CAN data bus – high	Ca3	⬌		1		
CAN data bus – low	Ca4	⬌		1		
Clutch pedal position (CPP) switch	Ce3	⬅	Ignition ON – clutch pedal released	11-14 V		
	Ce3	⬅	Ignition ON – clutch pedal depressed	0 V		

* Suggested settings - Voltage/time per division

Component/circuit description	ECM pin	Signal	Condition	Typical value	Oscilloscope setting*	Wave form
Crankshaft position (CKP) sensor	Bj4	←	Engine idling	1,4 V ac	1 V/2 ms per division	Reversed ⎍ 1
	Bk4	←	Engine idling	1,4 V ac	1 V/2 ms per division	⎍ 1
Data link connector (DLC)	Cb4	⇔	Ignition ON	0 V		
Earth	Ah2		Ignition ON	0 V		
	Bk2		Ignition ON	0 V		
	Cg4		Ignition ON	0 V		
	Ch1		Ignition ON	0 V		
	Ch4		Ignition ON	0 V		
Engine coolant blower motor relay	Cb2		Ignition ON	11-14 V		
	Cc4		Ignition ON	0 V		
	Cd4		Ignition ON	11-14 V		
Engine coolant heater relay 1	Cb1	⊐▷	Ignition ON	11-14 V		
Engine coolant heater relay 2	Cc1	⊐▷	Ignition ON	11-14 V		
Engine coolant temperature (ECT) sensor	Be1	⊐—	Ignition ON	0 V		
	Be4	←	Coolant temp. 85°C	0,9 V		
Exhaust gas recirculation (EGR) solenoid 1	Ag1	⊐▷	Ignition ON		2 V/2 ms per division	⎍ 66
	Ag1	⊐▷	Engine idling	41%	2 V/5 ms per division	⎍ 10
Exhaust gas recirculation (EGR) solenoid 2	Ah3	⊐▷	Engine idling		2 V/5 ms per division	⎍ 37
Fuel flow control valve	Ag3	⊐▷	Ignition ON	11-14 V		
	Ag3	⊐▷	Engine idling	10%	2 V/5 ms per division	⎍ 37
Fuel pressure control solenoid	Ah1	⊐▷	Ignition ON	11-14 V		
	Ah1	⊐▷	Engine idling		2 V/2 ms per division	⎍ 37
Fuel pressure sensor	Ad3	←	Ignition ON	0,5 V		
	Bd1	⇒	Ignition ON	5 V		
	Bf2	⊐—	Ignition ON	0 V		
Fuel temperature sensor	Bf3	←	Engine idling – coolant temp. 85°C	1,3 V		
	Bh4	⊐—	Ignition ON	0 V		
Glow plug timer relay	Ac1		Ignition ON	0 V		
	Be2		Ignition ON	11-14 V		
Injector 1	Bl3	⇒	Ignition ON	110 V		
	Bl3 (Bm2)	⇒	Engine idling	0,4 ms pilot + 0,7 ms main		
	Bl3 (Bm2)	⇒	Engine idling		20 V/0,5 ms per division	⎍ 68
	Bm2	⇒	Ignition ON	110 V		
	Bm2 (Bl3)	⇒	Engine idling	0,4 ms pilot + 0,7 ms main		
	Bm2 (Bl3)	⇒	Engine idling		20 V/0,5 ms per division	⎍ 68

★ Suggested settings - Voltage/time per division

Component/circuit description	ECM pin	Signal	Condition	Typical value	Oscilloscope setting*	Wave form
Injector 2	BI1	⇒	Ignition ON	110 V		
	BI1 (BI4)	⇒	Engine idling	0,4 ms pilot + 0,7 ms main		
	BI1 (BI4)	⇒	Engine idling		20 V/0,5 ms per division	〰〰 68
	BI4	⇒	Ignition ON	110 V		
	BI4 (BI1)	⇒	Engine idling	0,4 ms pilot + 0,7 ms main		
	BI4 (BI1)	⇒	Engine idling		20 V/0,5 ms per division	〰〰 68
Injector 3	BI2	⇒	Ignition ON	110 V		
	BI2 (Bm3)	⇒	Engine idling	0,4 ms pilot + 0,7 ms main		
	BI2 (Bm3)	⇒	Engine idling		20 V/0,5 ms per division	〰〰 68
	Bm3	⇒	Ignition ON	110 V		
	Bm3 (BI2)	⇒	Engine idling	0,4 ms pilot + 0,7 ms main		
	Bm3 (BI2)	⇒	Engine idling		20 V/0,5 ms per division	〰〰 68
Injector 4	Bm1	⇒	Ignition ON	110 V		
	Bm1 (Bm4)	⇒	Engine idling	0,4 ms pilot + 0,7 ms main		
	Bm1 (Bm4)	⇒	Engine idling		20 V/0,5 ms per division	〰〰 68
	Bm4	⇒	Ignition ON	110 V		
	Bm4 (Bm1)	⇒	Engine idling	0,4 ms pilot + 0,7 ms main		
	Bm4 (Bm1)	⇒	Engine idling		20 V/0,5 ms per division	〰〰 68
Intake air temperature (IAT) sensor	Be3	⇐	Ignition ON – air temp. 19°C	2,5 V		
Mass air flow (MAF) sensor	Aa3	⇐	Ignition ON	0,57 V		
	Aa3	⇐	Engine idling	2,6 V		
	Ab3	⊣⊢	Ignition ON	0 V		
	Bg2	⊣⊢	Ignition ON	0 V		
Multifunction control module 1 – CAN data bus – low	Ca3	⇔		1		
Multifunction control module 1 – CAN data bus – high	Ca4	⇔		1		
Multifunction control module 2	Ae3	⇐	Ignition ON	11-14 V		
	Af2	⇐	Ignition ON	11-14 V		
	Af3	⇐	Ignition ON	11-14 V		
	Bf1	⊣⇒	Ignition OFF	11-14 V		
	Bf1	⊣⇒	Ignition ON	0-1 V		
	Bh1		Ignition ON	0 V		
	Cc3	⇐	Ignition ON	11-14 V		

*Suggested settings - Voltage/time per division

1 Connected pin - no test data available or random digital signal

PEUGEOT

Magneti Marelli 1AP.20

Model:	Engine code:	Year:
406 1,8	LFX (XU7JB)	1997-02
Partner 1,8	LFX (XU7JB)	1996-02

ECM harness multi-plug

Terminal side

19 18 17 16 15 14 13 12 11 10 9 8 7 6 5 4 3 2 1
37 36 35 34 33 32 31 30 29 28 27 26 25 24 23 22 21 20
55 54 53 52 51 50 49 48 47 46 45 44 43 42 41 40 39 38

AD72618

Wire side

1 2 3 4 5 6 7 8 9 10 11 12 13 14 15 16 17 18 19
20 21 22 23 24 25 26 27 28 29 30 31 32 33 34 35 36 37
38 39 40 41 42 43 44 45 46 47 48 49 50 51 52 53 54 55

AD42077

Component/circuit description	ECM pin	Signal	Condition	Typical value	Oscilloscope setting*	Wave form
Air conditioning	26			1		
	50			1		
Crankshaft position (CKP) sensor	30	←	Engine cranking	2 V ac	2 V/1 ms	2
	30	←	Engine idling	5 V ac	2 V/1 ms	2
	30	←	3000 rpm	12 V ac	2 V/1 ms	2
	49	←	Engine cranking	2 V ac	2 V/1 ms	2
	49	←	Engine idling	5 V ac	2 V/1 ms	2
	49	←	3000 rpm	12 V ac	2 V/1 ms	2
Crankshaft position (CKP) sensor – shield wire	19	⌐	Ignition ON	0 V		
Data link connector (DLC)	12	←		1		
	31			1		
	42			1		
Earth	36		Ignition ON	0 V		
	54		Ignition ON	0 V		
Engine coolant temperature (ECT) sensor	47	←	Ignition ON – coolant temp. 20°C	1,7 V		
	47	←	Ignition ON – coolant temp. 80°C	0,4 V		
	53	⌐	Ignition ON	0 V		
Evaporative emission (EVAP) canister purge valve	24	⌐▷	Engine running	1-99%	10 V/50 ms	20
Heated oxygen sensor (HO2S)	4	⌐	Ignition ON	0 V		
	22	←	Engine idling – accelerate briefly	0-1 V fluctuating	0,2 V/1 sec.	21
Heated oxygen sensor (HO2S) – shield wire	19	⌐	Ignition ON	0 V		
Idle air control (IAC) valve	3 (20)	▷	Engine idling		5 V/0,5 sec.	Intermittent 26
	20 (3)	▷	Engine idling		5 V/0,5 sec.	Intermittent 26
	21 (40)	▷	Engine idling		5 V/0,5 sec.	Intermittent 26
	40 (21)	▷	Engine idling		5 V/0,5 sec.	Intermittent 26
Ignition coil – cylinders 1 & 4	55	⌐▷	Engine idling		5 V/2 ms	33
Ignition coil – cylinders 2 & 3	37	⌐▷	Engine idling		5 V/2 ms	33
Immobilizer control module	13	←	Ignition ON	11-14 V		
	27			1		
	48			1		

* Suggested settings - Voltage/time per division

Component/circuit description	ECM pin	Signal	Condition	Typical value	Oscilloscope setting*	Wave form
Inertia fuel shut-off (IFS) switch – Partner	7	⊐▷	Ignition ON	0-1 V briefly then 11-14 V		
	7	⊐▷	Engine running	11-14 V		
Injectors 1 & 4	2	⊐▷	Engine idling	4,2 ms	10 V/1 ms	〰 35
Injectors 2 & 3	1	⊐▷	Engine idling	4,2 ms	10 V/1 ms	〰 35
Intake air temperature (IAT) sensor	17	⊐—	Ignition ON	0 V		
	29	⟵	Ignition ON – air temp. 20°C	2,5 V		
Knock sensor (KS)	15	⟵	Engine idling – accelerate briefly		50 mV/1 ms	〰 38
	18	⊐—	Ignition ON	0-1 V		
Malfunction indicator lamp (MIL)	9	⊐▷	Ignition ON	0-1 V		
Manifold absolute pressure (MAP) sensor	17	⊐—	Ignition ON	0 V		
	34	⟹	Ignition ON	5 V		
	41	⟵	Ignition ON	4,5 V		
	41	⟵	Engine idling	1,3 V		
Power steering pressure (PSP) switch	14	⟵	Engine running – steering wheel not turned	0 V		
	14	⟵	Engine running – steering wheel turned	11-14 V		
Relay module	13	⟵	Ignition ON	11-14 V		
	35	⟵	Ignition ON	11-14 V		
	35	⟵	Engine running	11-14 V		
	52	⊐▷	Ignition ON	0-1 V		
	52	⊐▷	Engine running	0-1 V		
Relay module – 406	7	⊐▷	Ignition ON	0-1 V briefly then 11-14 V		
	7	⊐▷	Engine running	11-14 V		
Tachometer	42	⟹	Engine idling	28 Hz		
	42	⟹	3000 rpm	100 Hz		
Throttle position (TP) sensor	16	⟹	Ignition ON	5 V		
	23	⟵	Ignition ON – throttle closed	0,7 V		
	23	⟵	Ignition ON – throttle fully open	4,7 V		
	53	⊐—	Ignition ON	0 V		
Trip computer	5	⟹		1		
Vehicle speed sensor (VSS)	28	⟵	Ignition ON – vehicle moving	0-12 V fluctuating		

*Suggested settings - Voltage/time per division

1 Connected pin - no test data available or random digital signal

PEUGEOT

Bosch Motronic MP5.1.1

Model:	Engine code:	Year:
406 1,8i 16V	LFY (XU7JP4)	1995-02
406 2,0i 16V	RFV (XU10J4R)	1995-02
605 2,0i 16V	RFX (XU10J4R/L/Z)	1995-99

ECM harness multi-plug

Terminal side

19 18 17 16 15 14 13 12 11 10 9 8 7 6 5 4 3 2 1
37 36 35 34 33 32 31 30 29 28 27 26 25 24 23 22 21 20
55 54 53 52 51 50 49 48 47 46 45 44 43 42 41 40 39 38

AD72618

Wire side

1 2 3 4 5 6 7 8 9 10 11 12 13 14 15 16 17 18 19
20 21 22 23 24 25 26 27 28 29 30 31 32 33 34 35 36 37
38 39 40 41 42 43 44 45 46 47 48 49 50 51 52 53 54 55

AD42077

Component/circuit description	ECM pin	Signal	Condition	Typical value	Oscilloscope setting*	Wave form
Air conditioning	23			☐1		
	32			☐1		
	34			☐1		
Battery	18	←	Ignition OFF	11-14 V		
Coded keypad – some models	22			☐1		
	35	←		☐1		
Crankshaft position (CKP) sensor	11	⌐	Ignition ON	0 V		
	30	←	Engine idling	2,3 V ac		
	30	←	3000 rpm	3,9 V ac		
Data link connector (DLC)	6	⇒		☐1		
	13			☐1		
	16			☐1		
Data link connector (DLC) – some models	22			☐1		
Earth	2		Ignition ON	0 V		
	14		Ignition ON	0 V		
	19		Ignition ON	0 V		
Engine coolant temperature (ECT) sensor	25	←	Ignition ON – coolant temp. 20°C	3,5 V		
	25	←	Ignition ON – coolant temp. 80°C	1 V		
	26	⌐	Ignition ON	0 V		
Evaporative emission (EVAP) canister purge valve	5	⌐⊳	Ignition OFF	11-14 V		
	5	⌐⊳	Engine running		10 V/50 ms	⩘ 20
Heated oxygen sensor (HO2S)	10	⌐	Ignition ON	0 V		
	28	←	Engine idling – accelerate briefly	0,1-1 V fluctuating	0,2 V/1 sec.	⩘ 21
Idle air control (IAC) valve	15 (33)	⇒	Engine idling		5 V/0,5 sec.	Intermittent ⩘ 26
	21 (24)	⇒	Engine idling		5 V/0,5 sec.	Intermittent ⩘ 26
	24 (21)	⇒	Engine idling		5 V/0,5 sec.	Intermittent ⩘ 26
	33 (15)	⇒	Engine idling		5 V/0,5 sec.	Intermittent ⩘ 26
Ignition coil – cylinders 1 & 4	1	⌐⊳	Engine idling		5 V/2 ms	⩘ 33
Ignition coil – cylinders 2 & 3	20	⇒	Engine idling		5 V/2 ms	⩘ 33
Ignition switch – some models	35	←	Ignition ON	11-14 V		

* Suggested settings - Voltage/time per division

Component/circuit description	ECM pin	Signal	Condition	Typical value	Oscilloscope setting*	Wave form
Injectors	17	⊣▷	Ignition ON	11-14 V		
	17	⊣▷	Engine idling	2,1 ms	10 V/2 ms	⌇⌇ 35
	17	⊣▷	3000 rpm	1,8 ms	10 V/2 ms	⌇⌇ 35
Intake air temperature (IAT) sensor	26	⊣─	Ignition ON	0 V		
	27	◀	Ignition ON – air temp. 20°C	3,5 V		
Knock sensor (KS)	8	◀	Engine idling – accelerate briefly		50 mV/1 ms	⌇⌇ 38
	26	⊣─	Ignition ON	0 V		
Malfunction indicator lamp (MIL)	22	⊣▷	Ignition ON – MIL ON	0-1 V		
	22	⊣▷	Engine idling – MIL OFF	11-14 V		
Manifold absolute pressure (MAP) sensor	7	◀	Ignition ON	4,4 V		
	7	◀	Engine idling	1,3 V		
	7	◀	Accelerate briefly	1,3-4,4 V		
	12	⇨	Ignition ON	5 V		
	26	⊣─	Ignition ON	0 V		
Relay module	3	⊣▷	Ignition ON	0-1 V briefly then 11-14 V		
	3	⊣▷	Engine cranking	0-1 V		
	37	◀	Ignition ON	11-14 V		
Relay module – some models	36	⊣▷	Ignition OFF	11-14 V		
	36	⊣▷	Ignition ON	0-1 V		
Starter motor inhibitor switch relay	31			☐1		
Tachometer	6	⇨	Engine idling	30 Hz		
	6	⇨	3000 rpm	100 Hz		
Throttle position (TP) sensor	12	⇨	Ignition ON	5 V		
	26	⊣─	Ignition ON	0 V		
	29	◀	Ignition ON – throttle closed	0,4 V		
	29	◀	Ignition ON – throttle fully open	4,5 V		
Trip computer – some models	4			☐1		
Vehicle speed sensor (VSS) – some models	9	◀	Ignition ON – vehicle moving	Voltage varies with vehicle speed		
Vehicle speed sensor (VSS) signal amplifier – some models	9	◀	Ignition ON – vehicle moving	Voltage varies with vehicle speed		

*Suggested settings - Voltage/time per division

☐1 Connected pin - no test data available or random digital signal

PEUGEOT

Bosch AS3

Model:	Engine code:	Year:
406 1,9D Turbo	XUD9BTF/L3 (DHX)	1995-00
806 1,9D Turbo	XUD9BTF/L3 (DHX)	1995-00

ECM harness multi-plug

Terminal side

```
1  2  3  4  5  6  7  8  9  10  11  12  13  14  15  16  17  18
  19 20 21 22 23 24 25 26 27 28 29 30 31 32 33 34 35
```
AD71594

Wire side

```
18 17 16 15 14 13 12 11 10 9  8  7  6  5  4  3  2  1
  35 34 33 32 31 30 29 28 27 26 25 24 23 22 21 20 19
```
AD42073

Component/circuit description	ECM pin	Signal	Condition	Typical value	Oscilloscope setting*	Wave form
AC compressor clutch cut-off relay – 806	28			1		
AC control module – 406 – ATC	13			1		
	28	←	Engine idling – AC OFF	0 V		
	28	←	Engine idling – AC ON	11-14 V		
AC temperature sensors control module, 406 – MTC	13			1		
	28	←	Engine idling – AC OFF	0 V		
	28	←	Engine idling – AC ON	11-14 V		
Crankshaft position (CKP) sensor	8	←	Ignition ON	2,5 V		
	8	←	Engine idling	0,76 V ac	2 V/10 ms	〜 6
	25	←	Ignition ON	2,5 V		
	25	←	Engine idling	0,25 V ac	2 V/10 ms	Reversed 〜 6
Crankshaft position (CKP) sensor – shield wire	23	⅂	Ignition ON	0 V		
Data link connector (DLC)	10	⇨	Ignition ON	0 V		
	27	⇨	Ignition ON	0 V		
Data link connector (DLC) – engine RPM signal	11	⇨	Engine idling	33 Hz		
	11	⇨	3000 rpm	100 Hz		
Earth	17	⅂	Ignition ON	0 V		
	18	⅂	Ignition ON	0 V		
	34	⅂	Ignition ON	0 V		
	35	⅂	Ignition ON	0 V		
Engine coolant temperature (ECT) sensor	4	←	Ignition ON – coolant temp. 30°C	0,5 V		
	21	⅂	Ignition ON	0 V		
Exhaust gas recirculation (EGR) solenoid	32	⅂⇨	Ignition ON	11-14 V		
	32	⅂⇨	Engine idling	0-1 V		
	32	⅂⇨	Engine idling – accelerate briefly	11-14 V briefly then 0-1 V		

* Suggested settings - Voltage/time per division

Component/circuit description	ECM pin	Signal	Condition	Typical value	Oscilloscope setting*	Wave form
Fuel injection timing solenoid	15	⫟▷	Ignition ON	11,4 V		
	15	⫟▷	Engine idling		2 V/20 ms	〰22
Fuel lever position sensor	1	⟹	Ignition ON	5 V		
	2	⟸	Ignition ON – accelerator pedal released	1 V		
	2	⟸	Ignition ON – accelerator pedal depressed	2,9 V		
	19	⫞	Ignition ON	0 V		
Glow plug control module	6	⟹	Ignition ON – engine cold	11-14 V		
	29			1		
Glow plug warning lamp	12	⟹	Ignition ON – lamp ON	11-14 V		
	12	⟹	Ignition ON – lamp OFF	0 V		
Idle speed control (ISC) actuator	14	⫟▷	Ignition ON	0-1 V		
Injector needle lift sensor	7	⟸	Ignition ON	3,5 V		
	7	⟸	Engine idling	0,06 V ac	1 V/2 ms	〰7
	24	⫞	Ignition ON	0 V		
Injector needle lift sensor – shield wire	23	⫞	Ignition ON	0 V		
Malfunction indicator lamp (MIL)	30	⫟▷	Ignition ON – MIL ON	0-1 V		
	30	⫟▷	Ignition ON – MIL OFF	11-14 V		
	30	⫟▷	Engine idling – MIL OFF	11-14 V		
Relay module (RM)	16	⟸	Ignition OFF	0 V		
	16	⟸	Ignition ON	11-14 V		
	33	⟸	Ignition OFF	0 V		
	33	⟸	Ignition ON	11-14 V		
Tachometer	11	⟹	Engine idling	33 Hz		
	11	⟹	3000 rpm	100 Hz		
Wide open throttle (WOT) relay – 806	13			1		

*Suggested settings - Voltage/time per division

1 Connected pin - no test data available or random digital signal

Model:	Engine code:	Year:
406 2,0 HDi	DW10ATED (RHZ)	1998-04
406 2,0 HDi	DW10TD (RHY)	1999-04
406 2,2 HDi	DW12ATED (4HX)	2000-05
406 Coupe 2,2 HDi	DW12ATED (4HX)	2000-06

ECM harness multi-plug

Terminal side

AD20174

Wire side

AD20176

Component/circuit description	ECM pin	Signal	Condition	Typical value
AC control module (1998)	47	←		1
	84	⇥▷	Engine idling	11-14 V
	84	⇥▷	Ignition ON	0-1 V
AC refrigerant triple pressure switch	78	←		1
Accelerator pedal position (APP) sensor	15	←	Ignition ON – accelerator pedal released	0,5 V
	15	←	Ignition ON – accelerator pedal depressed	3,5 V
	22	⇤	Engine idling	0 V
	44	⇒	Ignition ON	5 V
	68	←	Ignition ON – accelerator pedal released	0,2 V
	68	←	Ignition ON – accelerator pedal depressed	2 V
Brake pedal position (BPP) switch	48	←	Ignition ON – brake pedal released	0 V
	48	←	Ignition ON – brake pedal depressed	11-14 V
Camshaft position (CMP) sensor	12	⇒	Ignition ON	5 V
	18	←	Engine idling	5 V/50 ms per division 〰〰 26
	18	←	Ignition ON	11 V
	40	⇤	Engine idling	0 V
Combination control module – glow plug warning lamp (1999→)	56	⇒	Ignition ON – lamp ON	11-14 V
	56	⇒	Ignition ON – lamp OFF	0 V
Combination control module (1999→)	23			1
	36	⬌		1
	47	←		1
	62	⇒	Ignition ON	0 V
	62	⇒	Engine idling	27 Hz
	62	⇒	3000 rpm	97 Hz
	63			1
	66	⬌		1
	81			1
	82	⇥▷	Ignition ON – MIL ON	0-1 V
	82	⇥▷	Engine idling – MIL OFF	11-14 V
	84	⇥▷		1

Component/circuit description	ECM pin	Signal	Condition	Typical value
Crankshaft position (CKP) sensor	14	←	Engine idling	1,72 V ac
	14 (41)	←	Engine idling	2 V/1 ms per division 〰〰 6
	41	←	Engine idling	1,72 V ac
	41 (14)	←	Engine idling	2 V/1 ms per division – wave form reversed 〰〰 6
Cruise control brake pedal switch	73	←	Ignition ON – brake pedal released	11-14 V
	73	←	Ignition ON – brake pedal depressed	0 V
Cruise control clutch pedal switch	21	←	Engine idling – clutch pedal released	11-14 V
	21	←	Engine idling – clutch pedal depressed	0 V
Cruise control switch (1999→)	17			1
	60			1
	61			1
Data link connector (DLC)	10		Ignition ON	0 V
	38		Ignition ON	0 V
	62	⇨	3000 rpm	97 Hz
	62	⇨	Engine idling	27 Hz
	62	⇨	Ignition ON	0 V
Data link connector (DLC) (1998)	8	←	Ignition ON – coolant blower motor OFF	0 V
	8	←	Ignition ON – coolant blower motor ON	11-14 V
Earth	33		Ignition ON	0 V
	49		Ignition ON	0 V
	51		Ignition ON	0 V
	53		Ignition ON	0 V
Engine coolant blower motor (1998)	8		Ignition ON – coolant blower motor OFF	0 V
	8		Ignition ON – coolant blower motor ON	11-14 V
Engine coolant blower motor relay I/II (1998)	8		Ignition ON – coolant blower motor OFF	0 V
	8		Ignition ON – coolant blower motor ON	11-14 V
	25	⊐▷	Engine idling – coolant blower motor OFF	11-14 V
	25	⊐▷	Engine idling – coolant blower motor ON	0-1 V
Engine coolant blower motor relay II (1999→)	25	⊐▷	Engine idling – coolant blower motor OFF	11-14 V
	25	⊐▷	Engine idling – coolant blower motor ON	0-1 V
	83	⊐▷	Ignition OFF	11-14 V
	83	⊐▷	Ignition ON	11-14 V
	83	⊐▷	Engine idling – coolant blower motor OFF	11-14 V
	83	⊐▷	Engine idling – coolant blower motor ON	0-1 V
Engine coolant blower motor relay II/III (1998)	8		Ignition ON – coolant blower motor OFF	0 V
	8		Ignition ON – coolant blower motor ON	11-14 V
Engine coolant blower motor relay III (1998)	83	⊐▷	Ignition OFF	11-14 V
	83	⊐▷	Ignition ON	11-14 V
	83	⊐▷	Engine idling – coolant blower motor OFF	11-14 V
	83	⊐▷	Engine idling – coolant blower motor ON	0-1 V
Engine coolant heater relay I (1998)	85	⊐▷	Ignition ON – engine coolant heater OFF	11-14 V
	85	⊐▷	Ignition ON – engine coolant heater ON	0-1 V
Engine coolant heater relay II/III (1998)	58	⊐▷	Ignition ON – engine coolant heater OFF	11-14 V
	58	⊐▷	Ignition ON – engine coolant heater ON	0-1 V
Engine coolant heater relay (1999→)	58	⊐▷	Ignition ON – engine coolant heater OFF	11-14 V
	58	⊐▷	Ignition ON – engine coolant heater ON	0-1 V
	85	⊐▷	Ignition ON – engine coolant heater OFF	11-14 V
	85	⊐▷	Ignition ON – engine coolant heater ON	0-1 V
Engine coolant temperature (ECT) sensor	45	⊐—	Engine idling	0 V
	46	←	Ignition ON – coolant temp. 20°C	3,2 V
	46	←	Ignition ON – coolant temp. 80°C	0,7 V

Component/circuit description	ECM pin	Signal	Condition	Typical value
Exhaust gas recirculation (EGR) solenoid I	52	⊐▷	Ignition ON	11-14 V for 2 seconds then 0 V
	52	⊐▷	Engine idling	25%
	52	⊐▷	Engine idling	5 V/2 ms per division 〰29
Exhaust gas recirculation (EGR) solenoid II – some models	55	⊐▷	Ignition ON	11-14 V for 2 seconds then 0 V
Fuel pressure control solenoid	50	⊐▷	4000 rpm	23-25%
	50	⊐▷	Engine idling	11-14 V
	50	⊐▷	Engine idling	1000 Hz
	50	⊐▷	Engine idling	15-17%
	50	⊐▷	Engine idling	2 V/1 ms per division 〰37
	50	⊐▷	Ignition ON	10 V
Fuel pressure sensor	34	⊐—	Engine idling	0 V
	44	⇨	Ignition ON	5 V
	74	⇦	3000 rpm	1,97 V
	74	⇦	Engine cranking	1,3 V
	74	⇦	Engine idling	1,3 V
	74	⇦	Ignition ON	0,5 V
Fuel temperature sensor	39	⇦	Ignition ON – air temp. 20°C	2,7 V
Fuel temperature sensor (1998)	40	⊐—	Engine idling	0 V
Fuel temperature sensor (1999→)	22	⊐—	Engine idling	0 V
Glow plug timer relay	67		Ignition ON – glow plugs OFF	0 V
	67		Ignition ON – glow plugs ON	11-14 V
	88		Ignition ON – glow plugs OFF	11-14 V
	88		Ignition ON – glow plugs ON	0 V
Glow plug warning lamp (1998)	56	⇨	Ignition ON – lamp ON	11-14 V
	56	⇨	Ignition ON – lamp OFF	0 V
Ignition switch	69	⇦	Ignition OFF	0 V
	69	⇦	Ignition ON	11-14 V
Immobilizer control module (1998)	36	⇦⇨		1
	66	⇦⇨		1
Inertia fuel shut-off (IFS) switch (1999→)	87	⇦	Ignition ON – button depressed	0-1 V for 2 seconds then 11-14 V
	87	⇦	Engine idling – button depressed	0-1 V
	87	⇦	Ignition ON – button released	0 V
Injector 1	2	⇨	Ignition ON	7 V
	2 (30)	⇨	Engine idling	1 ms pilot + 1 ms main
	2 (30)	⇨	Engine idling	10 V/0,5 ms per division 〰24
	30	⇨	Ignition ON	7 V
	30 (2)	⇨	Engine idling	1 ms pilot + 1 ms main
	30 (2)	⇨	Engine idling	10 V/0,5 ms per division 〰24
Injector 2	5	⇨	Ignition ON	7 V
	5 (6)	⇨	Engine idling	1 ms pilot + 1 ms main
	5 (6)	⇨	Engine idling	10 V/0,5 ms per division 〰24
	6	⇨	Ignition ON	7 V
	6 (5)	⇨	Engine idling	1 ms pilot + 1 ms main
	6 (5)	⇨	Engine idling	10 V/0,5 ms per division 〰24
Injector 3	3	⇨	Ignition ON	7 V
	3 (31)	⇨	Engine idling	1 ms pilot + 1 ms main
	3 (31)	⇨	Engine idling	10 V/0,5 ms per division 〰24
	31	⇨	Ignition ON	7 V
	31 (2)	⇨	Engine idling	1 ms pilot + 1 ms main
	31 (3)	⇨	Engine idling	10 V/0,5 ms per division 〰24

Component/circuit description	ECM pin	Signal	Condition	Typical value
Injector 4	4	⇒	Ignition ON	7 V
	4 (32)	⇒	Engine idling	1 ms pilot + 1 ms main
	4 (32)	⇒	Engine idling	10 V/0,5 ms per division [24]
	32	⇒	Ignition ON	7 V
	32 (4)	⇒	Engine idling	1 ms pilot + 1 ms main
	32 (4)	⇒	Engine idling	10 V/0,5 ms per division [24]
Instrument panel (1998)	23	⊐⇥▷		[1]
	62	⇒	3000 rpm	97 Hz
	62	⇒	Engine idling	27 Hz
	62	⇒	Ignition ON	0 V
Intake air temperature (IAT) sensor	11	⟵	Ignition ON – air temp. 18°C	2,4 V
Intake air temperature (IAT) sensor (1999→)	22	⊐⟵	Engine idling	0 V
Malfunction indicator lamp (MIL) (1998)	82	⊐⇥▷	Ignition ON – MIL ON	0-1 V
	82	⊐⇥▷	Engine idling – MIL OFF	11-14 V
Manifold absolute pressure (MAP) sensor – RHZ	34	⊐⟵	Engine idling	0 V
	44	⇒	Ignition ON	5 V
	71	⟵	Ignition ON	2,4 V
	71	⟵	Engine idling	2,4 V
	71	⟵	Engine running – accelerator pedal briefly fully depressed	3,35 V (briefly)
Manifold absolute pressure (MAP) sensor (1999→)	22	⊐⟵	Engine idling	0 V
Mass air flow (MAF) sensor	13	⟵	Engine idling	2 V
	13	⟵	Engine idling – accelerate briefly	4,4 V (briefly)
	13	⟵	Ignition ON	0,5 V
Mass air flow (MAF) sensor (1998)	40	⊐⟵	Engine idling	0 V
Mass air flow (MAF) sensor (1999→)	22	⊐⟵	Engine idling	0 V
Relay module	1	⟵	Ignition OFF	0 V
	1	⟵	Ignition ON	11-14 V
	29	⟵	Ignition OFF	0 V
	29	⟵	Ignition ON	11-14 V
	86	⊐⇥▷	Ignition OFF	11-14 V
	86	⊐⇥▷	Ignition ON	0-1 V
Relay module (1998)	87	⊐⇥▷	Engine idling	0-1 V
	87	⊐⇥▷	Ignition OFF	0 V
	87	⊐⇥▷	Ignition ON	0-1 V for 2 seconds then 11-14 V
Turbocharger (TC) wastegate regulating valve – RHZ	26	⊐⇥▷	Ignition ON	11-14 V for 2 seconds then 0 V
	26	⊐⇥▷	Engine idling	5 V/2 ms per division [29]
Vehicle speed sensor (VSS)	19	⟵	Ignition ON – vehicle pushed	0 V or 10 V
3rd piston cut-off solenoid	80	⊐⇥▷	Engine idling	11-14 V
	80	⊐⇥▷	Engine under full load	0-1 V
	80	⊐⇥▷	Ignition ON	11-14 V for 2 seconds then 0 V

[1] Connected pin - no test data available

PEUGEOT

Bosch EDC 15C2

Model:	Engine code:	Year:
406 2,0 HDi	DW10ATED (RHS)	2001-04

ECM harness multi-plug

Terminal side – A – Grey, B – Brown, C – Black

AD22744

Wire side – A – Grey, B – Brown, C – Black

AD22743

Component/circuit description	ECM pin	Signal	Condition	Typical value	Oscilloscope setting*	Wave form
ABS control module (without ESP) – CAN data bus	Bk2	⬅⇨		1		
ABS control module – CAN data bus	Aa3	⬅⇨		1		
	Aa4	⬅⇨		1		
AC refrigerant triple pressure switch	Af2	⇨	Ignition ON	5 V		
	Af4	⊐—	Ignition ON	0 V		
	Ah2	⬅	Ignition OFF	0 V		
	Ah2	⬅	Engine idling	1,1 V		
Accelerator pedal position (APP) sensor	Ac2	⬅	Ignition ON – accelerator pedal released	0,2 V		
	Ac2	⬅	Ignition ON – accelerator pedal depressed	1,85 V		
	Ag2	⇨	Ignition ON	5 V		
	Ag3	⬅	Ignition ON – accelerator pedal released	0,4 V		
	Ag3	⬅	Ignition ON – accelerator pedal depressed	3,7 V		
	Ah3	⊐—	Ignition ON	0 V		
Brake pedal position (BPP) switch 2	Ae4	⬅	Ignition ON – brake pedal released	11-14 V		
	Ae4	⬅	Ignition ON – brake pedal depressed	0 V		
Camshaft position (CMP) sensor	Bf2	⊐—	Ignition ON	0 V		
	Bg2	⬅	Engine idling		2 V/50 ms	〰️ 64
	Bh2	⇨	Ignition ON	5 V		
Clutch pedal position (CPP) switch	Ae3	⬅	Ignition ON – clutch pedal released	11-14 V		
	Ae3	⬅	Ignition ON – clutch pedal depressed	0 V		

* Suggested settings - Voltage/time per division

Autodata

Component/circuit description	ECM pin	Signal	Condition	Typical value	Oscilloscope setting*	Wave form
Crankshaft position (CKP) sensor	Bj1	←	Engine idling	1,5 V ac	1 V/2 ms	ᴡᴡ 1
	Bk1	←	Engine idling	1,5 V ac	1 V/2 ms	Reversed ᴡᴡ 1
Data link connector (DLC)	Ab4	⬌	Ignition ON	0 V		
Earth	Ag1		Ignition ON	0 V		
	Ah1		Ignition ON	0 V		
	Bl4		Ignition ON	0 V		
	Bm4		Ignition ON	0 V		
Engine coolant blower motor relay 1	Ad4	⊐▷	Ignition ON	11-14 V		
Engine coolant blower motor relay 2	Ab2	⊐▷	Ignition ON	0-1 V		
	Ab2	⊐▷	Engine idling	11-14 V		
	Ac4	←	Ignition ON	0 V		
Engine coolant heater relay	Ab1	⬌		[1]		
	Ac1	⬌		[1]		
Engine coolant temperature (ECT) sensor	Bd1	⊐—	Ignition ON	0 V		
	Be1	←	Ignition ON – coolant temp. 20°C	3 V		
	Be1	←	Ignition ON – coolant temp. 85°C	0,6 V		
Exhaust gas pressure sensor	Bd3	←	Ignition ON	0,49 V		
	Bd3	←	Engine idling	0,52 V		
	Bh2	⇒	Ignition ON	5 V		
	Bm3	⊐—	Ignition ON	0 V		
Exhaust gas recirculation (EGR) solenoid 1	Ba3	⊐▷	Ignition ON	Wave pattern for 5 secs then 0 V	2 V/2 ms	ᴡᴡ 66
	Ba3	⊐▷	Engine idling		2 V/5 ms	ᴡᴡ 37
Exhaust gas recirculation (EGR) solenoid 2	Ca4	⊐▷	Ignition ON	Wave pattern for 5 secs then 0 V	2 V/2 ms	ᴡᴡ 66
	Ca4	⊐▷	Engine idling		2 V/5 ms	ᴡᴡ 37
Exhaust gas temperature sensor	Be3	⊐—	Ignition ON	0 V		
	Bf3	←	Ignition ON	5 V		
Fuel pressure regulator control solenoid	Bl2	⊐▷	Ignition ON		2 V/0,5 ms	ᴡᴡ 43
	Bl2	⊐▷	Engine idling		2 V/1 ms	ᴡᴡ 37
Fuel pressure sensor	Bf1	⊐—	Ignition ON	0 V		
	Bg1	←	Ignition ON	0,5 V		
	Bg1	←	Engine idling	1,3 V		
	Bg1	←	3000 rpm	1,8 V		
	Bh1	⇒	Ignition ON	5 V		
Fuel temperature sensor	Bd2	⊐—	Ignition ON	0 V		
	Be2	←	Engine idling	2,2 V		
Glow plug timer relay	Cb1	⊐▷	Engine idling	140 Hz	5 V/5 ms	ᴡᴡ 12
	Cf1	⊐▷	Ignition ON	1,1 V		

* Suggested settings - Voltage/time per division

Component/circuit description	ECM pin	Signal	Condition	Typical value	Oscilloscope setting*	Wave form
Injector 1	Cg1	⇨	Ignition ON	1 V		
	Cg1	⇨	Engine idling	0,25 ms pilot + 0,5 ms main		
	Cg1	⇨	Engine idling		20 V/0,5 ms	⎍⋀⋁ 67
	Ch2	⇨	Ignition ON	1 V		
	Ch2	⇨	Engine idling	0,25 ms pilot + 0,5 ms main		
	Ch2	⇨	Engine idling		20 V/0,5 ms	⎍⋀⋁ 67
Injector 2	Ch3	⇨	Ignition ON	1 V		
	Ch3	⇨	Engine idling	0,25 ms pilot + 0,5 ms main		
	Ch3	⇨	Engine idling		20 V/0,5 ms	⎍⋀⋁ 67
	Ch4	⇨	Ignition ON	1 V		
	Ch4	⇨	Engine idling	0,25 ms pilot + 0,5 ms main		
	Ch4	⇨	Engine idling		20 V/0,5 ms	⎍⋀⋁ 67
Injector 3	Cg3	⇨	Ignition ON	1 V		
	Cg3	⇨	Engine idling	0,25 ms pilot + 0,5 ms main		
	Cg3	⇨	Engine idling		20 V/0,5 ms	⎍⋀⋁ 67
	Cg4	⇨	Ignition ON	1 V		
	Cg4	⇨	Engine idling	0,25 ms pilot + 0,5 ms main		
	Cg4	⇨	Engine idling		20 V/0,5 ms	⎍⋀⋁ 67
Injector 4	Cg2	⇨	Ignition ON	1 V		
	Cg2	⇨	Engine idling	0,25 ms pilot + 0,5 ms main		
	Cg2	⇨	Engine idling		20 V/0,5 ms	⎍⋀⋁ 67
	Ch1	⇨	Ignition ON	1 V		
	Ch1	⇨	Engine idling	0,25 ms pilot + 0,5 ms main		
	Ch1	⇨	Engine idling		20 V/0,5 ms	⎍⋀⋁ 67
Intake air heater coolant control valve	Bc2	⇉▷	Ignition ON	11-14 V for 5 secs then 0-1 V		
	Bc2	⇉▷	Engine idling	11-14 V		
Intake air temperature (IAT) sensor	Bj3	⬅	Ignition ON – air temp. 18°C	2,3 V		
Intake air valve control valve	Bb3	⇉▷	Engine idling		2 V/0,5 ms	⎍⋀⋁ 43
Manifold absolute pressure (MAP) sensor	Bb2	⇨	Ignition ON	5 V		
	Bc4	⌐	Ignition ON	0 V		
	Bd4	⬅	Engine idling	2,4 V		
	Bd4	⬅	Engine idling – accelerate briefly	3,9 V briefly		
Mass air flow (MAF) sensor	Bg3	⌐	Ignition ON	0 V		
	Bh3	⬅	Ignition ON	0,5 V		
	Bh3	⬅	Engine idling	2,1 V		
	Bh3	⬅	Engine idling – accelerate briefly	4 V briefly		

★ Suggested settings - Voltage/time per division

Component/circuit description	ECM pin	Signal	Condition	Typical value	Oscilloscope setting*	Wave form
Multifunction control module 1 – CAN data bus	Aa3	◆⇨		1		
	Aa4	◆⇨		1		
Multifunction control module 2	Ac3	⬅	Ignition OFF	0 V		
	Ac3	⬅	Ignition ON	11-14 V		
	Ba2	⇥⇨	Ignition OFF	11-14 V		
	Ba2	⇥⇨	Ignition ON	0-1 V		
	Ba4	⇥⇨	Ignition ON	0-1 V for 5 secs then 10,6 V		
	Bl1	⬅	Ignition ON	11-14 V		
	Bm1	⬅	Ignition ON	11-14 V		
Turbocharger (TC) wastegate regulating valve	Cb4	⇥⇨	Ignition ON	Wave pattern for 5 secs then 0 V	2 V/2 ms	∿∿ 66
3rd piston cut-off solenoid	Bc3	⇥⇨	Ignition ON	11-14 V for 5 secs then 0-1 V		
	Bc3	⇥⇨	Engine idling	11-14 V		
	Bc3	⇥⇨	Engine under full load	0-1 V		

*Suggested settings - Voltage/time per division

1 Connected pin - no test data available or random digital signal

PEUGEOT
Bosch EDC 15C2

Model:	Engine code:	Year:
806 2,0 HDi	DW10ATED (RHZ)	1999-02

ECM harness multi-plug

Terminal side

AD20174

Wire side

AD20176

Component/circuit description	ECM pin	Signal	Condition	Typical value	Oscilloscope setting*	Wave form
AC refrigerant triple pressure switch	78	←		1		
Accelerator pedal position (APP) sensor	15	←	Ignition ON – accelerator pedal released	0,5 V		
	15	←	Ignition ON – accelerator pedal fully depressed	3,5 V		
	22	⌐	Engine idling	0 V		
	44	⇒	Ignition ON	5 V		
	68	←	Ignition ON – accelerator pedal released	0,2 V		
	68	←	Ignition ON – accelerator pedal fully depressed	2 V		
Brake pedal position (BPP) switch	48	←	Ignition ON – brake pedal released	0 V		
	48	←	Ignition ON – Brake pedal depressed	11-14 V		
Camshaft position (CMP) sensor	12	⇒	Ignition ON	5 V		
	18	←	Engine idling		5 V/50 ms	26
	18	←	Ignition ON	11 V		
	40	⌐	Engine idling	0 V		
Clutch pedal position (CPP) switch	21	←	Ignition ON – clutch pedal released	11-14 V		
	21	←	Ignition ON – clutch pedal fully depressed	0 V		
Crankshaft position (CKP) sensor	14	←	Engine idling	1,72 V ac		
	14	←	Engine idling		2 V/1 ms	6
	41	←	Engine idling	1,72 V		
	41	←	Engine idling		2 V/1 ms	6
Cruise control brake pedal switch	73	←	Ignition ON – brake pedal released	11-14 V		
	73	←	Ignition ON – brake pedal depressed	0 V		
Cruise control switch	17	↔		1		
	60	↔		1		
	61	↔		1		

* Suggested settings - Voltage/time per division

Autodata

Component/circuit description	ECM pin	Signal	Condition	Typical value	Oscilloscope setting*	Wave form
Data link connector (DLC)	10		Ignition ON	0 V		
	38		Ignition ON	0 V		
	62	⇨	Ignition ON	0 V		
	62	⇨	Engine idling	27 Hz		
	62	⇨	3000 rpm	97 Hz		
	81	⬄		[1]		
Earth	33		Ignition ON	0 V		
	49		Ignition ON	0 V		
	51		Ignition ON	0 V		
	53		Ignition ON	0 V		
Engine coolant blower motor relay 1	83	⌐⇨	Ignition OFF	11-14 V		
	83	⌐⇨	Ignition ON	11-14 V		
	83	⌐⇨	Engine idling – coolant blower motor OFF	11-14 V		
	83	⌐⇨	Engine idling – coolant blower motor ON	0-1 V		
Engine coolant blower motor relay 2	8	⌐⇨	Ignition ON – coolant blower motor OFF	0 V		
	8	⌐⇨	Ignition ON – coolant blower motor ON	11-14 V		
	25	⌐⇨	Engine idling – coolant blower motor OFF	11-14 V		
	25	⌐⇨	Engine idling – coolant blower motor ON	0-1 V		
Engine coolant heater relay	85	⌐⇨	Ignition ON – engine coolant heater OFF	11-14 V		
	85	⌐⇨	Ignition ON – engine coolant heater ON	0-1 V		
Engine coolant temperature (ECT) sensor	45	⌐—	Engine idling	0 V		
	46	⬅	Ignition ON – coolant temp. 20°C	3,2 V		
	46	⬅	Ignition ON – coolant temp. 80°C	0,7 V		
Exhaust gas recirculation (EGR) solenoid 1	52	⌐⇨	Ignition ON	11-14 V for 2 secs then 0 V		
	52	⌐⇨	Engine idling	25%		
	52	⌐⇨	Engine idling		5 V/2 ms	〰〰 29
Exhaust gas recirculation (EGR) solenoid 2	55	⌐⇨	Ignition ON	11-14 V for 2 secs then 0 V		
Fuel pressure regulator control solenoid	50	⌐⇨	Ignition ON	10 V		
	50	⌐⇨	Engine idling	11-14 V		
	50	⌐⇨	Engine idling	1000 Hz		
	50	⌐⇨	Engine idling	15-17%		
	50	⌐⇨	4000 rpm	23-25%		
	50	⌐⇨	Engine idling		2 V/1 ms	〰〰 37
Fuel pressure sensor	74	⬅	3000 rpm	1,97 V		
Fuel rail pressure (FRP) sensor	34	⌐—	Engine idling	0 V		
	44	⇨	Ignition ON	5 V		
	74	⬅	Ignition ON	0,5 V		
	74	⬅	Engine cranking	1,3 V		
	74	⬅	Engine idling	1,3 V		

* Suggested settings - Voltage/time per division

Component/circuit description	ECM pin	Signal	Condition	Typical value	Oscilloscope setting*	Wave form
Fuel temperature sensor	22	⊣⊢	Engine idling	0 V		
	39	←	Ignition ON – air temp. 20°C	2,7 V		
Glow plug timer relay	67		Ignition ON – glow plugs OFF	0 V		
	67		Ignition ON – glow plugs ON	11-14 V		
	88		Ignition ON – glow plugs OFF	11-14 V		
	88		Ignition ON – glow plugs ON	0 V		
Glow plug warning lamp	56	⇒	Ignition ON – lamp ON	11-14 V		
	56	⇒	Ignition ON – lamp OFF	0 V		
Ignition switch	69	←	Ignition OFF	0 V		
	69	←	Ignition ON	11-14 V		
Immobiliser control module	36	⇔		1		
	66	⇔		1		
Inertia fuel shut-off (IFS) switch	87	←	Ignition ON – button depressed	0-1 V for 2 seconds then 11-14 V		
	87	←	Ignition ON – button released	0 V		
	87	←	Engine idling – button depressed	0-1 V		
Injector 1	2	⇒	Ignition ON	7 V		
	2	⇒	Engine idling	1 ms pilot + 1 ms main		
	2	⇒	Engine idling		10 V/0,5 ms	∿∿ 24
	30	⇒	Ignition ON	7 V		
	30	⇒	Engine idling	1 ms pilot + 1 ms main		
	30	⇒	Engine idling		10 V/0,5 ms	∿∿ 24
Injector 2	5	⇒	Ignition ON	7 V		
	5	⇒	Engine idling	1 ms pilot + 1 ms main		
	5	⇒	Engine idling		10 V/0,5 ms	∿∿ 24
	6	⇒	Ignition ON	7 V		
	6	⇒	Engine idling	1 ms pilot + 1 ms main		
	6	⇒	Engine idling		10 V/0,5 ms	∿∿ 24
Injector 3	3	⇒	Ignition ON	7 V		
	3	⇒	Engine idling	1 ms pilot + 1 ms main		
	3	⇒	Engine idling		10 V/0,5 ms	∿∿ 24
	31	⇒	Ignition ON	7 V		
	31	⇒	Engine idling	1 ms pilot + 1 ms main		
	31	⇒	Engine idling		10 V/0,5 ms	∿∿ 24
Injector 4	4	⇒	Ignition ON	7 V		
	4	⇒	Engine idling	1 ms pilot + 1 ms main		
	4	⇒	Engine idling		10 V/0,5 ms	∿∿ 24
	32	⇒	Ignition ON	7 V		
	32	⇒	Engine idling	1 ms pilot + 1 ms main		
	32	⇒	Engine idling		10 V/0,5 ms	∿∿ 24
Instrument panel	23	⊣⇒		1		
	63	⇔		1		

* Suggested settings - Voltage/time per division

Component/circuit description	ECM pin	Signal	Condition	Typical value	Oscilloscope setting*	Wave form
Intake air temperature (IAT) sensor	11	←	Ignition ON – air temp. 18°C	2,4 V		
Intake manifold air control solenoid	24	⇶▷		1		
Malfunction indicator lamp (MIL)	82	⇶▷	Ignition ON – MIL ON	0-1 V		
	82	⇶▷	Engine idling – MIL OFF	11-14 V		
Manifold absolute pressure (MAP) sensor	22	⇶⊢	Engine idling	0 V		
	44	⇨	Ignition ON	5 V		
	71	←	Ignition ON	2,4 V		
	71	←	Engine idling	2,4 V		
	71	←	Engine idling – accelerator pedal briefly fully depressed	3,35 V briefly		
Mass air flow (MAF) sensor	13	←	Engine idling	2 V		
	13	←	Engine idling – accelerate briefly	4,4 V briefly		
	13	←	Ignition ON	0,5 V		
Relay module (RM)	1	←	Ignition OFF	0 V		
	1	←	Ignition ON	11-14 V		
	29	←	Ignition OFF	0 V		
	29	←	Ignition ON	11-14 V		
	86	⇶▷	Ignition OFF	0-1 V		
	86	⇶▷	Ignition ON	11-14 V		
Turbocharger (TC) wastegate regulating valve	26	⇶▷	Ignition ON	11-14 V for 2 secs then 0 V		
	26	⇶▷	Engine idling		5 V/2 ms	⩗⩗ 29
Vehicle speed sensor (VSS)	19	←	Ignition ON – vehicle pushed	0 V or 10 V		
Wide open throttle (WOT) relay	47	←		1		
	84	⇶▷		1		
3rd piston cut-off solenoid	80	⇶▷	Engine idling	11-14 V		
	80	⇶▷	Engine under full load	0-1 V		
	80	⇶▷	Ignition ON	11-14 V for 2 secs then 0 V		

*Suggested settings - Voltage/time per division

1 Connected pin - no test data available or random digital signal

ECM harness multi-plug

Terminal side – A – Brown, B – Black

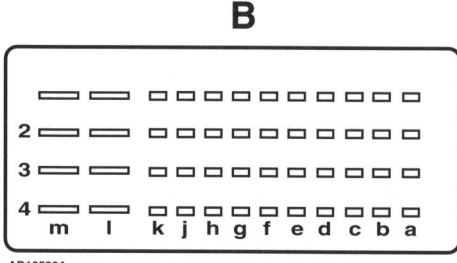

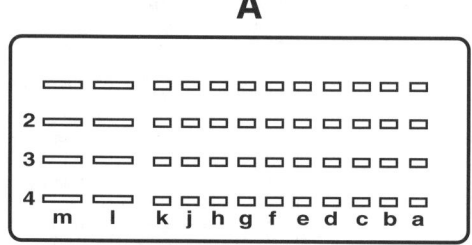

AD105964

Wire side – A – Brown, B – Black

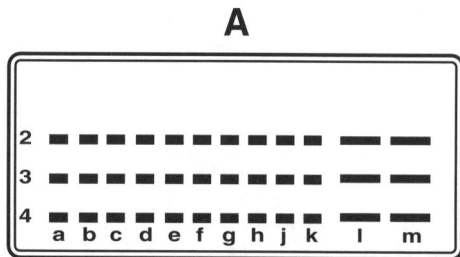

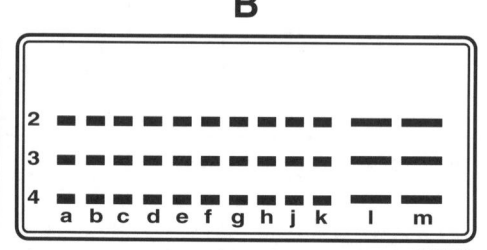

AD105963

Component/circuit description	ECM pin	Signal	Condition	Typical value	Oscilloscope setting*	Wave form
AC refrigerant triple pressure switch	Ae2			1		
Battery voltage – through relay module	Bb2	←	Ignition ON	11-14 V		
Crankshaft position (CKP) sensor	Bk2	⌐	Ignition ON	0 V		
	Bk4	←	Engine idling	1,3 V ac	5 V/2 ms	Reversed 〰 27
Data link connector (DLC)	Ab3			1		
	Af2			1		
	Ah2			1		
	Aj2	⇨	Engine idling	28 Hz		
	Aj2	⇨	Engine running – 3000 rpm	100 Hz		
Earth	Al4		Ignition ON	0 V		
	Am4		Ignition ON	0 V		
Engine coolant blower motor relay 1/2	Aj4			1		
Engine coolant blower motor relay 3	Ak4			1		
Engine coolant temperature (ECT) sensor	Bf2	⌐	Ignition ON	0 V		
	Bg4	←	Ignition ON – Coolant temp. 20°C	2,6 V		
	Bg4	←	Ignition ON – engine hot	0,6 V		
Exhaust gas recirculation (EGR) solenoid	Bb3	⌐▷	Ignition ON	11-14 V		
	Bb3	⌐▷	Engine running – solenoid operating	0-1 V		

* Suggested settings - Voltage/time per division

Component/circuit description	ECM pin	Signal	Condition	Typical value	Oscilloscope setting*	Wave form
Fuel lever position sensor	Bd4	←	Ignition ON – fuel lever closed	1 V		
	Bd4	←	Ignition ON – fuel lever fully open	4 V		
	Be2	⊣	Ignition ON	0 V		
	Bh4	⇨	Ignition ON	5 V		
Fuel shut-off solenoid	Bl2	⇨	Ignition ON	1		
Glow plug control module	Bc3	⇨	Ignition ON	0 V		
	Bc3	⇨	Engine idling	11-14 V		
	Bc4	←	Ignition ON	11,1 V		
	Bc4	←	Engine idling	1,3 V		
	Bl4	⊣	Ignition ON	0 V		
Ignition switch	Ab4	←	Ignition ON	11-14 V		
Injection pump advance solenoid	Bf4	⊣▷	Ignition ON	Wave pattern for 5 secs then 0-1 V	5 V/20 ms	33
	Bf4	⊣▷	Engine idling	50%	5 V/20 ms	33
Injector needle lift sensor	Bj2	⊣	Ignition ON	0 V		
	Bk3	←	Ignition ON	3,2 V		
	Bk3	←	Engine idling		1 V/5 ms	7
Intake air flap control actuator	Ba4	⊣▷	Ignition ON	11-14 V		
	Ba4	⊣▷	Engine idling – 11-14 V for 10 secs then wave pattern	56%	2 V/10 ms	64
Intake air temperature (IAT) sensor	Bj3	←	Ignition ON – air temp. 14°C	3,2 V		
Mass air flow (MAF) sensor	Bd2	←	Ignition ON	0,6 V		
	Bd2	←	Engine idling	2 V		
	Bd2	←	Engine idling – accelerate briefly	3,6 V		
	Be3	⊣	Ignition ON	0 V		
Multifunction control module	Aa4			1		
	Ac3			1		
	Ad3			1		
	Ac4			1		
	Af3			1		
	Af4			1		
	Aj3			1		
	Ak3			1		
Multifunction control module – tachometer signal	Aj2	⇨	Ignition ON	11,7 V		
	Aj2	⇨	Engine idling	28 Hz		
	Aj2	⇨	Engine running – 3000 rpm	100 Hz		
Relay module	Be4	⊣▷	Ignition OFF	11-14 V		
	Be4	⊣▷	Ignition ON	0-1 V		
	Bm2	←	Ignition OFF	0 V		
	Bm2	←	Ignition ON	11-14 V		
Vehicle speed sensor (VSS)	Ag2	←	Ignition ON – vehicle pushed	0-1 V or 10-11 V		

*Suggested settings - Voltage/time per division

1 Connected pin - no test data available or random digital signal

Model:	Engine code:	Year:
Partner 2,0 HDi	RHY (DW10TD)	2002-06

ECM harness multi-plug

Terminal side – A – Grey, B – Brown, C – Black

C

h1	g1	f1	e1	d1	c1	b1	a1
h2	g2	f2	e2	d2	c2	b2	a2
h3	g3	f3	e3	d3	c3	b3	a3
h4	g4	f4	e4	d4	c4	b4	a4

B

m1	l1	k1	j1	h1	g1	f1	e1	d1	c1	b1	a1
m2	l2	k2	j2	h2	g2	f2	e2	d2	c2	b2	a2
m3	l3	k3	j3	h3	g3	f3	e3	d3	c3	b3	a3
m4	l4	k4	j4	h4	g4	f4	e4	d4	c4	b4	a4

A

a4	b4	c4	d4	e4	f4	g4	h4
a3	b3	c3	d3	e3	f3	g3	h3
a2	b2	c2	d2	e2	f2	g2	h2
a1	b1	c1	d1	e1	f1	g1	h1

AD22744

Wire side – A – Grey, B – Brown, C – Black

A

h4	g4	f4	e4	d4	c4	b4	a4
h3	g3	f3	e3	d3	c3	b3	a3
h2	g2	f2	e2	d2	c2	b2	a2
h1	g1	f1	e1	d1	c1	b1	a1

B

a1	b1	c1	d1	e1	f1	g1	h1	j1	k1	l1	m1
a2	b2	c2	d2	e2	f2	g2	h2	j2	k2	l2	m2
a3	b3	c3	d3	e3	f3	g3	h3	j3	k3	l3	m3
a4	b4	c4	d4	e4	f4	g4	h4	j4	k4	l4	m4

C

a1	b1	c1	d1	e1	f1	g1	h1
a2	b2	c2	d2	e2	f2	g2	h2
a3	b3	c3	d3	e3	f3	g3	h3
a4	b4	c4	d4	e4	f4	g4	h4

AD22743

Component/circuit description	ECM pin	Signal	Condition	Typical value	Oscilloscope setting*	Wave form
AC refrigerant triple pressure switch	Cf2	⇨	Ignition ON	5 V		
	Cf4	⌐	Ignition ON	0 V		
	Ch2	⟵	Ignition OFF	0 V		
	Ch2	⟵	Ignition ON	0,8 V		
Accelerator pedal position (APP) sensor	Cc2	⟵	Ignition ON – accelerator pedal released	0,2 V		
	Cc2	⟵	Ignition ON – accelerator pedal depressed	1,85 V		
	Cg2	⇨	Ignition ON	5 V		
	Cg3	⟵	Ignition ON – accelerator pedal released	0,4 V		
	Cg3	⟵	Ignition ON – accelerator pedal depressed	3,7 V		
	Ch3	⌐	Ignition ON	0 V		
Battery	Bg4	⟵	Ignition OFF	11-14 V		
Brake pedal position (BPP) switch	Ce4	⟵	Ignition ON – brake pedal released	11-14 V		
	Ce4	⟵	Ignition ON – brake pedal depressed	0 V		
Camshaft position (CMP) sensor	Aa1	⌐	Ignition ON	0 V		
	Ad1	⟵	Engine idling		2 V/50 ms	∿ 64
	Bc3	⇨	Ignition ON	5 V		
Clutch pedal position (CPP) switch	Ce3	⟵	Ignition ON – clutch pedal released	11-14 V		
	Ce3	⟵	Ignition ON – clutch pedal depressed	0 V		
Crankshaft position (CKP) sensor	Bj4	⟵	Engine idling	1,4 V ac	1 V/2 ms	Reversed ∿ 1
	Bk4	⟵	Engine idling	1,4 V ac	1 V/2 ms	∿ 1
Data link connector (DLC)	Cb4	⟺	Ignition ON	0 V		

* Suggested settings - Voltage/time per division

Component/circuit description	ECM pin	Signal	Condition	Typical value	Oscilloscope setting*	Wave form
Earth	Ah2		Ignition ON	0 V		
	Bk2		Ignition ON	0 V		
	Cg4		Ignition ON	0 V		
	Ch4		Ignition ON	0 V		
Engine coolant blower motor relay	Cb2	⊐▷	Ignition ON	11-14 V		
	Cc4		Ignition ON	0 V		
	Cd4		Ignition ON	11-14 V		
Engine coolant heater relay	Cc1	⊐▷	Ignition ON	11-14 V		
Engine coolant temperature (ECT) sensor	Be1	⊐─	Ignition ON	0 V		
	Be4	◄	Coolant temp. 85°C	0,9 V		
Exhaust gas recirculation (EGR) solenoid	Ag1	⊐▷	Ignition ON		2 V/2 ms	66
	Ag1	⊐▷	Engine idling	41%	2 V/5 ms	10
Fuel flow control valve	Ag3	⊐▷	Ignition ON	11-14 V		
	Ag3	⊐▷	Engine idling	10%	2 V/5 ms	37
Fuel pressure control solenoid	Ah1	⊐▷	Ignition ON	11-14 V		
	Ah1	⊐▷	Engine idling		2 V/2 ms	37
Fuel pressure sensor	Ad3	◄	Ignition ON	0,5 V		
	Bd1	⇒	Ignition ON	5 V		
	Bf2	⊐─	Ignition ON	0 V		
Fuel temperature sensor	Bf3	◄	Engine idling – coolant temp. 85°C	1,3 V		
	Bh4	⊐─	Ignition ON	0 V		
Glow plug timer relay	Ac1		Ignition ON	0 V		
	Be2		Ignition ON	11-14 V		
Injector 1	Bl3	⇒	Ignition ON	110 V		
	Bl3	⇒	Engine idling	0,4 ms pilot + 0,7 ms main		
	Bl3	⇒	Engine idling		20 V/0,5 ms	68
	Bm2	⇒	Ignition ON	110 V		
	Bm2	⇒	Engine idling	0,4 ms pilot + 0,7 ms main		
	Bm2	⇒	Engine idling		20 V/0,5 ms	68
Injector 2	Bl1	⇒	Ignition ON	110 V		
	Bl1	⇒	Engine idling	0,4 ms pilot + 0,7 ms main		
	Bl1	⇒	Engine idling		20 V/0,5 ms	68
	Bl4	⇒	Ignition ON	110 V		
	Bl4	⇒	Engine idling	0,4 ms pilot + 0,7 ms main		
	Bl4	⇒	Engine idling		20 V/0,5 ms	68
Injector 3	Bl2	⇒	Ignition ON	110 V		
	Bl2	⇒	Engine idling	0,4 ms pilot + 0,7 ms main		
	Bl2	⇒	Engine idling		20 V/0,5 ms	68
	Bm3	⇒	Ignition ON	110 V		
	Bm3	⇒	Engine idling	0,4 ms pilot + 0,7 ms main		
	Bm3	⇒	Engine idling		20 V/0,5 ms	68

* Suggested settings - Voltage/time per division

Component/circuit description	ECM pin	Signal	Condition	Typical value	Oscilloscope setting*	Wave form
Injector 4	Bm1	⇒	Ignition ON	110 V		
	Bm1	⇒	Engine idling	0,4 ms pilot + 0,7 ms main		
	Bm1	⇒	Engine idling		20 V/0,5 ms	〜〜 68
	Bm4	⇒	Ignition ON	110 V		
	Bm4	⇒	Engine idling	0,4 ms pilot + 0,7 ms main		
	Bm4	⇒	Engine idling		20 V/0,5 ms	〜〜 68
Intake air temperature (IAT) sensor	Be3	⇐	Ignition ON – air temp. 19°C	2,5 V		
Mass air flow (MAF) sensor	Aa3	⇐	Ignition ON	0,57 V		
	Aa3	⇐	Engine idling	2,6 V		
	Ab3	⌐	Ignition ON	0 V		
	Bg2	⌐	Ignition ON	0 V		
Multifunction control module 1 – CAN data bus – low	Ca3	⇔		1		
Multifunction control module 1 – CAN data bus – high	Ca4	⇔		1		
Multifunction control module 2	Ae3	⇐	Ignition ON	11-14 V		
	Af2	⇐	Ignition ON	11-14 V		
	Af3	⇐	Ignition ON	11-14 V		
	Bf1	⊐▷	Ignition OFF	11-14 V		
	Bf1	⊐▷	Ignition ON	0-1 V		
	Bh1		Ignition ON	0 V		
	Cc3	⇐	Ignition ON	11-14 V		
Vehicle speed sensor (VSS)	Ab1	⇐	Ignition OFF	10,8 V		
	Ab1	⇐	Ignition ON – vehicle pushed	0 V or 11-14 V switching		

*Suggested settings - Voltage/time per division

1 Connected pin - no test data available or random digital signal

Model:	Engine code:	Year:
Clio 1,2 (X57)	D7F 730	1995-98
Clio 1,2 (XBO) – without AC	D7F 720	1998-06
Kangoo 1,2 (XCO) – without AC	D7F 710	1998-06

ECM harness multi-plug

Terminal side

AD71594

Wire side

AD42073

Component/circuit description	ECM pin	Signal	Condition	Typical value	Oscilloscope setting*	Wave form
Crankshaft position (CKP) sensor	13	←	Engine idling	0,7 V ac	5 V/1 ms	3
	13	←	3000 rpm	1,9 V ac		
	31	←	Engine idling	0,7 V ac	5 V/1 ms	3
	31	←	3000 rpm	1,9 V ac		
Data link connector (DLC)	9	←⇨	Ignition ON	2 V		
	10	←⇨	Ignition ON	2 V		
Digital multifunction display, fuel consumption signal – D7F 720	25	⇨		1		
Earth	4		Ignition ON	0 V		
	16		Ignition ON	0 V		
	34		Ignition ON	0 V		
Engine control relay	18	←	Ignition OFF	0 V		
	18	←	Ignition ON	11-14 V		
	26	⊐⊳	Ignition OFF	11-14 V		
	26	⊐⊳	Ignition ON	0 V		
Engine coolant blower motor relay – D7F 710/720	27	⊐—	Ignition ON – coolant blower motor OFF	11-14 V		
	27	⊐—	Engine running – coolant blower motor OFF	11-14 V		
	27	⊐—	Engine running – coolant blower motor ON	0 V		
Engine coolant temperature (ECT) sensor	6	←	Ignition ON – coolant temp. 20°C	3 V		
	6	←	Ignition ON – coolant temp. 80°C	0,5 V		
	15	⊐—	Ignition ON	0 V		
Evaporative emission (EVAP) canister purge valve	24	⊐⊳	Ignition ON	11-14 V briefly then 0 V		
	24	⊐⊳	Engine idling	11-14 V		
	24	⊐⊳	Engine running		10 V/50 ms	Intermittent 20
Fuel pump relay	20	⊐⊳	Ignition ON	1,8 V briefly then 11-14 V		
	20	⊐⊳	Engine idling	1,9 V		
Heated oxygen sensor (HO2S)	22	←	Engine idling	0-1 V fluctuating	0,2 V/1 sec.	21
	22	←	Engine running – mixture lean	0-0,15 V fluctuating		
	22	←	Engine running – mixture rich	0,6-1,1 V fluctuating		

* Suggested settings - Voltage/time per division

Component/circuit description	ECM pin	Signal	Condition	Typical value	Oscilloscope setting*	Wave form
Idle air control (IAC) valve	11 (29)	⇒	Ignition ON	10 V		
	11 (29)	⇒	Engine idling		5 V/0,5 sec.	Intermittent 〰 26
	12 (28)	⇒	Ignition ON	0,3 V		
	12 (28)	⇒	Engine idling		5 V/0,5 sec.	Intermittent 〰 26
	28 (12)	⇒	Ignition ON	0,3 V		
	28 (12)	⇒	Engine idling		5 V/0,5 sec.	Intermittent 〰 26
	29 (11)	⇒	Ignition ON	10 V		
	29 (11)	⇒	Engine idling		5 V/0,5 sec.	Intermittent 〰 26
Ignition coil – cylinders 1 & 4	35	⊐▷	Ignition ON	11-14 V		
	35	⊐▷	Engine idling		5 V/1 ms	〰 33
Ignition coil – cylinders 2 & 3	17	⊐▷	Ignition ON	11-14 V		
	17	⊐▷	Engine idling		5 V/1 ms	〰 33
Immobilizer control module	30	⬅		1		
Injectors 1 & 4	33	⊐▷	Ignition ON	11-14 V briefly then 0 V		
	33	⊐▷	Engine idling	3,1 ms	10 V/2 ms	〰 35
Injectors 2 & 3	32	⊐▷	Ignition ON	11-14 V briefly then 0 V		
	32	⊐▷	Engine idling	3,1 ms	10 V/2 ms	〰 35
Instruments – D7F 720	20	⊐▷	Engine idling	1,9 V		
Intake air temperature (IAT) sensor	2	⬅	Ignition ON – air temp. 10°C	2,75 V		
	15	⊐	Ignition ON	0 V		
Knock sensor (KS)	1	⬅	Engine idling – full throttle briefly		50 mV/1 ms	〰 38
	15	⊐	Ignition ON	0 V		
Malfunction indicator lamp (MIL)	19	⊐▷	Ignition ON – MIL ON	1,6 V		
	19	⊐▷	Engine idling – MIL OFF	11-14 V		
Manifold absolute pressure (MAP) sensor	5	⇒	Ignition ON	5 V		
	15	⊐	Ignition ON	0 V		
	23	⬅	Engine idling	1,6 V		
	23	⬅	Engine under load	4,9 V		
Power steering pressure (PSP) switch	7	⬅	Engine idling – steering wheel not turned	10 V		
	7	⬅	Engine idling – steering wheel turned	0 V		
Throttle position (TP) sensor	3	⬅	Ignition ON – throttle closed	0,5 V		
	3	⬅	Ignition ON – throttle fully open	4,4 V		
	5	⇒	Ignition ON	5 V		
	15	⊐	Ignition ON	0 V		
Vehicle speed sensor (VSS)	8	⬅	Ignition ON – vehicle pushed	0 V or 9,5 V switching		

*Suggested settings - Voltage/time per division

1 Connected pin - no test data available or random digital signal

Model:	Engine code:	Year:
Clio 1,2 (XBO) – with AC	D7F 720	1998-06
Megane 1,6	K7M 702/703	1995-99
Kangoo 1,2 (XCO) – with AC	D7F 710	1998-05

ECM harness multi-plug

Terminal side

27 26 25 24 23 22 21 20 19 18 17 16 15 14 13 12 11 10 9 8 7 6 5 4 3 2 1
55 54 53 52 51 50 49 48 47 46 45 44 43 42 41 40 39 38 37 36 35 34 33 32 31 30 29 28

AD81647

Wire side

1 2 3 4 5 6 7 8 9 10 11 12 13 14 15 16 17 18 19 20 21 22 23 24 25 26 27
28 29 30 31 32 33 34 35 36 37 38 39 40 41 42 43 44 45 46 47 48 49 50 51 52 53 54 55

AD42110

Component/circuit description	ECM pin	Signal	Condition	Typical value	Oscilloscope setting*	Wave form
Air conditioning	5			1		
	51			1		
Air conditioning – D7F 710/720	48	⊐▷	Engine idling	0 V		
AC control module – D7F 710/720	10	⊐─	Ignition ON – coolant blower motor OFF	11-14 V		
	10	⊐─	Engine running – coolant blower motor OFF	11-14 V		
	10	⊐─	Engine running – coolant blower motor ON	0 V		
Automatic transmission – K7M 702/703	41			1		
Automatic transmission – K7M 702/703, some models	7			1		
Battery – K7M 702/703	32	←	Ignition OFF	11-14 V		
Crankshaft position (CKP) sensor	33 (34)	←	Engine cranking	0,2 V ac		
	33 (34)	←	Engine idling	2 V ac	5 V/1 ms	∿∿ 3
	33 (34)	←	3000 rpm	7 V ac		
	34 (33)	←	Engine cranking	0,2 V ac		
	34 (33)	←	Engine idling	2 V ac	5 V/1 ms	Reversed ∿∿ 3
	34 (33)	←	3000 rpm	7 V ac		
Data link connector (DLC)	11	◀▷	Ignition ON	11 V		
	38	◀▷		1		
Earth	2		Ignition ON	0 V		
	3		Ignition ON	0 V		
	18		Ignition ON	0 V		
Engine control relay – D7F 710/720	1	←	Ignition OFF	0 V		
	1	←	Ignition ON	11-14 V		
	40	⊐▷	Ignition OFF	11-14 V		
	40	⊐▷	Ignition ON	0 V		
Engine coolant blower motor relay – D7F 710/720	10	⊐─	Ignition ON – coolant blower motor OFF	11-14 V		
	10	⊐─	Engine running – coolant blower motor OFF	11-14 V		
	10	⊐─	Engine running – coolant blower motor ON	0 V		

* Suggested settings - Voltage/time per division

Component/circuit description	ECM pin	Signal	Condition	Typical value	Oscilloscope setting*	Wave form
Engine coolant temperature (ECT) sensor	15	←	Ignition ON – engine cold	3,1 V		
	15	←	Engine idling – engine hot	0,38 V		
	44	⅃⊢	Ignition ON	0 V		
Evaporative emission (EVAP) canister purge valve	42	⅃⊢▷	Ignition ON	11-14 V briefly then 0 V		
	42	⅃⊢▷	Engine idling	11-14 V		
Exhaust gas recirculation (EGR) solenoid – some models – K7M 702/703	10	⅃⊢▷	Ignition ON	11-14 V briefly then 0 V		
Fuel pump relay	48	⅃⊢▷	Ignition ON	0 V briefly then 11-14 V		
	48	⅃⊢▷	Engine running	0 V		
Fuel pump relay – K7M 702/703	52	←	Ignition ON	11-14 V briefly then 0 V		
	52	←	Engine idling	11-14 V		
Heated oxygen sensor (HO2S)	17	←	Engine idling	0-1 V fluctuating	0,2 V/1 sec.	⩗⩗ 21
Heated rear window switch – K7M 702/703	6	←	Ignition ON – heated rear window OFF	11-14 V		
	6	←	Ignition ON – heated rear window ON	0 V		
Idle air control (IAC) valve – K7M 702/703	9 (36)	⇨	Ignition ON	0,2 V		
	9 (36)	⇨	Engine idling		5 V/0,5 sec.	Intermittent ⩗⩗ 26
	35 (40)	⇨	Ignition ON	0,2 V		
	35 (40)	⇨	Engine idling		5 V/0,5 sec.	Intermittent ⩗⩗ 26
	40 (35)	⇨	Ignition ON	0,2 V		
	40 (35)	⇨	Engine idling		5 V/0,5 sec.	Intermittent ⩗⩗ 26
	36 (9)	⇨	Ignition ON	11 V		
	36 (9)	⇨	Engine idling		5 V/0,5 sec.	Intermittent ⩗⩗ 26
Idle air control (IAC) valve – D7F 710/720	9 (35)	⇨	Ignition ON	0,2 V		
	9 (35)	⇨	Engine idling		5 V/0,5 sec.	Intermittent ⩗⩗ 26
	35 (9)	⇨	Ignition ON	0,2 V		
	35 (9)	⇨	Engine idling		5 V/0,5 sec.	Intermittent ⩗⩗ 26
	8 (30)	⇨	Ignition ON	0,2 V		
	8 (30)	⇨	Engine idling		5 V/0,5 sec.	Intermittent ⩗⩗ 26
	30 (8)	⇨	Ignition ON	11 V		
	30 (8)	⇨	Engine idling		5 V/0,5 sec.	Intermittent ⩗⩗ 26
Ignition coil – cylinders 1 & 4	28	⅃⊢▷	Ignition ON	11-14 V		
	28	⅃⊢▷	Engine idling		5 V/1 ms	⩗⩗ 33
Ignition coil – cylinders 2 & 3	29	⅃⊢▷	Ignition ON	11-14 V		
	29	⅃⊢▷	Engine idling		5 V/1 ms	⩗⩗ 33
Ignition switch – K7M 702/703	24	←	Ignition OFF	0 V		
	24	←	Ignition ON	11-14 V		
Immobilizer control module	37	←	Ignition ON	1-4 V fluctuating		
Injectors 1 & 4	30	⅃⊢▷	Ignition ON	11-14 V briefly then 0 V		
	30	⅃⊢▷	Engine idling	2,5 ms	10 V/0,5 ms	⩗⩗ 36

* Suggested settings - Voltage/time per division

Component/circuit description	ECM pin	Signal	Condition	Typical value	Oscilloscope setting*	Wave form
Injectors 2 & 3	4	⌐⊳	Ignition ON	11-14 V briefly then 0 V		
	4	⌐⊳	Engine idling	2,5 ms	10 V/0,5 ms	⋀⋀ 36
Instruments – D7F 710/720	48	⌐⊳	Engine idling	0 V		
Intake air temperature (IAT) sensor	20	⬅	Ignition ON – air temp. 10°C	3,3 V		
	46	⌐─	Ignition ON	0 V		
Knock sensor (KS)	44	⌐─	Ignition ON	0 V		
Knock sensor (KS) – K7M 702/703	8	⬅	Engine idling – full throttle briefly		50 mV/1 ms	⋀⋀ 38
Knock sensor (KS) – D7F 710/720	54	⬅	Engine idling – full throttle briefly		50 mV/1 ms	⋀⋀ 38
Knock sensor (KS) – shield wire	31	⌐─	Ignition ON	0 V		
Malfunction indicator lamp (MIL)	43	⌐⊳	Ignition ON – MIL ON	0-1 V		
	43	⌐⊳	Engine idling – MIL OFF	11-14 V		
Manifold absolute pressure (MAP) sensor	16	⬅	Engine idling	1 V		
	16	⬅	Engine under load	4,7 V		
	44	⌐─	Ignition ON	0 V		
	45	⇨	Ignition ON	5 V		
Power steering pressure (PSP) switch	13	⬅	Engine idling – steering wheel not turned	5 V		
	13	⬅	Engine idling – steering wheel turned	0 V		
Throttle position (TP) sensor	19	⬅	Ignition ON – throttle closed	0,78 V		
	19	⬅	Ignition ON – throttle fully open	4,3 V		
	45	⇨	Ignition ON	5 V		
	46	⌐─	Ignition ON	0 V		
Trip computer – some models	50	⇨	Ignition ON	11,4 V briefly then 0 V		
Vehicle speed sensor (VSS)	12	⬅	Ignition ON – vehicle pushed	0 V or 11 V switching		

*Suggested settings - Voltage/time per division

1 Connected pin - no test data available or random digital signal

RENAULT

Magneti Marelli 5NR

Model:	Engine code:	Year:
Clio 1,2 16V	D4F 712	2001-06

ECM harness multi-plug

Terminal side

B (br)   **A (sw)**

AD106429

Wire side

A (sw)   **B (br)**

AD106430

Component/circuit description	ECM pin	Signal	Condition	Typical value	Oscilloscope setting*	Wave form
AC compressor clutch relay	Aa4			[1]		
AC/heater function control panel	Ad2	←		[1]		
Accelerator pedal position (APP) sensor	Ab4	⌐⌐	Ignition ON	0 V		
	Ac4	⌐⌐	Ignition ON	0 V		
	Af1	⇒	Ignition ON	5 V		
	Ah1	←	Ignition ON – accelerator pedal released	0,73 V		
	Ah1	←	Ignition ON – accelerator pedal depressed	4 V		
	Ak1	←	Ignition ON – accelerator pedal released	0,6 V		
	Ak1	←	Ignition ON – accelerator pedal depressed	2 V		
	Ab1	⇒	Ignition ON	5 V		
Anti-percolation engine coolant blower relay	Ac2	⇒	Ignition ON	12 V		
Battery	Al4	←	Ignition OFF	11-14 V		
	Al4	←	Ignition ON	11-14 V		
Brake pedal position (BPP) switch	Ab3	←	Ignition ON – brake pedal released	0 V		
	Ab3	←	Ignition ON – brake pedal depressed	11-14 V		
	Ac3	←	Ignition ON – brake pedal released	11-14 V		
	Ac3	←	Ignition ON – brake pedal depressed	0 V		
Crankshaft position (CKP) sensor	Ba1	←	Engine idling	1,4 V ac	2 V/1 ms	〜〜 60
	Ba2	←	Engine idling	1,4 V ac	2 V/1 ms	Reversed 〜〜 60
Cruise control reversing switch	Af3	⌐⌐		[1]		
	Ag4			[1]		

* Suggested settings - Voltage/time per division

Component/circuit description	ECM pin	Signal	Condition	Typical value	Oscilloscope setting*	Wave form
Data link connector (DLC)	Ak4	⬅➡	Ignition ON	1		
Earth	Bl2	⬅	Ignition ON	0 V		
	Bl3	⬅	Ignition ON	0 V		
	Bl4	⬅	Ignition ON	0 V		
Engine control (EC) relay	Al3	⬅	Ignition OFF	0 V		
	Al3	⬅	Ignition ON	11-14 V		
	Am2	⊐➡	Ignition OFF	11-14 V		
	Am2	⊐➡	Ignition ON	0-1 V		
Engine coolant blower motor relay	Ad4	⊐➡		1		
Engine coolant temperature (ECT) sensor	Bd4	⬅	Ignition ON – coolant temp. 90°C	0,6 V		
	Bf1	⊐⊢	Ignition ON	0 V		
Evaporative emission (EVAP) canister purge valve	Am3	⊐➡	Ignition ON	11-14 V		
	Am3	⊐➡	Engine idling		2 V/1 ms	Intermittent ∿ 91
Fuel pump (FP) relay	Ag1	⊐➡	Ignition ON	0-1 V briefly then 11-14 V		
	Ag1	⊐➡	Engine idling	0-1 V		
Heated oxygen sensor (HO2S) 1	Bd1	⊐⊢	Ignition ON	0 V		
	Be3	⬅	Engine idling	0,1-0,9 V fluctuating		
	Bm4	⊐➡	Ignition ON	11-14 V		
	Bm4	⊐➡	Engine idling		2 V/1 ms	∿ 65
Heated oxygen sensor (HO2S) 2	Ae1	⊐➡	Ignition ON	0-1 V		
	Ah2	⬅	Engine idling	0,15 V		
	Am1	⊐➡	Ignition ON	11-14 V		
	Am1	⊐➡	Engine idling	0-1 V		
Ignition coil 1	Bm2	⊐➡	Ignition ON	0-1 V		
	Bm2	⊐➡	Engine idling		5 V/2 ms	∿ 33
Ignition coil 2	Bm3	⊐➡	Ignition ON	0-1 V		
	Bm3	⊐➡	Engine idling		5 V/2 ms	∿ 33
Ignition switch	Am4	⬅	Ignition OFF	0 V		
	Am4	⬅	Ignition ON	11-14 V		
Injector 1	Bj1	⊐➡	Ignition ON	11-14 V briefly then 0-1 V		
	Bj1	⊐➡	Engine idling	3,0 ms	10 V/2 ms	∿ 35
Injector 2	Bk1	⊐➡	Ignition ON	11-14 V briefly then 0-1 V		
	Bk1	⊐➡	Engine idling	3,0 ms	10 V/2 ms	∿ 35
Injector 3	Bk3	⊐➡	Ignition ON	11-14 V briefly then 0-1 V		
	Bk3	⊐➡	Engine idling	3,0 ms	10 V/2 ms	∿ 35
Injector 4	Bk4	⊐➡	Ignition ON	11-14 V briefly then 0-1 V		
	Bk4	⊐➡	Engine idling	3,0 ms	10 V/2 ms	∿ 35
Intake air temperature (IAT) sensor	Bd3	⊐⊢	Ignition ON	0 V		
	Be4	⬅	Ignition ON – air temp. 15°C	2,1 V		

* Suggested settings - Voltage/time per division

Component/circuit description	ECM pin	Signal	Condition	Typical value	Oscilloscope setting*	Wave form
Knock sensor (KS)	Bc2	⅃—	Ignition ON	0 V		
	Bc3	←	Engine idling – accelerate briefly		50 mV/1 ms	〰〰 38
Manifold absolute pressure (MAP) sensor	Bb2	⇨	Ignition ON	5 V		
	Bf2	⅃—	Ignition ON	0 V		
	Bf3	←	Ignition ON	4,8 V		
	Bf3	←	Engine idling	1,4 V		
	Bf3	←	Engine running – full throttle briefly	4,1 V		
Multifunction control module	Ah3			1		
	Aj4			1		
Power steering control module	Ae4	←		1		
Steering wheel multifunction switch	Ag2			1		
	Aj2	←	Ignition ON	5 V		
Throttle motor	Bl1	←	Ignition ON – accelerator pedal released	2,48 V		
	Bm1	⇨	Engine idling		2 V/0,5 ms	〰〰 64
Throttle motor position sensor	Bc1	⇨	Ignition ON	5 V		
	Bf4	←	Engine idling – accelerator pedal released	4,3 V		
	Bf4	←	Engine running – full throttle briefly	4,1 V		
	Bg1	⅃—	Ignition ON	0 V		
	Bg3	←	Engine idling – accelerator pedal released	0,6 V		
	Bg3	←	Engine running – full throttle briefly	4,0 V		
Transmission control module (TCM)	Aj3			1		
	Ak3			1		

*Suggested settings - Voltage/time per division

1 Connected pin - no test data available or random digital signal

Model:	Engine code:	Year:
Clio 1,4	E7J 780	1998-05
Clio 1,6	K7M 744/5	1998-03
Kangoo 1,4	E7J 780	1998-05

RENAULT

Siemens Fenix 5

ECM harness multi-plug

Terminal side

27 26 25 24 23 22 21 20 19 18 17 16 15 14 13 12 11 10 9 8 7 6 5 4 3 2 1
55 54 53 52 51 50 49 48 47 46 45 44 43 42 41 40 39 38 37 36 35 34 33 32 31 30 29 28

AD81647

Wire side

1 2 3 4 5 6 7 8 9 10 11 12 13 14 15 16 17 18 19 20 21 22 23 24 25 26 27
28 29 30 31 32 33 34 35 36 37 38 39 40 41 42 43 44 45 46 47 48 49 50 51 52 53 54 55

AD42110

Component/circuit description	ECM pin	Signal	Condition	Typical value	Oscilloscope setting*	Wave form
Air conditioning	5			1		
	51			1		
Automatic transmission	7			1		
	41			1		
	53			1		
Battery	32	←	Ignition OFF	11-14 V		
Crankshaft position (CKP) sensor	33	←	Ignition ON	3 V		
	33	←	Engine idling	1 V ac	0,5 V/1 ms	60
	34	←	Ignition ON	3 V		
	34	←	Engine idling	1 V ac	0,5 V/1 ms	Reversed 60
Data link connector (DLC)	11	←⇨	Ignition ON	0 V		
	38	←⇨	Ignition ON	0 V		
Earth	2	⊣⇨	Ignition ON	0 V		
	3	⊣⇨	Ignition ON	0 V		
	18	⊣–	Ignition ON	0 V		
Engine control relay	48	⊣⇨	Ignition ON	0 V briefly then 11-14 V		
	48	⊣⇨	Engine running	0 V		
	52	←	Ignition ON	11-14 V briefly then 0 V		
	52	←	Engine running	11-14 V		
Engine coolant blower motor relay – →1999	14	⊣⇨	Ignition OFF	11-14 V		
	14	⊣⇨	Engine running – coolant blower motor OFF	11-14 V		
	14	⊣⇨	Engine running – coolant blower motor ON	0 V		
Engine coolant blower motor relay – 2000→	55	←	Ignition OFF	11-14 V		
	55	←	Engine running – coolant blower motor OFF	11-14 V		
	55	←	Engine running – coolant blower motor ON	0,9 V		
Engine coolant temperature (ECT) sensor	15	←	Ignition ON – coolant temp. 10°C	2,5 V		
	15	←	Engine idling – engine hot	0,2 V		
	44	⊣–	Ignition ON	0 V		
Evaporative emission (EVAP) canister purge valve	42	⊣⇨	Ignition ON	11-14 V briefly then 0 V		
	42	⊣⇨	Engine idling	11-14 V		

* Suggested settings - Voltage/time per division

Component/circuit description	ECM pin	Signal	Condition	Typical value	Oscilloscope setting*	Wave form
Heated oxygen sensor (HO2S)	17	⬅	Ignition ON	0,4 V		
	17	⬅	Engine idling – engine hot	0,1-0,9 V fluctuating		
	17	⬅	Engine idling – engine hot		0,2 mV/0,5 sec.	〰 21
Idle air control (IAC) valve	9	⇨	Ignition ON	0,27 V		
	9	⇨	Engine idling – engine hot		4 V/50 ms	Intermittent 〰 14
	35	⇨	Ignition ON	11 V		
	35	⇨	Engine idling		4 V/50 ms	Intermittent 〰 14
	36	⇨	Ignition ON	0,26 V		
	36	⇨	Engine idling		4 V/50 ms	Intermittent 〰 14
	40	⇨	Ignition ON	11 V		
	40	⇨	Engine idling		4 V/50 ms	Intermittent 〰 14
Ignition coil – cylinders 1 & 4	28	⇥▷	Ignition ON	11-14 V		
	28	⇥▷	Engine idling		4 V/1 ms	〰 33
Ignition coil – cylinders 2 & 3	29	⇥▷	Ignition ON	11-14 V		
	29	⇥▷	Engine idling		4 V/1 ms	〰 33
Ignition switch	24	⬅	Ignition OFF	0 V		
	24	⬅	Ignition ON	11-14 V		
Immobilizer control module	37			1		
Injectors 1 & 4	30	⇥▷	Ignition ON	11-14 V briefly then 0 V		
	30	⇥▷	Engine idling	3 ms	10 V/2 ms	〰 35
Injectors 2 & 3	4	⇥▷	Ignition ON	11-14 V briefly then 0 V		
	4	⇥▷	Engine idling	3 ms	10 V/2 ms	〰 35
Instruments	48	⇥▷	Ignition ON	0 V briefly then 11-14 V		
	48	⇥▷	Engine running	0 V		
Instruments 2000→	47	⇥▷	Ignition ON	0 V		
	47	⇥▷	Engine running	11-14 V		
Intake air temperature (IAT) sensor	20	⬅	Ignition ON – air temp. 10°C	3 V		
	46	⇥	Ignition ON	0 V		
Knock sensor (KS)	8	⬅	Engine idling – accelerate briefly		50 mV/1 ms	〰 58
	44	⇥	Ignition ON	0 V		
Knock sensor (KS) – shield wire	31	⇥	Ignition ON	0 V		
Malfunction indicator lamp (MIL)	43	⇥▷	Ignition ON – MIL ON	0-1 V		
	43	⇥▷	Engine idling – MIL OFF	11-14 V		
Manifold absolute pressure (MAP) sensor	16	⬅	Ignition ON	4,7 V		
	16	⬅	Engine idling	1,9 V		
	16	⬅	Engine under load	4,4 V		
	44	⇥	Ignition ON	0 V		
	45	⇨	Ignition ON	5 V		
Power steering pressure (PSP) switch	13	⬅	Engine idling – steering wheel not turned	5 V		
	13	⬅	Engine idling – steering wheel turned	0 V		
Throttle position (TP) sensor	19	⬅	Ignition ON – throttle closed	0,6 V		
	19	⬅	Ignition ON – throttle fully open	4 V		
	45	⇨	Ignition ON	5 V		
	46	⇥	Ignition ON	0 V		
Trip computer	50			1		
Vehicle speed sensor (VSS)	12	⬅	Ignition ON – vehicle pushed	0 V or 11 V		

*Suggested settings - Voltage/time per division

1 Connected pin - no test data available or random digital signal

Model:	Engine code:	Year:
Clio 1,4 16V	K4J	1999-06
Megane/Megane Scenic/Scenic 1,4	K4J 750	1999-03
Megane/Scenic 1,6	K4M 700	1999-03
Megane/Scenic/RX4 2,0	F4R/F4R 740/741/744	1999-03
Laguna 1,6/1,8 16V	F4P 760/K4M 720/4	1998-01
Laguna 2,0 16V	F4R 780	1999-01

ECM harness multi-plug

Terminal side

```
61 62 63 64 65 66 67 68 69 70 71 72 73 74 75      76 77 78 79 80 81 82 83 84 85 86 87 88 89 90
31 32 33 34 35 36 37 38 39 40 41 42 43 44 45      46 47 48 49 50 51 52 53 54 55 56 57 58 59 60
 1  2  3  4  5  6  7  8  9 10 11 12 13 14 15      16 17 18 19 20 21 22 23 24 25 26 27 28 29 30
```
AD22771

Wire side

```
90 89 88 87 86 85 84 83 82 81 80 79 78 77 76      75 74 73 72 71 70 69 68 67 66 65 64 63 62 61
60 59 58 57 56 55 54 53 52 51 50 49 48 47 46      45 44 43 42 41 40 39 38 37 36 35 34 33 32 31
30 29 28 27 26 25 24 23 22 21 20 19 18 17 16      15 14 13 12 11 10  9  8  7  6  5  4  3  2  1
```
AD22770

Component/circuit description	ECM pin	Signal	Condition	Typical value	Oscilloscope setting*	Wave form
ABS control module – wheel speed signal – Laguna	52	←		1		
	53	←		1		
AC compressor clutch relay – some models	10	←	Ignition ON	11-14 V		
	10	←	Engine running – AC OFF	11-14 V		
	10	←	Engine running – AC ON	0,1 V		
AC control module – some models	10	←	Ignition ON	11-14 V		
	10	←	Engine running – AC OFF	11-14 V		
	10	←	Engine running – AC ON	0,1 V		
	23			1		
	46	←	Engine running – AC ON	0 V		
AC refrigerant pressure sensor – some models	18	←	Ignition ON	0,6 V		
	82	⌐—	Ignition ON	0 V		
	83	⇒	Ignition ON	5 V		
Air conditioning – heated windscreen signal – some models	88			1		
Battery	30	←	Ignition OFF	11-14 V		
Camshaft position (CMP) actuator – F4R	64	⌐⇒	Ignition ON	11-14 V		
	64	⌐⇒	Engine idling	11-14 V		
	64	⌐⇒	Engine idling – accelerate briefly	0 V briefly		
Crankshaft position (CKP) sensor	24	←	Ignition ON	1,9 V		
	24	←	Engine idling	0,9 V ac	1 V/1 ms	〰〰 3
	54	←	Ignition ON	1,9 V		
	54	←	Engine idling	0,9 V ac	1 V/1 ms	Reversed 〰〰 3
Data link connector (DLC)	26		Ignition ON	0 V		
	56		Ignition ON	0 V		
Earth	3	⌐—	Ignition ON	0 V		
	28	⌐—	Ignition ON	0 V		
	33	⌐—	Ignition ON	0 V		
Engine control relay	39	⌐⇒	Ignition OFF	0 V		
	39	⌐⇒	Ignition ON	0,1 V		
	66	←	Ignition ON	11-14 V		

* Suggested settings - Voltage/time per division

Component/circuit description	ECM pin	Signal	Condition	Typical value	Oscilloscope setting*	Wave form
Engine coolant blower motor relay	8	⊐⊳	Ignition ON	11-14 V		
	8	⊐⊳	Engine running – condenser blower motor OFF	11-14 V		
	8	⊐⊳	Engine running – condenser blower motor ON	0 V		
	38	⊐⊳	Ignition ON	11-14 V		
	38	⊐⊳	Engine running – coolant blower motor OFF	11-14 V		
	38	⊐⊳	Engine running – coolant blower motor ON	0,1 V		
Engine coolant 'hot' warning lamp	9	⊐⊳	Ignition ON – lamp OFF	11-14 V		
	9	⊐⊳	Engine running – lamp OFF	11-14 V		
	9	⊐⊳	Engine running – lamp ON	0 V		
Engine coolant temperature (ECT) sensor	13	⬅	Ignition ON – coolant temp. 10°C approx.	3,5 V		
	13	⬅	Ignition ON – coolant temp. 90°C approx.	0,5 V		
	73	⊐⊢	Ignition ON	0 V		
Evaporative emission (EVAP) canister purge valve	4	⊐⊳	Engine idling	1%		
	4	⊐⊳	Ignition ON	11-14 V		
Fuel pump relay	68	⊐⊳	Ignition OFF	0 V		
	68	⊐⊳	Ignition ON	0,9 V briefly then 11-14 V		
	68	⊐⊳	Engine running	0,9 V		
Heated oxygen sensor (HO2S) – front	45	⬅	Ignition ON	0,4 V		
	45	⬅	Engine idling	0,1-0,9 V		
	45	⬅	Engine idling		0,2 V/1 sec.	〰 21
	63	⊐⊳	Ignition ON	11-14 V		
	63	⊐⊳	Engine idling		5 V/2 ms	〰 62
	80	⊐⊢	Ignition ON	0 V		
Heated oxygen sensor (HO2S) – rear	44	⬅	Ignition ON	0,4 V		
	44	⬅	Engine idling	0,6 V		
	65	⊐⊳	Ignition ON	11-14 V		
	65	⊐⊳	Engine idling		5 V/2 ms	〰 62
	76	⊐⊢	Ignition ON	0 V		
Idle air control (IAC) valve	41 (72)	⇨	Engine idling		4 V/20 ms	Intermittent 〰 26
	12 (42)	⇨	Engine idling		4 V/20 ms	Intermittent 〰 26
	12	⇨	Ignition ON	11-14 V		
	42 (12)	⇨	Engine idling		4 V/20 ms	Intermittent 〰 26
	72 (41)	⇨	Engine idling		4 V/20 ms	Intermittent 〰 26
	41	⇨	Ignition ON	11-14 V		
	42	⇨	Ignition ON	0,3 V		
	72	⇨	Ignition ON	0,27 V		
Ignition coil – cylinder 1 & 4	32	⊐⊳	Ignition ON	11-14 V briefly then 0 V		
	32	⊐⊳	Engine running		4 V/3 ms	〰 33
Ignition coil – cylinder 2 & 3	1	⊐⊳	Ignition ON	11-14 V briefly then 0 V		
	1	⊐⊳	Engine running		4 V/3 ms	〰 33
Ignition switch	29	⬅	Ignition ON	11-14 V		
Immobilizer control module – some models	58		Ignition ON		2 V/50 ms	〰 61
Injector 1	59	⊐⊳	Ignition ON	11-14 V		
	59	⊐⊳	Engine idling	3,1 ms	10 V/2 ms	〰 35
Injector 2	90	⊐⊳	Ignition ON	11-14 V		
	90	⊐⊳	Engine idling	3,1 ms	10 V/2 ms	〰 35

★ Suggested settings - Voltage/time per division

Component/circuit description	ECM pin	Signal	Condition	Typical value	Oscilloscope setting*	Wave form
Injector 3	60	⊐⊢▷	Ignition ON	11-14 V		
	60	⊐⊢▷	Engine idling	3,1 ms	10 V/2 ms	∿∿ 35
Injector 4	89	⊐⊢▷	Ignition ON	11-14 V		
	89	⊐⊢▷	Engine idling	3,1 ms	10 V/2 ms	∿∿ 35
Instrumentation control module – engine speed signal	70	⇨	Engine idling	25 Hz approx.		
	70	⇨	3000 rpm	100 Hz approx.		
Instrumentation control module – fuel consumption signal – some models	11	⟵	Engine idling		4 V/0,2 sec.	∿∿ 24
Instrumentation control module – vehicle speed signal – some models	53	⟵		①		
Intake air temperature (IAT) sensor	49	⟵	Ignition ON – air temp. 10°C approx.	2,4 V		
	77	⊐⊢	Ignition ON	0 V		
Knock sensor (KS)	20	⟵	Engine idling – accelerate briefly		0,1 V/0,5 ms	∿∿ 38
	79	⊐⊢	Ignition ON	0 V		
Knock sensor (KS) – shield wire	19	⊐⊢	Ignition ON	0 V		
Manifold absolute pressure (MAP) sensor	15	⊐⊢	Ignition ON	0 V		
	16	⟵	Ignition ON	4,8 V		
	16	⟵	Engine idling	1,6 V		
	16	⟵	Engine idling – accelerate briefly	4,8 V		
	78	⇨	Ignition ON	5 V		
Malfunction indicator lamp (MIL) – some models	34		Ignition ON – MIL ON	0 V		
	34		Engine running – MIL OFF	1-14 V		
Multifunction control module – some models	58		Ignition ON		2 V/50 ms	∿∿ 61
Multifunction control module – some models	88			①		
	58			①		
Power steering pressure (PSP) switch – some models	85	⟵	Engine running – steering wheel not turned	11-14 V		
	85	⟵	Engine running – steering wheel turned	0 V		
Throttle position (TP) sensor	43	⟵	Ignition ON – throttle closed	0,5 V		
	43	⟵	Ignition ON – throttle fully open	4,5 V		
	74	⇨	Ignition ON	5 V		
	75	⊐⊢	Ignition ON	0 V		
Transmission control module (TCM)	27			①		
	57			①		

*Suggested settings - Voltage/time per division

① Connected pin - no test data available or random digital signal

Model:	Engine code:	Year:
Clio 1,5 dCi	K9K 702/704/710	2001-06

ECM harness multi-plug

Terminal side

C

1h	1g	1f	1e	1d	1c	1b	1a
2h	2g	2f	2e	2d	2c	2b	2a
3h	3g	3f	3e	3d	3c	3b	3a
4h	4g	4f	4e	4d	4c	4b	4a

B

1m	1l	1k	1j	1h	1g	1f	1e	1d	1c	1b	1a
2m	2l	2k	2j	2h	2g	2f	2e	2d	2c	2b	2a
3m	3l	3k	3j	3h	3g	3f	3e	3d	3c	3b	3a
4m	4l	4k	4j	4h	4g	4f	4e	4d	4c	4b	4a

A

4a	4b	4c	4d	4e	4f	4g	4h
3a	3b	3c	3d	3e	3f	3g	3h
2a	2b	2c	2d	2e	2f	2g	2h
1a	1b	1c	1d	1e	1f	1g	1h

AD29417

Wire side

A

4h	4g	4f	4e	4d	4c	4b	4a
3h	3g	3f	3e	3d	3c	3b	3a
2h	2g	2f	2e	2d	2c	2b	2a
1h	1g	1f	1e	1d	1c	1b	1a

B

1a	1b	1c	1d	1e	1f	1g	1h	1j	1k	1l	1m
2a	2b	2c	2d	2e	2f	2g	2h	2j	2k	2l	2m
3a	3b	3c	3d	3e	3f	3g	3h	3j	3k	3l	3m
4a	4b	4c	4d	4e	4f	4g	4h	4j	4k	4l	4m

C

1a	1b	1c	1d	1e	1f	1g	1h
2a	2b	2c	2d	2e	2f	2g	2h
3a	3b	3c	3d	3e	3f	3g	3h
4a	4b	4c	4d	4e	4f	4g	4h

AD29416

Component/circuit description	ECM pin	Signal	Condition	Typical value	Oscilloscope setting*	Wave form
AC compressor clutch relay	A2e	⊐▷	Engine idling – AC OFF	11-14 V		
	A2e	⊐▷	Engine idling – AC ON	0-1 V		
AC control module	C3e			①1		
AC refrigerant pressure sensor	C3c			①1		
	C3g			①1		
	C4c			①1		
Accelerator pedal position (APP) sensor	A2f	⇒	Ignition ON	5 V		
	A2g	⇒	Ignition ON	5 V		
	A2h	←	Ignition ON – accelerator pedal released	0,8 V		
	A2h	←	Ignition ON – accelerator pedal depressed	4,6 V		
	A3f	←	Ignition ON – accelerator pedal released	0,3 V		
	A3f	←	Ignition ON – accelerator pedal depressed	1,9 V		
	A3h	⊣⎺	Ignition ON	0 V		
	A4f	⊣⎺	Ignition ON	0 V		
Anti-percolation engine coolant blower relay	C1b	⊐▷	Engine idling – engine coolant blower motor OFF	11-14 V		
	C1b	⊐▷	Engine idling – engine coolant blower motor ON	0-1 V		
Brake pedal position (BPP) switch	A4e	←	Ignition ON – brake pedal released	0 V		
	A4e	←	Ignition ON – brake pedal depressed	11-14 V		
	C4d	←	Ignition ON – brake pedal released	11-14 V		
	C4d	←	Ignition ON – brake pedal depressed	0 V		
Camshaft position (CMP) sensor	B2e	←	Engine idling		2 V/50 ms	⌇⌇⌇ 3
	B3e	⊣⎺	Ignition ON	0 V		

* Suggested settings - Voltage/time per division

Autodata

Component/circuit description	ECM pin	Signal	Condition	Typical value	Oscilloscope setting*	Wave form
Clutch pedal position (CPP) switch (06/01→)	A4c	←	Ignition ON – clutch pedal released	0 V		
	A4c	←	Ignition ON – clutch pedal depressed	10,5 V		
Crankshaft position (CKP) sensor	B2f	←	Engine idling	5,7 V ac	5 V/2 ms	ᴡᴡᴡ 1
	B3f	⊐—	Ignition ON	0 V		
Cruise control reversing switch	A2d			☐1		
	A3d			☐1		
Data link connector (DLC)	A4b	⬅⇒		☐1		
Earth	C1g		Ignition ON	0 V		
	C1h		Ignition ON	0 V		
Engine control relay	A1g	←	Ignition OFF	0 V		
	A1g	←	Ignition ON	11-14 V		
	C1f	⊐⊳	Ignition OFF	11-14 V		
	C1f	⊐⊳	Ignition ON	0-1 V		
	C2g	←	Ignition ON	11-14 V		
	C2h	←	Ignition ON	11-14 V		
Engine coolant blower motor relay – some models	C2b			☐1		
Engine coolant heater relay 1	C2c	⊐⊳	Engine idling – engine coolant heater OFF	11-14 V		
	C2c	⊐⊳	Engine idling – engine coolant heater ON	0-1 V		
Engine coolant heater relay 2	C2d	⊐⊳	Engine idling – engine coolant heater OFF	11-14 V		
	C2d	⊐⊳	Engine idling – engine coolant heater ON	0-1 V		
Engine coolant temperature (ECT) sensor	B2h	←	Ignition ON – coolant temp. 20°C	3,5 V		
	B2h	←	Ignition ON – coolant temp. 80°C	0,7 V		
	B3h	⊐—	Ignition ON	0 V		
Exhaust gas recirculation (EGR) solenoid	B3l	⊐⊳	Ignition ON	11-14 V		
	B3l	⊐⊳	Engine idling		5 V/2 ms	Intermittent ᴡᴡᴡ 48
Exhaust gas recirculation (EGR) valve position sensor	B1b	⇒	Ignition ON	5 V		
	B2b	←	Ignition ON	1 V		
	B2b	←	Engine idling	1,3 V		
	B3b	⊐—	Ignition ON	0 V		
Fuel pressure control solenoid	B4m	⊐⊳	Engine idling		2 V/0,5 ms	ᴡᴡᴡ 37
Fuel pressure sensor	B1d	⇒	Ignition ON	5 V		
	B2d	←	Ignition ON	0,5 V		
	B2d	←	Engine idling	1 V		
	B2d	←	3000 rpm	2,2 V		
	B3d	⊐—	Ignition ON	0 V		
Fuel temperature sensor	B2g	←	Ignition ON – fuel temp. 20°C	3,1 V		
	B2g	←	Engine idling – engine hot	2,6 V		
	B3g	⊐—	Ignition ON	0 V		
Glow plug control module	C2f	⊐⊳	Ignition ON	0-1 V briefly then 11-14 V		
	C3d	⊐⊳	Ignition ON	0-1 V briefly then 11-14 V		

* Suggested settings - Voltage/time per division

Component/circuit description	ECM pin	Signal	Condition	Typical value	Oscilloscope setting*	Wave form
Ignition switch	A1d	←	Ignition OFF	0 V		
	A1d	←	Ignition ON	11-14 V		
Injector 1	B4a (B4b)		Engine idling	1 ms	5 V/1 ms	63
	B4b (B4a)		Engine idling	1 ms	5 V/1 ms	63
Injector 2	B4g (B4h)		Engine idling	1 ms	5 V/1 ms	63
	B4h (B4g)		Engine idling	1 ms	5 V/1 ms	63
Injector 3	B4c (B4d)		Engine idling	1 ms	5 V/1 ms	63
	B4d (B4c)		Engine idling	1 ms	5 V/1 ms	63
Injector 4	B4e (B4f)		Engine idling	1 ms	5 V/1 ms	63
	B4f (B4e)		Engine idling	1 ms	5 V/1 ms	63
Instrumentation control module – CAN data bus	A3a			1		
	A4a			1		
Intake air temperature (IAT) sensor	B2j	←	Ignition ON – air temp. 22°C	3 V		
	B3j	⌐	Ignition ON	0 V		
Knock sensor (KS)	B1f (B1g)	←	3000 rpm		50 mV/1 ms	62
	B1g (B1f)	←	3000 rpm		50 mV/1 ms	62
Manifold absolute pressure (MAP) sensor	B1c	⇨	Ignition ON	5 V		
	B2c	←	Ignition ON	1,8 V		
	B2c	←	Engine idling	1,8 V		
	B2c	←	Engine idling – accelerate briefly	3,9 V		
	B3c	⌐	Ignition ON	0 V		
Power steering control module	A2b			1		
Steering wheel multifunction switch	A2a			1		
	A3c			1		
Turbocharger (TC) boost air temperature sensor	B2k	←	Ignition ON – air temp. 22°C	2,1 V		
	B3k	⌐	Ignition ON	0 V		

*Suggested settings - Voltage/time per division

1 Connected pin - no test data available or random digital signal

Model:	Engine code:	Year:
Megane 1,6	K4M 760/761	2002-06
Scenic 1,6	K4M 760/761	2003-06

ECM harness multi-plug

Terminal side

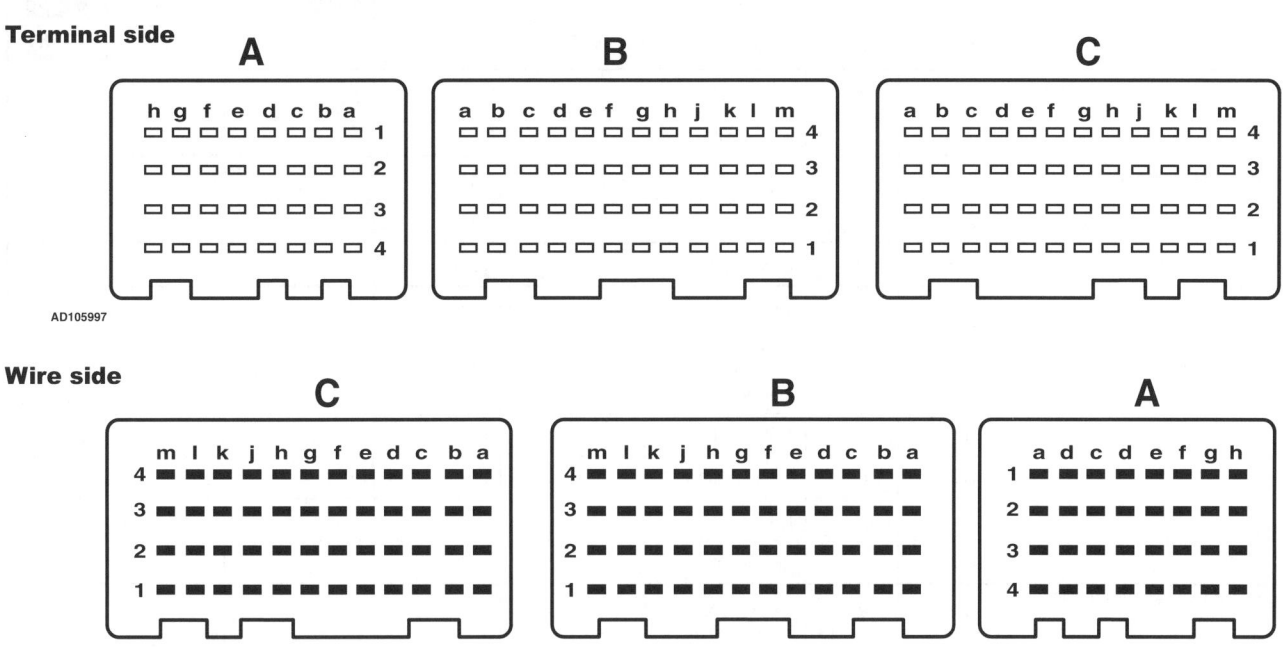

Wire side

Component/circuit description	ECM pin	Signal	Condition	Typical value	Oscilloscope setting*	Wave form
AC refrigerant pressure sensor	Cj2	⟹	Ignition ON	5 V		
	Cj3	⟸	Engine idling – AC ON	2,2 V		
	Cj3	⟸	Engine idling – AC OFF	0,8 V		
	Ck2	⌐⊢	Ignition ON	0 V		
Accelerator pedal position (APP) sensor	Af3	⟸	Ignition ON – accelerator pedal released	0,4 V		
	Af3	⟸	Ignition ON – accelerator pedal depressed	1,85 V		
	Af4	⌐⊢	Ignition ON	0 V		
	Ah2	⟸	Ignition ON – accelerator pedal released	0,76 V		
	Ah2	⟸	Ignition ON – accelerator pedal depressed	3,8 V		
	Ah3	⌐⊢	Ignition ON	0 V		
	Af2	⟹	Ignition ON	5 V		
	Ag2	⟹	Ignition ON	5 V		
Brake pedal position (BPP) switch	Ae4	⟸	Ignition ON – brake pedal released	11-14 V		
	Ae4	⟸	Ignition ON – brake pedal depressed	0 V		
Camshaft position (CMP) actuator	Cl3	⌐⟹	Engine idling	11-14 V		
	Cl3	⌐⟹	Engine idling		2 V/5 ms	⩗⩗ 64
Camshaft position (CMP) sensor	Be2	⌐⊢	Ignition ON	0 V		
	Bf1	⟸	Engine idling		5 V/50 ms	⩗⩗ 78

* Suggested settings - Voltage/time per division

Component/circuit description	ECM pin	Signal	Condition	Typical value	Oscilloscope setting*	Wave form
CAN data bus	Aa3	⟷		1		
	Aa4	⟷		1		
Clutch pedal position (CPP) switch	Ac4	←	Ignition ON – clutch pedal released	0 V		
	Ac4	←	Ignition ON – clutch pedal depressed	12 V		
Crankshaft position (CKP) sensor	Ce4	←	Ignition ON	2,5 V ac	0,5 V/1 ms	⟿ 60
	Cf3	←	Engine idling	2,5 V ac	0,5 V/1 ms	Reversed ⟿ 60
Steering wheel multifunction switch	Ad2	←	Ignition ON	5 V		
	Ad3	⌐	Ignition ON	0 V		
Cruise control reversing switch	Aa2	⌐		1		
	Ac3	⌐		1		
Data link connector (DLC)	Ab4	⟷	Ignition ON	0,25 V		
Earth	Ag4		Ignition ON	0 V		
	Ah1		Ignition ON	0 V		
	Ah4		Ignition ON	0 V		
	Bl1		Ignition ON	0 V		
	Bm1		Ignition ON	0 V		
	Cl1		Ignition ON	0 V		
	Cm1		Ignition ON	0 V		
Engine coolant temperature (ECT) sensor	Cf2	←	Ignition ON – coolant temp. 90°C	0,5 V		
	Cf4	⌐	Ignition ON	0 V		
Evaporative emission (EVAP) canister purge valve	Be1	⌐▷	Ignition ON	11-14 V		
	Be1	⌐▷	Engine idling		2 V/ 0,1 sec.	Intermittent ⟿ 71
Heated oxygen sensor (HO2S) 1	Bb1	←	Engine idling	0,1-0,9 V fluctuating		
	Bc1	⌐	Ignition ON	0 V		
	Bl2	⌐▷	Ignition ON	11-14 V		
	Bl2	⌐▷	Engine idling	0-1 V		
Heated oxygen sensor (HO2S) 2	Ba2	←	Engine idling	0,5 V		
	Bb2	⌐	Ignition ON	0 V		
	Bl3	⌐▷	Engine idling	0-1 V		
Ignition coil 1 & 2	Bm4	▷	Ignition ON	0 V		
	Bm4	▷	Engine idling		2 V/20 ms	⟿ 91
Ignition coil 3 & 4	Bm3	▷	Ignition ON	0 V		
	Bm3	▷	Engine idling		2 V/20 ms	⟿ 91
Injector 1	Ca1	⌐▷	Ignition ON	11-14 V briefly then 0-1 V		
	Ca1	⌐▷	Engine idling	3,7 ms	10 V/2 ms	⟿ 35
Injector 2	Ca2	⌐▷	Ignition ON	11-14 V briefly then 0-1 V		
	Ca2	⌐▷	Engine idling	3,7 ms	10 V/2 ms	⟿ 35
Injector 3	Ca3	⌐▷	Ignition ON	11-14 V briefly then 0-1 V		
	Ca3	⌐▷	Engine idling	3,7 ms	10 V/2 ms	⟿ 35

★ Suggested settings - Voltage/time per division

Component/circuit description	ECM pin	Signal	Condition	Typical value	Oscilloscope setting*	Wave form
Injector 4	Ca4	⊐▷	Ignition ON	11-14 V briefly then 0-1 V		
	Ca4	⊐▷	Engine idling	3,7 ms	10 V/2 ms	〰 35
Intake air temperature (IAT) sensor	Ce2	⬅	Ignition ON – air temp. 14°C	2,3 V		
	Ce2	⬅	Ignition ON – air temp. 26°C	1,5 V		
	Ce3	⊐—	Ignition ON	0 V		
Knock sensor (KS)	Cb3	⬅	Engine idling – accelerate briefly		50 mV/1 ms	〰 38
	Cb4	⬅	Engine idling – accelerate briefly		50 mV/1 ms	〰 38
Knock sensor (KS) – shield wire	Cb2	⊐—	Ignition ON	0 V		
Manifold absolute pressure (MAP) sensor	Ch2	⇨	Ignition ON	5 V		
	Ch3	⬅	Ignition ON	5 V		
	Ch3	⬅	Engine idling	1,5 V		
	Ch3	⬅	Engine running – full throttle briefly	4,2 V		
	Ch4	⊐—	Ignition ON	0 V		
Multifunction control module	Ad1	⬅	Ignition ON	11-14 V		
	Ag1	⬅	Ignition ON	11-14 V		
	Bd1	⊐▷	Ignition ON	11-14 V		
	Bd1	⊐▷	Engine idling	0-1 V		
	Cd4	⊐▷	Ignition OFF	11-14 V		
	Cd4	⊐▷	Ignition ON	0-1 V		
	Cm2	⬅	Ignition ON	0-1 V		
Throttle motor	Cm3	⇨	Ignition ON – accelerator pedal released	0,1 V		
	Cm3	⇨	Ignition ON – accelerator pedal depressed	3,2 V		
	Cm4	⇨	Ignition ON – accelerator pedal released	3,2 V		
	Cm4	⇨	Ignition ON – accelerator pedal depressed	0,1 V		
Throttle motor position sensor	Cd3	⬅	Engine idling – accelerator pedal released	4,4 V		
	Cd3	⬅	Engine idling – accelerator pedal depressed	2 V		
	Cg2	⇨	Ignition ON	5 V		
	Cg3	⬅	Engine idling – accelerator pedal released	0,6 V		
	Cg3	⬅	Engine running – full throttle briefly	3,0 V		
	Cg4	⊐—	Ignition ON	0 V		
Transmission control module (TCM)	Ck3	⬅▷		1		
	Ck4	⬅▷		1		

*Suggested settings - Voltage/time per division

1 Connected pin - no test data available or random digital signal

RENAULT

Bosch MSA 15.5

Model:	Engine code:	Year:
Mégane 1,9D Turbo	F9Q 730/734	1997-99
Mégane Scénic 1,9D Turbo	F9Q 730/734	1997-99
Mégane 1,9dTi	F9Q 731/736/744	1999-03

ECM harness multi-plug

Terminal side

AD81718

Wire side

AD42119

Component/circuit description	ECM pin	Signal	Condition	Typical value
AC/heater function control panel	28			1
	37			1
Accelerator pedal position (APP) sensor	15	←	Ignition ON – accelerator pedal released	0,4 V
	15	←	Ignition ON – accelerator pedal depressed	3,1 V
	55	⌐	Engine idling	0 V
	57	⇒	Ignition ON	5 V
Accelerator pedal position (APP) switch	65	←	Ignition ON – accelerator pedal released	0 V
	65	←	Ignition ON – accelerator pedal depressed	2,8 V
Accelerator pedal position (APP) switch – some models	33	⌐	Engine idling	0 V
Anti-percolation engine coolant blower motor relay – some models	3	⌐▷		1
Brake pedal position (BPP) switch	20	←	Ignition ON – brake pedal released	11-14 V
	20	←	Ignition ON – brake pedal depressed	0 V
	44	←	Ignition ON – brake pedal released	0 V
	44	←	Ignition ON – brake pedal depressed	11-14 V
Clutch pedal position (CPP) switch	17	←	Ignition ON – clutch pedal released	0 V
	17	←	Ignition ON – clutch pedal depressed	11-14 V
Combination control module	35	←		1
Crankshaft position (CKP) sensor	8	←	Engine idling	1,8 V ac
	8	←	Engine idling	5 V/5 ms per division 〰6
	21	⌐	Engine idling	0 V
Data link connector (DLC)	61	⬌⇒		1
	66	⬌⇒		1
Earth	1		Ignition ON	0 V
	24		Ignition ON	0 V
	46		Ignition ON	0 V

Autodata

Component/circuit description	ECM pin	Signal	Condition	Typical value
Engine control relay	23	←	Ignition OFF	0 V
	23	←	Ignition ON	11-14 V
	42	⊐▷	Ignition OFF	11-14 V
	42	⊐▷	Ignition ON	0-1 V
	45	←	Ignition OFF	0 V
	45	←	Ignition ON	11-14 V
	68	←	Ignition OFF	0 V
	68	←	Ignition ON	11-14 V
Engine coolant blower motor relay – some models	6	⊐▷	Engine idling – coolant blower motor OFF	11-14 V
	6	⊐▷	Engine idling – coolant blower motor ON	0-1 V
Engine coolant heater relay I – if fitted	47	⊐▷	Ignition ON – engine coolant heater OFF	11-14 V
	47	⊐▷	Ignition ON – engine coolant heater ON	0-1 V
Engine coolant heater relay II – if fitted	27	⊐▷	Ignition ON – engine coolant heater OFF	11-14 V
	27	⊐▷	Ignition ON – engine coolant heater ON	0-1 V
Engine coolant 'hot' warning lamp – some models	48	⊐▷	Ignition ON – lamp ON	0-1 V
	48	⊐▷	Ignition ON – lamp OFF	11-14 V
Engine coolant temperature (ECT) sensor	14	←	Ignition ON – coolant temp. 20°C	2,9 V
	14	←	Ignition ON – coolant temp. 80°C	0,6 V
	33	⊐–	Engine idling	0 V
Exhaust gas recirculation (EGR) solenoid	25	⊐▷	Ignition ON	11-14 V
	25	⊐▷	Engine idling	11-14 V
	25	⊐▷	Engine idling	5 V/2 ms per division 31
Fuel injection timing solenoid	51	⊐▷	Engine idling	2 V/10 ms per division 10
Fuel quantity adjuster	4	⊐▷	Engine idling	2 V/2 ms per division 30
	5	⊐▷	Engine idling	2 V/2 ms per division 30
	49	⊐▷	Engine idling	2 V/2 ms per division 30
Fuel quantity adjuster position sensor	7	⇒	Ignition ON	2,49 V
	7	⇒	Engine idling	2,49 V
	29	←	Ignition ON	2,48 V
	29	←	Engine idling	2,5 V
	29	←	Engine idling	0,5 V/0,1 ms per division 8
	52	←	Ignition ON	2,5 V
	52	←	Engine idling	2,5 V
	52	←	Engine idling	0,5 V/0,1 ms per division 8
Fuel shut-off solenoid valve	53	⇒	Engine idling	11-14 V
	53	⇒	Ignition OFF	0 V
	53	⇒	Ignition ON	0 V
Fuel temperature sensor	33	⊐–	Engine idling	0 V
	63	←	Ignition ON – fuel temp. 20°C	3,4 V

Component/circuit description	ECM pin	Signal	Condition	Typical value
Glow plug control module	30		Engine idling – glow plugs OFF	0,17 V
	30		Ignition ON – glow plugs ON	11-14 V
	30		Ignition ON – glow plugs OFF	0,15 V
	50		Engine idling – glow plugs OFF	11-14 V
	50		Ignition ON – glow plugs ON	0 V
	50		Ignition ON – glow plugs OFF	10,5 V
Glow plug warning lamp – F9Q736	26	⊣▷	Ignition ON – lamp ON	0-1 V
	26	⊣▷	Ignition ON – lamp OFF	11-14 V
Glow plug warning lamp	54	⊣▷	Ignition ON – lamp ON	0-1 V
	54	⊣▷	Ignition ON – lamp OFF	11-14 V
Immobilizer control module	59	←		☐1
Inertia fuel shut-off (IFS) switch	38	←	Ignition ON – button depressed	11-14 V
	38	←	Ignition ON – button released	0 V
Injector needle lift sensor	11	⊣—	Engine idling	0 V
	12	←	Engine idling	0,016 V ac
	12	←	Engine idling	0,2 V/1 ms per division ⎍⎍ 7
Intake air temperature (IAT) sensor	21	⊣—	Engine idling	0 V
	64	←	Ignition ON – air temp. 17°C	3,8 V
Malfunction indicator lamp (MIL) – some models	26	⊣▷	Ignition ON – MIL ON	0-1 V
	26	⊣▷	Ignition ON – MIL OFF	11-14 V
Mass air flow (MAF) sensor	13	←	Engine idling	1,8 V
	13	←	Engine idling – accelerate briefly	4 V (briefly)
	13	←	Ignition ON	0,5 V
	21	⊣—	Engine idling	0 V
Mass air flow (MAF) sensor – F9Q736	19	⇒	Ignition ON	5 V
Tachometer – some models	2	⇒	3000 rpm	100 Hz
	2	⇒	Engine idling	28 Hz
	2	⇒	Engine idling	5 V/10 ms per division ⎍⎍ 2
	2	⇒	Ignition ON	11-14 V
Transmission control module (TCM)	9			☐1
	16			☐1
	31			☐1
	39			☐1
Trip computer – if fitted	32	⇒	Ignition ON	☐1
Vehicle speed sensor (VSS) signal – ABS control module/instrument panel – except F9Q736 2000→	43	←	Ignition ON – vehicle pushed	Switching voltage
Vehicle speed sensor (VSS) – F9Q736 2000→	43	←	Ignition ON – vehicle pushed	Switching voltage

☐1 Connected pin - no test data available

Model:	Engine code:	Year:
Mégane 1,9 dCi	F9Q 732/733	1999-03
Scénic 1,9 dCi	F9Q 732	1999-03
Scénic RX4 1,9 dCi	F9Q 740/746/748	2000-03

RENAULT
Bosch EDC15C3

ECM harness multi-plug

Terminal side

C

1m	1l	1k	1j	1h	1g	1f	1e	1d	1c	1b	1a	
2m	2l	2k	2j	2h	2g	2f	2e	2d	2c	2b	2a	
3m	3l	3k	3j	3h	3g	3f	3e	3d	3c	3b	3a	
4m	4l	4k	4j	4h	4g	4f	4e	4d	4c	4b	4a	

B

1m	1l	1k	1j	1h	1g	1f	1e	1d	1c	1b	1a	
2m	2l	2k	2j	2h	2g	2f	2e	2d	2c	2b	2a	
3m	3l	3k	3j	3h	3g	3f	3e	3d	3c	3b	3a	
4m	4l	4k	4j	4h	4g	4f	4e	4d	4c	4b	4a	

A

4a	4b	4c	4d	4e	4f	4g	4h
3a	3b	3c	3d	3e	3f	3g	3h
2a	2b	2c	2d	2e	2f	2g	2h
1a	1b	1c	1d	1e	1f	1g	1h

AD20837

Wire side

A

4h	4g	4f	4e	4d	4c	4b	4a
3h	3g	3f	3e	3d	3c	3b	3a
2h	2g	2f	2e	2d	2c	2b	2a
1h	1g	1f	1e	1d	1c	1b	1a

B

1a	1b	1c	1d	1e	1f	1g	1h	1j	1k	1l	1m	
2a	2b	2c	2d	2e	2f	2g	2h	2j	2k	2l	2m	
3a	3b	3c	3d	3e	3f	3g	3h	3j	3k	3l	3m	
4a	4b	4c	4d	4e	4f	4g	4h	4j	4k	4l	4m	

C

1a	1b	1c	1d	1e	1f	1g	1h	1j	1k	1l	1m	
2a	2b	2c	2d	2e	2f	2g	2h	2j	2k	2l	2m	
3a	3b	3c	3d	3e	3f	3g	3h	3j	3k	3l	3m	
4a	4b	4c	4d	4e	4f	4g	4h	4j	4k	4l	4m	

AD20838

Component/circuit description	ECM pin	Signal	Condition	Typical value	Oscilloscope setting*	Wave form
AC compressor clutch relay	A4f	⊐–▷	Engine idling – AC OFF	11-14 V		
	A4f	⊐–▷	Engine idling – AC ON	0-1 V		
AC master switch	A4g			1		
Accelerator pedal position (APP) sensor	A1c	←	Ignition ON – accelerator pedal released	0,8 V		
	A1c	←	Ignition ON – accelerator pedal depressed	4,5 V		
	A1e	⇒	Ignition ON	5 V		
	A1f	←	Ignition ON – accelerator pedal released	0,4 V		
	A1f	←	Ignition ON – accelerator pedal depressed	2,1 V		
	A2h	⇒	Ignition ON	5 V		
	A3a	⌐—	Ignition ON	0 V		
	A3b	⌐—	Ignition ON	0 V		
Brake pedal position (BPP) switch	A3f	←	Ignition ON – brake pedal released	0 V		
	A3f	←	Ignition ON – brake pedal depressed	11-14 V		
Camshaft position (CMP) sensor	C1c	⌐—	Ignition ON	0 V		
	C4k	←	Engine idling		5 V/50 ms	⎍⌁ 3
CAN data bus – high	A4b	←▷		1		
CAN data bus – low	A4a	←▷		1		
Clutch pedal position (CPP) switch	A2e	←	Ignition ON – clutch pedal released	0 V		
	A2e	←	Ignition ON – clutch pedal depressed	10,5 V		
Crankshaft position (CKP) sensor	B3g	←	Engine idling	5,8 V ac	5 V/2 ms	⌁⎍ 1
	B3h	←	Engine idling	5,8 V ac	5 V/2 ms	Reversed ⌁⎍ 1
Data link connector (DLC)	A3c	←▷		1		
	A3d	←▷		1		
Earth	B3l		Ignition ON	0 V		
	B4l		Ignition ON	0 V		
	B4m		Ignition ON	0 V		

★ Suggested settings - Voltage/time per division

Component/circuit description	ECM pin	Signal	Condition	Typical value	Oscilloscope setting*	Wave form
Engine control relay	B2m	←	Ignition ON	11-14 V		
	B3m	←	Ignition ON	11-14 V		
	B4d	⊣▷	Ignition OFF	11-14 V		
	B4d	⊣▷	Ignition ON	0-1 V		
Engine coolant blower motor relay	C2a	⊣▷	Engine idling – engine coolant blower motor OFF	11-14 V		
	C2a	⊣▷	Engine idling – engine coolant blower motor ON	0-1 V		
Engine coolant blower motor relay – some models	C4b			1		
Engine coolant heater relay 1	C4j	⊣▷	Engine idling – engine coolant heater OFF	11-14 V		
	C4j	⊣▷	Engine idling – engine coolant heater ON	0-1 V		
Engine coolant heater relay 2	C4e	⊣▷	Engine idling – engine coolant heater OFF	11-14 V		
	C4e	⊣▷	Engine idling – engine coolant heater ON	0-1 V		
Engine coolant 'hot' warning lamp	A3g	⊣▷	Ignition ON – engine coolant 'hot' warning lamp ON	0-1 V		
	A3g	⊣▷	Ignition ON – engine coolant 'hot' warning lamp OFF	11-14 V		
	A4h	⊣▷	Ignition ON – engine coolant 'hot' warning lamp ON	0-1 V		
	A4h	⊣▷	Ignition ON – engine coolant 'hot' warning lamp OFF	11-14 V		
Engine coolant temperature (ECT) sensor	B1e	⊣—	Ignition ON	0 V		
	B3k	←	Ignition ON – coolant temp. 20°C	2,7 V		
	B3k	←	Ignition ON – coolant temp. 80°C	0,5 V		
Exhaust gas recirculation (EGR) solenoid	B1m	⊣▷	Ignition ON	11-14 V		
	B1m	⊣▷	Engine idling		5 V/2 ms	Intermittent ⋀⋁⋀ 3
Exhaust gas recirculation (EGR) valve position sensor	B2b	⊣—	Ignition ON	0 V		
	B2c	←	Ignition ON	1 V		
	B2c	←	Engine idling	0,8 V		
	B2f	⇨	Ignition ON	5 V		
Fuel lift pump relay	C1a	⊣▷	Ignition ON – fuel pump ON	0-1 V		
	C1a	⊣▷	Ignition ON – fuel pump OFF	11-14 V		
	C1a	⊣▷	Engine idling	0-1 V		
Fuel pressure control solenoid	B1l	⊣▷	Engine idling		2 V/1 ms	⋀⋁⋀ 37
Fuel pressure sensor	B1d	←	Ignition ON	0,5 V		
	B1d	←	Engine idling	1,2 V		
	B1d	←	3000 rpm	1,8 V		
	B2h	⇨	Ignition ON	5 V		
	C3b	⊣—	Ignition ON	0 V		
Fuel temperature sensor	B1g	⊣—	Ignition ON	0 V		
	B3j	←	Ignition ON – fuel temp. 18°C	2,9 V		
	B3j	←	Engine idling – engine hot	1,3 V		
Glow plug control module	B3b	⊣▷	Ignition ON	0-1 V for 5 secs then 11-14 V		
	B3c	⊣▷	Ignition ON	0-1 V for 10 secs then 11-14 V		
Glow plug warning lamp	A1g	⊣▷	Ignition ON – lamp ON	0-1 V		
	A1g	⊣▷	Ignition ON – lamp OFF	11-14 V		
Heated rear window switch	A1b			1		
Ignition switch	B3e	←	Ignition OFF	0 V		
	B3e	←	Ignition ON	11-14 V		
Immobilizer control module	A2g			1		

* Suggested settings - Voltage/time per division

Component/circuit description	ECM pin	Signal	Condition	Typical value	Oscilloscope setting*	Wave form
Injector 1	C1m (C3m)		Engine idling	1 ms	10 V/0,5 ms	60
	C3m (C1m)		Engine idling	1 ms	10 V/0,5 ms	60
Injector 2	C3l (C4l)		Engine idling	1 ms	10 V/0,5 ms	60
	C4l (C3l)		Engine idling	1 ms	10 V/0,5 ms	60
Injector 3	C2l (C2m)		Engine idling	1 ms	10 V/0,5 ms	60
	C2m (C2l)		Engine idling	1 ms	10 V/0,5 ms	60
Injector 4	C1l (C4m)		Engine idling	1 ms	10 V/0,5 ms	60
	C4m (C1l)		Engine idling	1 ms	10 V/0,5 ms	60
Intake air temperature (IAT) sensor	B3d	←	Ignition ON – air temp. 22°C	2,3 V		
	C3a	⊣	Ignition ON	0 V		
Malfunction indicator lamp (MIL) – some models	A3h	⊣▷	Ignition ON – MIL ON	0-1 V		
	A3h	⊣▷	Ignition ON – MIL OFF	11-14 V		
Manifold absolute pressure (MAP) sensor	B1c	←	Ignition ON	0,5 V		
	B1c	←	Engine idling	1,9 V		
	B1c	←	3000 rpm	2,6 V		
	B2j	⇒	Ignition ON	5 V		
	C4a	⊣	Ignition ON	0 V		
Mass air flow (MAF) sensor	B2g	⇒	Ignition ON	5 V		
	B4h	←	Ignition ON	0,6 V		
	B4h	←	Engine idling	2,5 V		
	B4h	←	3000 rpm	3,7 V		
Tachometer	A4d	⇒	Engine idling	28 Hz	5 V/10 ms	2
	A4d	⇒	3000 rpm	100 Hz		
Trip computer	A3e			[1]		
Turbocharger (TC) wastegate regulating valve	B2l	⊣▷	Ignition ON	11-14 V		
	B2l	⊣▷	Engine idling	68%	5 V/5 ms	12
Vehicle speedometer – VSS signal	A4e			[1]		

*Suggested settings - Voltage/time per division

[1] Connected pin - no test data available

RENAULT

Fenix 5

Model:	Engine code:	Year:
Megane 2,0	F3R 750/751	1995-99
Megane 2,0 16V	F7R 710	1996-99
Laguna 1,8	F3P 670	1996-99
Laguna 2,0	F3R 611/728/729	1996-01
Laguna 2,0 16V	N7Q 700	1996-99
Safrane 2,0 16V	N7Q 710/711	1996-01

ECM harness multi-plug

Terminal side

27 26 25 24 23 22 21 20 19 18 17 16 15 14 13 12 11 10 9 8 7 6 5 4 3 2 1
55 54 53 52 51 50 49 48 47 46 45 44 43 42 41 40 39 38 37 36 35 34 33 32 31 30 29 28

AD81647

Wire side

1 2 3 4 5 6 7 8 9 10 11 12 13 14 15 16 17 18 19 20 21 22 23 24 25 26 27
28 29 30 31 32 33 34 35 36 37 38 39 40 41 42 43 44 45 46 47 48 49 50 51 52 53 54 55

AD42110

Component/circuit description	ECM pin	Signal	Condition	Typical value	Oscilloscope setting*	Wave form
Air conditioning	51	⊐⊢▷	Engine idling – AC OFF	11-14 V		
	51	⊐⊢▷	Engine idling – AC ON	0 V		
Air conditioning – except Safrane	6	◀—	Ignition ON – AC OFF	0 V		
	6	◀—	Ignition ON – AC ON	11-14 V		
Air conditioning – Safrane	42			1		
Anti percolation engine coolant blower relay – some models	23	⊐⊢▷	Ignition OFF – engine cold – coolant blower motor OFF	11-14 V		
	23	⊐⊢▷	Ignition OFF – engine hot – coolant blower motor ON	0 V		
Automatic transmission	1			1		
	7			1		
	41			1		
Automatic transmission – some models	37			1		
	7			1		
Battery	32	◀—	Ignition OFF	11-14 V		
Camshaft position (CMP) sensor – except Safrane	42	◀—	Engine idling		5 V/20 ms	∿∿ 12
Camshaft position (CMP) sensor – Safrane	6	◀—	Engine idling		5 V/20 ms	∿∿ 12
Crankshaft position (CKP) sensor	33	◀—	Engine idling		5 V/1 ms	∿∿ 3
	34	◀—	Engine idling		5 V/1 ms	Reversed ∿∿ 3
Data link connector (DLC)	11	◀⊏▷		1		
	38	◀⊏▷		1		
Earth	2		Ignition ON	0 V		
	3		Ignition ON	0 V		
Engine control relay – some models	47	⊐⊢▷	Ignition OFF	11-14 V		
	47	⊐⊢▷	Ignition ON	0 V		
Engine coolant temperature (ECT) sensor	15	◀—	Ignition ON – coolant temp. 10°C	2,6 V		
	15	◀—	Engine idling – engine hot	0,3 V		
	44	⊐⊢	Ignition ON	0 V		

* Suggested settings - Voltage/time per division

Autodata

Component/circuit description	ECM pin	Signal	Condition	Typical value	Oscilloscope setting*	Wave form
Evaporative emission (EVAP) canister purge valve	50	⊐▷	Ignition ON	11-14 V briefly then 0 V		
	50	⊐▷	Engine idling		10 V/50 ms	ᴧᴧᴡ 20
Exhaust gas recirculation (EGR) solenoid – some models	49	⊐▷	Ignition ON	11-14 V briefly then 0 V		
	49	⊐▷	Engine idling	11-14 V		
Fuel pump relay	48	⊐▷	Ignition ON	0 V briefly then 11-14 V		
	48	⊐▷	Engine idling	0 V		
	52	◀	Ignition ON	11-14 V briefly then 0 V		
	52	◀	Engine idling	11-14 V		
Heated oxygen sensor (HO2S)	17	◀	Engine idling	0-1 V fluctuating	0,2 V/1 sec.	ᴧᴧᴡ 21
	18	⊐⊢	Ignition ON	0 V		
Heated rear window switch	5	◀	Ignition ON – heated rear window OFF	0 V		
	5	◀	Ignition ON – heated rear window ON	11-14 V		
Idle air control (IAC) valve	54	⇨	Ignition ON	7 V briefly then 0 V		
	54	⇨	Engine idling	32%	5 V/5 ms	ᴧᴧᴡ 24
Ignition coil – cylinders 1 & 4	28	⇨	Engine idling		5 V/1 ms	ᴧᴧᴡ 33
Ignition coil – cylinders 2 & 3	29	⇨	Engine idling		5 V/1 ms	ᴧᴧᴡ 33
Ignition switch	24	◀	Ignition OFF	0 V		
	24	◀	Ignition ON	11-14 V		
Immobilizer control module	35	◀	Ignition ON	2-5 V fluctuating		
Injector 1	53	⊐▷	Ignition ON	11-14 V briefly then 0 V		
	53	⊐▷	Engine idling	3,4 ms	10 V/2 ms	ᴧᴧᴡ 36
Injector 2	25	⊐▷	Ignition ON	11-14 V briefly then 0 V		
	25	⊐▷	Engine idling	3,4 ms	10 V/2 ms	ᴧᴧᴡ 36
Injector 3	4	⊐▷	Ignition ON	11-14 V briefly then 0 V		
	4	⊐▷	Engine idling	3,4 ms	10 V/2 ms	ᴧᴧᴡ 36
Injector 4	30	⊐▷	Ignition ON	11-14 V briefly then 0 V		
	30	⊐▷	Engine idling	3,4 ms	10 V/2 ms	ᴧᴧᴡ 36
Intake air temperature (IAT) sensor	20	◀	Ignition ON – air temp. 10°C	3,2 V		
	46	⊐⊢	Ignition ON	0 V		
Intake manifold air control solenoid – F7R 710	55	⊐▷	Engine running – valve not operating	11-14 V		
	55	⊐▷	Engine running – valve operating	0 V		
Knock sensor (KS)	8	◀	Engine idling – full throttle briefly		50 mV/1 ms	ᴧᴧᴡ 38
	44	⊐⊢	Ignition ON	0 V		
Knock sensor (KS) – shield wire	31	⊐⊢	Ignition ON	0 V		

* Suggested settings - Voltage/time per division

Component/circuit description	ECM pin	Signal	Condition	Typical value	Oscilloscope setting*	Wave form
Malfunction indicator lamp (MIL) – except F3R 611	26	⇥▷	Ignition ON – MIL ON	0-1 V		
	26	⇥▷	Engine idling – MIL OFF	11-14 V		
Malfunction indicator lamp (MIL) – F3R 611	36	⇥▷	Ignition ON – MIL ON	0-1 V		
	26	⇥▷	Engine idling – MIL OFF	11-14 V		
Manifold absolute pressure (MAP) sensor	16	⬅	Engine idling	1 V		
	16	⬅	Engine under load	4,8 V		
	44	⊣⊢	Ignition ON	0 V		
	45	⇨	Ignition ON	5 V		
Power steering pressure (PSP) switch – except N7Q 710/711, F3R 611	9	⬅	Engine idling – steering wheel not turned	11-14 V		
	9	⬅	Engine idling – steering wheel turned	0 V		
Secondary air injection (AIR) pump/ solenoid relay – some models	27	⇥▷	Engine idling – engine cold	0 V		
	27	⇥▷	Engine idling – engine hot	11-14 V		
Tachometer	43	⇨	Engine idling	26 Hz		
	43	⇨	3000 rpm	100 Hz		
Throttle position (TP) sensor	19	⬅	Ignition ON – throttle closed	0,33 V		
	19	⬅	Ignition ON – throttle fully open	4,3 V		
	45	⇨	Ignition ON	5 V		
	46	⊣⊢	Ignition ON	0 V		
Trip computer – if fitted	13	⇨		1		
Vehicle speed sensor (VSS)	12	⬅	Ignition ON – vehicle pushed	0 V or 11-14 V switching		

*Suggested settings - Voltage/time per division

1 Connected pin - no test data available or random digital signal

ECM harness multi-plug

Terminal side

AD81718

Wire side

AD42119

Component/circuit description	ECM pin	Signal	Condition	Typical value	Oscilloscope setting★	Wave form
Accelerator pedal position (APP) sensor	15	←	Ignition ON – accelerator pedal released	0,4 V		
	15	←	Ignition ON – accelerator pedal fully depressed	3,1 V		
	55	⌐	Ignition ON	0 V		
	57	⇨	Ignition ON	5 V		
	65	←	Ignition ON – accelerator pedal released	0,4 V		
	65	←	Ignition ON – accelerator pedal fully depressed	3,1 V		
Brake pedal position (BPP) switch	20	←	Ignition ON – brake pedal released	11-14 V		
	20	←	Ignition ON – brake pedal depressed	0 V		
	44	←	Ignition ON – brake pedal released	0 V		
	44	←	Ignition ON – brake pedal depressed	11-14 V		
Crankshaft position (CKP) sensor	8	←	Engine idling	1,8 V ac	5 V/5 ms	〰 6
	21	⌐	Ignition ON	0 V		
Data link connector (DLC)	61	⬌		1		
	66	⬌		1		
Earth	1		Ignition ON	0 V		
	24		Ignition ON	0 V		
	46		Ignition ON	0 V		
Engine control (EC) relay	23	←	Ignition OFF	0 V		
	23	←	Ignition ON	11-14 V		
	42	⌐⇨	Ignition OFF	11-14 V		
	42	⌐⇨	Ignition ON	0-1 V		
	45	←	Ignition OFF	0 V		
	45	←	Ignition ON	11-14 V		
	68	←	Ignition OFF	0 V		
	68	←	Ignition ON	11-14 V		

★ Suggested settings - Voltage/time per division

Component/circuit description	ECM pin	Signal	Condition	Typical value	Oscilloscope setting*	Wave form
Engine coolant blower motor relay	3	⊐▷		1		
Engine coolant heater relay 1	47	⊐▷	Ignition ON – engine coolant heater OFF	11-14 V		
	47	⊐▷	Ignition ON – engine coolant heater ON	0-1 V		
Engine coolant heater relay 2	27	⊐▷	Ignition ON – engine coolant heater OFF	11-14 V		
	27	⊐▷	Ignition ON – engine coolant heater ON	0-1 V		
Engine coolant 'hot' warning lamp	48	⊐▷	Ignition ON – lamp ON	0-1 V		
	48	⊐▷	Ignition ON – lamp OFF	11-14 V		
Engine coolant temperature (ECT) sensor	14	⬅	Ignition ON – coolant temp. 20°C	3 V		
	14	⬅	Ignition ON – coolant temp. 80°C	0,6 V		
	33	⅂	Ignition ON	0 V		
Exhaust gas recirculation (EGR) solenoid	25	⊐▷	Ignition ON	11-14 V		
	25	⊐▷	Engine idling		5 V/2 ms	〰 31
Fuel injection timing solenoid	51	⊐▷	Engine idling		2 V/10 ms	〰 10
Fuel quantity adjuster	4	⊐▷	Engine idling		2 V/2 ms	〰 30
	5	⊐▷	Engine idling		2 V/2 ms	〰 30
	49	⊐▷	Engine idling		2 V/2 ms	〰 30
Fuel quantity adjuster position sensor	7	⇨	Ignition ON	2,49 V		
	7	⇨	Engine idling	2,49 V		
	29	⬅	Ignition ON	2,48 V		
	29	⬅	Engine idling	2,5 V	0,5 V/0,1 ms	〰 8
	52	⬅	Ignition ON	2,48 V		
	52	⬅	Engine idling	2,5 V	0,5 V/0,1 ms	〰 8
Fuel shut-off solenoid	53	⇨	Ignition ON	0 V		
	53	⇨	Engine idling	11-14 V		
Fuel temperature sensor	33	⅂	Ignition ON	0 V		
	63	⬅	Ignition ON – fuel temp. 20°C	3,4 V		
Glow plug control module	30		Ignition ON – glow plugs ON	11-14 V		
	30		Ignition ON – glow plugs OFF	0,15 V		
	30		Engine idling – glow plugs OFF	0,17 V		
	50		Engine idling – glow plugs OFF	11-14 V		
	50		Ignition ON – glow plugs ON	0 V		
	50		Ignition ON – glow plugs OFF	10,5 V		
Glow plug warning lamp	26	⊐▷	Ignition ON – lamp ON	0-1 V		
	26	⊐▷	Ignition ON – lamp OFF	11-14 V		
	54	⊐▷	Ignition ON – lamp ON	0-1 V		
	54	⊐▷	Ignition ON – lamp OFF	11-14 V		
Ignition switch	38	⬅	Ignition ON	11-14 V		
Injector needle lift sensor	11	⅂	Engine idling	0 V		
	12	⬅	Ignition ON	3,24 V		
	12	⬅	Engine idling		0,2 V/5 ms	〰 7
Instrument panel	32			1		

* Suggested settings - Voltage/time per division

Component/circuit description	ECM pin	Signal	Condition	Typical value	Oscilloscope setting*	Wave form
Intake air temperature (IAT) sensor	21	⅂—	Ignition ON	0 V		
	64	⬅	Ignition ON – air temp. 17°C	3,8 V		
Mass air flow (MAF) sensor	13	⬅	Ignition ON	0,5 V		
	13	⬅	Engine idling	1,8 V		
	13	⬅	Engine idling – accelerate briefly	4 V briefly		
	19	⟹	Ignition ON	5 V		
	21	⅂—	Ignition ON	0 V		
Multifunction control module	35			☐1		
	59			☐1		
Tachometer	2	⟹		☐1		
Transmission control module (TCM)	2			☐1		
	9			☐1		
	16			☐1		
	31			☐1		
	39			☐1		
Transmission range (TR) switch – reverse gear engaged	17			☐1		
Vehicle speedometer	43	⬅		☐1		

*Suggested settings - Voltage/time per division

☐1 Connected pin - no test data available or random digital signal

RENAULT

Bosch MSA 15.5

Model:	Engine code:	Year:
Laguna 1,9 dTi	F9Q 710/716	1998-01
Espace 1,9 dTi	F9Q 720/722	1999-01

ECM harness multi-plug

Terminal side

AD81718

Wire side

AD42119

Component/circuit description	ECM pin	Signal	Condition	Typical value
ABS control module – vehicle speed sensor (VSS) signal	43	←	Ignition ON – vehicle pushed	Switching voltage
AC connector – F9Q722	3			☐1
	6			☐1
AC control module	28			☐1
	37			☐1
AC refrigerant triple pressure switch – F9Q710	3			☐1
	6			☐1
AC/heater function control panel – Laguna	35			☐1
Accelerator pedal position (APP) sensor	15	←	Ignition ON – accelerator pedal released	0,4 V
	15	←	Ignition ON – accelerator pedal depressed	3,1 V
	55	⌐	Engine idling	0 V
	57	⇒	Ignition ON	5 V
Accelerator pedal position (APP) switch	65	←	Ignition ON – accelerator pedal released	0 V
	65	←	Ignition ON – accelerator pedal depressed	2,74 V
Airbag control module – some models	38			☐1
Brake pedal position (BPP) switch	20	←	Ignition ON – brake pedal released	11-14 V
	20	←	Ignition ON – brake pedal depressed	0 V
	44	←	Ignition ON – brake pedal released	0 V
	44	←	Ignition ON – brake pedal depressed	11-14 V
Clutch pedal position (CPP) switch	17	←	Ignition ON – clutch pedal released	0 V
	17	←	Ignition ON – clutch pedal depressed	11-14 V
Combination control module – Espace	26			☐1
	54			☐1
	59			☐1
Combination control module – F9Q722	48			☐1

Component/circuit description	ECM pin	Signal	Condition	Typical value
Crankshaft position (CKP) sensor	8	←	Engine idling	1,8 V ac
	8	←	Engine idling	5 V/5 ms per division 〰️ 6
	21	⅂—	Engine idling	0 V
Data link connector (DLC)	61	⇔		1
	66	⇔		1
Earth	1		Ignition ON	0 V
	24		Ignition ON	0 V
	46		Ignition ON	0 V
Engine control relay	23	←	Ignition OFF	0 V
	23	←	Ignition ON	11-14 V
	42	⅂▷	Ignition OFF	11-14 V
	42	⅂▷	Ignition ON	0-1 V
	45	←	Ignition OFF	0 V
	45	←	Ignition ON	11-14 V
	68	←	Ignition OFF	0 V
	68	←	Ignition ON	11-14 V
Engine coolant heater relay I – if fitted	47	⅂▷	Ignition ON – engine coolant heater OFF	11-14 V
	47	⅂▷	Ignition ON – engine coolant heater ON	0-1 V
Engine coolant heater relay II – if fitted	27	⅂▷	Ignition ON – engine coolant heater OFF	11-14 V
	27	⅂▷	Ignition ON – engine coolant heater ON	0-1 V
Engine coolant 'hot' warning lamp – F9Q710	48	⅂▷	Ignition ON – lamp ON	0-1 V
	48	⅂▷	Ignition ON – lamp OFF	11-14 V
Engine coolant temperature (ECT) sensor	14	←	Ignition ON – coolant temp. 20°C	2,7 V
	14	←	Ignition ON – coolant temp. 80°C	0,5 V
	33	⅂—	Engine idling	0 V
Exhaust gas recirculation (EGR) solenoid	25	⅂▷	Ignition ON	11-14 V
	25	⅂▷	Engine idling	11-14 V
	25	⅂▷	Engine idling	5 V/2 ms per division 〰️ 31
Fuel injection timing solenoid	51	⅂▷	Engine idling	2 V/10 ms per division 〰️ 10
Fuel quantity adjuster	4	⅂▷	Engine idling	2 V/2 ms per division 〰️ 30
	5	⅂▷	Engine idling	2 V/2 ms per division 〰️ 30
	49	⅂▷	Engine idling	2 V/2 ms per division 〰️ 30
Fuel quantity adjuster position sensor	7	⇨	Ignition ON	2,48 V
	7	⇨	Engine idling	2,49 V
	29	←	Ignition ON	2,47 V
	29	←	Engine idling	2,48 V
	29	←	Engine idling	0,5 V/0,1 ms per division 〰️ 8
	52	←	Ignition ON	2,47 V
	52	←	Engine idling	2,48 V
	52	←	Engine idling	0,5 V/0,1 ms per division 〰️ 8

Component/circuit description	ECM pin	Signal	Condition	Typical value
Fuel shut-off solenoid	53	⇨	Engine idling	11-14 V
	53	⇨	Ignition OFF	0 V
	53	⇨	Ignition ON	0 V
Fuel temperature sensor	33	⊣⊢	Engine idling	0 V
	63	⇦	Ignition ON – fuel temp. 20°C	3,4 V
Glow plug control module	30		Engine idling – glow plugs OFF	0,17 V
	30		Ignition ON – glow plugs ON	11-14 V
	30		Ignition ON – glow plugs OFF	0,15 V
	50		Engine idling – glow plugs OFF	11-14 V
	50		Ignition ON – glow plugs ON	0 V
	50		Ignition ON – glow plugs OFF	10,5 V
Glow plug warning lamp – Laguna	54	⊣▷	Ignition ON – lamp ON	0-1 V
	54	⊣▷	Ignition ON – lamp OFF	11-14 V
Immobilizer control module – Laguna	59	⇦		[1]
Inertia fuel shut-off (IFS) switch – some models	38	⇦	Ignition ON – button depressed	11-14 V
	38	⇦	Ignition ON – button released	0 V
Injector needle lift sensor	11	⊣⊢	Engine idling	0 V
	12	⇦	Engine idling	0,016 V ac
	12	⇦	Engine idling	0,2 V/1 ms per division ⎍ 7
Intake air temperature (IAT) sensor	21	⊣⊢	Engine idling	0 V
	64	⇦	Ignition ON – air temp. 20°C	3 V
Malfunction indicator lamp (MIL) – Laguna	26	⊣▷	Ignition ON – MIL ON	0-1 V
	26	⊣▷	Ignition ON – MIL OFF	11-14 V
Mass air flow (MAF) sensor – F9Q710 & F9Q722	19	⇦	Ignition ON	5 V
	13	⇦	Engine idling	2,4 V
	13	⇦	Engine idling – accelerate briefly	4,3 V (briefly)
	13	⇦	Ignition ON	0,5 V
	21	⊣⊢	Engine idling	0 V
Reverse gear position switch – F9Q710 MT	16	⇦	Ignition ON – except reverse	0 V
	16	⇦	Ignition ON – in reverse	11-14 V
Tachometer	2	⇨	3000 rpm	100 Hz
	2	⇨	Engine idling	28 Hz
	2	⇨	Engine idling	5 V/10 ms per division ⎍ 2
	2	⇨	Ignition ON	11-14 V
Trip computer – some models	32	⇨	Ignition ON	[1]

[1] Connected pin - no test data available

ECM harness multi-plug

Terminal side

C

1m	1l	1k	1j	1h	1g	1f	1e	1d	1c	1b	1a
2m	2l	2k	2j	2h	2g	2f	2e	2d	2c	2b	2a
3m	3l	3k	3j	3h	3g	3f	3e	3d	3c	3b	3a
4m	4l	4k	4j	4h	4g	4f	4e	4d	4c	4b	4a

B

1m	1l	1k	1j	1h	1g	1f	1e	1d	1c	1b	1a
2m	2l	2k	2j	2h	2g	2f	2e	2d	2c	2b	2a
3m	3l	3k	3j	3h	3g	3f	3e	3d	3c	3b	3a
4m	4l	4k	4j	4h	4g	4f	4e	4d	4c	4b	4a

A

4a	4b	4c	4d	4e	4f	4g	4h
3a	3b	3c	3d	3e	3f	3g	3h
2a	2b	2c	2d	2e	2f	2g	2h
1a	1b	1c	1d	1e	1f	1g	1h

AD20837

Wire side

A

4h	4g	4f	4e	4d	4c	4b	4a
3h	3g	3f	3e	3d	3c	3b	3a
2h	2g	2f	2e	2d	2c	2b	2a
1h	1g	1f	1e	1d	1c	1b	1a

B

1a	1b	1c	1d	1e	1f	1g	1h	1j	1k	1l	1m
2a	2b	2c	2d	2e	2f	2g	2h	2j	2k	2l	2m
3a	3b	3c	3d	3e	3f	3g	3h	3j	3k	3l	3m
4a	4b	4c	4d	4e	4f	4g	4h	4j	4k	4l	4m

C

1a	1b	1c	1d	1e	1f	1g	1h	1j	1k	1l	1m
2a	2b	2c	2d	2e	2f	2g	2h	2j	2k	2l	2m
3a	3b	3c	3d	3e	3f	3g	3h	3j	3k	3l	3m
4a	4b	4c	4d	4e	4f	4g	4h	4j	4k	4l	4m

AD20838

Component/circuit description	ECM pin	Signal	Condition	Typical value
ABS control module – vehicle speed sensor (VSS) signal	A4e	←		1
AC connector	A4f	←		1
	A4g	←		1
Accelerator pedal position (APP) sensor	A3a	⌐—	Engine idling	0 V
	A3b	⌐—	Engine idling	0 V
	A1c	←	Ignition ON – accelerator pedal released	0,1 V
	A1c	←	Ignition ON – accelerator pedal depressed	2,7 V
	A1e	⇒	Ignition ON	5 V
	A1f	←		1
	A2h	⇒	Ignition ON	5 V
Brake pedal position (BPP) switch	A3f	←	Ignition ON – brake pedal released	0 V
	A3f	←	Ignition ON – brake pedal depressed	11-14 V
Camshaft position (CMP) sensor	C1c	⌐—	Engine idling	0 V
	C4k	←	Engine idling	5 V/50 ms per division 〰 3
Clutch pedal position (CPP) switch	A2e	←	Ignition ON – clutch pedal released	0 V
	A2e	←	Ignition ON – clutch pedal depressed	2,6 V
Crankshaft position (CKP) sensor	B3g	←	Engine idling	0,58 V ac
	B3g	←	Engine idling	5 V/2 ms per division 〰 1
	B3h	←	Engine idling	0,58 V ac
	B3h	←	Engine idling	5 V/2 ms per division – wave form reversed 〰 1
Data link connector (DLC)	A3c	⇔		1
	A3d	⇔		1
Earth	B3l		Ignition ON	0 V
	B4l		Ignition ON	0 V
	B4m		Ignition ON	0 V

Component/circuit description	ECM pin	Signal	Condition	Typical value
Engine control relay	B2m	←	Ignition ON	11-14 V
	B3m	←	Ignition ON	11-14 V
	B4d	⊐▷	Ignition OFF	11-14 V
	B4d	⊐▷	Ignition ON	0-1 V
Engine coolant blower motor relay – high speed	C4b			1
Engine coolant blower motor relay – low speed	C2a			1
Engine coolant heater relay I	C4e	⊐▷	Engine idling – engine coolant heater OFF	11-14 V
	C4e	⊐▷	Engine idling – engine coolant heater ON	0-1 V
Engine coolant heater relay II	C4j	⊐▷	Engine idling – engine coolant heater OFF	11-14 V
	C4j	⊐▷	Engine idling – engine coolant heater ON	0-1 V
Engine coolant 'hot' warning lamp	A4h			1
Engine coolant temperature (ECT) sensor	B1e	⊣—	Engine idling	0 V
	B3k	←	Ignition ON – coolant temp. 20°C	2,7 V
	B3k	←	Ignition ON – coolant temp. 80°C	0,5 V
Exhaust gas recirculation (EGR) solenoid	B1m	⊐▷	Ignition ON	11-14 V
	B1m	⊐▷	Engine idling	30%
	B1m	⊐▷	Engine idling	5 V/5 ms per division ⎍⎍ 39
Exhaust gas recirculation (EGR) valve position sensor	B2b	⊣—	Engine idling	0 V
	B2c	←	Ignition ON	1 V
	B2c	←	Engine idling	1,75 V
	B2f	⇨	Ignition ON	5 V
Fuel lift pump relay	C1a	⊐▷	Engine idling	0-1 V
	C1a	⊐▷	Ignition ON – fuel pump ON	0-1 V
	C1a	⊐▷	Ignition ON – fuel pump OFF	11-14 V
Fuel pressure control solenoid	B1l	⊐▷	Engine idling	5 V/1 ms per division ⎍⎍ 56
	B1l	⊐▷	Ignition ON	9,2 V
Fuel pressure sensor	B1d	←	Engine idling	1,2 V
	B1d	←	Ignition ON	0,5 V
	B2h	⇨	Ignition ON	5 V
	C3b	⊣—	Engine idling	0 V
Fuel temperature sensor	B1g	⊣—	Engine idling	0 V
	B3j	←	Ignition ON – fuel temp. 18°C	2,9 V
Glow plug control module	B3b		Ignition ON	11-14 V
	B3c		Ignition ON	11-14 V
Glow plug warning lamp	A1g	⊐▷	Ignition ON – lamp ON	0-1 V
	A1g	⊐▷	Ignition ON – lamp OFF	11-14 V
Heated rear window switch	A1b			1
Ignition switch	B3e	←	Ignition OFF	0 V
	B3e	←	Ignition ON	11-14 V
Immobilizer control module	A2g	←		1
Injector 1	C1m (C3m)		Engine idling	1,5 ms pilot + 1,5 ms main
	C1m (C3m)		Engine idling	10 V/1 ms per division ⎍⎍ 24
	C1m		Ignition ON	7 V
	C3m (C1m)		Engine idling	1,5 ms pilot + 1,5 ms main
	C3m (C1m)		Engine idling	10 V/1 ms per division ⎍⎍ 24
	C3m		Ignition ON	7 V

Component/circuit description	ECM pin	Signal	Condition	Typical value
Injector 2	C3l (C4l)		Engine idling	1,5 ms pilot + 1,5 ms main
	C3l (C4l)		Engine idling	10 V/1 ms per division ᴧᴧᴧ 24
	C3l		Ignition ON	7 V
	C4l (C3l)		Engine idling	1,5 ms pilot + 1,5 ms main
	C4l (C3l)		Engine idling	10 V/1 ms per division ᴧᴧᴧ 24
	C4l		Ignition ON	7 V
Injector 3	C2l (C2m)		Engine idling	1,5 ms pilot + 1,5 ms main
	C2l (C2m)		Engine idling	10 V/1 ms per division ᴧᴧᴧ 24
	C2l		Ignition ON	7 V
	C2m (C2l)		Engine idling	1,5 ms pilot + 1,5 ms main
	C2m (C2l)		Engine idling	10 V/1 ms per division ᴧᴧᴧ 24
	C2m		Ignition ON	7 V
Injector 4	C1l (C4m)		Engine idling	1,5 ms pilot + 1,5 ms main
	C1l (C4m)		Engine idling	10 V/1 ms per division ᴧᴧᴧ 24
	C1l		Ignition ON	7 V
	C4m (C1l)		Engine idling	1,5 ms pilot + 1,5 ms main
	C4m (C1l)		Engine idling	10 V/1 ms per division ᴧᴧᴧ 24
	C4m		Ignition ON	7 V
Intake air temperature (IAT) sensor	B3d	←	Ignition ON – air temp. 20°C	3 V
	C3a	⌐	Engine idling	0 V
Malfunction indicator lamp (MIL) I	A3h	⊐▷	Ignition ON – MIL ON	0-1 V
	A3h	⊐▷	Ignition ON – MIL OFF	11-14 V
Malfunction indicator lamp (MIL) II	A3g	⊐▷	Ignition ON – MIL ON	0-1 V
	A3g	⊐▷	Ignition ON – MIL OFF	11-14 V
Manifold absolute pressure (MAP) sensor	B1c	←	Ignition ON	1,88 V
	B1c	←	Engine idling	1,86 V
	B1c	←	Engine running – accelerator pedal briefly fully depressed	3,75 V (briefly)
	B2j	⇒	Ignition ON	5 V
	C4a	⌐	Engine idling	0 V
Mass air flow (MAF) sensor	B2g	⇒	Ignition ON	5 V
	B4h	←	Engine idling	2,4 V
	B4h	←	Engine idling – accelerate briefly	4,2 V (briefly)
	B4h	←	Ignition ON	0,6 V
Tachometer	A4d	⇒	3000 rpm	100 Hz
	A4d	⇒	Engine idling	28 Hz
	A4d	⇒	Engine idling	5 V/10 ms per division ᴧᴧᴧ 2
Trip computer	A3e	⇒		1
Turbocharger (TC) wastegate regulating valve	B2l	⊐▷	Ignition ON	11-14 V
	B2l	⊐▷	Engine idling	5 V/2 ms per division ᴧᴧᴧ 29

1 Connected pin - no test data available

Model:	Engine code:	Year:
Laguna 1,9 dCi	F9Q 750	2001-10/02

ECM harness multi-plug

Terminal side

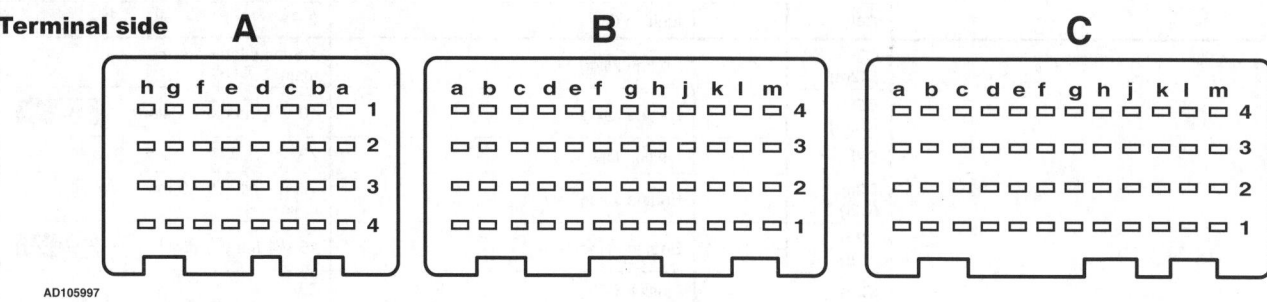

AD105997

Wire side

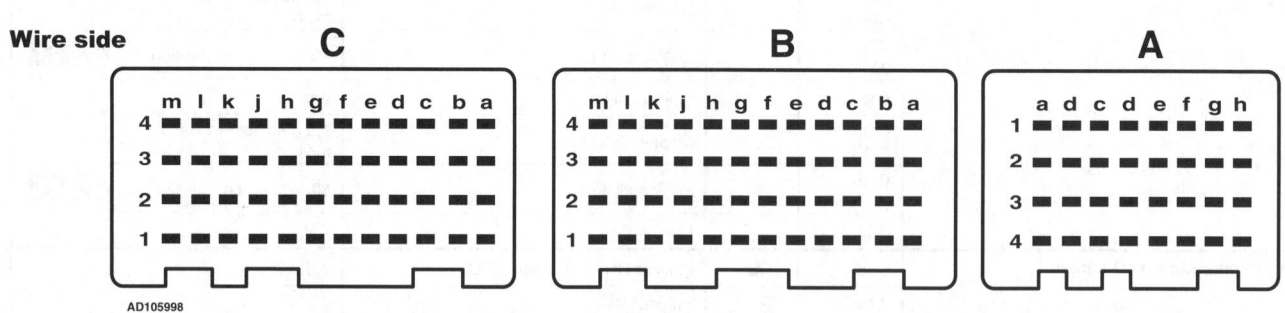

AD105998

Component/circuit description	ECM pin	Signal	Condition	Typical value	Oscilloscope setting*	Wave form
Accelerator pedal position (APP) sensor	Ac1	←	Ignition ON – accelerator pedal released	0,5-1,1 V		
	Ac1	←	Ignition ON – accelerator pedal fully depressed	4,3-4,7 V		
	Ae1	⇒	Ignition ON	5 V		
	Af1	←	Ignition ON – accelerator pedal released	0,1-0,6 V		
	Af1	←	Ignition ON – accelerator pedal fully depressed	2-2,4 V		
	Ah2	⇒	Ignition ON	5 V		
	Aa3	⌐	Engine idling	0 V		
	Ab3	⌐	Engine idling	0 V		
Airbag spiral cable	Aa2			1		
	Ab2			1		
Anti-percolation engine coolant blower relay	Ca2			1		
Brake pedal position (BPP) switch	Af3	←	Ignition ON – brake pedal released	0 V		
	Af3	←	Ignition ON – brake pedal depressed	11-14 V		
Camshaft position (CMP) sensor	Cc1	⌐	Engine idling	0 V		
	Ck4	←	Engine idling		5 V/50 ms	〰 3
Clutch pedal position (CPP) switch	Ae2	←	Ignition ON – clutch pedal released	0 V		
	Ae2	←	Ignition ON – clutch pedal depressed	2,6 V		
Crankshaft position (CKP) sensor	Bg3	←	Engine idling	0,58 V ac	5 V/2 ms	〰 1
	Bh3	←	Engine idling	0,58 V ac	5 V/2 ms	Reversed 〰 1
Cruise control reversing switch	Ad2			1		
	Af2			1		

★ Suggested settings - Voltage/time per division

Autodata

Component/circuit description	ECM pin	Signal	Condition	Typical value	Oscilloscope setting*	Wave form
Data link connector (DLC)	Ac3	⇄		1		
	Aa4	⇄		1		
	Ab4	⇄		1		
Earth	Bl3		Ignition ON	0 V		
	Bl4		Ignition ON	0 V		
	Bm4		Ignition ON	0 V		
Engine control relay	Bm2	←	Ignition ON	11-14 V		
	Bm3	←	Ignition ON	11-14 V		
	Bd4	⊣▷	Ignition OFF	11-14 V		
	Bd4	⊣▷	Ignition ON	0-1 V		
Engine coolant blower motor relay	Cb4			1		
Engine coolant heater relay 1	Cj4	⊣▷	Engine idling – engine coolant heater OFF	11-14 V		
	Cj4	⊣▷	Engine idling – engine coolant heater ON	0-1 V		
Engine coolant heater relay 2	Bf3	⊣▷	Engine idling – engine coolant heater OFF	11-14 V		
	Bf3	⊣▷	Engine idling – engine coolant heater ON	0-1 V		
Engine coolant heater relay 3	Ce4	⊣▷	Engine idling – engine coolant heater OFF	11-14 V		
	Ce4	⊣▷	Engine idling – engine coolant heater ON	0-1 V		
Engine coolant temperature (ECT) sensor	Be1	⊣—	Engine idling	0 V		
	Bk3	←	Ignition ON – coolant temp. 20°C	2,7 V		
	Bk3	←	Ignition ON – coolant temp. 80°C	0,5 V		
Exhaust gas recirculation (EGR) solenoid	Bm1	⊣▷	Ignition ON	11-14 V		
	Bm1	⊣▷	Engine idling	30%	5 V/5 ms	〰 39
Exhaust gas recirculation (EGR) valve position sensor	Bb2	⊣—	Engine idling	0 V		
	Bc2	←	Ignition ON	1 V		
	Bc2	←	Engine idling	1,75 V		
	Bf2	⇒	Ignition ON	5 V		
Fuel pressure regulator control solenoid	Bl1	⊣▷	Ignition ON	9,2 V		
	Bl1	⊣▷	Engine idling		5 V/1 ms	〰 56
Fuel pressure sensor	Cb3	⊣—	Engine idling	0 V		
Fuel rail pressure (FRP) sensor	Bd1	←	Ignition ON	0,5 V		
	Bd1	←	Engine idling	1,2 V		
	Bh2	⇒	Ignition ON	5 V		
Fuel temperature sensor	Bg1	⊣—	Engine idling	0 V		
	Bj3	←	Ignition ON – fuel temp. 18°C	2,9 V		
Fuel/water separator sensor	Ah1			1		
Glow plug control module	Bb3		Ignition ON	11-14 V		
	Bc3		Ignition ON	11-14 V		
Ignition main circuits relay	Be3	←	Ignition OFF	0 V		
	Be3	←	Ignition ON	11-14 V		
Injector 1	Cm1	⊣▷	Ignition ON	7 V		
	Cm1 (Cm3)	⊣▷	Engine idling	1,5 ms pilot + 1,5 ms main	10 V/1 ms	〰 24
	Cm3	⊣▷	Ignition ON	7 V		
	Cm3 (Cm1)	⊣▷	Engine idling	1,5 ms pilot + 1,5 ms main	10 V/1 ms	〰 24

* Suggested settings - Voltage/time per division

Component/circuit description	ECM pin	Signal	Condition	Typical value	Oscilloscope setting*	Wave form
Injector 2	CI3		Ignition ON	7 V		
	CI3 (CI4)	⊐▷	Engine idling	1,5 ms pilot + 1,5 ms main	10 V/1 ms	24
	CI4	⊐▷	Ignition ON	7 V		
	CI4 (CI3)	⊐▷	Engine idling	1,5 ms pilot + 1,5 ms main	10 V/1 ms	24
Injector 3	CI2	⊐▷	Ignition ON	7 V		
	CI2 (Cm2)	⊐▷	Engine idling	1,5 ms pilot + 1,5 ms main	10 V/1 ms	24
	Cm2	⊐▷	Ignition ON	7 V		
	Cm2 (CI2)	⊐▷	Engine idling	1,5 ms pilot + 1,5 ms main	10 V/1 ms	24
Injector 4	CI1	⊐▷	Ignition ON	7 V		
	CI1 (Cm4)	⊐▷	Engine idling	1,5 ms pilot + 1,5 ms main	10 V/1 ms	24
	Cm4	⊐▷	Ignition ON	7 V		
	Cm4 (CI1)	⊐▷	Engine idling	1,5 ms pilot + 1,5 ms main	10 V/1 ms	24
Intake air temperature (IAT) sensor	Bd3	⬅	Ignition ON – air temp. 20°C	3 V		
	Ca3	⊐—	Engine idling	0 V		
Intake manifold air control solenoid	Bf4			1		
Mass air flow (MAF) sensor	Bg2	⇨	Ignition ON	5 V		
	Bh4	⬅	Ignition ON	0,6 V		
	Bh4	⬅	Engine idling	2,4 V		
	Bh4	⬅	Engine idling – accelerate briefly	4,2 V briefly		
Turbocharger (TC) boost pressure sensor	Bc1	⬅	Ignition ON	1,88 V		
	Bc1	⬅	Engine idling	1,86 V		
	Bc1	⬅	Engine idling – accelerate briefly	3,75 V briefly		
	Bj2	⇨	Ignition ON	5 V		
	Ca4	⊐—	Engine idling	0 V		
Turbocharger (TC) wastegate regulating valve	Bl2	⊐▷	Ignition ON	11-14 V		
	Bl2	⊐▷	Engine idling		5 V/2 ms	29

*Suggested settings - Voltage/time per division

1 Connected pin - no test data available or random digital signal

ECM harness multi-plug

Terminal side

C
1h	1g	1f	1e	1d	1c	1b	1a
2h	2g	2f	2e	2d	2c	2b	2a
3h	3g	3f	3e	3d	3c	3b	3a
4h	4g	4f	4e	4d	4c	4b	4a

B
1m	1l	1k	1j	1h	1g	1f	1e	1d	1c	1b	1a
2m	2l	2k	2j	2h	2g	2f	2e	2d	2c	2b	2a
3m	3l	3k	3j	3h	3g	3f	3e	3d	3c	3b	3a
4m	4l	4k	4j	4h	4g	4f	4e	4d	4c	4b	4a

A
4a	4b	4c	4d	4e	4f	4g	4h
3a	3b	3c	3d	3e	3f	3g	3h
2a	2b	2c	2d	2e	2f	2g	2h
1a	1b	1c	1d	1e	1f	1g	1h

AD29417

Wire side

A
4h	4g	4f	4e	4d	4c	4b	4a
3h	3g	3f	3e	3d	3c	3b	3a
2h	2g	2f	2e	2d	2c	2b	2a
1h	1g	1f	1e	1d	1c	1b	1a

B
1a	1b	1c	1d	1e	1f	1g	1h	1j	1k	1l	1m
2a	2b	2c	2d	2e	2f	2g	2h	2j	2k	2l	2m
3a	3b	3c	3d	3e	3f	3g	3h	3j	3k	3l	3m
4a	4b	4c	4d	4e	4f	4g	4h	4j	4k	4l	4m

C
1a	1b	1c	1d	1e	1f	1g	1h
2a	2b	2c	2d	2e	2f	2g	2h
3a	3b	3c	3d	3e	3f	3g	3h
4a	4b	4c	4d	4e	4f	4g	4h

AD29416

Component/circuit description	ECM pin	Signal	Condition	Typical value	Oscilloscope setting*	Wave form
AC compressor clutch relay	A2e	⊐▷	Engine idling – AC OFF	11-14 V		
	A2e	⊐▷	Engine idling – AC ON	0-1 V		
AC control module	C3e			[1]		
AC refrigerant pressure sensor	C3c			[1]		
	C3g			[1]		
	C4c			[1]		
Accelerator pedal position (APP) sensor	A2f	⇨	Ignition ON	5 V		
	A2g	⇨	Ignition ON	5 V		
	A2h	◀	Ignition ON – accelerator pedal released	0,8 V		
	A2h	◀	Ignition ON – accelerator pedal depressed	4,6 V		
	A3f	◀	Ignition ON – accelerator pedal released	0,3 V		
	A3f	◀	Ignition ON – accelerator pedal depressed	1,9 V		
	A3h	⊐	Ignition ON	0 V		
	A4f	⊐	Ignition ON	0 V		
Anti-percolation engine coolant blower relay	C1b	⊐▷	Engine idling – engine coolant blower motor OFF	11-14 V		
	C1b	⊐▷	Engine idling – engine coolant blower motor ON	0-1 V		
Brake pedal position (BPP) switch	A4e	◀	Ignition ON – brake pedal released	0 V		
	A4e	◀	Ignition ON – brake pedal depressed	11-14 V		
	C4d	◀	Ignition ON – brake pedal released	11-14 V		
	C4d	◀	Ignition ON – brake pedal depressed	0 V		
Camshaft position (CMP) sensor	B2e	◀	Engine idling		2 V/50 ms	∿∿ 3
	B3e	⊐	Ignition ON	0 V		

* Suggested settings - Voltage/time per division

Component/circuit description	ECM pin	Signal	Condition	Typical value	Oscilloscope setting*	Wave form
Clutch pedal position (CPP) switch (06/01→)	A4c	←	Ignition ON – clutch pedal released	0 V		
	A4c	←	Ignition ON – clutch pedal depressed	10,5 V		
Crankshaft position (CKP) sensor	B2f	←	Engine idling	5,7 V ac	5 V/2 ms	∿ 1
	B3f	⊣⊢	Ignition ON	0 V		
Data link connector (DLC)	A4b	⟷		1		
Earth	C1g		Ignition ON	0 V		
	C1h		Ignition ON	0 V		
Engine control relay	A1g	←	Ignition OFF	0 V		
	A1g	←	Ignition ON	11-14 V		
	C1f	⊣▷	Ignition OFF	11-14 V		
	C1f	⊣▷	Ignition ON	0-1 V		
	C2g	←	Ignition ON	11-14 V		
	C2h	←	Ignition ON	11-14 V		
Engine coolant blower motor relay – some models	C2b			1		
Engine coolant heater relay 1	C2c	⊣▷	Engine idling – engine coolant heater OFF	11-14 V		
	C2c	⊣▷	Engine idling – engine coolant heater ON	0-1 V		
Engine coolant heater relay 2	C2d	⊣▷	Engine idling – engine coolant heater OFF	11-14 V		
	C2d	⊣▷	Engine idling – engine coolant heater ON	0-1 V		
Engine coolant temperature (ECT) sensor	B2h	←	Ignition ON – coolant temp. 20°C	3,5 V		
	B2h	←	Ignition ON – coolant temp. 80°C	0,7 V		
	B3h	⊣⊢	Ignition ON	0 V		
Exhaust gas recirculation (EGR) solenoid	B3l	⊣▷	Ignition ON	11-14 V		
	B3l	⊣▷	Engine idling		5 V/2 ms	Intermittent ∿ 48
Exhaust gas recirculation (EGR) valve position sensor	B1b	▷	Ignition ON	5 V		
	B2b	←	Ignition ON	1 V		
	B2b	←	Engine idling	1,3 V		
	B3b	⊣⊢	Ignition ON	0 V		
Fuel pressure control solenoid	B4m	⊣▷	Engine idling		2 V/0,5 ms	∿ 37
Fuel pressure sensor	B1d	▷	Ignition ON	5 V		
	B2d	←	Ignition ON	0,5 V		
	B2d	←	Engine idling	1 V		
	B2d	←	3000 rpm	2,2 V		
	B3d	⊣⊢	Ignition ON	0 V		
Fuel temperature sensor	B2g	←	Ignition ON – fuel temp. 20°C	3,1 V		
	B2g	←	Engine idling – engine hot	2,6 V		
	B3g	⊣⊢	Ignition ON	0 V		
Fuel/water separator sensor – some models	C2a			1		
	C3b			1		
Glow plug control module	C2f	⊣▷	Ignition ON	0-1 V briefly then 11-14 V		
	C3d	⊣▷	Ignition ON	0-1 V briefly then 11-14 V		

* Suggested settings - Voltage/time per division

Component/circuit description	ECM pin	Signal	Condition	Typical value	Oscilloscope setting*	Wave form
Ignition switch	A1d	←	Ignition OFF	0 V		
	A1d	←	Ignition ON	11-14 V		
Injector 1	B4a (B4b)		Engine idling	1 ms	5 V/1 ms	63
	B4b (B4a)		Engine idling	1 ms	5 V/1 ms	63
Injector 2	B4g (B4h)		Engine idling	1 ms	5 V/1 ms	63
	B4h (B4g)		Engine idling	1 ms	5 V/1 ms	63
Injector 3	B4c (B4d)		Engine idling	1 ms	5 V/1 ms	63
	B4d (B4c)		Engine idling	1 ms	5 V/1 ms	63
Injector 4	B4e (B4f)		Engine idling	1 ms	5 V/1 ms	63
	B4f (B4e)		Engine idling	1 ms	5 V/1 ms	63
Instrumentation control module – CAN data bus	A3a			[1]		
	A4a			[1]		
Intake air temperature (IAT) sensor	B2j	←	Ignition ON – air temp. 22°C	3 V		
	B3j	⊣	Ignition ON	0 V		
Knock sensor (KS)	B1f (B1g)	←	3000 rpm		50 mV/1 ms	62
	B1g (B1f)	←	3000 rpm		50 mV/1 ms	62
Knock sensor (KS) – shield wire	B1k	⊣	Ignition ON	0 V		
Manifold absolute pressure (MAP) sensor	B1c	⇒	Ignition ON	5 V		
	B2c	←	Ignition ON	1,8 V		
	B2c	←	Engine idling	1,8 V		
	B2c	←	Engine idling – accelerate briefly	3,9 V		
	B3c	⊣	Ignition ON	0 V		
Power steering control module	C1c			[1]		
Turbocharger (TC) boost air temperature sensor	B2k	←	Ignition ON – air temp. 22°C	2,1 V		
	B3k	⊣	Ignition ON	0 V		
Vehicle speedometer – VSS signal (10/02→)	C1e			[1]		

*Suggested settings - Voltage/time per division

[1] Connected pin - no test data available or random digital signal

Model:	Engine code:	Year:
Mini 1,3i	12A2LK70	1996-01

ECM harness multi-plug

Terminal side – A – Red, B – Black

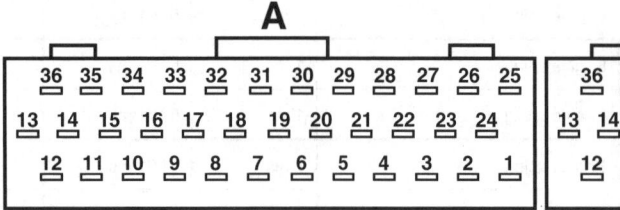

AD42363

Wire side – A – Red, B – Black

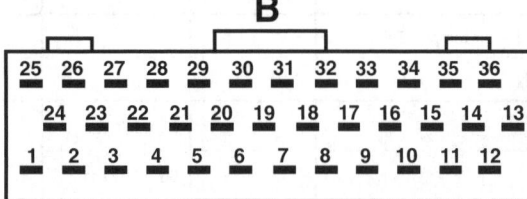

AD42364

Component/circuit description	ECM pin	Signal	Condition	Typical value	Oscilloscope setting*	Wave form
AC refrigerant pressure switch	B34	←		1		
Air conditioning	B19			1		
Camshaft position (CMP) sensor	A1 (A2)	←	Engine idling		5 V/20 ms	⟋⟍ 11
	A2 (A1)	←	Engine idling		5 V/20 ms	Reversed ⟋⟍ 11
Camshaft position (CMP) sensor – shield wire	A23	⌐	Ignition ON	0 V		
Crankshaft position (CKP) sensor	A25 (A26)	←	Engine idling		5 V/5 ms	⟋⟍ 7
	A26 (A25)	←	Engine idling		5 V/5 ms	Reversed ⟋⟍ 7
Crankshaft position (CKP) sensor – shield wire	A23	⌐	Ignition ON	0 V		
Data link connector (DLC)	A31			1		
Earth	A16		Ignition ON	0 V		
	A24		Ignition ON	0 V		
	B21		Ignition ON	0 V		
Engine coolant blower motor relay	B28	⌐▷	Ignition OFF	11-14 V		
	B28	⌐▷	Engine running – coolant blower motor OFF	11-14 V		
	B28	⌐▷	Engine running – coolant blower motor ON	0-1 V		
Engine coolant temperature gauge	B31	⇨		1		
Engine coolant temperature gauge sensor	B13	⌐	Ignition ON	0 V		
	B15	←	Ignition ON – coolant temp. 10°C	2,7 V		
	B15	←	Ignition ON – coolant temp. 80°C	0,5 V		

★ Suggested settings - Voltage/time per division

Component/circuit description	ECM pin	Signal	Condition	Typical value	Oscilloscope setting*	Wave form
Evaporative emission (EVAP) canister purge valve	A17	⊐▷	Engine running	1-99%		
	A17	⊐▷	Engine running		10 V/50 ms	〜〜 20
Heated oxygen sensor (HO2S)	A27	←	Engine idling – accelerate briefly	0-1 V	0,2 V/1 sec.	〜〜 21
	A28	⊐—	Ignition ON	0 V		
Heated oxygen sensor (HO2S) – shield wire	A23	⊐—	Ignition ON	0 V		
Idle air control (IAC) valve	A10	⊐▷	Ignition ON	11-14 V		
	A10	⊐▷	Engine idling		5 V/0,1 ms	Intermittent 〜〜 30
	A15	⊐▷	Ignition ON	11-14 V		
	A15	⊐▷	Engine idling		5 V/0,1 ms	Intermittent 〜〜 30
	A33	⊐▷	Ignition ON	11-14 V		
	A33	⊐▷	Engine idling		5 V/0,1 ms	Intermittent 〜〜 30
	A34	⊐▷	Ignition ON	11-14 V		
	A34	⊐▷	Engine idling		5 V/0,1 ms	Intermittent 〜〜 30
Ignition coil	B25	⊐▷	Ignition OFF	0 V after 5 minutes		
	B25	⊐▷	Ignition ON	11-14 V		
	B25	⊐▷	Engine running		5 V/2 ms	〜〜 33
	B26	⊐▷	Ignition OFF	0 V after 5 minutes		
	B26	⊐▷	Ignition ON	11-14 V		
	B26	⊐▷	Engine running		5 V/2 ms	〜〜 33
Ignition switch	B33	←	Ignition ON	11-14 V		
Immobilizer	B17			[1]		
Injector 1	A12	⊐▷	Ignition OFF	0 V after 5 minutes		
	A12	⊐▷	Ignition ON	11-14 V		
	A12	⊐▷	Engine idling	2,8 ms	10 V/2 ms	〜〜 35
	A13	⊐▷	Ignition OFF	0 V after 5 minutes		
	A13	⊐▷	Ignition ON	11-14 V		
	A13	⊐▷	Engine idling	2,8 ms	10 V/2 ms	〜〜 35
Injector 2	A14	⊐▷	Ignition OFF	0 V after 5 minutes		
	A14	⊐▷	Ignition ON	11-14 V		
	A14	⊐▷	Engine idling	2,8 ms	10 V/2 ms	〜〜 35
	A35	⊐▷	Ignition OFF	0 V after 5 minutes		
	A35	⊐▷	Ignition ON	11-14 V		
	A35	⊐▷	Engine idling	2,8 ms	10 V/2 ms	〜〜 35
Intake air temperature (IAT) sensor	B13	⊐—	Ignition ON	0 V		
	B14	←	Ignition ON – air temp. 10°C	2,8 V		
Manifold absolute pressure (MAP) sensor	B8	⇨	Ignition ON	5 V		
	B13	⊐—	Ignition ON	0 V		
	B36	←	Engine idling	1,5 V		
	B36	←	3000 rpm	1,2 V		
	B36	←	Engine idling – accelerate briefly	4,6 V briefly		

* Suggested settings - Voltage/time per division

Component/circuit description	ECM pin	Signal	Condition	Typical value	Oscilloscope setting*	Wave form
Relay module	B20	⊐▷	Ignition ON	11-14 V		
	B20	⊐▷	Engine running	0-1 V		
	B22	⊐▷	Ignition OFF	11-14 V after 5 minutes		
	B22	⊐▷	Ignition ON	0-1 V		
	B27	⟵	Ignition OFF	0 V after 5 minutes		
	B27	⟵	Ignition ON	11-14 V		
	B30	⊐▷	Ignition ON	0-1 V briefly then 11-14 V		
	B30	⊐▷	Engine cranking	0-1 V briefly then 11-14 V		
	B30	⊐▷	Engine running	0-1 V briefly then 11-14 V		
Tachometer	B25	⊐▷	Engine running		5 V/2 ms	ᴡᴡ 33
Throttle position (TP) sensor	B12	⟵	Ignition ON – throttle closed	0,5 V		
	B12	⟵	Ignition ON – throttle fully open	3,7 V		
	B13	⊐—	Ignition ON	0 V		
	B18	⇨	Ignition ON	5 V		

*Suggested settings - Voltage/time per division

1 Connected pin - no test data available or random digital signal

Model:	Engine code:	Year:
111i/114i/214i	K8/14K8	1996-98
214/216/218 16V	14K16/16K16/18K16	1995-99
216 Cabrio/Coupe/416 Tourer	K16	1996-99
414i/416i	K16	1995-98
420i	T16	1995-98
MGF 1,8i	K16	1995-02

ECM harness multi-plug

Terminal side

AD73893

Wire side

AD42080

Component/circuit description	ECM pin	Signal	Condition	Typical value	Oscilloscope setting*	Wave form
Air conditioning	5	⇨		1		
	15	⬅		1		
	35	⬅		1		
Air conditioning – if fitted	19	⇨		1		
Crankshaft position (CKP) sensor	31 (32)	⬅	Engine running		2 V/5 ms	7
	32 (31)	⬅	Engine running		2 V/5 ms	Reversed 7
Cruise control system relay – except 1,8 – if fitted	26			1		
Data link connector (DLC)	10	⬄		1		
Earth	29		Ignition ON	0 V		
Engine bay air temperature sensor – 1,8	30	⌐	Ignition ON	0 V		
	34	⬅		1		
Engine bay blower motor – 1,8	26	⇨		1		
Engine bay temperature warning lamp – 1,8	17	⇨		1		
Engine coolant blower motor relay – without AC	6	⌐⇨	Engine running – coolant blower motor OFF	11-14 V		
	6	⌐⇨	Engine running – coolant blower motor ON	0-1 V		
Engine coolant temperature (ECT) sensor	30	⌐	Ignition ON	0 V		
	33	⬅	Ignition ON – coolant temp. 10°C	2,8 V		
	33	⬅	Ignition ON – coolant temp. 80°C	0,5 V		
Evaporative emission (EVAP) canister purge valve	21	⌐⇨	Ignition OFF	0 V after 5 minutes		
	21	⌐⇨	Ignition ON	11-14 V		
	21	⌐⇨	Engine running	1-99%	10 V/50 ms	20
Fuel temperature sensor – 2,0	30	⌐	Ignition ON	0 V		
	34	⬅	Ignition ON – fuel temp. 10°C	3,1 V		
Heated oxygen sensor (HO2S)	7	⬅	Engine idling – accelerate briefly	0-1 V fluctuating	0,2 V/1 sec.	21
	18	⌐	Ignition ON	0 V		

* Suggested settings - Voltage/time per division

Component/circuit description	ECM pin	Signal	Condition	Typical value	Oscilloscope setting*	Wave form
Idle speed control (ISC) actuator	2	⟹	Ignition ON	11-14 V		
	2	⟹	Engine idling		5 V/0,1 ms	Intermittent 〰 30
	3	⟹	Ignition ON	11-14 V		
	3	⟹	Engine idling		5 V/0,1 ms	Intermittent 〰 30
	22	⟹	Ignition ON	11-14 V		
	22	⟹	Engine idling		5 V/0,1 ms	Intermittent 〰 30
	27	⟹	Ignition ON	11-14 V		
	27	⟹	Engine idling		5 V/0,1 ms	Intermittent 〰 30
Ignition coil	25	⇥▷	Ignition OFF	0 V after 5 minutes		
	25	⇥▷	Ignition ON	11-14 V		
	25	⇥▷	Engine running		5 V/2 ms	〰 33
Ignition coil – 2,0	1	⇥▷	Ignition OFF	0 V after 5 minutes		
	1	⇥▷	Ignition ON	11-14 V		
	1	⇥▷	Engine running		5 V/2 ms	〰 33
Ignition switch	11	⟸	Ignition OFF	0 V		
	11	⟸	Ignition ON	11-14 V		
Immobilizer control module	13	⟸		[1]		
Injectors 1 & 4	24	⇥▷	Ignition OFF	0 V after 5 minutes		
	24	⇥▷	Ignition ON	11-14 V		
Injectors 1 & 4 – 2,0	24	⇥▷	Engine idling	2,1 ms	10 V/2 ms	〰 35
Injectors 1 & 4 – except 2,0	24	⇥▷	Engine idling	3,3 ms	10 V/2 ms	〰 35
Injectors 2 & 3	23	⇥▷	Ignition OFF	0 V after 5 minutes		
	23	⇥▷	Ignition ON	11-14 V		
Injectors 2 & 3 – 2,0	23	⇥▷	Engine idling	2,1 ms	10 V/2 ms	〰 35
Injectors 2 & 3 – except 2,0	23	⇥▷	Engine idling	3,3 ms	10 V/2 ms	〰 35
Intake air temperature (IAT) sensor	16	⟸	Ignition ON – air temp. 10°C	2,8 V		
	30	⇥—	Ignition ON	0 V		
Knock sensor (KS) – 2,0	17	⟸	Engine idling – accelerate briefly		50 mV/1 ms	〰 38
	30	⇥—	Ignition ON	0 V		
Park/neutral position (PNP) switch – AT	14	⟸		[1]		
Relay module 1	4	⇥▷	Ignition OFF	11-14 V after 5 minutes		
	4	⇥▷	Ignition ON	1 V		
	20	⇥▷	Ignition ON	0,7 V briefly then 11-14 V		
	20	⇥▷	Engine running	0,7 V		
	28	⟸	Ignition OFF	0 V after 5 minutes		
	28	⟸	Ignition ON	11-14 V		
	36	⇥▷	Ignition OFF	0 V after 5 minutes		
	36	⇥▷	Ignition ON	11-14 V		
	36	⇥▷	Engine idling	0-1 V		
Relay module 2 – with AC	6	⇥▷	Engine running – coolant blower motor OFF	11-14 V		
	6	⇥▷	Engine running – coolant blower motor ON	0-1 V		
Tachometer – some models	12	⟹	Engine idling	30 Hz		
	12	⟹	3000 rpm	100 Hz		
Throttle position (TP) sensor	8	⟸	Ignition ON – throttle closed	0,6 V		
	8	⟸	Ignition ON – throttle fully open	4,3 V		
	9	⟹	Ignition ON	5 V		
	30	⇥—	Ignition ON	0 V		

*Suggested settings - Voltage/time per division

[1] Connected pin - no test data available or random digital signal

Model:	Engine code:	Year:
200 vi	18K16	1995-99
218 Coupe VVC	18K16	1996-99
MGF 1,8i VVC	K16-1,8	1995-02

ROVER

Rover MEMS 2J MPI

ECM harness multi-plug

Terminal side – A – Black, B – Red

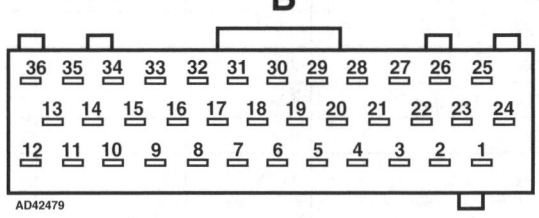
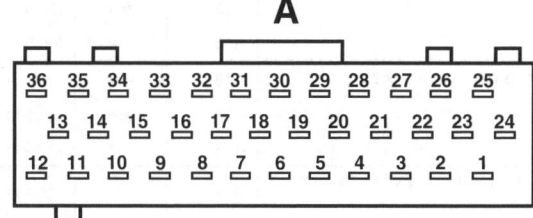

Wire side – A – Black, B – Red

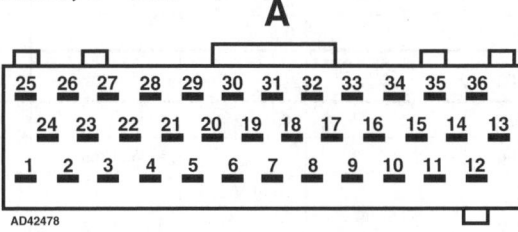
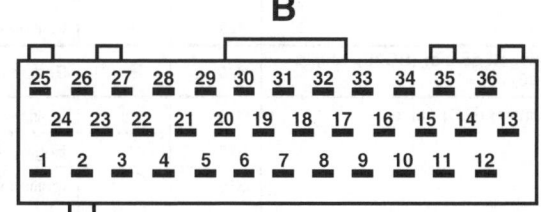

Component/circuit description	ECM pin	Signal	Condition	Typical value	Oscilloscope setting*	Wave form
Air conditioning	A9			1		
	A29			1		
Air conditioning – except MGF 2000→	B19			1		
Air conditioning – MGF 2000→	A19			1		
Camshaft position (CMP) sensor	B1	←	Engine idling	0,3 V ac	0,5 V/20 ms	15
	B2	⌐	Ignition ON	0 V		
Camshaft position (CMP) sensor, shield wire	B23	⌐	Ignition ON	0 V		
Camshaft timing control solenoid 1	A23	⌐⊳	Ignition ON	11-14 V		
	A23	⌐⊳	Engine idling	11-14 V		
	A23	⌐⊳	Engine idling – accelerate briefly	0-1 V briefly		
Camshaft timing control solenoid 2	A2	⌐⊳	Ignition ON	11-14 V		
	A2	⌐⊳	Engine idling	11-14 V		
	A2	⌐⊳	Engine idling – accelerate briefly	0-1 V		
Crankshaft position (CKP) sensor	B25	←	Engine idling	3,8 V ac	2 V/5 ms	7
	B26	⌐	Ignition ON	0 V		
Crankshaft position (CKP) sensor, shield wire	B23	⌐	Ignition ON	0 V		
Data link connector (DLC)	B31		Ignition ON	3,7 V		
Earth	A21		Ignition ON	0 V		
	B16		Ignition ON	0 V		
	B24		Ignition ON	0 V		
Engine bay air temperature sensor – MGF	A11	←	Ignition ON – air temp. 10°C	2,3 V		
	A13	⌐	Ignition ON	0 V		
Engine bay blower motor relay – MGF	B32	⌐⊳	Ignition ON – engine bay blower motor OFF	11-14 V		
	B32	⌐⊳	Engine idling – engine bay blower motor ON	0-1 V		

* Suggested settings - Voltage/time per division

Component/circuit description	ECM pin	Signal	Condition	Typical value	Oscilloscope setting*	Wave form
Engine bay temperature warning lamp – MGF	A31	→▷	Ignition ON – warning lamp OFF	11-14 V		
	A31	→▷	Ignition ON – warning lamp ON	0-1 V		
Engine coolant blower motor relay – without AC	A4	→▷	Engine running – coolant blower motor OFF	11-14 V		
	A4	→▷	Engine running – coolant blower motor ON	0-1 V		
Engine coolant temperature (ECT) sensor	A13	→—	Ignition ON	0 V		
	A15	←	Ignition ON – coolant temp. 10°C	2,2 V		
	A15	←	Ignition ON – coolant temp. 80°C	0,5 V		
Engine oil temperature sensor	A10	←	Ignition ON – oil temp. 10°C	2 V		
	A10	←	Ignition ON – oil temp. 80°C	1 V		
	A13	→—	Ignition ON	0 V		
Evaporative emission (EVAP) canister purge valve	B17	→▷	Ignition ON	11-14 V		
	B17	→▷	Engine running		10 V/50 ms	〰 20
Heated oxygen sensor (HO2S)	B27	←	Engine idling – accelerate briefly	0-1 V fluctuating	0,2 V/1 sec.	〰 21
	B28	→—	Ignition ON	0 V		
Heated oxygen sensor (HO2S), shield wire – 2000→	B23	→—	Engine idling	0 V		
Idle air control (IAC) valve	B10	→▷	Ignition ON	11-14 V		
	B10	→▷	Engine idling		5 V/0,1 ms	Intermittent 〰 30
	B15	→▷	Ignition ON	11-14 V		
	B15	→▷	Engine idling		5 V/0,1 ms	Intermittent 〰 30
	B33	→▷	Ignition ON	11-14 V		
	B33	→▷	Engine idling		5 V/0,1 ms	Intermittent 〰 30
	B34	→▷	Ignition ON	11-14 V		
	B34	→▷	Engine idling		5 V/0,1 ms	Intermittent 〰 30
Ignition coil 1	A25	→▷	Ignition OFF	0 V after 5 minutes		
	A25	→▷	Ignition ON	11-14 V		
	A25	→▷	Engine idling	11-14 V		
	A25	→▷	Engine idling		5 V/2 ms	〰 33
Ignition coil 2	A26	→▷	Ignition OFF	0 V after 5 minutes		
	A26	→▷	Ignition ON	11-14 V		
	A26	→▷	Engine idling	11-14 V		
	A26	→▷	Engine idling		5 V/2 ms	〰 33
Ignition switch	A33	←	Ignition ON	11-14 V		
Immobilizer control module	A17			1		
Injector 1	B12	→▷	Ignition OFF	0 V after 5 minutes		
	B12	→▷	Ignition ON	11-14 V		
	B12	→▷	Engine idling	3 ms	10 V/2 ms	〰 35
Injector 2	B13	→▷	Ignition OFF	0 V after 5 minutes		
	B13	→▷	Ignition ON	11-14 V		
	B13	→▷	Engine idling	3 ms	10 V/2 ms	〰 35
Injector 3	B14	→▷	Ignition OFF	0 V after 5 minutes		
	B14	→▷	Ignition ON	11-14 V		
	B14	→▷	Engine idling	3 ms	10 V/2 ms	〰 35
Injector 4	B35	→▷	Ignition OFF	0 V after 5 minutes		
	B35	→▷	Ignition ON	11-14 V		
	B35	→▷	Engine idling	3 ms	10 V/2 ms	〰 35

* Suggested settings - Voltage/time per division

Component/circuit description	ECM pin	Signal	Condition	Typical value	Oscilloscope setting*	Wave form
Intake air temperature (IAT) sensor	A13	⌐ー	Ignition ON	0 V		
	A14	←	Ignition ON – air temp. 10°C	2,3 V		
Manifold absolute pressure (MAP) sensor	A8	⇨	Ignition ON	5 V		
	A13	⌐ー	Ignition ON	0 V		
	A36	←	Ignition ON	4,6 V		
	A36	←	Engine idling	1 V		
	A36	←	Engine idling – accelerate briefly	4,6 V briefly		
Relay module 1	A20	⌐▷	Ignition ON	11-14 V		
	A20	⌐▷	Engine idling	0-1 V		
	A22	⌐▷	Ignition OFF	11-14 V after 5 minutes		
	A22	⌐▷	Ignition ON	0-1 V		
	A27	←	Ignition OFF	0 V after 5 minutes		
	A27	←	Ignition ON	11-14 V		
	A30	⌐▷	Ignition ON	0-1 V briefly then 11-14 V		
	A30	⌐▷	Engine cranking	0-1 V		
	A30	⌐▷	Engine idling	0-1 V		
Relay module 2 – with AC	A4	⌐▷	Engine running – coolant/condenser blower motors OFF	11-14 V		
	A4	⌐▷	Engine running – coolant/condenser blower motors ON, fast speed	0-1 V		
	A28	⌐▷	Engine running – coolant/condenser blower motors OFF	11-14 V		
	A28	⌐▷	Engine running – coolant/condenser blower motors ON, slow/fast speed	0-1 V		
Tachometer	B9	⇨	Engine idling	30 Hz		
Throttle position (TP) sensor	A12	←	Ignition ON – throttle closed	0,5 V		
	A12	←	Ignition ON – throttle fully open	4 V		
	A13	⌐ー	Ignition ON	0 V		
	A18	⇨	Ignition ON	5 V		
Vehicle speed sensor (VSS) – 200	B30	←		1		

*Suggested settings - Voltage/time per division

1 Connected pin - no test data available or random digital signal

Model:		Engine code:	Year:
220 2,0D Turbo		20T2N	1995-99
420 2,0D Turbo		20T2N	1995-99

ECM harness multi-plug

Terminal side

19 18 17 16 15 14 13 12 11 10 9 8 7 6 5 4 3 2 1
37 36 35 34 33 32 31 30 29 28 27 26 25 24 23 22 21 20
55 54 53 52 51 50 49 48 47 46 45 44 43 42 41 40 39 38

AD72618

Wire side

1 2 3 4 5 6 7 8 9 10 11 12 13 14 15 16 17 18 19
20 21 22 23 24 25 26 27 28 29 30 31 32 33 34 35 36 37
38 39 40 41 42 43 44 45 46 47 48 49 50 51 52 53 54 55

AD42077

Component/circuit description	ECM pin	Signal	Condition	Typical value
AC refrigerant triple pressure switch – 220	44	←	Ignition ON	10 V
	44	←	Ignition ON – AC OFF	10,5 V
	44	←	Ignition ON – AC ON	0,1 V
	44	←	Engine idling – AC OFF	11-14 V
	44	←	Engine idling – AC ON	0,1 V
AC refrigerant triple pressure switch, through engine oil temperature switch – 420	44	←	Ignition ON	10 V
	44	←	Ignition ON – AC OFF	10,5 V
	44	←	Ignition ON – AC ON	0,1 V
	44	←	Engine idling – AC OFF	11-14 V
	44	←	Engine idling – AC ON	0,1 V
Accelerator pedal position (APP) sensor	13	⊣	Ignition ON	0 V
	25	←	Ignition ON – accelerator pedal released	0,4 V
	25	←	Ignition ON – accelerator pedal slightly depressed	6 V
	33	⇒	Ignition ON	5 V
	37	←	Ignition ON – accelerator pedal released	0,4 V
	37	←	Ignition ON – accelerator pedal fully depressed	3,7 V
Brake pedal position (BPP) switch	26	←	Ignition ON – brake pedal released	0 V
	26	←	Ignition ON – brake pedal depressed	11-14 V
	31	←	Ignition ON – brake pedal released	0 V
	31	←	Ignition ON – brake pedal depressed	9,5 V
Crankshaft position (CKP) sensor	13	⊣	Ignition ON	0 V
	47	←	Engine idling	3,6 V ac
	47	←	Engine idling	10 V/5 ms per division ⎍⎍ 6
	47	←	Ignition ON	0 V
Data link connector (DLC)	27	←	Ignition ON	9,5 V
	42	⇒	Ignition ON	6,8 V

Component/circuit description	ECM pin	Signal	Condition	Typical value
Earth	18		Ignition ON	0 V
	19		Ignition ON	0 V
Engine control (EC) relay – 420	15	⊣▷	Ignition OFF	0 V
	15	⊣▷	Ignition ON	0,2 V
	16	⟵	Ignition ON	11-14 V
	16	⟵	Ignition OFF	0 V
	17	⟵	Ignition OFF	0 V
	17	⟵	Ignition ON	11-14 V
Engine coolant temperature (ECT) sensor	13	⊣—	Ignition ON	0 V
	53	⟵	Ignition ON – coolant temp. 20°C	3,8 V
	53	⟵	Engine idling – coolant temp. 80°C	1,5 V
Exhaust gas recirculation (EGR) solenoid	6	⊣▷	Ignition ON	11-14 V
	6	⊣▷	Engine idling	5 V/2 ms per division 〰 31
Fuel injection timing solenoid	10	⊣▷	Ignition ON	5 V/2 ms per division 〰 31
	10	⊣▷	Ignition ON	8,5-9,5 V (fluctuating)
Fuel quantity adjuster	1	⊣▷	Engine idling	2 V/2 ms per division 〰 5
	1	⊣▷	Ignition ON	11-14 V after 30 seconds
	2	⊣▷	Engine idling	2 V/2 ms per division 〰 5
	2	⊣▷	Ignition ON	11-14 V after 30 seconds
Fuel quantity adjuster position sensor	14	⟹	Engine idling	2,5 V
	14	⟹	Ignition ON	2,5 V
	21	⟵	Ignition ON	2,5 V
	21	⟵	Engine idling	2,5 V
	21	⟵	Engine idling	0,5 V/0,5 ms per division 〰 8
	39	⟵	Ignition ON	2,5 V
	39	⟵	Engine idling	2,5 V
	39	⟵	Engine idling	0,5 V/0,5 ms per division 〰 8
Fuel shut-off solenoid	3	⟹	Ignition OFF	0 V
	3	⟹	Ignition ON	11-14 V
Fuel temperature sensor	13	⊣—	Ignition ON	0 V
	35	⟵	Engine idling	3,3 V
	35	⟵	Ignition ON	3,7 V
Glow plug relay	8	⊣▷	Ignition ON – glow plugs ON	0 V
	8	⊣▷	Ignition ON – glow plugs OFF	11-14 V
Glow plug warning lamp	11	⊣▷	Ignition ON – lamp ON	0 V
	11	⊣▷	Ignition ON – lamp OFF	11-14 V
Ignition switch – 420	55	⟵	Ignition OFF	0 V
	55	⟵	Ignition ON	11-14 V
Immobilizer	45	⟵	Ignition ON	0 to 11-14 V (fluctuating)

Component/circuit description	ECM pin	Signal	Condition	Typical value
Injector needle lift sensor	5	←	Engine idling	0,5 V/1 ms per division ∿ **7**
	5	←	Engine idling	0,03 V ac
	5	←	Ignition ON	3,5 V
	12	⊣▷	Ignition ON	0 V
Intake air temperature (IAT) sensor	13	⊣	Ignition ON	0 V
	36	←	Ignition ON – air temp. 20°C	3,8 V
Malfunction indicator lamp (MIL)	4	⊣▷	Ignition ON – MIL ON	0 V
	4	⊣▷	Ignition ON – MIL OFF	11-14 V
Manifold absolute pressure (MAP) sensor	51	⇨	Ignition ON	5 V
	51	⇨	Engine idling	5 V
	54	←	Ignition ON	1,9 V
	54	←	Engine idling	1,9 V
	54	←	Accelerate briefly	3,4 V
Mass air flow (MAF) sensor	13	⊣	Ignition ON	0 V
	38	←	Engine idling	1,1 V
	38	←	Engine idling – accelerate briefly	3,6 V
	38	←	Ignition ON	0,1 V
Relay module, AC compressor clutch contacts	9	⊣▷	Engine idling – AC compressor OFF	11-14 V
	9	⊣▷	Engine idling – AC compressor ON	0,14 V
	9	⊣▷	Ignition ON	11-14 V
Relay module, engine control (EC) contacts – 220	15	⊣▷	Ignition OFF	0 V
	15	⊣▷	Ignition ON	0,2 V
	16	←	Ignition ON	11-14 V
	16	←	Ignition OFF	0 V
	17	←	Ignition OFF	0 V
	17	←	Ignition ON	11-14 V
Relay module, ignition main circuits contacts – 220	55	←	Ignition OFF	0 V
	55	←	Ignition ON	11-14 V
Tachometer	50	⇨	Engine idling	27 Hz
	50	⇨	Ignition ON	10,6 V
Vehicle speed sensor (VSS)	29	←	Drive vehicle at 10 mph min.	0 to 11-14 V (fluctuating)
	29	←	Drive vehicle at 10 mph min.	5 V/50 ms per division ∿ **2**
	29	←	Ignition ON	10,6 V

1 Connected pin - no test data available

Model:	Engine code:	Year:
220 2,0D Turbo	20T2R	1995-99
420 2,0D Turbo	20T2R	1995-00

ROVER

Rover EDC

ECM harness multi-plug

Terminal side

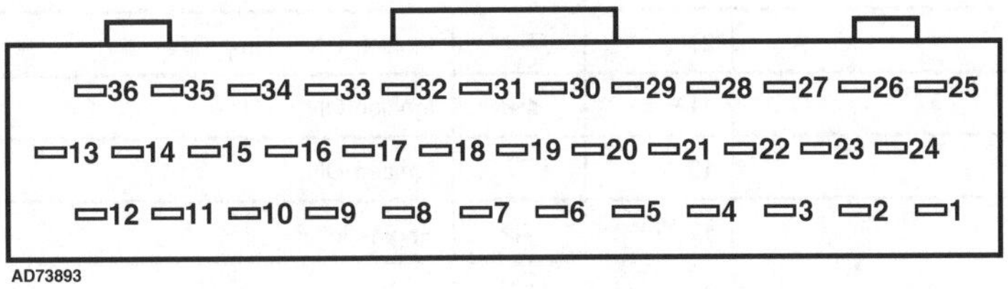

```
  □36 □35 □34 □33 □32 □31 □30 □29 □28 □27 □26 □25
  □13 □14 □15 □16 □17 □18 □19 □20 □21 □22 □23 □24
  □12 □11 □10 □9 □8 □7 □6 □5 □4 □3 □2 □1
```
AD73893

Wire side

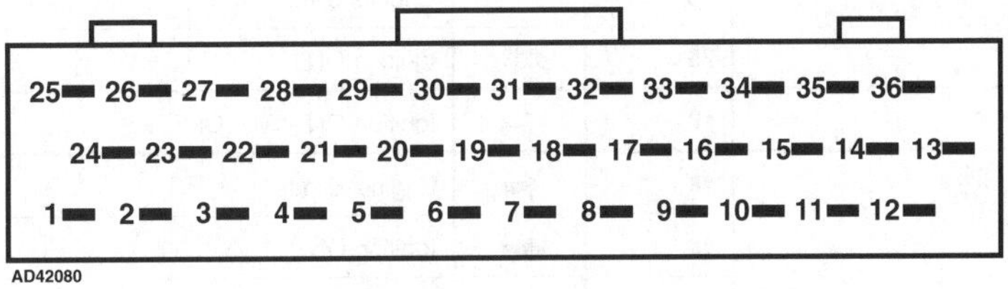

```
  25■ 26■ 27■ 28■ 29■ 30■ 31■ 32■ 33■ 34■ 35■ 36■
  24■ 23■ 22■ 21■ 20■ 19■ 18■ 17■ 16■ 15■ 14■ 13■
  1■ 2■ 3■ 4■ 5■ 6■ 7■ 8■ 9■ 10■ 11■ 12■
```
AD42080

Component/circuit description	ECM pin	Signal	Condition	Typical value	
AC compressor clutch relay	19	⊐⊢▷	Engine idling – AC compressor OFF	11-14 V	
	19	⊐⊢▷	Engine idling – AC compressor ON	0-1 V	
AC refrigerant triple pressure switch	15	⊐⊢▷		[1]	
Crankshaft position (CKP) sensor	31	⬅	Engine idling	1 V/5 ms per division	� 6
	32	⬅	Engine idling	0,05 V	
	32	⬅	Ignition ON	0 V	
Data link connector (DLC)	10	⬅▷	Ignition ON	0 V	
Earth	29		Ignition ON	0 V	
Engine control relay	4	▷	Ignition OFF	11-14 V	
	4	▷	Ignition ON	1,1 V	
	28	⬅	Ignition ON	11-14 V	
Engine coolant blower motor relay I	5	⊐⊢▷	Ignition OFF	11-14 V	
	5	⊐⊢▷	Engine idling – coolant blower motor OFF	11-14 V	
	5	⊐⊢▷	Engine idling – coolant blower motor ON	0-1 V	
Engine coolant blower motor relay II	6	⊐⊢▷	Ignition ON	11-14 V	
	6	⊐⊢▷	Engine idling – coolant blower motor OFF	11-14 V	
	6	⊐⊢▷	Engine idling – coolant blower motor ON	0-1 V	
Engine coolant temperature (ECT) sensor	7	⊐⊢▷	Ignition ON	0 V	
	30	⊐⊢	Ignition ON	0 V	
	33	▷	Ignition ON – coolant temp. 20°C	2,3 V	
	33	▷	Ignition ON – coolant temp. 80°C	0,7 V	
Engine oil temperature switch	35			[1]	
Exhaust gas recirculation (EGR) solenoid	21	⊐⊢▷	Ignition ON	11-14 V	
	21	⊐⊢▷	Engine idling	2 V/5 ms per division	⟋ᴡ 53

Component/circuit description	ECM pin	Signal	Condition	Typical value
Fuel injection timing solenoid	36	⇨	Engine idling	2 V/10 ms per division ⎍⎍⎍ **6**
	36	⇨	Ignition ON	11-14 V
Fuel shut-off solenoid relay	20	⇨	Ignition ON	0 V
	26	⇨	Ignition ON	0 V
Glow plug relay	3	⇨	Ignition ON	11-14 V
Glow plug warning lamp	27	⇨	Ignition ON – lamp OFF	11-14 V
Ignition switch	11	⬅	Ignition ON	11-14 V
Immobilizer control module	13	⇨	Ignition ON	4,4-6,8 V (fluctuating)
Injector needle lift sensor	1	⇨	Engine idling	0,2 V/2 ms per division ⎍⎍⎍ **7**
	1	⇨	Ignition ON	3,5 V
	25	⌐⊳	Engine idling	0,003 V ac
	25	⌐⊳	Ignition ON	0 V
Malfunction indicator (MIL) lamp	17	⇨	Ignition ON – MIL OFF	11-14 V
Mass air flow (MAF) sensor	18	⬅	Engine idling	1,6 V
	18	⬅	Ignition ON	0,1 V
	30	⌐−	Ignition ON	0 V
Tachometer	12	⇨	3000 rpm	100 Hz
	12	⇨	Engine idling	30 Hz

1 Connected pin - no test data available

Model:	Engine code:	Year:
25 1,4	14K4	1999-05
25 1,6	16K4	1999-05
25 1,8	18K4	1999-05
25 1,8 VVC	18K4	1999-04

ECM harness multi-plug

Terminal side

AD42344

Wire side

AD42345

Component/circuit description	ECM pin	Signal	Condition	Typical value	Oscilloscope setting*	Wave form
ABS control module – rough road signal	78	←		1		
AC compressor clutch relay	53	⊐▷	Engine idling – AC OFF	11-14 V		
	53	⊐▷	Engine idling – AC ON – AC compressor ON	0-1 V		
AC condenser blower motor relay 1	60	⊐▷	Engine idling – condenser blower motor OFF	11-14 V		
	60	⊐▷	Engine idling – condenser blower motor ON, low speed	11-14 V		
	60	⊐▷	Engine idling – condenser blower motor ON, high speed	0-1 V		
AC condenser blower motor relay 2 – CVT	60	⊐▷	Engine idling – condenser blower motor OFF	11-14 V		
	60	⊐▷	Engine idling – condenser blower motor ON, low speed	11-14 V		
	60	⊐▷	Engine idling – condenser blower motor ON, high speed	0-1 V		
AC evaporator temperature sensor	37	⊐—	Ignition ON	0 V		
	47	←		1		
AC master switch	56	←		1		
AC refrigerant pressure sensor	37	⊐—	Ignition ON	0 V		
	57	⇨	Ignition ON	5 V		
	70	←		1		
Alarm system control module	72			1		
Alternator	35	←		1		
Battery	80	←	Ignition OFF	11-14 V		
Camshaft position (CMP) sensor – screened lead – with variable valve control (VVC)	17	⊐—	Ignition ON	0 V		
Camshaft position (CMP) sensor – with variable valve control (VVC)	16 (42)	←	Engine idling		0,5 V/50 ms	∿∿ 17
	42 (16)	←	Engine idling		0,5 V/50 ms	Reversed ∿∿ 17
Camshaft position (CMP) sensor – without variable valve control (VVC)	16	←	Engine idling		5 V/50 ms	∿∿ 18
	42	⊐—	Ignition ON	0 V		
Camshaft timing control solenoid 1 – with variable valve control (VVC)	12	⊐▷	Ignition ON	11-14 V		
	12	⊐▷	Engine idling	11-14 V		
	12	⊐▷	Engine idling – accelerate briefly – valve operating	0-1 V		

* Suggested settings - Voltage/time per division

Component/circuit description	ECM pin	Signal	Condition	Typical value	Oscilloscope setting*	Wave form
Camshaft timing control solenoid 2 – with variable valve control (VVC)	49	⊐▷	Ignition ON	11-14 V		
	49	⊐▷	Engine idling	11-14 V		
	49	⊐▷	Engine idling – accelerate briefly – valve operating	0-1 V		
Crankshaft position (CKP) sensor	4	⬅	Engine idling	1,9 V ac	2 V/5 ms	⎍⎍ 7
	30	⬅	Engine idling	1,9 V ac	2 V/5 ms	Reversed ⎍⎍ 7
Data link connector (DLC)	58	⬅▷		1		
Earth	59		Ignition ON	0 V		
	66		Ignition ON	0 V		
	73		Ignition ON	0 V		
Engine control relay	19	⬅	Ignition OFF	0 V		
	19	⬅	Ignition ON	11-14 V		
	54	⊐▷	Ignition OFF	11-14 V		
	54	⊐▷	Ignition ON	0-1 V		
Engine coolant blower motor relay 1	67	⊐▷	Engine idling – coolant blower motor OFF	11-14 V		
	67	⊐▷	Engine idling – coolant blower motor ON	0-1 V		
Engine coolant blower motor relay 2 – AC	60	⊐▷	Engine idling – coolant blower motor OFF	11-14 V		
	60	⊐▷	Engine idling – coolant blower motor ON, low speed	11-14 V		
	60	⊐▷	Engine idling – coolant blower motor ON, high speed	0-1 V		
Engine coolant temperature (ECT) sensor	7	⊐⎯	Ignition ON	0 V		
	33	⬅	Ignition ON – coolant temp. 10°C	3 V		
	33	⬅	Ignition ON – coolant temp. 80°C	0,5 V		
Engine oil temperature sensor	6	⊐⎯	Ignition ON	0 V		
	32	⬅	Ignition ON – oil temp. 10°C	3 V		
	32	⬅	Ignition ON – oil temp. 80°C	0,5 V		
Evaporative emission (EVAP) canister purge valve	38	⊐▷	Ignition ON	11-14 V		
	38	⊐▷	Engine running – valve operating		5 V/50 ms	⎍⎍ 67
Fuel gauge tank sensor	76	⬅		1		
Fuel pump relay	68	⊐▷	Ignition ON	0-1 V briefly then 11-14 V		
	68	⊐▷	Engine cranking	0-1 V		
Heated oxygen sensor (HO2S) 1	15	⬅	Engine idling – engine hot	0-1 V fluctuating	0,2 V/1 sec.	⎍⎍ 21
	41	⊐⎯	Engine idling	0 V		
Heated oxygen sensor (HO2S) 1 – heater control	1	⊐▷	Ignition ON	11-14 V		
	1	⊐▷	Engine idling		5 V/0,1 sec.	⎍⎍ 49
Heated oxygen sensor (HO2S) 1 – screened lead	28	⊐⎯	Ignition ON	0 V		
Heated oxygen sensor (HO2S) 2	3	⬅	Engine idling	0,3-0,7 V	0,2 V/0,5 sec.	⎍⎍ 76
	29	⊐⎯	Ignition ON	0 V		
Heated oxygen sensor (HO2S) 2 – heater control	27	⊐▷	Ignition ON	11-14 V		
	27	⊐▷	Engine idling – engine hot		5 V/0,1 sec.	⎍⎍ 32
Idle air control (IAC) valve	13	▷	Engine idling	0 V or 11-14 V	5 V/5 ms	⎍⎍ 18
	24	▷	Engine idling	0 V or 11-14 V	5 V/5 ms	⎍⎍ 18
	39	▷	Engine idling	0 V or 11-14 V	5 V/5 ms	⎍⎍ 18
	50	▷	Engine idling	0 V or 11-14 V	5 V/5 ms	⎍⎍ 18
Ignition coil – cylinders 1 & 4	52	⊐▷	Ignition ON	11-14 V		
	52	⊐▷	Engine idling	2,9 ms	5 V/2 ms	⎍⎍ 33

* Suggested settings - Voltage/time per division

Component/circuit description	ECM pin	Signal	Condition	Typical value	Oscilloscope setting*	Wave form
Ignition coil – cylinders 2 & 3	26		Ignition ON	11-14 V		
	26		Engine idling	2,9 ms	5 V/2 ms	33
Ignition switch	61		Ignition ON	11-14 V		
Injector 1	25		Ignition ON	11-14 V		
	25		Engine idling	2,9 ms	10 V/2 ms	35
Injector 2	51		Ignition ON	11-14 V		
	51		Engine idling	2,9 ms	10 V/2 ms	35
Injector 3	14		Ignition ON	11-14 V		
	14		Engine idling	2,9 ms	10 V/2 ms	35
Injector 4	40		Ignition ON	11-14 V		
	40		Engine idling	2,9 ms	10 V/2 ms	35
Instrument panel – CVT	48			1		
	62			1		
Intake air temperature (IAT) sensor	18		Ignition ON	0 V		
	44		Ignition ON – air temp. 15°C	2,8 V		
Malfunction indicator lamp (MIL)	69		Ignition ON – MIL ON	0-1 V		
	69		Engine running – MIL OFF	11-14 V		
Manifold absolute pressure (MAP) sensor	8		Ignition ON	5 V		
	31		Ignition ON	0 V		
	45		Ignition ON	4 V		
	45		Engine idling	1,5 V		
	45		Engine idling – accelerate briefly	4 V		
Manifold absolute pressure (MAP) sensor – not used	10		Ignition ON	0 V		
	10		Engine idling	0 V		
Starter motor relay – AT (except CVT)	63		Engine cranking	0 V		
Tachometer	55		Engine idling	28 Hz		
	55		3000 rpm	100 Hz	2 V/20 ms	55
Throttle position (TP) sensor	34		Ignition ON	0 V		
	46		Ignition ON	5 V		
	20		Ignition ON – throttle closed	0,6 V		
	20		Ignition ON – throttle fully open	4,6 V		
Transmission control module (TCM)	75			1		
	77			1		
Transmission vehicle speed sensor – CVT	9			1		
Wheel speed sensor LH front – rough road signal – without ABS	64			1		
	78			1		

*Suggested settings - Voltage/time per division

1 Connected pin - no test data available or random digital signal

Model:	Engine code:	Year:
25 2,0D Turbo	20T	1999-05
MG ZR 2,0D 101	20T	2001-05

ECM harness multi-plug

Terminal side

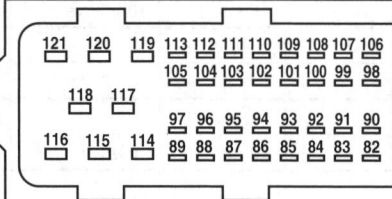
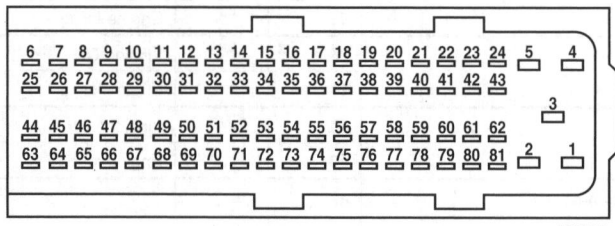

AD20712

Wire side

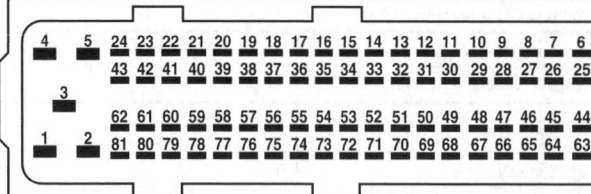
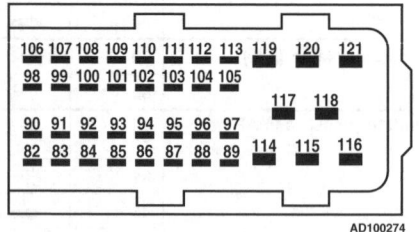

AD100274

Component/circuit description	ECM pin	Signal	Condition	Typical value	Oscilloscope setting*	Wave form
AC compressor clutch relay	41	⌐▷	AC compressor OFF	11-14 V		
	41	⌐▷	AC compressor ON	0-1 V		
AC evaporator temperature sensor	36	←		[1]		
	51	⌐	Ignition ON	0 V		
AC master switch	33	←	Engine running – AC ON	0 V		
AC refrigerant pressure sensor	50	⌐	Ignition ON	0 V		
	55	▷	Ignition ON	5 V		
	81	←		[1]		
Accelerator pedal position (APP) sensor	38	←	Ignition ON – accelerator pedal released	0,43 V		
	38	←	Ignition ON – accelerator pedal fully depressed	2,83 V		
	49	⌐	Ignition ON	0 V		
	57	▷	Ignition ON	5 V		
	69	←	Ignition ON – accelerator pedal released	3,44 V		
	69	←	Ignition ON – accelerator pedal slightly depressed	0,1 V		
Alarm system control module	37	←		[1]		
Brake pedal position (BPP) switch	30	←	Ignition ON – brake pedal released	0 V		
	30	←	Ignition ON – brake pedal depressed	11-14 V		
Crankshaft position (CKP) sensor	90	←	Engine idling	3,95 V ac	5 V/5 ms	〰〰 6
	98	⌐	Ignition ON	0 V		
Crankshaft position (CKP) sensor – shield wire	101	⌐	Ignition ON	0 V		
Data link connector (DLC)	35	◄►	Ignition ON	0 V		
Earth	1		Ignition ON	0 V		
	2		Ignition ON	0 V		
Engine control relay	3	←	Ignition ON	11-14 V		
	58	⌐▷	Ignition ON	0-1 V		

* Suggested settings - Voltage/time per division

Component/circuit description	ECM pin	Signal	Condition	Typical value	Oscilloscope setting*	Wave form
Engine coolant blower motor relay	40	⊣▷	Engine running – coolant blower motor OFF	11-14 V		
	40	⊣▷	Engine running – coolant blower motor ON	0-1 V		
Engine coolant blower motor relay – AC	61	⊣▷	Engine running – coolant blower motor OFF	11-14 V		
	61	⊣▷	Engine running – coolant blower motor ON, high speed	0-1 V		
Engine coolant temperature (ECT) sensor	89	◀—	Ignition ON – coolant temp. 17°C	3,82 V		
	89	◀—	Ignition ON – coolant temp. 80°C	1,4 V		
	93	⊣—	Ignition ON	0 V		
Exhaust gas recirculation (EGR) solenoid	97	⇨	Ignition ON	11-14 V		
	97	⇨	Engine idling		5 V/3 ms	∿ 31
Fuel pump control module – CAN data bus, high	100	◀⇨	Ignition ON	2,5 V		
Fuel pump control module – CAN data bus, low	99	◀⇨	Ignition ON	2,4 V		
Fuel pump control module – engine speed signal	91	⇨	Engine idling	56 Hz	2 V/5 ms	∿ 15
Fuel pump control module – fuel shut-off signal	105	⇨			0,1 V/10 ms	∿ 17
Glow plug relay	94	⊣▷	Ignition ON – coolant temp. 17°C	0 V for 6 secs then 11-14 V		
Glow plug warning lamp	43	⊣▷	Ignition ON – lamp ON	0-1 V		
	43	⊣▷	Ignition ON – lamp OFF	11-14 V		
Ignition switch	39	◀—	Ignition ON	11-14 V		
Injector needle lift sensor	102	⊣—	Ignition ON	0 V		
	103	◀—	Ignition ON	3,2 V		
	103	◀—	Engine idling		0,2 V/2 ms	∿ 55
Intake air temperature (IAT) sensor	84	◀—	Ignition ON – air temp. 17°C	2,5 V		
	92	⊣—	Ignition ON	0 V		
Malfunction indicator lamp (MIL)	42	⊣▷	Ignition ON – MIL ON	0-1 V		
	42	⊣▷	Ignition ON – MIL OFF	11-14 V		
Manifold absolute pressure (MAP) sensor	82	⇨	Ignition ON	5 V		
	85	◀—	Ignition ON	1,86 V		
	85	◀—	Engine idling	1,84 V		
	85	◀—	Engine idling – accelerate briefly	3,2 V briefly		
	93	⊣—	Ignition ON	0 V		
Mass air flow (MAF) sensor	83	⇨	Ignition ON	5 V		
	88	◀—	Ignition ON	1 V		
	88	◀—	Engine idling	1,6 V		
	88	◀—	3000 rpm	3,3 V		
Reverse gear position switch – 11/02→	44	◀—	Ignition ON – gear lever not in reverse	0 V		
	44	◀—	Ignition ON – gear lever in reverse	11-14 V		
Tachometer	27	◀—	Engine idling	30 Hz	2 V/20 ms	∿ 10
Transmission warning lamp – AT	59	⊣▷	Ignition ON – lamp OFF	11-14 V		
	59	⊣▷	Ignition ON – lamp ON	0-1 V		
Vehicle speed sensor (VSS)	68	◀—	Ignition ON – vehicle pushed	0-10,4 V switching		

*Suggested settings - Voltage/time per division

1 Connected pin - no test data available or random digital signal

ROVER

Rover MEMS 3

Model:	Engine code:	Year:
45 1,4	14K4	1999-05
45 1,6	16K4	1999-05
45/75 1,8	18K4	1999-05

ECM harness multi-plug

Terminal side

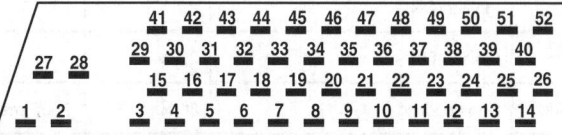

AD42344

Wire side

AD42345

Component/circuit description	ECM pin	Signal	Condition	Typical value	Oscilloscope setting*	Wave form
ABS control module – rough road signal – 45	78	←		1		
ABS control module – rough road signal – 75	64	←		1		
AC compressor clutch relay	53	⇥▷	Engine idling – AC OFF	11-14 V		
	53	⇥▷	Engine idling – AC ON – AC compressor ON	0-1 V		
AC evaporator temperature sensor – 45	37	⊣	Ignition ON	0 V		
	47	←		1		
AC master switch – 45	56	←		1		
AC refrigerant pressure sensor – 45	57	⇨	Ignition ON	5 V		
	70	←		1		
	71	⊣	Ignition ON	0 V		
AC refrigerant triple pressure switch – 75	56	←		1		
	70	←		1		
Alternator	35	←		1		
Battery	80	←	Ignition OFF	11-14 V		
Camshaft position (CMP) sensor	16	←	Engine idling		5 V/50 ms	〰〰 18
	42	⊣	Ignition ON	0 V		
Crankshaft position (CKP) sensor – 45	4	←	Engine idling	1,9 V ac	2 V/5 ms	〰〰 7
Crankshaft position (CKP) sensor – 75	4	←	Ignition ON	0 or 11-14 V		
	4	←	Engine idling		2 V/5 ms	〰〰 54
	30	⊣	Ignition ON	0 V		
Crankshaft position (CKP) sensor – screened lead – 45	17	⊣	Ignition ON	0 V		
Data link connector (DLC)	58	⬌		1		
Earth	59		Ignition ON	0 V		
	66		Ignition ON	0 V		
	73		Ignition ON	0 V		
Engine control relay	19	←	Ignition OFF	0 V		
	19	←	Ignition ON	11-14 V		
	54	⇥▷	Ignition OFF	11-14 V		
	54	⇥▷	Ignition ON	0-1 V		

* Suggested settings - Voltage/time per division

Component/circuit description	ECM pin	Signal	Condition	Typical value	Oscilloscope setting*	Wave form
Engine coolant blower motor relay – 75	74			[1]		
Engine coolant blower motor relay – with AC	60			[1]		
	67			[1]		
Engine coolant blower motor relay – without AC	60	→	Engine idling – condenser blower motor OFF	11-14 V		
	60	→	Engine idling – condenser blower motor ON	0-1 V		
Engine coolant temperature (ECT) sensor	7	⊣	Ignition ON	0 V		
	33	←	Ignition ON – coolant temp. 15°C	3 V		
	33	←	Ignition ON – coolant temp. 85°C	0,5 V		
Engine oil temperature sensor	6	⊣	Ignition ON	0 V		
	32	←	Ignition ON – oil temp. 10°C	3 V		
	32	←	Ignition ON – oil temp. 80°C	0,5 V		
Evaporative emission (EVAP) canister purge valve	38	→	Ignition ON	11-14 V		
	38	→	Engine running – valve operating		5 V/50 ms	67
Fuel gauge tank sensor – 45	76	←		[1]		
Fuel pump relay	68	→	Ignition ON	0-1 V briefly then 11-14 V		
	68	→	Engine cranking	0-1 V		
Heated oxygen sensor (HO2S) 1	15	←	Engine idling – engine hot	0-1 V fluctuating	0,2 V/1 sec.	21
	41	⊣	Engine idling	0 V		
Heated oxygen sensor (HO2S) 1 – heater control	1	→	Ignition ON	11-14 V		
	1	→	Engine idling		5 V/0,1 sec.	49
Heated oxygen sensor (HO2S) 1 – screened lead	28	⊣	Ignition ON	0 V		
Heated oxygen sensor (HO2S) 2 – heater control – if fitted	27	→	Ignition ON	11-14 V		
	27	→	Engine idling – engine hot		5 V/0,1 sec.	32
Heated oxygen sensor (HO2S) 2 – if fitted	3	←	Engine idling	0,3-0,7 V	0,2 V/0,5 sec.	76
	29	⊣	Ignition ON	0 V		
Idle air control (IAC) valve	13	⇒	Engine idling	0 V or 11-14 V	5 V/5 ms	18
	24	⇒	Engine idling	0 V or 11-14 V	5 V/5 ms	18
	39	⇒	Engine idling	0 V or 11-14 V	5 V/5 ms	18
	50	⇒	Engine idling	0 V or 11-14 V	5 V/5 ms	18
Ignition coil – cylinders 1 & 4	52	→	Ignition ON	11-14 V		
	52	→	Engine idling	2,9 ms	5 V/2 ms	33
Ignition coil – cylinders 2 & 3	26	→	Ignition ON	11-14 V		
	26	→	Engine idling	2,9 ms	5 V/2 ms	33
Ignition switch	61	←	Ignition ON	11-14 V		
Immobilizer control module	72			[1]		
Injector 1	25	→	Ignition ON	11-14 V		
	25	→	Engine idling	2,9 ms	10 V/2 ms	35
Injector 2	51	→	Ignition ON	11-14 V		
	51	→	Engine idling	2,9 ms	10 V/2 ms	35
Injector 3	14	→	Ignition ON	11-14 V		
	14	→	Engine idling	2,9 ms	10 V/2 ms	35
Injector 4	40	→	Ignition ON	11-14 V		
	40	→	Engine idling	2,9 ms	10 V/2 ms	35
Instrument panel – 45 CVT	48	⇒		[1]		
	62			[1]		

* Suggested settings - Voltage/time per division

Component/circuit description	ECM pin	Signal	Condition	Typical value	Oscilloscope setting*	Wave form
Instrument panel – CAN data bus – 75	65	⬅⇨		1		
	79	⬅⇨		1		
Intake air temperature (IAT) sensor	18	⌐—	Ignition ON	0 V		
	44	⬅	Ignition ON – air temp. 0°C	3,8 V		
	44	⬅	Ignition ON – air temp. 20°C	2,8 V		
Malfunction indicator lamp (MIL) – 45	69	⌐⇨	Ignition ON – MIL ON	0-1 V		
	69	⌐⇨	Engine running – MIL OFF	11-14 V		
Manifold absolute pressure (MAP) sensor	8	⇨	Ignition ON	5 V		
	31	⌐—	Ignition ON	0 V		
	45	⬅	Ignition ON	4 V		
	45	⬅	Engine idling	1,5 V		
	45	⬅	Engine idling – accelerate briefly	4 V		
Manifold absolute pressure (MAP) sensor – not used	10		Ignition ON	0 V		
	10		Engine idling	0 V		
Park/neutral position (PNP) switch – 45	63	⬅		1		
Power steering pressure (PSP) sensor – 75	21	⬅	Engine idling – steering wheel not turned	0,5 V		
	21	⬅	Engine idling – steering – full lock	4,5 V		
	23	⇨	Ignition ON	5 V		
	37	⌐—	Ignition ON	0 V		
Tachometer – 45	55	⇨	Engine idling	28 Hz		
	55	⇨	3000 rpm	100 Hz	2 V/20 ms	⟋⟍ 55
Throttle position (TP) sensor	34	⌐—	Ignition ON	0 V		
	46	⇨	Ignition ON	5 V		
	20	⬅	Ignition ON – throttle closed	0,6 V		
	20	⬅	Ignition ON – throttle fully open	4,6 V		
Transmission control module (TCM) – 45	75			1		
	77			1		
Transmission vehicle speed sensor – 45 CVT	9	⬅		1		
Wheel speed sensor LH front – rough road signal – 45, without ABS	64			1		
	78			1		

*Suggested settings - Voltage/time per division

1 Connected pin - no test data available or random digital signal

Model:		Engine code:		Year:
45 2,0D Turbo		20T		1999-05
MG ZS 2,0D 101		20T		2001-05

ROVER

Bosch EDC15M

ECM harness multi-plug

Terminal side

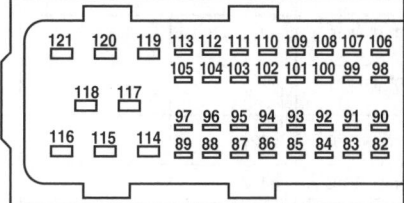
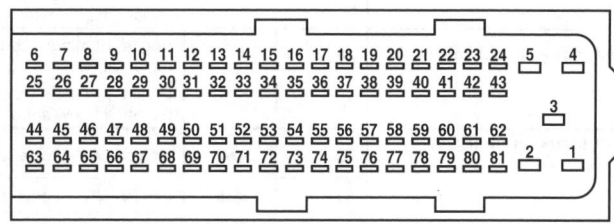

AD20712

Wire side

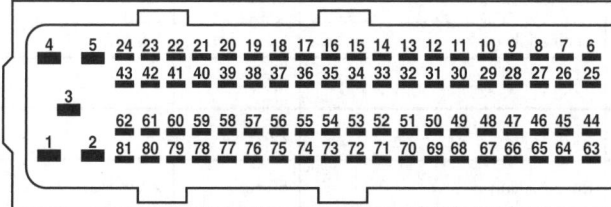
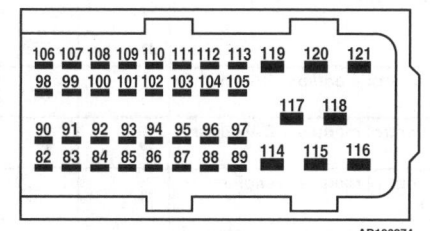

AD100274

Component/circuit description	ECM pin	Signal	Condition	Typical value	Oscilloscope setting★	Wave form
ABS control module	35	←	Ignition ON	0 V		
AC compressor clutch relay	41	⇥	AC compressor OFF	11-14 V		
	41	⇥	AC compressor ON	0-1 V		
AC evaporator temperature sensor	36	←		1		
	51	⊣	Ignition ON	0 V		
AC master switch	33	←	Engine running – AC ON	0 V		
AC refrigerant pressure sensor	50	⊣	Ignition ON	0 V		
	55	⇒	Ignition ON	5 V		
	81	←		1		
Accelerator pedal position (APP) sensor	38	←	Ignition ON – accelerator pedal released	0,43 V		
	38	←	Ignition ON – accelerator pedal fully depressed	2,83 V		
	49	⊣	Ignition ON	0 V		
	57	⇒	Ignition ON	5 V		
	69	←	Ignition ON – accelerator pedal released	3,44 V		
	69	←	Ignition ON – accelerator pedal slightly depressed	0,1 V		
Alarm system control module	37	←		1		
Brake pedal position (BPP) switch	30	←	Ignition ON – brake pedal released	0 V		
	30	←	Ignition ON – brake pedal depressed	11-14 V		
Clutch pedal position (CPP) switch – →10/02	31	←	Ignition ON – clutch pedal released	0 V		
	31	←	Ignition ON – clutch pedal depressed	11-14 V		
Crankshaft position (CKP) sensor	90	←	Engine idling	3,95 V ac	5 V/5 ms	〰 6
	98	⊣	Ignition ON	0 V		
Crankshaft position (CKP) sensor – shield wire	101	⊣	Ignition ON	0 V		
Data link connector (DLC)	35	←	Ignition ON	0 V		

★ Suggested settings - Voltage/time per division

Component/circuit description	ECM pin	Signal	Condition	Typical value	Oscilloscope setting*	Wave form
Earth	1		Ignition ON	0 V		
	2		Ignition ON	0 V		
Engine control relay	3	←	Ignition ON	11-14 V		
	58	⊐▷	Ignition ON	0-1 V		
Engine coolant blower motor relay	61	⊐▷	Engine running – coolant blower motor OFF	11-14 V		
	61	⊐▷	Engine running – coolant blower motor ON, high speed	0-1 V		
Engine coolant blower motor relay – AC	40	⊐▷	Engine running – coolant blower motor OFF	11-14 V		
	40	⊐▷	Engine running – coolant blower motor ON, low speed	0-1 V		
Engine coolant temperature (ECT) sensor	89	←	Ignition ON – coolant temp. 17°C	3,82 V		
	89	←	Ignition ON – coolant temp. 80°C	1,4 V		
	93	⊐─	Ignition ON	0 V		
Exhaust gas recirculation (EGR) solenoid	97	⇒	Ignition ON	11-14 V		
	97	⇒	Engine idling		5 V/3 ms	31
Fuel pump control module – CAN data bus, high	100	◆▷		2,5 V		
Fuel pump control module – CAN data bus, low	99	◆▷		2,4 V		
Fuel pump control module – engine speed signal	91	⇒	Engine idling	56 Hz	2 V/5 ms	15
Fuel pump control module – fuel shut-off signal	105	⇒			2 V/5 ms	17
Glow plug relay	94	⊐▷	Ignition ON – coolant temp. 17°C	0 V for 6 secs then 11-14 V		
Glow plug warning lamp	43	⊐▷	Ignition ON – lamp ON	0-1 V		
	43	⊐▷	Ignition ON – lamp OFF	11-14 V		
Ignition switch	39	←	Ignition ON	11-14 V		
Injector needle lift sensor	102	⊐─	Ignition ON	0 V		
	103	←	Ignition ON	3,2 V		
	103	←	Engine idling		0,2 V/2 ms	55
Intake air temperature (IAT) sensor	84	←	Ignition ON – air temp. 17°C	2,5 V		
	92	⊐─	Ignition ON	0 V		
Malfunction indicator lamp (MIL)	42	⊐▷	Ignition ON – MIL ON	0-1 V		
	42	⊐▷	Ignition ON – MIL OFF	11-14 V		
Manifold absolute pressure (MAP) sensor	82	⇒	Ignition ON	5 V		
	85	←	Ignition ON	1,86 V		
	85	←	Engine idling	1,84 V		
	85	←	Engine idling – accelerate briefly	3,2 V briefly		
	93	⊐─	Ignition ON	0 V		
Mass air flow (MAF) sensor	83	⇒	Ignition ON	5 V		
	88	←	Ignition ON	1 V		
	88	←	Engine idling	1,6 V		
	88	←	3000 rpm	3,3 V		
Tachometer	27	←	Engine idling	30 Hz	2 V/20 ms	10
Transmission warning lamp – AT	59	⊐▷	Ignition ON – lamp OFF	11-14 V		
	59	⊐▷	Ignition ON – lamp ON	0-1 V		
Vehicle speed sensor (VSS)	68	←	Ignition ON – vehicle pushed	0-10,4 V switching		

*Suggested settings - Voltage/time per division

1 Connected pin - no test data available or random digital signal

Model:	Engine code:	Year:
75 2,0 CDT/CDTi	M47R	1999-05
MG ZT 2,0 CDT/CDTi	M47R	1999-05

ECM harness multi-plug

Terminal side

Wire side

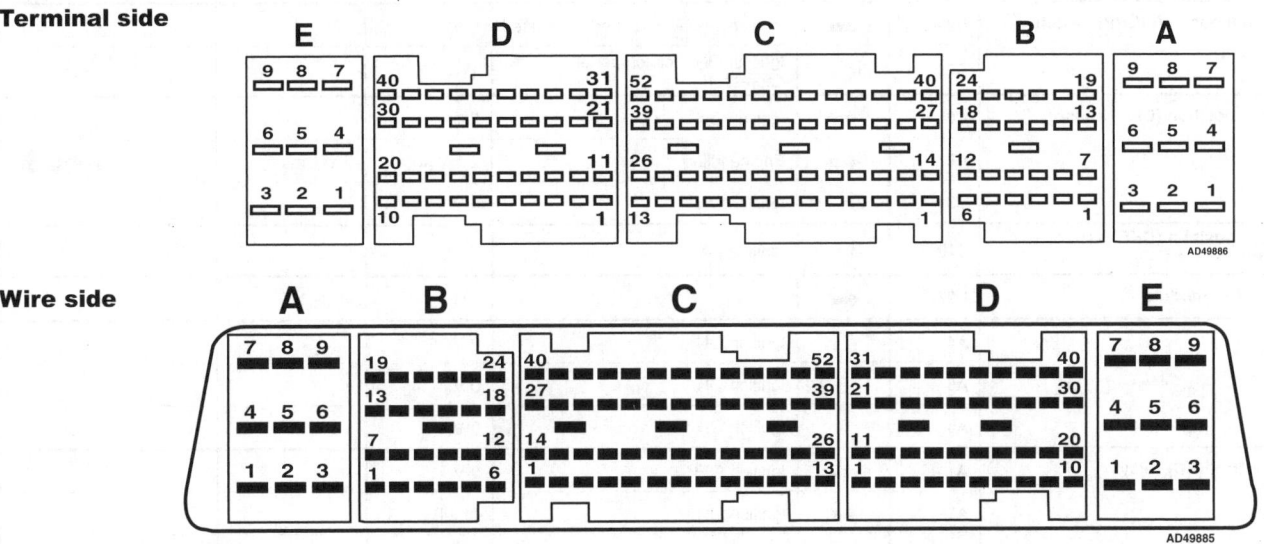

AD49886

AD49885

Component/circuit description	ECM pin	Signal	Condition	Typical value	Oscilloscope setting*	Wave form
ABS control module – vehicle speed signal	D22	←	Ignition ON – vehicle pushed	0-11 V switching		
AC refrigerant triple pressure switch	D29	⌐→	Ignition ON	11-14 V		
	D29	⌐→	Engine running – AC compressor OFF	11-14 V		
	D29	⌐→	Engine running – AC compressor ON	0-1 V		
Accelerator pedal position (APP) sensor	D7	⌐	Ignition ON	0 V		
	D8	←	Ignition ON – accelerator pedal released	0,8 V		
	D8	←	Ignition ON – accelerator pedal fully depressed	3,6 V		
	D9	⇒	Ignition ON	5 V		
	D12	⌐	Ignition ON	0 V		
	D13	←	Ignition ON – accelerator pedal released	0,4 V		
	D13	←	Ignition ON – accelerator pedal fully depressed	1,6 V		
	D14	⇒	Ignition ON	5 V		
Alternator	C50	←	Ignition ON	1 V		
	C50	←	Engine idling	11-14 V		
	D1	⇒	Ignition ON	1 V		
	D1	⇒	Engine running	11-14 V		
Brake pedal position (BPP) switch	D24	←	Ignition ON – brake pedal released	0,2 V		
	D24	←	Ignition ON – brake pedal depressed	8,6 V		
	D28	←	Ignition ON – brake pedal released	0 V		
	D28	←	Ignition ON – brake pedal depressed	11-14 V		

* Suggested settings - Voltage/time per division

Component/circuit description	ECM pin	Signal	Condition	Typical value	Oscilloscope setting*	Wave form
Camshaft position (CMP) sensor	C4	←	Ignition ON	0 or 12 V		
	C4	←	Engine idling		5 V/50 ms	ᴡᴡ 3
	C17	⌐⌐	Ignition ON	0 V		
CAN data bus – high	D36	←▷		1		
CAN data bus – low	D37	←▷		1		
Clutch pedal position (CPP) switch	D23	←	Ignition ON – clutch pedal released	0 V		
	D23	←	Ignition ON – clutch pedal depressed	11-14 V		
Crankshaft position (CKP) sensor	C6	←	Ignition ON	2,4 V		
	C6	←	Engine idling	2,1 V ac	2 V/1 ms	ᴡᴡ 1
	C31	⌐⌐	Ignition ON	0 V		
Crankshaft position (CKP) sensor – shield wire	C19	⌐⌐	Ignition ON	0 V		
Cruise control module	D27	←		1		
Earth	A4		Ignition ON	0 V		
	A5		Ignition ON	0 V		
	A6		Ignition ON	0 V		
Engine control (EC) relay	A1	←	Ignition OFF	0 V		
	A1	←	Ignition ON	11-14 V		
	A8	←	Ignition ON	11-14 V		
	A9	⌐▷	Ignition OFF	11-14 V		
	A9	⌐▷	Ignition ON	0-1 V		
Engine coolant blower motor control module	D4	▷	Ignition ON – coolant blower motor OFF		5 V/2 ms	ᴡᴡ 3
	D4	▷	Engine running – coolant blower motor ON		5 V/2 ms	ᴡᴡ 48
Engine coolant temperature (ECT) sensor	C28	←	Ignition ON – coolant temp. 20°C	3,5 V		
	C28	←	Ignition ON – coolant temp. 80°C	1 V		
	C32	⌐⌐	Ignition ON	0 V		
Engine oil pressure switch	C41	←	Ignition ON	0 V		
	C41	←	Engine running	11-14 V		
Engine oil pressure warning lamp	D11	▷	Ignition ON	0 V		
	D11	▷	Engine running	11-14 V		
Exhaust gas recirculation (EGR) solenoid	C10	▷	Ignition ON	11-14 V		
	C10	▷	Engine idling		5 V/1 ms	ᴡᴡ 31
Fuel lift pump relay	D10	⌐▷	Ignition ON	0-1 V for 1-20 seconds then 11-14 V		
	D10	⌐▷	Engine running	0-1 V		
Fuel pressure control solenoid	C38	▷	Ignition ON		2 V/1 ms	ᴡᴡ 37
	C38	▷	Engine idling		2 V/1 ms	ᴡᴡ 37
Fuel pressure sensor	B9	▷	Ignition ON	5 V		
	B10	⌐⌐	Ignition ON	0 V		
	B17	←	Ignition ON	4,4 V		
	B17	←	Engine running	4,4 V		

★ Suggested settings - Voltage/time per division

Component/circuit description	ECM pin	Signal	Condition	Typical value	Oscilloscope setting*	Wave form
Fuel rail pressure (FRP) sensor	C20	⌐⊢	Ignition ON	0 V		
	C33	⟵	Ignition ON	0,5 V		
	C33	⟵	Engine idling	1,3 V		
	C33	⟵	3000 rpm	2,1 V		
	C35	⟹	Ignition ON	5 V		
Glow plug control module	C12	⟹	Ignition ON	11-14 V		
	C12	⟹	Engine idling – engine hot	11-14 V		
	C52	⟵	Ignition ON	1 V		
	C52	⟵	Engine running	1 V		
Ignition switch	A7	⟵	Ignition OFF	0 V		
	A7	⟵	Ignition ON	11-14 V		
Immobilizer control module	D33	⟺		1		
Injector 1	E4	⟹	Ignition ON	1 V		
	E5	⟹	Ignition ON	1 V		
	E5 (E4)	⟹	Engine idling	0,3 ms pilot + 0,7 ms main	10 V/0,5 ms	ᴧᴧᴡ 59
Injector 2	E1	⟹	Ignition ON	1 V		
	E3	⟹	Ignition ON	1 V		
	E3 (E1)	⟹	Engine idling	0,3 ms pilot + 0,7 ms main	10 V/0,5 ms	ᴧᴧᴡ 59
Injector 3	E1	⟹	Ignition ON	1 V		
	E9	⟹	Ignition ON	1 V		
	E9 (E1)	⟹	Engine idling	0,3 ms pilot + 0,7 ms main	10 V/0,5 ms	ᴧᴧᴡ 59
Injector 4	E4	⟹	Ignition ON	1 V		
	E7	⟹	Ignition ON	1 V		
	E7 (E4)	⟹	Engine idling	0,3 ms pilot + 0,7 ms main	10 V/0,5 ms	ᴧᴧᴡ 59
Intake air temperature (IAT) sensor	C29	⟵	Ignition ON – air temp. 20°C	3,5 V		
Manifold absolute pressure (MAP) sensor	C14	⟹	Ignition ON	5 V		
	C15	⟵	Ignition ON	1,8 V		
	C15	⟵	Engine idling	1,8 V		
	C15	⟵	Engine idling – accelerate briefly	3,4 V briefly		
	C16	⌐⊢	Ignition ON	0 V		
Mass air flow (MAF) sensor	C1	⟹	Ignition ON	5 V		
	C2	⟵	Ignition ON	1 V		
	C2	⟵	Engine idling	2 V		
	C2	⟵	3000 rpm	3,5 V		

*Suggested settings - Voltage/time per division

1 Connected pin - no test data available or random digital signal

Model:	Engine code:	Year:
825i	KV6	1996-99

ECM harness multi-plug

Terminal side – A – Black, B – Red

B

36	35	34	33	32	31	30	29	28	27	26	25
13	14	15	16	17	18	19	20	21	22	23	24
12	11	10	9	8	7	6	5	4	3	2	1

AD42479

A

36	35	34	33	32	31	30	29	28	27	26	25
13	14	15	16	17	18	19	20	21	22	23	24
12	11	10	9	8	7	6	5	4	3	2	1

Wire side – A – Black, B – Red

A

25	26	27	28	29	30	31	32	33	34	35	36
24	23	22	21	20	19	18	17	16	15	14	13
1	2	3	4	5	6	7	8	9	10	11	12

AD42478

B

25	26	27	28	29	30	31	32	33	34	35	36
24	23	22	21	20	19	18	17	16	15	14	13
1	2	3	4	5	6	7	8	9	10	11	12

Component/circuit description	ECM pin	Signal	Condition	Typical value	Oscilloscope setting*	Wave form
AC compressor clutch relay	A29	⊐+▷	Engine idling – AC compressor OFF	11-14 V		
	A29	⊐+▷	Engine idling – AC compressor ON	0,1 V		
AC condenser blower motor relay	A4	⊐+▷	Ignition ON	11-14 V		
	A4	⊐+▷	Engine running – condenser blower motor OFF	11-14 V		
	A4	⊐+▷	Engine running – condenser blower motor ON	0-1 V		
AC refrigerant pressure switch	A9			[1]		
	A19			[1]		
Camshaft position (CMP) sensor	B1	←	Engine idling	3 V ac		
	B1	←	Engine idling		0,2 V/20 ms	⋀⋁⋀ 2
	B2	⊐−	Ignition ON	0 V		
Camshaft position (CMP) sensor – shield wire	B23	⊐−	Ignition ON	0 V		
Combination control module	A17			[1]		
Crankshaft position (CKP) sensor	B25	←	Engine idling		0,5 V/10 ms	⋀⋁⋀ 7
	B26	⊐−	Ignition ON	0 V		
Crankshaft position (CKP) sensor – shield wire	B23	⊐−	Ignition ON	0 V		
Cruise control relay	B18			[1]		
Data link connector (DLC)	B31		Ignition ON	5 V		
Earth	A21		Ignition ON	0 V		
	B16		Ignition ON	0 V		
	B24		Ignition ON	0 V		
Engine control relay	A22	⊐+▷	Ignition OFF	11-14 V after 5 minutes		
	A22	⊐+▷	Ignition ON	0-1 V		
	A27	←	Ignition OFF	0 V after 5 minutes		
	A27	←	Ignition ON	11-14 V		

* Suggested settings - Voltage/time per division

Component/circuit description	ECM pin	Signal	Condition	Typical value	Oscilloscope setting*	Wave form
Engine coolant blower motor relay	A28	⊐▷	Ignition ON	0,4 V		
	A28	⊐▷	Engine idling – coolant blower motor OFF	11-14 V		
	A28	⊐▷	Engine idling – coolant blower motor ON	0,1 V		
Engine coolant temperature (ECT) sensor	A13	⊐—	Ignition ON	0 V		
	A15	←	Ignition ON – coolant temp. 10°C	2,8 V		
	A15	←	Ignition ON – coolant temp. 80°C	0,5 V		
Engine oil temperature sensor	A10	←	Ignition ON – coolant temp. 10°C	2,8 V		
	A10	←	Ignition ON – coolant temp. 80°C	0,5 V		
	A13	⊐—	Ignition ON	0 V		
Evaporative emission (EVAP) canister purge valve	B17	⊐▷	Ignition ON	11-14 V		
	B17	⊐▷	Engine running		10 V/50 ms	⩥ 20
Fuel pump relay	A30	⊐▷	Ignition ON	0-1 V briefly then 11-14 V		
	A30	⊐▷	Engine cranking	0-1 V		
	A30	⊐▷	Engine running	0-1 V		
Fuel temperature sensor	A13	⊐—	Ignition ON	0 V		
	A34	←	Ignition ON – fuel temp. 10°C	3 V		
Heated oxygen sensor (HO2S) 1	B5	←	Engine idling – accelerate briefly	0-1 V fluctuating	0,2 V/1 sec.	⩥ 21
	B6	⊐—	Ignition ON	0 V		
Heated oxygen sensor (HO2S) 2	B27	←	Engine idling – accelerate briefly	0-1 V fluctuating	0,2 V/1 sec.	⩥ 21
	B28	⊐—	Ignition ON	0 V		
Heated oxygen sensor (HO2S) 1 – shield wire	B23	⊐—	Ignition ON	0 V		
Heated oxygen sensor (HO2S) 2 – shield wire	B23	⊐—	Ignition ON	0 V		
Idle air control (IAC) valve	B10	⊐▷	Ignition ON	11-14 V		
	B10	⊐▷	Engine idling		5 V/0,1 ms	Intermittent ⩥ 30
	B15	⊐▷	Ignition ON	0,5 V		
	B15	⊐▷	Engine idling		5 V/0,1 ms	Intermittent ⩥ 30
	B33	⊐▷	Ignition ON	11-14 V		
	B33	⊐▷	Engine idling		5 V/0,1 ms	Intermittent ⩥ 30
	B34	⊐▷	Ignition ON	11-14 V		
	B34	⊐▷	Engine idling		5 V/0,1 ms	Intermittent ⩥ 30
Ignition coil 1	A25	⊐▷	Ignition OFF	0 V after 5 minutes		
	A25	⊐▷	Ignition ON	11-14 V		
	A25	⊐▷	Engine idling		5 V/2 ms	⩥ 33
Ignition coil 2	A26	⊐▷	Ignition OFF	0 V after 5 minutes		
	A26	⊐▷	Ignition ON	11-14 V		
	A26	⊐▷	Engine idling		5 V/2 ms	⩥ 33
Ignition coil 3	B36	⊐▷	Ignition OFF	0 V after 5 minutes		
	B36	⊐▷	Ignition ON	11-14 V		
	B36	⊐▷	Engine idling		5 V/2 ms	⩥ 33
Ignition switch	A33	←	Ignition OFF	0 V		
	A33	←	Ignition ON	11-14 V		
Injector 1	B12	⊐▷	Ignition OFF	0 V after 5 minutes		
	B12	⊐▷	Ignition ON	11-14 V		
	B12	⊐▷	Engine idling	3,3 ms	10 V/2 ms	⩥ 35

★ Suggested settings - Voltage/time per division

Component/circuit description	ECM pin	Signal	Condition	Typical value	Oscilloscope setting*	Wave form
Injector 2	B13	⊐▷	Ignition OFF	0 V after 5 minutes		
	B13	⊐▷	Ignition ON	11-14 V		
	B13	⊐▷	Engine idling	3,3 ms	10 V/2 ms	∿∿ 35
Injector 3	B14	⊐▷	Ignition OFF	0 V after 5 minutes		
	B14	⊐▷	Ignition ON	11-14 V		
	B14	⊐▷	Engine idling	3,3 ms	10 V/2 ms	∿∿ 35
Injector 4	B35	⊐▷	Ignition OFF	0 V after 5 minutes		
	B35	⊐▷	Ignition ON	11-14 V		
	B35	⊐▷	Engine idling	3,3 ms	10 V/2 ms	∿∿ 35
Injector 5	A1	⊐▷	Ignition OFF	0 V after 5 minutes		
	A1	⊐▷	Ignition ON	11-14 V		
	A1	⊐▷	Engine idling	3,3 ms	10 V/2 ms	∿∿ 35
Injector 6	A24	⊐▷	Ignition OFF	0 V after 5 minutes		
	A24	⊐▷	Ignition ON	11-14 V		
	A24	⊐▷	Engine idling	3,3 ms	10 V/2 ms	∿∿ 35
Intake air temperature (IAT) sensor	A13	⊐—	Ignition ON	0 V		
	A14	◀	Ignition ON – air temp. 10°C	2,8 V		
Intake manifold air control solenoid 1	A2	⊐▷	Ignition ON	11-14 V		
	A2	⊐▷	Engine idling	11-14 V		
	A2	⊐▷	Engine idling – accelerate briefly	0 V		
Intake manifold air control solenoid 2	A23	⊐▷	Ignition ON – accelerate briefly	0 V briefly		
Manifold absolute pressure (MAP) sensor	A8	▷	Ignition ON	5 V		
	A13	⊐—	Ignition ON	0 V		
	A36	◀	Ignition ON	4,8 V		
	A36	◀	Engine idling	1,3 V		
	A36	◀	Engine idling – accelerate briefly	4,8 V briefly		
Tachometer	B9	▷	Engine idling	25 Hz		
Throttle position (TP) sensor	A12	◀	Ignition ON – throttle closed	0,5 V		
	A12	◀	Ignition ON – throttle fully open	4,4 V		
	A13	⊐—	Ignition ON	0 V		
	A18	▷	Ignition ON	5 V		
Transmission control module (TCM)	B30			1		
	B19			1		

*Suggested settings - Voltage/time per division

1 Connected pin - no test data available or random digital signal

Model:	Engine code:	Year:
9-3 2,0 Turbo	B205L	1999-03
9-3 2,0 Turbo	B205E	2000-03
9-3 2,0 Turbo	B205R	1999-03
9-3 2,3 Turbo	B235R	1999-01
9-5 2,0 Turbo	B205E/F	1997-06
9-5 2,3 Turbo	B235R/TK	1999-06
9-5 2,3 Turbo	B235E	1997-06

ECM harness multi-plug

Terminal side

Wire side

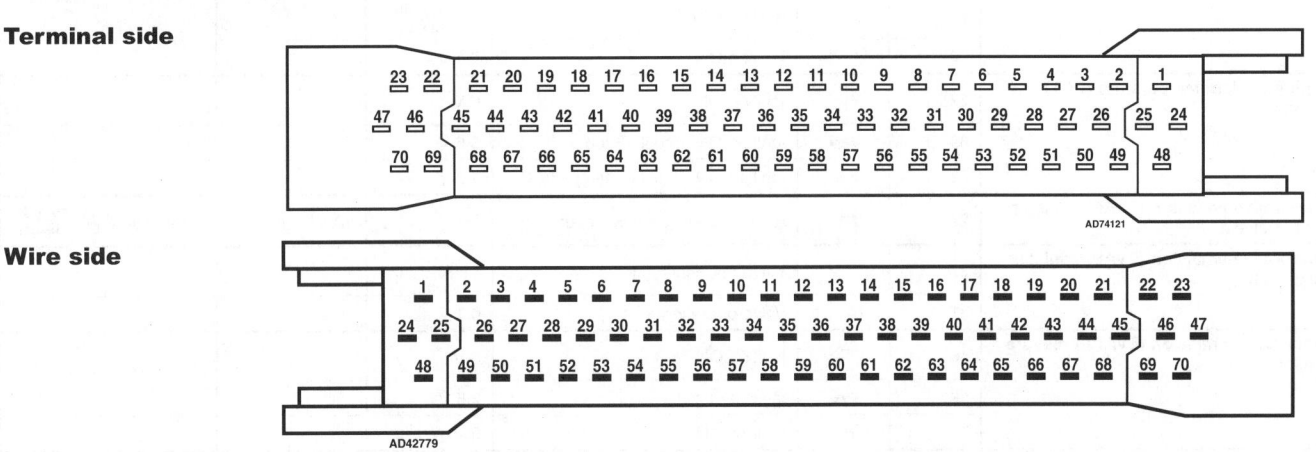

Component/circuit description	ECM pin	Signal	Condition	Typical value	Oscilloscope setting*	Wave form
AC compressor clutch relay	4	⅂▷	Engine running – AC compressor OFF	11-14 V		
	4	⅂▷	Engine running – AC compressor ON	0-1 V		
Accelerator pedal position (APP) sensor	9	⬅	Ignition ON – throttle closed	0,3-1 V		
	9	⬅	Ignition ON – throttle fully open	3,9-4,6 V		
	22	⅂	Ignition ON	0 V		
	56	⬅	Ignition ON – throttle closed	3,9-4,6 V		
	56	⬅	Ignition ON – throttle fully open	0,4-1 V		
	69	⇨	Ignition ON	5 V		
Battery	23	⬅	Ignition OFF	11-14 V		
Brake pedal position (BPP) switch	63	⬅	Ignition ON – brake pedal depressed	11-14 V		
	63	⬅	Ignition ON – brake pedal released	0 V		
Brake pedal position (BPP) switch – cruise control	29	⬅	Ignition ON – brake pedal depressed	0 V		
	29	⬅	Ignition ON – brake pedal released	11-14 V		
Clutch pedal position (CPP) switch	29	⬅	Ignition ON – clutch pedal depressed	0 V		
	29	⬅	Ignition ON – clutch pedal released	11-14 V		
Crankshaft position (CKP) sensor	17	⬅	Engine idling	5-15 V ac	5 V/1 ms	∿ 2
	18	⬅	Engine idling	5-10 V ac	5 V/1 ms	∿ 2
Cruise control master switch	5	⬅	Ignition ON	0 V		
	5	⬅	Ignition ON – cruise control master switch activated	11-14 V		
	30	⬅	Ignition ON	0 V		
	30	⬅	Ignition ON – cruise control master switch activated	11-14 V		
	52	⬅	Ignition ON	0 V		
	52	⬅	Ignition ON – cruise control master switch activated	11-14 V		
Data link connector (DLC)	19	⬅⇨	Ignition ON	2-3 V		
	66	⬅⇨	Ignition ON	2-3 V		

* Suggested settings - Voltage/time per division

Component/circuit description	ECM pin	Signal	Condition	Typical value	Oscilloscope setting*	Wave form
Earth	25		Ignition ON	0 V		
	47		Ignition ON	0 V		
	62		Ignition ON	0 V		
Engine control (EC) relay	1	←	Ignition OFF	0 V		
	1	←	Ignition ON	11-14 V		
	26	⊐▷	Ignition OFF	0-1 V for 10 secs.		
	26	⊐▷	Ignition OFF	11-14 V after 10 secs.		
	26	⊐▷	Ignition ON	0-1 V		
Engine coolant temperature (ECT) sensor	22	⊐—	Ignition ON	0 V		
	39	←	Ignition ON – coolant temp. 20°C	3,6 V		
	39	←	Ignition ON – coolant temp. 80°C	1,2 V		
Evaporative emission (EVAP) canister purge valve 1	27	⊐▷	Engine running – valve operating		10 V/50 ms	Intermittent 〰 20
Evaporative emission (EVAP) canister purge valve 2	37	⇨	Valve not operating	11-14 V		
	37	⇨	Valve operating	0,1 V		
Evaporative emission (EVAP) pressure sensor	46	⇨	Ignition ON	5 V		
	59	←	Ignition ON	2,5 V		
	70	⊐—	Ignition ON	0 V		
Fuel pump (FP) relay	50	⊐▷	Ignition ON	0,1 V briefly then 11-14 V		
	50	⊐▷	Engine cranking	0-1 V		
	50	⊐▷	Engine running	0-1 V		
Heated oxygen sensor (HO2S) 1	34	←	Engine idling – accelerate briefly	0-1 V fluctuating	0,2 V/1 sec.	〰 21
	49	⊐▷	Ignition ON	0-1 V		
	49	⊐▷	Engine idling	0-1 V		
	58	⊐—	Ignition ON	0 V		
Heated oxygen sensor (HO2S) 1 – shield wire	22	⊐—	Ignition ON	0 V		
Heated oxygen sensor (HO2S) 2	2	⊐▷	Ignition ON	0-1 V		
	2	⊐▷	Engine idling	0-1 V		
	57	←	Engine idling	0,6 V		
	58	⊐—	Ignition ON	0 V		
Heated oxygen sensor (HO2S) 2 – some models – shield wire	22	⊐—	Ignition ON	0 V		
Ignition control module (ICM)	6	←	Engine idling	15-90 Hz		
	7	⊐▷	Ignition ON	0-1 V		
	7	⊐▷	Engine idling	7 Hz	5 V/50 ms	〰 68
	8	⊐▷	Ignition ON	0-1 V		
	8	⊐▷	Engine idling	7 Hz	5 V/50 ms	〰 68
	38	←	Engine idling	2,5 V		
	53	←	Engine idling	15-90 Hz		
	54	⊐▷	Ignition ON	0-1 V		
	54	⊐▷	Engine idling	7 Hz	5 V/50 ms	〰 68
	55	⊐▷	Ignition ON	0-1 V		
	55	⊐▷	Engine idling	7 Hz	5 V/50 ms	〰 68
Ignition switch	43	←	Ignition ON	11-14 V		
Injector 1	45	⊐▷	Ignition ON	0-1 V		
	45	⊐▷	Engine idling	2,5-4,5 ms		
Injector 2	44	⊐▷	Ignition ON	0-1 V		
	44	⊐▷	Engine idling	2,5-4,5 ms		
Injector 3	67	⊐▷	Ignition ON	0-1 V		
	67	⊐▷	Engine idling	2,5-4,5 ms		

* Suggested settings - Voltage/time per division

Component/circuit description	ECM pin	Signal	Condition	Typical value	Oscilloscope setting*	Wave form
Injector 4	**68**	⊣▷	Ignition ON	0-1 V		
	68	⊣▷	Engine idling	2,5-4,5 ms		
Intake air temperature (IAT) sensor	**15**	⬅	Ignition ON – air temp. 20°C	2,4 V		
	15	⬅	Ignition ON – air temp. 40°C	1,5 V		
	22	⏚	Ignition ON	0 V		
Limp-home solenoid relay	**36**	⊣▷	Ignition ON – relay OFF	11-14 V		
Manifold absolute pressure (MAP) sensor	**11**	⬅	Ignition ON	2,1 V		
	11	⬅	Engine idling	0,6 V		
	11	⬅	Engine idling – accelerate briefly	2,1 V		
	22	⏚	Ignition ON	0 V		
	69	⇨	Ignition ON	5 V		
Mass air flow (MAF) sensor	**65**	⇨	Engine idling		5 V/1 ms	68
Throttle motor	**24**	⇨	Engine idling		5 V/1 ms	24
	48	⇨	Engine idling		5 V/1 ms	24
Throttle motor position sensor	**10**	⬅	Ignition ON – throttle closed	3,9-4,9 V		
	10	⬅	Ignition ON – throttle fully open	0-1 V		
	33	⬅	Ignition ON – throttle closed	0-1 V		
	33	⬅	Ignition ON – throttle fully open	3,9-4,8 V		
	46	⇨	Ignition ON	5 V		
	70	⏚	Ignition ON	0 V		
Turbocharger (TC) boost pressure sensor	**35**	⬅	Ignition ON	2,1 V		
	46	⇨	Ignition ON	5 V		
	70	⏚	Ignition ON	0 V		
Turbocharger (TC) bypass valve	**51**	⇨	Engine running – valve operating	11-14 V		
	51	⇨	Engine running – valve not operating	0,1 V		
Turbocharger (TC) wastegate regulating valve	**13**	⇨	Engine running	32 Hz		
	13	⇨	Engine running	2%		
Vehicle speed sensor (VSS)	**64**	⬅	Vehicle speed 12 mph	15 Hz		

*Suggested settings - Voltage/time per division

[1] Connected pin - no test data available or random digital signal

SAAB

Bosch EDC 15M

Model:	Engine code:	Year:
9-3 2,2 TiD	D223L	1998-02

ECM harness multi-plug

Terminal side

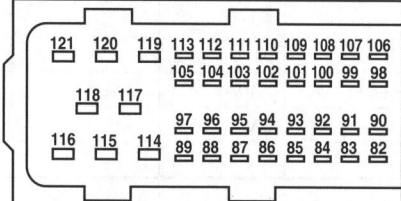
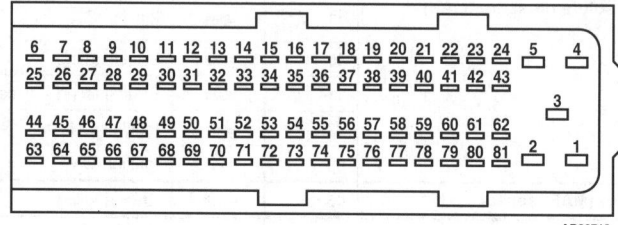

AD20712

Wire side

A   B

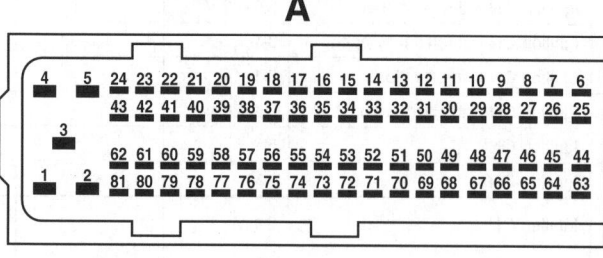
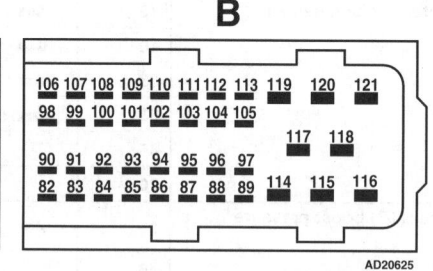

AD20625

Component/circuit description	ECM pin	Signal	Condition	Typical value
ABS control module – vehicle speed sensor (VSS) signal	68	←	Ignition ON – RH front wheel turned at 60 rpm	29 Hz
	68	←	Ignition ON – RH front wheel turned	5 V/10 ms per division ⎍⎍ 4
AC compressor clutch relay	41	⊐⇾	Ignition ON – AC compressor ON	0 V
	41	⊐⇾	Ignition ON – AC compressor OFF	11-14 V
Accelerator pedal position (APP) sensor	38	←	Ignition ON – accelerator pedal in idle position	0,5 V
	38	←	Ignition ON – accelerator pedal in full load position	3,5 V
	49	⊐⊢	Ignition ON	0 V
	57	⇾	Ignition ON	5 V
	69	←	Ignition ON – accelerator pedal in idle position	3,7 V
	69	←	Ignition ON – accelerator pedal slightly depressed	0 V
Brake pedal position (BPP) switch	30	←	Ignition ON – brake pedal released	0 V
	30	←	Ignition ON – brake pedal depressed	11-14 V
Brake pedal position (BPP) switch (cruise control)	65	←	Ignition ON – brake pedal released	11-14 V
	65	←	Ignition ON – brake pedal depressed	0 V
CAN data bus – bus line negative	99	⬄	Ignition ON	2-3 V
	100	⬄	Ignition ON	2-3 V
Clutch pedal position (CPP) switch (cruise control)	31	←	Ignition ON – clutch pedal released	0 V
	31	←	Ignition ON – clutch pedal depressed	11-14 V
Crankshaft position (CKP) sensor	90	←	Engine idling	60 Hz/900 rpm
	90	←	Engine idling	5 V/10 ms per division ⎍⎍ 6
	98	⊐⊢	Ignition ON	0 V
Crankshaft position (CKP) sensor – screened lead	101	⊐⊢	Ignition ON	0 V

Component/circuit description	ECM pin	Signal	Condition	Typical value
Cruise control switch	45	←	Ignition ON – cruise control switch OFF	11-14 V
	63	←	Ignition ON – cruise control switch in 'RES' position	11-14 V
	64	←	Ignition ON – cruise control switch in 'SET' position	11-14 V
Data link connector (DLC)	35	⟺	Ignition ON	11-14 V
Earth	1		Ignition ON	0 V
	2		Ignition ON	0 V
Engine control relay	3	←	Ignition OFF	0 V
	3	←	Ignition ON	11-14 V
	58	⊐▷	Ignition OFF	11-14 V
	58	⊐▷	Ignition ON	0,4 V
Engine coolant temperature (ECT) sensor	89	←	Ignition ON – coolant temp. 20°C	3,5 V
	89	←	Ignition ON – coolant temp. 80°C	1 V
	93	⊐	Ignition ON	0 V
Engine oil temperature sensor	86	←	Ignition ON – oil temp. 90°C	0,9 V
	93	⊐	Ignition ON	0 V
Exhaust gas recirculation (EGR) solenoid	97	⊐▷	Ignition ON	140 Hz
	97	⊐▷	Engine running – accelerate briefly	5 V/5 ms per division 〰31
Fuel injection pump control module	91	⟹	Engine idling	60 Hz/900 rpm
	91	⟹	Engine idling	2 V/5 ms per division 〰15
Fuel injection pump control module – shut-off signal	105	⟹	Ignition OFF	10 V
	105	⟹	Engine idling	0,5 V
	105	⟹	Engine idling	38 Hz
	105	⟹	3000 rpm	150 Hz
	105	⟹	Engine idling	0,1 V/10 ms per division 〰17
Glow plug control module	87	←	Ignition ON – glow plugs OFF	11-14 V
	87	←	Ignition ON – glow plugs ON	0 V
	94	⟹	Ignition ON – glow plugs ON	0,2 V
Ignition switch	39	←	Ignition OFF	0 V
	39	←	Ignition ON	11-14 V
Intake air temperature (IAT) sensor	84	←	Ignition ON – air temp. 20°C	3,5 V
	92	⊐	Ignition ON	0 V
Intake manifold air control solenoid	60	⊐▷	Ignition ON	140 Hz
	60	⊐▷	Engine running – accelerate briefly	5 V/2 ms per division 〰31
Manifold absolute pressure (MAP) sensor	82	⟹	Ignition ON	5 V
	85	←	Ignition ON	2 V
	85	←	Engine idling	1,5 V
	85	←	Engine idling – accelerate briefly	4,5 V
	93	⊐	Ignition ON	0 V
Mass air flow (MAF) sensor	83	⟹	Ignition ON	5 V
	88	←	Engine idling	1,4 V
	88	←	Engine running – accelerate briefly	4,5 V
	88	←	Ignition ON	1 V
	92	⊐	Ignition ON	0 V
Turbocharger (TC) wastegate regulating valve	96	⊐▷	Ignition ON	140 Hz
	96	⊐▷	Engine running – accelerate briefly	5 V/10 ms per division 〰29

1 Connected pin - no test data available

SAAB

Saab Trionic

Model:	Engine code:	Year:
9000 2,0	B204S	1994-98
9000 2,0 Turbo	B204S	1994-95
9000 2,0 Turbo	B204E	1996-99
9000 2,0 Turbo	B204L	1994-97
9000 2,3	B234I	1994-97
9000 2,3 Turbo	B234	1993-94
9000 2,3 Turbo	B234L	1994-98
9000 2,3 ECO Turbo	B234E	1994-98
9000 Aero	B234R	1994-98

ECM harness multi-plug

Terminal side

Wire side

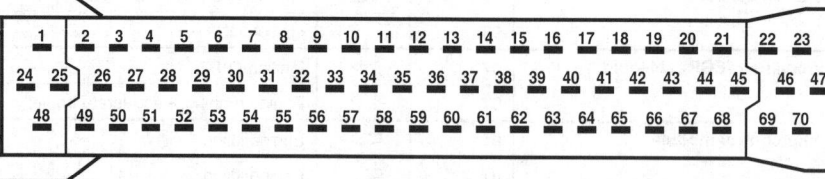

Component/circuit description	ECM pin	Signal	Condition	Typical value	Oscilloscope setting*	Wave form
AC compressor clutch relay	54	⊐▷	Engine running – AC compressor OFF	11-14 V		
	54	⊐▷	Engine running – AC compressor ON	0-1 V		
Air conditioning	59	←	Ignition ON – AC OFF	0 V		
	59	←	Ignition ON – AC ON	11-14 V		
Alarm system control module – some models	60	←	Ignition ON	11-14 V		
Battery	1	←	Ignition OFF	11-14 V		
	48	←	Ignition OFF	11-14 V		
Brake pedal position (BPP) switch	15	←	Ignition ON – brake pedal depressed	11-14 V		
	15	←	Ignition ON – brake pedal released	0 V		
Crankshaft position (CKP) sensor	41	←	Engine idling	8-10 V ac	5 V/1 ms	⊶ 2
	66	⊐⊢	Ignition ON	0 V		
	67	⊐⊢	Ignition ON	0 V		
Crankshaft position (CKP) sensor – shield wire	66	⊐⊢	Ignition ON	0 V		
	67	⊐⊢	Ignition ON	0 V		
Cruise control module	36	←	Ignition ON	10 V		
Data link connector (DLC)	33	◀▷	Ignition ON	11-14 V		
Earth	24		Ignition ON	0 V		
	25		Ignition ON	0 V		
Engine control relay	31	⊐▷	Ignition OFF	11-14 V		
	31	⊐▷	Ignition ON	11-14 V		
	31	⊐▷	Engine cranking	0-1 V		
	31	⊐▷	Engine running	0-1 V		
Engine coolant temperature (ECT) sensor	66	⊐⊢	Ignition ON	0 V		
	67	⊐⊢	Ignition ON	0 V		
	68	←	Ignition ON – coolant temp. 20°C	2,4 V		
	68	←	Ignition ON – coolant temp. 80°C	0,5 V		

* Suggested settings - Voltage/time per division

Autodata

Component/circuit description	ECM pin	Signal	Condition	Typical value	Oscilloscope setting*	Wave form
Evaporative emission (EVAP) canister purge valve →1996	21	←	Ignition ON	0 V		
	21	←	Engine running	50%	10 V/50 ms	Intermittent ⎍ 20
	27	⊐▷	Ignition ON	0 V		
	27	⊐▷	Engine running	50%	10 V/50 ms	Intermittent ⎍ 20
Evaporative emission (EVAP) canister purge valve 1997→	27	←	Ignition ON	0 V		
	27	←	Engine running	50%	10 V/50 ms	Intermittent ⎍ 20
Fuel pump relay	56	⊐▷	Ignition ON	0,1 V briefly then 11-14 V		
	56	⊐▷	Engine cranking	0,1 V		
	56	⊐▷	Engine running	0,1 V		
Heated oxygen sensor (HO2S) – 1	47	⊐—	Ignition ON	0 V		
	23	←	Engine idling – accelerate briefly	0-1 V fluctuating	0,2 V/1 sec.	21
	50	⊐▷	Ignition ON	0 V		
	50	⊐▷	Engine idling	0,3 V		
Heated oxygen sensor (HO2S) – 1 – shield wire	66	⊐—	Ignition ON	0 V		
	67	⊐—	Ignition ON	0 V		
Heated oxygen sensor (HO2S) – 2 – some models	47	⊐—	Ignition ON	0 V		
	51	⊐▷	Ignition ON	0 V		
	51	⊐▷	Engine idling	0,3 V		
	70	←	Engine idling – accelerate briefly	0-1 V fluctuating	0,2 V/1 sec.	21
Heated oxygen sensor (HO2S) – 2 – some models – shield wire	66	⊐—	Ignition ON	0 V		
	67	⊐—	Ignition ON	0 V		
Idle air control (IAC) valve	49	⊐▷	Ignition ON	0 V		
	49	⊐▷	Engine idling	30-50%	5 V/1 ms	24
Ignition control module (ICM)	9	⊐▷	Ignition ON	0 V		
	9	⊐▷	Engine idling	7,6 Hz	5 V/50 ms	68
	10	⊐▷	Ignition ON	0 V		
	10	⊐▷	Engine idling	7,6 Hz	5 V/50 ms	68
	11	⊐▷	Ignition ON	0 V		
	11	⊐▷	Engine idling	7,6 Hz	5 V/50 ms	68
	12	⊐▷	Ignition ON	0 V		
	12	⊐▷	Engine idling	7,6 Hz	5 V/50 ms	68
	17	←	Ignition ON	10 V		
	17	←	Engine idling	1,5 V	5 V/10 ms	81
	18	←	Ignition ON	10 V		
	18	←	Engine idling	1,5 V	5 V/10 ms	81
	44	←	Ignition ON	0 V		
	44	←	Engine idling	50-100 mV ac	50 mV/1 ms	38
Ignition switch – some models	60	←	Ignition ON	11-14 V		
Injector 1	3	⊐▷	Ignition ON	0 V		
	3	⊐▷	Engine idling	2,5-4,5 ms		
Injector 2	4	⊐▷	Ignition ON	0 V		
	4	⊐▷	Engine idling	2,5-4,5 ms		
Injector 3	5	⊐▷	Ignition ON	0 V		
	5	⊐▷	Engine idling	2,5-4,5 ms		
Injector 4	6	⊐▷	Ignition ON	0 V		
	6	⊐▷	Engine idling	2,5-4,5 ms		

* Suggested settings - Voltage/time per division

Component/circuit description	ECM pin	Signal	Condition	Typical value	Oscilloscope setting*	Wave form
Intake air temperature (IAT) sensor	46	←	Ignition ON – air temp. 10°C	2,6 V		
	46	←	Ignition ON – air temp. 40°C	1,5 V		
	66	⊣⊢	Ignition ON	0 V		
	67	⊣⊢	Ignition ON	0 V		
Manifold absolute pressure (MAP) sensor	22	←	Ignition ON	1,9 V		
	22	←	Engine idling	0,7 V		
	22	←	Engine idling – accelerate briefly	2,3 V		
	43	⇒	Ignition ON	5 V		
	66	⊣⊢	Ignition ON	0 V		
	67	⊣⊢	Ignition ON	0 V		
Reversing lamp/s relay	13	⇒	Ignition ON – gear lever not in reverse	0-1 V		
	13	⇒	Ignition ON – gear lever in reverse	11-14 V		
Secondary air injection (AIR) pump relay – some models	52	⊣⊳		[1]		
Tachometer	58	⇒	Engine idling	28 Hz		
Test connector	62			[1]		
	63			[1]		
	65			[1]		
Throttle control module – if fitted	57	←	Engine idling	0,7 V		
	57	←	Engine idling	200 Hz		
	57	←	Engine idling	5%		
Throttle control module – some models	35	⇒	Engine idling	28 Hz		
	35	⇒	2500 rpm	85 Hz		
Throttle position (TP) sensor	42	⇒	Ignition ON	5 V		
	45	←	Ignition ON – throttle closed	0,5 V		
	45	←	Ignition ON – throttle fully open	4,3 V		
	66	⊣⊢	Ignition ON	0 V		
	67	⊣⊢	Ignition ON	0 V		
Transmission range (TR) switch	14	←	Ignition ON – AT in P or N	0 V		
	14	←	Ignition ON – AT not in P or N	11-14 V		
Transmission shift warning lamp	55	⊣⊳	Ignition ON	0-1 V briefly then 11-14 V		
Trip computer – MIL signal	32	⊣⊳	Ignition ON	0-0,5 V for 3 secs then 11-14 V		
Trip computer	34	⇒	Engine idling	7,1 Hz		
	34	⇒	Engine idling	2,5-4,5 ms		
	38			[1]		
Turbocharger (TC) wastegate regulating valve	2	⊣⊳	Ignition ON	11-14 V		
	2	⊣⊳	Engine running – below 2500 rpm	90 Hz		
	2	⊣⊳	Engine running – above 2500 rpm	70 Hz		
	26	⊣⊳	Ignition ON	11-14 V		
	26	⊣⊳	Engine running – below 2500 rpm	90 Hz		
	26	⊣⊳	Engine running – above 2500 rpm	70 Hz		
Vehicle speed sensor (VSS)	39	←	Vehicle speed 12 mph	6,5 V		
	39	←	Vehicle speed 12 mph	15 Hz		

*Suggested settings - Voltage/time per division

[1] Connected pin - no test data available or random digital signal

Model:	Engine code:	Year:
Arosa 1,0/1,4	AER/AEX/ALL	1997-05
Ibiza/Cordoba 1,4	AEX/APQ	1996-99

ECM harness multi-plug

Terminal side

AD81645

Wire side

AD42108

Component/circuit description	ECM pin	Signal	Condition	Typical value	Oscilloscope setting*	Wave form
AC condenser blower motor relay – Ibiza/Cordoba	35	⇨		1		
AC master switch – Ibiza/Cordoba	33	⟵	AC ON – heater motor switch in position 2, 3 or 4	11-14 V		
AC refrigerant pressure switch – Ibiza/Cordoba	33	⟵	Engine idling – AC ON	11-14 V		
Automatic transmission	12			1		
Battery	21	⟵	Ignition OFF	11-14 V		
Closed throttle position (CTP) switch	10	⟵	Ignition ON – throttle closed	0 V		
	10	⟵	Ignition ON – throttle slightly open	11-14 V		
Closed throttle position (CTP) switch – Arosa	17	⫞	Ignition ON	0 V		
Crankshaft position (CKP) sensor	8	⇨	Ignition ON	11-14 V		
	13	⟵	Ignition ON – engine turned	0 V or 9-14 V switching		
	13	⟵	Engine cranking	10 Hz		
	13	⟵	Engine idling	30 Hz	5 V/20 ms	〰〰 4
	13	⟵	3000 rpm	100 Hz		
Crankshaft position (CKP) sensor – Arosa	17	⫞	Ignition ON	0 V		
Earth	1		Ignition ON	0 V		
Earth – Ibiza/Cordoba	17		Ignition ON	0 V		
Engine coolant blower motor control module/AC compressor control module – Arosa 1,4, with AC 1998→	12	⟵		1		
Engine coolant blower motor control module/AC compressor control module – Arosa, with AC	33	⟵		1		
	35	⟵		1		
Engine coolant temperature (ECT) sensor	42	⟵	Ignition ON – coolant temp. 10°C	4,2 V		
	42	⟵	Ignition ON – coolant temp. 80°C	1,7 V		
Engine coolant temperature (ECT) sensor – Arosa	17	⫞	Ignition ON	0 V		

* Suggested settings - Voltage/time per division

Component/circuit description	ECM pin	Signal	Condition	Typical value	Oscilloscope setting*	Wave form
Evaporative emission (EVAP) canister purge valve	3	⊣▷	Ignition ON	11-14 V		
	3	⊣▷	Engine hot – valve operating		10 V/20 ms	⎍⎍ 20
Fuel pump relay	25	⊣▷	Ignition ON	0-1 V briefly then 11-14 V		
	25	⊣▷	Engine cranking	0-1 V		
	25	⊣▷	Engine running	0-1 V		
Heated oxygen sensor (HO2S)	15	⊣⊢	Ignition ON	0 V		
	38	◀	Engine idling – accelerate briefly	0,1-1 V fluctuating	0,2 V/1 sec.	⎍⎍ 21
Heated rear window switch – Arosa 1,0 1998→	12	◀	Ignition ON – heated rear window OFF	0 V		
	12	◀	Ignition ON – heated rear window ON	11-14 V		
Heated rear window switch – Arosa 1,4 1998→	33	◀	Ignition ON – heated rear window OFF	0 V		
	33	◀	Ignition ON – heated rear window ON	11-14 V		
Idle speed control (ISC) actuator	2	▷	Engine idling	16-24%	5 V/2 ms	⎍⎍ 28
	26	⊣⊢	Ignition ON	0 V		
Idle speed control (ISC) actuator position sensor	14	▷	Ignition ON	5 V		
	16	◀	Ignition ON	2,3-3,4 V		
	16	◀	Engine idling	3 V		
Idle speed control (ISC) actuator position sensor – Arosa	17	⊣⊢	Ignition ON	0 V		
Ignition amplifier	24	▷	Engine cranking	10 Hz		
	24	▷	Engine idling	30 Hz	1 V/10 ms	⎍⎍ 32
	24	▷	3000 rpm	100 Hz		
Ignition switch	23	◀	Ignition OFF	0 V		
	23	◀	Ignition ON	11-14 V		
Immobilizer control module	29	◀	Ignition ON	11-14 V		
	29	◀	Engine idling	11-14 V		
Injector 1	7	⊣▷	Ignition ON	11-14 V briefly then 0 V		
	7	⊣▷	Engine idling	4,8 ms	10 V/2 ms	⎍⎍ 35
Injector 2	6	⊣▷	Ignition ON	11-14 V briefly then 0 V		
	6	⊣▷	Engine idling	4,8 ms	10 V/2 ms	⎍⎍ 35
Injector 3	28	⊣▷	Ignition ON	11-14 V briefly then 0 V		
	28	⊣▷	Engine idling	4,8 ms	10 V/2 ms	⎍⎍ 35
Injector 4	4	⊣▷	Ignition ON	11-14 V briefly then 0 V		
	4	⊣▷	Engine idling	4,8 ms	10 V/2 ms	⎍⎍ 35
Instrument panel – engine RPM signal	9	▷	Engine idling	30 Hz		
	9	▷	3000 rpm	100 Hz		
Instrument panel – Ibiza/Cordoba	27			1		
Instrument panel – vehicle speed signal	36	◀	Ignition ON – vehicle pushed	0 V or 11-14 V switching		

* Suggested settings - Voltage/time per division

Component/circuit description	ECM pin	Signal	Condition	Typical value	Oscilloscope setting*	Wave form
Intake air temperature (IAT) sensor	43	←	Ignition ON – air temp. 10°C	3,7 V		
Intake air temperature (IAT) sensor – Arosa	17	⌐—	Ignition ON	0 V		
Knock sensor (KS)	19	⌐—	Ignition ON	0 V		
	39	←	Engine idling – accelerate briefly		50 mV/1 ms	〰〰 38
Knock sensor (KS) – shield wire	45	⌐—	Ignition ON	0 V		
Manifold absolute pressure (MAP) sensor	18	←	Ignition ON	4 V		
	18	←	Engine idling	0,9 V		
	18	←	3000 rpm	0,5 V		
	18	←	Engine idling – accelerate briefly	3,8 V briefly		
	37	⇒	Ignition ON	5 V		
Manifold absolute pressure (MAP) sensor – Arosa	17	⌐—	Ignition ON	0 V		
Power steering pressure (PSP) switch – Arosa 1,0	11			1		
Throttle position (TP) sensor	14	⇒	Ignition ON	5 V		
	41	←	Ignition ON – throttle closed	4,2 V		
	41	←	Ignition ON – throttle fully open	0,7 V		
Throttle position (TP) sensor – Arosa	17	⌐—	Ignition ON	0 V		
Transmission control module (TCM)	30			1		
	34			1		
Transmission control module (TCM) – engine RPM signal	9	⇒	Engine idling	30 Hz		
	9	⇒	3000 rpm	100 Hz		

*Suggested settings - Voltage/time per division

1 Connected pin - no test data available or random digital signal

SEAT
Bosch Motronic ME7.5.10

Model:	Engine code:	Year:
Arosa 1,0	ALD	1999-03
Arosa 1,4	AKK	1999-03
Ibiza 1,0/1,4	ALD/AKK	1999-02
Cordoba 1,0/1,4	ALD/AKK	1999-02

ECM harness multi-plug

Terminal side

AD42344

Wire side

AD42345

Component/circuit description	ECM pin	Signal	Condition	Typical value	Oscilloscope setting*	Wave form
Accelerator pedal position (APP) sensor	7	⌐	Ignition ON	0 V		
	6	⟹	Ignition ON	5 V		
	8	⟹	Ignition ON	5 V		
	19	⌐	Ignition ON	0 V		
	33	⟸	Ignition ON – accelerator pedal released	0,8 V		
	33	⟸	Ignition ON – accelerator pedal depressed	3,8 V		
	45	⟸	Ignition ON – accelerator pedal released	0,4 V		
	45	⟸	Ignition ON – accelerator pedal depressed	1,8 V		
Air conditioning	17			1		
	42			1		
Alternator	11	⟹	Engine idling		2 V/10 ms	89
Battery	15	⟸	Ignition OFF	11-14 V		
Brake pedal position (BPP) switch 1	51	⟸	Ignition ON – brake pedal released	11-14 V		
	51	⟸	Ignition ON – brake pedal depressed	0 V		
Brake pedal position (BPP) switch 2	23	⟸	Ignition ON – brake pedal released	0 V		
	23	⟸	Ignition ON – brake pedal depressed	11-14 V		
Camshaft position (CMP) sensor	62	⟹	Ignition ON	5 V		
	54	⌐	Ignition ON	0 V		
	60	⟸	Ignition ON	0 or 11-14 V		
	60	⟸	Engine idling		4 V/20 ms	14
CAN data bus – high	31	⟺		1		
CAN data bus – low	32	⟺		1		
Crankshaft position (CKP) sensor	53	⟸	Ignition ON	0 V		
	53	⟸	Engine idling		2 V/2 ms	73
	62	⟹	Ignition ON	5 V		
	67	⌐	Ignition ON	0 V		
Earth	2		Ignition ON	0 V		
	28		Ignition ON	0 V		
Engine coolant 'low' sensor – Arosa	54	⌐	Ignition ON	0 V		
Engine coolant temperature (ECT) sensor	54	⌐	Ignition ON	0 V		
	74	⟸	Ignition ON – coolant temp. 20°C	1,9 V		
	74	⟸	Ignition ON – coolant temp. 80°C	0,5 V		

★ Suggested settings - Voltage/time per division

Component/circuit description	ECM pin	Signal	Condition	Typical value	Oscilloscope setting*	Wave form
Evaporative emission (EVAP) canister purge valve	14	⇥▷	Engine running – engine hot – valve operating		10 V/5 ms	35
Fuel pump (FP) relay	26	⇥▷	Ignition ON	0-1 V briefly then 11-14 V		
	26	⇥▷	Engine idling	0-1 V		
Heated oxygen sensor (HO2S)	21	⊣	Ignition ON	0 V		
	47	⇐	Engine idling – engine hot		0,2 V/1 sec.	21
Heated oxygen sensor (HO2S) – heater control	13	⇥▷	Engine idling – engine hot		5 V/50 ms	18
Ignition amplifier	57	⇨	Ignition ON	0 V		
	57	⇨	Engine idling		1 V/20 ms	32
	71	⇨	Ignition ON	0 V		
	71	⇨	Engine idling		1 V/20 ms	32
Ignition switch	27	⇐	Ignition OFF	0 V		
	27	⇐	Ignition ON	11-14 V		
Immobilizer control module – diagnosis signal – Arosa	29			1		
Injector 1	79	⇥▷	Engine idling	4,2 ms	10 V/2 ms	35
Injector 2	59	⇥▷	Engine idling	4,2 ms	10 V/2 ms	35
Injector 3	73	⇥▷	Engine idling	4,2 ms	10 V/2 ms	35
Injector 4	65	⇥▷	Engine idling	4,2 ms	10 V/2 ms	35
Instrumentation control module	30			1		
Instrumentation control module – diagnosis signal – Ibiza/Cordoba	29			1		
Instrumentation control module – engine RPM signal	41	⇨	Engine idling	26 Hz		
Instrumentation control module – vehicle speed signal	5	⇐	Ignition ON – vehicle pushed	0 V or 11-14 V switching		
Intake air temperature (IAT) sensor	54	⊣	Ignition ON	0 V		
	56	⇐	Ignition ON – air temp. 15°C	2,2 V		
Knock sensor (KS)	63	⇐	Engine idling – accelerate briefly		50 mV/1 ms	38
	77	⇐	Engine idling – accelerate briefly		50 mV/1 ms	38
Manifold absolute pressure (MAP) sensor	54	⊣	Ignition ON	0 V		
	62	⇨	Ignition ON	5 V		
	70	⇐	Ignition ON	4,1 V		
	70	⇐	Engine idling	0,9 V		
	70	⇐	Engine running – full throttle briefly	4,1 V		
Power steering pressure (PSP) switch – if fitted	21	⊣	Ignition ON	0 V		
	49	⇐		1		
Throttle motor	66	⇨	Ignition ON	11-14 V		
	66	⇨	Engine idling	11-14 V		
	80	⇨	Ignition ON	11-14 V for 30 seconds then 3 V		
	80	⇨	Ignition ON – accelerator pedal released		2 V/0,5 ms	(30 seconds only) 64
	80	⇨	Ignition ON – accelerator pedal depressed		2 V/0,5 ms	71
Throttle motor position sensor	55	⇨	Ignition ON	5 V		
	61	⊣	Ignition ON	0 V		
	68	⇐	Ignition ON – accelerator pedal released	0,6 V		
	68	⇐	Ignition ON – accelerator pedal depressed	4,4 V		
	75	⇐	Ignition ON – accelerator pedal depressed	0,7 V		
	75	⇐	Ignition ON – accelerator pedal released	4,5 V		

*Suggested settings - Voltage/time per division

1 Connected pin - no test data available or random digital signal

SEAT
Bosch Motronic ME7.5.10

Model:	Engine code:	Year:
Arosa 1,0	ANV/AUC	1999-03
Arosa 1,4	ANW/AUD	1999-03
Ibiza 1,0/1,4	ANV/ANW/AUC/AUD	1999-02
Cordoba 1,0/1,4	ANV/ANW/AUC/AUD	1999-02
Leon 1,4	APE/AXP	2000-05
Toledo 1,4	APE/AXP	2000-05

ECM harness multi-plug

Terminal side

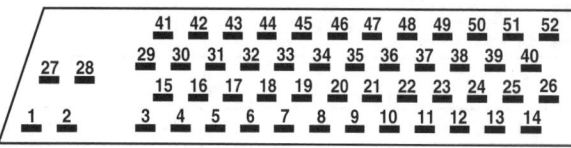

AD42344

Wire side

AD42345

Component/circuit description	ECM pin	Signal	Condition	Typical value	Oscilloscope setting*	Wave form
Accelerator pedal position (APP) sensor	6	⇨	Ignition ON	5 V		
	7	⌐	Ignition ON	0 V		
	8	⇨	Ignition ON	5 V		
	19	⌐	Ignition ON	0 V		
	33	⬅	Ignition ON – accelerator pedal released	0,8 V		
	33	⬅	Ignition ON – accelerator pedal depressed	3,8 V		
	45	⬅	Ignition ON – accelerator pedal released	0,4 V		
	45	⬅	Ignition ON – accelerator pedal depressed	1,8 V		
Air conditioning	42			1		
Air conditioning/engine coolant blower motor control module	17			1		
Alternator	11	⇨	Engine idling		2 V/10 ms	∿∿ 89
Battery	15	⬅	Ignition OFF	11-14 V		
Brake pedal position (BPP) switch 1	23	⬅	Ignition ON – brake pedal released	0 V		
	23	⬅	Ignition ON – brake pedal depressed	11-14 V		
Brake pedal position (BPP) switch 2	51	⬅	Ignition ON – brake pedal released	11-14 V		
	51	⬅	Ignition ON – brake pedal depressed	0 V		
Camshaft position (CMP) sensor	62	⇨	Ignition ON	5 V		
	54	⌐	Ignition ON	0 V		
	60	⬅	Ignition ON	0 or 11-14 V		
	60	⬅	Engine idling		2 V/20 ms	∿∿ 14
CAN data bus – high	31	⬅⇨		1		
CAN data bus – low	32	⬅⇨		1		
Clutch pedal position (CPP) switch – Leon/Toledo – if fitted	38	⬅	Ignition ON – clutch pedal released	11-14 V		
	38	⬅	Ignition ON – clutch pedal depressed		0 V	
Crankshaft position (CKP) sensor	53	⬅	Ignition ON	0 V		
	53	⬅	Engine idling		2 V/2 ms	∿∿ 73
	62	⇨	Ignition ON	5 V		
	67	⌐	Ignition ON	0 V		

* Suggested settings - Voltage/time per division

Component/circuit description	ECM pin	Signal	Condition	Typical value	Oscilloscope setting*	Wave form
Earth	2		Ignition ON	0 V		
	28		Ignition ON	0 V		
Engine coolant temperature (ECT) sensor	54		Ignition ON	0 V		
	74	←	Ignition ON – coolant temp. 20°C	1,9 V		
	74	←	Ignition ON – coolant temp. 80°C	0,5 V		
Evaporative emission (EVAP) canister purge valve	14	→	Engine running – engine hot – valve operating		10 V/5 ms	35
Exhaust gas recirculation (EGR) valve actuator	78	→	Ignition ON	11-14 V		
	78	→	Engine idling		5 V/1 ms – intermittent	53
Exhaust gas recirculation (EGR) valve position sensor	54		Ignition ON	0 V		
	62	⇒	Ignition ON	5 V		
	69	←	Ignition ON	0,92 V		
	69	←	Engine idling	0,95 V		
Fuel pump (FP) relay	26	→	Ignition ON	0-1 V briefly then 11-14 V		
	26	→	Engine idling	0-1 V		
Heated oxygen sensor (HO2S) 1	20	←	Engine idling	2,55 V		
	20 (46)	←	Engine idling	0,45 V		
	34	⇔	Engine idling	2,33-2,55 V		
	35	⇔	Engine idling	2,33-2,55 V		
	46	←	Engine idling	3 V		
	46 (20)	←	Engine idling	0,45 V		
Heated oxygen sensor (HO2S) 1 – heater control	1	→	Engine idling – engine hot	58%	2 V/0,2 secs.	55
Heated oxygen sensor (HO2S) 2	21		Ignition ON	0 V		
	47	←	Engine idling – engine hot	0,6 V		
Heated oxygen sensor (HO2S) 2 – heater control	13	→	Ignition ON	11-14 V briefly then 0-1 V		
	13	→	Engine idling	0-1 V		
Ignition amplifier	57	⇒	Ignition ON	0 V		
	57	⇒	Engine idling		1 V/20 ms	32
	71	⇒	Ignition ON	0 V		
	71	⇒	Engine idling		1 V/20 ms	32
Ignition switch	27	←	Ignition OFF	0 V		
	27	←	Ignition ON	11-14 V		
Immobilizer control module – diagnosis signal – Arosa	29			1		
Injector 1	79	→	Engine idling	4,2 ms	10 V/2 ms	35
Injector 2	59	→	Engine idling	4,2 ms	10 V/2 ms	35
Injector 3	73	→	Engine idling	4,2 ms	10 V/2 ms	35
Injector 4	65	→	Engine idling	4,2 ms	10 V/2 ms	35
Instrumentation control module – diagnosis signal – Ibiza/Cordoba/Leon/Toledo	29			1		
Instrumentation control module – engine RPM signal	41	⇒	Engine idling	26 Hz		
Instrumentation control module – some models	3			1		
	12	→		1		
	16	→		1		
	30	→		1		
Instrumentation control module – vehicle speed signal	5	←	Ignition ON – vehicle pushed	0 V or 11-14 V (switching)		

* Suggested settings - Voltage/time per division

Component/circuit description	ECM pin	Signal	Condition	Typical value	Oscilloscope setting*	Wave form
Intake air temperature (IAT) sensor	54	⌐—	Ignition ON	0 V		
	56	←	Ignition ON – air temp. 15°C	2,2 V		
Knock sensor (KS)	63	←	Engine idling – accelerate briefly		50 mV/1 ms	∿ 38
	77	←	Engine idling – accelerate briefly		50 mV/1 ms	∿ 38
Malfunction indicator lamp (MIL) – Arosa – if fitted	12	⌐▷		1		
Malfunction indicator lamp (MIL) – Ibiza/Cordoba – if fitted	16	⌐▷		1		
Manifold absolute pressure (MAP) sensor	54	⌐—	Ignition ON	0 V		
	62	⇨	Ignition ON	5 V		
	70	←	Ignition ON	4,1 V		
	70	←	Engine idling	0,9 V		
	70	←	Engine running – full throttle briefly	4,1 V		
Power steering pressure (PSP) switch – Ibiza/Cordoba 1,0/Arosa	49	←		1		
Spare cable – Leon/Toledo	12			1		
	16			1		
	30			1		
Throttle control system warning lamp – some models	30	⌐▷		1		
Throttle motor	66	⇨	Ignition ON	11-14 V		
	66	⇨	Engine idling	11-14 V		
	80	⇨	Ignition ON	11-14 V for 30 seconds then 3 V		
	80	⇨	Ignition ON – accelerator pedal released		2 V/0,5 ms	(30 seconds only) ∿ 64
	80	⇨	Ignition ON – accelerator pedal depressed		2 V/0,5 ms	∿ 71
Throttle motor position sensor	55	⇨	Ignition ON	5 V		
	61	⌐—	Ignition ON	0 V		
	68	←	Ignition ON – accelerator pedal released	0,6 V		
	68	←	Ignition ON – accelerator pedal depressed	4,4 V		
	75	←	Ignition ON – accelerator pedal released	4,5 V		
	75	←	Ignition ON – accelerator pedal depressed	0,7 V		

*Suggested settings - Voltage/time per division

1 Connected pin - no test data available or random digital signal

Model:	Engine code:	Year:
Ibiza/Cordoba 1,05	AAU	1993-97
Ibiza/Cordoba 1,4	ABD	1994-99
Ibiza/Cordoba 1,6	ABU/1F	1993-97
Ibiza/Cordoba 1,8	ADZ	1995-99
Toledo 1,6/1,8	1F/ABS/ADZ	1994-97
Inca 1,6	1F	1995-00

SEAT

Bosch Mono-Motronic

ECM harness multi-plug

Terminal side

AD81645

Wire side

AD42108

Component/circuit description	ECM pin	Signal	Condition	Typical value	Oscilloscope setting★	Wave form
Air conditioning	33			1		
	35			1		
Automatic transmission	12			1		
	34			1		
Battery – some models	21	←	Ignition OFF	11-14 V		
Closed throttle position (CTP) switch	10	←	Ignition ON – throttle closed	0-1 V		
	10	←	Ignition ON – throttle slightly open	11-14 V		
Crankshaft position (CKP) sensor	8	⇒	Ignition ON	10 V		
	13	←	Ignition ON – engine turned	0 V or 11-14 V switching		
	13	←	Engine cranking	9 Hz		
	13	←	Engine idling	30 Hz	5 V/20 ms	〜〜 4
	13	←	3000 rpm	100 Hz		
Data link connector (DLC)	29	↔	Ignition ON	11-14 V		
Data link connector (DLC) – some models	11	↔		1		
Earth	1		Ignition ON	0 V		
	20		Ignition ON	0 V		
Earth – some models	15		Ignition ON	0 V		
	17		Ignition ON	0 V		
Engine coolant temperature (ECT) sensor	42	←	Ignition ON – coolant temp. 20°C	2 V		
	42	←	Ignition ON – coolant temp. 80°C	0,3 V		
Engine coolant temperature (ECT) sensor – some models	17	⌐	Ignition ON	0 V		
Evaporative emission (EVAP) canister purge valve	3	⌐▷	Engine hot – valve operating		10 V/20 ms	〜〜 20
Fuel pump relay	25	⌐▷	Ignition ON	0-1 V briefly then 11-14 V		
	25	⌐▷	Engine cranking	0-1 V		
	25	⌐▷	Engine running	0-1 V		
Fuel pump relay – some models	21	←	Engine running	11-14 V		
Heated oxygen sensor (HO2S)	38	←	Engine idling	0,1-1 V fluctuating	0,2 V/2 ms	〜〜 21
Heated oxygen sensor (HO2S) – shield wire	44	⌐	Ignition ON	0 V		

★ Suggested settings - Voltage/time per division

Component/circuit description	ECM pin	Signal	Condition	Typical value	Oscilloscope setting*	Wave form
Heated oxygen sensor (HO2S) – some models	15	ㄱ—	Ignition ON	0 V		
Idle speed control (ISC) actuator	2 (26)	⇨	Engine idling		5 V/2 ms	Intermittent ᴧᴧᴧ 27
	26 (2)	⇨	Engine idling		5 V/2 ms	Intermittent ᴧᴧᴧ 27
Idle speed control (ISC) actuator position sensor – ABU & 1F	16	⇦	Engine idling	3 V or 11-14 V – intermittent	10 V/50 ms	Intermittent ᴧᴧᴧ 31
Ignition amplifier	24	⇨	Engine cranking	12 Hz		
	24	⇨	Engine idling	30 Hz	1 V/10 ms	ᴧᴧᴧ 32
	24	⇨	3000 rpm	100 Hz		
Ignition switch	23	⇦	Ignition ON	11-14 V		
Ignition switch – some models	40	⇦	Ignition ON	11-14 V		
Injector	7	ㄱ▷	Ignition ON	11-14 V briefly then 0 V		
	7	ㄱ▷	Engine idling	1,5 ms	10 V/2 ms	ᴧᴧᴧ 35
Instrument panel	27			1		
Instrument panel – some models	36			1		
Intake air temperature (IAT) sensor	43	⇦	Ignition ON – air temp. 20°C	2,5 V		
Intake air temperature (IAT) sensor – some models	17	ㄱ—	Ignition ON	0 V		
Intake manifold heater relay	28	ㄱ▷	Engine running – engine cold	0-1 V		
	28	ㄱ▷	Engine running – engine hot	11-14 V		
Spare cable – some models	36			1		
Tachometer	9	⇨	Engine idling	30 Hz		
	9	⇨	3000 rpm	100 Hz		
Throttle position (TP) sensor	14	⇦	Ignition ON	5 V		
	18	⇦	Ignition ON – throttle closed	0,5 V		
	18	⇦	Ignition ON – throttle fully open	4,5 V		
	41	⇦	Ignition ON – throttle closed	1,9 V		
	41	⇦	Ignition ON – throttle fully open	4,9 V		
Throttle position (TP) sensor – some models	17	ㄱ—	Ignition ON	0 V		

*Suggested settings - Voltage/time per division

1 Connected pin - no test data available or random digital signal

Model:		Engine code:	Year:
Ibiza 1,2 12V		AZQ	2002-06
Cordoba 1,2 12V		AZQ	2002-06

ECM harness multi-plug

Terminal side

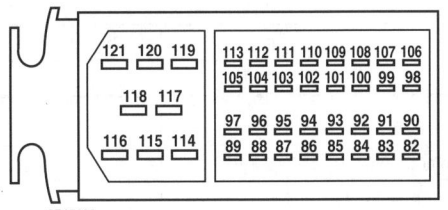

AD25036

Wire side

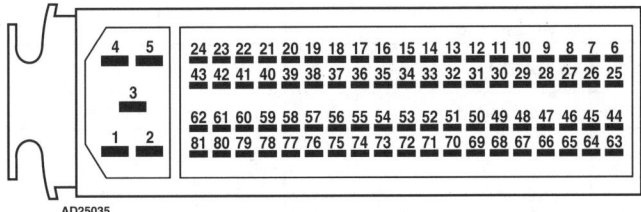

AD25035

Component/circuit description	ECM pin	Signal	Condition	Typical value	Oscilloscope setting*	Wave form
Accelerator pedal position (APP) sensor	18	⇨	Ignition ON	5 V		
	19	⇨	Ignition ON	5 V		
	45	⌐⌐	Ignition ON	0 V		
	50	⌐⌐	Ignition ON	0 V		
	51	⬅	Ignition ON – accelerator pedal released	0,7 V		
	51	⬅	Ignition ON – accelerator pedal depressed	4,1 V		
	64	⬅	Ignition ON – accelerator pedal released	0,4 V		
	64	⬅	Ignition ON – accelerator pedal depressed	2 V		
Alternator	13	⇨		1		
Audio unit – vehicle speed signal	9	⬅		1		
Brake pedal position (BPP) switch	53	⬅	Ignition ON – brake pedal released	0 V		
	53	⬅	Ignition ON – brake pedal depressed	11-14 V		
	63	⬅	Ignition ON – brake pedal released	11-14 V		
	63	⬅	Ignition ON – brake pedal depressed	0 V		
Camshaft position (CMP) sensor	83	⌐⌐	Ignition ON	0 V		
	96	⇨	Ignition ON	5 V		
	105	⬅	Ignition ON	0 or 5 V		
	105	⬅	Engine idling		2 V/0,1 sec.	〰 4
CAN data bus – high	20	⬅⇨		1		
CAN data bus – low	21	⬅⇨		1		
Clutch pedal position (CPP) switch	65	⬅	Ignition ON – clutch pedal released	11-14 V		
	65	⬅	Ignition ON – clutch pedal depressed	0 V		
Crankshaft position (CKP) sensor	89	⇨	Ignition ON	5 V		
	99	⌐⌐	Ignition ON	0 V		
	106	⬅	Engine idling		2 V/2 ms	〰104

* Suggested settings - Voltage/time per division

Component/circuit description	ECM pin	Signal	Condition	Typical value	Oscilloscope setting*	Wave form
Cruise control master switch	28			☐1		
Cruise control selector switch	28			☐1		
Data link connector (DLC) – diagnosis signal	17			☐1		
Diagnostic module – diagnosis signal	17			☐1		
Earth	1		Ignition ON	0 V		
	2		Ignition ON	0 V		
Engine control (EC) relay	3	←	Ignition OFF	0 V		
	3	←	Ignition ON	11-14 V		
Engine coolant temperature (ECT) sensor	83	⊣	Ignition ON	0 V		
	104	←	Ignition ON – coolant temp. 20°C	2,2 V		
	104	←	Ignition ON – coolant temp. 80°C	0,5 V		
Evaporative emission (EVAP) canister purge valve	61	⊣▷	Ignition ON	11-14 V briefly then 0-1 V		
	61	⊣▷	Engine running – engine hot – valve operating		10 V/20 ms	Intermittent 〰 20
Exhaust gas recirculation (EGR) valve actuator	115	⊣▷	Ignition ON	11-14 V		
	115	⊣▷	Engine idling		5 V/1 ms	Intermittent 〰 53
Exhaust gas recirculation (EGR) valve position sensor	84	⊣	Ignition ON	0 V		
	96	⇒	Ignition ON	5 V		
	108	←	Ignition ON	0,8 V		
	108	←	Engine idling	0,8 V		
Fuel pump (FP) relay	80	⊣▷	Ignition ON	0-1 V briefly then 11-14 V		
	80	⊣▷	Engine idling	0-1 V		
Heated oxygen sensor (HO2S) 1	14	←	Engine idling	2,9 V		
	14 (34)	←	Engine idling	0,45 V		
	15	←⇒	Engine idling	2,34-2,55 V		
	33	←⇒	Engine idling	2,34-2,55 V		
	34	←	Engine idling	2,5 V		
	34 (14)	←	Engine idling	0,45 V		
Heated oxygen sensor (HO2S) 1 – heater control	4	⊣▷	Ignition ON	11-14 V briefly then 0-1 V		
	4	⊣▷	Engine idling – engine hot		2 V/0,1 sec.	〰 72
Heated oxygen sensor (HO2S) 2	16	←	Engine idling – engine hot	0,6 V		
	35	⊣	Ignition ON	0 V		
Heated oxygen sensor (HO2S) 2 – heater control	5	⊣▷	Ignition ON	11-14 V briefly then 0-1 V		
	5	⊣▷	Engine idling – engine hot	0,2 V		
Ignition coil 1	112	⇒	Ignition ON	0 V		
	112	⇒	Engine idling		2 V/5 ms	〰 62
Ignition coil 2	113	⇒	Ignition ON	0 V		
	113	⇒	Engine idling		2 V/5 ms	〰 62
Ignition coil 3	100	⇒	Ignition ON	0 V		
	100	⇒	Engine idling		2 V/5 ms	〰 62
Ignition switch	55	←	Ignition OFF	0 V		
	55	←	Ignition ON	0 V		
	55	←	Engine cranking	9 V		
	62	←	Ignition OFF	0 V		
	62	←	Ignition ON	11-14 V		

★ Suggested settings - Voltage/time per division

Component/circuit description	ECM pin	Signal	Condition	Typical value	Oscilloscope setting*	Wave form
Ignition switch – through engine control (EC) relay	23	←	Ignition OFF	0 V		
	23	←	Ignition ON	11-14 V		
Injector 1	88	⊐▷	Ignition ON	11-14 V briefly then 0-1 V		
	88	⊐▷	Engine idling	3,4 ms	10 V/2 ms	⩗⩗ 35
Injector 2	87	⊐▷	Ignition ON	11-14 V briefly then 0-1 V		
	87	⊐▷	Engine idling	3,4 ms	10 V/2 ms	⩗⩗ 35
Injector 3	85	⊐▷	Ignition ON	11-14 V briefly then 0-1 V		
	85	⊐▷	Engine idling	3,4 ms	10 V/2 ms	⩗⩗ 35
Instrumentation control module – vehicle speed signal	9	←		[1]		
Intake air temperature (IAT) sensor	83	⊐—	Ignition ON	0 V		
	93	←	Ignition ON – air temp. 20°C	2 V		
Knock sensor (KS)	101	⊐—	Engine idling	0 V		
	109	←	Engine idling – accelerate briefly		50 mV/1 ms	⩗⩗ 38
Knock sensor (KS) – screened lead	102	⊐—	Engine idling	0 V		
Manifold absolute pressure (MAP) sensor	83	⊐—	Ignition ON	0 V		
	95	←	Ignition ON	4 V		
	95	←	Engine idling	1 V		
	95	←	Engine running – full throttle briefly	4,1 V		
	96	⇒	Ignition ON	5 V		
Multifunction control module	28			[1]		
Throttle motor	119	⇒	Ignition ON – accelerator pedal released		2 V/2 ms	(30 seconds only) ⩗⩗ 64
	121	⇒	Ignition ON – accelerator pedal released		2 V/2 ms	(30 seconds only) ⩗⩗ 64
Throttle motor position sensor	90	←	Ignition ON – accelerator pedal released	0,9 V		
	90	←	Ignition ON – accelerator pedal depressed	4,4 V		
	91	⊐—	Ignition ON	0 V		
	92	←	Ignition ON – accelerator pedal released	4,1 V		
	92	←	Ignition ON – accelerator pedal depressed	0,7 V		
	97	⇒	Ignition ON	5 V		

*Suggested settings - Voltage/time per division

[1] Connected pin - no test data available or random digital signal

SEAT

Magneti-Marelli 1AV

Model:	Engine code:	Year:
Ibiza/Cordoba 1,4	AFH	1997-99
Ibiza/Cordoba 1,6	AEE/ALM	1996-99
Inca 1,6	AEE/ALM	1998-00

ECM harness multi-plug

Terminal side

AD81645

Wire side

AD42108

Component/circuit description	ECM pin	Signal	Condition	Typical value	Oscilloscope setting*	Wave form
Air conditioning	33			☐1		
	35			☐1		
Battery	21	←	Ignition OFF	11-14 V		
Closed throttle position (CTP) switch	10	←	Ignition ON – throttle closed	0 V		
	10	←	Ignition ON – throttle slightly open	9 V min.		
	17	⌐	Ignition ON	0 V		
Crankshaft position (CKP) sensor	8	⇒	Ignition ON	9 V min.		
	13	←	Ignition ON – engine turned	0 V or 5 V switching		
	13	←	Engine idling		2 V/20 ms	⟿ 4
	17	⌐	Ignition ON	0 V		
Earth	1		Ignition ON	0 V		
Engine coolant temperature (ECT) sensor	17	⌐	Ignition ON	0 V		
	42	←	Ignition ON – coolant temp. 10°C	3,2 V		
	42	←	Ignition ON – coolant temp. 80°C	0,5 V		
Evaporative emission (EVAP) canister purge valve	3	⌐▷	Ignition ON	11-14 V		
	3	⌐▷	Engine hot – valve operating		10 V/20 ms	⟿ 20
Fuel pump relay	25	⌐▷	Ignition ON	0-1 V briefly then 11-14 V		
	25	⌐▷	Engine cranking	0-1 V		
Heated oxygen sensor (HO2S)	15	⌐	Engine idling	0 V		
	38	←	Engine idling – engine hot	0,1-1 V fluctuating	0,2 V/1 sec.	⟿ 21
Idle speed control (ISC) actuator	2	⇒	Engine idling – engine hot	60-65%		
	26	⇒	Engine idling – engine hot	35-40%	5 V/2 ms	⟿ 28
Idle speed control (ISC) actuator position sensor	14	⇒	Ignition ON	4,5 V min.		
	16	←	Engine idling – engine hot	3 V		
	17	⌐	Ignition ON	0 V		
Ignition amplifier	24	⇒	Engine idling		2 V/10 ms	⟿ 32
Ignition switch	23	←	Ignition OFF	0 V		
	23	←	Ignition ON	11-14 V		
Immobilizer control module	29	←▷		☐1		

* Suggested settings - Voltage/time per division

Component/circuit description	ECM pin	Signal	Condition	Typical value	Oscilloscope setting*	Wave form
Injector 1	7	⊣▷	Ignition ON	11-14 V briefly then 0 V		
	7	⊣▷	Engine idling – engine hot	4 ms	10 V/2 ms	ᴡᴡᴡ 35
Injector 2	6	⊣▷	Ignition ON	11-14 V briefly then 0 V		
	6	⊣▷	Engine idling – engine hot	4 ms	10 V/2 ms	ᴡᴡᴡ 35
Injector 3	28	⊣▷	Ignition ON	11-14 V briefly then 0 V		
	28	⊣▷	Engine idling – engine hot	4 ms	10 V/2 ms	ᴡᴡᴡ 35
Injector 4	4	⊣▷	Ignition ON	11-14 V briefly then 0 V		
	4	⊣▷	Engine idling – engine hot	4 ms	10 V/2 ms	ᴡᴡᴡ 35
Instrument panel – engine RPM signal	9	⇨	Engine idling – engine hot	25-30 Hz		
Instrument panel	36			①		
	27			①		
Intake air temperature (IAT) sensor	17	⊣—	Ignition ON	0 V		
	43	⬅	Ignition ON – air temp. 10°C	3,2 V		
Knock sensor (KS)	19 (39)	⬅	Engine idling – accelerate briefly		50 mV/1 ms	ᴡᴡᴡ 38
	39 (19)	⬅	Engine idling – accelerate briefly		50 mV/1 ms	ᴡᴡᴡ 38
Knock sensor (KS) – shield wire	45	⊣—	Engine idling	0 V		
Manifold absolute pressure (MAP) sensor	17	⊣—	Ignition ON	0 V		
	18	⬅	Ignition ON	4 V		
	18	⬅	Engine idling – engine hot	1,3 V		
	18	⬅	Engine idling – accelerator pedal briefly fully depressed	4,2 V		
	37	⇨	Ignition ON	5 V		
Throttle position (TP) sensor	14	⇨	Ignition ON	4,5 V min.		
	17	⊣—	Ignition ON	0 V		
	41	⬅	Ignition ON – throttle closed	4 V		
	41	⬅	Ignition ON – throttle fully open	0,8 V		

*Suggested settings - Voltage/time per division

① Connected pin - no test data available or random digital signal

Model:	Engine code:	Year:
Ibiza 1,4	APE/AQQ/AUA/AUB	1999-02
Cordoba 1,4	APE/AQQ/AUA/AUB	1999-02

ECM harness multi-plug

Terminal side

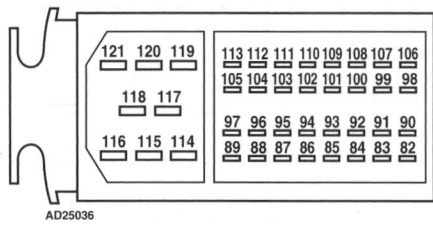
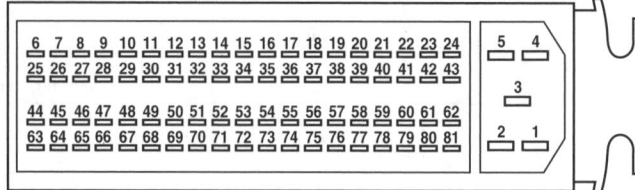

AD25036

Wire side

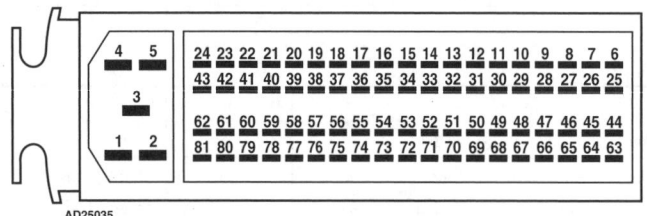
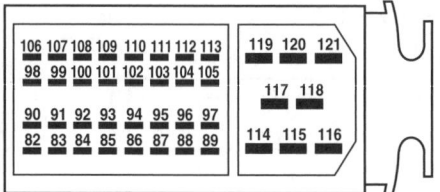

AD25035

Component/circuit description	ECM pin	Signal	Condition	Typical value	Oscilloscope setting*	Wave form
AC control module	40			①		
Accelerator pedal position (APP) sensor	33	⌐—	Ignition ON	0 V		
	34	←	Ignition ON – accelerator pedal fully depressed	2 V		
	34	←	Ignition ON – accelerator pedal released	0,4 V		
	35	←	Ignition ON – accelerator pedal fully depressed	4,1 V		
	35	←	Ignition ON – accelerator pedal released	0,8 V		
	36	⌐—	Ignition ON	0 V		
	72	⟹	Ignition ON	5 V		
	73	⟹	Ignition ON	5 V		
Alternator	28	←	Engine idling		1 V/10 ms	〰89
Battery	3	←	Ignition OFF	11-14 V		
Brake pedal position (BPP) switch 1	55	←	Ignition ON – brake pedal released	11-14 V		
	55	←	Ignition ON – brake pedal depressed	0 V		
Brake pedal position (BPP) switch 2	56	←	Ignition OFF – brake pedal released	0 V		
	56	←	Ignition OFF – brake pedal depressed	11-14 V		
Camshaft position (CMP) sensor	86	←	Ignition ON	0 or 5 V		
	86	←	Engine idling		2 V/50 ms	〰69
	98	⟹	Ignition ON	5 V		
	108	⌐—	Ignition ON	0 V		
CAN data bus – high	60	◆⟹		①		
CAN data bus – low	58	◆⟹		①		
Clutch pedal position (CPP) switch	39	←	Ignition ON – clutch pedal released	11-14 V		
	39	←	Ignition ON – clutch pedal depressed	0 V		
Crankshaft position (CKP) sensor	82	←	Engine idling		2 V/2 ms	〰73
	87	⟹	Ignition ON	5 V		
	108	⌐—	Ignition ON	0 V		

* Suggested settings - Voltage/time per division

Component/circuit description	ECM pin	Signal	Condition	Typical value	Oscilloscope setting*	Wave form
Earth	1		Ignition ON	0 V		
	2		Ignition ON	0 V		
Engine coolant blower motor control module	41			1		
	61			1		
Engine coolant temperature (ECT) sensor	93	←	Ignition ON – coolant temp. 20°C	2,2 V		
	93	←	Ignition ON – coolant temp. 80°C	0,5 V		
	108	⊣⊢	Ignition ON	0 V		
Evaporative emission (EVAP) canister purge valve	64	⊣▷	Ignition ON	11-14 V briefly then 0 V		
	64	⊣▷	Engine running – engine hot – valve operating		10 V/20 ms	20
Exhaust gas recirculation (EGR) valve	114	⊣▷	Ignition ON	11-14 V		
	114	⊣▷	Engine idling		5 V/1 ms	Intermittent 53
Exhaust gas recirculation (EGR) valve position sensor	98	⇒	Ignition ON	5 V		
	100	←	Ignition ON	0,92 V		
	100	←	Engine idling	0,95 V		
	108	⊣⊢	Ignition ON	0 V		
Fuel pump (FP) relay	65	⊣▷	Ignition ON	0-1 V briefly then 11-14 V		
	65	⊣▷	Engine idling	0-1 V		
Heated oxygen sensor (HO2S) 1	51	←	Engine idling	3,79 V		
	51 (70)	←	Engine idling	0,46 V		
	52	←	Engine idling	3,94 V		
	70	←	Engine idling	4,25 V		
	70 (51)	←	Engine idling	0,46 V		
	71	←	Engine idling	8,24 V		
Heated oxygen sensor (HO2S) 1 – heater control	5	⊣▷	Engine idling – engine hot		2 V/20 ms	65
Heated oxygen sensor (HO2S) 2	68	⊣⊢	Ignition ON	0 V		
	69	←	Engine idling – engine hot	0,6 V		
Heated oxygen sensor (HO2S) 2 – heater control	63	⊣▷	Ignition ON	11-14 V briefly then 0 V		
	63	⊣▷	Engine idling – engine hot		2 V/10 ms	65
Ignition amplifier	102	⇒	Ignition ON	0 V		
	102	⇒	Engine idling		2 V/20 ms	62
	103	⇒	Ignition ON	0 V		
	103	⇒	Engine idling		2 V/20 ms	62
Ignition switch	62	←	Ignition OFF	0 V		
	62	←	Ignition ON	11-14 V		
Injector 1	96	⊣▷	Ignition ON	11-14 V briefly then 0 V		
	96	⊣▷	Engine idling	2,5 ms	10 V/2 ms	35
Injector 2	97	⊣▷	Ignition ON	11-14 V briefly then 0 V		
	97	⊣▷	Engine idling	2,5 ms	10 V/2 ms	35
Injector 3	88	⊣▷	Ignition ON	11-14 V briefly then 0 V		
	88	⊣▷	Engine idling	2,5 ms	10 V/2 ms	35
Injector 4	89	⊣▷	Ignition ON	11-14 V briefly then 0 V		
	89	⊣▷	Engine idling	2,5 ms	10 V/2 ms	35

* Suggested settings - Voltage/time per division

Component/circuit description	ECM pin	Signal	Condition	Typical value	Oscilloscope setting*	Wave form
Instrumentation control module	30			1		
	37			1		
	47			1		
	48			1		
	81			1		
Instrumentation control module – diagnosis signal	43	⬌		1		
Instrumentation control module – vehicle speed signal	54	⬅	Ignition ON – vehicle pushed	0 V or 11-14 V (switching)		
Intake air temperature (IAT) sensor	85	⬅	Ignition ON – air temp. 20°C	2,4 V		
	108	ⅎ	Ignition ON	0 V		
Knock sensor (KS)	99	ⅎ	Engine idling	0 V		
	106	⬅	Engine idling – accelerate briefly		50 mV/1 ms	〰 38
Knock sensor (KS) – shield wire	108	ⅎ	Ignition ON	0 V		
Manifold absolute pressure (MAP) sensor	98	⇨	Ignition ON	5 V		
	108	ⅎ	Ignition ON	0 V		
	109	⬅	Ignition ON	4 V		
	109	⬅	Engine idling	0,9 V		
	109	⬅	Engine running – full throttle briefly	4,3 V briefly		
Power steering pressure (PSP) switch – →10/99	49	⬅		1		
Spare cable	115			1		
Throttle motor	117	⇨	Ignition ON – accelerator pedal released		2 V/2 ms	(30 seconds only) 〰 64
	118	⇨	Ignition ON – accelerator pedal released		2 V/2 ms	(30 seconds only) 〰 64
Throttle motor position sensor	83	⇨	Ignition ON	5 V		
	84	⬅	Ignition ON – accelerator pedal fully depressed	0,7 V		
	84	⬅	Ignition ON – accelerator pedal released	4,3 V		
	91	ⅎ	Ignition ON	0 V		
	92	⬅	Ignition ON – accelerator pedal fully depressed	4,4 V		
	92	⬅	Ignition ON – accelerator pedal released	0,7 V		

*Suggested settings - Voltage/time per division

1 Connected pin - no test data available or random digital signal

Model:	Engine code:	Year:
Ibiza 1,4	BBY/BBZ	2002-06
Cordoba 1,4	BBY/BBZ	2002-06

ECM harness multi-plug

Terminal side

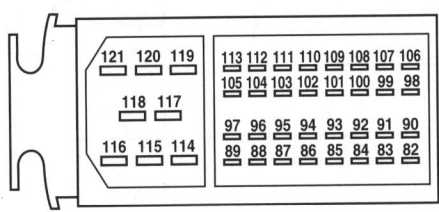

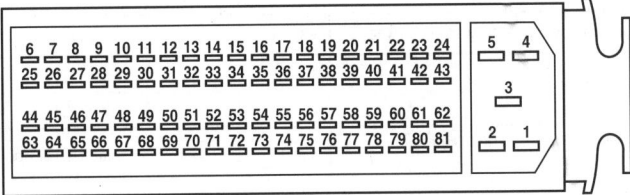

AD25036

Wire side

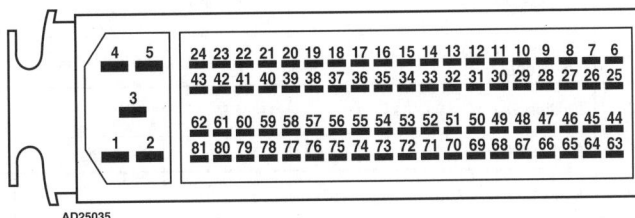

AD25035

Component/circuit description	ECM pin	Signal	Condition	Typical value	Oscilloscope setting*	Wave form
Accelerator pedal position (APP) sensor	33	⌐⌐	Ignition ON	0 V		
	34	←	Ignition ON – accelerator pedal released	0,4 V		
	34	←	Ignition ON – accelerator pedal depressed	2 V		
	35	←	Ignition ON – accelerator pedal released	0,8 V		
	35	←	Ignition ON – accelerator pedal depressed	4,1 V		
	36	⌐⌐	Ignition ON	0 V		
	72	⇒	Ignition ON	5 V		
	73	⇒	Ignition ON	5 V		
Alternator	28	⇒	Engine idling		1 V/10 ms	∿∿ 89
Audio unit – vehicle speed signal	54	←		1		
Battery	3	←	Ignition OFF	11-14 V		
Brake pedal position (BPP) switch	55	←	Ignition ON – brake pedal released	11-14 V		
	55	←	Ignition ON – brake pedal depressed	0 V		
	56	←	Ignition ON – brake pedal released	0 V		
	56	←	Ignition ON – brake pedal depressed	11-14 V		
Camshaft position (CMP) sensor	86	←	Ignition ON	0 or 5 V		
	86	←	Engine idling		2 V/50 ms	∿∿ 69
	98	⇒	Ignition ON	5 V		
	108	⌐⌐	Ignition ON	0 V		
CAN data bus – high	60	⟷⇒		1		
CAN data bus – low	58	⟷⇒		1		
Clutch pedal position (CPP) switch	39	←	Ignition ON – clutch pedal released	11-14 V		
	39	←	Ignition ON – clutch pedal depressed	0 V		

★ Suggested settings - Voltage/time per division

Component/circuit description	ECM pin	Signal	Condition	Typical value	Oscilloscope setting*	Wave form
Crankshaft position (CKP) sensor	82	⬅	Engine idling		2 V/1 ms	〰 73
	87	⮕	Ignition ON	5 V		
	108	⌐	Ignition ON	0 V		
Cruise control master switch	38			1		
Cruise control selector switch	38			1		
Data link connector (DLC) – diagnosis signal	43			1		
Diagnostic module – diagnosis signal	43			1		
Earth	1		Ignition ON	0 V		
	2		Ignition ON	0 V		
Engine coolant temperature (ECT) sensor	93	⬅	Ignition ON – coolant temp. 20°C	2,2 V		
	93	⬅	Ignition ON – coolant temp. 80°C	0,5 V		
	108	⌐	Ignition ON	0 V		
Evaporative emission (EVAP) canister purge valve	64	⊣▷	Ignition ON	11-14 V briefly then 0-1 V		
	64	⊣▷	Engine running – engine hot – valve operating		10 V/20 ms	〰 20
Exhaust gas recirculation (EGR) valve actuator	114	⊣▷	Ignition ON	11-14 V		
	114	⊣▷	Engine idling		5 V/1 ms	Intermittent 〰 53
Exhaust gas recirculation (EGR) valve position sensor	98	⮕	Ignition ON	5 V		
	100	⬅	Ignition ON	0,92 V		
	100	⬅	Engine idling	0,95 V		
	108	⌐	Ignition ON	0 V		
Fuel pump (FP) relay	65	⊣▷	Ignition ON	0-1 V briefly then 11-14 V		
	65	⊣▷	Engine idling	0-1 V		
Heated oxygen sensor (HO2S) 1	51	⬅	Engine idling	3,79 V		
	51 (70)	⬅	Engine idling	0,46 V		
	52	⬅⮕	Engine idling	3,94 V		
	70	⬅	Engine idling	4,25 V		
	70 (51)	⬅	Engine idling	0,46 V		
	71	⬅⮕	Engine idling	8,24 V		
Heated oxygen sensor (HO2S) 1 – heater control	5	⊣▷	Engine idling – engine hot		2 V/10 ms	〰 65
Heated oxygen sensor (HO2S) 2	68	⌐	Ignition ON	0 V		
	69	⬅	Engine idling – engine hot	0,6 V		
Heated oxygen sensor (HO2S) 2 – heater control	63	⊣▷	Ignition ON	11-14 V briefly then 0-1 V		
	63	⊣▷	Engine idling – engine hot		2 V/5 ms	〰 65
Ignition coil 1	102	⮕	Ignition ON	0 V		
	102	⮕	Engine idling		2 V/20 ms	〰 62
Ignition coil 2	103	⮕	Ignition ON	0 V		
	103	⮕	Engine idling		2 V/20 ms	〰 62
Ignition coil 3	94	⮕	Ignition ON	0 V		
	94	⮕	Engine idling		2 V/20 ms	〰 62
Ignition coil 4	95	⮕	Ignition ON	0 V		
	95	⮕	Engine idling		2 V/20 ms	〰 62
Ignition switch	4	⬅	Ignition OFF	0 V		
	4	⬅	Ignition ON	11-14 V		
Injector 1	96	⊣▷	Ignition ON	11-14 V briefly then 0-1 V		
	96	⊣▷	Engine idling	2,5 ms	10 V/2 ms	〰 35

* Suggested settings - Voltage/time per division

Component/circuit description	ECM pin	Signal	Condition	Typical value	Oscilloscope setting*	Wave form
Injector 2	97	→▷	Ignition ON	11-14 V briefly then 0-1 V		
	97	→▷	Engine idling	2,5 ms	10 V/2 ms	35
Injector 3	88	→▷	Ignition ON	11-14 V briefly then 0-1 V		
	88	→▷	Engine idling	2,5 ms	10 V/2 ms	35
Injector 4	89	→▷	Ignition ON	11-14 V briefly then 0-1 V		
	89	→▷	Engine idling	2,5 ms	10 V/2 ms	35
Instrumentation control module – vehicle speed signal	54	←		[1]		
Intake air temperature (IAT) sensor	85	←	Ignition ON – air temp. 20°C	2,4 V		
	108	⊣	Ignition ON	0 V		
Knock sensor (KS)	99	⊣	Engine idling	0 V		
	106	←	Engine idling – accelerate briefly		50 mV/1 ms	38
Manifold absolute pressure (MAP) sensor	98	⇒	Ignition ON	5 V		
	108	⊣	Ignition ON	0 V		
	109	←	Ignition ON	4 V		
	109	←	Engine idling	0,8 V		
	109	←	Engine running – full throttle briefly	4,3 V		
Multifunction control module	38			[1]		
Throttle motor	117	⇒	Ignition ON	11-14 V for 30 seconds then 3 V		
	117	⇒	Ignition ON – accelerator pedal released		2 V/2 ms	(30 seconds only) 64
	118	⇒	Ignition ON	11-14 V for 30 seconds then 3 V		
	118	⇒	Ignition ON – accelerator pedal released		2 V/2 ms	(30 seconds only) 64
Throttle motor position sensor	83	⇒	Ignition ON	5 V		
	84	←	Ignition ON – accelerator pedal released	4,3 V		
	84	←	Ignition ON – accelerator pedal depressed	0,7 V		
	91	⊣	Ignition ON	0 V		
	92	←	Ignition ON – accelerator pedal released	0,7 V		
	92	←	Ignition ON – accelerator pedal depressed	4,4 V		

*Suggested settings - Voltage/time per division

[1] Connected pin - no test data available or random digital signal

Model:	Engine code:	Year:
Ibiza/Cordoba 1,6	AFT	1996-99
Ibiza/Cordoba 2,0	ADY/AGG	1995-99
Toledo 1,6	AFT	1996-99
Toledo 2,0	AGG	1994-99
Alhambra 2,0	ADY	1996-99

ECM harness multi-plug

Terminal side

AD81718

Wire side

AD42119

Component/circuit description	ECM pin	Signal	Condition	Typical value	Oscilloscope setting*	Wave form
Air conditioning	13			1		
	39			1		
Camshaft position (CMP) sensor	44	←	Ignition ON – engine turned	0 V or 10-14 V switching		
	44	←	Engine idling	8 Hz	5 V/20 ms	⤳ 12
	44	←	3000 rpm	25 Hz		
	45	⇨	Ignition ON	11-14 V		
Closed throttle position (CTP) switch	18	←	Ignition ON – throttle closed	0 V		
	18	←	Ignition ON – throttle slightly open	11-14 V		
Crankshaft position (CKP) sensor	16	⊐	Ignition ON	0 V		
	67	←	Engine idling		2 V/1 ms	⤳ 5
	68	←	Ignition ON	11-14 V		
Earth	1		Ignition ON	0 V		
	35		Ignition ON	0 V		
Engine control relay	8	←	Ignition OFF	0 V after 30 seconds		
	8	←	Ignition ON	11-14 V		
	8	←	Engine running	11-14 V		
	23	←	Ignition OFF	0 V after 30 seconds		
	23	←	Ignition ON	11-14 V		
	23	←	Engine running	11-14 V		
Engine coolant temperature (ECT) switch	12	←	Ignition ON – coolant temp. 10°C	2,8 V		
	12	←	Ignition ON – coolant temp. 80°C	0,4 V		
Evaporative emission (EVAP) canister purge valve	33	⊐▷	Ignition ON	11-14 V		
	33	⊐▷	Engine hot – valve operating		10 V/20 ms	⤳ 20
Fuel pump relay	31	⊐▷	Ignition ON	0-1 V briefly then 11-14 V		
	31	⊐▷	Engine cranking	0-1 V		
	31	⊐▷	Engine running	0-1 V		
Heated oxygen sensor (HO2S)	17	←	Engine idling	0,1-1 V fluctuating	0,2 V/1 sec.	⤳ 21
	20	⊐▷	Ignition ON – engine cold	0 V		
	20	⊐▷	Engine idling – engine hot	0 V		
	42	⊐	Ignition ON	0 V		

* Suggested settings - Voltage/time per division

Autodata

Component/circuit description	ECM pin	Signal	Condition	Typical value	Oscilloscope setting*	Wave form
Heated oxygen sensor (HO2S) – shield wire	21	⌐─	Ignition ON	0 V		
Idle speed control (ISC) actuator	25 (30)	⇒	Engine idling		5 V/2 ms	Intermittent ∿ **27**
	30 (25)	⇒	Engine idling		5 V/2 ms	Intermittent ∿ **27**
Idle speed control (ISC) actuator position sensor	28	⟵	Ignition ON	3,7 V		
	28	⟵	Engine idling	3,7 V		
	41	⇒	Ignition ON	5 V		
Ignition amplifier	7	⇒	Engine idling		2 V/10 ms	∿ **32**
Ignition switch	38	⟵	Ignition OFF	0 V		
	38	⟵	Ignition ON	11-14 V		
Ignition switch, start signal – some models	32	⟵	Engine cranking	10 V min.		
Immobilizer control module	43	⟵	Ignition OFF	0 V after 30 seconds		
	43	⟵	Ignition ON	11-14 V		
Injector 1	2	⌐⇒	Engine idling	3,8 ms	10 V/2 ms	∿ **35**
Injector 2	46	⌐⇒	Engine idling	3,8 ms	10 V/2 ms	∿ **35**
Injector 3	47	⌐⇒	Engine idling	3,8 ms	10 V/2 ms	∿ **35**
Injector 4	48	⌐⇒	Engine idling	3,8 ms	10 V/2 ms	∿ **35**
Instrument panel	10			1		
Instrument panel – engine RPM signal	19	⇒	Engine idling	30 Hz		
	19	⇒	3000 rpm	100 Hz		
Intake air temperature (IAT) sensor	37	⟵	Ignition ON – air temp. 10°C	2 V		
Intake air temperature (IAT) sensor – except Ibiza/Cordoba 1,6	29	⌐─	Ignition ON	0 V		
Intake manifold air control solenoid – some models	22	⌐⇒	Ignition ON	11-14 V briefly then 0 V		
	22	⌐⇒	Engine idling	11-14 V		
	22	⌐⇒	Engine running – above 4000 rpm	0-1 V		
Knock sensor (KS)	34	⟵	Engine running – accelerate briefly		50 mV/1 ms	∿ **38**
	36	⌐─	Engine idling	0 V		
Knock sensor (KS) – shield wire	9	⌐─	Ignition ON	0 V		
Mass air flow (MAF) sensor	14	⟵	Engine idling	1,2 V		
	14	⟵	3000 rpm	1,7 V		
	26	⌐─	Ignition ON	0 V		
Throttle position (TP) sensor	40	⟵	Ignition ON – throttle closed	4,3 V		
	40	⟵	Ignition ON – throttle fully open	0,7 V		
	41	⇒	Ignition ON	5 V		
Transmission control module (TCM) – some models	5			1		
	15			1		
	13			1		
Vehicle speed sensor (VSS)	11	⟵	Ignition ON – vehicle pushed	0 V or 11-14 V switching		

*Suggested settings - Voltage/time per division

1 Connected pin - no test data available or random digital signal

SEAT

Siemens Simos 2

Model:	Engine code:	Year:
Ibiza/Cordoba 1,6	AEH/AKL	1999-02
Leon/Toledo 1,6	AEH/AKL	1999-02

ECM harness multi-plug

Terminal side

AD42344

Wire side

AD42345

Component/circuit description	ECM pin	Signal	Condition	Typical value	Oscilloscope setting*	Wave form
Air conditioning – except Toledo →08/99	11			1		
Air conditioning, AC ON signal	10	←		1		
Air conditioning, compressor ON/shut-off signal	8	←⇨		1		
Battery	3	←	Ignition OFF	11-14 V		
Camshaft position (CMP) sensor	62	⇨	Ignition ON	5 V		
	70	⌐	Engine idling	0 V		
	76	←	Ignition ON – engine turned	0 V or 5 V switching		
	76	←	Engine idling	2 V/50 ms	⩗ 45
CAN data bus	29	←⇨		1		
	31	←⇨		1		
Closed throttle position (CTP) switch	69	←	Ignition ON – throttle closed	0 V		
	69	←	Ignition ON – throttle open	9 V min.		
	70	⌐	Engine idling	0 V		
Clutch pedal position (CPP) switch – if fitted	21	←	Ignition ON – clutch pedal released	11-14 V		
	21	←	Ignition ON – clutch pedal depressed	0 V		
Crankshaft position (CKP) sensor	56	←	Engine idling	13,7 V ac	10 V/1 ms	⩗ 2
	63	←	Engine idling	0 V		
Crankshaft position (CKP) sensor, shield wire	70	⌐	Engine idling	0 V		
Earth	2		Ignition ON	0 V		
Engine control module (ECM), pin 22 – Toledo/Leon, MT	70	⌐	Ignition ON	0 V		
Engine control module (ECM), pin 70 – Toledo/Leon, MT	22	←	Ignition ON	0 V		
Engine coolant temperature (ECT) sensor	53	←	Ignition ON – coolant temp. 15°C	2,1 V		
	53	←	Ignition ON – coolant temp. 80°C	0,4 V		
	70	⌐	Engine idling	0 V		

* Suggested settings - Voltage/time per division

Component/circuit description	ECM pin	Signal	Condition	Typical value	Oscilloscope setting*	Wave form
Evaporative emission (EVAP) canister purge valve	15	⊐⊳	Ignition ON	11-14 V briefly then 0 V		
	15	⊐⊳	Engine idling – engine hot	10%	10 V/20 ms	〰 59
Fuel pump relay	4	⊐⊳	Ignition ON	0-1 V briefly then 11-14 V		
	4	⊐⊳	Engine idling	0-1 V		
Heated oxygen sensor (HO2S)	25	⊐—	Engine idling	0 V		
	26	⟵	Engine idling – engine hot	0,1-1 V fluctuating	0,2 V/1 sec.	〰 21
	27	⊐⊳	Ignition ON	11-14 V briefly then 0 V		
	27	⊐⊳	Engine idling	0-1 V		
Idle speed control (ISC) actuator	59	⟹	Ignition ON	11-14 V		
	66	⟹	Ignition ON	11-14 V		
	66	⟹	Engine idling	10-20%	2 V/2 ms	〰 71
Idle speed control (ISC) actuator position sensor	62	⟹	Ignition ON	5 V		
	70	⊐—	Engine idling	0 V		
	74	⟵	Ignition ON	3,8 V		
	74	⟵	Engine idling	3,8 V		
Ignition amplifier	71	⟹	Engine idling		2 V/10 ms	〰 32
	78	⟹	Engine idling		2 V/10 ms	〰 32
Ignition switch	1	⟵	Ignition OFF	0 V		
	1	⟵	Ignition ON	11-14 V		
Ignition switch, start signal – Ibiza/ Cordoba	22	⟵	Engine cranking	8 V min.		
Injector 1	73	⊐⊳	Ignition ON	11-14 V briefly then 0 V		
	73	⊐⊳	Engine idling – engine hot	2-4,1 ms	10 V/2 ms	〰 35
Injector 2	80	⊐⊳	Ignition ON	11-14 V briefly then 0 V		
	80	⊐⊳	Engine idling – engine hot	2-4,1 ms	10 V/2 ms	〰 35
Injector 3	58	⊐⊳	Ignition ON	11-14 V briefly then 0 V		
	58	⊐⊳	Engine idling – engine hot	2-4,1 ms	10 V/2 ms	〰 35
Injector 4	65	⊐⊳	Ignition ON	11-14 V briefly then 0 V		
	65	⊐⊳	Engine idling – engine hot	2-4,1 ms	10 V/2 ms	〰 35
Instrumentation control module, engine RPM signal	6	⟹	Engine idling	30 Hz		
	6	⟹	3000 rpm	100 Hz		
Instrumentation control module, fuel consumption signal – with digital multifunction display	18			1		
Instrumentation control module, immobilization/diagnosis signal	19	⟵⟹		1		
Instrumentation control module, vehicle speed signal	20	⟵	Ignition ON – vehicle pushed	0 V or 11-14 V switching		

★ Suggested settings - Voltage/time per division

Component/circuit description	ECM pin	Signal	Condition	Typical value	Oscilloscope setting*	Wave form
Intake manifold air control solenoid	64	⊐▷	Ignition ON	11-14 V briefly then 0 V		
	64	⊐▷	Engine idling	11-14 V		
	64	⊐▷	Engine idling – full throttle briefly	0-1 V briefly then 11-14 V		
Knock sensor (KS)	67	⊐—	Engine idling	0 V		
	68	⟵	Engine idling – full throttle briefly		50 mV/1 ms	58
Knock sensor (KS), shield wire	67	⊐—	Engine idling	0 V		
Mass air flow (MAF) sensor	12	⊐—	Engine idling	0 V		
	13	⟵	Engine idling	1 V		
	13	⟵	Engine idling – full throttle briefly	4,2 V		
Mass air flow (MAF) sensor, IAT signal	9	⟵	Ignition ON – air temp. 15°C	1,5 V		
Power steering pressure (PSP) switch	14	⟵		1		
	24	⟵		1		
Starter motor relay/reversing lamp/s relay – Toledo/Leon, AT	22	⟵		1		
Throttle position (TP) sensor	62	⟹	Ignition ON	5 V		
	70	⊐—	Engine idling	0 V		
	75	⟵	Ignition ON – throttle closed	4,3 V		
	75	⟵	Ignition ON – throttle fully open	0,6 V		
Transmission control module (TCM), torque reduction signal – some models	23	⟵		1		
Transmission control module (TCM), TP signal – some models	7	⟹		1		
Transmission control module (TCM), engine RPM signal – some models	6	⟹	Engine idling	30 Hz		
	6	⟹	3000 rpm	100 Hz		

*Suggested settings - Voltage/time per division

1 Connected pin - no test data available or random digital signal

Model:	Engine code:	Year:
Ibiza 1,9 TDI PD	ASZ, ATD	2002-06
Cordoba 1,9 TDI PD	ASZ, ATD	2002-06

SEAT

Bosch EDC 15P

ECM harness multi-plug

Terminal side

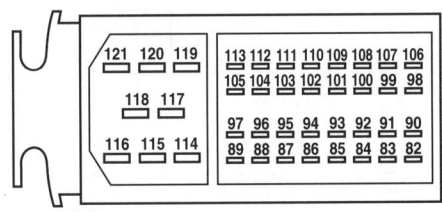

AD25036

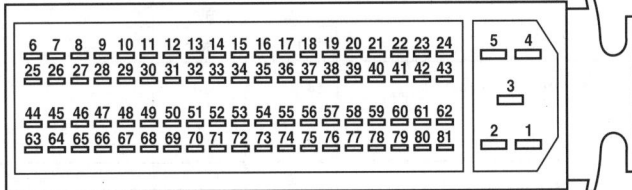

Wire side

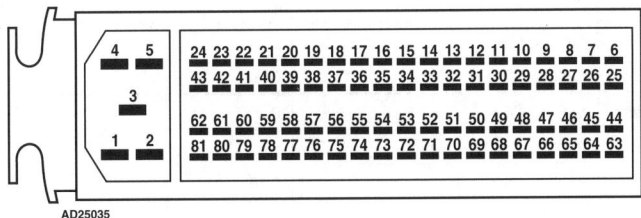

AD25035

Component/circuit description	ECM pin	Signal	Condition	Typical value	Oscilloscope setting*	Wave form
Accelerator pedal position (APP) sensor	12	⇒	Ignition ON	5 V		
	50	⌐	Ignition ON	0 V		
	69	←	Ignition ON – accelerator pedal released	0,4 V		
	69	←	Ignition ON – accelerator pedal fully depressed	4,4 V		
Accelerator pedal position (APP) switch	51	⌐	Ignition ON	0 V		
	70	←	Ignition ON – accelerator pedal released	0,2 V		
	70	←	Ignition ON – accelerator pedal depressed	5 V		
Alternator, charging signal	38	⇒	Ignition ON		2 V/20 ms	〰 43
Auxiliary heater switch – if fitted	15			1		
Battery – 11/02→	88	←	Ignition ON	11-14 V		
Brake pedal position (BPP) switch	32	←	Ignition OFF – brake pedal released	0 V		
	32	←	Ignition OFF – brake pedal depressed	11-14 V		
	65	←	Ignition ON – brake pedal released	11-14 V		
	65	←	Ignition ON – brake pedal depressed	0 V		
Camshaft position (CMP) sensor	101	⌐	Ignition ON	0 V		
	109	←	Engine idling		2 V/0,5 ms	〰 58
CAN data bus – high	7	⟺		1		
CAN data bus – low	6	⟺		1		
Clutch pedal position (CPP) switch	66	←	Ignition ON – clutch pedal released	11-14 V		
	66	←	Ignition ON – clutch pedal depressed	0 V		

★ Suggested settings - Voltage/time per division

Component/circuit description	ECM pin	Signal	Condition	Typical value	Oscilloscope setting*	Wave form
Crankshaft position (CKP) sensor	102	←	Ignition ON	2,5 V		
	102	←	Engine idling	1,9 V ac		
	102	←	Engine idling		2 V/1 ms	⩘⩘ 25
	102	←	3000 rpm	3,1 V		
	110	←	Ignition ON	2,5 V		
	110	←	Engine idling	1,9 V ac		
	110	←	Engine idling		2 V/1 ms	Reversed ⩘⩘ 25
	110	←	3000 rpm	3,1 V		
Cruise control master switch	14	←	Ignition ON – selector switch set to 'OFF'	0 V		
	14	←	Ignition ON – selector switch set to 'ON'	11-14 V		
Cruise control selector switch	14	←	Ignition ON – selector switch set to 'OFF'	0 V		
	14	←	Ignition ON – selector switch set to 'ON'	11-14 V		
Data link connector (DLC)	16	⬌		1		
Earth	4		Ignition ON	0 V		
	5		Ignition ON	0 V		
Engine control (EC) relay	1	←	Ignition OFF	0 V		
	1	←	Ignition ON	11-14 V		
	2	←	Ignition OFF	0 V		
	2	←	Ignition ON	11-14 V		
	18	⊐▷	Ignition OFF	11-14 V		
	18	⊐▷	Ignition ON	0-1 V		
Engine coolant blower motor relay – ASZ →10/02 without AC	11	⊐▷		1		
Engine coolant heater relay 1, low output – if fitted	21	⊐▷		1		
Engine coolant heater relay 2, high output – if fitted	22	⊐▷		1		
Engine coolant temperature (ECT) sensor	104	⊐⊢	Ignition ON	0 V		
	112	←	Ignition ON – coolant temp. 10°C	4 V		
	112	←	Ignition ON – coolant temp. 80°C	1,2 V		
Exhaust gas recirculation (EGR) solenoid	61	⊐▷	Ignition ON	11-14 V		
	61	⊐▷	Engine idling		5 V/1 ms	⩘⩘ 2
Fuel lift pump relay	80	⊐▷	Ignition ON	0-1 V briefly then 11-14 V		
	80	⊐▷	Engine idling	0-1 V		
Fuel temperature sensor	103	⊐⊢	Ignition ON	0 V		
	111	←	Ignition ON – fuel temp. 5°C	4,6 V		
Glow plug relay	42	⊐▷	Ignition ON – glow plugs ON	0-1 V		
	42	⊐▷	Ignition ON – glow plugs OFF	11-14 V		
Ignition switch	37	←	Ignition OFF	0 V		
	37	←	Ignition ON	11-14 V		
	37	←	Engine cranking	11-14 V		
	37	←	Engine idling	11-14 V		
Injector 1	114	⇒	Ignition ON	0,3 V		
	116	⇒	Ignition ON	0,3 V		
	116 (114)	⇒	Engine idling	2,2 ms		
	116 (114)	⇒	Engine idling		10 V/0,5 ms	⩘⩘ 57

* Suggested settings - Voltage/time per division

Component/circuit description	ECM pin	Signal	Condition	Typical value	Oscilloscope setting*	Wave form
Injector 2	114	⇒	Ignition ON	0,3 V		
	117	⇒	Ignition ON	0,3 V		
	117 (114)	⇒	Engine idling	2,2 ms		
	117 (114)	⇒	Engine idling		10 V/0,5 ms	∿∿ 57
Injector 3	114	⇒	Ignition ON	0,3 V		
	118	⇒	Ignition ON	0,3 V		
	118 (114)	⇒	Engine idling	2,2 ms		
	118 (114)	⇒	Engine idling		10 V/0,5 ms	∿∿ 57
Injector 4	114	⇒	Ignition ON	0,3 V		
	121	⇒	Ignition ON	0,3 V		
	121 (114)	⇒	Engine idling	2,2 ms		
	121 (114)	⇒	Engine idling		10 V/0,5 ms	∿∿ 57
Instrumentation control module – vehicle speed signal	20	⇐	Ignition ON – vehicle pushed	0 V or 10 V min. (switching)		
Intake air temperature (IAT) sensor	52	⊣—	Ignition ON	0 V		
	73	⇐	Ignition ON – air temp. 10°C	3 V		
Intake manifold air control solenoid	81	⊣▷	Ignition ON	11-14 V		
	81	⊣▷	Engine idling	11-14 V		
	81	⊣▷	Engine idling – switch ignition OFF	0-1 V for 2,5 secs., 11-14 V for 0,5 sec., then 0-1 V		
Mass air flow (MAF) sensor	30	⇒	Ignition ON	5 V		
	49	⊣—	Ignition ON	0 V		
	68	⇐	Ignition ON	1 V		
	68	⇐	Engine idling	1,5-2,1 V		
	68	⇐	3000 rpm	3,2 V		
Transmission kick-down switch	51	⊣—	Ignition ON	0 V		
	63	⇐	Ignition ON – accelerator pedal released	5 V		
	63	⇐	Ignition ON – accelerator pedal fully depressed	0 V		
Turbocharger (TC) boost pressure sensor	31	⇒	Ignition ON	5 V		
	52	⊣—	Ignition ON	0 V		
	71	⇐	Ignition ON	1,6 V		
	71	⇐	Engine idling	1,7 V		
Turbocharger (TC) wastegate regulating valve	62	⊣▷	Ignition ON	11-14 V		
	62	⊣▷	Engine idling	11-14 V		
	62	⊣▷	Engine idling – accelerator pedal briefly fully depressed	0-1 V briefly		
	62	⊣▷	Engine running – valve not operating	11-14 V		
	62	⊣▷	Engine running – valve operating	0-1 V		

*Suggested settings - Voltage/time per division

1 Connected pin - no test data available or random digital signal

SEAT
VAG Digifant

Model:	Engine code:	Year:
Ibiza 2,0 16V	ABF	1996-99
Cordoba 2,0 16V	ABF	1996-99
Toledo 2,0 16V	ABF	1994-99

ECM harness multi-plug

Terminal side

AD81718

Wire side

AD42119

Component/circuit description	ECM pin	Signal	Condition	Typical value	Oscilloscope setting*	Wave form
Camshaft position (CMP) sensor	33	⌐	Ignition ON	0 V		
	44	←	Engine idling		5 V/20 ms	12
	45	⇒	Ignition ON	11-14 V		
Closed throttle position (CTP) switch	21	←	Ignition ON – throttle closed	0 V		
	21	←	Ignition ON – throttle fully open	11-14 V		
	33	⌐	Ignition ON	0 V		
Crankshaft position (CKP) sensor	33	⌐	Ignition ON	0 V		
	67	←	Engine idling		2 V/1 ms	5
	68	⇒	Ignition ON	11-14 V		
Data link connector (DLC) – without immobilizer	43		Engine idling	11-14 V		
Earth	1		Ignition ON	0 V		
Engine control relay	23	←	Ignition OFF	0 V		
	23	←	Ignition ON	11 V min.		
Engine coolant temperature (ECT) sensor	14	←	Ignition ON – coolant temp. 10°C	1 V		
	14	←	Ignition ON – coolant temp. 80°C	0,2 V		
	33	⌐	Ignition ON	0 V		
Evaporative emission (EVAP) canister purge valve	31	⌐⇒	Ignition ON	11-14 V		
	31	⌐⇒	Engine hot – valve operating		10 V/20 ms	20
Fuel pump relay	6	⌐⇒	Ignition ON	0-1 V briefly then 11-14 V		
	6	⌐⇒	Engine cranking	0-1 V		
Heated oxygen sensor (HO2S)	20	←	Engine idling – engine hot	0,1-1 V fluctuating	0,2 V/1 sec.	21
	42	⌐	Engine idling	0 V		
Heated oxygen sensor (HO2S) – shield wire	65	⌐	Engine idling	0 V		
Idle air control (IAC) valve	27	⌐⇒	Engine idling – engine hot	50%	5 V/5 ms	24
Ignition amplifier	8	⇒	Engine idling	30 Hz	2 V/10 ms	32
	8	⇒	3000 rpm	100 Hz		
Ignition switch	7	←	Engine cranking	8 V min.		
	38	←	Ignition OFF	0 V		
	38	←	Ignition ON	11 V min.		

★ Suggested settings - Voltage/time per division

Component/circuit description	ECM pin	Signal	Condition	Typical value	Oscilloscope setting*	Wave form
Ignition switch – through engine control relay	9	←	Ignition OFF	0 V		
	9	←	Ignition ON	9 V min.		
Immobilizer control module	43		Engine idling	11-14 V		
Injector 1	24	⇥▷	Ignition ON	11-14 V briefly then 0 V		
	24	⇥▷	Engine idling – engine hot	3,4 ms	10 V/2 ms	⎍ 35
Injector 2	25	⇥▷	Ignition ON	11-14 V briefly then 0 V		
	25	⇥▷	Engine idling – engine hot	3,4 ms	10 V/2 ms	⎍ 35
Injector 3	26	⇥▷	Ignition ON	11-14 V briefly then 0 V		
	26	⇥▷	Engine idling – engine hot	3,4 ms	10 V/2 ms	⎍ 35
Injector 4	2	⇥▷	Ignition ON	11-14 V briefly then 0 V		
	2	⇥▷	Engine idling – engine hot	3,4 ms	10 V/2 ms	⎍ 35
Instrument panel	51			1		
Intake air temperature (IAT) sensor	33	⇥–	Ignition ON	0 V		
	36	←	Ignition ON – air temp. 10°C	1,6 V		
Knock sensor (KS) 1	32 (34)	←	Engine idling – accelerate briefly		50 mV/1 ms	⎍ 38
	34 (32)	←	Engine idling – accelerate briefly		50 mV/1 ms	⎍ 38
	10	⇥–	Engine idling	0 V		
Knock sensor (KS) 2	56 (57)	←	Engine idling – accelerate briefly		50 mV/1 ms	⎍ 38
	57 (56)	←	Engine idling – accelerate briefly		50 mV/1 ms	⎍ 38
	55	⇥–	Engine idling	0 V		
Oxygen sensor heater relay	28	⇥▷	Ignition ON	0-1 V		
Throttle position (TP) sensor	33	⇥–	Ignition ON	0 V		
	40	←	Ignition ON – throttle closed	0,5-1,5 V		
	40	←	Ignition ON – throttle fully open	3-5 V		
	41	⇨	Ignition ON	5 V		

*Suggested settings - Voltage/time per division

1 Connected pin - no test data available or random digital signal

ECM harness multi-plug

Terminal side

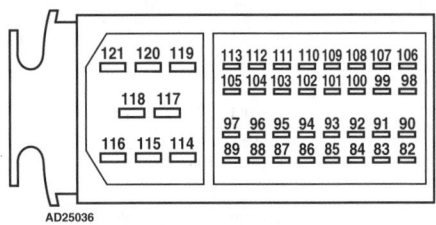
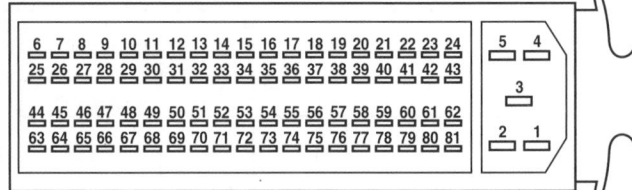

AD25036

Wire side

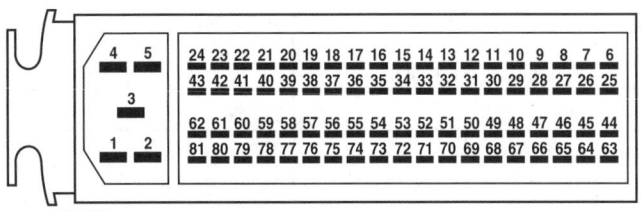
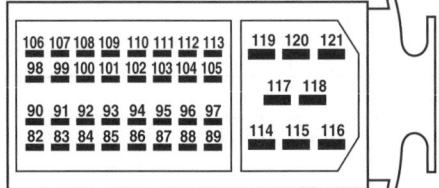

AD25035

Component/circuit description	ECM pin	Signal	Condition	Typical value	Oscilloscope setting*	Wave form
AC control module – ATC	40			1		
	41			1		
AC refrigerant pressure sensor	61			1		
AC/heater function control panel – MTC	40			1		
Accelerator pedal position (APP) sensor	33	⌐	Ignition ON	0 V		
	34	←	Ignition ON – accelerator pedal released	0,4 V		
	34	←	Ignition ON – accelerator pedal depressed	2 V		
	35	←	Ignition ON – accelerator pedal released	0,8 V		
	35	←	Ignition ON – accelerator pedal depressed	4,1 V		
	36	⌐	Ignition ON	0 V		
	72	⇒	Ignition ON	5 V		
	73	⇒	Ignition ON	5 V		
Alternator	28	⇒	Engine idling		1 V/10 ms	⋀⋁⋀ 89
Battery	3	←	Ignition OFF	11-14 V		
Brake pedal position (BPP) switch	55	←	Ignition ON – brake pedal released	11-14 V		
	55	←	Ignition ON – brake pedal depressed	0 V		
	56	←	Ignition ON – brake pedal released	0 V		
	56	←	Ignition ON – brake pedal depressed	11-14 V		
Camshaft position (CMP) sensor	86	←	Ignition ON	0 or 5 V		
	86	←	Engine idling		2 V/50 ms	⋀⋁⋀ 69
	98	⇒	Ignition ON	5 V		
	108	⌐	Ignition ON	0 V		
CAN data bus – high	60	⇔		1		
CAN data bus – low	58	⇔		1		
Clutch pedal position (CPP) switch	39	←	Ignition ON – clutch pedal released	11-14 V		
	39	←	Ignition ON – clutch pedal depressed	0 V		

* Suggested settings - Voltage/time per division

Component/circuit description	ECM pin	Signal	Condition	Typical value	Oscilloscope setting*	Wave form
Crankshaft position (CKP) sensor	82	←	Engine idling		5 V/1 ms	⩓⩓ 5
	87	⇒	Ignition ON	5 V		
	108	⊣⁻	Ignition ON	0 V		
Cruise control master switch	38			☐1		
	57			☐1		
Cruise control selector switch	38			☐1		
	75			☐1		
	76			☐1		
Earth	1		Ignition ON	0 V		
	2		Ignition ON	0 V		
Engine coolant blower motor control module	61			☐1		
Engine coolant blower motor control module – MTC	40			☐1		
	41			☐1		
Engine coolant temperature (ECT) sensor	93	←	Ignition ON – coolant temp. 20°C	2,2 V		
	93	←	Ignition ON – coolant temp. 80°C	0,5 V		
	108	⊣⁻	Ignition ON	0 V		
Evaporative emission (EVAP) canister purge valve	64	⊣▷	Ignition ON	11-14 V briefly then 0-1 V		
	64	⊣▷	Engine idling	11-14 V		
	64	⊣▷	Engine running – engine hot – valve operating		10 V/20 ms	⩓⩓ 20
Exhaust gas recirculation (EGR) valve actuator	114	⊣▷	Ignition ON	11-14 V		
	114	⊣▷	Engine idling		5 V/1 ms	Intermittent ⩓⩓ 53
Exhaust gas recirculation (EGR) valve position sensor	98	⇒	Ignition ON	5 V		
	100	←	Ignition ON	0,92 V		
	100	←	Engine idling	0,95 V		
	108	⊣⁻	Ignition ON	0 V		
Fuel pump (FP) relay	65	⊣▷	Ignition ON	0-1 V briefly then 11-14 V		
	65	⊣▷	Engine idling	0-1 V		
Heated oxygen sensor (HO2S) 1	51	←	Engine idling	3,79 V		
	51 (70)	←	Engine idling	0,46 V		
	52	⇐▷	Engine idling	3,94 V		
	70	←	Engine idling	4,25 V		
	70 (51)	←	Engine idling	0,46 V		
	71	⇔	Engine idling	8,24 V		
Heated oxygen sensor (HO2S) 1 – heater control	5	⊣▷	Engine idling – engine hot		2 V/10 ms	⩓⩓ 65
Heated oxygen sensor (HO2S) 2	68	⊣⁻	Ignition ON	0 V		
	69	←	Engine idling – engine hot	0,6 V		
Heated oxygen sensor (HO2S) 2 – heater control	63	⊣▷	Ignition ON	11-14 V briefly then 0-1 V		
	63	⊣▷	Engine idling – engine hot		2 V/5 ms	⩓⩓ 65
Ignition amplifier	102	⊣▷	Engine idling		1 V/20 ms	⩓⩓ 32
	103	⊣▷	Engine idling		1 V/20 ms	⩓⩓ 32
Ignition switch	4	←	Ignition OFF	0 V		
	4	←	Ignition ON	11-14 V		
Injector 1	96	⊣▷	Ignition ON	11-14 V briefly then 0-1 V		
	96	⊣▷	Engine idling	2,8 ms	10 V/2 ms	⩓⩓ 35

* Suggested settings - Voltage/time per division

Component/circuit description	ECM pin	Signal	Condition	Typical value	Oscilloscope setting*	Wave form
Injector 2	97	⌐▷	Ignition ON	11-14 V briefly then 0-1 V		
	97	⌐▷	Engine idling	2,8 ms	10 V/2 ms	⋀⋁⋀ 35
Injector 3	88	⌐▷	Ignition ON	11-14 V briefly then 0-1 V		
	88	⌐▷	Engine idling	2,8 ms	10 V/2 ms	⋀⋁⋀ 35
Injector 4	89	⌐▷	Ignition ON	11-14 V briefly then 0-1 V		
	89	⌐▷	Engine idling	2,8 ms	10 V/2 ms	⋀⋁⋀ 35
Instrumentation control module – diagnosis signal	43			1		
Instrumentation control module – engine RPM signal	37	⟹	Engine idling	28 Hz		
Instrumentation control module – vehicle speed signal	54	⟸		1		
Intake air temperature (IAT) sensor	85	⟸	Ignition ON – air temp. 20°C	2,4 V		
	108	⌐—	Ignition ON	0 V		
Knock sensor (KS)	99	⌐—	Engine idling	0 V		
	106	⟸	Engine idling – accelerate briefly		50 mV/1 ms	⋀⋁⋀ 38
Manifold absolute pressure (MAP) sensor	98	⟹	Ignition ON	5 V		
	108	⌐—	Ignition ON	0 V		
	109	⟸	Ignition ON	4 V		
	109	⟸	Engine idling	0,8 V		
	109	⟸	Engine running – full throttle briefly	4,3 V		
Spare cable – some models	66			1		
Throttle motor	117	⟹	Ignition ON	11-14 V for 30 seconds then 3 V		
	117	⟹	Ignition ON – accelerator pedal released		2 V/2 ms	(30 seconds only) ⋀⋁⋀ 64
	118	⟹	Ignition ON	11-14 V for 30 seconds then 3 V		
	118	⟹	Ignition ON – accelerator pedal released		2 V/2 ms	(30 seconds only) ⋀⋁⋀ 64
Throttle motor position sensor	83	⟹	Ignition ON	5 V		
	84	⟸	Ignition ON – accelerator pedal released	4,3 V		
	91	⌐—	Ignition ON	0 V		
	92	⟸	Ignition ON – accelerator pedal released	0,7 V		

*Suggested settings - Voltage/time per division

1 Connected pin - no test data available or random digital signal

Model:	Engine code:	Year:
Leon 1,6 16V	AZD/BCB	2001-05
Toledo 1,6 16V	AZD/BCB	2001-05

SEAT

Magneti Marelli 4MV

ECM harness multi-plug

Terminal side

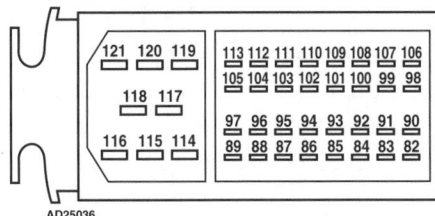

AD25036

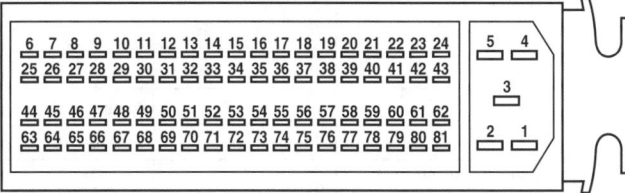

Wire side

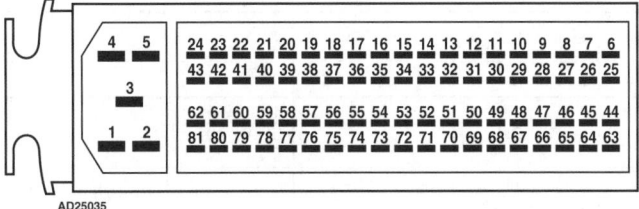

AD25035

Component/circuit description	ECM pin	Signal	Condition	Typical value	Oscilloscope setting★	Wave form
AC control module – ATC	40			1		
	41			1		
AC control module – engine RPM signal – ATC	37	⟹	Engine idling	28 Hz		
AC/heater function control panel – MTC	40			1		
Accelerator pedal position (APP) sensor	33	⌐⌐	Ignition ON	0 V		
	34	⟸	Ignition ON – accelerator pedal released	0,4 V		
	34	⟸	Ignition ON – accelerator pedal depressed	2 V		
	35	⟸	Ignition ON – accelerator pedal released	0,8 V		
	35	⟸	Ignition ON – accelerator pedal depressed	4,1 V		
	36	⌐⌐	Ignition ON	0 V		
	72	⟹	Ignition ON	5 V		
	73	⟹	Ignition ON	5 V		
Alternator	28	⟹	Engine idling		1 V/10 ms	⩗⩗ 89
Battery	3	⟸	Ignition OFF	11-14 V		
Brake pedal position (BPP) switch	55	⟸	Ignition ON – brake pedal released	11-14 V		
	55	⟸	Ignition ON – brake pedal depressed	0 V		
	56	⟸	Ignition ON – brake pedal released	0 V		
	56	⟸	Ignition ON – brake pedal depressed	11-14 V		
Camshaft position (CMP) sensor	86	⟸	Ignition ON	0 or 5 V		
	86	⟸	Engine idling		2 V/50 ms	⩗⩗ 69
	98	⟹	Ignition ON	5 V		
	108	⌐⌐	Ignition ON	0 V		
CAN data bus – high	60	⟸⟹		1		
CAN data bus – low	58	⟸⟹		1		
Clutch pedal position (CPP) switch	39	⟸	Ignition ON – clutch pedal released	11-14 V		
	39	⟸	Ignition ON – clutch pedal depressed	0 V		

★ Suggested settings - Voltage/time per division

Component/circuit description	ECM pin	Signal	Condition	Typical value	Oscilloscope setting*	Wave form
Crankshaft position (CKP) sensor	82	←	Engine idling		5 V/1 ms	5
	87	⇒	Ignition ON	5 V		
	108	⊣−	Ignition ON	0 V		
Cruise control master switch	38			1		
	57	←		1		
Cruise control selector switch	38			1		
	75	←		1		
	76	←		1		
Earth	1		Ignition ON	0 V		
	2		Ignition ON	0 V		
Engine coolant blower motor control module	61			1		
Engine coolant blower motor control module – MTC	41			1		
Engine coolant temperature (ECT) sensor	93	←	Ignition ON – coolant temp. 20°C	2,2 V		
	93	←	Ignition ON – coolant temp. 80°C	0,5 V		
Evaporative emission (EVAP) canister purge valve	64	⊣⊳	Ignition ON	11-14 V briefly then 0-1 V		
	64	⊣⊳	Engine running – engine hot – valve operating		10 V/20 ms	20
Exhaust gas recirculation (EGR) valve actuator	114	⊣⊳	Ignition ON	11-14 V		
	114	⊣⊳	Engine idling		5 V/1 ms	Intermittent 53
Exhaust gas recirculation (EGR) valve position sensor	98	⇒	Ignition ON	5 V		
	100	←	Ignition ON	0,92 V		
	100	←	Engine idling	0,95 V		
	108	⊣−	Ignition ON	0 V		
Fuel pump (FP) relay	65	⊣⊳	Ignition ON	0-1 V briefly then 11-14 V		
	65	⊣⊳	Engine idling	0-1 V		
Heated oxygen sensor (HO2S) 1	51	←	Engine idling	3,79 V		
	51 (70)	←	Engine idling	0,46 V		
	52	←⇒	Engine idling	3,94 V		
	70	←	Engine idling	4,25 V		
	70 (51)	←	Engine idling	0,46 V		
	71	←⇒	Engine idling	8,24 V		
Heated oxygen sensor (HO2S) 1 – heater control	5	⊣⊳	Engine idling – engine hot		2 V/10 ms	65
Heated oxygen sensor (HO2S) 2	68	⊣−	Ignition ON	0 V		
	69	←	Engine idling – engine hot	0,6 V		
Heated oxygen sensor (HO2S) 2 – heater control	63	⊣⊳	Ignition ON	11-14 V briefly then 0-1 V		
	63	⊣⊳	Engine idling – engine hot		2 V/5 ms	65
Ignition coil 1	102	⇒	Ignition ON	0 V		
	102	⇒	Engine idling		2 V/20 ms	62
Ignition coil 2	103	⇒	Ignition ON	0 V		
	103	⇒	Engine idling		2 V/20 ms	62
Ignition coil 3	94	⇒	Ignition ON	0 V		
	94	⇒	Engine idling		2 V/20 ms	62
Ignition coil 4	95	⇒	Ignition ON	0 V		
	95	⇒	Engine idling		2 V/20 ms	62
Ignition switch	4	←	Ignition OFF	0 V		
	4	←	Ignition ON	11-14 V		

* Suggested settings - Voltage/time per division

Component/circuit description	ECM pin	Signal	Condition	Typical value	Oscilloscope setting*	Wave form
Injector 1	96	⅃⊸▷	Ignition ON	11-14 V briefly then 0-1 V		
	96	⅃⊸▷	Engine idling	2,5 ms	10 V/2 ms	∿∿ 35
Injector 2	97	⅃⊸▷	Ignition ON	11-14 V briefly then 0-1 V		
	97	⅃⊸▷	Engine idling	2,5 ms	10 V/2 ms	∿∿ 35
Injector 3	88	⅃⊸▷	Ignition ON	11-14 V briefly then 0-1 V		
	88	⅃⊸▷	Engine idling	2,5 ms	10 V/2 ms	∿∿ 35
Injector 4	89	⅃⊸▷	Ignition ON	11-14 V briefly then 0-1 V		
	89	⅃⊸▷	Engine idling	2,5 ms	10 V/2 ms	∿∿ 35
Instrumentation control module – diagnosis signal	43			1		
Instrumentation control module – engine RPM signal	37	⇨	Engine idling	28 Hz		
Instrumentation control module – vehicle speed signal	54	⬅		1		
Intake air temperature (IAT) sensor	85	⬅	Ignition ON – air temp. 20°C	2,4 V		
	108	⅃⊣	Ignition ON	0 V		
Knock sensor (KS)	99	⅃⊣	Engine idling	0 V		
	106	⬅	Engine idling – accelerate briefly		50 mV/1 ms	∿∿ 38
Manifold absolute pressure (MAP) sensor	98	⇨	Ignition ON	5 V		
	108	⅃⊣	Ignition ON	0 V		
	109	⬅	Ignition ON	4 V		
	109	⬅	Engine idling	0,8 V		
	109	⬅	Engine running – full throttle briefly	4,3 V		
Spare cable	66			1		
Throttle motor	117	⇨	Ignition ON	11-14 V for 30 seconds then 3 V		
	117	⇨	Ignition ON – accelerator pedal released		2 V/2 ms	(30 seconds only) ∿∿ 64
	118	⇨	Ignition ON	11-14 V for 30 seconds then 3 V		
	118	⇨	Ignition ON – accelerator pedal released		2 V/2 ms	(30 seconds only) ∿∿ 64
Throttle motor position sensor	83	⇨	Ignition ON	5 V		
	84	⬅	Ignition ON – accelerator pedal released	4,3 V		
	91	⅃⊣	Ignition ON	0 V		
	92	⬅	Ignition ON – accelerator pedal released	0,7 V		

*Suggested settings - Voltage/time per division

1 Connected pin - no test data available or random digital signal

ECM harness multi-plug

Terminal side

AD81718

Wire side

AD42119

Component/circuit description	ECM pin	Signal	Condition	Typical value	Oscilloscope setting*	Wave form
Accelerator pedal position (APP) sensor	15	←	Ignition ON – accelerator pedal released	0,4 V		
	15	←	Ignition ON – accelerator pedal fully depressed	3 V		
	55	⌐	Ignition ON	0 V		
	57	⇨	Ignition ON	5 V		
Accelerator pedal position (APP) switch	33	⌐	Ignition ON	0 V		
	65	←	Ignition ON – accelerator pedal released	0 V		
	65	←	Ignition ON – accelerator pedal depressed	2,8 V		
AC compressor clutch cut-off relay – except AFN/AHU 05/98→ & AVG	28			1		
	37	←	Engine idling – AC OFF	0 V		
	37	←	Engine idling – AC ON	11-14 V		
AC control module – AFN/AHU 05/98→ & AVG	28			1		
	37	←	Engine idling – AC OFF	0 V		
	37	←	Engine idling – AC ON	11-14 V		
Alternator – AHU 09/97→ some models	39			1		
Brake pedal position (BPP) switch 1	44	←	Ignition OFF – brake pedal released	0 V		
	44	←	Ignition OFF – brake pedal depressed	11-14 V		
Brake pedal position (BPP) switch 2	20	←	Ignition ON – brake pedal released	0 V		
	20	←	Ignition ON – brake pedal depressed	11-14 V		
	33	⌐	Ignition ON	0 V		
Clutch pedal position (CPP) switch	17	←	Ignition ON – clutch pedal released	0 V		
	17	←	Ignition ON – clutch pedal depressed	11-14 V		
	33	⌐	Ignition ON	0 V		
Crankshaft position (CKP) sensor	8	←	Engine idling	3,6 V ac		
	8	←	Engine idling		5 V/5 ms	∿ 6
	33	⌐	Engine idling	0 V		
Cruise control master switch	35			1		
	66			1		

* Suggested settings - Voltage/time per division

Component/circuit description	ECM pin	Signal	Condition	Typical value	Oscilloscope setting*	Wave form
Cruise control selector switch	34			1		
	58			1		
	66			1		
Earth	1		Ignition ON	0 V		
	24		Ignition ON	0 V		
	46		Ignition ON	0 V		
Earth – except 1Z/AHU →08/97	39		Ignition ON	0 V		
Engine control (EC) relay	23	←	Ignition OFF	0 V		
	23	←	Ignition ON	11-14 V		
	42	⌐▷	Ignition OFF	11-14 V		
	42	⌐▷	Ignition ON	0-1 V		
	45	←	Ignition OFF	0 V		
	45	←	Ignition ON	11-14 V		
	68	←	Ignition OFF	0 V		
	68	←	Ignition ON	11-14 V		
Engine coolant blower motor run-on relay – AFN/AVG 05/98→	3	⌐▷	Engine idling	11-14 V		
	3	⌐▷	Ignition OFF – coolant blower motor ON	0-1 V		
Engine coolant heater relay, high output – if fitted	26	⌐▷	Engine idling – relay contacts open	11-14 V		
	26	⌐▷	Engine idling – relay contacts closed	0-1 V		
Engine coolant heater relay, low output – if fitted	6	⌐▷	Engine idling – relay contacts open	11-14 V		
	6	⌐▷	Engine idling – relay contacts closed	0-1 V		
Engine coolant temperature (ECT) sensor	14	←	Ignition ON – coolant temp. 20°C	3,5 V		
	14	←	Ignition ON – coolant temp. 80°C	1,4 V		
	33	⌐	Ignition ON	0 V		
Exhaust gas recirculation (EGR) solenoid	25	⌐▷	Ignition ON	11-14 V		
	25	⌐▷	Engine running – valve operating		5 V/1 ms	2
Fuel injection timing solenoid	51	⌐▷	Ignition ON	0,8 V then 11-14 V		
	51	⌐▷	Engine idling		2 V/10 ms	10
Fuel quantity adjuster	4	⌐▷	Ignition ON	9,3 V then 11-14 V		
	4	⌐▷	Engine idling		2 V/2 ms	5
	5	⌐▷	Ignition ON	9,3 V then 11-14 V		
	5	⌐▷	Engine idling		2 V/2 ms	5
	49	⌐▷	Ignition ON	9,3 V then 11-14 V		
	49	⌐▷	Engine idling		2 V/2 ms	5
Fuel quantity adjuster position sensor	7	⇒	Ignition ON	2,5 V		
	29	←	Ignition ON	2,5 V		
	29	←	Engine idling		0,5 V/0,1 ms	8
	52	←	Ignition ON	2,5 V		
	52	←	Engine idling		0,5 V/0,1 ms	8
Fuel shut-off solenoid – →04/98	53	⇒	Engine idling	11-14 V		
	53	⇒	Ignition ON	11-14 V then 0 V		
Fuel shut-off solenoid, through crash control module – 05/98→	53	⇒	Engine idling	11-14 V		
	53	⇒	Ignition ON	11-14 V then 0 V		
Fuel temperature sensor	33	⌐	Ignition ON	0 V		
	63	←	Ignition ON – fuel temp. 20°C	3,6 V		

★ Suggested settings - Voltage/time per division

Component/circuit description	ECM pin	Signal	Condition	Typical value	Oscilloscope setting*	Wave form
Glow plug relay	50		Ignition ON – glow plugs ON	0-1 V		
	50		Ignition ON – glow plugs OFF	11-14 V		
Glow plug warning lamp	48		Ignition ON – lamp ON	0-1 V		
	48		Ignition ON – lamp OFF	11-14 V		
Ignition switch	38		Ignition OFF	0 V		
	38		Ignition ON	11-14 V		
Immobilizer control module, immobilization/diagnosis signal	61		Ignition ON	11-14 V		
	61		Engine idling	11-14 V		
Injector needle lift sensor	11		Engine idling	0 V		
	12		Engine idling	0,014 V ac		
	12		Engine idling		0,2 V/1 ms	⌁ 7
Instrumentation control module	2			1		
	9			1		
Instrumentation control module, vehicle speed signal	43		Ignition ON – vehicle pushed	0 V or 5 V min. – switching		
Intake air temperature (IAT) sensor	33		Ignition ON	0 V		
	64		Ignition ON – air temp. 20°C	3,5 V		
Mass air flow (MAF) sensor	13		Ignition ON	0,3 V		
	13		Engine idling	1,5 V		
	19		Ignition ON	5 V		
Mass air flow (MAF) sensor – →08/97	33		Ignition ON	0 V		
Mass air flow (MAF) sensor – 09/97→	21		Ignition ON	0 V		
Transmission control module (TCM) – except 1Z & AFN/AHU →08/97	18			1		
	31			1		
	32			1		
Transmission kick-down switch	33		Ignition ON	0 V		
	62			1		
Turbocharger (TC) wastegate regulating valve	47		Ignition ON	11-14 V		
	47		Engine running – valve not operating	11-14 V		
	47		Engine running – valve operating	0-1 V		

*Suggested settings - Voltage/time per division

1 Connected pin - no test data available or random digital signal

Model:	Engine code:	Year:
Alhambra 1,9 TDI PD	ANU	1999-06
Alhambra 1,9 TDI PD	AUY	2000-06
Alhambra 1,9 TDI PD	ASZ	2002-06

SEAT

Bosch EDC 15P

ECM harness multi-plug

Terminal side

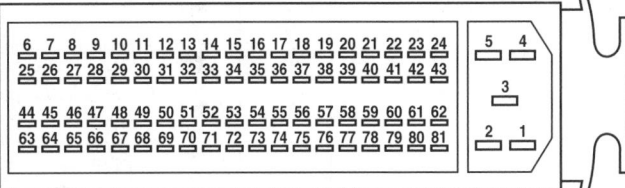

AD25036

Wire side

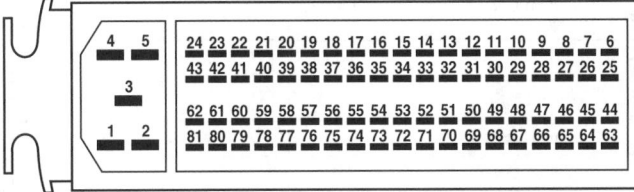

AD25035

Component/circuit description	ECM pin	Signal	Condition	Typical value	Oscilloscope setting*	Wave form
AC control module – except ASZ	34			1		
AC control module – →04/00	29			1		
AC refrigerant pressure sensor – ASZ	96	←		1		
Accelerator pedal position (APP) sensor	12	⇨	Ignition ON	5 V		
	50	⌐	Ignition ON	0 V		
	69	←	Ignition ON – accelerator pedal released	0,4 V		
	69	←	Ignition ON – accelerator pedal fully depressed	4,4 V		
Accelerator pedal position (APP) switch	51	⌐	Ignition ON	0 V		
	70	←	Ignition ON – accelerator pedal released	0,2 V		
	70	←	Ignition ON – accelerator pedal depressed	5 V		
Alternator, charging signal – 05/00→	38	⇨	Ignition ON		2 V/20 ms	〰 43
Brake pedal position (BPP) switch	32	←	Ignition OFF – brake pedal released	0 V		
	32	←	Ignition OFF – brake pedal depressed	11-14 V		
	65	←	Ignition ON – brake pedal released	11-14 V		
	65	←	Ignition ON – brake pedal depressed	0 V		
Camshaft position (CMP) sensor	101	⌐	Ignition ON	0 V		
	109	←	Engine idling		2 V/0,5 ms	〰 58
CAN data bus – high – 05/00→	7	⇄		1		
CAN data bus – low – 05/00→	6	⇄		1		
Clutch pedal position (CPP) switch	66	←	Ignition ON – clutch pedal released	11-14 V		
	66	←	Ignition ON – clutch pedal depressed	0 V		
Crankshaft position (CKP) sensor	102	←	Ignition ON	2,5 V		
	102	←	Engine idling	1,9 V ac		
	102	←	Engine idling		2 V/1 ms	〰 25
	110	←	Ignition ON	2,5 V		
	110	←	Engine idling	1,9 V ac		
	110	←	Engine idling		2 V/1 ms	Reversed 〰 25

* Suggested settings - Voltage/time per division

Component/circuit description	ECM pin	Signal	Condition	Typical value	Oscilloscope setting★	Wave form
Cruise control master switch	14	←	Ignition ON – selector switch set to 'OFF'	0 V		
	14	←	Ignition ON – selector switch set to 'ON'	11-14 V		
	44	←	Ignition ON – master switch released	0 V		
	44	←	Ignition ON – master switch depressed	11-14 V		
Cruise control selector switch	14	←	Ignition ON – selector switch set to 'OFF'	0 V		
	14	←	Ignition ON – selector switch set to 'ON'	11-14 V		
	45	←	Ignition ON – selector switch set to 'ON'	0 V		
	45	←	Ignition ON – selector switch set to 'RES'	11-14 V		
	46	←	Ignition ON – selector switch set to 'OFF'	0 V		
	46	←	Ignition ON – selector switch set to 'ON'	11-14 V		
Data link connector (DLC)	6	⬌		1		
	7	⬌		1		
Earth	4		Ignition ON	0 V		
	5		Ignition ON	0 V		
Engine control (EC) relay	1	←	Ignition OFF	0 V		
	1	←	Ignition ON	11-14 V		
	2	←	Ignition OFF	0 V		
	2	←	Ignition ON	11-14 V		
	18	⊐▷	Ignition OFF	11-14 V		
	18	⊐▷	Ignition ON	0-1 V		
Engine coolant blower motor – ASZ	11			1		
Engine coolant blower motor control module – 05/00→	29			1		
Engine coolant blower motor control module – 05/00→, except ASZ	11			1		
Engine coolant pump relay – ASZ	41			1		
Engine coolant temperature (ECT) sensor	104	⊐—	Ignition ON	0 V		
	112	←	Ignition ON – coolant temp. 10°C	4 V		
	112	←	Ignition ON – coolant temp. 80°C	1,2 V		
Exhaust gas recirculation (EGR) solenoid	61	⊐▷	Ignition ON	11-14 V		
	61	⊐▷	Engine idling		5 V/1 ms	〰〰 2
Fuel lift pump relay – 05/00→	80	⊐▷	Ignition ON	0-1 V briefly then 11-14 V		
	80	⊐▷	Engine idling	0-1 V		
Fuel temperature sensor	103	⊐—	Ignition ON	0 V		
	111	←	Ignition ON – fuel temp. 5°C	4,6 V		
Glow plug relay	42	⊐▷	Ignition ON – glow plugs ON	0-1 V		
	42	⊐▷	Ignition ON – glow plugs OFF	11-14 V		
Glow plug warning lamp – →04/00	40	⊐▷	Ignition ON – warning lamp ON	0-1 V		
	40	⊐▷	Ignition ON – warning lamp OFF	11-14 V		
Ignition auxiliary circuits relay – 05/00→	88	←	Ignition OFF	0 V		
	88	←	Ignition ON	11-14 V		
	88	←	Engine cranking	0 V		
	88	←	Engine idling	11-14 V		
Ignition switch	37	←	Ignition OFF	0 V		
	37	←	Ignition ON	11-14 V		
	37	←	Engine cranking	11-14 V		
	37	←	Engine idling	11-14 V		

★ Suggested settings - Voltage/time per division

Component/circuit description	ECM pin	Signal	Condition	Typical value	Oscilloscope setting*	Wave form
Immobilizer control module	16	⬅➡		1		
Injector 1	114	➡	Ignition ON	0,3 V		
	116	➡	Ignition ON	0,3 V		
	116 (114)	➡	Engine idling	2,2 ms		
	116 (114)	➡	Engine idling		10 V/0,5 ms	⎍ 57
Injector 2	114	➡	Ignition ON	0,3 V		
	117	➡	Ignition ON	0,3 V		
	117 (114)	➡	Engine idling	2,2 ms		
	117 (114)	➡	Engine idling		10 V/0,5 ms	⎍ 57
Injector 3	114	➡	Ignition ON	0,3 V		
	118	➡	Ignition ON	0,3 V		
	118 (114)	➡	Engine idling	2,2 ms		
	118 (114)	➡	Engine idling		10 V/0,5 ms	⎍ 57
Injector 4	114	➡	Ignition ON	0,3 V		
	121	➡	Ignition ON	0,3 V		
	121 (114)	➡	Engine idling	2,2 ms		
	121 (114)	➡	Engine idling		10 V/0,5 ms	⎍ 57
Instrumentation control module	27			1		
	28			1		
Instrumentation control module – vehicle speed signal	20	⬅	Ignition ON – vehicle pushed	0 V or 10 V min. (switching)		
Intake air temperature (IAT) sensor	52	⌐–	Ignition ON	0 V		
	73	⬅	Ignition ON – air temp. 10°C	3 V		
Intake manifold air control solenoid	81	⌐➡	Ignition ON	11-14 V		
	81	⌐➡	Engine idling	11-14 V		
	81	⌐➡	Engine idling – switch ignition OFF	0-1 V for 2,5 secs., 11-14 V for 0,5 sec., then 0-1 V		
Mass air flow (MAF) sensor	30	➡	Ignition ON	5 V		
	49	⌐–	Ignition ON	0 V		
	68	⬅	Ignition ON	1 V		
	68	⬅	Engine idling	1,5-2,1 V		
	68	⬅	3000 rpm	3,2 V		
Transmission kick-down switch	51	⌐–	Ignition ON	0 V		
	63	⬅	Ignition ON – accelerator pedal released	5 V		
	63	⬅	Ignition ON – accelerator pedal fully depressed	0 V		
Turbocharger (TC) boost pressure sensor	31	➡	Ignition ON	5 V		
	52	⌐–	Ignition ON	0 V		
	71	⬅	Ignition ON	1,6 V		
	71	⬅	Engine idling	1,7 V		
Turbocharger (TC) wastegate regulating valve	62	⌐➡	Ignition ON	11-14 V		
	62	⌐➡	Engine idling	11-14 V		
	62	⌐➡	Engine idling – accelerator pedal briefly fully depressed	0-1 V briefly		
	62	⌐➡	Engine running – valve not operating	11-14 V		
	62	⌐➡	Engine running – valve operating	0-1 V		

*Suggested settings - Voltage/time per division

1 Connected pin - no test data available or random digital signal

SKODA
Siemens Simos 3PD

Model:	Engine code:	Year:
Fabia 1,2	AWY	2002-04

ECM harness multi-plug

Terminal side

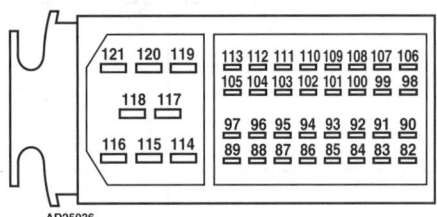 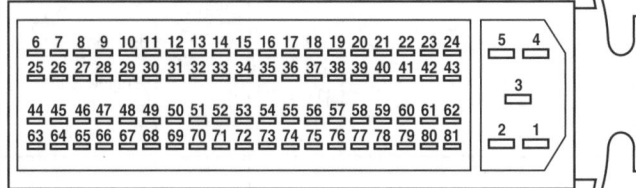

AD25036

Wire side

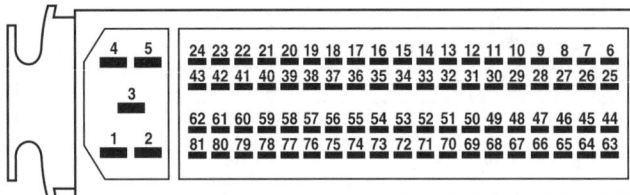 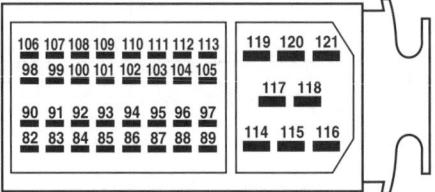

AD25035

Component/circuit description	ECM pin	Signal	Condition	Typical value	Oscilloscope setting*	Wave form
Accelerator pedal position (APP) sensor	18	⇨	Ignition ON	5 V		
	19	⇨	Ignition ON	5 V		
	45	⌐	Ignition ON	0 V		
	50	⌐	Ignition ON	0 V		
	51	⟵	Ignition ON – accelerator pedal released	0,7 V		
	51	⟵	Ignition ON – accelerator pedal fully depressed	4,1 V		
	64	⟵	Ignition ON – accelerator pedal released	0,4 V		
	64	⟵	Ignition ON – accelerator pedal fully depressed	2 V		
Alternator	13	⇨		①		
Brake pedal position (BPP) switch	53	⟵	Ignition ON – brake pedal released	0 V		
	53	⟵	Ignition ON – brake pedal depressed	11-14 V		
	63	⟵	Ignition ON – brake pedal released	11-14 V		
	63	⟵	Ignition ON – brake pedal depressed	0 V		
Camshaft position (CMP) sensor	89	⇨	Ignition ON	5 V		
	105	⟵	Ignition ON	0 or 5 V		
	105	⟵	Engine idling		2 V/0,1 sec.	⑷
	111	⌐	Ignition ON	0 V		
CAN data bus – high	20	⬌		①		
CAN data bus – low	21	⬌		①		
Clutch pedal position (CPP) switch	65	⟵	Ignition ON – clutch pedal released	11-14 V		
	65	⟵	Ignition ON – clutch pedal depressed	0 V		

* Suggested settings - Voltage/time per division

Component/circuit description	ECM pin	Signal	Condition	Typical value	Oscilloscope setting*	Wave form
Crankshaft position (CKP) sensor	89	⇨	Ignition ON	5 V		
	99	⌐⌐	Ignition ON	0 V		
	106	⬅	Engine idling		2 V/2 ms	∿∿104
Cruise control master switch – if fitted	69			1		
	28			1		
Cruise control selector switch – if fitted	69			1		
	28			1		
Data link connector (DLC) – diagnosis signal	17	⬌		1		
Diagnostic module – diagnosis signal	17	⬌		1		
Earth	1		Ignition ON	0 V		
	2		Ignition ON	0 V		
Engine control (EC) relay	3	⬅	Ignition OFF	0 V		
	3	⬅	Ignition ON	11-14 V		
Engine coolant temperature (ECT) sensor	83	⌐⌐	Ignition ON	0 V		
	104	⬅	Ignition ON – coolant temp. 20°C	2,2 V		
	104	⬅	Ignition ON – coolant temp. 80°C	0,5 V		
Evaporative emission (EVAP) canister purge valve	61	⌐⇨	Ignition ON	11-14 V briefly then 0 V		
	61	⌐⇨	Engine running – engine hot – valve operating		10 V/20 ms	Intermittent ∿∿20
Fuel pump (FP) relay	80	⌐⇨	Ignition ON	0-1 V briefly then 11-14 V		
	80	⌐⇨	Engine idling	0-1 V		
Heated oxygen sensor (HO2S) 1	14	⬅	Engine idling – engine hot	0,1-1 V fluctuating	0,2 V/2 ms	∿∿21
	31	⌐⌐	Engine idling	0 V		
Heated oxygen sensor (HO2S) 1 – heater control	4	⌐⇨	Ignition ON	11-14 V briefly then 0 V		
	4	⌐⇨	Engine idling – engine hot		0-1 V	
Heated oxygen sensor (HO2S) 2	16	⬅	Engine idling – engine hot	0,6 V		
	35	⌐⌐	Ignition ON	0 V		
Heated oxygen sensor (HO2S) 2 – heater control	5	⌐⇨	Ignition ON	11-14 V briefly then 0 V		
	5	⌐⇨	Engine idling – engine hot	0-1 V		
Ignition amplifier – cylinder 1	112	⇨	Ignition ON	0 V		
	112	⇨	Engine idling		2 V/5 ms	∿∿62
	120	⌐⌐	Ignition ON	0 V		
Ignition amplifier – cylinder 2	113	⇨	Ignition ON	0 V		
	113	⇨	Engine idling		2 V/5 ms	∿∿62
	120	⌐⌐	Ignition ON	0 V		
Ignition amplifier – cylinder 3	100	⇨	Ignition ON	0 V		
	100	⇨	Engine idling		2 V/5 ms	∿∿62
	120	⌐⌐	Ignition ON	0 V		
Ignition switch	62	⬅	Ignition OFF	0 V		
	62	⬅	Ignition ON	11-14 V		

* Suggested settings - Voltage/time per division

Component/circuit description	ECM pin	Signal	Condition	Typical value	Oscilloscope setting*	Wave form
Ignition switch – through engine control (EC) relay	23	⬅	Ignition OFF	0 V		
	23	⬅	Ignition ON	11-14 V		
Injector 1	88	⇥▷	Ignition ON	11-14 V briefly then 0 V		
	88	⇥▷	Engine idling	3,2 ms	10 V/2 ms	ᴧᴧᴠᴠᴠ 35
Injector 2	87	⇥▷	Ignition ON	11-14 V briefly then 0 V		
	87	⇥▷	Engine idling	3,2 ms	10 V/2 ms	ᴧᴧᴠᴠᴠ 35
Injector 3	85	⇥▷	Ignition ON	11-14 V briefly then 0 V		
	85	⇥▷	Engine idling	3,2 ms	10 V/2 ms	ᴧᴧᴠᴠᴠ 35
Instrumentation control module – vehicle speed signal	9	⬅	Ignition ON – vehicle pushed	0 V or 10 V switching		
Intake air temperature (IAT) sensor	93	⬅	Ignition ON – air temp. 20°C	2 V		
	107	⇥⊢	Ignition ON	0 V		
Knock sensor (KS)	101	⇥⊢	Engine idling	0 V		
	109	⬅	Engine idling – accelerate briefly		50 mV/1 ms	ᴧᴧᴠᴠᴠ 38
Knock sensor (KS) – screened lead	102	⇥⊢	Ignition ON	0 V		
Manifold absolute pressure (MAP) sensor	95	⬅	Ignition ON	4 V		
	95	⬅	Engine idling	1 V		
	95	⬅	Engine running – full throttle briefly	4,1 V briefly		
	96	⇨	Ignition ON	5 V		
	107	⇥⊢	Ignition ON	0 V		
Throttle motor	119	⇨	Ignition ON – accelerator pedal released		2 V/2 ms	(30 seconds only) ᴧᴧᴠᴠᴠ 64
	121	⇨	Ignition ON – accelerator pedal released		2 V/2 ms	(30 seconds only) ᴧᴧᴠᴠᴠ 64
Throttle motor position sensor	90	⬅	Ignition ON – accelerator pedal released	0,9 V		
	90	⬅	Ignition ON – accelerator pedal fully depressed	4,4 V		
	91	⇥⊢	Ignition ON	0 V		
	92	⬅	Ignition ON – accelerator pedal released	4,1 V		
	92	⬅	Ignition ON – accelerator pedal fully depressed	0,7 V		
	97	⇨	Ignition ON	5 V		

*Suggested settings - Voltage/time per division

1 Connected pin - no test data available or random digital signal

ECM harness multi-plug

Terminal side

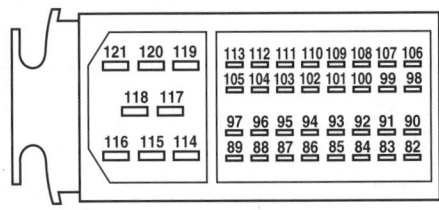

Wire side

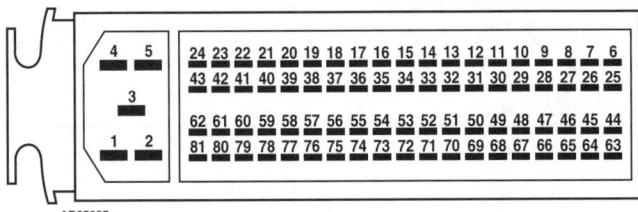

Component/circuit description	ECM pin	Signal	Condition	Typical value	Oscilloscope setting*	Wave form
Accelerator pedal position (APP) sensor	18	⇒	Ignition ON	5 V		
	19	⇒	Ignition ON	5 V		
	45	⌐	Ignition ON	0 V		
	50	⌐	Ignition ON	0 V		
	51	⟵	Ignition ON – accelerator pedal released	0,7 V		
	51	⟵	Ignition ON – accelerator pedal depressed	4,1 V		
	64	⟵	Ignition ON – accelerator pedal released	0,4 V		
	64	⟵	Ignition ON – accelerator pedal depressed	2 V		
Alternator	13	⇒		[1]		
Brake pedal position (BPP) switch	53	⟵	Ignition ON – brake pedal released	0 V		
	53	⟵	Ignition ON – brake pedal depressed	11-14 V		
	63	⟵	Ignition ON – brake pedal released	11-14 V		
	63	⟵	Ignition ON – brake pedal depressed	0 V		
Camshaft position (CMP) sensor	83	⌐	Ignition ON	0 V		
	96	⇒	Ignition ON	5 V		
	105	⟵	Ignition ON	0 or 5 V		
	105	⟵	Engine idling		2 V/0,1 sec.	∿ 4
CAN data bus – high	20	⟺		[1]		
CAN data bus – low	21	⟺		[1]		
Clutch pedal position (CPP) switch	65	⟵	Ignition ON – clutch pedal released	11-14 V		
	65	⟵	Ignition ON – clutch pedal depressed	0 V		
Crankshaft position (CKP) sensor	89	⇒	Ignition ON	5 V		
	99	⌐	Ignition ON	0 V		
	106	⟵	Engine idling		2 V/2 ms	∿ 104
Cruise control master switch	28			[1]		

* Suggested settings - Voltage/time per division

Component/circuit description	ECM pin	Signal	Condition	Typical value	Oscilloscope setting*	Wave form
Cruise control selector switch	28			[1]		
Data link connector (DLC) – diagnosis signal	17			[1]		
Diagnostic module – diagnosis signal	17			[1]		
Earth	1		Ignition ON	0 V		
	2		Ignition ON	0 V		
Engine control (EC) relay	3	←	Ignition OFF	0 V		
	3	←	Ignition ON	11-14 V		
Engine coolant temperature (ECT) sensor	83	⌐—	Ignition ON	0 V		
	104	←	Ignition ON – coolant temp. 20°C	2,2 V		
	104	←	Ignition ON – coolant temp. 80°C	0,5 V		
Evaporative emission (EVAP) canister purge valve	61	⊐▷	Ignition ON	11-14 V briefly then 0-1 V		
	61	⊐▷	Engine running – engine hot – valve operating		10 V/20 ms	Intermittent ⩘⩘ 20
Exhaust gas recirculation (EGR) valve actuator	115	⊐▷	Ignition ON	11-14 V		
	115	⊐▷	Engine idling		5 V/1 ms	Intermittent ⩘⩘ 53
Exhaust gas recirculation (EGR) valve position sensor	84	⌐—	Ignition ON	0 V		
	96	⇨	Ignition ON	5 V		
	108	←	Ignition ON	0,8 V		
	108	←	Engine idling	0,8 V		
Fuel pump (FP) relay	80	⊐▷	Ignition ON	0-1 V briefly then 11-14 V		
	80	⊐▷	Engine idling	0-1 V		
Heated oxygen sensor (HO2S) 1	14	←	Engine idling	2,9 V		
	14 (34)	←	Engine idling	0,45 V		
	15	◄⇨	Engine idling	2,34-2,55 V		
	33	◄⇨	Engine idling	2,34-2,55 V		
	34	←	Engine idling	2,5 V		
	34 (14)	←	Engine idling	0,45 V		
Heated oxygen sensor (HO2S) 1 – heater control	4	⊐▷	Ignition ON	11-14 V briefly then 0-1 V		
	4	⊐▷	Engine idling – engine hot		2 V/0,1 sec.	⩘⩘ 72
Heated oxygen sensor (HO2S) 2	16	←	Engine idling – engine hot	0,6 V		
	35	⌐—	Ignition ON	0 V		
Heated oxygen sensor (HO2S) 2 – heater control	5	⊐▷	Ignition ON	11-14 V briefly then 0-1 V		
	5	⊐▷	Engine idling – engine hot	0,2 V		
Ignition coil 1	112	⇨	Ignition ON	0 V		
	112	⇨	Engine idling		2 V/5 ms	⩘⩘ 62
Ignition coil 2	113	⇨	Ignition ON	0 V		
	113	⇨	Engine idling		2 V/5 ms	⩘⩘ 62
Ignition coil 3	100	⇨	Ignition ON	0 V		
	100	⇨	Engine idling		2 V/5 ms	⩘⩘ 62
Ignition switch	55	←	Ignition OFF	0 V		
	55	←	Ignition ON	0 V		
	55	←	Engine cranking	9 V		
	62	←	Ignition OFF	0 V		
	62	←	Ignition ON	11-14 V		
Ignition switch – through engine control (EC) relay	23	←	Ignition OFF	0 V		
	23	←	Ignition ON	11-14 V		

* Suggested settings - Voltage/time per division

Component/circuit description	ECM pin	Signal	Condition	Typical value	Oscilloscope setting*	Wave form
Injector 1	88	⌐▷	Ignition ON	11-14 V briefly then 0-1 V		
	88	⌐▷	Engine idling	3,4 ms	10 V/2 ms	〰 35
Injector 2	87	⌐▷	Ignition ON	11-14 V briefly then 0-1 V		
	87	⌐▷	Engine idling	3,4 ms	10 V/2 ms	〰 35
Injector 3	85	⌐▷	Ignition ON	11-14 V briefly then 0-1 V		
	85	⌐▷	Engine idling	3,4 ms	10 V/2 ms	〰 35
Instrumentation control module – vehicle speed signal	9	⬅		[1]		
Intake air temperature (IAT) sensor	83	⌐	Ignition ON	0 V		
	93	⬅	Ignition ON – air temp. 20°C	2 V		
Knock sensor (KS)	101	⌐	Engine idling	0 V		
	109	⬅	Engine idling – accelerate briefly		50 mV/1 ms	〰 38
Knock sensor (KS) – screened lead	102	⌐	Engine idling	0 V		
Manifold absolute pressure (MAP) sensor	83	⌐	Ignition ON	0 V		
	95	⬅	Ignition ON	4 V		
	95	⬅	Engine idling	1 V		
	95	⬅	Engine running – full throttle briefly	4,1 V		
	96	⇨	Ignition ON	5 V		
Multifunction control module	28			[1]		
Throttle motor	119	⇨	Ignition ON – accelerator pedal released		2 V/2 ms	(30 seconds only) 〰 64
	121	⇨	Ignition ON – accelerator pedal released		2 V/2 ms	(30 seconds only) 〰 64
Throttle motor position sensor	90	⬅	Ignition ON – accelerator pedal released	0,9 V		
	90	⬅	Ignition ON – accelerator pedal depressed	4,4 V		
	91	⌐	Ignition ON	0 V		
	92	⬅	Ignition ON – accelerator pedal released	4,1 V		
	92	⬅	Ignition ON – accelerator pedal depressed	0,7 V		
	97	⇨	Ignition ON	5 V		

*Suggested settings - Voltage/time per division

[1] Connected pin - no test data available or random digital signal

SKODA

Bosch EDC 15P

Model:	Engine code:	Year:
Fabia 1,9 TDI PD	ATD	2000-06
Fabia 1,9 TDI PD vRS	ASZ	2003-06
Octavia 1,9 TDI PD	ATD	2000-05
Octavia 1,9 TDI PD	ASZ	2003-05

ECM harness multi-plug

Terminal side

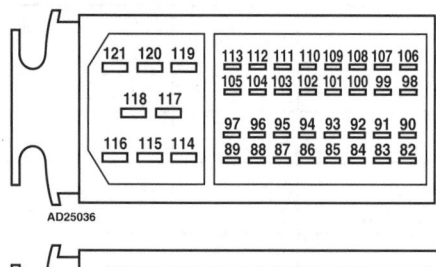

AD25036

Wire side

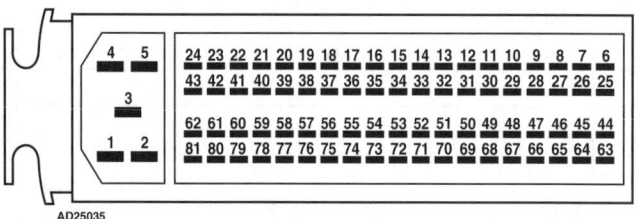

AD25035

Component/circuit description	ECM pin	Signal	Condition	Typical value	Oscilloscope setting*	Wave form
Accelerator pedal position (APP) sensor	12	⇒	Ignition ON	5 V		
	50	⌐	Ignition ON	0 V		
	69	⟵	Ignition ON – accelerator pedal released	0,4 V		
	69	⟵	Ignition ON – accelerator pedal fully depressed	4,4 V		
Accelerator pedal position (APP) switch	51	⌐	Ignition ON	0 V		
	70	⟵	Ignition ON – accelerator pedal released	0,2 V		
	70	⟵	Ignition ON – accelerator pedal depressed	5 V		
Air conditioning – Octavia	27			1		
	34			1		
Air conditioning/engine coolant blower motor control module – Octavia	29			1		
Alternator, charging signal	38	⇒	Ignition ON		2 V/20 ms	43
Auxiliary heater switch – Fabia without AC	15			1		
Brake pedal position (BPP) switch	32	⟵	Ignition OFF – brake pedal released	0 V		
	32	⟵	Ignition OFF – brake pedal depressed	11-14 V		
	65	⟵	Ignition ON – brake pedal released	11-14 V		
	65	⟵	Ignition ON – brake pedal depressed	0 V		
Camshaft position (CMP) sensor	101	⌐	Ignition ON	0 V		
	109	⟵	Engine idling		2 V/0,5 ms	58
CAN data bus – high	7	⟷		1		
CAN data bus – low	6	⟷		1		
Clutch pedal position (CPP) switch	66	⟵	Ignition ON – clutch pedal released	11-14 V		
	66	⟵	Ignition ON – clutch pedal depressed	0 V		

★ Suggested settings - Voltage/time per division

Component/circuit description	ECM pin	Signal	Condition	Typical value	Oscilloscope setting*	Wave form
Crankshaft position (CKP) sensor	102	←	Ignition ON	2,5 V		
	102	←	Engine idling	1,9 V ac		
	102	←	Engine idling		2 V/1 ms	⎍⎍ **25**
	102	←	3000 rpm	3,1 V		
	110	←	Ignition ON	2,5 V		
	110	←	Engine idling	1,9 V ac		
	110	←	Engine idling		2 V/1 ms	Reversed ⎍⎍ **25**
	110	←	3000 rpm	3,1 V		
Cruise control master switch	14	←	Ignition ON – selector switch set to 'OFF'	0 V		
	14	←	Ignition ON – selector switch set to 'ON'	11-14 V		
Cruise control master switch – Octavia	44	←	Ignition ON – master switch released	0 V		
	44	←	Ignition ON – master switch depressed	11-14 V		
Cruise control selector switch	14	←	Ignition ON – selector switch set to 'OFF'	0 V		
	14	←	Ignition ON – selector switch set to 'ON'	11-14 V		
Cruise control selector switch – Octavia	45	←	Ignition ON – selector switch set to 'ON'	0 V		
	45	←	Ignition ON – selector switch set to 'RES'	11-14 V		
	46	←	Ignition ON – selector switch set to 'OFF'	0 V		
	46	←	Ignition ON – selector switch set to 'ON'	11-14 V		
Data link connector (DLC) – Fabia	16	↔		1		
Earth	4		Ignition ON	0 V		
	5		Ignition ON	0 V		
Engine control (EC) relay	1	←	Ignition OFF	0 V		
	1	←	Ignition ON	11-14 V		
	2	←	Ignition OFF	0 V		
	2	←	Ignition ON	11-14 V		
	18	⊐▷	Ignition OFF	11-14 V		
	18	⊐▷	Ignition ON	0-1 V		
Engine coolant blower motor control module – Octavia with AC	11			1		
Engine coolant blower motor relay – Octavia without AC	11	⊐▷		1		
Engine coolant heater relay 1, low output – if fitted	21	⊐▷		1		
Engine coolant heater relay 2, high output – if fitted	22	⊐▷		1		
Engine coolant temperature (ECT) sensor	104	⊐⎯	Ignition ON	0 V		
	112	←	Ignition ON – coolant temp. 10°C	4 V		
	112	←	Ignition ON – coolant temp. 80°C	1,2 V		
Exhaust gas recirculation (EGR) solenoid	61	⊐▷	Ignition ON	11-14 V		
	61	⊐▷	Engine idling		5 V/1 ms	⎍⎍ **2**
Fuel lift pump relay	80	⊐▷	Ignition ON	0-1 V briefly then 11-14 V		
	80	⊐▷	Engine idling	0-1 V		
Fuel temperature sensor	103	⊐⎯	Ignition ON	0 V		
	111	←	Ignition ON – fuel temp. 5°C	4,6 V		
Glow plug relay	42	⊐▷	Ignition ON – glow plugs ON	0-1 V		
	42	⊐▷	Ignition ON – glow plugs OFF	11-14 V		

* Suggested settings - Voltage/time per division

Component/circuit description	ECM pin	Signal	Condition	Typical value	Oscilloscope setting*	Wave form
Ignition switch	37	←	Ignition OFF	0 V		
	37	←	Ignition ON	11-14 V		
	37	←	Engine cranking	11-14 V		
	37	←	Engine idling	11-14 V		
Ignition switch (auxiliary circuits) – Fabia, ASZ	88	←	Ignition OFF	0 V		
	88	←	Ignition ON	11-14 V		
	88	←	Engine idling	11-14 V		
Ignition switch (auxiliary circuits) – Octavia	88	←	Ignition OFF	0 V		
	88	←	Ignition ON	11-14 V		
	88	←	Engine cranking	0 V		
	88	←	Engine idling	11-14 V		
Injector 1	114	⇒	Ignition ON	0,3 V		
	116	⇒	Ignition ON	0,3 V		
	116 (114)	⇒	Engine idling	2,2 ms		
	116 (114)	⇒	Engine idling		10 V/0,5 ms	〰〰 57
Injector 2	114	⇒	Ignition ON	0,3 V		
	117	⇒	Ignition ON	0,3 V		
	117 (114)	⇒	Engine idling	2,2 ms		
	117 (114)	⇒	Engine idling		10 V/0,5 ms	〰〰 57
Injector 3	114	⇒	Ignition ON	0,3 V		
	118	⇒	Ignition ON	0,3 V		
	118 (114)	⇒	Engine idling	2,2 ms		
	118 (114)	⇒	Engine idling		10 V/0,5 ms	〰〰 57
Injector 4	114	⇒	Ignition ON	0,3 V		
	121	⇒	Ignition ON	0,3 V		
	121 (114)	⇒	Engine idling	2,2 ms		
	121 (114)	⇒	Engine idling		10 V/0,5 ms	〰〰 57
Instrumentation control module – diagnosis signal – Octavia	16	←⇒		1		
Instrumentation control module – vehicle speed signal	20	←	Ignition ON – vehicle pushed	0 V or 10 V min. (switching)		
Intake air temperature (IAT) sensor	52	⌐⎍	Ignition ON	0 V		
	73	←	Ignition ON – air temp. 10°C	3 V		
Intake manifold air control solenoid	81	⌐⊳	Ignition ON	11-14 V		
	81	⌐⊳	Engine idling	11-14 V		
	81	⌐⊳	Engine idling – switch ignition OFF	0-1 V for 2,5 secs., 11-14 V for 0,5 sec., then 0-1 V		
Mass air flow (MAF) sensor	30	⇒	Ignition ON	5 V		
	49	⌐⎍	Ignition ON	0 V		
	68	←	Ignition ON	1 V		
	68	←	Engine idling	1,5-2,1 V		
	68	←	3000 rpm	3,2 V		
Spare cable – Fabia, ATD 11/02→	88			1		

* Suggested settings - Voltage/time per division

Component/circuit description	ECM pin	Signal	Condition	Typical value	Oscilloscope setting*	Wave form
Spare cable – Octavia	28			1		
	33			1		
	40			1		
	47			1		
Transmission kick-down switch	51	⊐—	Ignition ON	0 V		
	63	⬅	Ignition ON – accelerator pedal released	5 V		
	63	⬅	Ignition ON – accelerator pedal fully depressed	0 V		
Turbocharger (TC) boost pressure sensor	31	⇨	Ignition ON	5 V		
	52	⊐—	Ignition ON	0 V		
	71	⬅	Ignition ON	1,6 V		
	71	⬅	Engine idling	1,7 V		
Turbocharger (TC) wastegate regulating valve	62	⊐▷	Ignition ON	11-14 V		
	62	⊐▷	Engine idling	11-14 V		
	62	⊐▷	Engine idling – accelerator pedal briefly fully depressed	0-1 V briefly		
	62	⊐▷	Engine running – valve not operating	11-14 V		
	62	⊐▷	Engine running – valve operating	0-1 V		

*Suggested settings - Voltage/time per division

1 Connected pin - no test data available or random digital signal

SKODA

Siemens Simos 2

Model:	Engine code:	Year:
Octavia 1,6	AEH/AKL	1997-05

ECM harness multi-plug

Terminal side

AD42344

Wire side

AD42345

Component/circuit description	ECM pin	Signal	Condition	Typical value	Oscilloscope setting*	Wave form
Air conditioning – 08/98→	11			1		
Air conditioning, AC ON signal	10	←		1		
Air conditioning, compressor ON/shut-off signal	8	←→		1		
Air conditioning, engine RPM signal – ATC	6	⇒	Engine idling	30 Hz		
	6	⇒	3000 rpm	100 Hz		
Battery	3	←	Ignition OFF	11-14 V		
Camshaft position (CMP) sensor	62	⇒	Ignition ON	5 V		
	76	←	Ignition ON – engine turned	0 V or 5 V switching		
	76	←	Engine idling		2 V/50 ms	⟋⟍ 45
Camshaft position (CMP) sensor – →07/97	67	⊣	Engine idling	0 V		
Camshaft position (CMP) sensor – 08/97→	70	⊣	Engine idling	0 V		
CAN data bus – 08/97→	29	←→		1		
	31	←→		1		
Closed throttle position (CTP) switch	69	←	Ignition ON – throttle closed	0 V		
	69	←	Ignition ON – throttle open	9 V min.		
Closed throttle position (CTP) switch – →07/97	67	⊣	Engine idling	0 V		
Closed throttle position (CTP) switch – 08/97→	70	⊣	Engine idling	0 V		
Clutch pedal position (CPP) switch – 08/97-07/98	21	←	Ignition ON	11-14 V briefly then 0 V		
	21	←	Engine idling – clutch pedal released	11-14 V		
	21	←	Engine idling – clutch pedal depressed	0 V		
Clutch pedal position (CPP) switch – 08/98→	21	←	Ignition ON – clutch pedal released	11-14 V		
	21	←	Ignition ON – clutch pedal depressed	0 V		
Crankshaft position (CKP) sensor	56	←	Engine idling	13,7 V ac	10 V/1 ms	⟋⟍ 2
	63	⊣	Engine idling	0 V		

* Suggested settings - Voltage/time per division

Autodata

Component/circuit description	ECM pin	Signal	Condition	Typical value	Oscilloscope setting*	Wave form
Crankshaft position (CKP) sensor – shield wire – 08/97→	70	⊣−	Engine idling	0 V		
Crankshaft position (CKP) sensor, shield wire – →07/97	67	⊣−	Engine idling	0 V		
Earth	2		Ignition ON	0 V		
Engine coolant temperature (ECT) sensor	53	⟵	Ignition ON – coolant temp. 15°C	2,1 V		
	53	⟵	Ignition ON – coolant temp. 80°C	0,4 V		
Engine coolant temperature (ECT) sensor – →07/97	67	⊣−	Engine idling	0 V		
Engine coolant temperature (ECT) sensor – 08/97→	70	⊣−	Engine idling	0 V		
Evaporative emission (EVAP) canister purge valve	15	⊣▷	Ignition ON	11-14 V briefly then 0 V		
	15	⊣▷	Engine idling – engine hot	10%	10 V/20 ms	59
Fuel pump relay	4	⊣▷	Ignition ON	0-1 V briefly then 11-14 V		
	4	⊣▷	Engine idling	0-1 V		
Heated oxygen sensor (HO2S)	25	⊣−	Engine idling	0 V		
	26	⟵	Engine idling – engine hot	0,1-1 V fluctuating	0,2 V/1 sec.	21
	27	⊣▷	Ignition ON	11-14 V briefly then 0 V		
	27	⊣▷	Engine idling	0-1 V		
Idle speed control (ISC) actuator	59	⟹	Ignition ON	11-14 V		
	66	⟹	Ignition ON	11-14 V		
	66	⟹	Engine idling	10-20%	2 V/2 ms	71
Idle speed control (ISC) actuator position sensor	62	⟹	Ignition ON	5 V		
	74	⟵	Ignition ON	3,8 V		
	74	⟵	Engine idling	3,8 V		
Idle speed control (ISC) actuator position sensor – →07/97	67	⊣−	Engine idling	0 V		
Idle speed control (ISC) actuator position sensor – 08/97→	70	⊣−	Engine idling	0 V		
Ignition amplifier	71	⟹	Engine idling		2 V/10 ms	32
	78	⟹	Engine idling		2 V/10 ms	32
Ignition switch	1	⟵	Ignition OFF	0 V		
	1	⟵	Ignition ON	11-14 V		
Ignition switch, start signal – MT	22	⟵	Engine cranking	8 V min.		
Injector 1	73	⊣▷	Ignition ON	11-14 V briefly then 0 V		
	73	⊣▷	Engine idling – engine hot	2-4,1 ms	10 V/2 ms	35
Injector 2	80	⊣▷	Ignition ON	11-14 V briefly then 0 V		
	80	⊣▷	Engine idling – engine hot	2-4,1 ms	10 V/2 ms	35
Injector 3	58	⊣▷	Ignition ON	11-14 V briefly then 0 V		
	58	⊣▷	Engine idling – engine hot	2-4,1 ms	10 V/2 ms	35
Injector 4	65	⊣▷	Ignition ON	11-14 V briefly then 0 V		
	65	⊣▷	Engine idling – engine hot	2-4,1 ms	10 V/2 ms	35

* Suggested settings - Voltage/time per division

Component/circuit description	ECM pin	Signal	Condition	Typical value	Oscilloscope setting*	Wave form
Instrumentation control module, engine RPM signal – →07/00	6	⇨	Engine idling	30 Hz		
	6	⇨	3000 rpm	100 Hz		
Instrumentation control module, fuel consumption signal – with digital multifunction display	18	⇨		1		
Instrumentation control module, immobilization/diagnosis signal	19	◆⇨		1		
Instrumentation control module, vehicle speed signal	20	⬅	Ignition ON – vehicle pushed	0 V or 11-14 V switching		
Intake air temperature (IAT) sensor – →07/97	54	⬅	Ignition ON – air temp. 15°C	1,5 V		
	67	⊣⊢	Engine idling	0 V		
Intake manifold air control solenoid	64	⊣▷	Ignition ON	11-14 V briefly then 0 V		
	64	⊣▷	Engine idling	11-14 V		
	64	⊣▷	Engine idling – full throttle briefly	0-1 V briefly then 11-14 V		
Knock sensor (KS)	67	⊣⊢	Engine idling	0 V		
	68	⬅	Engine idling – full throttle briefly		50 mV/1 ms	
Knock sensor (KS), shield wire	67	⊣⊢	Engine idling	0 V		
Mass air flow (MAF) sensor	12	⊣⊢	Engine idling	0 V		
	13	⬅	Engine idling	1 V		
	13	⬅	Engine idling – full throttle briefly	4,2 V		
Mass air flow (MAF) sensor, IAT signal – 08/97→	9	⬅	Ignition ON – air temp. 15°C	1,5 V		
Power steering pressure (PSP) switch – 08/97→	14			1		
	24			1		
Throttle position (TP) sensor	62	⇨	Ignition ON	5 V		
	75	⬅	Ignition ON – throttle closed	4,3 V		
	75	⬅	Ignition ON – throttle fully open	0,6 V		
Throttle position (TP) sensor – →07/97	67	⊣⊢	Engine idling	0 V		
Throttle position (TP) sensor – 08/97→	70	⊣⊢	Engine idling	0 V		
Transmission control module (TCM)	8	◆⇨		1		
Transmission control module (TCM), torque reduction signal – →07/97	23	⬅		1		
Transmission control module (TCM), TP signal – →07/97	7	⇨		1		
Transmission control module (TCM), engine RPM signal – →07/97	6	⇨	Engine idling	30 Hz		
	6	⇨	3000 rpm	100 Hz		

*Suggested settings - Voltage/time per division

1 Connected pin - no test data available or random digital signal

Model:		Engine code:	Year:
Octavia 1,8		AGN	1996-99
Octavia 1,8 Turbo		AGU	1998-05

SKODA
Bosch Motronic
M3.8.2/3/5

ECM harness multi-plug

Terminal side

AD42344

Wire side

AD42345

Component/circuit description	ECM pin	Signal	Condition	Typical value	Oscilloscope setting*	Wave form
AC control module, engine RPM signal	6	⇒	Ignition ON	0,26 V		
	6	⇒	Engine idling	41 Hz	4 V/10 ms	24
	6	⇒	3000 rpm	100 Hz		
Air conditioning, compressor clutch signal	8	←	Engine idling – AC OFF	0 V		
	8	←	Engine idling – AC ON, AC compressor OFF	0 V		
	8	←	Engine idling – AC ON, AC compressor ON	11-14 V		
Air conditioning, load signal	10	←	Engine idling – AC OFF	0 V		
	10	←	Engine idling – AC ON	11-14 V		
Barometric pressure (BARO) sensor – Turbo	61	←	Ignition ON – at sea level	4 V		
	61	←	Ignition ON – 1000 m above sea level	3 V		
	61	←	Ignition ON – 2000 m above sea level	2,1 V		
	62	⇒	Ignition ON	5 V		
	67	⊣⊢	Ignition ON	0 V		
Battery	3	←	Ignition ON	11-14 V		
Brake pedal position (BPP) switch – with cruise control	48	←	Ignition ON – brake pedal released	11-14 V		
	48	←	Ignition ON – brake pedal depressed	0 V		
Camshaft position (CMP) actuator – non-Turbo	55	⊣▷	Ignition ON	11-14 V briefly then 0 V		
	55	⊣▷	Engine idling	11-14 V		
	55	⊣▷	Engine idling – accelerate briefly	0,4 V briefly		
Camshaft position (CMP) sensor	62	⇒	Ignition ON	5 V		
	67	⊣⊢	Ignition ON	0 V		
Camshaft position (CMP) sensor – Motronic M3.8.2/3	76	←	Engine idling		5 V/20 ms	12
Camshaft position (CMP) sensor – Motronic M3.8.5	76	←	Engine idling		5 V/20 ms	14

* Suggested settings - Voltage/time per division

Component/circuit description	ECM pin	Signal	Condition	Typical value	Oscilloscope setting*	Wave form
CAN data bus – 08/97→	29	◆▷		1		
	41	◆▷		1		
Closed throttle position (CTP) switch	67	⌐	Ignition ON	0 V		
	69	◀	Ignition ON – throttle closed	0 V		
	69	◀	Ignition ON – throttle slightly open	11-14 V		
Crankshaft position (CKP) sensor	56	◀	Ignition ON	1,53 V		
	56	◀	Engine idling	3 V ac		
	56	◀	Engine idling		2 V/2 ms	∿ 2
	63	◀	Ignition ON	1,53 V		
	63	◀	Engine idling	3 V ac		
	63	◀	Engine idling		2 V/2 ms	Reversed ∿ 2
	67	⌐	Ignition ON	0 V		
Crankshaft position (CKP) sensor, shield wire	67	⌐	Ignition ON	0 V		
Clutch pedal position (CPP) switch – 08/97→	9	◀	Ignition ON – clutch pedal released	11-14 V briefly then 0 V		
	9	◀	Engine idling – clutch pedal released	11-14 V		
	9	◀	Engine idling – clutch pedal depressed	0 V		
Cruise control master switch	34			1		
	46			1		
Cruise control selector switch	35			1		
	36			1		
	46			1		
Data link connector (DLC), pin 13 – 08/97→	43			1		
Earth	2	⌐	Ignition ON	0 V		
Earth – MT →07/97	22	⌐	Ignition ON	0 V		
Engine coolant temperature (ECT) sensor	53	◀	Ignition ON – coolant temp. 12°C approx.	2,3 V		
	53	◀	Ignition ON – coolant temp. 85°C approx.	0,5 V		
	67	⌐	Ignition ON	0 V		
Evaporative emission (EVAP) canister purge valve	15	⌐▷	Ignition ON	11-14 V briefly then 0 V		
	15	⌐▷	Engine idling	11-14 V		
	15	⌐▷	Engine hot – valve operating		10 V/20 ms	∿ 20
Fuel pump relay	4	⌐▷	Ignition ON	0-1 V briefly then 11-14 V		
	4	⌐▷	Engine cranking	0,6 V		
	4	⌐▷	Engine idling	0,6 V		
Heated oxygen sensor (HO2S)	25	⌐	Ignition ON	0 V		
	26	◀	Ignition ON	0,68 V		
	26	◀	Engine running	0,1-0,9 V fluctuating	0,2 V/1 sec.	∿ 21
	27	⌐▷	Ignition ON	11-14 V briefly then 0 V		
	27	⌐▷	Engine idling	0,3 V		

* Suggested settings - Voltage/time per division

Component/circuit description	ECM pin	Signal	Condition	Typical value	Oscilloscope setting*	Wave form
Idle speed control (ISC) actuator	59	⇨	Ignition ON	8,4 V		
	59	⇨	Engine idling	60%		
	59	⇨	Engine idling		2 V/2 ms	⌇⌇ 64
	66	⇦	Ignition ON	11-14 V		
	66	⇦	Engine idling	0,1 V		
Idle speed control (ISC) actuator position sensor	62	⇨	Ignition ON	5 V		
	67	⌐	Ignition ON	0 V		
	74	⇦	Ignition ON	3,2 V		
	74	⇦	Engine idling	3,7 V		
Ignition amplifier	71	⇨	Ignition ON	0 V		
	71	⇨	Engine idling		1 V/20 ms	⌇⌇ 56
	78	⇨	Ignition ON	0 V		
	78	⇨	Engine idling		1 V/20 ms	⌇⌇ 56
Ignition amplifier – Turbo	70	⇨	Ignition ON	0 V		
	70	⇨	Engine idling		1 V/20 ms	⌇⌇ 56
	77	⇨	Ignition ON	0 V		
	77	⇨	Engine idling		1 V/20 ms	⌇⌇ 56
Ignition switch	1	⇦	Ignition OFF	0 V		
	1	⇦	Ignition ON	11-14 V		
Injector 1	73	⌐⇨	Ignition ON	11-14 V briefly then 0 V		
	73	⌐⇨	Engine idling	3,5 ms	10 V/2 ms	⌇⌇ 35
Injector 2	80	⌐⇨	Ignition ON	11-14 V briefly then 0 V		
	80	⌐⇨	Engine idling	3,5 ms	10 V/2 ms	⌇⌇ 35
Injector 3	58	⌐⇨	Ignition ON	11-14 V briefly then 0 V		
	58	⌐⇨	Engine idling	3,5 ms	10 V/2 ms	⌇⌇ 35
Injector 4	65	⌐⇨	Ignition ON	11-14 V briefly then 0 V		
	65	⌐⇨	Engine idling	3,5 ms	10 V/2 ms	⌇⌇ 35
Instrumentation control module, immobilization/diagnosis signal	19			[1]		
Instrumentation control module, fuel consumption signal – with digital multifunction display	18			[1]		
Instrumentation control module, engine RPM signal – →07/00	6	⇨	Ignition ON	0,26 V		
	6	⇨	Engine idling	41 Hz	4 V/10 ms	⌇⌇ 24
	6	⇨	3000 rpm	100 Hz		
Instrumentation control module – vehicle speed signal	20	⇦	Ignition ON – vehicle pushed	0 V or 11-14 V switching		
Intake air temperature (IAT) sensor – Turbo 08/97→	54	⇦	Ignition ON – air temp. 10°C	2 V		
	67	⌐	Ignition ON	0 V		

* Suggested settings - Voltage/time per division

Component/circuit description	ECM pin	Signal	Condition	Typical value	Oscilloscope setting*	Wave form
Intake manifold air control solenoid – non-Turbo 08/97→	64	⊐▷	Ignition ON	11-14 V briefly then 0 V		
	64	⊐▷	Engine idling	11-14 V		
	64	⊐▷	Engine idling – accelerate briefly	0,2 V briefly		
Knock sensor (KS) 1 – Turbo 08/98-04/99	60	⟵	Ignition ON	0 V		
	60	⟵	Engine idling – accelerate briefly		50 mV/1 ms	∿∿ 58
Knock sensor (KS) 1 – except Turbo 08/98-04/99	68	⟵	Ignition ON	0 V		
	68	⟵	Engine idling – accelerate briefly		50 mV/1 ms	∿∿ 58
Knock sensor (KS) 1 – shield wire	67	⊐—	Ignition ON	0 V		
Knock sensor (KS) 2 – except Turbo 08/98-04/99	60	⟵	Ignition ON	0 V		
	60	⟵	Engine idling – accelerate briefly		50 mV/1 ms	∿∿ 58
Knock sensor (KS) 2 – Turbo 08/98-04/99	68	⟵	Ignition ON	0 V		
	68	⟵	Engine idling – accelerate briefly		50 mV/1 ms	∿∿ 58
Knock sensor (KS) 2 – shield wire	67	⊐—	Ignition ON	0 V		
Mass air flow (MAF) sensor	12	⊐—	Ignition ON	0 V		
	13	⟵	Ignition ON	1 V briefly then 0 V		
	13	⟵	Engine idling	1,44 V		
	13	⟵	Engine idling – accelerate briefly	3,6 V briefly		
Mass air flow (MAF) sensor – non-Turbo 08/97→	11	⟹	Ignition ON	5 V		
Mass air flow (MAF) sensor, IAT signal – non-Turbo 08/97→	40	⟵	Ignition ON – air temp. 10°C approx.	2,4 V		
Power steering pressure (PSP) switch	14	⊐—	Ignition ON	0 V		
	49	⟵	Engine idling – steering wheel not turned	11-14 V		
	49	⟵	Engine idling – steering wheel turned	0 V		
Stop lamp switch – with cruise control	47	⟵	Ignition OFF – brake pedal released	0 V		
	47	⟵	Ignition OFF – brake pedal depressed	11-14 V		
Throttle position (TP) sensor	62	⟹	Ignition ON	5 V		
	67	⊐—	Ignition ON	0 V		
	75	⟵	Ignition ON – throttle closed	4,16 V		
	75	⟵	Ignition ON – throttle fully open	0,65 V		
Transmission control module (TCM) – →07/97	23				①	
	7				①	
Transmission control module (TCM), engine RPM signal – →07/97	6	⟹	Ignition ON	0,26 V		
	6	⟹	Engine idling	41 Hz	4 V/10 ms	∿∿ 24
	6	⟹	3000 rpm	100 Hz		
Turbocharger (TC) wastegate regulating valve	64	⊐▷	Ignition ON	11-14 V briefly then 0 V		
	64	⊐▷	Engine idling	11-14 V		
	64	⊐▷	Vehicle moving – accelerate, full load	1-99%		

*Suggested settings - Voltage/time per division

① Connected pin - no test data available or random digital signal

Model:	Engine code:	Year:
Octavia 2,0	AQY	1999-02
Octavia 2,0	APK/AEG	1999-05

ECM harness multi-plug

Terminal side

AD42344

Wire side

AD42345

Component/circuit description	ECM pin	Signal	Condition	Typical value	Oscilloscope setting*	Wave form
Air conditioning	8	←	Engine idling – AC OFF	0 V		
	8	←	Engine idling – AC ON – AC compressor ON	11-14 V		
	10	⇒	Engine idling – AC OFF	0 V		
	10	⇒	Engine idling – AC ON – AC compressor ON	11-14 V		
Battery	3	←	Ignition OFF	11-14 V		
Camshaft position (CMP) sensor	67	⊣⎓	Ignition ON	0 V		
	76	←	Engine idling		5 V/20 ms	∿ 14
Closed throttle position (CTP) switch	67	⊣⎓	Ignition ON	0 V		
	69	←	Ignition ON – throttle closed	0 V		
	69	←	Ignition ON – throttle open	11-14 V		
Crankshaft position (CKP) sensor	56	←	Engine idling	1,6 V ac	5 V/1 ms	∿ 2
	63	←	Engine idling	1,6 V ac	5 V/1 ms	Reversed ∿ 2
Crankshaft position (CKP) sensor – shield wire	67	⊣⎓	Ignition ON	0 V		
CAN data bus	29	◄⇒		1		
	41	◄⇒		1		
Data link connector (DLC)	43	◄⇒		1		
Digital multifunction display – some models	18			1		
Earth	2		Ignition ON	0 V		
Engine coolant temperature (ECT) sensor	53	←	Ignition ON – coolant temp. 20°C	2,2 V		
	53	←	Ignition ON – coolant temp. 90°C	0,36 V		
	67	⊣⎓	Ignition ON	0 V		
Evaporative emission (EVAP) canister purge valve	15	⊣⊳	Engine idling – engine hot – valve operating		10 V/20 ms	∿ 20
Fuel pump relay	4	⊣⊳	Ignition ON	0 V briefly then 11-14 V		
	4	⊣⊳	Engine idling	0-1 V		
Heated oxygen sensor (HO2S) 1	25	⊣⎓	Engine idling	0 V		
	26	←	Engine idling – engine hot	0,1-1 V fluctuating	0,2 V/2 ms	∿ 21
	27	⊣⊳	Engine idling	0,2 V		
Heated oxygen sensor (HO2S) 2	28	⊣⊳	Engine idling	0,2 V		
	51	⊣⎓	Engine idling	0 V		
	52	←	3000 rpm – engine hot	0,6 V		
Idle speed control (ISC) actuator	59	⇒	Engine idling		5 V/2 ms	∿ 28
	66	⇒	Engine idling	0,1 V		

* Suggested settings - Voltage/time per division

Component/circuit description	ECM pin	Signal	Condition	Typical value	Oscilloscope setting*	Wave form
Idle speed control (ISC) actuator position sensor	62	⇨	Ignition ON	5 V		
	67	⇥	Ignition ON	0 V		
	74	⇦	Engine idling	3,6-3,9 V		
Ignition amplifier	71	⇨	Ignition ON	0,15 V		
	71	⇨	Engine idling		1 V/20 ms	〰 32
	78	⇨	Ignition ON	0,15 V		
	78	⇨	Engine idling		1 V/20 ms	〰 32
Ignition switch	1	⇦	Ignition OFF	0 V		
	1	⇦	Ignition ON	11-14 V		
Injector 1	73	⇥▷	Engine idling	3,6 ms	10 V/2 ms	〰 35
Injector 2	80	⇥▷	Engine idling	3,6 ms	10 V/2 ms	〰 35
Injector 3	58	⇥▷	Engine idling	3,6 ms	10 V/2 ms	〰 35
Injector 4	65	⇥▷	Engine idling	3,6 ms	10 V/2 ms	〰 35
Instrumentation control module	21			1		
Instrumentation control module – engine RPM signal	6	⇨	Engine idling	26 Hz		
Immobilizer control module	19		Engine idling	11-14 V		
Instrumentation control module – vehicle speed signal	20	⇦	Ignition ON	10,5 V		
Knock sensor (KS) 1	60	⇦	Engine idling – accelerate briefly		50 mV/1 ms	〰 38
	67	⇥	Ignition ON	0 V		
Knock sensor (KS) 2	67	⇥	Ignition ON	0 V		
	68	⇦	Engine idling – accelerate briefly		50 mV/1 ms	〰 38
Knock sensor (KS) 1 – shield wire	67	⇥	Ignition ON	0 V		
Knock sensor (KS) 2 – shield wire	67	⇥	Ignition ON	0 V		
Malfunction indicator lamp (MIL) – AQY	17	⇥▷	Ignition ON – MIL ON	0-1 V		
	17	⇥▷	Engine running – MIL OFF	11-14 V		
Mass air flow (MAF) sensor	11	⇨	Ignition ON	5 V		
	12	⇥	Engine idling	0 V		
	13	⇦	Engine idling	1,4 V		
	13	⇦	Engine idling – full throttle briefly	4 V briefly		
	40	⇦	Ignition ON – air temp. 20°C	2 V		
Secondary air injection (AIR) pump relay – AQY	30	⇥▷	Ignition ON	11-14 V briefly then 0 V		
	30	⇥▷	Engine running – pump OFF	11-14 V		
	30	⇥▷	Engine running – pump ON	0 V		
Secondary air injection (AIR) solenoid – AQY – if fitted	33	⇥▷	Ignition ON	11-14 V briefly then 0 V		
	33	⇥▷	Engine running – solenoid OFF	11-14 V		
	33	⇥▷	Engine running – solenoid ON	0 V		
Spare cable – some models	18			1		
Spare cable – APK	17			1		
Throttle position (TP) sensor	62	⇨	Ignition ON	5 V		
	67	⇥	Ignition ON	0 V		
	75	⇦	Ignition ON – throttle closed	4 V		
	75	⇦	Ignition ON – throttle fully open	0,6 V		
Transmission control module (TCM) – engine RPM signal	6	⇨	Engine idling	26 Hz		
	8	⇦	Engine idling – AC ON – AC compressor ON	11-14 V		
	22			1		
	32			1		

*Suggested settings - Voltage/time per division

1 Connected pin - no test data available or random digital signal

Model:	Engine code:	Year:
Corolla 1,6i	4A-FE	1992-97
Carina E 1,6i (MT)	4A-FE	1992-95
Avensis 1,6i	4A-FE	1997-01

TOYOTA

Toyota TCCS

ECM harness multi-plug

Terminal side

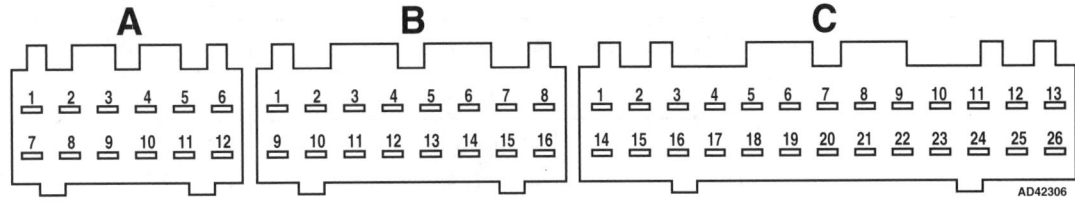

Wire side

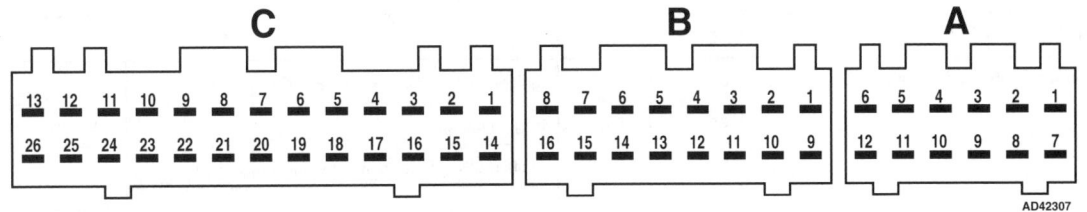

Component/circuit description	ECM pin	Signal	Condition	Typical value	Oscilloscope setting★	Wave form
AC control module	A6	←	Ignition ON – AC ON	9-10 V		
	A10	←	Ignition ON – AC ON	2 V max.		
Auxiliary air valve – AC/Carina/Corolla	C23	⊣▷	Ignition ON	9-14 V		
	C23	⊣▷	Engine idling – AC ON	0 V		
Battery	A2	←	Ignition OFF	10-14 V		
Brake pedal position (BPP) switch – Avensis	A1			1		
Camshaft position (CMP) sensor	C5 (C18)	←	Engine idling		2 V/20 ms	∿∿ 11
	C18 (C5)	←	Engine idling		2 V/20 ms	∿∿ 11
Closed throttle position (CTP) switch – Carina/Corolla	B12	←	Ignition ON – throttle closed	0 V		
	B12	←	Ignition ON – throttle slightly open	9-14 V		
Data link connector (DLC)	B7	←▷		1		
	B8	←▷		1		
	B15	←▷		1		
Data link connector (DLC) – Avensis	B16	←▷		1		
Earth	C13		Ignition ON	0 V		
	C24		Ignition ON	0 V		
	C26		Ignition ON	0 V		
Engine control relay	A1	←	Ignition OFF	0 V		
	A1	←	Ignition ON	10-14 V		
	A7	←	Ignition OFF	0 V		
	A7	←	Ignition ON	10-14 V		

★ Suggested settings - Voltage/time per division

Component/circuit description	ECM pin	Signal	Condition	Typical value	Oscilloscope setting*	Wave form
Engine coolant temperature (ECT) sensor	B4	←	Ignition ON – coolant temp. 20°C	3,5 V		
	B4	←	Ignition ON – coolant temp. 80°C	0,2-1 V		
	B9	⅃—	Ignition ON	0 V		
Engine coolant temperature (ECT) sensor – Corolla/Carina-E	B16	⅃—	Ignition ON	0 V		
Engine coolant temperature gauge sensor – Avensis	C9			1		
Engine speed (RPM) sensor	C4 (C17)	←	Engine idling		2 V/5 ms	17
	C17 (C4)	←	Engine idling		2 V/5 ms	17
Fuel pump relay	A4	⅃▷	Ignition ON	10-14 V		
	A4	⅃▷	Engine idling	0 V		
Heated oxygen sensor (HO2S)	B6	←	Engine idling – engine hot	0,2-0,8 V fluctuating	0,2 V/1 sec.	21
	C14	⅃—	Ignition ON	0 V		
Heated rear window fuse – Avensis	A5			1		
Idle air control (IAC) valve	C9	⇨	Ignition ON – ECM disconnected	9-14 V		
	C9	⇨	Engine idling		5 V/5 ms	25
	C10	⇨	Ignition ON – ECM disconnected	9-14 V		
	C10	⇨	Engine idling		5 V/5 ms	25
Ignition amplifier	C3	←	Engine idling		1 V/10 ms	32
	C22	⇨	Engine idling		1 V/10 ms	32
Ignition switch – start signal	C2	←	Engine cranking	6-14 V		
Injectors 1 & 3	C12	⅃▷	Ignition OFF	0 V		
	C12	⅃▷	Ignition ON	9-14 V		
	C12	⅃▷	Engine idling		10 V/2 ms	35
Injectors 2 & 4	C25	⅃▷	Ignition OFF	0 V		
	C25	⅃▷	Ignition ON	9-14 V		
	C25	⅃▷	Engine idling		10 V/2 ms	35
Intake air temperature (IAT) sensor	B3	←	Ignition ON – air temp. 20°C	3,4 V		
	B9	⅃—	Ignition ON	0 V		
Intake air temperature (IAT) sensor – Corolla/Carina-E	B16	⅃—	Ignition ON	0 V		
Knock sensor (KS)	B14	←	Engine idling – accelerate briefly		50 mV/1 ms	38
Malfunction indicator lamp (MIL)	A8	⅃▷	Ignition ON – MIL ON	0-1 V		
	A8	⅃▷	Engine running – MIL OFF	10-14 V		
Manifold absolute pressure (MAP) sensor	B2	←	Ignition ON	3,3-3,9 V		
	B9	⅃—	Ignition ON	0 V		
	B11	⇨	Ignition ON	4,5-5,5 V		
Manifold absolute pressure (MAP) sensor – Corolla/Carina-E	B16	⅃—	Ignition ON	0 V		
Octane coding plug – Carina	A3			1		
Octane coding plug – Avensis	B1			1		
Overdrive solenoid – Avensis	C7			1		
Park/neutral position (PNP) switch – Avensis	C15	←	Ignition ON – AT in P or N	0-3 V		
	C15	←	Ignition ON – AT not in P or N	9-14 V		

* Suggested settings - Voltage/time per division

Component/circuit description	ECM pin	Signal	Condition	Typical value	Oscilloscope setting*	Wave form
Rear fog lamps switch/side lamps relay	A12	←	Ignition ON – fog lamps OFF – side lamps OFF	0 V		
	A12	←	Ignition ON – fog lamps ON – side lamps ON	10-14 V		
Starter motor relay	C15	←	Ignition ON	0-3 V		
Throttle position (TP) sensor	B9	⌐	Ignition ON	0 V		
	B10	←	Ignition ON – throttle closed	0,3-0,8 V		
	B10	←	Ignition ON – throttle fully open	3,2-4,9 V		
	B11	⇒	Ignition ON	4,5-5,5 V		
Throttle position (TP) sensor – Corolla/Carina-E	B16	⌐	Ignition ON	0 V		
Transmission mode selection switch – Avensis	B5			1		
Transmission range (TR) switch – Avensis	C6			1		
	C19			1		
	C20			1		
Transmission shift control valve 1 – Avensis	C21			1		
Transmission shift control valve 2 – Avensis	C21			1		
Vehicle speed sensor (VSS)	A11	←	Ignition ON – vehicle pushed	0 V or 5 V		

*Suggested settings - Voltage/time per division

1 Connected pin - no test data available or random digital signal

Model:	Engine code:	Year:
Avensis 1,8	7A-FE	1997-01

ECM harness multi-plug

Terminal side

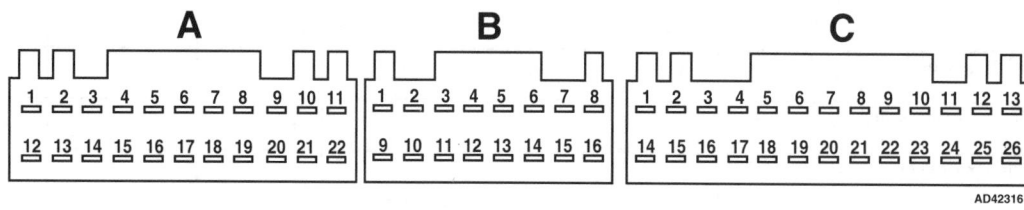

Wire side

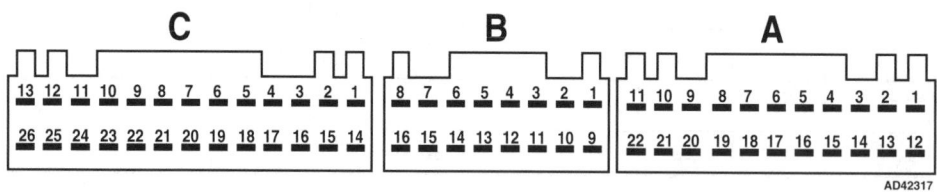

Component/circuit description	ECM pin	Signal	Condition	Typical value	Oscilloscope setting*	Wave form
AC control module	A10	←	Ignition ON – AC OFF	2 V max.		
	A10	←	Ignition ON – AC ON	11-14 V		
	A21	←	Engine idling – AC OFF	2 V max.		
	A21	←	Engine idling – AC ON	11-14 V		
Battery	A1	←	Ignition OFF	11-14 V		
Brake pedal position (BPP) switch – AT	A4	←	Ignition ON – brake pedal released	0 V		
	A4	←	Ignition ON – brake pedal depressed	11-14 V		
Camshaft position (CMP) sensor	C5	←	Engine idling		5 V/20 ms	⩗⩗ 11
	C17	⌐	Ignition ON	0 V		
Crankshaft position (CKP) sensor	C4	←	Engine idling		5 V/2 ms	⩗⩗ 2
	C17	⌐	Ignition ON	0 V		
Data link connector (DLC)	B7	⇄		1		
	B8	⇄		1		
	B16	⇄		1		
	C16	⇒	Engine idling	30 Hz		
Earth	C13		Ignition ON	0 V		
	C14		Ignition ON	0 V		
	C15		Ignition ON	0 V		
	C26		Ignition ON	0 V		
Earth – AT, RHD	B10		Ignition ON	0 V		
Engine control relay	A12	←	Ignition OFF	0 V		
	A12	←	Ignition ON	11-14 V		
Engine coolant blower motor relay	B5	⊐▷	Ignition ON	11-14 V		
	B5	⊐▷	Engine running – coolant temp. 90°C max.	11-14 V		
	B5	⊐▷	Engine running – coolant temp. 105°C min.	0-3 V		
Engine coolant temperature (ECT) gauge	C9	⇒		1		

* Suggested settings - Voltage/time per division

Component/circuit description	ECM pin	Signal	Condition	Typical value	Oscilloscope setting*	Wave form
Engine coolant temperature (ECT) sensor	B4	⟵	Ignition ON – coolant temp. 20°C	3,5 V		
	B4	⟵	Ignition ON – coolant temp. 80°C	0,2-1 V		
	B9	⊣⎯	Ignition ON	0 V		
Fuel pump relay	A14	⊣▷	Ignition ON	11-14 V		
	A14	⊣▷	Engine idling	0 V		
Heated oxygen sensor (HO2S)	B6	⟵	Engine idling – engine hot	0,2-0,8 V fluctuating	0,2 V/1 sec.	〰 21
	B9	⊣⎯	Ignition ON	0 V		
	C1	⊣▷	Ignition ON	11-14 V		
	C1	⊣▷	Engine idling	3 V max.		
Heated rear window relay	B14	⟵	Ignition ON – heated rear window OFF	0 V		
	B14	⟵	Ignition ON – heated rear window ON	11-14 V		
Heater blower motor relay	B15	⟵	Ignition ON – heater blower motor switch OFF	3 V max.		
	B15	⟵	Ignition ON – heater blower motor switch ON	11-14 V		
Idle air control (IAC) valve	C10	⊣▷	Ignition ON	11-14 V		
	C10	⊣▷	Engine idling		5 V/5 ms	〰 24
Ignition amplifier – cylinders 1 & 4	C3	⟵	Engine idling		1 V/10 ms	〰 56
	C20	⟹	Engine idling		1 V/20 ms	〰 56
Ignition amplifier – cylinders 2 & 3	C3	⟵	Engine idling		1 V/10 ms	〰 56
	C19	⟹	Engine idling		1 V/20 ms	〰 56
Ignition switch – start signal	A22	⟵	Engine cranking	6-14 V		
Immobilizer control module	A15			1		
	A16			1		
Injector 1	C12	⊣▷	Ignition OFF	0 V		
	C12	⊣▷	Ignition ON	11-14 V		
	C12	⊣▷	Engine idling	3 ms	10 V/2 ms	〰 35
Injector 2	C11	⊣▷	Ignition OFF	0 V		
	C11	⊣▷	Ignition ON	11-14 V		
	C11	⊣▷	Engine idling	3 ms	10 V/2 ms	〰 35
Injector 3	C25	⊣▷	Ignition OFF	0 V		
	C25	⊣▷	Ignition ON	11-14 V		
	C25	⊣▷	Engine idling	3 ms	10 V/2 ms	〰 35
Injector 4	C24	⊣▷	Ignition OFF	0 V		
	C24	⊣▷	Ignition ON	11-14 V		
	C24	⊣▷	Engine idling	3 ms	10 V/2 ms	〰 35
Instrument panel – econolight	A13	⊣▷	Engine running – econolight OFF	11-14 V		
	A13	⊣▷	Engine running – econolight ON	0 V		
Instrument panel – snow mode warning lamp – AT	A8	⊣▷	Engine running – normal mode selected	11-14 V		
	A8	⊣▷	Engine running – snow mode selected	0 V		
Instrument panel – sport mode warning lamp – AT	A6	⟵	Engine running – normal mode selected	0 V		
	A6	⟵	Engine running – sport mode selected	11-14 V		
Intake air temperature (IAT) sensor	B3	⟵	Ignition ON – air temp. 20°C	3,4 V		
	B9	⊣⎯	Ignition ON	0 V		
Intake manifold air control solenoid	C2	⊣▷	Ignition ON	11-14 V		
	C2	⊣▷	Engine idling – full throttle briefly	0 V briefly		
Knock sensor (KS)	B13	⟵	Engine idling – accelerate briefly		50 mV/1 ms	〰 38
Malfunction indicator lamp (MIL)	A5	⊣▷	Ignition ON – MIL ON	0-1 V		
	A5	⊣▷	Engine running – MIL OFF	11-14 V		

* Suggested settings - Voltage/time per division

Component/circuit description	ECM pin	Signal	Condition	Typical value	Oscilloscope setting*	Wave form
Manifold absolute pressure (MAP) sensor	B1	⇨	Ignition ON	5 V		
	B2	⬅	Ignition ON	3,3-3,9 V		
	B2	⬅	Engine idling	1,3 V		
	B2	⬅	Engine idling – full throttle briefly	3,6 V briefly		
	B9	⌐	Ignition ON	0 V		
Overdrive selection switch – AT	A7	⬅	Ignition ON – overdrive OFF	11-14 V		
	A7	⬅	Ignition ON – overdrive ON	0-3 V		
Park/neutral position (PNP) switch	A11	⬅	Ignition ON – AT in P or N	0-3 V		
	A11	⬅	Ignition ON – AT not in P or N	11-14 V		
Power steering pressure (PSP) switch	B12	⬅	Ignition ON – steering wheel not turned	11-14 V		
	B12	⬅	Ignition ON – steering wheel turned	3 V max.		
Tachometer	C16	⇨	Engine idling	30 Hz		
Tail lamps relay	A2	⬅	Tail lamps OFF	0 V		
	A2	⬅	Tail lamps ON	11-14 V		
Throttle position (TP) sensor	B1	⇨	Ignition ON	5 V		
	B9	⌐	Ignition ON	0 V		
	B11	⬅	Ignition ON – throttle closed	0,3-1 V		
	B11	⬅	Ignition ON – throttle fully open	3,2-4,9 V		
Transmission kick-down switch – LHD	A3	⬅	Ignition ON – throttle closed	11-14 V		
	A3	⬅	Ignition ON – throttle fully open	0-3 V		
Transmission mode selection switch	A6	⬅	Ignition ON – normal mode selected	0 V		
	A6	⬅	Ignition ON – sport mode selected	11-14 V		
	A17	⬅	Ignition ON – normal mode selected	0 V		
	A17	⬅	Ignition ON – snow mode selected	11-14 V		
Transmission range (TR) switch	A18	⬅	Ignition ON – AT in 2	7,5-14 V		
	A18	⬅	Ignition ON – AT not in 2	0-1,5 V		
	A19	⬅	Ignition ON – AT in L	7,5-14 V		
	A19	⬅	Ignition ON – AT not in L	0-1,5 V		
Transmission range (TR) switch	A20			1		
Transmission shift control valve 1	C8			1		
Transmission shift control valve 2	C7			1		
Transmission shift control valve 3	C6			1		
Vehicle speed sensor (VSS)	A9	⬅	Ignition ON – vehicle pushed	0 V or 5 V fluctuating		

*Suggested settings - Voltage/time per division

1 Connected pin - no test data available or random digital signal

ECM harness multi-plug

Terminal side

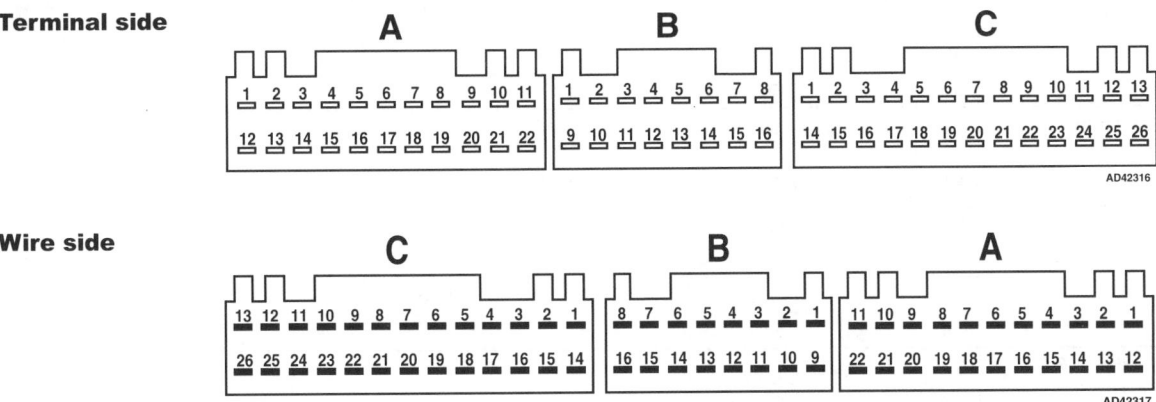

Wire side

Component/circuit description	ECM pin	Signal	Condition	Typical value	Oscilloscope setting*	Wave form
AC control module	A10	←	Ignition ON – AC OFF	2 V max.		
	A10	←	Ignition ON – AC ON	11-14 V		
	A21	←	Engine idling – AC OFF	2 V max.		
	A21	←	Engine idling – AC ON	11-14 V		
Battery	A1	←	Ignition OFF	11-14 V		
Brake pedal position (BPP) switch – AT	A4	←	Ignition ON – brake pedal released	0 V		
	A4	←	Ignition ON – brake pedal depressed	11-14 V		
Camshaft position (CMP) sensor	C5	←	Engine idling		5 V/20 ms	ᴡᴡ 11
	C17	⌐	Ignition ON	0 V		
Crankshaft position (CKP) sensor	C4	←	Engine idling		5 V/2 ms	ᴡᴡ 2
	C17	⌐	Ignition ON	0 V		
Data link connector (DLC)	A8	⇒	Engine idling	30 Hz		
	A15	⟷		1		
	A16	⟷		1		
	C7	⟷		1		
Earth	C13		Ignition ON	0 V		
	C14		Ignition ON	0 V		
	C26		Ignition ON	0 V		
Engine control relay	A12	←	Ignition OFF	0 V		
	A12	←	Ignition ON	11-14 V		
Engine coolant blower motor relay	B14	⊐▷	Ignition ON	11-14 V		
	B14	⊐▷	Engine running – coolant temp. 90°C max.	11-14 V		
	B14	⊐▷	Engine running – coolant temp. 105°C min.	0-3 V		
Engine coolant temperature (ECT) gauge	A20	⇒		1		

* Suggested settings - Voltage/time per division

Component/circuit description	ECM pin	Signal	Condition	Typical value	Oscilloscope setting*	Wave form
Engine coolant temperature (ECT) sensor	B4	←	Ignition ON – coolant temp. 20°C	3,5 V		
	B4	←	Ignition ON – coolant temp. 80°C	0,2-1 V		
	B9	⌐	Ignition ON	0 V		
Exhaust gas recirculation (EGR) solenoid	C2	⌐▷	Ignition ON	11-14 V		
Fuel pump relay	A14	⌐▷	Ignition ON	11-14 V		
	A14	⌐▷	Engine idling	0 V		
Heated oxygen sensor (HO2S)	B6	←	Engine idling – engine hot	0,2-0,8 V fluctuating	0,2 V/1 sec.	〰 21
	B8	⌐▷	Ignition ON	11-14 V		
	B8	⌐▷	Engine idling	3 V max.		
Heated rear window relay – through diode	A2	←	Ignition ON – heated rear window OFF	0 V		
	A2	←	Ignition ON – heated rear window ON	11-14 V		
Idle air control (IAC) valve	C9	⌐▷	Ignition ON	11-14 V		
	C9	⌐▷	Engine idling		5 V/5 ms	〰 24
	C10	⌐▷	Ignition ON	11-14 V		
	C10	⌐▷	Engine idling		5 V/5 ms	〰 24
Ignition amplifier – cylinders 1 & 4	C16	←	Engine idling		1 V/10 ms	〰 56
	C20	▷	Engine idling		1 V/20 ms	〰 56
Ignition amplifier – cylinders 2 & 3	C16	←	Engine idling		1 V/10 ms	〰 56
	C19	▷	Engine idling		1 V/20 ms	〰 56
Ignition switch – start signal	A22	←	Engine cranking	6-14 V		
Immobilizer control module	A6			[1]		
	A7			[1]		
Injector 1	C12	⌐▷	Ignition OFF	0 V		
	C12	⌐▷	Ignition ON	11-14 V		
	C12	⌐▷	Engine idling	3 ms	10 V/2 ms	〰 35
Injector 2	C11	⌐▷	Ignition OFF	0 V		
	C11	⌐▷	Ignition ON	11-14 V		
	C11	⌐▷	Engine idling	3 ms	10 V/2 ms	〰 35
Injector 3	C25	⌐▷	Ignition OFF	0 V		
	C25	⌐▷	Ignition ON	11-14 V		
	C25	⌐▷	Engine idling	3 ms	10 V/2 ms	〰 35
Injector 4	C24	⌐▷	Ignition OFF	0 V		
	C24	⌐▷	Ignition ON	11-14 V		
	C24	⌐▷	Engine idling	3 ms	10 V/2 ms	〰 35
Instrument panel – snow mode warning lamp – AT	A3	⌐▷	Engine running – normal mode selected	11-14 V		
	A3	⌐▷	Engine running – snow mode selected	0 V		
Instrument panel – sport mode warning lamp – AT	C3	←	Engine running – normal mode selected	0 V		
	C3	←	Engine running – sport mode selected	11-14 V		
Intake air temperature (IAT) sensor	B3	←	Ignition ON – air temp. 20°C	3,4 V		
	B9	⌐	Ignition ON	0 V		
Knock sensor (KS)	B13	←	Engine idling – accelerate briefly		50 mV/1 ms	〰 38
Malfunction indicator lamp (MIL)	A5	⌐▷	Ignition ON – MIL ON	0-1 V		
	A5	⌐▷	Engine running – MIL OFF	11-14 V		

* Suggested settings - Voltage/time per division

Component/circuit description	ECM pin	Signal	Condition	Typical value	Oscilloscope setting*	Wave form
Manifold absolute pressure (MAP) sensor	B1	⇒	Ignition ON	5 V		
	B2	⬅	Ignition ON	3,3-3,9 V		
	B2	⬅	Engine idling	1,3 V		
	B2	⬅	Engine idling – full throttle briefly	3,6 V briefly		
	B9	⏚	Ignition ON	0 V		
Overdrive selection switch – AT	A11	⬅	Ignition ON – overdrive OFF	0-1 V		
	A11	⬅	Ignition ON – overdrive ON	11-14 V		
Park/neutral position (PNP) switch	C1	⬅	Ignition ON – AT in P or N	0-3 V		
	C1	⬅	Ignition ON – AT not in P or N	9-14 V		
Power steering pressure (PSP) switch	C6	⬅	Ignition ON – steering wheel not turned	11-14 V		
	C6	⬅	Ignition ON – steering wheel turned	3 V max.		
Tachometer	A8	⇒	Engine idling	30 Hz		
Tail lamps relay – through diode	A2	⬅	Tail lamps OFF	0 V		
	A2	⬅	Tail lamps ON	11-14 V		
Throttle position (TP) sensor	B1	⇒	Ignition ON	5 V		
	B9	⏚	Ignition ON	0 V		
	B11	⬅	Ignition ON – throttle closed	0,3-1 V		
	B11	⬅	Ignition ON – throttle fully open	3,2-4,9 V		
Transmission kick-down switch – LHD	A17	⬅	Ignition ON – throttle closed	11-14 V		
	A17	⬅	Ignition ON – throttle fully open	0-3 V		
Transmission mode selection switch	C3	⬅	Ignition ON – normal mode selected	0 V		
	C3	⬅	Ignition ON – sport mode selected	11-14 V		
	C18	⬅	Ignition ON – normal mode selected	0 V		
	C18	⬅	Ignition ON – snow mode selected	11-14 V		
Transmission range (TR) switch	A18	⬅	Ignition ON – AT in 2	7,5-14 V		
	A18	⬅	Ignition ON – AT not in 2	0-1,5 V		
	A19	⬅	Ignition ON – AT in L	7,5-14 V		
	A19	⬅	Ignition ON – AT not in L	0-1,5 V		
Transmission shift control valve 1	C23			1		
Transmission shift control valve 2	C22			1		
Transmission shift control valve SL	C21			1		
Vehicle speed sensor (VSS)	A9	⬅	Ignition ON – vehicle pushed	0 V or 5 V fluctuating		

*Suggested settings - Voltage/time per division

1 Connected pin - no test data available or random digital signal

ECM harness multi-plug

Terminal side

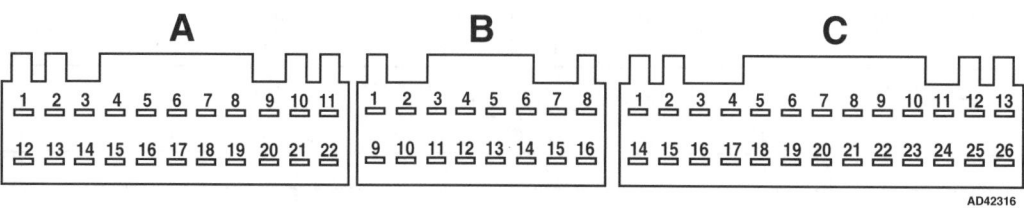

AD42316

Wire side

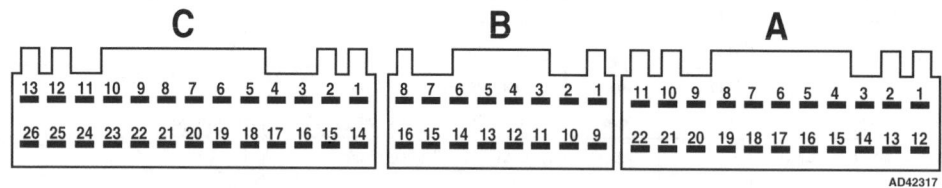

AD42317

Component/circuit description	ECM pin	Signal	Condition	Typical value	Oscilloscope setting★	Wave form
AC compressor clutch	A10	←	Engine idling – AC OFF	0-1 V		
	A10	←	Engine idling – AC ON	11-14 V		
Air conditioning	A21			1		
Battery	A1	←	Ignition OFF	11-14 V		
Brake pedal position (BPP) switch	A4	←	Ignition ON – brake pedal depressed	9-14 V		
	A4	←	Ignition ON – brake pedal released	0 V		
Closed throttle position (CTP) switch	B12	←	Ignition ON – throttle closed	0 V		
	B12	←	Ignition ON – throttle slightly open	10-14 V		
CO adjustment resistor – without cat	B1	⇨	Ignition ON	5 V		
	B9	⤙	Ignition ON	0 V		
	B13	←	Ignition ON	0-5 V		
Cold start injector – if fitted	C10	⇉		1		
Crankshaft position (CKP) sensor 1	B16 (C15)	←	Engine cranking	0,1-0,2 V ac		
	B16 (C15)	←	Engine idling	0,4 V ac	0,5 V/20 ms	⩗ 1
	B16 (C15)	←	3000 rpm	1,3 V ac		
	C15 (B16)	←	Engine cranking	0,1-0,2 V ac		
	C15 (B16)	←	Engine idling	0,4 V ac	0,5 V/20 ms	⩗ 1
	C15 (B16)	←	3000 rpm	1,2 V ac		

★ Suggested settings - Voltage/time per division

Component/circuit description	ECM pin	Signal	Condition	Typical value	Oscilloscope setting*	Wave form
Crankshaft position (CKP) sensor 2	B16 (C2)	←	Engine cranking	0,1-0,2 V ac		
	B16 (C2)	←	Engine idling	0,4 V ac	0,5 V/20 ms	1
	B16 (C2)	←	3000 rpm	1,3 V ac		
	C2 (B16)	←	Engine cranking	0,1-0,2 V ac		
	C2 (B16)	←	Engine idling	0,4 V ac	0,5 V/20 ms	1
	C2 (B16)	←	Engine running – 3000 rpm	1,3 V ac		
Data link connector (DLC)	B8	←→		1		
	B14	←→		1		
	B15	←→		1		
Earth	C13		Ignition ON	0 V		
	C14		Ignition ON	0 V		
	C26		Ignition ON	0 V		
Engine control relay	A12	←	Ignition OFF	0 V		
	A12	←	Ignition ON	11-14 V		
	A13	←	Ignition OFF	0 V		
	A13	←	Ignition ON	11-14 V		
Engine coolant temperature (ECT) sensor	B4	←	Ignition ON – coolant temp. 20°C	3 V		
	B4	←	Ignition ON – coolant temp. 80°C	1 V max.		
	B9	⌐—	Ignition ON	0 V		
Engine speed (RPM) sensor	B16 (C1)	←	Engine cranking	0,5 V ac		
	B16 (C1)	←	Engine idling	1,2 V ac	2 V/5 ms	17
	B16 (C1)	←	3000 rpm	2,6 V ac		
	C1 (B16)	←	Engine cranking	0,5 V ac		
	C1 (B16)	←	Engine idling	1,2 V ac	2 V/5 ms	17
	C1 (B16)	←	3000 rpm	2,6 V ac		
Fuel pressure regulator control solenoid	C5	⌐▷	Ignition OFF	0 V		
	C5	⌐▷	Ignition ON – engine cold	2,7 V		
	C5	⌐▷	Ignition ON – engine hot	11-14 V		
	C5	⌐▷	Engine idling – engine hot	11-14 V		
Fuel pump relay	A14	⌐▷	Ignition ON	11-14 V		
	A14	⌐▷	Engine idling	0 V		
Heated oxygen sensor (HO2S)	C8	⇒	Ignition ON	9-14 V		
	B6	←	Engine idling – engine hot	0,2-0,8 V fluctuating	0,2 V/1 sec.	21
Idle air control (IAC) valve	C9	⇒	Ignition ON	8-14 V		
	C9	⇒	Engine idling		5 V/5 ms	25
	C22	⇒	Ignition ON	8-14 V		
	C22	⇒	Engine idling		5 V/5 ms	25

* Suggested settings - Voltage/time per division

Component/circuit description	ECM pin	Signal	Condition	Typical value	Oscilloscope setting*	Wave form
Ignition amplifier	C3	⇨	Engine cranking	11 Hz		
	C3	⇨	Engine idling	27 Hz	1 V/10 ms	32
	C3	⇨	3000 rpm	109 Hz		
	C20	⇨	Engine cranking	11 Hz		
	C20	⇨	Engine idling	27 Hz	1 V/10 ms	32
	C20	⇨	3000 rpm	109 Hz		
Ignition switch – start signal	A11	⬅	Engine cranking	6-14 V		
Injector 1	C12	⏚⇨	Ignition ON	11-14 V		
	C12	⏚⇨	Engine idling	2,5 ms	10 V/2 ms	35
Injector 2	C11	⏚⇨	Ignition ON	11-14 V		
	C11	⏚⇨	Engine idling	2,5 ms	10 V/2 ms	35
Injector 3	C25	⏚⇨	Ignition ON	11-14 V		
	C25	⏚⇨	Engine idling	2,5 ms	10 V/2 ms	35
Injector 4	C24	⏚⇨	Ignition ON	11-14 V		
	C24	⏚⇨	Engine idling	2,5 ms	10 V/2 ms	35
Intake air temperature (IAT) sensor	B3	⬅	Ignition ON – air temp. 20°C	3 V		
	B9	⏚	Ignition ON	0 V		
Intake manifold air control solenoid	C18	⇨	Ignition ON	3,7 V		
	C18	⇨	Engine idling	3,7 V		
	C18	⇨	Engine idling – accelerate briefly	11-14 V briefly		
Knock sensor (KS)	B5	⬅	Engine idling – accelerate briefly	0,25 V ac	50 mV/1 ms	38
Malfunction indicator lamp (MIL)	A5	⏚⇨	Ignition ON – MIL ON	0-1 V		
	A5	⏚⇨	Engine running – MIL OFF	8-14 V		
Manifold absolute pressure (MAP) sensor	B1	⇨	Ignition ON	5 V		
	B2	⬅	Ignition ON	2,5-4,5 V		
	B9	⏚	Ignition ON	0 V		
Rear fog lamps switch/side lamps relay	A2	⬅	Ignition ON – fog lamps ON – side lamps ON	9-14 V		
Throttle position (TP) sensor	B1	⇨	Ignition ON	5 V		
	B9	⏚	Ignition ON	0 V		
	B11	⬅	Ignition ON – throttle closed	0,5 V		
	B11	⬅	Ignition ON – throttle fully open	3,85 V		
Vehicle speed sensor (VSS)	A9	⬅	Ignition ON – vehicle pushed	0 V or 5 V		

*Suggested settings - Voltage/time per division

[1] Connected pin - no test data available or random digital signal

ECM harness multi-plug

Terminal side

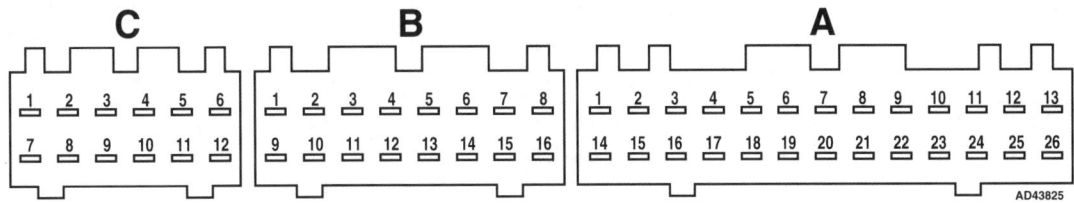

Wire side

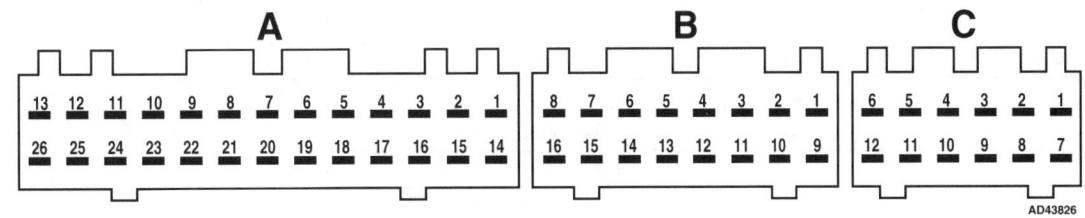

Component/circuit description	ECM pin	Signal	Condition	Typical value	Oscilloscope setting*	Wave form
AC control module	C6	←	Ignition ON – AC ON	9-10 V		
	C10	←		1		
Auxiliary air valve – AC	A1	⌐⊳	Ignition ON	9-14 V		
	A1	⌐⊳	Engine idling – AC ON	0 V		
Battery	C2	←	Ignition OFF	10-14 V		
Camshaft position (CMP) sensor	A5 (A18)	←	Engine idling		2 V/50 ms	11
	A18 (A5)	←	Engine idling		2 V/50 ms	11
Closed throttle position (CTP) switch	B12	←	Ignition ON – throttle closed	0 V		
	B12	←	Ignition ON – throttle slightly open	11-14 V		
Data link connector (DLC)	B7	⇄		1		
	B8	⇄		1		
	B15	⇄		1		
	A24	⇄		1		
Earth	A13		Ignition ON	0 V		
	A26		Ignition ON	0 V		
Electrical load sensor	C12	←	Ignition ON – electrical loads OFF	0 V		
	C12	←	Ignition ON – electrical loads ON	10-14 V		
Engine control relay	C7	←	Ignition OFF	0 V		
	C7	←	Ignition ON	10-14 V		
Engine coolant temperature (ECT) sensor	B4	←	Ignition ON – coolant temp. 10°C	2,7 V		
	B4	←	Engine idling – coolant temp. 80°C	0,3 V		
	B9	⌐	Ignition ON	0 V		
Engine speed (RPM) sensor	A4 (A17)	←	Engine idling		2 V/5 ms	17
	A17 (A4)	←	Engine idling		2 V/5 ms	17

* Suggested settings - Voltage/time per division

Component/circuit description	ECM pin	Signal	Condition	Typical value	Oscilloscope setting*	Wave form
Exhaust gas recirculation (EGR) solenoid	A23	←	Ignition ON	0 V		
	A23	←	Engine idling	0 V		
Fuel pressure regulator control solenoid	A15	⊐▷	Ignition ON – engine cold	2,7 V		
	A15	⊐▷	Engine idling – engine hot	11-14 V		
Fuel pump relay	C4	⊐▷	Ignition ON	10-14 V		
	C4	⊐▷	Engine idling	0 V		
Heated oxygen sensor (HO2S)	B6	←	Engine idling – engine hot	0-1 V fluctuating	0,2 V/1 sec.	⩗⩗ 21
	A11	⊐▷	Ignition ON	11-14 V		
	A11	⊐▷	Engine idling	0 V		
Idle air control (IAC) valve	A9	⇒	Ignition ON	0,7 V		
	A9	⇒	Engine idling	60%	5 V/5 ms	⩗⩗ 25
	A10	⇒	Ignition ON	11-14 V		
	A10	⇒	Engine idling	40%	5 V/5 ms	⩗⩗ 25
Ignition amplifier	A22	⇒	Engine idling	30 Hz	1 V/10 ms	⩗⩗ 32
	A22	⇒	3000 rpm	100 Hz		
Ignition switch – start signal	A2	←	Engine cranking	9 V		
Injectors 1 & 3	A12	⊐▷	Ignition ON	9-14 V		
	A12	⊐▷	Engine idling	3,1 ms	10 V/2 ms	⩗⩗ 35
Injectors 2 & 4	A25	⊐▷	Ignition ON	9-14 V		
	A25	⊐▷	Engine idling	3,1 ms	10 V/2 ms	⩗⩗ 35
Intake air temperature (IAT) sensor	B3	←	Ignition ON – air temp. 5°C	3 V		
	B9	⊣	Ignition ON	0 V		
Knock sensor (KS)	B5	←	Engine idling – accelerate briefly		50 mV/1 ms	⩗⩗ 38
Malfunction indicator lamp (MIL)	C8	⊐▷	Ignition ON – MIL ON	0-1 V		
	C8	⊐▷	Engine idling – MIL OFF	10-14 V		
Manifold absolute pressure (MAP) sensor	B2	←	Ignition ON	3,6 V		
	B2	←	Engine idling	1,3 V		
	B2	←	3000 rpm	1,4 V		
	B2	←	Engine under load	3,6 V		
	B9	⊣	Ignition ON	0 V		
	B11	⇒	Ignition ON	5 V		
Throttle position (TP) sensor	B9	⊣	Ignition ON	0 V		
	B10	←	Ignition ON – throttle closed	0,5 V		
	B10	←	Ignition ON – throttle fully open	4 V		
	B11	⇒	Ignition ON	5 V		
Vehicle speed sensor (VSS)	C11	←	Ignition ON – vehicle pushed	0 V or 5 V		

*Suggested settings - Voltage/time per division

1 Connected pin - no test data available or random digital signal

ECM harness multi-plug

Terminal side

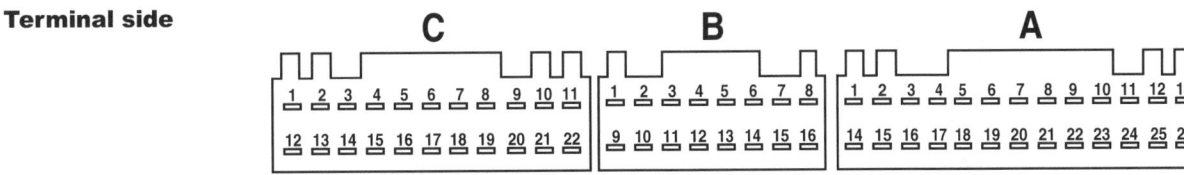

AD29991

Wire side

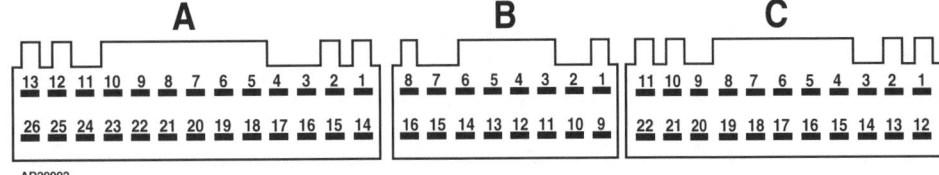

AD29992

Component/circuit description	ECM pin	Signal	Condition	Typical value	Oscilloscope setting*	Wave form
AC control module	C10	←		1		
	C21	←		1		
Automatic transmission	C6			1		
	C7			1		
	C8			1		
	C18			1		
	C19			1		
	B5			1		
	A1			1		
	A2			1		
	A6			1		
	A7			1		
	A8			1		
	A15			1		
	A16			1		
	A19			1		
	A21			1		
	A22			1		
Auxiliary air valve – AC	A23	⊐▷	Engine idling – AC OFF	11-14 V		
	A23	⊐▷	Engine idling – AC ON	0 V		
Battery	C1	←	Ignition OFF	11-14 V		
Brake pedal position (BPP) switch	C4	←	Ignition ON – brake pedal depressed	11-14 V		
	C4	←	Ignition ON – brake pedal released	0 V		

★ Suggested settings - Voltage/time per division

Component/circuit description	ECM pin	Signal	Condition	Typical value	Oscilloscope setting*	Wave form
Camshaft position (CMP) sensor	A5 (A18)	←	Engine idling		2 V/20 ms	11
	A18 (A5)	←	Engine idling		2 V/20 ms	11
Closed throttle position (CTP) switch	B12	←	Ignition ON – throttle closed	0 V		
	B12	←	Ignition ON – throttle slightly open	11-14 V		
Data link connector (DLC)	B7	↔		1		
	B8	↔		1		
	B14	↔		1		
	B15	↔		1		
Earth	A13		Ignition ON	0 V		
	A14		Ignition ON	0 V		
	A26		Ignition ON	0 V		
Earth – some models	C3		Ignition ON	0 V		
Electrical load sensor	C2	←	Ignition ON – electrical loads OFF	0 V		
	C2	←	Ignition ON – electrical loads ON	11-14 V		
Engine control relay	C12	←	Ignition OFF	0 V		
	C12	←	Ignition ON	11-14 V		
Engine coolant temperature (ECT) sensor	B4	←	Ignition ON – coolant temp. 20°C	3,4 V		
	B4	←	Engine idling – coolant temp. 80°C	0,5 V		
	B9	⊣⊢	Ignition ON	0 V		
Engine speed (RPM) sensor	A4 (A17)	←	Engine idling		2 V/5 ms	17
	A17 (A4)	←	Engine idling		2 V/5 ms	17
Exhaust gas recirculation (EGR) solenoid	A25	←	Ignition ON	0 V		
	A25	←	Engine idling – valve operating	0 V		
Fuel pressure regulator control solenoid	B16	⊣▷	Ignition ON – engine cold	2,7 V		
	B16	⊣▷	Engine idling – engine hot	11-14 V		
Fuel pump relay	C14	⊣▷	Ignition ON	11-14 V		
	C14	⊣▷	Engine idling	0 V		
Heated oxygen sensor (HO2S)	B6	←	Engine idling – engine hot	0-1 V fluctuating	0,2 V/1 sec.	21
	A24	⊣▷	Ignition ON	11-14 V		
	A24	⊣▷	Engine idling	0 V		
Idle air control (IAC) valve	A9	⇒	Ignition ON	0,7 V		
	A9	⇒	Engine idling	60%	5 V/5 ms	25
	A10	⇒	Ignition ON	11-14 V		
	A10	⇒	Engine idling	40%	5 V/5 ms	25
Ignition amplifier	A3	←	Engine idling	30 Hz	1 V/10 ms	32
	A3	←	3000 rpm	100 Hz		
	A20	⇒	Engine idling	30 Hz	1 V/10 ms	32
	A20	⇒	3000 rpm	100 Hz		
Injectors 1 & 3	A12	⊣▷	Ignition ON	11-14 V		
	A12	⊣▷	Engine idling	3,1 ms	10 V/2 ms	35

* Suggested settings - Voltage/time per division

Component/circuit description	ECM pin	Signal	Condition	Typical value	Oscilloscope setting*	Wave form
Injectors 2 & 4	A11	→⊳	Ignition ON	11-14 V		
	A11	→⊳	Engine idling	3,1 ms	10 V/2 ms	35
Intake air temperature (IAT) sensor	B3	←	Ignition ON – air temp. 20°C	3,4 V		
	B9	⅂—	Ignition ON	0 V		
Knock sensor (KS)	B13	←	Engine idling – accelerate briefly		50 mV/1 ms	38
Malfunction indicator lamp (MIL)	C5	→⊳	MIL ON	0-1 V		
	C5	→⊳	Engine idling – MIL OFF	11-14 V		
Manifold absolute pressure (MAP) sensor	B1	⇨	Ignition ON	5 V		
	B2	←	Ignition ON	3,6 V		
	B2	←	Engine idling	1,3 V		
	B2	←	Engine under load	3,6 V		
	B9	⅂—	Ignition ON	0 V		
Octane coding plug – some models	C15	←	Ignition ON	0 V		
Park/neutral position (PNP) switch	C22	←	Ignition ON – AT in P or N	0 V		
	C22	←	Ignition ON – AT not in P or N	11-14 V		
Starter motor relay	C11	←	Engine cranking	9 V		
Throttle position (TP) sensor	B1	⇨	Ignition ON	5 V		
	B9	⅂—	Ignition ON	0 V		
	B11	←	Ignition ON – throttle closed	0,5 V		
	B11	←	Ignition ON – throttle fully open	4 V		
Vehicle speed sensor (VSS)	C9	←	Ignition ON – vehicle pushed	0 V or 5 V		

*Suggested settings - Voltage/time per division

1 Connected pin - no test data available or random digital signal

Model:	Engine code:	Year:
Landcruiser Colorado 3,0D Turbo	1KZ-TE	1996-02

ECM harness multi-plug

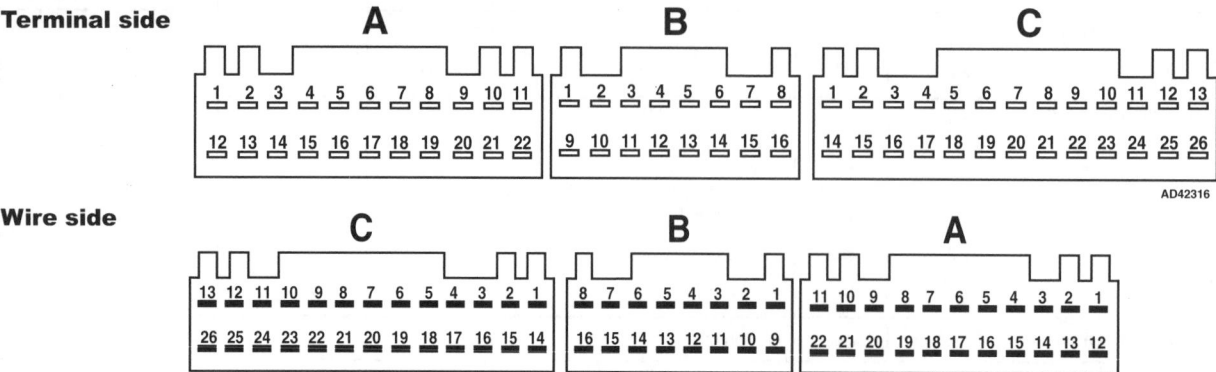

Terminal side

Wire side

AD42316

AD42317

Component/circuit description	ECM pin	Signal	Condition	Typical value	Oscilloscope setting*	Wave form
AC compressor clutch	C10	⇨	Engine idling – AC OFF	0-1 V		
	C10	⇨	Engine idling – AC ON, AC compressor OFF	0-1 V		
	C10	⇨	Engine idling – AC ON, AC compressor ON	11-14 V		
AC compressor control module	C19	⬅	Ignition ON	11-14 V		
	C19	⬅	Vehicle moving – 48 mph max. – AC ON – accelerator pedal fully depressed for 5 secs.	0-1 V		
Battery	C1	⬅	Ignition OFF	11-14 V		
Brake pedal position (BPP) switch	C4	⬅	Ignition ON – brake pedal released	0-1 V		
	C4	⬅	Ignition ON – brake pedal depressed	7,5-14 V		
Closed throttle position (CTP) switch	B9	⅃	Ignition ON	0 V		
	B12	⬅	Ignition ON – throttle closed	0-1 V		
	B12	⬅	Ignition ON – throttle slightly open	11-14 V		
Crankshaft position (CKP) sensor	A5	⬅	Engine idling	0,25 V ac		
	A5	⬅	Engine idling		1 V/20 ms	∿∿ 6
	A18	⅃	Engine idling	0 V		
Data link connector (DLC)	B7		Ignition ON	11-14 V		
	B8			1		
	B15		Ignition ON	11-14 V		
Data link connector (DLC) – AT	B16			1		
Earth	A13		Ignition ON	0 V		
	A14		Ignition ON	0 V		
	A26		Ignition ON	0 V		
Engine control (EC) relay	C3	⇨	Ignition OFF	0-1 V		
	C3	⇨	Ignition ON	11-14 V		
	C12	⬅	Ignition OFF	0 V		
	C12	⬅	Ignition ON	11-14 V		
Engine coolant temperature (ECT) sensor	B4	⬅	Ignition ON – coolant temp. 20°C	2 V		
	B4	⬅	Ignition ON – coolant temp. 80°C	0,5 V		
	B9	⅃	Ignition ON	0 V		

★ Suggested settings - Voltage/time per division

Component/circuit description	ECM pin	Signal	Condition	Typical value	Oscilloscope setting*	Wave form
Exhaust gas recirculation (EGR) solenoid	A24	⊐⊳	Ignition ON	11-14 V		
	A24	⊐⊳	Engine running – engine hot – valve operating		2 V/1 ms	⎍⎍⎍ 10
Fuel injection timing solenoid	A12	⊐⊳	Ignition ON	11-14 V		
	A12	⊐⊳	Engine running		5 V/20 ms	⎍⎍⎍ 33
Fuel quantity adjuster	A11	⊐⊳	Ignition ON	11-14 V		
	A11	⊐⊳	Engine idling – engine hot	11-14 V	2 V/20 µs	⎍⎍⎍ 10
Fuel quantity adjuster relay	C13	⊐⊳	Ignition ON	0-1 V		
Fuel temperature sensor	B5	⟵	Ignition ON – fuel temp. 18°C	2,2 V		
	B9	⊐—	Ignition ON	0 V		
Glow plug relay	C2	⟹	Ignition ON – glow plugs ON	11-14 V		
	C2	⟹	Ignition ON – glow plugs OFF	0-1 V		
	C2	⟹	Engine cranking	6 V min.		
Glow plug warning lamp	C7	⊐⊳	Ignition ON – lamp ON	0-1 V		
	C7	⊐⊳	Ignition ON – lamp OFF	11-14 V		
Idle speed adjustment switch	C20	⟹	Engine idling – 'idle up' switch ON	0-1 V		
	C20	⟹	Engine idling – 'idle up' switch OFF	11-14 V		
Ignition switch	C14	⟵	Ignition OFF	0 V		
	C14	⟵	Ignition ON	11-14 V		
Immobilizer control module	C8			[1]		
	C17			[1]		
Injection pump calibration resistor 1	B9	⊐—	Ignition ON	0 V		
	B14	⟵	Ignition ON	0,2-4,5 V		
Injection pump calibration resistor 2	B6	⟵	Ignition ON	0,2-4,5 V		
	B9	⊐—	Ignition ON	0 V		
Injection pump position sensor	A4	⟵	Engine idling	0,6 V ac		
	A4	⟵	Engine idling		0,5 V/5 ms	⎍⎍⎍ 1
	A17	⊐—	Engine idling	0 V		
Intake air temperature (IAT) sensor	B3	⟵	Ignition ON – air temp. 18°C	2,2 V		
	B9	⊐—	Ignition ON	0 V		
Intake manifold air control solenoid 1	A10	⊐⊳	Engine idling	11-14 V		
	A10	⊐⊳	Engine idling – switch ignition OFF	0-1 V for 2 seconds		
Intake manifold air control solenoid 2	A9	⊐⊳	Engine idling	11-14 V		
	A9	⊐⊳	Engine idling – switch ignition OFF	0-1 V for 2 seconds		
Malfunction indicator lamp (MIL)	C5	⊐⊳	Ignition ON – MIL ON	0-1 V		
	C5	⊐⊳	Engine idling – MIL OFF	11-14 V		
Overdrive selection switch	C16	⟵	Ignition ON – overdrive selected	11-14 V		
	C16	⟵	Ignition ON – overdrive 'OFF' selected	3 V max.		
Second gear pull-away selection switch	A23	⟵	Ignition ON – '2nd' switch ON	3 V max.		
	A23	⟵	Ignition ON – '2nd' switch OFF	11-14 V		
Second gear pull-away warning lamp	A22	⊐⊳	Ignition ON – lamp ON	3 V max.		
	A22	⊐⊳	Ignition ON – lamp OFF	11-14 V		
Starter motor relay	C11	⟵	Engine cranking	6 V min.		
Tachometer	C18	⟹		[1]		
Throttle position (TP) sensor	B1	⟹	Ignition ON	5 V		
	B9	⊐—	Ignition ON	0 V		
	B11	⟵	Ignition ON – throttle closed	0,3-0,8 V		
	B11	⟵	Ignition ON – throttle fully open	3,2-4,9 V		
Transfer box low ratio switch	A7			[1]		

* Suggested settings - Voltage/time per division

Component/circuit description	ECM pin	Signal	Condition	Typical value	Oscilloscope setting*	Wave form
Transfer box neutral switch	A8	←	Ignition ON – transfer box in neutral	0-1 V		
	A8	←	Ignition ON – transfer box not in neutral	11-14 V		
Transmission fluid temperature (TFT) sensor	B13	←	Engine idling – engine hot	0-1 V		
Transmission lock-up control valve	A1	⇒	Ignition ON	1,5 V max.		
Transmission mode selection switch	C15	←	Ignition ON – 'ECT/PWR' switch ON	11-14 V		
	C15	←	Ignition ON – 'ECT/PWR' switch OFF	0-1 V		
Transmission fluid temperature warning lamp	C6	⌐⇒	Ignition ON – lamp ON	0-1 V		
	C6	⌐⇒	Engine idling – lamp OFF	11-14 V		
Transmission range (TR) sensor	A20	←	Selector lever in L	11-14 V		
	A20	←	Selector lever not in L	0-1 V		
	A21	←	Selector lever in 2	11-14 V		
	A21	←	Selector lever not in 2	0-1 V		
	C22	←	Engine cranking – AT in P or N	11-14 V		
	C22	←	Engine cranking – AT not in P or N	0-1 V		
Transmission shift solenoid (SS) 1	A2	⇒	Ignition ON	11-14 V		
	A2	⇒	Ignition ON – AT in 1 or 2	11-14 V		
	A2	⇒	Ignition ON – AT in 3 or overdrive	0-1 V		
Transmission shift solenoid (SS) 2	A15	⇒	Ignition ON – AT in 3 or overdrive	0-1 V		
	A15	⇒	Ignition ON – AT in 2 or 3	11-14 V		
	A15	⇒	Ignition ON – AT in 1 or overdrive	0-1 V		
Transmission vehicle speed sensor	A3	←		1		
	A16	⌐⊢		1		
Turbocharger (TC) boost pressure sensor	B1	⇒	Ignition ON	5 V		
	B2	←	Ignition ON	1,3-1,9 V		
	B2	←	Ignition ON – 0,4 bar vacuum	0,2-0,8 V		
	B2	←	Ignition ON – 0,69 bar vacuum	3,2-3,8 V		
	B2	←	Engine running – full throttle briefly	3,3 V		
	B9	⌐⊢	Ignition ON	0 V		
Vehicle speedometer	C9	←	Ignition ON – vehicle pushed	0-1 V or 11-14 V switching		

*Suggested settings - Voltage/time per division

1 Connected pin - no test data available or random digital signal

Model:	Engine code:	Year:
Corsa-B 1,0/1,2	X10XE/X12XE	1997-00
Astra-G 1,2	X12XE	1998-02

OPEL-VAUXHALL

Bosch Motronic M1.5.5

ECM harness multi-plug

Terminal side

Wire side

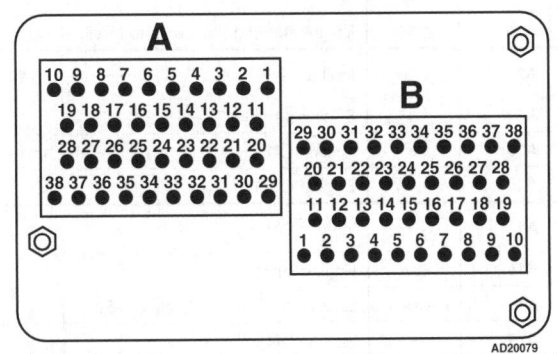

AD20078

AD20079

Component/circuit description	ECM pin	Signal	Condition	Typical value	Oscilloscope setting*	Wave form
ABS control module/traction control module – vehicle speed signal – Astra	B36	←		①		
AC compressor clutch relay – Corsa	B5	⇥▷		①		
AC control module – Astra	B5	⇥▷		①		
	B6			①		
	B26			①		
AC heater blower relay – Astra	B35	←		①		
AC master switch	B35	←		①		
AC refrigerant pressure switch – Corsa	B21	←		①		
Battery	B18	←	Ignition OFF	11-14 V		
Camshaft position (CMP) sensor	A9	⇥	Ignition ON	0 V		
	A23	←	Ignition ON	0 or 5 V		
	A23	←	Engine idling		2 V/20 ms	〰14
	A29	⇨	Ignition ON	5 V		
Camshaft position (CMP) sensor – shield wire	A9	⇥	Ignition ON	0 V		
Closed throttle position (CTP) switch	A4	←	Ignition ON – throttle closed	11-14 V		
	A37	⇥	Ignition ON	0 V		
Crankshaft position (CKP) sensor	A22	←	Engine cranking	1 V		
	A22	←	Engine idling	3,1 V	2 V/10 ms	〰10
	A22	←	3000 rpm	8,2 V		
	A32	⇥	Ignition ON	0 V		
Crankshaft position (CKP) sensor – shield wire	A9	⇥	Ignition ON	0 V		
Data link connector (DLC) – Astra	B10	←⇨		①		
Data link connector (DLC) – Corsa	B11	←⇨		①		

* Suggested settings - Voltage/time per division

Component/circuit description	ECM pin	Signal	Condition	Typical value	Oscilloscope setting*	Wave form
Earth – Corsa MT	B25		Ignition ON	0 V		
Engine control relay	B7	⬅	Ignition OFF	0 V		
	B7	⬅	Ignition ON	11-14 V		
	B9	⏚⇨	Ignition OFF	11-14 V		
	B9	⏚⇨	Ignition ON	0-1 V		
	B17	⬅	Ignition OFF	0 V		
	B17	⬅	Ignition ON	11-14 V		
Engine coolant blower motor relay – non-AC – Astra	B13	⏚		[1]		
Engine coolant temperature (ECT) gauge – Astra	B6	⇨		[1]		
Engine coolant temperature (ECT) sensor	A1	⏚	Ignition ON	0 V		
	A5	⬅	Ignition ON – coolant temp. 80°C	0,8 V		
Evaporative emission (EVAP) canister purge valve	A34	⏚⇨	Ignition ON	11-14 V		
	A34	⏚⇨	Engine running – accelerate briefly		10 V/20 ms	59
Exhaust gas recirculation (EGR) solenoid	A24	⏚⇨	Ignition ON	11-14 V		
	A24	⏚⇨	Engine running		10 V/5 ms	25
	A25	⏚⇨	Ignition ON	11-14 V		
	A25	⏚⇨	Engine running		10 V/5 ms	25
Exhaust gas recirculation (EGR) valve position sensor	A1	⏚	Ignition ON	0 V		
	A14	⬅	Engine idling	1 V		
	A14	⬅	Engine idling – accelerate briefly	2,2 V		
	A29	⇨	Ignition ON	5 V		
Fuel pump relay	B3	⏚⇨	Ignition ON	0-1 V briefly then 11-14 V		
	B3	⏚⇨	Engine idling	0-1 V		
Heated oxygen sensor (HO2S)	A8	⏚⇨	Engine running	0-1 V		
	A18	⏚⇨	Engine running	0-1 V		
	A21	⏚	Ignition ON	0 V		
	A30	⬅	Engine idling – engine hot	0-1 V fluctuating	0,2 V/1 sec.	21
Heated oxygen sensor (HO2S) – shield wire	A9	⏚	Ignition ON	0 V		
Idle speed control (ISC) actuator	A26	⏚⇨	Engine idling		2 V/10 ms	8
	A35	⏚⇨	Engine idling		2 V/10 ms	8
Ignition coil – cylinder 1	A38	⏚⇨	Ignition ON	11-14 V		
	A38	⏚⇨	Engine idling		5 V/2 ms	33
Ignition coil – cylinder 2	A10	⏚⇨	Ignition ON	11-14 V		
	A10	⏚⇨	Engine idling		5 V/2 ms	33
Ignition coil – cylinder 3	A19	⏚⇨	Ignition ON	11-14 V		
	A19	⏚⇨	Engine idling		5 V/2 ms	33
Ignition coil – cylinder 4 – X12XE	A28	⏚⇨	Ignition ON	11-14 V		
	A28	⏚⇨	Engine idling		5 V/2 ms	33
Ignition switch	B8	⬅	Ignition OFF	0 V		
	B8	⬅	Ignition ON	11-14 V		
Ignition switch – start signal – Corsa AT	B25	⬅	Engine cranking	11-14 V		
Immobilizer control module – Astra	B11	⬅⇨		[1]		
Immobilizer control module – vehicle speed signal – Corsa	B36	⬅		[1]		
Injector 1 – X10XE	A6	⏚⇨	Ignition ON	11-14 V		
	A6	⏚⇨	Engine idling – engine hot	3,7 ms	10 V/2 ms	35
Injector 1 – X12XE	A6	⏚⇨	Ignition ON	11-14 V		
	A6	⏚⇨	Engine idling – engine hot	5,5 ms	10 V/5 ms	35

* Suggested settings - Voltage/time per division

Component/circuit description	ECM pin	Signal	Condition	Typical value	Oscilloscope setting*	Wave form
Injector 2 – X10XE	A16	⊐▷	Ignition ON	11-14 V		
	A16	⊐▷	Engine idling – engine hot	3,7 ms	10 V/2 ms	〰 35
Injector 2 – X12XE	A17	⊐▷	Ignition ON	11-14 V		
	A17	⊐▷	Engine idling – engine hot	5,5 ms	10 V/5 ms	〰 35
Injector 3 – X10XE	A7	⊐▷	Ignition ON	11-14 V		
	A7	⊐▷	Engine idling – engine hot	3,7 ms	10 V/2 ms	〰 35
Injector 3 – X12XE	A16	⊐▷	Ignition ON	11-14 V		
	A16	⊐▷	Engine idling – engine hot	5,5 ms	10 V/5 ms	〰 35
Injector 4 – X12XE	A7	⊐▷	Ignition ON	11-14 V		
	A7	⊐▷	Engine idling – engine hot	5,5 ms	10 V/5 ms	〰 35
Intake air temperature (IAT) sensor	A3	⬅	Ignition ON – air temp. 20°C	3 V		
Knock sensor (KS)	A2 (A11)	⬅	Engine running – accelerate briefly		50 mV/1 ms	〰 38
	A11 (A2)	⬅	Engine running – accelerate briefly		50 mV/1 ms	〰 38
Malfunction indicator lamp (MIL)	B12	⊐▷	Ignition ON – MIL ON	0-1 V		
	B12	⊐▷	Engine idling – MIL OFF	11-14 V		
Mass air flow (MAF) sensor	A1	⊐─	Ignition ON	0 V		
	A12	⬅	Ignition ON	5 V		
	A12	⬅	Engine idling	1,5 V		
	A12	⬅	Engine idling – accelerate briefly	4,2 V		
	A29	⇨	Ignition ON	5 V		
Tachometer	B2	⇨	Engine idling		2 V/10 ms	〰 32
Throttle position (TP) sensor	A1	⊐─	Ignition ON	0 V		
	A13	⬅	Ignition ON – throttle closed	1 V		
	A13	⬅	Ignition ON – throttle fully open	4,3 V		
	A29	⇨	Ignition ON	5 V		
Transmission control module (TCM) – Corsa	B15	⬅		1		
	B27	⬅		1		
Vehicle speed sensor (VSS) – without ABS/traction control – Astra	B36	⬅		1		

*Suggested settings - Voltage/time per division

1 Connected pin - no test data available or random digital signal

VAUXHALL-OPEL

GM Multec S

Model:	Engine code:	Year:
Corsa-B 1,4/1,6	X14XE/X16XE	1994-00
Astra-F 1,4	X14XE	1995-98
Astra-F 1,6 16V	X16XEL	1994-99
Vectra-B 1,6	X16SEJ	1996-98
Vectra-B 1,6 16V	X16XEL	1995-02
Tigra 1,4/1,6	X14XE/X16XE	1995-00

ECM harness multi-plug

Terminal side

C1 C2 C3 C4 C5 C6 C7 C8 C9 C10 C11 C12 C13 C14 C15 C16
D1 D2 D3 D4 D5 D6 D7 D8 D9 D10 D11 D12 D13 D14 D15 D16

A1 A2 A3 A4 A5 A6 A7 A8 A9 A10 A11 A12 A13 A14 A15 A16
B1 B2 B3 B4 B5 B6 B7 B8 B9 B10 B11 B12 B13 B14 B15 B16

AD42410

Wire side

A16 A15 A14 A13 A12 A11 A10 A9 A8 A7 A6 A5 A4 A3 A2 A1
B16 B15 B14 B13 B12 B11 B10 B9 B8 B7 B6 B5 B4 B3 B2 B1

C16 C15 C14 C13 C12 C11 C10 C9 C8 C7 C6 C5 C4 C3 C2 C1
D16 D15 D14 D13 D12 D11 D10 D9 D8 D7 D6 D5 D4 D3 D2 D1

AD42411

Component/circuit description	ECM pin	Signal	Condition	Typical value	Oscilloscope setting*	Wave form
Air conditioning	A8	←	Ignition ON – AC OFF	0 V		
	A8	←	Ignition ON – AC ON	11-14 V		
	A15	⊐⊳	Engine idling – engine hot – AC OFF	11-14 V		
	A15	⊐⊳	Engine idling – engine hot – AC ON	0-1 V		
	A15	⊐⊳	Engine running – engine hot – AC ON – accelerator pedal briefly fully depressed	11-14 V		
	B5	⊐⊳	Engine idling – AC ON – AC compressor ON	0-1 V		
	B5	⊐⊳	Engine running – accelerate briefly – AC ON – AC compressor OFF	11-14 V		
Battery	A6	←	Ignition OFF	11-14 V		
Camshaft position (CMP) sensor	A5	←	Engine cranking		2 V/50 ms	⩗ 12
Crankshaft position (CKP) sensor	A16 (B14)	←	Engine cranking		1 V/1 ms	⩗ 2
	B14 (A16)	←	Engine cranking		1 V/1 ms	Reversed ⩗ 2
Crankshaft position (CKP) sensor – shield wire	D16	⊐	Ignition ON	0 V		
Data link connector (DLC)	B9	←		1		
	D11	⇔		1		
Earth	B1		Ignition ON	0 V		
	C7		Ignition ON	0 V		
	C9		Ignition ON	0 V		
	D7		Ignition ON	0 V		
	D16		Ignition ON	0 V		
Engine coolant temperature (ECT) sensor	B2	⊐	Ignition ON	0 V		
	B3	←	Engine idling – coolant temp. 85-110°C	0,5-1 V		
Evaporative emission (EVAP) canister purge valve	A13	⊐⊳	Engine running – accelerate briefly		10 V/20 ms	⩗ 20
Exhaust gas recirculation (EGR) solenoid	D1	⊐⊳	Ignition ON	11-14 V		
	D1	⊐⊳	Vehicle moving – 19 mph min.	1% min.		
Exhaust gas recirculation (EGR) valve position sensor	B2	⊐	Ignition ON	0 V		
	D2	←	Ignition ON	0,7 V		
	D8	⇒	Ignition ON	5 V		
Fuel pump relay	A12	⊐⊳	Ignition ON	0-1 V briefly then 11-14 V		
	A12	⊐⊳	Engine idling	0-1 V		

* Suggested settings - Voltage/time per division

Component/circuit description	ECM pin	Signal	Condition	Typical value	Oscilloscope setting*	Wave form
Fuel pump relay – Astra-F	D3	←	Engine idling	11-14 V		
Heated oxygen sensor (HO2S) – except Vectra-B	D9	←	Engine idling – engine hot	0,1-1 V fluctuating	0,2 V/1 sec.	
Heated oxygen sensor (HO2S) – shield wire – except Vectra-B	D16	⊣	Ignition ON	0 V		
Idle air control (IAC) valve	A1	⇨	Ignition ON	10,4 V		
	A1 (A3)	⇨	Engine idling		5 V/0,1 sec.	Intermittent
	A2	⇨	Ignition ON	0,8 V		
	A2 (A4)	⇨	Engine idling		5 V/0,1 sec.	Intermittent
	A3	⇨	Ignition ON	10,4 V		
	A3 (A1)	⇨	Engine idling		5 V/0,1 sec.	Intermittent
	A4	⇨	Ignition ON	0,8 V		
	A4 (A2)	⇨	Engine idling		5 V/0,1 sec.	Intermittent
Ignition amplifier	C14	⇨	Engine idling – engine hot		2 V/0,1 sec.	
	D14	⇨	Engine idling – engine hot		2 V/0,1 sec.	
Ignition switch	C16	←	Ignition ON	11-14 V		
Ignition switch – except Astra-F	D3	←	Ignition ON	11-14 V		
Injector 1	C4	⊣▷	Engine idling – engine hot	2,8 ms	10 V/2 ms	
Injector 2	C3	⊣▷	Engine idling – engine hot	2,8 ms	10 V/2 ms	
Injector 3	C2	⊣▷	Engine idling – engine hot	2,8 ms	10 V/2 ms	
Injector 4	C6	⊣▷	Engine idling – engine hot	2,8 ms	10 V/2 ms	
Instrument panel – except Corsa	B12	⇨		1		
Intake air temperature (IAT) sensor	B4	←	Ignition ON – air temp. 0-10°C	3,2 V		
	D15	⊣	Ignition ON	0 V		
Knock sensor (KS) – Vectra-B	C11	←	Engine running – accelerate briefly		50 mV/1 ms	
Knock sensor (KS) – except Vectra-B	C1	←	Engine running – accelerate briefly		50 mV/1 ms	
Knock sensor (KS) – shield wire – Vectra-B	D15	⊣	Ignition ON	0 V		
Malfunction indicator lamp (MIL)	B10	⊣▷	Ignition ON – MIL ON	0-1 V		
	B10	⊣▷	Engine idling – MIL OFF	11-14 V		
Manifold absolute pressure (MAP) sensor	A7	←	Engine idling – engine hot	1,3 V		
	D8	⇨	Ignition ON	5 V		
	D15	⊣	Ignition ON	0 V		
Oxygen sensor (O2S) – Vectra-B	D9	←	Engine idling – engine hot	0,1-1 V fluctuating	0,2 V/1 sec.	
Oxygen sensor (O2S) – shield wire – Vectra-B	D16	⊣	Ignition ON	0 V		
Secondary air injection (AIR) solenoid – Vectra-B	A11	⊣▷	Engine running – engine cold – throttle slightly open	0-1 V		
Secondary air injection (AIR) solenoid relay	A10	⊣▷	Engine running – engine cold – throttle slightly open	0-1 V		
Tachometer	B13	⇨	Ignition ON	11-14 V		
	B13	⇨	Engine idling	27 Hz		
	B13	⇨	3000 rpm	100 Hz		
Throttle position (TP) sensor	B2	⊣	Ignition ON	0 V		
	D5	←	Ignition ON – throttle closed	0,7 V		
	D5	←	Ignition ON – throttle fully open	4,6 V		
	D8	⇨	Ignition ON	5 V		
Transmission control module (TCM)	A9			1		
	B8	←	Engine idling – AT in P or N	0 V		
	B8	←	Engine idling – AT not in P or N	11-14 V		
	C10			1		
Vehicle speed sensor (VSS)	D10	←	Ignition ON – vehicle moving	0-10 V fluctuating	5 V/1 sec.	

*Suggested settings - Voltage/time per division

1 Connected pin - no test data available or random digital signal

Model:	Engine code:	Year:
Corsa-B 1,4	X14SZ	1996-99
Astra-F 1,6	X16SZR	1996-98
Vectra-B 1,6	X16SZR	1995-02

ECM harness multi-plug

Terminal side

Wire side

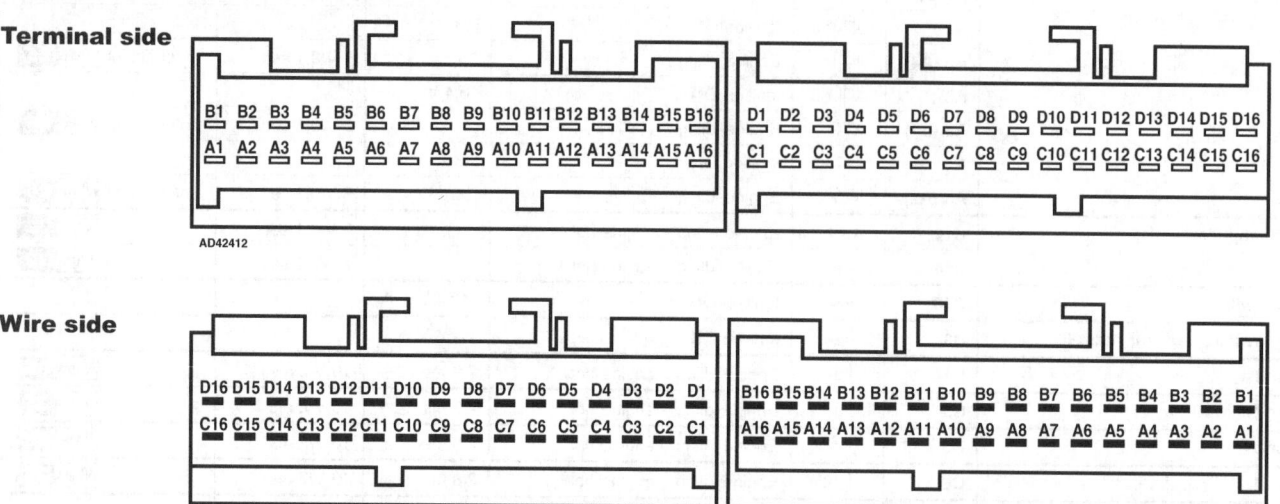

AD42412

AD42413

Component/circuit description	ECM pin	Signal	Condition	Typical value	Oscilloscope setting*	Wave form
Air conditioning	A8			1		
	A15			1		
	B5			1		
Battery	A6	←	Ignition OFF	11-14 V		
Crankshaft position (CKP) sensor	A16 (B14)	←	Engine cranking		1 V/1 ms	⎍ 2
	B14 (A16)	←	Engine cranking		1 V/1 ms	Reversed ⎍ 2
Crankshaft position (CKP) sensor – shield wire	B1	⅃—	Ignition ON	0 V		
Data link connector (DLC)	B9	←	Ignition ON	11-14 V		
	D11	↔	Ignition ON	0 V		
Earth	B1		Ignition ON	0 V		
	C9		Ignition ON	0 V		
	D16		Ignition ON	0 V		
Engine control module (ECM) – pin C7	C8			1		
Engine control module (ECM) – pin C8	C7			1		
Engine coolant temperature (ECT) sensor	B2	⅃—	Ignition ON	0 V		
	B3	←	Engine idling – engine hot	1,8 V		
Evaporative emission (EVAP) canister purge valve	A13	⅃▷	Engine idling – engine hot	11-14 V		
	A13	⅃▷	Engine running – accelerate briefly		10 V/20 ms	⎍ 20
Exhaust gas recirculation (EGR) solenoid	D1	⅃▷	Ignition ON	11-14 V		
	D1	⅃▷	3000 rpm	45%	5 V/0,1 sec.	⎍ 19
Exhaust gas recirculation (EGR) valve position sensor	B2	⅃—	Ignition ON	0 V		
	D2	←	Engine idling	0,65 V		
	D8	⇒	Ignition ON	5 V		

★ Suggested settings - Voltage/time per division

Component/circuit description	ECM pin	Signal	Condition	Typical value	Oscilloscope setting*	Wave form
Fuel pump relay	A12	⊐⊳	Ignition OFF	0 V		
	A12	⊐⊳	Ignition ON	0-1 V briefly then 11-14 V		
	A12	⊐⊳	Engine idling	0-1 V		
Idle air control (IAC) valve	A1	⇨	Ignition ON	10,8 V		
	A1 (A3)	⇨	Engine idling		5 V/0,1 sec.	Intermittent ⋀⋁⋀ 26
	A2	⇨	Ignition ON	0,9 V		
	A2 (A4)	⇨	Engine idling		5 V/0,1 sec.	Intermittent ⋀⋁⋀ 26
	A3	⇨	Ignition ON	0,9 V		
	A3 (A1)	⇨	Engine idling		5 V/0,1 sec.	Intermittent ⋀⋁⋀ 26
	A4	⇨	Ignition ON	10,8 V		
	A4 (A2)	⇨	Engine idling		5 V/0,1 sec.	Intermittent ⋀⋁⋀ 26
Ignition amplifier	C14	⇨	Engine idling – engine hot		2 V/10 ms	⋀⋁⋀ 32
	D14	⇨	Engine idling – engine hot		2 V/10 ms	⋀⋁⋀ 32
Ignition switch	C16	⟵	Ignition ON	11-14 V		
	D3	⟵	Ignition ON	11-14 V		
Ignition switch – AT	B8	⟵	Engine cranking	11-14 V		
Injector	C4	⊐⊳	Ignition ON	11-14 V		
	C4	⊐⊳	Engine idling – engine hot	0,97 ms	10 V/2 ms	⋀⋁⋀ 36
Instrument panel	B12	⇨		[1]		
Knock sensor (KS)	C11	⟵	Engine running – accelerate briefly		50 mV/1 ms	⋀⋁⋀ 38
Knock sensor (KS) – shield wire	D15	⊐⟋	Ignition ON	0 V		
Malfunction indicator lamp (MIL)	B10	⊐⊳	Ignition ON – MIL ON	0-1 V		
	B10	⊐⊳	Engine idling – MIL OFF	11-14 V		
Manifold absolute pressure (MAP) sensor	A7	⟵	Ignition ON	4,8 V		
	A7	⟵	Engine idling – engine hot	1,4 V		
	D8	⇨	Ignition ON	5 V		
	D15	⊐⟋	Ignition ON	0 V		
Oxygen sensor (O2S)	D9	⟵	Engine idling – engine hot	0,1-1 V fluctuating	0,2 V/1 sec.	⋀⋁⋀ 21
Tachometer	B13	⇨	Ignition ON	11-14 V		
	B13	⇨	Engine idling	27 Hz		
	B13	⇨	3000 rpm	100 Hz		
Throttle position (TP) sensor	B2	⊐⟋	Ignition ON	0 V		
	D5	⟵	Ignition ON – throttle closed	0,6 V		
	D5	⟵	Ignition ON – throttle fully open	4,5 V		
	D8	⇨	Ignition ON	5 V		
Transmission control module (TCM)	A9			[1]		
	C10			[1]		
Vehicle speed sensor (VSS)	D10	⟵	Ignition ON – vehicle moving	0-10 V fluctuating	5 V/1 sec.	⋀⋁⋀ 39

*Suggested settings - Voltage/time per division

[1] Connected pin - no test data available or random digital signal

Model:	Engine code:	Year:
Corsa-C 1,0	Z10XE	2000-06

ECM harness multi-plug

Terminal side

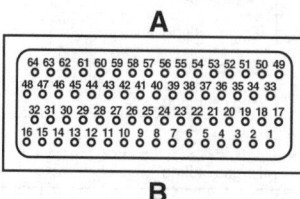

Wire side

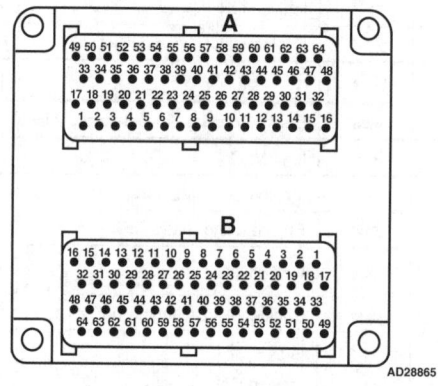

AD28865

Component/circuit description	ECM pin	Signal	Condition	Typical value	Oscilloscope setting*	Wave form
ABS control module	B59			1		
AC compressor clutch relay	B30			1		
	B39			1		
	B53			1		
Accelerator pedal position (APP) sensor	B4	⇒	Ignition ON	5 V		
	B5	⌐	Ignition ON	0 V		
	B21	⇒	Ignition ON	5 V		
	B22	⌐	Ignition ON	0 V		
	B37	←	Ignition ON – accelerator pedal released	0,5 V		
	B37	←	Ignition ON – accelerator pedal fully depressed	2 V		
	B54	←	Ignition ON – accelerator pedal released	1 V		
	B54	←	Ignition ON – accelerator pedal fully depressed	4,2 V		
Battery	B18	←	Ignition OFF	11-14 V		
	B51	←	Ignition ON	11-14 V		
Brake pedal position (BPP) switch	B25	←	Ignition ON – brake pedal released	0 V		
	B25	←	Ignition ON – brake pedal depressed	11-14 V		
	B57	←	Ignition ON – brake pedal released	11-14 V		
	B57	←	Ignition ON – brake pedal depressed	0 V		

★ Suggested settings - Voltage/time per division

Component/circuit description	ECM pin	Signal	Condition	Typical value	Oscilloscope setting*	Wave form
Camshaft position (CMP) sensor	A7	⇒	Ignition ON	5 V		
	A36	←	Engine idling		2 V/20 ms	〰 14
	A45	⊣—	Ignition ON	0 V		
Camshaft position (CMP) sensor – shield wire	A45	⊣—	Ignition ON	0 V		
Clutch pedal position (CPP) switch	B8	←	Ignition ON – clutch pedal released	0 V		
	B8	←	Ignition ON – clutch pedal depressed	11-14 V		
Crankshaft position (CKP) sensor	A10 (A42)	←	Engine idling	2,4 V	2 V/1 ms	Reversed 〰 2
	A42 (A10)	←	Engine idling	2,4 V	2 V/1 ms	〰 2
Crankshaft position (CKP) sensor – shield wire	A45	⊣—	Ignition ON	0 V		
Engine control relay	B17	←	Engine idling	11-14 V		
	B19	⊣▷	Ignition OFF	11-14 V		
	B19	⊣▷	Ignition ON	0-1 V		
	B33	←	Ignition ON	11-14 V		
	B49	←	Ignition ON	11-14 V		
Engine coolant blower motor relay	B14	⊣▷	Ignition OFF	11-14 V		
	B14	⊣▷	Ignition ON	11-14 V		
	B14	⊣▷	Engine idling – coolant blower motor OFF	11-14 V		
	B14	⊣▷	Engine idling – coolant blower motor ON	0-1 V		
	B45			[1]		
Engine coolant temperature (ECT) sensor	A9	⊣—	Ignition ON	0 V		
	A38	←	Ignition ON – coolant temp. 20°C	3,4 V		
	A38	←	Ignition ON – coolant temp. 80°C	0,9 V		
Engine oil pressure warning lamp switch	B56	⇒	Ignition OFF	0 V		
	B56	⇒	Engine idling	11-14 V		
Evaporative emission (EVAP) canister purge valve	A33	⊣▷	Ignition ON	11-14 V		
Exhaust gas recirculation (EGR) solenoid	A1	⊣▷	Ignition ON	11-14 V		
	A1	⊣▷	Accelerate briefly		5 V/5 ms	〰 24
	A50	⊣▷	Ignition ON	11-14 V briefly then 0-1 V		
	A50	⊣▷	Accelerate briefly	11-14 V	5 V/5 ms	〰 24
Exhaust gas recirculation (EGR) valve position sensor	A7	⇒	Ignition ON	5 V		
	A9	⊣—	Ignition ON	0 V		
	A54	←	Engine idling	1 V		
Fuel gauge tank sensor	B55	←		[1]		
Fuel pump relay	B46	⊣—	Ignition ON	0-1 V briefly then 11-14 V		
	B46	⊣—	Engine idling	0-1 V		
Heated oxygen sensor (HO2S) 1	A8	←	Engine idling	0-1 V fluctuating	0,2 V/1 sec.	〰 21
	A25	⊣—	Ignition ON	0 V		
	A49	⊣▷	Engine idling		4 V/0,1 sec.	〰 28
Heated oxygen sensor (HO2S) 1 – shield wire	A45	⊣—	Ignition ON	0 V		
Heated oxygen sensor (HO2S) 2	A17	⊣▷	Ignition ON	11-14 V		
	A17	⊣▷	Engine idling		4 V/0,1 sec.	〰 28
	A41	⊣—	Ignition ON	0 V		
	A57	←	Ignition ON	0,4 V		
	A57	←	Engine idling	0,6 V		
Heated oxygen sensor (HO2S) 2 – shield wire	A45	⊣—	Ignition ON	0 V		

* Suggested settings - Voltage/time per division

Component/circuit description	ECM pin	Signal	Condition	Typical value	Oscilloscope setting*	Wave form
Ignition coil	A15	⇥▷	Ignition ON	11-14 V		
	A15	⇥▷	Engine idling		5 V/2 ms	
	A16	⇥▷	Ignition ON	11-14 V		
	A16	⇥▷	Engine idling		5 V/2 ms	
	A32	⇥▷	Ignition ON	11-14 V		
	A32	⇥▷	Engine idling		5 V/2 ms	
Immobilizer control module	B2	⇨	Ignition ON	11-14 V		
	B2	⇨	Engine idling	11-14 V		
	B13	⬅	Engine idling	11-14 V		
Injector 1	A51	⇥▷	Ignition ON	11-14 V briefly then 0 V		
	A51	⇥▷	Engine idling	3,1 ms	10 V/2 ms	
Injector 2	A2	⇥▷	Ignition ON	11-14 V briefly then 0-1 V		
	A2	⇥▷	Engine idling	3,1 ms	10 V/2 ms	
Injector 3	A34	⇥▷	Ignition ON	11-14 V briefly then 0-1 V		
	A34	⇥▷	Engine idling	3,1 ms	10 V/2 ms	
Intake air temperature (IAT) sensor	A55	⬅	Ignition ON	3,2 V		
	A55	⬅	Engine idling	3 V		
Knock sensor (KS)	A21	⬅	Engine running – accelerate briefly		50 mV/1 ms	
	A37	⬅	Accelerate briefly		50 mV/1 ms	
Mass air flow (MAF) sensor	A6	⬅	Engine idling	1,3 V		
	A6	⬅	Accelerate briefly	4,2 V		
	A6	⬅	Ignition ON	1 V		
	A7	⇨	Ignition ON	5 V		
	A9	⇥−	Ignition ON	0 V		
Multifunction control module	B11			1		
	B43			1		
Power steering control module	B20	⬅	Engine idling – steering wheel not turned	8,5 V		
Throttle motor	A11	⇨	Ignition ON	0,1 V – for 10 seconds		
	A11	⇨	Ignition ON	3 V – after 10 seconds		
	A28	⇨	Ignition ON	11-14 V – for 10 seconds	4 V/0,2 ms	Reversed
	A28	⇨	Ignition ON	3 V – after 10 seconds		
	A43	⇨	Ignition ON	0,1 V – for 10 seconds		
	A43	⇨	Ignition ON	3 V – after 10 seconds		
	A60	⇨	Ignition ON	11-14 V – for 10 seconds	4 V/0,2 ms	Reversed
	A60	⇨	Ignition ON	3 V – after 10 seconds		
Throttle motor position sensor	A23	⬅	Ignition ON – accelerator pedal released	1 V		
	A23	⬅	Ignition ON – accelerator pedal fully depressed	4,2 V		
	A39	⬅	Ignition ON – accelerator pedal released	4 V		
	A39	⬅	Ignition ON – accelerator pedal fully depressed	1 V		
	A56	⇨	Ignition ON	5 V		
	A58	⬅	Ignition ON	0 V		
Vehicle speed sensor (VSS) signal amplifier	B59			1		

*Suggested settings - Voltage/time per division

1 Connected pin - no test data available or random digital signal

ECM harness multi-plug

Terminal side

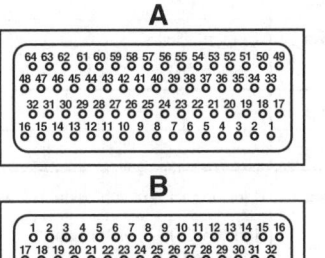

Wire side

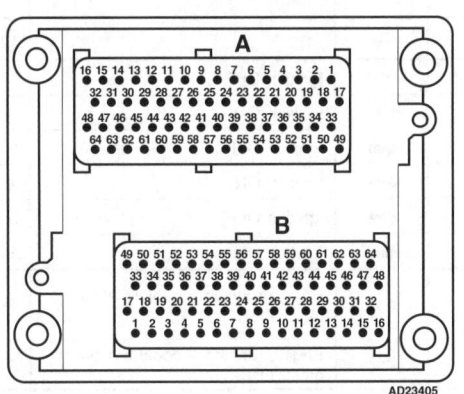

Component/circuit description	ECM pin	Signal	Condition	Typical value	Oscilloscope setting*	Wave form
ABS control module – VSS signal	B59	←	Ignition ON – vehicle pushed	0 V or 11-14 V fluctuating		
AC compressor clutch relay	B30	⇥▷	Engine idling – AC OFF	11-14 V		
	B30	⇥▷	Engine idling – AC ON – AC compressor OFF	11-14 V		
	B30	⇥▷	Engine idling – AC ON – AC compressor ON	0-1 V		
AC refrigerant pressure sensor	B39	←		①		
	B53	⇨	Ignition ON	5 V		
Accelerator pedal position (APP) sensor	B4	⇨	Ignition ON	5 V		
	B5	⇥	Ignition ON	0 V		
	B21	⇨	Ignition ON	5 V		
	B22	⇥	Ignition ON	0 V		
	B37	←	Ignition ON – accelerator pedal released	0,6 V		
	B37	←	Ignition ON – accelerator pedal fully depressed	2 V		
	B54	←	Ignition ON – accelerator pedal released	1 V		
	B54	←	Ignition ON – accelerator pedal fully depressed	4,1 V		
Battery	B18	←	Ignition OFF	11-14 V		

★ Suggested settings - Voltage/time per division

Component/circuit description	ECM pin	Signal	Condition	Typical value	Oscilloscope setting*	Wave form
Brake pedal position (BPP) switch	B25	←	Ignition ON – brake pedal released	0 V		
	B25	←	Ignition ON – brake pedal depressed	11-14 V		
	B57	←	Ignition ON – brake pedal released	11-14 V		
	B57	←	Ignition ON – brake pedal depressed	0 V		
Camshaft position (CMP) sensor	A3	⇒	Ignition ON	5 V		
	A4	←	Ignition ON	0 V or 5 V		
	A4	←	Engine idling		2 V/20 ms	14
	A21	⌐	Ignition ON	0 V		
CAN data bus	B11	⟷		[1]		
	B43	⟷		[1]		
Clutch pedal position (CPP) switch – with cruise control	B8	←	Ignition ON – clutch pedal released	0 V		
	B8	←	Ignition ON – clutch pedal depressed	11-14 V		
Crankshaft position (CKP) sensor	A27 (A43)	←	Engine idling		2 V/2 ms	Reversed 2
	A43 (A27)	←	Engine idling		2 V/2 ms	2
Digital multifunction display – 2005→	B35	⇒		[1]		
Engine control (EC) relay	B19	⌐⇒	Ignition OFF	11-14 V		
	B19	⌐⇒	Ignition ON	0-1 V		
	B33	←	Ignition OFF	0 V		
	B33	←	Ignition ON	11-14 V		
	B49	←	Ignition OFF	0 V		
	B49	←	Ignition ON	11-14 V		
Engine coolant blower motor relay – without AC, with single speed engine coolant blower motor	B14	⌐⇒	Engine running – coolant blower motor OFF	11-14 V		
	B14	⌐⇒	Engine running – coolant blower motor ON	0-1 V		
Engine coolant blower motor relay 1 – with AC, with 2 speed engine coolant blower motor	B62	⌐⇒	Engine running – coolant blower motor OFF	11-14 V		
	B62	⌐⇒	Engine running – coolant blower motor ON, 1st speed	0-1 V		
	B62	⌐⇒	Engine running – coolant blower motor ON, 2nd speed	11-14 V		
Engine coolant blower motor relay 1 – with AC, with 3 speed engine coolant blower motor	B14	⌐⇒	Engine running – coolant blower motor OFF	11-14 V		
	B14	⌐⇒	Engine running – coolant blower motor ON, 1st speed	0-1 V		
	B14	⌐⇒	Engine running – coolant blower motor ON, 2nd speed	11-14 V		
	B14	⌐⇒	Engine running – coolant blower motor ON, 3rd speed	11-14 V		
Engine coolant blower motor relay 1 – without AC, with 2 speed engine coolant blower motor	B14	⌐⇒	Engine running – coolant blower motor OFF	11-14 V		
	B14	⌐⇒	Engine running – coolant blower motor ON, 1st speed	0-1 V		
	B14	⌐⇒	Engine running – coolant blower motor ON, 2nd speed	11-14 V		
Engine coolant blower motor relay 2 – with AC, with 2 speed engine coolant blower motor	B45	⌐⇒	Engine running – coolant blower motor OFF	11-14 V		
	B45	⌐⇒	Engine running – coolant blower motor ON, 1st speed	11-14 V		
	B45	⌐⇒	Engine running – coolant blower motor ON, 2nd speed	0-1 V		

* Suggested settings - Voltage/time per division

Component/circuit description	ECM pin	Signal	Condition	Typical value	Oscilloscope setting*	Wave form
Engine coolant blower motor relay 2 – with AC, with 3 speed engine coolant blower motor	B62	⊐▷	Engine running – coolant blower motor OFF	11-14 V		
	B62	⊐▷	Engine running – coolant blower motor ON, 1st speed	11-14 V		
	B62	⊐▷	Engine running – coolant blower motor ON, 2nd speed	0-1 V		
	B62	⊐▷	Engine running – coolant blower motor ON, 3rd speed	11-14 V		
Engine coolant blower motor relay 2 – without AC, with 2 speed engine coolant blower motor	B62	⊐▷	Engine running – coolant blower motor OFF	11-14 V		
	B62	⊐▷	Engine running – coolant blower motor ON, 1st speed	11-14 V		
	B62	⊐▷	Engine running – coolant blower motor ON, 2nd speed	0-1 V		
Engine coolant blower motor relay 3 – with AC, with 3 speed engine coolant blower motor	B45	⊐▷	Engine running – coolant blower motor OFF	11-14 V		
	B45	⊐▷	Engine running – coolant blower motor ON, 1st speed	11-14 V		
	B45	⊐▷	Engine running – coolant blower motor ON, 2nd speed	11-14 V		
	B45	⊐▷	Engine running – coolant blower motor ON, 3rd speed	0-1 V		
Engine coolant temperature (ECT) sensor	A38	⬅	Ignition ON – coolant temp. 20°C	3,4 V		
	A38	⬅	Ignition ON – coolant temp. 80°C	0,9 V		
	A42	⊐—	Ignition ON	0 V		
Engine oil pressure warning lamp switch	A5	⬅	Ignition ON	0 V		
	A5	⬅	Engine idling	11-14 V		
Evaporative emission (EVAP) canister purge valve	A33	⊐▷	Ignition ON	11-14 V		
	A33	⊐▷	Engine running – valve operating	1-99 %	10 V/20 ms	⌇⌇ 20
Exhaust gas recirculation (EGR) valve actuator	A50	⊐▷	Ignition ON	11-14 V		
	A50	⊐▷	Accelerate briefly		5 V/5 ms	⌇⌇ 24
Exhaust gas recirculation (EGR) valve position sensor	A7	⇨	Ignition ON	5 V		
	A9	⊐—	Ignition ON	0 V		
	A54	⬅	Engine idling	0,9 V		
Fuel gauge tank sensor	B55	⬅		[1]		
Fuel pump (FP) relay	B46	⊐▷	Ignition ON	0-1 V briefly then 11-14 V		
	B46	⊐▷	Engine idling	0-1 V		
Heated oxygen sensor (HO2S) 1	A8	⬅	Engine idling	0,1-0,9 V fluctuating	0,2 V/1 sec.	⌇⌇ 21
	A25	⊐—	Ignition ON	0 V		
	A49	⊐▷	Ignition ON	11-14 V		
	A49	⊐▷	Engine idling	0-1 V		
Heated oxygen sensor (HO2S) 2	A35	⊐▷	Ignition ON	11-14 V		
	A35	⊐▷	Engine idling	0-1 V		
	A41	⊐—	Ignition ON	0 V		
	A57	⬅	Engine idling	0,6 V		
Ignition coil – cylinder 1	A48	⊐▷	Ignition ON	11-14 V		
	A48	⊐▷	Engine idling		5 V/2 ms	⌇⌇ 33
Ignition coil – cylinder 2	A64	⊐▷	Ignition ON	11-14 V		
	A64	⊐▷	Engine idling		5 V/2 ms	⌇⌇ 33
Ignition coil – cylinder 3	A47	⊐▷	Ignition ON	11-14 V		
	A47	⊐▷	Engine idling		5 V/2 ms	⌇⌇ 33
Ignition switch	B51	⬅	Ignition OFF	0 V		
	B51	⬅	Ignition ON	11-14 V		

* Suggested settings - Voltage/time per division

Component/circuit description	ECM pin	Signal	Condition	Typical value	Oscilloscope setting*	Wave form
Immobilizer control module	B2	←⇨		1		
	B29	←⇨		1		
Injector 1	A18	⊐⇨	Ignition ON	11-14 V briefly then 0 V		
	A18	⊐⇨	Engine idling	3,2 ms	10 V/2 ms	35
Injector 2	A2	⊐⇨	Ignition ON	11-14 V briefly then 0 V		
	A2	⊐⇨	Engine idling	3,2 ms	10 V/2 ms	35
Injector 3	A19	⊐⇨	Ignition ON	11-14 V briefly then 0 V		
	A19	⊐⇨	Engine idling	3,2 ms	10 V/2 ms	35
Intake air temperature (IAT) sensor	A26	⊐—	Ignition ON	0 V		
	A55	←	Ignition ON – air temp. 20°C	3,2 V		
Intake manifold air control actuator position sensor	A10	⊐—	Ignition ON	0 V		
	A44	←	Engine idling	2,7 V		
Intake manifold air control solenoid	A34	⊐⇨	Engine idling	0-1 V		
Knock sensor (KS)	A20 (A52)	←	Engine running – accelerate briefly		50 mV/1 ms	38
	A52 (A20)	←	Engine running – accelerate briefly		50 mV/1 ms	38
Mass air flow (MAF) sensor	A6	←	Ignition ON	1 V		
	A6	←	Engine idling	1,3 V		
	A6	←	Engine idling – accelerate briefly	4,2 V briefly		
	A24	⇨	Ignition ON	5 V		
	A26	⊐—	Ignition ON	0 V		
Power steering control module	B20	←	Engine idling – steering wheel not turned	8,5 V		
Throttle motor	A14	⇨	Engine idling		2 V/50 ms	71
	A30	⇨	Ignition ON	0 V		
Throttle motor position sensor	A23	←	Ignition ON – accelerator pedal released	0,8 V		
	A23	←	Ignition ON – accelerator pedal fully depressed	4 V		
	A39	←	Ignition ON – accelerator pedal released	4,1 V		
	A39	←	Ignition ON – accelerator pedal fully depressed	1 V		
	A56	⇨	Ignition ON	5 V		
	A58	⊐—	Ignition ON	0 V		
Vehicle speed sensor (VSS) signal amplifier – without ABS	B59	←	Ignition ON – vehicle pushed	0 V or 11-14 V fluctuating		

*Suggested settings - Voltage/time per division

1 Connected pin - no test data available or random digital signal

ECM harness multi-plug

Terminal side

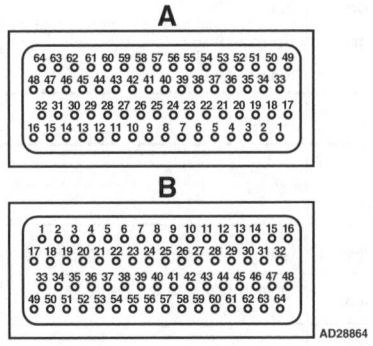

Wire side

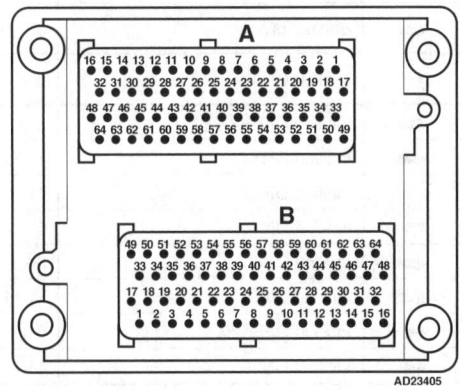

Component/circuit description	ECM pin	Signal	Condition	Typical value	Oscilloscope setting*	Wave form
ABS control module – VSS signal	B59	←	Ignition ON – vehicle pushed	0 V or 11-14 V fluctuating		
AC compressor clutch relay	B30	⊐▷	Engine idling – AC OFF	11-14 V		
	B30	⊐▷	Engine idling – AC ON – AC compressor OFF	11-14 V		
	B30	⊐▷	Engine idling – AC ON – AC compressor ON	0-1 V		
AC refrigerant pressure sensor	B5	⊐—	Ignition ON	0 V		
	B39			☐1		
	B53			☐1		
Accelerator pedal position (APP) sensor	B4	⇨	Ignition ON	5 V		
	B5	⊐—	Ignition ON	0 V		
	B21	⇨	Ignition ON	5 V		
	B22	⊐—	Ignition ON	0 V		
	B37	←	Ignition ON – accelerator pedal released	0,5 V		
	B37	←	Ignition ON – accelerator pedal fully depressed	2 V		
	B54	←	Ignition ON – accelerator pedal released	1 V		
	B54	←	Ignition ON – accelerator pedal fully depressed	4,2 V		
Battery	B18	←	Ignition OFF	11-14 V		

* Suggested settings - Voltage/time per division

Component/circuit description	ECM pin	Signal	Condition	Typical value	Oscilloscope setting*	Wave form
Brake pedal position (BPP) switch	B25	←	Ignition ON – brake pedal released	0 V		
	B25	←	Ignition ON – brake pedal depressed	11-14 V		
	B57	←	Ignition ON – brake pedal released	11-14 V		
	B57	←	Ignition ON – brake pedal depressed	0 V		
Camshaft position (CMP) sensor	A7	⇒	Ignition ON	5 V		
	A36	←	Ignition ON	0 V or 5 V		
	A36	←	Engine idling		2 V/20 ms	⎍⎍ 4
	A45	⊣⎽	Ignition ON	0 V		
Camshaft position (CMP) sensor – shield wire	A45	⊣⎽	Ignition ON	0 V		
CAN data bus	B11	⬌		1		
	B43	⬌		1		
Clutch pedal position (CPP) switch – with cruise control	B8	←	Ignition ON – clutch pedal released	0 V		
	B8	←	Ignition ON – clutch pedal depressed	11-14 V		
Crankshaft position (CKP) sensor	A10 (A42)	←	Engine idling	3 V ac	2 V/1 ms	Reversed ⎍⎍ 2
	A42 (A10)	←	Engine idling	3 V ac	2 V/1 ms	⎍⎍ 2
Crankshaft position (CKP) sensor – shield wire	A45	⊣⎽	Ignition ON	0 V		
Engine control (EC) relay	B17	←	Ignition OFF	0 V		
	B17	←	Ignition ON	11-14 V		
	B19	⊣⊳	Ignition OFF	11-14 V		
	B19	⊣⊳	Ignition ON	0-1 V		
	B33	←	Ignition OFF	0 V		
	B33	←	Ignition ON	11-14 V		
	B49	←	Ignition OFF	0 V		
	B49	←	Ignition ON	11-14 V		
Engine coolant blower motor relay 1	B14	⊣⊳	Engine running – coolant blower motor OFF	11-14 V		
	B14	⊣⊳	Engine running – coolant blower motor ON	0-1 V		
Engine coolant blower motor relay 2 – with AC	B62	⊣⊳	Engine running – coolant blower motor OFF	11-14 V		
	B62	⊣⊳	Engine running – coolant blower motor ON, 2nd speed	0-1 V		
Engine coolant blower motor relay 3 – with AC	B45	⊣⊳	Engine running – coolant blower motor OFF	11-14 V		
	B45	⊣⊳	Engine running – coolant blower motor ON, 1st speed	11-14 V		
	B45	⊣⊳	Engine running – coolant blower motor ON, 2nd speed	0-1 V		
Engine coolant temperature (ECT) sensor	A9	⊣⎽	Ignition ON	0 V		
	A38	←	Ignition ON – coolant temp. 20°C	3,4 V		
	A38	←	Ignition ON – coolant temp. 80°C	0,9 V		
Engine oil pressure warning lamp switch	B56	←	Ignition ON	0 V		
	B56	←	Engine idling	11-14 V		
Evaporative emission (EVAP) canister purge valve	A33	⊣⊳	Ignition ON	11-14 V		
	A33	⊣⊳	Engine idling	11-14 V		
	A33	⊣⊳	Engine running – valve operating	0-1 V		
Exhaust gas recirculation (EGR) valve actuator – →2002	A1	⊣⊳	Ignition ON	11-14 V		
	A1	⊣⊳	Accelerate briefly		5 V/5 ms	⎍⎍ 24
	A50	⊣⊳	Ignition ON	11-14 V		
	A50	⊣⊳	Accelerate briefly		5 V/5 ms	⎍⎍ 24

* Suggested settings - Voltage/time per division

Component/circuit description	ECM pin	Signal	Condition	Typical value	Oscilloscope setting*	Wave form
Exhaust gas recirculation (EGR) valve position sensor – →2002	A7	⇨	Ignition ON	5 V		
	A9	⌐	Ignition ON	0 V		
	A54	⇐	Engine idling	1 V		
Fuel gauge tank sensor	B55	⇐		1		
Fuel pump (FP) relay	B46	⌐⇨	Ignition ON	0-1 V briefly then 11-14 V		
	B46	⌐⇨	Engine idling	0-1 V		
Heated oxygen sensor (HO2S) 1	A8	⇐	Engine idling	0,1-0,9 V fluctuating	0,2 V/1 sec.	21
	A25	⌐	Ignition ON	0 V		
	A49	⌐⇨	Engine idling		4 V/0,1 sec.	28
Heated oxygen sensor (HO2S) 1 – shield wire	A45	⌐	Ignition ON	0 V		
Heated oxygen sensor (HO2S) 2	A17	⌐⇨	Ignition ON	11-14 V		
	A17	⌐⇨	Engine idling		4 V/0,1 sec.	28
	A41	⌐	Ignition ON	0 V		
	A57	⇐	Engine idling	0,6 V		
Heated oxygen sensor (HO2S) 2 – shield wire	A45	⌐	Ignition ON	0 V		
Ignition coil	A15	⌐⇨	Ignition ON	11-14 V		
	A15	⌐⇨	Engine idling		5 V/2 ms	33
	A16	⌐⇨	Ignition ON	11-14 V		
	A16	⌐⇨	Engine idling		5 V/2 ms	33
	A31	⌐⇨	Ignition ON	11-14 V		
	A31	⌐⇨	Engine idling		5 V/2 ms	33
	A32	⌐⇨	Ignition ON	11-14 V		
	A32	⌐⇨	Engine idling		5 V/2 ms	33
Ignition switch	B51	⇐	Ignition OFF	0 V		
	B51	⇐	Ignition ON	11-14 V		
Immobilizer control module	B2	⇔		1		
	B13	⇔		1		
Injector 1	A51	⌐⇨	Ignition ON	11-14 V briefly then 0-1 V		
	A51	⌐⇨	Engine idling	3,2 ms	10 V/2 ms	35
Injector 2	A18	⌐⇨	Ignition ON	11-14 V briefly then 0-1 V		
	A18	⌐⇨	Engine idling	3,2 ms	10 V/2 ms	35
Injector 3	A2	⌐⇨	Ignition ON	11-14 V briefly then 0-1 V		
	A2	⌐⇨	Engine idling	3,2 ms	10 V/2 ms	35
Injector 4	A34	⌐⇨	Ignition ON	11-14 V briefly then 0-1 V		
	A34	⌐⇨	Engine idling	3,2 ms	10 V/2 ms	35
Intake air temperature (IAT) sensor	A9	⌐	Ignition ON	0 V		
	A55	⇐	Ignition ON – air temp. 20°C	3,2 V		
Knock sensor (KS)	A21 (A37)	⇐	Engine running – accelerate briefly		50 mV/1 ms	38
	A37 (A21)	⇐	Engine running – accelerate briefly		50 mV/1 ms	38
Mass air flow (MAF) sensor	A6	⇐	Ignition ON	1 V		
	A6	⇐	Engine idling	1,3 V		
	A6	⇐	Engine idling – accelerate briefly	4,2 V		
	A7	⇨	Ignition ON	5 V		
	A9	⌐	Ignition ON	0 V		

* Suggested settings - Voltage/time per division

Component/circuit description	ECM pin	Signal	Condition	Typical value	Oscilloscope setting*	Wave form
Power steering control module	B20	←	Engine idling – steering wheel not turned	8,5 V		
Throttle motor	A11	⇒	Ignition ON	0,1 V for 10 secs.		
	A11	⇒	Ignition ON	3 V after 10 seconds		
	A28	⇒	Ignition ON	11-14 V for 10 secs.	4 V/0,2 ms	Reversed 〰〰 67
	A28	⇒	Ignition ON	3 V after 10 secs.		
	A43	⇒	Ignition ON	0,1 V for 10 secs.		
	A43	⇒	Ignition ON	3 V after 10 secs.		
	A60	⇒	Ignition ON	11-14 V for 10 secs.	4 V/0,2 ms	Reversed 〰〰 67
	A60	⇒	Ignition ON	3 V after 10 secs.		
Throttle motor position sensor	A23	←	Ignition ON – accelerator pedal released	1 V		
	A23	←	Ignition ON – accelerator pedal fully depressed	4,2 V		
	A39	←	Ignition ON – accelerator pedal released	4 V		
	A39	←	Ignition ON – accelerator pedal fully depressed	1 V		
	A56	⇒	Ignition ON	5 V		
	A58	⌐	Ignition ON	0 V		
Vehicle speed sensor (VSS) signal amplifier – without ABS	B59	←	Ignition ON – vehicle pushed	0 V or 11-14 V fluctuating		

*Suggested settings - Voltage/time per division

1 Connected pin - no test data available or random digital signal

Model:		Engine code:		Year:
Corsa-C 1,2		Z12XEP		2004-06
Corsa-C 1,4		Z14XEP		2003-06

ECM harness multi-plug

Terminal side

Wire side

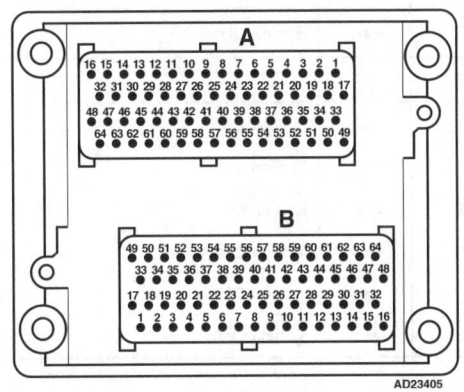

Component/circuit description	ECM pin	Signal	Condition	Typical value	Oscilloscope setting*	Wave form
ABS control module – VSS signal	B59	←	Ignition ON – vehicle pushed	0 V or 11-14 V fluctuating		
AC compressor clutch relay	B30	⇥▷	Engine idling – AC OFF	11-14 V		
	B30	⇥▷	Engine idling – AC ON – AC compressor OFF	11-14 V		
	B30	⇥▷	Engine idling – AC ON – AC compressor ON	0-1 V		
AC refrigerant pressure sensor	B5	⇥	Ignition ON	0 V		
	B39	←		1		
	B53	⇨	Ignition ON	5 V		
Accelerator pedal position (APP) sensor	B4	⇨	Ignition ON	5 V		
	B5	⇥	Ignition ON	0 V		
	B21	⇨	Ignition ON	5 V		
	B22	⇥	Ignition ON	0 V		
	B37	←	Ignition ON – accelerator pedal released	0,5 V		
	B37	←	Ignition ON – accelerator pedal fully depressed	2 V		
	B54	←	Ignition ON – accelerator pedal released	1 V		
	B54	←	Ignition ON – accelerator pedal fully depressed	4,2 V		
Battery	B18	←	Ignition OFF	11-14 V		

* Suggested settings - Voltage/time per division

Component/circuit description	ECM pin	Signal	Condition	Typical value	Oscilloscope setting*	Wave form
Brake pedal position (BPP) switch	B25	⬅	Ignition ON – brake pedal released	0 V		
	B25	⬅	Ignition ON – brake pedal depressed	11-14 V		
	B57	⬅	Ignition ON – brake pedal released	11-14 V		
	B57	⬅	Ignition ON – brake pedal depressed	0 V		
Camshaft position (CMP) sensor	A3	⮕	Ignition ON	5 V		
	A4	⬅	Ignition ON	0 V or 5 V		
	A4	⬅	Engine idling		2 V/20 ms	⟿ 14
	A21	⌐	Ignition ON	0 V		
CAN data bus	B11	⬌		1		
	B43	⬌		1		
Clutch pedal position (CPP) switch – with cruise control	B8	⬅	Ignition ON – clutch pedal released	0 V		
	B8	⬅	Ignition ON – clutch pedal depressed	11-14 V		
Crankshaft position (CKP) sensor	A27 (A43)	⬅	Engine idling		2 V/2 ms	Reversed ⟿ 2
	A43 (A27)	⬅	Engine idling		2 V/2 ms	⟿ 2
Digital multifunction display – 2005→	B35	⮕		1		
Engine control (EC) relay	B19	⊣▷	Ignition OFF	11-14 V		
	B19	⊣▷	Ignition ON	0-1 V		
	B33	⬅	Ignition OFF	0 V		
	B33	⬅	Ignition ON	11-14 V		
	B49	⬅	Ignition OFF	0 V		
	B49	⬅	Ignition ON	11-14 V		
Engine coolant blower motor relay 1	B14	⊣▷	Engine running – coolant blower motor OFF	11-14 V		
	B14	⊣▷	Engine running – coolant blower motor ON, 1st speed	0-1 V		
	B14	⊣▷	Engine running – coolant blower motor ON, 2nd speed	11-14 V		
Engine coolant blower motor relay 1 – with AC	B14	⊣▷	Engine running – coolant blower motor ON, 3rd speed	11-14 V		
Engine coolant blower motor relay 2	B62	⊣▷	Engine running – coolant blower motor OFF	11-14 V		
	B62	⊣▷	Engine running – coolant blower motor ON, 1st speed	11-14 V		
	B62	⊣▷	Engine running – coolant blower motor ON, 2nd speed	0-1 V		
Engine coolant blower motor relay 2 – with AC	B62	⊣▷	Engine running – coolant blower motor ON, 3rd speed	11-14 V		
Engine coolant blower motor relay 3 – with AC	B45	⊣▷	Engine running – coolant blower motor OFF	11-14 V		
	B45	⊣▷	Engine running – coolant blower motor ON, 1st speed	11-14 V		
	B45	⊣▷	Engine running – coolant blower motor ON, 2nd speed	11-14 V		
	B45	⊣▷	Engine running – coolant blower motor ON, 3rd speed	0-1 V		
Engine coolant temperature (ECT) sensor	A38	⬅	Ignition ON – coolant temp. 20°C	3,4 V		
	A38	⬅	Ignition ON – coolant temp. 80°C	0,9 V		
	A42	⌐	Ignition ON	0 V		
Engine oil pressure warning lamp switch	A5	⬅	Ignition ON	0 V		
	A5	⬅	Engine idling	11-14 V		

✱ Suggested settings - Voltage/time per division

Component/circuit description	ECM pin	Signal	Condition	Typical value	Oscilloscope setting*	Wave form
Evaporative emission (EVAP) canister purge valve	A33	⊐▷	Ignition ON	11-14 V		
	A33	⊐▷	Engine idling	11-14 V		
	A33	⊐▷	Engine running – valve operating	1-99 %		
Exhaust gas recirculation (EGR) valve actuator	A50	⊐▷	Ignition ON	11-14 V		
	A50	⊐▷	Accelerate briefly		5 V/5 ms	∿ 24
Exhaust gas recirculation (EGR) valve position sensor	A7	⇨	Ignition ON	5 V		
	A9	⊐—	Ignition ON	0 V		
	A54	⬅	Engine idling	0,9 V		
Fuel gauge tank sensor	B55	⬅		1		
Fuel pump (FP) relay	B46	⊐▷	Ignition ON	0-1 V briefly then 11-14 V		
	B46	⊐▷	Engine idling	0-1 V		
Heated oxygen sensor (HO2S) 1	A8	⬅	Engine idling	0,1-0,9 V fluctuating	0,2 V/1 sec.	∿ 21
	A25	⊐—	Ignition ON	0 V		
	A49	⊐▷	Ignition ON	11-14 V		
	A49	⊐▷	Engine idling	0-1 V		
Heated oxygen sensor (HO2S) 2	A35	⊐▷	Ignition ON	11-14 V		
	A35	⊐▷	Engine idling	0-1 V		
	A41	⊐—	Ignition ON	0 V		
	A57	⬅	Engine idling	0,6 V		
Ignition coil	A47	⊐▷	Ignition ON	11-14 V		
	A47	⊐▷	Engine idling		5 V/2 ms	∿ 33
	A48	⊐▷	Ignition ON	11-14 V		
	A48	⊐▷	Engine idling		5 V/2 ms	∿ 33
	A63	⊐▷	Ignition ON	11-14 V		
	A63	⊐▷	Engine idling		5 V/2 ms	∿ 33
	A64	⊐▷	Ignition ON	11-14 V		
	A64	⊐▷	Engine idling		5 V/2 ms	∿ 33
Ignition switch	B51	⬅	Ignition OFF	0 V		
	B51	⬅	Ignition ON	11-14 V		
Immobilizer control module	B2	⬄		1		
	B29	⬄		1		
Injector 1	A18	⊐▷	Ignition ON	11-14 V briefly then 0 V		
	A18	⊐▷	Engine idling	3,2 ms	10 V/2 ms	∿ 35
Injector 2	A17	⊐▷	Ignition ON	11-14 V briefly then 0 V		
	A17	⊐▷	Engine idling	3,2 ms	10 V/2 ms	∿ 35
Injector 3	A2	⊐▷	Ignition ON	11-14 V briefly then 0 V		
	A2	⊐▷	Engine idling	3,2 ms	10 V/2 ms	∿ 35
Injector 4	A19	⊐▷	Ignition ON	11-14 V briefly then 0 V		
	A19	⊐▷	Engine idling	3,2 ms	10 V/2 ms	∿ 35

* Suggested settings - Voltage/time per division

Component/circuit description	ECM pin	Signal	Condition	Typical value	Oscilloscope setting*	Wave form
Intake air temperature (IAT) sensor	A26	⊣—	Ignition ON	0 V		
	A55	⬅	Ignition ON – air temp. 20°C	3,2 V		
Intake manifold air control actuator position sensor	A10	⊣—	Ignition ON	0 V		
	A44	⬅	Engine idling	2,7 V		
Intake manifold air control solenoid	A34	⊣▷	Engine idling	0-1 V		
Knock sensor (KS)	A20 (A52)	⬅	Engine running – accelerate briefly		50 mV/1 ms	〰 38
	A52 (A20)	⬅	Engine running – accelerate briefly		50 mV/1 ms	〰 38
Mass air flow (MAF) sensor	A6	⬅	Ignition ON	1 V		
	A6	⬅	Engine idling	1,3 V		
	A6	⬅	Engine idling – accelerate briefly	4,2 V		
	A24	⟹	Ignition ON	5 V		
	A26	⊣—	Ignition ON	0 V		
Power steering control module	B20	⬅	Engine idling – steering wheel not turned	8,5 V		
Throttle motor	A14	⟹	Engine idling		2 V/50 ms	〰 71
	A30	⟹	Ignition ON	0 V		
Throttle motor position sensor	A23	⬅	Ignition ON – accelerator pedal released	0,8 V		
	A23	⬅	Ignition ON – accelerator pedal fully depressed	4,2 V		
	A39	⬅	Ignition ON – accelerator pedal released	4,1 V		
	A39	⬅	Ignition ON – accelerator pedal fully depressed	1 V		
	A56	⟹	Ignition ON	5 V		
	A58	⊣—	Ignition ON	0 V		
Vehicle speed sensor (VSS) signal amplifier – without ABS	B59	⬅	Ignition ON – vehicle pushed	0 V or 11-14 V fluctuating		

*Suggested settings - Voltage/time per division

1 Connected pin - no test data available or random digital signal

Model:	Engine code:	Year:
Corsa-C 1,3 CDTi	Z13DT	2003-06
Combo-C 1,3 CDTi	Z13DT	2003-06

OPEL-VAUXHALL

Magneti Marelli 6JF

ECM harness multi-plug

Terminal side

A

B

AD105533

Wire side

B

A

AD105522

Component/circuit description	ECM pin	Signal	Condition	Typical value	Oscilloscope setting*	Wave form
ABS control module – VSS signal	A89	←	Ignition ON – vehicle pushed	0 V or 11-14 V fluctuating		
AC compressor clutch relay	A79	⊰▷	Engine idling – AC OFF	11-14 V		
	A79	⊰▷	Engine idling – AC ON – AC compressor OFF	11-14 V		
	A79	⊰▷	Engine idling – AC ON – AC compressor ON	0-1 V		
AC refrigerant pressure sensor	A10	⊰—	Ignition ON	0 V		
	A37	⟹	Ignition ON	5 V		
	A87	←		1		
Accelerator pedal position (APP) sensor	A15	⟹	Ignition ON	5 V		
	A32	⊰—	Ignition ON	0 V		
	A35	⊰—	Ignition ON	0 V		
	A41	←	Ignition ON – accelerator pedal released	0,5 V		
	A41	←	Ignition ON – accelerator pedal depressed	2,1 V		
	A65	←	Ignition ON – accelerator pedal released	0,9 V		
	A65	←	Ignition ON – accelerator pedal depressed	4 V		
	A83	⟹	Ignition ON	5 V		
Battery	A50	←	Ignition OFF	11-14 V		

* Suggested settings - Voltage/time per division

Component/circuit description	ECM pin	Signal	Condition	Typical value	Oscilloscope setting*	Wave form
Brake pedal position (BPP) switch	A68	←	Ignition ON – brake pedal released	11-14 V		
	A68	←	Ignition ON – brake pedal depressed	0 V		
	A81	←	Ignition ON – brake pedal released	0 V		
	A81	←	Ignition ON – brake pedal depressed	11-14 V		
Camshaft position (CMP) sensor	B21	⌐⊢	Ignition ON	0 V		
	B25	⇨	Ignition ON	5 V		
	B56	←	Engine idling		2 V/50 ms	∿∿ 3
CAN data bus	A40	⬄		1		
	A64	⬄		1		
Clutch pedal position (CPP) switch	A22	←	Ignition ON – clutch pedal released	11-14 V		
	A22	←	Ignition ON – clutch pedal depressed	0 V		
Crankshaft position (CKP) sensor	B43	←	Engine idling	4,3 V ac		
	B43	←	Engine idling		2 V/2 ms	∿∿ 1
	B59	←	Engine idling	4,3 V ac		
	B59	←	Engine idling		2 V/2 ms	Reversed ∿∿ 1
Earth	A1		Ignition ON	0 V		
	A2		Ignition ON	0 V		
	A3		Ignition ON	0 V		
	A72		Ignition ON	0 V		
Engine control (EC) relay	A4	←	Ignition OFF	0 V		
	A4	←	Ignition ON	11-14 V		
	A5	←	Ignition OFF	0 V		
	A5	←	Ignition ON	11-14 V		
	A6	←	Ignition OFF	0 V		
	A6	←	Ignition ON	11-14 V		
	A80	⌐⊢▷	Ignition OFF	11-14 V		
	A80	⌐⊢▷	Ignition ON	0-1 V		
Engine control (EC) relay – 2004	B5	←	Ignition OFF	0 V		
	B5	←	Ignition ON	11-14 V		
Engine coolant blower motor relay 1	A7	⌐⊢▷		1		
Engine coolant blower motor relay 2 – without AC	A8	⌐⊢▷		1		
Engine coolant blower motor relay 2/4 – with AC	A8	⌐⊢▷		1		
Engine coolant blower motor relay 3 – with AC	A30	⌐⊢▷		1		
Engine coolant temperature (ECT) sensor	B29	⌐⊢	Ignition ON	0 V		
	B54	←	Ignition ON – coolant temp. 15°C	3 V		
	B54	←	Engine idling – engine hot	0,5 V		
Engine oil level sensor	A26	←		1		
Engine oil pressure switch	B9	←	Ignition ON	0 V		
	B9	←	Engine idling	5 V		

* Suggested settings - Voltage/time per division

Component/circuit description	ECM pin	Signal	Condition	Typical value	Oscilloscope setting*	Wave form
Exhaust gas recirculation (EGR) solenoid	B15	⇥▷	Ignition ON	11-14 V		
	B15	⇥▷	Engine idling – valve operating		5 V/2 ms	〜〰 2
Exhaust gas recirculation (EGR) solenoid – 2005	B5	⇒	Ignition ON	11-14 V		
Fuel heater relay	A76	⇥▷	Engine running – fuel heater ON	0-1 V		
	A76	⇥▷	Engine running – fuel heater OFF	11-14 V		
Fuel lift pump relay	A75	⇥▷	Ignition ON	0-1 V for 10 seconds then 11-14 V		
	A75	⇥▷	Engine idling	0-1 V		
Fuel rail pressure (FRP) control valve	B4	⇒	Ignition ON	11-14 V		
	B4	⇒	Engine idling	11-14 V		
	B34	⟵	Ignition ON		2 V/0,2 ms	〜〰 66
	B34	⟵	Engine idling		2 V/1 ms	〜〰 37
Fuel rail pressure (FRP) sensor	B6	⇥—	Ignition ON	0 V		
	B8	⇒	Ignition ON	5 V		
	B38	⟵	Ignition ON	0,5 V		
	B38	⟵	Engine idling	1 V		
	B38	⟵	3000 rpm	2,3 V		
Fuel temperature sensor	A13	⇥—	Ignition ON	0 V		
	A61	⟵	Ignition ON – fuel temp. 15°C	3,1 V		
Fuel/water separator sensor	A90	⟵		☐1		
Glow plug control module	A70	⇒	Engine idling	0,3 V		
	A74	⟵	Engine idling	11-14 V		
Ignition main circuits relay	A23	⟵	Ignition OFF	0 V		
	A23	⟵	Ignition ON	11-14 V		
Immobilizer control module	A66	⟷		☐1		
	A78	⟷		☐1		
Injector 1	B16	⇒	Ignition ON	11-14 V		
	B16 (B47)	⇒	Engine idling	0,6 ms pilot + 4,5 ms main		
	B16 (B47)	⇒	Engine idling		20 V/1 ms	〜〰 70
	B47	⇒	Ignition ON	11-14 V		
	B47 (B16)	⇒	Engine idling	0,6 ms pilot + 4,5 ms main		
	B47 (B16)	⇒	Engine idling		20 V/1 ms	〜〰 70
Injector 2	B17	⇒	Ignition ON	11-14 V		
	B17 (B49)	⇒	Engine idling	0,6 ms pilot + 4,5 ms main		
	B17 (B49)	⇒	Engine idling		20 V/1 ms	〜〰 70
	B49	⇒	Ignition ON	11-14 V		
	B49 (B17)	⇒	Engine idling	0,6 ms pilot + 4,5 ms main		
	B49 (B17)	⇒	Engine idling		20 V/1 ms	〜〰 70

★ Suggested settings - Voltage/time per division

Component/circuit description	ECM pin	Signal	Condition	Typical value	Oscilloscope setting*	Wave form
Injector 3	B31	⇨	Ignition ON	11-14 V		
	B31 (B48)	⇨	Engine idling	0,6 ms pilot + 4,5 ms main		
	B31 (B48)	⇨	Engine idling		20 V/1 ms	⎍⎍ 70
	B48	⇨	Ignition ON	11-14 V		
	B48 (B31)	⇨	Engine idling	0,6 ms pilot + 4,5 ms main		
	B48 (B31)	⇨	Engine idling		20 V/1 ms	⎍⎍ 70
Injector 4	B1	⇨	Ignition ON	11-14 V		
	B1 (B46)	⇨	Engine idling	0,6 ms pilot + 4,5 ms main		
	B1 (B46)	⇨	Engine idling		20 V/1 ms	⎍⎍ 70
	B46	⇨	Ignition ON	11-14 V		
	B46 (B1)	⇨	Engine idling	0,6 ms pilot + 4,5 ms main		
	B46 (B1)	⇨	Engine idling		20 V/1 ms	⎍⎍ 70
Intake air temperature (IAT) sensor	A34	⊣⊢	Ignition ON	0 V		
	A62	⬅	Ignition ON – air temp. 15°C	2,6 V		
Manifold absolute pressure (MAP) sensor	B23	⇨	Ignition ON	5 V		
	B24	⊣⊢	Ignition ON	0 V		
	B41	⬅	Ignition ON	1,9 V		
	B41	⬅	Engine idling	1,9 V		
	B41	⬅	Full load	3,1 V		
Mass air flow (MAF) sensor	A34	⊣⊢	Ignition ON	0 V		
	A36	⇨	Ignition ON	5 V		
	A56	⬅	Ignition ON	1 V		
	A56	⬅	Engine idling	1,8 V		
	A56	⬅	Engine idling – accelerate briefly	3,5 V		
Power steering control module	A29	⬅		1		
Vehicle speed sensor (VSS) signal amplifier – without ABS	A89	⬅	Ignition ON – vehicle pushed	0 V or 11-14 V fluctuating		

*Suggested settings - Voltage/time per division

1 Connected pin - no test data available or random digital signal

Autodata

ECM harness multi-plug

Terminal side

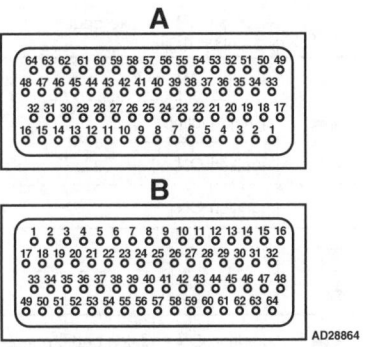

AD28864

Wire side

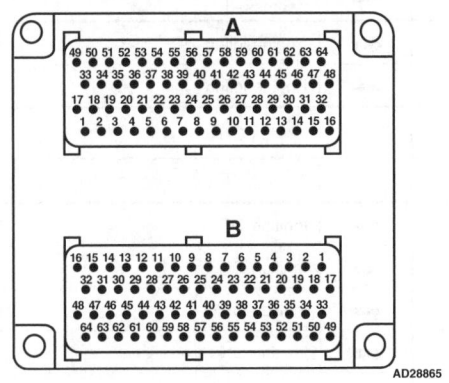

AD28865

Component/circuit description	ECM pin	Signal	Condition	Typical value	Oscilloscope setting★	Wave form
ABS control module – VSS signal	B41	←	Ignition ON – vehicle pushed	0 V or 11-14 V fluctuating		
AC compressor clutch relay	B7	ꓱ▷	Engine idling – AC OFF	11-14 V		
	B7	ꓱ▷	Engine idling – AC ON – AC compressor OFF	11-14 V		
	B7	ꓱ▷	Engine idling – AC ON – AC compressor ON	0-1 V		
AC refrigerant pressure sensor	B3			1		
	B4			1		
	B49			1		
Accelerator pedal position (APP) sensor	B20	⇨	Ignition ON	5 V		
	B33	ꓱ−	Ignition ON	0 V		
	B35	⇨	Ignition ON	5 V		
	B36	←	Ignition ON – accelerator pedal released	0,5 V		
	B36	←	Ignition ON – accelerator pedal depressed	2 V		
	B37	←	Ignition ON – accelerator pedal released	1 V		
	B37	←	Ignition ON – accelerator pedal depressed	4,1 V		
	B50	ꓱ−	Ignition ON	0 V		

★ Suggested settings - Voltage/time per division

Component/circuit description	ECM pin	Signal	Condition	Typical value	Oscilloscope setting*	Wave form
Battery	B2	←	Ignition OFF	11-14 V		
	B19	←	Ignition OFF	11-14 V		
Brake pedal position (BPP) switch	B5	←	Ignition ON – brake pedal released	0 V		
	B5	←	Ignition ON – brake pedal depressed	11-14 V		
	B13	←	Ignition ON – brake pedal released	11-14 V		
	B13	←	Ignition ON – brake pedal depressed	0 V		
Camshaft position (CMP) sensor	A23	←	Ignition ON	0 or 5 V		
	A23	←	Engine idling		2 V/100 ms	4
	A29	⊣	Ignition ON	0 V		
	A30	⇨	Ignition ON	5 V		
CAN data bus	B11	⬄		1		
	B43	⬄		1		
Clutch pedal position (CPP) switch – with cruise control	B61	←	Ignition ON – clutch pedal released	0 V		
	B61	←	Ignition ON – clutch pedal depressed	11-14 V		
Crankshaft position (CKP) sensor	A5	←	Engine idling	1,6 V ac	1 V/2 ms	Reversed 2
	A22	←	Engine idling	2,4 V ac	1 V/2 ms	2
Crankshaft position (CKP) sensor – shield wire	A37	⊣	Ignition ON	0 V		
Digital multifunction display – 2005→	B42			1		
Engine control (EC) relay	A47	←	Ignition OFF	0 V		
	A47	←	Ignition ON	11-14 V		
	A48	←	Ignition OFF	0 V		
	A48	←	Ignition ON	11-14 V		
	A64	←	Ignition OFF	0 V		
	A64	←	Ignition ON	11-14 V		
	B16	⊣▷	Ignition OFF	11-14 V		
	B16	⊣▷	Ignition ON	0-1 V		
Engine coolant blower motor relay 1 – →2003 with AC	B39	⊣▷	Engine idling – coolant blower motors OFF	11-14 V		
	B39	⊣▷	Engine idling – coolant blower motors ON, 1st speed	0-1 V		
	B39	⊣▷	Engine idling – coolant blower motors ON, 2nd speed	0-1 V		
Engine coolant blower motor relay 1 – 2004→ with AC	B39	⊣▷	Engine idling – coolant blower motor OFF	11-14 V		
	B39	⊣▷	Engine idling – coolant blower motor ON, 1st speed	0-1 V		
	B39	⊣▷	Engine idling – coolant blower motor ON, 2nd speed	11-14 V		
	B39	⊣▷	Engine idling – coolant blower motor ON, 3rd speed	11-14 V		
Engine coolant blower motor relay 1 – without AC	B39	⊣▷	Engine idling – coolant blower motor OFF	11-14 V		
	B39	⊣▷	Engine idling – coolant blower motor ON, 1st speed	0-1 V		
	B39	⊣▷	Engine idling – coolant blower motor ON, 2nd speed	11-14 V		
Engine coolant blower motor relay 2 – →2003 with AC	B31	⊣▷	Engine idling – coolant blower motors OFF	11-14 V		
	B31	⊣▷	Engine idling – coolant blower motors ON, 1st speed	11-14 V		
	B31	⊣▷	Engine idling – coolant blower motors ON, 2nd speed	0-1 V		

★ Suggested settings - Voltage/time per division

Component/circuit description	ECM pin	Signal	Condition	Typical value	Oscilloscope setting*	Wave form
Engine coolant blower motor relay 2 – 2004→ with AC	B31	→▷	Engine idling – coolant blower motor OFF	11-14 V		
	B31	→▷	Engine idling – coolant blower motor ON, 1st speed	11-14 V		
	B31	→▷	Engine idling – coolant blower motor ON, 2nd speed	0-1 V		
	B31	→▷	Engine idling – coolant blower motor ON, 3rd speed	11-14 V		
Engine coolant blower motor relay 2 – without AC	B31	→▷	Engine idling – coolant blower motor OFF	11-14 V		
	B31	→▷	Engine idling – coolant blower motor ON, 1st speed	11-14 V		
	B31	→▷	Engine idling – coolant blower motor ON, 2nd speed	0-1 V		
Engine coolant blower motor relay 4 – →2003 with AC	B23	→▷	Engine idling – coolant blower motors OFF	11-14 V		
	B23	→▷	Engine idling – coolant blower motors ON, 1st speed	11-14 V		
	B23	→▷	Engine idling – coolant blower motors ON, 2nd speed	0-1 V		
Engine coolant blower motor relay 4 – 2004→ with AC	B23	→▷	Engine idling – coolant blower motor OFF	11-14 V		
	B23	→▷	Engine idling – coolant blower motor ON, 1st speed	11-14 V		
	B23	→▷	Engine idling – coolant blower motor ON, 2nd speed	11-14 V		
	B23	→▷	Engine idling – coolant blower motor ON, 3rd speed	0-1 V		
Engine coolant temperature (ECT) sensor	A10	←	Ignition ON – coolant temp. 20°C	1,9 V		
	A10	←	Ignition ON – coolant temp. 80°C	2,3 V		
	A62	⊣–	Ignition ON	0 V		
Engine oil level sensor – 2004→	A27	←		1		
Engine oil pressure warning lamp switch	A56	←	Ignition ON	0 V		
	A56	←	Engine idling	11-14 V		
Evaporative emission (EVAP) canister purge valve	A3	⊣▷	Ignition ON	11-14 V		
	A3	⊣▷	Engine idling		5 V/2 ms	Intermittent 〰〰 68
Exhaust gas recirculation (EGR) solenoid	A21	⊣▷	Ignition ON	11-14 V		
	A21	⊣▷	Engine idling – engine hot		5 V/2 ms	Intermittent 〰〰 68
Exhaust gas recirculation (EGR) valve position sensor	A28	←	Ignition ON	1,2 V		
	A28	←	Engine idling	1,2 V		
	A30	⇒	Ignition ON	5 V		
	A62	⊣–	Ignition ON	0 V		
Fuel gauge tank sensor signal	B53	←		1		
Fuel pump (FP) relay	B24	⊣▷	Ignition ON	0-1 V briefly then 11-14 V		
	B24	⊣▷	Engine idling	0-1 V		
Heated oxygen sensor (HO2S) 1	A44	←	Engine idling	0,1-0,9 V fluctuating	0,2 V/1 sec.	〰〰 21
	A52	⊣▷	Ignition ON	11-14 V		
	A52	⊣▷	Engine idling	0-1 V		
	A62	⊣–	Ignition ON	0 V		
Heated oxygen sensor (HO2S) 2	A53	⊣▷	Ignition ON	11-14 V		
	A53	⊣▷	Engine idling	0-1 V		
	A61	←	Engine idling	0,6 V		
	A62	⊣–	Ignition ON	0 V		

* Suggested settings - Voltage/time per division

Component/circuit description	ECM pin	Signal	Condition	Typical value	Oscilloscope setting*	Wave form
Ignition coil	A1	⊐▷	Ignition ON	11-14 V		
	A1	⊐▷	Engine idling		5 V/2 ms	�〜 33
	A2	⊐▷	Ignition ON	11-14 V		
	A2	⊐▷	Engine idling		5 V/2 ms	�〜 33
	A17	⊐▷	Ignition ON	11-14 V		
	A17	⊐▷	Engine idling		5 V/2 ms	⧸〜 33
	A18	⊐▷	Ignition ON	11-14 V		
	A18	⊐▷	Engine idling		5 V/2 ms	⧸〜 33
	A33	⊐▷	Ignition ON	11-14 V		
	A33	⊐▷	Engine idling		5 V/2 ms	⧸〜 33
	A34	⊐▷	Ignition ON	11-14 V		
	A34	⊐▷	Engine idling		5 V/2 ms	⧸〜 33
	A49	⊐▷	Ignition ON	11-14 V		
	A49	⊐▷	Engine idling		5 V/2 ms	⧸〜 33
	A50	⊐▷	Ignition ON	11-14 V		
	A50	⊐▷	Engine idling		5 V/2 ms	⧸〜 33
Ignition switch	B52	⟵	Ignition OFF	0 V		
	B52	⟵	Ignition ON	11-14 V		
Immobilizer control module	B54	⟷		[1]		
	B64	⟷		[1]		
Injector 1	A57	⊐▷	Ignition ON	11-14 V briefly then 0-1 V		
	A57	⊐▷	Engine idling	3,5 ms	10 V/2 ms	⧸〜 35
Injector 2	A60	⊐▷	Ignition ON	11-14 V briefly then 0-1 V		
	A60	⊐▷	Engine idling	3,5 ms	10 V/2 ms	⧸〜 35
Injector 3	A58	⊐▷	Ignition ON	11-14 V briefly then 0-1 V		
	A58	⊐▷	Engine idling	3,5 ms	10 V/2 ms	⧸〜 35
Injector 4	A59	⊐▷	Ignition ON	11-14 V briefly then 0-1 V		
	A59	⊐▷	Engine idling	3,5 ms	10 V/2 ms	⧸〜 35
Intake air temperature (IAT) sensor	A29	⊐—	Ignition ON	0 V		
	A43	⟵	Ignition ON – air temp. 20°C	3,7 V		
Knock sensor (KS)	A39	⟵	Engine idling – accelerate briefly		50 mV/1 ms	⧸〜 58
Knock sensor (KS) – shield wire	A62	⊐—	Ignition ON	0 V		
Manifold absolute pressure (MAP) sensor	A26	⟵	Ignition ON	4,9 V		
	A26	⟵	Engine idling	1,3 V		
	A26	⟵	Engine running – full throttle briefly	4,9 V		
	A45	⊐—	Ignition ON	0 V		
	A63	⟹	Ignition ON	5 V		
Power steering control module	B46	⟵		[1]		

★ Suggested settings - Voltage/time per division

Component/circuit description	ECM pin	Signal	Condition	Typical value	Oscilloscope setting*	Wave form
Throttle motor	A15	⇨	Ignition ON	11-14 V		
	A15	⇨	Engine idling		5 V/0,2 ms	〰〰 68
	A16	⇨	Ignition ON		5 V/0,2 ms	(intermittent for 10 seconds only) 〰〰 68
	A16	⇨	Engine idling	11-14 V		
	A31	⇨	Ignition ON	11-14 V		
	A31	⇨	Engine idling		5 V/0,2 ms	〰〰 68
	A32	⇨	Ignition ON		5 V/0,2 ms	(intermittent for 10 seconds only) 〰〰 68
	A32	⇨	Engine idling	11-14 V		
Throttle motor position sensor	A9	⬅	Ignition ON – accelerator pedal released	1 V		
	A9	⬅	Ignition ON – accelerator pedal depressed	4,4 V		
	A12	⬅	Ignition ON – accelerator pedal released	4,1 V		
	A12	⬅	Ignition ON – accelerator pedal depressed	0,7 V		
	A13	╤	Ignition ON	0 V		
	A14	⇨	Ignition ON	5 V		
	A29	╤	Ignition ON	0 V		
	A46	⇨	Ignition ON	5 V		
Vehicle speed sensor (VSS) signal amplifier – without ABS	B41	⬅	Ignition ON – vehicle pushed	0 V or 11-14 V fluctuating		

*Suggested settings - Voltage/time per division

1 Connected pin - no test data available or random digital signal

VAUXHALL-OPEL
Denso V5

Model:	Engine code:	Year:
Corsa-C 1,7 Di	Y17DTL	2000-05
Corsa-C 1,7 DTi	Y17DT	2000-05
Combo-C 1,7 Di	Y17DTL	2001-05
Combo-C 1,7 DTi	Y17DT	2001-05

ECM harness multi-plug

Terminal side

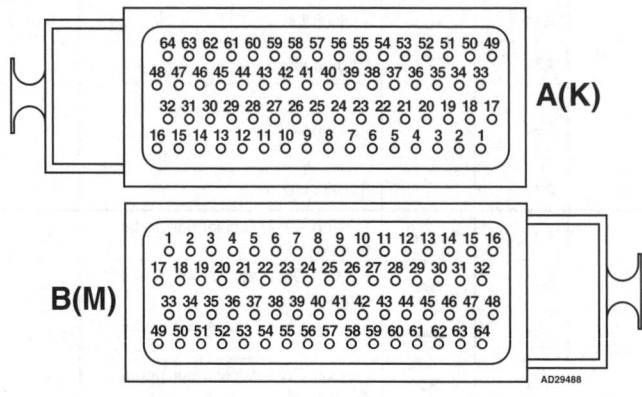

Wire side

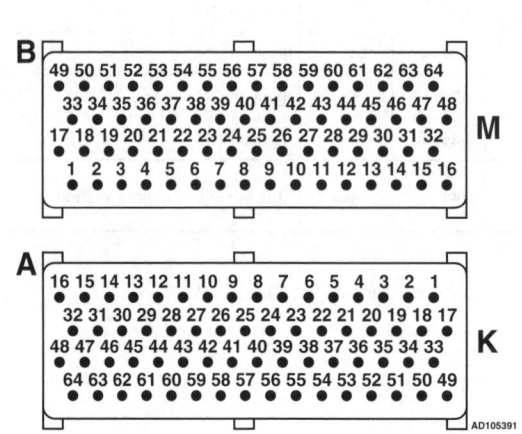

Component/circuit description	ECM pin	Signal	Condition	Typical value	Oscilloscope setting*	Wave form
ABS control module – VSS signal	A40	←	Ignition ON – vehicle pushed	0 V or 11-14 V fluctuating		
AC compressor clutch relay	A7	⊐▷	Engine idling – AC OFF	11-14 V		
	A7	⊐▷	Engine idling – AC ON – AC compressor OFF	11-14 V		
	A7	⊐▷	Engine idling – AC ON – AC compressor ON	0-1 V		
AC refrigerant pressure sensor	A4			1		
	A50	⊐⊢	Ignition ON	0 V		
	A51			1		
Accelerator pedal position (APP) sensor	A3	⇨	Ignition ON	5 V		
	A33	⊐⊢	Ignition ON	0 V		
	A35	⇨	Ignition ON	5 V		
	A36	←	Ignition ON – accelerator pedal released	0,5 V		
	A36	←	Ignition ON – accelerator pedal depressed	1,9 V		
	A37	←	Ignition ON – accelerator pedal released	1 V		
	A37	←	Ignition ON – accelerator pedal depressed	3,9 V		
	A49	⊐⊢	Ignition ON	0 V		

* Suggested settings - Voltage/time per division

Autodata

Component/circuit description	ECM pin	Signal	Condition	Typical value	Oscilloscope setting*	Wave form
Barometric pressure (BARO) sensor	B14	→	Ignition ON	5 V		
	B61	←	Ignition ON	4,9 V		
	B61	←	Engine idling	4,8 V		
	B62	⊣	Ignition ON	0 V		
Battery	A2	←	Ignition OFF	11-14 V		
	A19	←	Ignition OFF	11-14 V		
Brake pedal position (BPP) switch	A12	←	Ignition ON – brake pedal released	0 V		
	A12	←	Ignition ON – brake pedal depressed	11-14 V		
	A13	←	Ignition ON – brake pedal released	11-14 V		
	A13	←	Ignition ON – brake pedal depressed	0 V		
CAN data bus	A48	↔		1		
	A64	↔		1		
Clutch pedal position (CPP) switch	A59	←	Ignition ON – clutch pedal released	11-14 V		
	A59	←	Ignition ON – clutch pedal depressed	0 V		
Crankshaft position (CKP) sensor	B23	←	Ignition ON	0 V or 5 V		
	B23	←	Engine idling		1 V/5 ms	49
Earth	B38		Ignition ON	0 V		
	B54		Ignition ON	0 V		
	B55		Ignition ON	0 V		
Engine control (EC) relay	A1	←	Ignition OFF	0 V		
	A1	←	Ignition ON	11-14 V		
	A15	⊣→	Ignition OFF	11-14 V		
	A15	⊣→	Ignition ON	0-1 V		
	A17	←	Ignition OFF	0 V		
	A17	←	Ignition ON	11-14 V		
Engine control module (ECM) – pin 60 – 2004→	A61			1		
Engine control module (ECM) – pin 61 – 2004→	A60			1		
Engine coolant blower motor relay 1	A56	⊣→	Engine running – coolant blower motor OFF	11-14 V		
	A56	⊣→	Engine running – coolant blower motor ON, 1st speed	0-1 V		
Engine coolant blower motor relay 2 – with AC	A16	⊣→		1		
Engine coolant blower motor relay 2 – without AC	A39	⊣→	Engine running – coolant blower motor OFF	11-14 V		
	A39	⊣→	Engine running – coolant blower motor ON, 2nd speed	0-1 V		
Engine coolant blower motor relay 3/4 – with AC	A39	⊣→		1		
	A39	⊣→		1		
Engine coolant temperature (ECT) sensor	B42	←	Ignition ON – coolant temp. 20°C	3,7 V		
	B45	⊣	Ignition ON	0 V		
Engine oil level sensor – 2004→	B40	←		1		
Engine oil pressure switch	B8	←	Ignition ON	0 V		
	B8	←	Engine idling	11-14 V		
Exhaust gas recirculation (EGR) solenoid – →2003	B26	⊣→	Ignition ON	11-14 V		
	B26	⊣→	Engine idling – valve operating		5 V/5 ms	12
Exhaust gas recirculation (EGR) valve actuator – 2004→	B26	⊣→	Ignition ON	11-14 V		
	B26	⊣→	Engine idling – valve operating	0-1 V		
Exhaust gas recirculation (EGR) valve position sensor – 2004→	B28	←		1		
	B29	⊣	Ignition ON	0 V		
	B63	→	Ignition ON	5 V		

* Suggested settings - Voltage/time per division

Component/circuit description	ECM pin	Signal	Condition	Typical value	Oscilloscope setting*	Wave form
Fuel injection pump control module	B33	⇨	Ignition ON	1 V for 10 seconds then 4,5 V		
	B33	⇨	Engine idling		1 V/2 ms	〜 69
	B34	⇨	Ignition ON	0 V		
	B34	⇨	Engine idling		1 V/2 ms	〜 69
Fuel quantity adjuster	B25	⇥⇨	Engine idling		5 V/20 ms	〜 33
Fuel quantity adjuster relay	A24	⇥▷	Ignition ON	0-1 V for 10 seconds then 11-14 V		
	A24	⇥▷	Engine running	0-1 V		
Fuel shut-off solenoid	B49	⬅	Ignition OFF	0 V		
	B49	⬅	Ignition ON	0 V		
	B50	⇨	Ignition OFF	0 V		
	B50	⇨	Ignition ON	5 V		
Fuel temperature sensor	B41	⬅	Ignition ON – fuel temp. 20°C	3,5 V		
	B45	⊣	Ignition ON	0 V		
Glow plug control module	A9	⇨	Engine idling	11-14 V		
	A43			[1]		
Ignition switch	A52	⬅	Ignition OFF	0 V		
	A52	⬅	Ignition ON	11-14 V		
Immobilizer control module	A32	⬅⇨		[1]		
	A54	⬅⇨		[1]		
Injection pump position sensor	B1	⬅	Engine idling	0,32 V ac	0,2 V/5 ms	〜 1
	B17	⬅	Engine idling	0,32 V ac	0,2 V/5 ms	Reversed 〜 1
Injection pump position sensor – shield wire	B37	⊣	Ignition ON	0 V		
Intake air temperature (IAT) sensor	A42	⬅	Ignition ON – air temp. 20°C	3,5 V		
Manifold absolute pressure (MAP) sensor	B14	⇨	Ignition ON	5 V		
	B58	⬅	Ignition ON	1,8 V		
	B58	⬅	Engine idling	2,3 V		
	B58	⬅	Full load	4,2 V		
	B62	⊣	Ignition ON	0 V		
Mass air flow (MAF) sensor	A5	⬅	Ignition ON	1 V		
	A5	⬅	Engine idling	1,8 V		
	A5	⬅	3000 rpm	3,4 V		
	A20	⇨	Ignition ON	5 V		
	A50	⊣	Ignition ON	0 V		
Power steering control module	A11	⬅		[1]		
Turbocharger (TC) wastegate regulating valve	B9	⇥▷	Ignition ON	11-14 V		
	B9	⇥▷	Engine idling – valve operating		2 V/1 ms	〜 66
Vehicle speed sensor (VSS) signal amplifier – without ABS	A40	⬅	Ignition ON – vehicle pushed	0 V or 11-14 V fluctuating		

*Suggested settings - Voltage/time per division

[1] Connected pin - no test data available or random digital signal

Model:	Engine code:	Year:
Astra-G 1,4 16V	X14XE	1998-02
Astra-G 1,6 16V	X16XEL	1998-02
Zafira 1,6 16V	X16XEL	1999-02

ECM harness multi-plug

Terminal side

```
16 15 14 13 12 11 10 9 8 7 6 5 4 3 2 1
32 31 30 29 28 27 26 25 24 23 22 21 20 19 18 17    ) B
```

```
17 18 19 20 21 22 23 24 25 26 27 28 29 30 31 32
1  2  3  4  5  6  7  8  9 10 11 12 13 14 15 16    ) A
```
AD22886

Wire side

```
1  2  3  4  5  6  7  8  9 10 11 12 13 14 15 16
17 18 19 20 21 22 23 24 25 26 27 28 29 30 31 32   ) B
```

```
32 31 30 29 28 27 26 25 24 23 22 21 20 19 18 17
16 15 14 13 12 11 10 9 8 7 6 5 4 3 2 1            ) A
```
AD23541

Component/circuit description	ECM pin	Signal	Condition	Typical value	Oscilloscope setting*	Wave form
AC control module	A9	←		1		
Battery	A3	←	Ignition OFF	11-14 V		
	A18	←	Ignition OFF	11-14 V		
Camshaft position (CMP) sensor	B10	←	Ignition ON – engine turned	0-5 V fluctuating		
	B10	←	Engine idling		2 V/20 ms	~ 63
Crankshaft position (CKP) sensor	B7	⌐	Ignition ON	0 V		
	B23	←	Ignition ON	0 V		
	B23	←	Engine idling	1,5 V ac	4 V/20 ms	~ 2
Data link connector (DLC)	A10		Ignition OFF	0,5 V		
	A10		Ignition ON	11-14 V		
Digital multifunction display	A21	⇒	Ignition ON	11-14 V		
Earth	B3	⌐	Ignition ON	0 V		
	B4	⌐	Ignition ON	0 V		
	B19	⌐	Ignition ON	0 V		
	B20	⌐	Ignition ON	0 V		
Engine coolant blower control module – some models	A15		Ignition ON	11-14 V		
	A15		Engine running – AC OFF	11-14 V		
	A15		Engine running – AC ON	0 V		
Engine coolant blower control module – AC	A8	⇒	Engine idling	30 Hz		
	A8	⇒	3000 rpm	100 Hz		
	A26	⇒	Ignition ON	11-14 V		
Engine coolant blower motor relay	A12			1		
	A14	⌐▷	Engine idling – coolant blower motor OFF	11-14 V		
	A14	⌐▷	Engine idling – coolant blower motor ON	0 V		
Engine coolant temperature (ECT) gauge	A30	⇒	Ignition ON	11-14 V		
Engine coolant temperature (ECT) sensor	B27	←	Ignition ON – coolant temp. 10°C approx.	4 V		
	B27	←	Ignition ON – coolant temp. 85°C approx.	1,8 V		
	B32	⌐	Ignition ON	0 V		

★ Suggested settings - Voltage/time per division

Component/circuit description	ECM pin	Signal	Condition	Typical value	Oscilloscope setting*	Wave form
Evaporative emission (EVAP) canister purge valve	B22	⊐▷	Ignition ON	11-14 V briefly then 0 V		
	B22	⊐▷	Engine idling	11-14 V		
	B22	⊐▷	Engine idling	0%		
	B22	⊐▷	Engine running – throttle slightly open	0,1% min.		
Exhaust gas recirculation (EGR) solenoid	B21	⊐▷	Ignition ON	11-14 V briefly then 0 V		
	B21	⊐▷	Engine idling	11-14 V		
	B21	⊐▷	Engine running – EGR system operating		4 V/5 ms	⟊ 24
Exhaust gas recirculation (EGR) valve position sensor	B14	⊐—	Ignition ON	0 V		
	B28	◀━	Ignition ON	0,68 V		
	B28	◀━	Engine idling	0,75 V		
	B28	◀━	Engine running – EGR system operating	2 V approx.		
	B32	⊐—	Ignition ON	0 V		
Fuel pump relay	A28	⊐▷	Ignition OFF	0 V		
	A28	⊐▷	Ignition ON	0 V briefly then 11-14 V		
	A28	⊐▷	Engine cranking	0 V		
	A28	⊐▷	Engine running	0 V		
	A32	◀━	Ignition ON	11-14 V briefly then 0 V		
	A32	◀━	Engine cranking	11-14 V		
	A32	◀━	Engine running	11-14 V		
Heated oxygen sensor (HO2S)	B6	⊐▷	Ignition ON	11-14 V briefly then 0 V		
	B6	⊐▷	Engine idling	0 V		
	B12	◀━	Ignition ON	0,5 V		
	B12	◀━	Engine running	0,3-0,95 V fluctuating		
	B12	◀━	Engine running		0,2 V/1 sec.	⟊ 21
	B32	⊐—	Ignition ON	0 V		
Idle air control (IAC) valve	B15	⇨	Ignition ON	10,4 V		
	B15 (B16)	⇨	Engine idling		5 V/50 ms	Intermittent ⟊ 26
	B16	⇨	Ignition ON	10,4 V		
	B16 (B15)	⇨	Engine idling		5 V/50 ms	Intermittent ⟊ 26
	B30	◀━	Ignition ON	0,68 V		
	B30 (B31)	◀━	Engine idling		5 V/50 ms	Intermittent ⟊ 26
	B31	◀━	Ignition ON	0,9 V		
	B31 (B30)	◀━	Engine idling		5 V/50 ms	Intermittent ⟊ 26
Ignition coil	B1	⊐▷	Ignition ON	11-14 V briefly then 0 V		
	B1	⊐▷	Engine running		4 V/3 ms	⟊ 33
	B2	⊐▷	Ignition ON	11-14 V briefly then 0 V		
	B2	⊐▷	Engine running		4 V/3 ms	⟊ 33
	B17	⊐▷	Ignition ON	11-14 V briefly then 0 V		
	B17	⊐▷	Engine running		4 V/3 ms	⟊ 33
	B18	⊐▷	Ignition ON	11-14 V briefly then 0 V		
	B18	⊐▷	Engine running		4 V/3 ms	⟊ 33

* Suggested settings - Voltage/time per division

Component/circuit description	ECM pin	Signal	Condition	Typical value	Oscilloscope setting*	Wave form
Ignition switch	A31	←	Ignition ON	11-14 V		
Immobilizer control module	A20	←	Ignition ON	11-14 V		
	A29	→▷	Ignition ON – MIL ON	0,6-1,6 V		
	A29	→▷	Engine running – MIL OFF	11-14 V		
Injector 1	B8	→▷	Ignition ON	11-14 V briefly then 0 V		
	B8	→▷	Engine idling	2,7-3,7 ms		
	B8	→▷	Engine idling		10 V/2 ms	35
Injector 2	B9	→▷	Ignition ON	11-14 V briefly then 0 V		
	B9	→▷	Engine idling	2,7-3,7 ms		
	B9	→▷	Engine idling		10 V/2 ms	35
Injector 3	B24	→▷	Ignition ON	11-14 V briefly then 0 V		
	B24	→▷	Engine idling	2,7-3,7 ms		
	B24	→▷	Engine idling		10 V/2 ms	35
Injector 4	B25	→▷	Ignition ON	11-14 V briefly then 0 V		
	B25	→▷	Engine idling	2,7-3,7 ms		
	B25	→▷	Engine idling		10 V/2 ms	35
Intake air temperature (IAT) sensor	B11	←	Ignition ON – air temp. 10°C approx.	4 V		
	B11	←	Engine idling – air temp. 50°C approx.	2,2 V		
	B32	⌐	Ignition ON	0 V		
Knock sensor (KS)	B26	←	Ignition ON	0,1 V		
	B26	←	Engine idling – accelerate briefly		50 mV/ 1 ms	58
Knock sensor (KS) – shield wire	B32	⌐	Ignition ON	0 V		
Malfunction indicator lamp (MIL)	A29	→▷	Ignition ON – MIL ON	0,6-1,6 V		
	A29	→▷	Engine running – MIL OFF	11-14 V		
Manifold absolute pressure (MAP) sensor	B13	←	Ignition ON	5 V		
	B13	←	Engine idling	1,5 V		
	B13	←	Engine idling – accelerate briefly	4,8 V briefly		
	B14	⌐	Ignition ON	0 V		
	B32	⌐	Ignition ON	0 V		
Tachometer	A8	⇒	Engine idling	30 Hz		
	A8	⇒	3000 rpm	100 Hz		
Throttle position (TP) sensor	B14	⌐	Ignition ON	0 V		
	B29	←	Ignition ON – throttle closed	0,68 V		
	B29	←	Ignition ON – throttle fully open	4,5 V		
	B32	⌐	Ignition ON	0 V		
Transmission control module (TCM) – AT	A5			1		
	A7			1		
	A25			1		
Vehicle speed sensor (VSS)	A27	←	Ignition ON	0,8 or 11-14 V		
	A27	←	Ignition ON – vehicle pushed	0,8 or 11-14 V fluctuating	5 V/0,5 sec.	45

*Suggested settings - Voltage/time per division

1 Connected pin - no test data available or random digital signal

Model:	Engine code:	Year:
Astra-G 1,4	Z14XE	2000-06
Astra-G 1,6	Z16XE	2000-06

ECM harness multi-plug

Terminal side

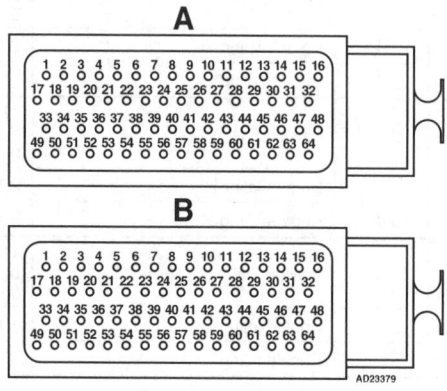

Wire side

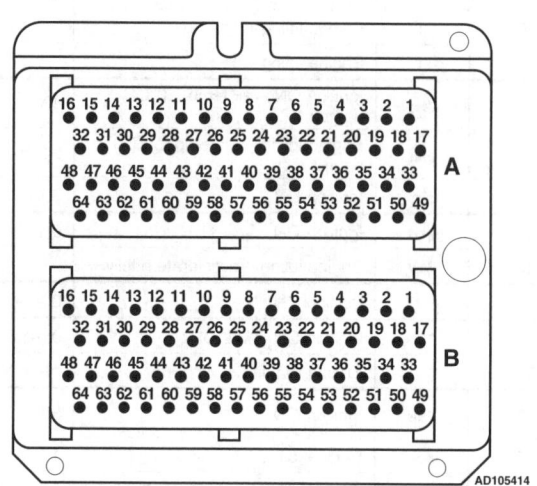

Component/circuit description	ECM pin	Signal	Condition	Typical value	Oscilloscope setting★	Wave form
ABS control module – VSS signal	B41	←	Ignition ON – vehicle pushed	0 V or 11-14 V fluctuating		
AC compressor clutch relay – 2003→	B7	⊐▷	Engine idling – AC OFF	11-14 V		
	B7	⊐▷	Engine idling – AC ON – AC compressor OFF	11-14 V		
	B7	⊐▷	Engine idling – AC ON – AC compressor ON	0-1 V		
AC control module – ATC	B45	←	Ignition ON – AC OFF	0 V		
	B45	←	Ignition ON – AC ON	11-14 V		
AC master switch – MTC	B45	←	Ignition ON – AC OFF	0 V		
	B45	←	Ignition ON – AC ON	11-14 V		
AC refrigerant pressure sensor – 2003→	B3			1		
	B4			1		
	B49			1		

★ Suggested settings - Voltage/time per division

Component/circuit description	ECM pin	Signal	Condition	Typical value	Oscilloscope setting*	Wave form
Accelerator pedal position (APP) sensor	B20	⇨	Ignition ON	5 V		
	B33	⊣	Ignition ON	0 V		
	B35	⇨	Ignition ON	5 V		
	B36	←	Ignition ON – accelerator pedal released	0,5 V		
	B36	←	Ignition ON – accelerator pedal depressed	2 V		
	B37	←	Ignition ON – accelerator pedal released	1 V		
	B37	←	Ignition ON – accelerator pedal depressed	4,1 V		
	B50	⊣	Ignition ON	0 V		
Battery	B2	←	Ignition OFF	11-14 V		
	B19	←	Ignition OFF	11-14 V		
Brake pedal position (BPP) switch	B5	←	Ignition ON – brake pedal released	0 V		
	B5	←	Ignition ON – brake pedal depressed	11-14 V		
	B13	←	Ignition ON – brake pedal released	11-14 V		
	B13	←	Ignition ON – brake pedal depressed	0 V		
Camshaft position (CMP) sensor	A23	←	Ignition ON	0 or 5 V		
	A23	←	Engine idling		2 V/100 ms	〰 4
	A29	⊣	Ignition ON	0 V		
	A30	⇨	Ignition ON	5 V		
Clutch pedal position (CPP) switch – with cruise control	B61	←	Ignition ON – clutch pedal released	0 V		
	B61	←	Ignition ON – clutch pedal depressed	11-14 V		
Crankshaft position (CKP) sensor	A5	←	Engine idling	1,6 V ac	1 V/2 ms	Reversed 〰 2
	A22	←	Engine idling	2,4 V ac	1 V/2 ms	〰 2
Crankshaft position (CKP) sensor – shield wire	A37	⊣	Ignition ON	0 V		
Cruise control master switch	B29			1		
	B44			1		
	B62			1		
Digital multifunction display	B47			1		
Engine control (EC) relay	A47	←	Ignition OFF	0 V		
	A47	←	Ignition ON	11-14 V		
	A48	←	Ignition OFF	0 V		
	A48	←	Ignition ON	11-14 V		
	A64	←	Ignition OFF	0 V		
	A64	←	Ignition ON	11-14 V		
	B16	⊣⇨	Ignition OFF	11-14 V		
	B16	⊣⇨	Ignition ON	0-1 V		
Engine coolant blower motor control module – →2002 with AC	B7			1		
	B55			1		
	B57			1		
Engine coolant blower motor control module – tachometer signal – →2002 with AC	B46	⇨	Engine idling	25 Hz		
	B46	⇨	3000 rpm	100 Hz		
Engine coolant blower motor relay 1 – 2003→, MT with AC	B39	⊣⇨	Engine idling – coolant blower motor OFF	11-14 V		
	B39	⊣⇨	Engine idling – coolant blower motor ON, 1st speed	0-1 V		
	B39	⊣⇨	Engine idling – coolant blower motor ON, 2nd speed	11-14 V		
	B39	⊣⇨	Engine idling – coolant blower motor ON, 3rd speed	11-14 V		

* Suggested settings - Voltage/time per division

Component/circuit description	ECM pin	Signal	Condition	Typical value	Oscilloscope setting*	Wave form
Engine coolant blower motor relay 1 – without AC	B39	⊐→▷	Engine idling – coolant blower motor OFF	11-14 V		
	B39	⊐→▷	Engine idling – coolant blower motor ON, 1st speed	0-1 V		
	B39	⊐→▷	Engine idling – coolant blower motor ON, 2nd speed	11-14 V		
Engine coolant blower motor relay 1/2 – 2003→, AT with AC	B31	⊐→▷		1		
Engine coolant blower motor relay 2 – 2003→, MT with AC	B31	⊐→▷	Engine idling – coolant blower motor OFF	11-14 V		
	B31	⊐→▷	Engine idling – coolant blower motor ON, 1st speed	11-14 V		
	B31	⊐→▷	Engine idling – coolant blower motor ON, 2nd speed	0-1 V		
	B31	⊐→▷	Engine idling – coolant blower motor ON, 3rd speed	11-14 V		
Engine coolant blower motor relay 2 – without AC	B31	⊐→▷	Engine idling – coolant blower motor OFF	11-14 V		
	B31	⊐→▷	Engine idling – coolant blower motor ON, 1st speed	11-14 V		
	B31	⊐→▷	Engine idling – coolant blower motor ON, 2nd speed	0-1 V		
Engine coolant blower motor relay 3 – 2003→, AT with AC	B24	⊐→▷		1		
Engine coolant blower motor relay 3 – 2003→, MT with AC	B24	⊐→▷	Engine idling – coolant blower motor OFF	11-14 V		
	B24	⊐→▷	Engine idling – coolant blower motor ON, 1st speed	11-14 V		
	B24	⊐→▷	Engine idling – coolant blower motor ON, 2nd speed	11-14 V		
	B24	⊐→▷	Engine idling – coolant blower motor ON, 3rd speed	0-1 V		
Engine coolant blower motor relay 4 – 2003→, AT with AC	B39	⊐→▷		1		
Engine coolant temperature (ECT) sensor	A10	←	Ignition ON – coolant temp. 20°C	1,9 V		
	A10	←	Ignition ON – coolant temp. 80°C	2,3 V		
	A62	⊐—	Ignition ON	0 V		
Evaporative emission (EVAP) canister purge valve	A3	⊐→▷	Ignition ON	11-14 V		
	A3	⊐→▷	Engine idling		5 V/2 ms	Intermittent ⋀⋁⋀ 68
Exhaust gas recirculation (EGR) valve actuator – →2003	A21	⊐→▷	Ignition ON	11-14 V		
	A21	⊐→▷	Engine idling – engine hot		5 V/2 ms	Intermittent ⋀⋁⋀ 68
Exhaust gas recirculation (EGR) valve position sensor – →2003	A28	←	Ignition ON	1,2 V		
	A28	←	Engine idling	1,2 V		
	A30	⇨	Ignition ON	5 V		
	A62	⊐—	Ignition ON	0 V		
Fuel gauge tank sensor signal	B53	←		1		
Fuel pump (FP) relay	B23	⊐→▷	Ignition ON	0-1 V briefly then 11-14 V		
	B23	⊐→▷	Engine idling	0-1 V		
Heated oxygen sensor (HO2S) 1	A44	←	Engine idling	0,1-0,9 V fluctuating	0,2 V/1 sec.	⋀⋁⋀ 21
	A52	⊐→▷	Ignition ON	11-14 V		
	A52	⊐→▷	Engine idling	0-1 V		
	A62	⊐—	Ignition ON	0 V		
Heated oxygen sensor (HO2S) 2	A53	⊐→▷	Ignition ON	11-14 V		
	A53	⊐→▷	Engine idling	0-1 V		
	A61	←	Engine idling	0,6 V		
	A62	⊐—	Ignition ON	0 V		

★ Suggested settings - Voltage/time per division

Component/circuit description	ECM pin	Signal	Condition	Typical value	Oscilloscope setting*	Wave form
Ignition coil	A1	→▷	Ignition ON	11-14 V		
	A1	→▷	Engine idling		5 V/2 ms	〰 33
	A2	→▷	Ignition ON	11-14 V		
	A2	→▷	Engine idling		5 V/2 ms	〰 33
	A17	→▷	Ignition ON	11-14 V		
	A17	→▷	Engine idling		5 V/2 ms	〰 33
	A18	→▷	Ignition ON	11-14 V		
	A18	→▷	Engine idling		5 V/2 ms	〰 33
	A33	→▷	Ignition ON	11-14 V		
	A33	→▷	Engine idling		5 V/2 ms	〰 33
	A34	→▷	Ignition ON	11-14 V		
	A34	→▷	Engine idling		5 V/2 ms	〰 33
	A49	→▷	Ignition ON	11-14 V		
	A49	→▷	Engine idling		5 V/2 ms	〰 33
	A50	→▷	Ignition ON	11-14 V		
	A50	→▷	Engine idling		5 V/2 ms	〰 33
Ignition switch	B52	⟵	Ignition OFF	0 V		
	B52	⟵	Ignition ON	11-14 V		
Immobilizer control module	B54	⟷		1		
Injector 1	A57	→▷	Ignition ON	11-14 V briefly then 0-1 V		
	A57	→▷	Engine idling	3,5 ms	10 V/2 ms	〰 35
Injector 2	A60	→▷	Ignition ON	11-14 V briefly then 0-1 V		
	A60	→▷	Engine idling	3,5 ms	10 V/2 ms	〰 35
Injector 3	A58	→▷	Ignition ON	11-14 V briefly then 0-1 V		
	A58	→▷	Engine idling	3,5 ms	10 V/2 ms	〰 35
Injector 4	A59	→▷	Ignition ON	11-14 V briefly then 0-1 V		
	A59	→▷	Engine idling	3,5 ms	10 V/2 ms	〰 35
Instrumentation control module	B55			1		
Instrumentation control module – tachometer signal	B46	⟹	Engine idling	25 Hz		
	B46	⟹	3000 rpm	100 Hz		
Intake air temperature (IAT) sensor	A29	⊣	Ignition ON	0 V		
	A43	⟵	Ignition ON – air temp. 20°C	3,7 V		
Knock sensor (KS)	A39	⟵	Engine idling – accelerate briefly		50 mV/1 ms	〰 58
Knock sensor (KS) – shield wire	A62	⊣	Ignition ON	0 V		
Malfunction indicator lamp (MIL)	B64	→▷	Ignition ON – MIL ON	0-1 V		
	B64	→▷	Ignition ON – MIL OFF	11-14 V		
Manifold absolute pressure (MAP) sensor	A26	⟵	Ignition ON	4,9 V		
	A26	⟵	Engine idling	1,3 V		
	A26	⟵	Engine running – full throttle briefly	4,9 V		
	A45	⊣	Ignition ON	0 V		
	A63	⟹	Ignition ON	5 V		
Power steering control module	B15	⟵		1		
Service indicator	B32	→▷	Ignition ON – service indicator ON	0-1 V		
	B32	→▷	Ignition ON – service indicator OFF	11-14 V		

* Suggested settings - Voltage/time per division

Component/circuit description	ECM pin	Signal	Condition	Typical value	Oscilloscope setting*	Wave form
Throttle motor	A15	⇒	Ignition ON	11-14 V		
	A15	⇒	Engine idling		5 V/0,2 ms	⎍⎍ 68
	A16	⇒	Ignition ON		5 V/0,2 ms	(intermittent for 10 seconds only) ⎍⎍ 68
	A16	⇒	Engine idling	11-14 V		
	A31	⇒	Ignition ON	11-14 V		
	A31	⇒	Engine idling		5 V/0,2 ms	⎍⎍ 68
	A32	⇒	Ignition ON		5 V/0,2 ms	(intermittent for 10 seconds only) ⎍⎍ 68
	A32	⇒	Engine idling	11-14 V		
Throttle motor position sensor	A9	⇐	Ignition ON – accelerator pedal released	1 V		
	A9	⇐	Ignition ON – accelerator pedal depressed	4,4 V		
	A12	⇐	Ignition ON – accelerator pedal released	4,1 V		
	A12	⇐	Ignition ON – accelerator pedal depressed	0,7 V		
	A13	⊣—	Ignition ON	0 V		
	A14	⇒	Ignition ON	5 V		
	A29	⊣—	Ignition ON	0 V		
	A46	⇒	Ignition ON	5 V		
Transmission control module (TCM)	B11	⬌		1		
	B43	⬌		1		
Vehicle speed sensor (VSS) signal amplifier – without ABS	B41	⇐	Ignition ON – vehicle pushed	0 V or 11-14 V fluctuating		

*Suggested settings - Voltage/time per division

1 Connected pin - no test data available or random digital signal

ECM harness multi-plug

Terminal side – A – White, B – Blue

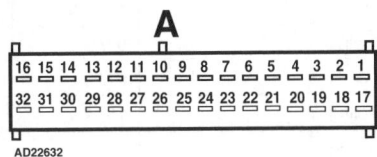

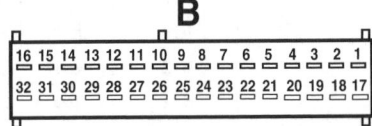

AD22632

Wire side – A – White, B – Blue

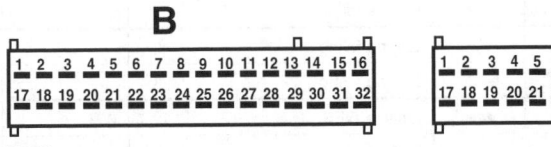

AD22960

Component/circuit description	ECM pin	Signal	Condition	Typical value	Oscilloscope setting★	Wave form
AC control module	A10	⇨	Engine idling	99 Hz		
	A11	⌐⇨	Engine idling	99 Hz		
	A28	⬅	Engine idling	11-14 V		
AC control module – engine speed signal	A8	⇨	Engine idling	27 Hz	2 V/20 ms	⩗ 55
	A8	⇨	3000 rpm	95 Hz		
Air conditioning	A6	⬅	Ignition ON	0 V		
	A6	⬅	Engine idling – AC OFF	0 V		
	A6	⬅	Engine idling – AC ON	11-14 V		
Battery	A1	⬅	Ignition OFF	11-14 V		
Crankshaft position (CKP) sensor	B1	⬅	Engine idling	1,3 V ac	1 V/1 ms	Reversed ⩗ 2
	B21	⬅	Engine idling	1,3 V ac	1 V/1 ms	⩗ 2
Crankshaft position (CKP) sensor – shield wire	B19		Ignition ON	0 V		
Data link connector (DLC)	A4	⬅⇨	Ignition OFF	0 V		
	A4	⬅⇨	Ignition ON	0 V		
Digital multifunction display	A9	⇨		1		
Earth	B19		Ignition ON	0 V		
	B20		Ignition ON	0 V		
	B29		Ignition ON	0 V		
Engine control module (ECM) – pin B13	B8		Ignition ON	0 V		
Engine control module (ECM) – pin B8	B13		Ignition ON	0 V		
Engine coolant blower motor relay – non-AC	A12	⌐⇨		1		
	A14	⌐⇨		1		
Engine coolant temperature (ECT) sensor	B18	⌐	Ignition ON	0 V		
	B23	⬅	Ignition ON – coolant temp. 10°C	2,31 V		
	B23	⬅	Ignition ON – coolant temp. 85-90°C	1,88 V		
Engine coolant temperature gauge	A10	⇨	Engine idling	99 Hz		
Evaporative emission (EVAP) canister purge valve	B31	⌐⇨	Engine idling – engine hot	11-14 V		

★ Suggested settings - Voltage/time per division

Component/circuit description	ECM pin	Signal	Condition	Typical value	Oscilloscope setting*	Wave form
Exhaust gas recirculation (EGR) solenoid	B16	⊃⊳	Ignition ON	0 V		
	B16	⊃⊳	3000 rpm		5 V/0,5 ms	
Exhaust gas recirculation (EGR) valve position sensor	B9	⟵	Ignition ON	0 V		
	B9	⟵	Engine idling	0,7 V		
	B17	⊣	Ignition ON	0 V		
	B26	⟹	Ignition ON	5 V		
Fuel pump relay	A26	⊃⊳	Ignition ON	11-14 V		
	A26	⊃⊳	Engine idling	0 V		
	B12	⟵	Ignition ON	0 V		
	B12	⟵	Engine idling	11-14 V		
Idle air control (IAC) valve	B2 (B3)	⟹	Engine idling		4 V/0,1 sec.	
	B3 (B2)	⟹	Engine idling		4 V/0,1 sec.	
	B4 (B5)	⟹	Engine idling		4 V/0,1 sec.	
	B5 (B4)	⟹	Engine idling		4 V/0,1 sec.	
Ignition amplifier	B6	⟹	Engine idling		1 V/20 ms	
	B7	⟹	Engine idling		1 V/20 ms	
Ignition switch	A2	⟵	Ignition OFF	0 V		
	A2	⟵	Ignition ON	11-14 V		
Immobilizer control module	A31	⟵⟹	Engine idling	11-14 V		
Injector	B10	⊃⊳	Ignition ON	11-14 V		
	B10	⊃⊳	Engine idling		10 V/0,5 ms	
Knock sensor (KS)	B25	⟵	Engine running – accelerate briefly		50 mV/1 ms	
Knock sensor (KS) – shield wire	B17	⊣	Ignition ON	0 V		
Malfunction indicator lamp (MIL)	A29	⊃⊳	Ignition ON – MIL ON	0 V		
	A29	⊃⊳	Engine idling – MIL OFF	11-14 V		
Manifold absolute pressure (MAP) sensor	B17	⊣	Ignition ON	0 V		
	B26	⟹	Ignition ON	5 V		
	B30	⟵	Ignition ON	4,9 V		
	B30	⟵	Engine idling	1,2 V		
	B30	⟵	Engine idling – accelerate briefly	5 V briefly		
Oxygen sensor (O2S)	B27	⟵	Engine idling – engine hot	0,1-1 V fluctuating	0,2 V/1 sec.	
Tachometer	A8	⟹	Engine idling	27 Hz	2 V/20 ms	
	A8	⟹	3000 rpm	95 Hz		
Throttle position (TP) sensor	B18	⊣	Ignition ON	0 V		
	B24	⟵	Ignition ON – throttle closed	0,5 V		
	B24	⟵	Ignition ON – throttle fully open	4,36 V		
	B26	⟹	Ignition ON	5 V		
Transmission control module (TCM)	A5			1		
	A9			1		
	A11		Engine idling	99 Hz		
	A16			1		
	A32			1		
Vehicle speed sensor (VSS)	A20	⟵	Ignition ON – vehicle pushed	0 V or 10,5 V fluctuating		

*Suggested settings - Voltage/time per division

1 Connected pin - no test data available or random digital signal

ECM harness multi-plug

Terminal side

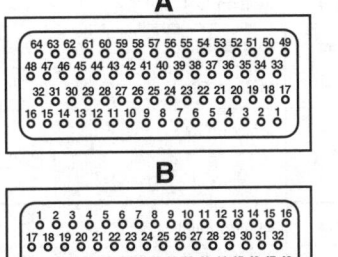

Wire side

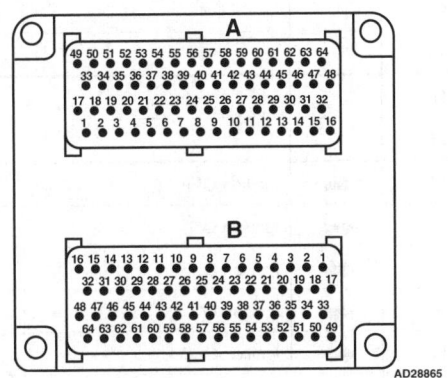

Component/circuit description	ECM pin	Signal	Condition	Typical value	Oscilloscope setting*	Wave form
ABS control module – VSS signal	B41	←	Ignition ON – vehicle pushed	0 V or 11-14 V fluctuating		
AC control module	B45	←	Ignition ON – AC OFF	0 V		
	B45	←	Ignition ON – AC ON	11-14 V		
Accelerator pedal position (APP) sensor	B20	⇒	Ignition ON	5 V		
	B33	⌐⎯	Ignition ON	0 V		
	B35	⇒	Ignition ON	5 V		
	B36	←	Ignition ON – accelerator pedal released	0,5 V		
	B36	←	Ignition ON – accelerator pedal depressed	2 V		
	B37	←	Ignition ON – accelerator pedal released	1 V		
	B37	←	Ignition ON – accelerator pedal depressed	4,1 V		
	B50	⌐⎯	Ignition ON	0 V		
Battery	B2	←	Ignition OFF	11-14 V		
	B19	←	Ignition OFF	11-14 V		

* Suggested settings - Voltage/time per division

Component/circuit description	ECM pin	Signal	Condition	Typical value	Oscilloscope setting*	Wave form
Brake pedal position (BPP) switch	B5	←	Ignition ON – brake pedal released	0 V		
	B5	←	Ignition ON – brake pedal depressed	11-14 V		
	B13	←	Ignition ON – brake pedal released	11-14 V		
	B13	←	Ignition ON – brake pedal depressed	0 V		
Camshaft position (CMP) sensor	A23	←	Ignition ON	0 or 5 V		
	A23	←	Engine idling		2 V/100 ms	⎍ 4
	A29	⊣—	Ignition ON	0 V		
	A30	⇒	Ignition ON	5 V		
Clutch pedal position (CPP) switch – with cruise control	B61			1		
Crankshaft position (CKP) sensor	A5	←	Engine idling	1,6 V ac	1 V/2 ms	Reversed ⎍ 2
	A22	←	Engine idling	2,4 V ac	1 V/2 ms	⎍ 2
Crankshaft position (CKP) sensor – shield wire	A37	⊣—	Ignition ON	0 V		
Cruise control master switch	B29			1		
	B44			1		
	B62			1		
Digital multifunction display	B47			1		
	B55			1		
Engine control (EC) relay	A47	←	Ignition OFF	0 V		
	A47	←	Ignition ON	11-14 V		
	A48	←	Ignition OFF	0 V		
	A48	←	Ignition ON	11-14 V		
	A64	←	Ignition OFF	0 V		
	A64	←	Ignition ON	11-14 V		
	B16	⊣▷	Ignition OFF	11-14 V		
	B16	⊣▷	Ignition ON	0-1 V		
Engine coolant blower motor control module – with AC	B7	⊣▷	Engine idling – AC ON	0-1 V		
	B7	⊣▷	Engine idling – AC OFF	11-14 V		
	B57			1		
Engine coolant blower motor relay 1 – without AC	B39	⊣▷	Engine idling – coolant blower motor OFF	11-14 V		
	B39	⊣▷	Engine idling – coolant blower motor ON	0-1 V		
Engine coolant blower motor relay 2 – without AC	B31	⊣▷	Engine idling – coolant blower motor OFF	11-14 V		
	B31	⊣▷	Engine idling – coolant blower motor ON	0-1 V		
Engine coolant temperature (ECT) sensor	A10	←	Ignition ON – engine cold	1,7 V		
	A10	←	Engine idling – engine hot	1,9 V		
	A62	⊣—	Ignition ON	0 V		
Evaporative emission (EVAP) canister purge valve	A3	⊣▷	Ignition ON	11-14 V		
	A3	⊣▷	Engine idling		5 V/2 ms	Intermittent ⎍ 68
Exhaust gas recirculation (EGR) solenoid	A21	⊣▷	Ignition ON	11-14 V		
	A21	⊣▷	Engine idling – engine hot		5 V/2 ms	Intermittent ⎍ 68

* Suggested settings - Voltage/time per division

Component/circuit description	ECM pin	Signal	Condition	Typical value	Oscilloscope setting*	Wave form
Exhaust gas recirculation (EGR) valve position sensor	A28	←	Ignition ON	1,2 V		
	A28	←	Engine idling	1,2 V		
	A30	⇨	Ignition ON	5 V		
	A62	⊣⊢	Ignition ON	0 V		
Fuel gauge tank sensor	B53	←	Ignition ON – fuel level low	6 V		
Fuel pump (FP) relay	B23	⊣▷	Ignition ON	0-1 V briefly then 11-14 V		
	B23	⊣▷	Engine idling	0-1 V		
Heated oxygen sensor (HO2S) 1	A44	←	Ignition ON	0,2 V		
	A44	←	Engine idling – engine hot		0,2 V/1 sec.	21
	A52	⊣▷	Ignition ON	11-14 V		
	A52	⊣▷	Engine idling	0-1 V		
	A62	⊣⊢	Ignition ON	0 V		
Heated oxygen sensor (HO2S) 2	A53	⊣▷	Ignition ON	11-14 V		
	A53	⊣▷	Engine idling	0-1 V		
	A61	←	Ignition ON	0,2 V		
	A61	←	Engine idling	0,7 V		
	A62	⊣⊢	Ignition ON	0 V		
Ignition coil	A1	⊣▷	Ignition ON	11-14 V		
	A1	⊣▷	Engine idling		5 V/1 ms	33
	A17	⊣▷	Ignition ON	11-14 V		
	A17	⊣▷	Engine idling		5 V/1 ms	33
	A33	⊣▷	Ignition ON	11-14 V		
	A33	⊣▷	Engine idling		5 V/1 ms	33
	A49	⊣▷	Ignition ON	11-14 V		
	A49	⊣▷	Engine idling		5 V/1 ms	33
Ignition switch	B52	←	Ignition OFF	0 V		
	B52	←	Ignition ON	11-14 V		
Immobilizer control module	B54	←	Ignition ON	11 V		
Injector 1	A57	⊣▷	Ignition ON	11-14 V briefly then 0-1 V		
	A57	⊣▷	Engine idling	3,5 ms	10 V/2 ms	35
Injector 2	A60	⊣▷	Ignition ON	11-14 V briefly then 0-1 V		
	A60	⊣▷	Engine idling	3,5 ms	10 V/2 ms	35
Injector 3	A58	⊣▷	Ignition ON	11-14 V briefly then 0-1 V		
	A58	⊣▷	Engine idling	3,5 ms	10 V/2 ms	35
Injector 4	A59	⊣▷	Ignition ON	11-14 V briefly then 0-1 V		
	A59	⊣▷	Engine idling	3,5 ms	10 V/2 ms	35
Intake air temperature (IAT) sensor	A29	⊣⊢	Ignition ON	0 V		
	A43	←	Ignition ON – air temp. 20°C	3,7 V		
Knock sensor (KS)	A39	←	Engine idling – accelerate briefly		50 mV/1 ms	58
Knock sensor (KS) – shield wire	A62	⊣⊢	Ignition ON	0 V		

* Suggested settings - Voltage/time per division

Component/circuit description	ECM pin	Signal	Condition	Typical value	Oscilloscope setting*	Wave form
Malfunction indicator lamp (MIL)	B64	⌐⊳	Ignition ON – MIL ON	0-1 V		
	B64	⌐⊳	Ignition ON – MIL OFF	11-14 V		
Manifold absolute pressure (MAP) sensor	A26	⬅	Ignition ON	4,9 V		
	A26	⬅	Engine idling	1,3 V		
	A26	⬅	Engine running – full throttle briefly	4,9 V		
	A45	⌐	Ignition ON	0 V		
	A63	⇨	Ignition ON	5 V		
Power steering control module	B15	⬅	Engine idling – steering wheel not turned	8,5 V		
	B15	⬅	Engine idling – steering wheel turned	7,7 V		
Service indicator	B32	⌐⊳	Ignition ON – service indicator ON	0-1 V		
	B32	⌐⊳	Ignition ON – service indicator OFF	11-14 V		
Tachometer	B46	⇨	Engine idling	25 Hz		
	B46	⇨	3000 rpm	100 Hz		
Throttle motor	A15	⇨	Ignition ON	11-14 V		
	A15	⇨	Engine idling		5 V/0,2 ms	⎍⎍ 68
	A16	⇨	Ignition ON		5 V/0,2 ms	(intermittent for 10 seconds only) ⎍⎍ 68
	A16	⇨	Engine idling	11-14 V		
	A31	⇨	Ignition ON	11-14 V		
	A31	⇨	Engine idling		5 V/0,2 ms	⎍⎍ 68
	A32	⇨	Ignition ON		5 V/0,2 ms	(intermittent for 10 seconds only) ⎍⎍ 68
	A32	⇨	Engine idling	11-14 V		
Throttle motor position sensor	A9	⬅	Ignition ON – accelerator pedal released	1 V		
	A9	⬅	Ignition ON – accelerator pedal depressed	4,4 V		
	A12	⬅	Ignition ON – accelerator pedal released	4,1 V		
	A12	⬅	Ignition ON – accelerator pedal depressed	0,7 V		
	A13	⌐	Ignition ON	0 V		
	A14	⇨	Ignition ON	5 V		
	A29	⌐	Ignition ON	0 V		
	A46	⇨	Ignition ON	5 V		
Transmission control module (TCM)	B11			☐1		
	B43			☐1		
Vehicle speed sensor (VSS) – without ABS	B41	⬅	Ignition ON – vehicle pushed	0 V or 11-14 V fluctuating		

*Suggested settings - Voltage/time per division

☐1 Connected pin - no test data available or random digital signal

ECM harness multi-plug

Terminal side

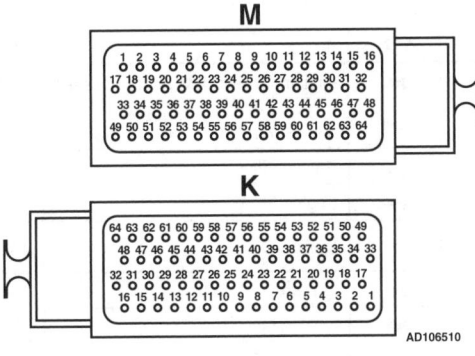

Wire side

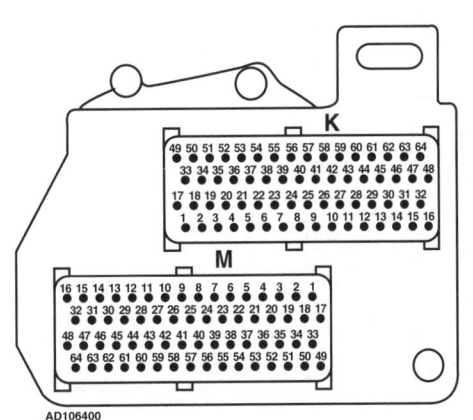

AD106400

Component/circuit description	ECM pin	Signal	Condition	Typical value	Oscilloscope setting★	Wave form
AC compressor clutch relay	K7	⊐▷	Engine idling – AC OFF	11-14 V		
	K7	⊐▷	Engine idling – AC ON – AC compressor ON	0-1 V		
AC refrigerant pressure sensor	K3	⇨	Ignition ON	5 V		
	K4	⬅	Ignition ON	0,6 V		
	K34	⊐⊢	Ignition ON	0 V		
Accelerator pedal position (APP) sensor	K20	⇨	Ignition ON	5 V		
	K33	⊐⊢	Ignition ON	0 V		
	K35	⇨	Ignition ON	5 V		
	K36	⬅	Ignition ON – accelerator pedal released	0,5 V		
	K36	⬅	Ignition ON – accelerator pedal fully depressed	1,8 V		
	K37	⬅	Ignition ON – accelerator pedal released	1 V		
	K37	⬅	Ignition ON – accelerator pedal fully depressed	3,7 V		
	K50	⊐⊢	Ignition ON	0 V		
Alternator	M8	⬅	Ignition ON	1,3 V		
	M8	⬅	Engine idling	11-14 V		
Brake pedal position (BPP) switch	K5	⬅	Ignition ON – brake pedal released	0 V		
	K5	⬅	Ignition ON – brake pedal depressed	11-14 V		
	K13	⬅	Ignition ON – brake pedal released	11-14 V		
	K13	⬅	Ignition ON – brake pedal depressed	0 V		

★ Suggested settings - Voltage/time per division

Component/circuit description	ECM pin	Signal	Condition	Typical value	Oscilloscope setting*	Wave form
Camshaft position (CMP) sensor	M23	←	Ignition ON	0 or 5 V		
	M23	←	Engine idling		2 V/0,1 sec.	⎍ 4
	M29	⊣⊢	Ignition ON	0 V		
	M30	⇨	Ignition ON	5 V		
	M36	⊣⊢	Ignition ON	0 V		
CAN data bus	K11	⬄		①		
	K43	⬄		①		
Clutch pedal position (CPP) switch	K61	←	Ignition ON – clutch pedal released	11-14 V		
	K61	←	Ignition ON – clutch pedal depressed	0 V		
Crankshaft position (CKP) sensor	M5	←	Engine idling		2 V/2 ms	Reversed ⎍ 2
	M22	←	Engine idling		2 V/2 ms	⎍ 2
Crankshaft position (CKP) sensor – shield wire	M37	⊣⊢	Ignition ON	0 V		
Engine control (EC) relay	M47	←	Ignition OFF	0 V		
	M47	←	Ignition ON	11-14 V		
	M48	←	Ignition OFF	0 V		
	M48	←	Ignition ON	11-14 V		
	M64	←	Ignition OFF	0 V		
	M64	←	Ignition ON	11-14 V		
	K2	←	Ignition OFF	0 V		
	K2	←	Ignition ON	11-14 V		
	K14	←	Ignition OFF	0 V		
	K14	←	Ignition ON	11-14 V		
	K16	⊣⊢⇨	Ignition OFF	11-14 V		
	K16	⊣⊢⇨	Ignition ON	0-1 V		
	K19	←	Ignition OFF	0 V		
	K19	←	Ignition ON	11-14 V		
Engine coolant blower motor relay – with AC	K24	⊣⊢⇨	Engine idling – coolant blower motor OFF	11-14 V		
	K24	⊣⊢⇨	Engine idling – coolant blower motor ON	0-1 V		
	K39	⊣⊢⇨	Engine idling – coolant blower motor OFF	11-14 V		
	K39	⊣⊢⇨	Engine idling – coolant blower motor ON	0-1 V		
Engine coolant blower motor relay – without AC	K31	⊣⊢⇨	Engine idling – coolant blower motor OFF	11-14 V		
	K31	⊣⊢⇨	Engine idling – coolant blower motor ON	0-1 V		
Engine coolant blower motor temperature sensor	K21			①		
	K49			①		
Engine coolant temperature (ECT) sensor	M10	←	Ignition ON – coolant temp. 7°C	2,5 V		
	M10	←	Ignition ON – coolant temp. 70°C	1,5 V		
	M62	⊣⊢	Ignition ON	0 V		
Engine coolant thermostat	M55	⊣⊢⇨	Ignition ON	11-14 V		
	M55	⊣⊢⇨	Engine running – valve operating	0-1 V		
Engine oil level sensor	M27			①		
Engine oil pressure switch 1	M54			①		
Engine oil pressure switch 2	M56			①		
Evaporative emission (EVAP) canister purge valve	M3	⊣⊢⇨	Ignition ON	11-14 V		
	M3	⊣⊢⇨	Engine idling		5 V/2 ms	Intermittent ⎍ 68
Exhaust gas recirculation (EGR) valve actuator	M21	⊣⊢⇨	Ignition ON	11-14 V		
	M21	⊣⊢⇨	Engine running – valve operating		5 V/2 ms	⎍ 68

★ Suggested settings - Voltage/time per division

Component/circuit description	ECM pin	Signal	Condition	Typical value	Oscilloscope setting*	Wave form
Exhaust gas recirculation (EGR) valve position sensor	M28	←	Ignition ON	1 V		
	M28	←	Engine idling	1 V		
	M62	⌐	Ignition ON	0 V		
Fuel pump (FP) relay	K28	⌐▷	Ignition ON	11-14 V briefly then 0-1 V		
	K28	⌐▷	Engine idling	11-14 V		
Heated oxygen sensor (HO2S) 1	M42	⌐	Ignition ON	0 V		
	M44	←	Engine idling – engine hot	0,1-0,9 V fluctuating	0,2 V/1 sec.	
	M52	⌐▷	Ignition ON	11-14 V		
	M52	⌐▷	Engine idling	0-1 V		
Heated oxygen sensor (HO2S) 2	M6	⌐	Ignition ON	0 V		
	M53	⌐▷	Ignition ON	11-14 V		
	M53	⌐▷	Engine idling	0-1 V		
	M61	←	Engine idling	0,5 V		
Ignition coil – cylinder 1	M33	⌐▷	Ignition ON	11-14 V		
	M33	⌐▷	Engine idling		5 V/2 ms	
	M49	⌐▷	Ignition ON	11-14 V		
	M49	⌐▷	Engine idling		5 V/2 ms	
Ignition coil – cylinder 2	M2	⌐▷	Ignition ON	11-14 V		
	M2	⌐▷	Engine idling		5 V/2 ms	
	M18	⌐▷	Ignition ON	11-14 V		
	M18	⌐▷	Engine idling		5 V/2 ms	
Ignition coil – cylinder 3	M1	⌐▷	Ignition ON	11-14 V		
	M1	⌐▷	Engine idling		5 V/2 ms	
	M17	⌐▷	Ignition ON	11-14 V		
	M17	⌐▷	Engine idling		5 V/2 ms	
Ignition coil – cylinder 4	M34	⌐▷	Ignition ON	11-14 V		
	M34	⌐▷	Engine idling		5 V/2 ms	
	M50	⌐▷	Ignition ON	11-14 V		
	M50	⌐▷	Engine idling		5 V/2 ms	
Ignition main circuits relay	K52	←	Ignition OFF	0 V		
	K52	←	Ignition ON	11-14 V		
Injector 1	M57	⌐▷	Ignition ON	11-14 V briefly then 0-1 V		
	M57	⌐▷	Engine idling	1,9 ms	10 V/2 ms	
Injector 2	M60	⌐▷	Ignition ON	11-14 V briefly then 0-1 V		
	M60	⌐▷	Engine idling	1,9 ms	10 V/2 ms	
Injector 3	M58	⌐▷	Ignition ON	11-14 V briefly then 0-1 V		
	M58	⌐▷	Engine idling	1,9 ms	10 V/2 ms	
Injector 4	M59	⌐▷	Ignition ON	11-14 V briefly then 0-1 V		
	M59	⌐▷	Engine idling	1,9 ms	10 V/2 ms	
Intake air temperature (IAT) sensor	M29	⌐	Ignition ON	0 V		
	M36	⌐	Ignition ON	0 V		
	M43	←	Ignition ON – air temp. 9°C	3,2 V		
	M43	←	Ignition ON – air temp. 24°C	2,4 V		
Intake manifold air control actuator	M7	⌐▷	Ignition ON	11-14 V		
	M7	⌐▷	Engine idling	0-1 V		

* Suggested settings - Voltage/time per division

Component/circuit description	ECM pin	Signal	Condition	Typical value	Oscilloscope setting*	Wave form
Intake manifold air control actuator position sensor	M38	←	Ignition ON	0,3 V		
	M38	←	Engine idling	4,7 V		
	M38	←	Engine idling – accelerate briefly	0,3 V briefly		
Knock sensor (KS)	M39	←	Engine idling – accelerate briefly		50 mV/1 ms	
Knock sensor (KS) – shield wire	M62	⌐—	Ignition ON	0 V		
Manifold absolute pressure (MAP) sensor	M26	←	Ignition ON	4,8 V		
	M26	←	Engine idling	0,9 V		
	M26	←	Engine running – full throttle briefly	4,2 V briefly		
	M45	⌐—	Ignition ON	0 V		
	M63	⇒	Ignition ON	5 V		
Throttle motor	M15	⇒	Ignition ON	11-14 V		
	M15	⇒	Engine idling		5 V/0,2 ms	
	M16	⇒	Ignition ON	10,5 V for 5 secs then 11-14 V		
	M16	⇒	Engine idling	11-14 V		
	M31	⇒	Ignition ON	11-14 V		
	M31	⇒	Engine idling		5 V/0,2 ms	
	M32	⇒	Ignition ON	10,5 V for 5 secs then 11-14 V		
	M32	⇒	Engine idling	11-14 V		
Throttle motor position sensor	M9	←	Ignition ON – accelerator pedal released	1,2 V		
	M9	←	Ignition ON – accelerator pedal fully depressed	1,4 V		
	M12	←	Ignition ON – accelerator pedal released	3,8 V		
	M12	←	Ignition ON – accelerator pedal fully depressed	3,5 V		
	M13	⌐—	Ignition ON	0 V		
	M14	⇒	Ignition ON	5 V		
	M29	⌐—	Ignition ON	0 V		
	M36	⌐—	Ignition ON	0 V		
	M46	⇒	Ignition ON	5 V		

*Suggested settings - Voltage/time per division

1 Connected pin - no test data available or random digital signal

Model:	Engine code:	Year:
Astra-G 1,7 TD	X17DTL	1998-01
Astra-G 2,0 TD	X20DTL	1998-01

OPEL-VAUXHALL

Bosch EDC 15M

ECM harness multi-plug

Terminal side

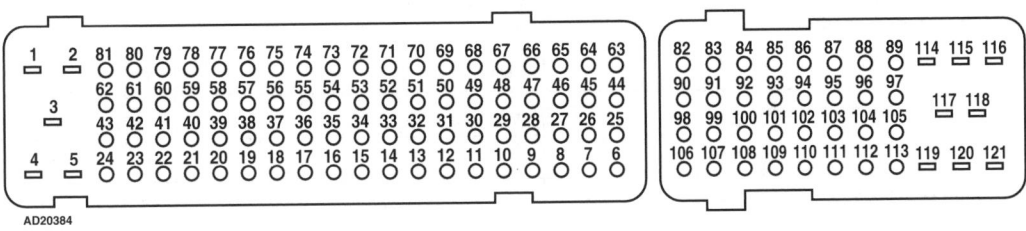

AD20384

Wire side

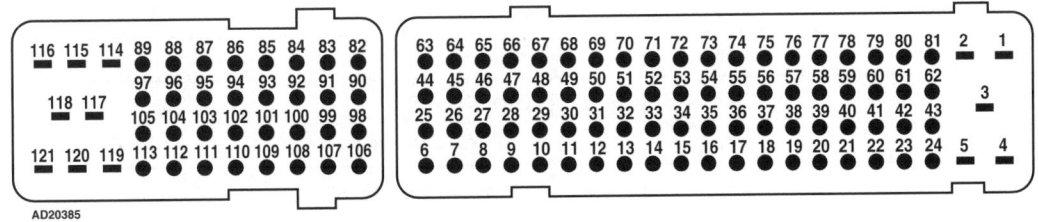

AD20385

Component/circuit description	ECM pin	Signal	Condition	Typical value
AC relay	33			1
Accelerator pedal position (APP) sensor	38	←	Ignition ON – accelerator pedal released	0,5 V
	38	←	Ignition ON – accelerator pedal depressed	3,5 V
	49		Ignition ON	0 V
	57	⇒	Ignition OFF	0 V
	57	⇒	Ignition ON	5 V
	69	←	Ignition ON – accelerator pedal released	3,5 V
	69	←	Ignition ON – accelerator pedal depressed	0,1 V
Brake pedal position (BPP) switch	30	←	Ignition ON – brake pedal released	0 V
	30	←	Ignition ON – brake pedal depressed	11-14 V
	65	←	Ignition ON – brake pedal released	11-14 V
	65	←	Ignition ON – brake pedal depressed	0 V
Clutch pedal position (CPP) switch	31	←	Ignition ON – clutch pedal released	11-14 V
	31	←	Ignition ON – clutch pedal depressed	0 V
Crankshaft position (CKP) sensor	90	←	Engine idling	3,8 V ac
	90	←	Engine idling	5 V/5 ms per division 〰〰 6
	98	⌐	Ignition ON	0 V
Crankshaft position (CKP) sensor – screened lead	101	⌐	Ignition ON	0 V
Cruise control master switch	45			1
	63			1
	64			1
Digital multifunction display	29	⇒	Engine idling	11-14 V
	29	⇒	Ignition ON	11-14 V

Component/circuit description	ECM pin	Signal	Condition	Typical value
Earth	1		Ignition ON	0 V
	2		Ignition ON	0 V
Engine control relay	3	←	Ignition OFF	0 V
	3	←	Ignition ON	11-14 V
	58	⇥	Ignition OFF	11-14 V
	58	⇥	Ignition ON	0 V
Engine coolant blower motor control module	27	⇨	Engine idling	5 V/10 ms per division ⌁ 4
	28	⇨	Engine idling	1
Engine coolant blower motor control module – AC	41			1
	66			1
Engine coolant temperature (ECT) sensor	89	←	Ignition ON – coolant temp. 20°C	3,7 V
	89	←	Engine idling – engine hot	1,1 V
	93	⊣	Ignition ON	0 V
Engine coolant temperature gauge	28	⇨	Engine idling	1
Engine malfunction indicator lamp (MIL)	42	⇨	Ignition ON – MIL ON	0 V
	42	⇨	Ignition ON – MIL OFF	11-14 V
Engine oil temperature sensor	86	←	Engine idling – engine hot	2,47 V
	86	←	Ignition ON – engine cold	3,7 V
	93	⊣	Ignition ON	0 V
Exhaust gas recirculation (EGR) solenoid	97	⇨	Ignition ON	11-14 V
	97	⇨	Engine idling	5 V/1 ms per division ⌁ 12
Exhaust gas recirculation (EGR) throttle control valve – 2,0	60	←	Ignition ON	11-14 V
	60	←	Engine idling	5 V/2 ms per division ⌁ 31
Fuel injection pump control module	91	⇨	Engine idling	2 V/5 ms per division ⌁ 15
	99	⇔	Engine idling	1,5-2,5 V
	99	⇔	Engine idling	0,5 V/10 µs per division ⌁ 16
	99	⇔	Ignition ON	2,5 V
	100	⇔	Ignition ON	2,5 V
	100	⇔	Engine idling	2,5-3,5 V
	100	⇔	Engine idling	0,5 V/10 µs per division ⌁ 19
	105	⇔	Ignition ON	0 V
	105	⇔	Engine idling	0,1 V/10 ms per division ⌁ 17
Glow plug control module	87	⇨	Engine idling	0,3 V
	87	⇨	Ignition ON	0,3 V
	94	⇨	Ignition OFF	0 V
	94	⇨	Engine idling	11-14 V
	94	⇨	Ignition ON	0 V
Glow plug warning lamp	43	⇨	Ignition ON – lamp ON	0 V
	43	⇨	Ignition ON – lamp OFF	11-14 V
Ignition switch	39	←	Ignition OFF	0 V
	39	←	Ignition ON	11-14 V

Component/circuit description	ECM pin	Signal	Condition	Typical value
Immobilizer control module	35	←	Ignition OFF	0 V
	35	←	Ignition ON	11-14 V
Manifold absolute pressure (MAP) sensor	82	⇒		5 V
	93	⌐	Ignition ON	0 V
	85	←	Engine idling	1,9 V
	85	←	Engine idling – accelerate briefly	2,85 V
Mass air flow (MAF) sensor	83	⇒	Ignition ON	5 V
	88	←		1,1 V
	88	←	Engine idling	1,9 V
	88	←	Engine idling – accelerate briefly	3,7 V
	92	⌐	Ignition ON	0 V
Mass air flow (MAF) sensor – intake air temperature	84	←	Ignition ON – air temp. 20°C	2,2 V
Tachometer	27	⇒	Engine idling	5 V/10 ms per division 〰 4
Transmission control module (TCM) – 2,0	31			1
	34			1
	67			1
Turbocharger (TC) wastegate regulating valve – 2,0	96	←	Engine running	5 V/10 ms per division 〰 29
	96	←	Ignition ON	11-14 V
Vehicle speed sensor (VSS)	68	←	Ignition ON	0 or 11-14 V
	68	←	Ignition ON – vehicle moving	5 V/10 ms per division 〰 4

1 Connected pin - no test data available

Model:	Engine code:	Year:
Astra-G 1,7 DTi	Y17DT	2000-06

ECM harness multi-plug

Terminal side

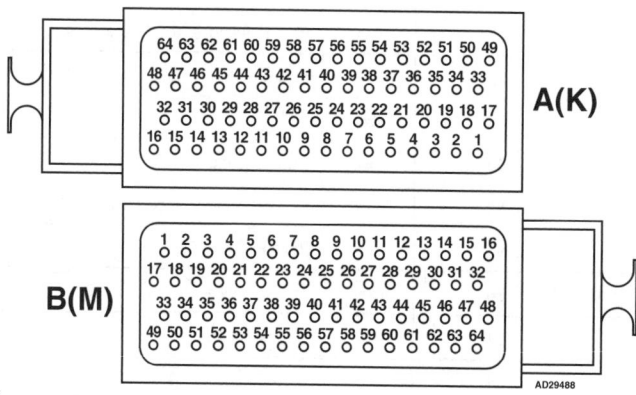

Wire side

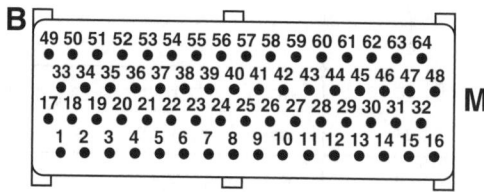

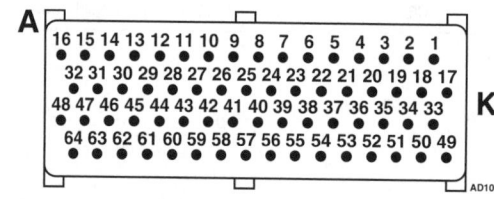

Component/circuit description	ECM pin	Signal	Condition	Typical value	Oscilloscope setting*	Wave form
ABS control module – VSS signal	A40	←	Ignition ON – vehicle pushed	0 V or 11-14 V fluctuating		
AC control module/AC master switch	A45	←		1		
Accelerator pedal position (APP) sensor	A3	⇨	Ignition ON	5 V		
	A33	⌐	Ignition ON	0 V		
	A35	⇨	Ignition ON	5 V		
	A36	←	Ignition ON – accelerator pedal released	0,6 V		
	A36	←	Ignition ON – accelerator pedal depressed	1,9 V		
	A37	←	Ignition ON – accelerator pedal released	1 V		
	A37	←	Ignition ON – accelerator pedal depressed	4 V		
	A49	⌐	Ignition ON	0 V		
Barometric pressure (BARO) sensor	B14	⇨	Ignition ON	5 V		
	B61	←	Ignition ON	4,9 V		
	B61	←	Engine idling	4,8 V		
	B62	⌐	Ignition ON	0 V		
Battery	A2	←	Ignition OFF	11-14 V		
	A19	←	Ignition OFF	11-14 V		

* Suggested settings - Voltage/time per division

Component/circuit description	ECM pin	Signal	Condition	Typical value	Oscilloscope setting*	Wave form
Brake pedal position (BPP) switch	A12	←	Ignition ON – brake pedal released	0 V		
	A12	←	Ignition ON – brake pedal depressed	11-14 V		
	A13	←	Ignition ON – brake pedal released	11-14 V		
	A13	←	Ignition ON – brake pedal depressed	0 V		
Clutch pedal position (CPP) switch	A59	←	Ignition ON – clutch pedal released	11-14 V		
	A59	←	Ignition ON – clutch pedal depressed	0 V		
Crankshaft position (CKP) sensor	B23	←	Ignition ON	0 V or 5 V		
	B23	←	Engine idling		1 V/5 ms	〜 49
Cruise control selector switch	A29			1		
	A44			1		
	A62			1		
Digital multifunction display	A47	⇒		1		
Earth	B38		Ignition ON	0 V		
	B54		Ignition ON	0 V		
	B55		Ignition ON	0 V		
Engine control (EC) relay	A1	←	Ignition OFF	0 V		
	A1	←	Ignition ON	11-14 V		
	A15	⊐⇒	Ignition OFF	11-14 V		
	A15	⊐⇒	Ignition ON	0-1 V		
	A17	←	Ignition OFF	0 V		
	A17	←	Ignition ON	11-14 V		
Engine coolant blower motor control module – engine coolant temperature signal – with AC	A55	⇒		1		
	A55	⇒		1		
Engine coolant blower motor control module – tachometer signal – with AC	A11	⇒	Engine idling	25 Hz		
	A11	⇒	3000 rpm	100 Hz		
Engine coolant blower motor control module – with AC	A7			1		
	A8			1		
Engine coolant blower motor relay 1 – without AC	A56	⊐⇒	Engine running – coolant blower motor OFF	11-14 V		
	A56	⊐⇒	Engine running – coolant blower motor ON, 1st speed	0-1 V		
Engine coolant blower motor relay 2 – without AC	A39	⊐⇒	Engine running – coolant blower motor OFF	11-14 V		
	A39	⊐⇒	Engine running – coolant blower motor ON, 2nd speed	0-1 V		
Engine coolant temperature (ECT) sensor	B42	←	Ignition ON – coolant temp. 20°C	3,7 V		
	B45	⊐─	Ignition ON	0 V		
Engine oil pressure switch	B8	←	Ignition ON	0 V		
	B8	←	Engine idling	11-14 V		
Exhaust gas recirculation (EGR) solenoid	B26	⊐⇒	Ignition ON	11-14 V		
	B26	⊐⇒	Engine idling – valve operating		5 V/5 ms	〜 12
Fuel injection pump control module	B33	⇒	Ignition ON	1 V for 10 seconds then 4,5 V		
	B33	⇒	Engine idling		1 V/2 ms	〜 69
	B34	⇒	Ignition ON	0 V		
	B34	⇒	Engine idling		1 V/2 ms	〜 69
Fuel quantity adjuster	B25	⊐⇒	Engine idling		5 V/20 ms	〜 33

* Suggested settings - Voltage/time per division

Component/circuit description	ECM pin	Signal	Condition	Typical value	Oscilloscope setting*	Wave form
Fuel quantity adjuster relay	A16	⏚⇨	Ignition OFF	11-14 V		
	A16	⏚⇨	Ignition ON	0-1 V for 10 seconds then 11-14 V		
	A16	⏚⇨	Engine running	0-1 V		
Fuel temperature sensor	B41	⬅	Ignition ON – fuel temp. 20°C	3,5 V		
	B45	⏚	Ignition ON	0 V		
Glow plug control module	A9	⇨	Engine idling	11-14 V		
	A43			[1]		
Ignition switch	A52	⬅	Ignition OFF	0 V		
	A52	⬅	Ignition ON	11-14 V		
Immobilizer control module	A54	⬅⇨		[1]		
Immobilizer warning lamp – 2004	A27	⏚⇨	Ignition ON – lamp ON	0-1 V		
	A27	⏚⇨	Engine idling – lamp OFF	11-14 V		
Injection pump assembly	B49	⬅	Ignition ON	0 V		
	B50	⇨	Ignition ON	5 V		
Injection pump position sensor	B1	⬅	Engine idling	0,32 V ac	0,2 V/5 ms	1
	B17	⬅	Engine idling	0,32 V ac	0,2 V/5 ms	Reversed 1
Injection pump position sensor – shield wire	B37	⏚	Ignition ON	0 V		
Instrument panel – engine coolant temperature signal	A55	⇨		[1]		
	A55	⇨		[1]		
Instrument panel – engine oil pressure warning lamp	A63	⏚⇨	Ignition ON – lamp ON	0-1 V		
	A63	⏚⇨	Engine idling – lamp OFF	11-14 V		
Instrument panel – glow plug warning lamp	A26	⏚⇨	Ignition ON – lamp ON	0-1 V		
	A26	⏚⇨	Ignition ON – lamp OFF	11-14 V		
Instrument panel – immobilizer warning lamp – →2003	A32	⏚⇨	Ignition ON – lamp ON	0-1 V		
	A32	⏚⇨	Engine idling – lamp OFF	11-14 V		
Instrument panel – malfunction indicator lamp (MIL) – 2004→	A32	⏚⇨	Ignition ON – MIL ON	0-1 V		
	A32	⏚⇨	Engine idling – MIL OFF	11-14 V		
Instrument panel – tachometer signal	A11	⇨	Engine idling	28 Hz		
	A11	⇨	3000 rpm	100 Hz		
Intake air temperature (IAT) sensor	A42	⬅	Ignition ON – air temp. 20°C	3,5 V		
Manifold absolute pressure (MAP) sensor	B14	⇨	Ignition ON	5 V		
	B58	⬅	Ignition ON	1,8 V		
	B58	⬅	Engine idling	2,3 V		
	B58	⬅	Full load	4,2 V		
	B62	⏚	Ignition ON	0 V		
Mass air flow (MAF) sensor	A5	⬅	Ignition ON	1 V		
	A5	⬅	Engine idling	1,85 V		
	A5	⬅	3000 rpm	3,46 V		
	A20	⇨	Ignition ON	5 V		
	A50	⏚	Ignition ON	0 V		
Turbocharger (TC) wastegate regulating valve	B9	⏚⇨	Ignition ON	11-14 V		
	B9	⏚⇨	Engine idling – valve operating		2 V/1 ms	66
Vehicle speed sensor (VSS) – without ABS	A40	⬅	Ignition ON – vehicle pushed	0 V or 11-14 V fluctuating		

*Suggested settings - Voltage/time per division

[1] Connected pin - no test data available or random digital signal

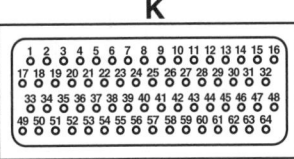
ECM harness multi-plug

Terminal side

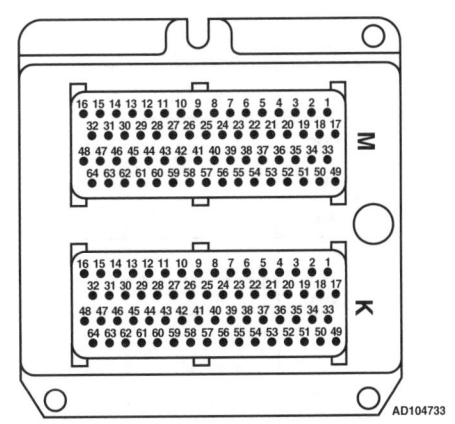

AD105170

Wire side

M

K

AD104733

Component/circuit description	ECM pin	Signal	Condition	Typical value	Oscilloscope setting★	Wave form
ABS control module – VSS signal	K41	⬅	Ignition ON – vehicle pushed	0 V or 11-14 V fluctuating		
AC compressor clutch relay	K51	⊐⊳	Engine idling – AC OFF	11-14 V		
	K51	⊐⊳	Engine idling – AC ON – AC compressor OFF	11-14 V		
	K51	⊐⊳	Engine idling – AC ON – AC compressor ON	0-1 V		
AC refrigerant pressure sensor	K7	⬅		☐1		
	K23	⇨	Ignition ON	5 V		
	K34	⅂	Ignition ON	0 V		
AC/heater function control panel	K11	⬅		☐1		
Accelerator pedal position (APP) sensor	K8	⬅	Ignition ON – accelerator pedal released	1 V		
	K8	⬅	Ignition ON – accelerator pedal depressed	4,3 V		
	K24	⬅	Ignition ON – accelerator pedal released	0,5 V		
	K24	⬅	Ignition ON – accelerator pedal depressed	2,1 V		
	K39	⇨	Ignition ON	5 V		
	K40	⅂	Ignition ON	0 V		
	K55	⇨	Ignition ON	5 V		
	K56	⅂	Ignition ON	0 V		
Battery	K32	⬅	Ignition OFF	11-14 V		

★ Suggested settings - Voltage/time per division

Component/circuit description	ECM pin	Signal	Condition	Typical value	Oscilloscope setting*	Wave form
Brake pedal position (BPP) switch	K28	←	Ignition ON – brake pedal released	0 V		
	K28	←	Ignition ON – brake pedal depressed	11-14 V		
	K42	←	Ignition ON – brake pedal released	11-14 V		
	K42	←	Ignition ON – brake pedal depressed	0 V		
Camshaft position (CMP) sensor	M1	⊣	Ignition ON	0 V		
	M11	←	Ignition ON	0 or 5 V		
	M11	←	Engine idling		2 V/100 ms	∿ 4
	M52	⇒	Ignition ON	5 V		
CAN data bus – high	K6	⇆		1		
CAN data bus – low	K38	⇆		1		
Clutch pedal position (CPP) switch – with cruise control	K10	←		1		
Crankshaft position (CKP) sensor	M5	←	Engine idling	2,8 V ac	2 V/2 ms	Reversed ∿ 2
	M37	←	Engine idling	2,8 V ac	2 V/2 ms	∿ 2
Crankshaft position (CKP) sensor – shield wire	M33	⊣	Ignition ON	0 V		
Cruise control master switch	K27	←		1		
	K43	←		1		
	K59	←		1		
Digital multifunction display	K20	⇒		1		
Engine control (EC) relay	K31	←	Ignition OFF	0 V		
	K31	←	Ignition ON	11-14 V		
	K36	⊣⇒	Ignition OFF	11-14 V		
	K36	⊣⇒	Ignition ON	0-1 V		
	K47	←	Ignition OFF	0 V		
	K47	←	Ignition ON	11-14 V		
	M23	←	Ignition OFF	0 V		
	M23	←	Ignition ON	11-14 V		
Engine coolant blower motor control module – 2002 with AC	K2	⇒		1		
Engine coolant blower motor control module – tachometer signal – 2002 with AC	K62	⇒	Engine idling	25 Hz		
	K62	⇒	3000 rpm	100 Hz		
Engine coolant blower motor relay 1	K30	⊣⇒		1		
Engine coolant blower motor relay 2	K29	⊣⇒		1		
Engine coolant blower motor relay 3 – AT with AC	K29	⊣⇒		1		
Engine coolant blower motor relay 3 – MT with AC	K46	⊣⇒		1		
Engine coolant blower motor relay 4 – AT with AC	K46	⊣⇒		1		
Engine coolant temperature (ECT) sensor	M1	⊣	Ignition ON	0 V		
	M25	←	Ignition ON – engine cold	3,6 V		
	M25	←	Engine idling – engine hot	0,8 V		
Engine malfunction indicator lamp (MIL)	K14	⊣⇒	Ignition ON – MIL ON	0-1 V		
	K14	⊣⇒	Ignition ON – MIL OFF	11-14 V		
Evaporative emission (EVAP) canister purge valve	M34	⊣⇒	Ignition ON	11-14 V		
	M34	⊣⇒	Engine idling		5 V/2 ms	Intermittent ∿ 68
Fuel pump (FP) relay	K19	⊣⇒	Ignition ON	0 V briefly then 11-14 V		
	K19	⊣⇒	Engine idling	0-1 V		

★ Suggested settings - Voltage/time per division

Component/circuit description	ECM pin	Signal	Condition	Typical value	Oscilloscope setting*	Wave form
Heated oxygen sensor (HO2S) 1	M8	⊣—	Ignition ON	0 V		
	M19	⊣▷	Ignition ON	11-14 V		
	M19	⊣▷	Engine idling	0-1 V		
	M35	⊣▷	Ignition ON	11-14 V		
	M35	⊣▷	Engine idling	0-1 V		
	M57	⟵	Ignition ON	0,4 V		
	M57	⟵	Engine idling – engine hot	0,1-0,9 V fluctuating	0,2 V/1 sec.	21
Heated oxygen sensor (HO2S) 1 – shield wire	M33	⊣—	Ignition ON	0 V		
Heated oxygen sensor (HO2S) 2	M18	⊣▷	Ignition ON	11-14 V		
	M18	⊣▷	Engine idling	0-1 V		
	M24	⊣—	Ignition ON	0 V		
	M40	⟵	Ignition ON	0,4 V		
	M40	⟵	Engine idling	0,6 V		
	M51	⊣▷	Ignition ON	11-14 V		
	M51	⊣▷	Engine idling	0-1 V		
Heated oxygen sensor (HO2S) 2 – shield wire	M33	⊣—	Ignition ON	0 V		
Ignition coil	M15	⊣▷	Ignition ON	11-14 V		
	M15	⊣▷	Engine idling		5 V/1 ms	33
	M16	⊣▷	Ignition ON	11-14 V		
	M16	⊣▷	Engine idling		5 V/1 ms	33
	M31	⊣▷	Ignition ON	11-14 V		
	M31	⊣▷	Engine idling		5 V/1 ms	33
	M32	⊣▷	Ignition ON	11-14 V		
	M32	⊣▷	Engine idling		5 V/1 ms	33
	M47	⊣▷	Ignition ON	11-14 V		
	M47	⊣▷	Engine idling		5 V/1 ms	33
	M48	⊣▷	Ignition ON	11-14 V		
	M48	⊣▷	Engine idling		5 V/1 ms	33
	M63	⊣▷	Ignition ON	11-14 V		
	M63	⊣▷	Engine idling		5 V/1 ms	33
	M64	⊣▷	Ignition ON	11-14 V		
	M64	⊣▷	Engine idling		5 V/1 ms	33
Ignition switch	K64	⟵	Ignition OFF	0 V		
	K64	⟵	Ignition ON	11-14 V		
Immobilizer control module	K5	⟷		1		
Injector 1	M29	⊣▷	Ignition ON	11-14 V briefly then 0 V		
	M29	⊣▷	Engine idling	3,2 ms	10 V/2 ms	35
Injector 2	M61	⊣▷	Ignition ON	11-14 V briefly then 0 V		
	M61	⊣▷	Engine idling	3,2 ms	10 V/2 ms	35
Injector 3	M44	⊣▷	Ignition ON	11-14 V briefly then 0 V		
	M44	⊣▷	Engine idling	3,2 ms	10 V/2 ms	35
Injector 4	M12	⊣▷	Ignition ON	11-14 V briefly then 0 V		
	M12	⊣▷	Engine idling	3,2 ms	10 V/2 ms	35
Instrumentation control module	K2	▷		1		
Instrumentation control module – fuel level signal	K57	⟵		1		

* Suggested settings - Voltage/time per division

Component/circuit description	ECM pin	Signal	Condition	Typical value	Oscilloscope setting*	Wave form
Instrumentation control module – tachometer signal	K62	⇨	Engine idling	25 Hz		
	K62	⇨	3000 rpm	100 Hz		
Intake air temperature (IAT) sensor	M41	⬅	Ignition ON – air temp. 20°C	1,9 V		
Intake manifold air control solenoid	M2	⊐⊳	Ignition ON	11-14 V		
	M2	⊐⊳	Engine idling	11-14 V		
	M2	⊐⊳	Engine idling – full throttle briefly	0 V briefly		
Knock sensor (KS)	M17	⬅	Engine idling – accelerate briefly		50 mV/1 ms	〜〰 58
	M49	⊐—	Ignition ON	0 V		
Knock sensor (KS) – shield wire	M33	⊐—	Ignition ON	0 V		
Mass air flow (MAF) sensor	M27	⊐—	Ignition ON	0 V		
	M43	⬅	Ignition ON	0 V		
	M43	⬅	Engine idling	0,8 V		
	M43	⬅	Engine idling – accelerate briefly	4 V		
Power steering pump	K35	⬅		1		
Service indicator	K13	⊐⊳	Ignition ON – service indicator ON	0-1 V		
	K13	⊐⊳	Ignition ON – service indicator OFF	11-14 V		
Throttle motor	M13	⇨	Ignition ON	11-14 V briefly then 0 V		
	M13	⇨	Engine idling		2 V/2 ms	〜〰 64
	M30	⇨	Ignition ON	11-14 V briefly then 0 V		
	M30	⇨	Engine idling		2 V/50 ms	〜〰 91
	M45	⇨	Ignition ON	11-14 V briefly then 0 V		
	M45	⇨	Engine idling		2 V/2 ms	〜〰 64
	M62	⇨	Ignition ON	11-14 V briefly then 0 V		
	M62	⇨	Engine idling		2 V/50 ms	〜〰 91
Throttle motor position sensor	M3	⇨	Ignition ON	5 V		
	M10	⬅	Ignition ON	0,7 V		
	M10	⬅	Engine idling	0,5 V		
	M20	⇨	Ignition ON	5 V		
	M26	⬅	Ignition ON	4,2 V		
	M26	⬅	Engine idling	4,5 V		
	M42	⊐—	Ignition ON	0 V		
	M58	⊐—	Ignition ON	0 V		
Vehicle speed sensor (VSS) signal amplifier – without ABS	K41	⬅	Ignition ON – vehicle pushed	0 V or 11-14 V fluctuating		

*Suggested settings - Voltage/time per division

1 Connected pin - no test data available or random digital signal

Model:	Engine code:	Year:
Astra-G 1,8 16V	X18XE1	1998-02
Astra-G 2,0 16V	X20XEV	1998-02
Vectra-B 1,8 16V	X18XE1	1998-02
Zafira 1,8 16V	X18XE1	1999-02

OPEL-VAUXHALL

Siemens Simtec 70

ECM harness multi-plug

Terminal side

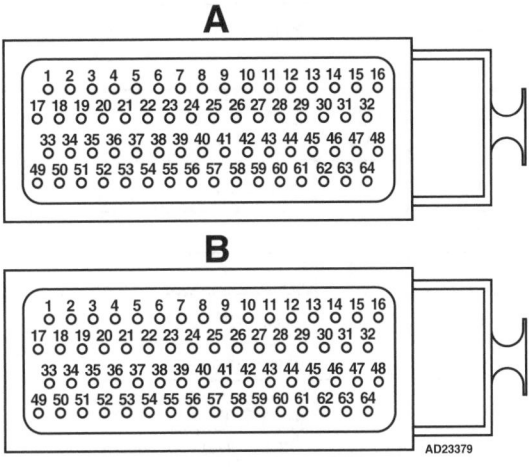

Wire side

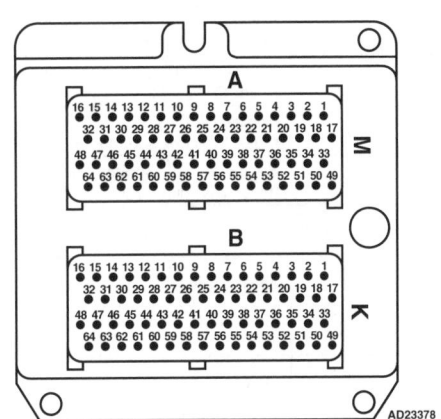

Component/circuit description	ECM pin	Signal	Condition	Typical value	Oscilloscope setting*	Wave form
ABS control module/traction control module	B17	←	Ignition ON – vehicle moving	0 V or 11-14 V fluctuating		
ABS control module/traction control module – Astra	B24			$\boxed{1}$		
ABS control module/traction control module – Astra/Zafira	B33			$\boxed{1}$		
AC compressor clutch relay – Vectra	B49	⌐▷	Engine idling – AC OFF	11-14 V		
	B49	⌐▷	Engine idling – AC ON	0-1 V		
AC control module – Astra	B8	⇒		$\boxed{1}$		
AC control module – Astra/Zafira	B34			$\boxed{1}$		
	B49	⌐▷	Engine idling – AC OFF	11-14 V		
	B49	⌐▷	Engine idling – AC ON	0-1 V		
AC control module – engine speed signal – Astra	B2	⇒	Engine idling	25 Hz		
	B2	⇒	3000 rpm	100 Hz	2 V/20 ms	Ⱳ⋀⋁ 55
AC refrigerant triple pressure switch – Vectra	B25			$\boxed{1}$		
AC/heater function control panel	B63	←	Engine idling – AC OFF	0 V		
	B63	←	Engine idling – AC ON	11-14 V		
Battery	B48	←	Ignition OFF	11-14 V		

★ Suggested settings - Voltage/time per division

Component/circuit description	ECM pin	Signal	Condition	Typical value	Oscilloscope setting*	Wave form
Camshaft position (CMP) sensor	A7		Ignition ON	0 V		
	A8		Ignition ON	5 V		
	A26		Ignition ON	0 or 5 V		
	A26		Engine idling		2 V/50 ms	66
Closed throttle position (CTP) switch	A36		Ignition ON – throttle open	11-14 V		
Closed throttle position (CTP) switch – X18XE1	A7		Ignition ON	0 V		
	A36		Ignition ON – throttle closed	0 V		
Crankshaft position (CKP) sensor	A37		Engine idling	1,4 V ac	1 V/2 ms	2
	A53		Engine idling	1,4 V ac	1 V/2 ms	Reversed 2
Crankshaft position (CKP) sensor – shield wire – Astra	A24		Ignition ON	0 V		
Data link connector (DLC)	B47			[1]		
Digital multifunction display	B5			[1]		
Engine control relay	B53		Ignition ON	0-1 V briefly then 11-14 V		
	B53		Engine idling	0-1 V		
Engine coolant blower motor relay 1 – non-AC – Astra/Zafira	B35		Engine idling – coolant blower motor OFF	11-14 V		
	B35		Engine idling – coolant blower motor ON, low speed	0-1 V		
	B35		Engine idling – coolant blower motor ON, high speed	11-14 V		
Engine coolant blower motor relay 2 – non-AC – Astra/Zafira	B51		Engine idling – coolant blower motor OFF	11-14 V		
	B51		Engine idling – coolant blower motor ON, low speed	11-14 V		
	B51		Engine idling – coolant blower motor ON, high speed	0-1 V		
Engine coolant temperature (ECT) gauge – Astra/Zafira	B8			[1]		
Engine coolant temperature (ECT) sensor	A7		Ignition ON	0 V		
	A63		Ignition ON – coolant temp. 80-110°C	1,1-2 V		
Evaporative emission (EVAP) canister purge valve	A29		Ignition ON	11-14 V		
	A29		Engine idling – engine hot	1,2%	5 V/20 ms	67
Exhaust gas recirculation (EGR) solenoid	A31		Ignition ON	11-14 V		
	A31		Engine idling – engine hot		5 V/2 ms	68
Exhaust gas recirculation (EGR) valve position sensor – X18XE1	A7		Ignition ON	0 V		
	A8		Ignition ON	5 V		
	A60		Ignition ON	0,8 V		
	A60		Engine idling, engine hot – EGR system operating	0,7 V		
Heated oxygen sensor (HO2S)	A15		Ignition ON	11-14 V		
	A15		Engine idling – engine hot	96%	2 V/20 ms	65
	A40		Ignition ON	4,8 V		
	A40		Engine idling – engine hot	0,4-4,8 V fluctuating	2 V/1 sec.	70
	A57		Ignition ON	0 V		
Heated oxygen sensor (HO2S) – shield wire	A24		Ignition ON	0 V		
Idle air control (IAC) valve – X20XEV	A45			[1]		
	A61			[1]		
Idle speed control (ISC) actuator – X18XE1	A45		Ignition ON	11-14 V		
	A45		Engine idling	500 Hz	2 V/2 ms	71
	A61		Ignition ON	11-14 V		

* Suggested settings - Voltage/time per division

Component/circuit description	ECM pin	Signal	Condition	Typical value	Oscilloscope setting*	Wave form
Idle speed control (ISC) actuator position sensor – X18XE1	A7		Ignition ON	0 V		
	A8		Ignition ON	5 V		
	A44		Ignition ON	3,9 V		
	A44		Engine idling – engine hot	3,9 V		
Ignition coil – cylinder 1 – X18XE1	A1		Ignition ON	11-14 V		
	A1		Engine idling		5 V/1 ms	33
	A2		Ignition ON	11-14 V		
	A2		Engine idling		5 V/1 ms	33
Ignition coil – cylinder 2 – X18XE1	A17		Ignition ON	11-14 V		
	A17		Engine idling		5 V/1 ms	33
	A18		Ignition ON	11-14 V		
	A18		Engine idling		5 V/1 ms	33
Ignition coil – cylinder 3 – X18XE1	A20		Ignition ON	11-14 V		
	A20		Engine idling		5 V/1 ms	33
	A21		Ignition ON	11-14 V		
	A21		Engine idling		5 V/1 ms	33
Ignition coil – cylinder 4 – X18XE1	A4		Ignition ON	11-14 V		
	A4		Engine idling		5 V/1 ms	33
	A5		Ignition ON	11-14 V		
	A5		Engine idling		5 V/1 ms	33
Ignition coil – cylinder 1 & 4 – X20XEV	A1		Ignition ON	11-14 V		
	A1		Engine idling		5 V/1 ms	33
	A2		Ignition ON	11-14 V		
	A2		Engine idling		5 V/1 ms	33
Ignition coil – cylinder 2 & 3 – X20XEV	A17		Ignition ON	11-14 V		
	A17		Engine idling		5 V/1 ms	33
	A18		Ignition ON	11-14 V		
	A18		Engine idling		5 V/1 ms	33
Ignition switch	B31		Ignition ON	11-14 V		
	B32		Ignition ON	11-14 V		
Ignition switch – X18XE1	A13		Ignition ON	11-14 V		
Immobilizer control module	B44		Engine idling	11-14 V		
Injector 1	A33		Ignition ON	11-14 V briefly then 0 V		
Injector 1 – except Zafira	A33		Engine idling	2,2-3,8 ms	10 V/2 ms	35
Injector 1 – Zafira	A33		Engine idling	3,2-5 ms	10 V/2 ms	35
Injector 2	A34		Ignition ON	11-14 V briefly then 0 V		
Injector 2 – except Zafira	A34		Engine idling	2,2-3,8 ms	10 V/2 ms	35
Injector 2 – Zafira	A34		Engine idling	3,2-5 ms	10 V/2 ms	35
Injector 3	A50		Ignition ON	11-14 V briefly then 0 V		
Injector 3 – except Zafira	A50		Engine idling	2,2-3,8 ms	10 V/2 ms	35
Injector 3 – Zafira	A50		Engine idling	3,2-5 ms	10 V/2 ms	35
Injector 4	A49		Ignition ON	11-14 V briefly then 0 V		
Injector 4 – except Zafira	A49		Engine idling	2,2-3,8 ms	10 V/2 ms	35
Injector 4 – Zafira	A49		Engine idling	3,2-5 ms	10 V/2 ms	35
Intake air temperature (IAT) sensor	A47		Ignition ON – air temp. 10°C	3 V		
	A47		Ignition ON – air temp. 80°C	0,5 V		

* Suggested settings - Voltage/time per division

Component/circuit description	ECM pin	Signal	Condition	Typical value	Oscilloscope setting*	Wave form
Intake manifold air control solenoid	A52	⊐↦	Ignition ON	11-14 V		
	A52	⊐↦	Engine running – accelerator pedal briefly fully depressed	0-1 V		
Knock sensor (KS)	A41	⊐⊢	Ignition ON	0 V		
	A58	⟵	Engine idling – accelerate briefly		50 mV/1 ms	ᴡᴡ 58
Knock sensor (KS) – shield wire	A24	⊐⊢	Ignition ON	0 V		
Malfunction indicator lamp (MIL)	B37	⊐↦	Ignition ON – MIL ON	0-1 V		
	B37	⊐↦	Engine running – MIL OFF	11-14 V		
Mass air flow (MAF) sensor	A48	⊐⊢	Ignition ON	0 V		
	A64	⟵	Engine idling	0,6 V		
	A64	⟵	Engine idling – accelerate briefly	4 V		
Tachometer	B2	⟹	Engine idling	25 Hz	2 V/20 ms	ᴡᴡ 55
	B2	⟹	3000 rpm	100 Hz		
Throttle position (TP) sensor	A7	⊐⊢	Ignition ON	0 V		
	A8	⟹	Ignition ON	5 V		
Throttle position (TP) sensor – X18XE1	A32	⟵	Ignition ON – throttle closed	3,9-4,9 V		
	A32	⟵	Ignition ON – throttle fully open	0,1-0,9 V		
Throttle position (TP) sensor – X20XEV	A32	⟵	Ignition ON – throttle closed	0,1-0,9 V		
	A32	⟵	Ignition ON – throttle fully open	3,9-4,9 V		
Transmission control module (TCM)	B18			1		
	B21			1		
	B24			1		
	B60		Ignition ON – AT in P or N	0-1 V		
	B60		Ignition ON – AT not in P or N	11-14 V		
Transmission control module (TCM) – Astra/Zafira	B3			1		
Transmission control module (TCM) – engine speed signal – Astra	B2	⟹	Engine idling	25 Hz		
	B2	⟹	3000 rpm	100 Hz	2 V/20 ms	ᴡᴡ 55
Transmission control module (TCM) – X18XE1	B49	⊐↦	Engine idling – AC OFF	11-14 V		
	B49	⊐↦	Engine idling – AC ON	0-1 V		
Vehicle speed sensor (VSS) – without ABS/traction control	B17	⟵	Ignition ON – vehicle moving	0 V or 11-14 V fluctuating		

*Suggested settings - Voltage/time per division

1 Connected pin - no test data available or random digital signal

NOTE: *Multi-plug A designated 'M' on engine control module (ECM). Multi-plug B designated 'K' on engine control module (ECM).*

ECM harness multi-plug

Terminal side

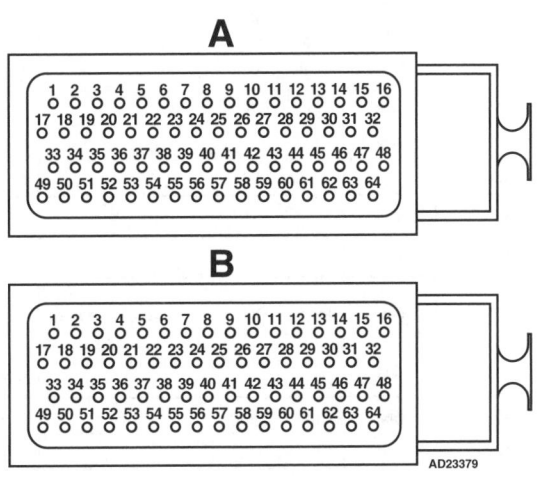

Wire side

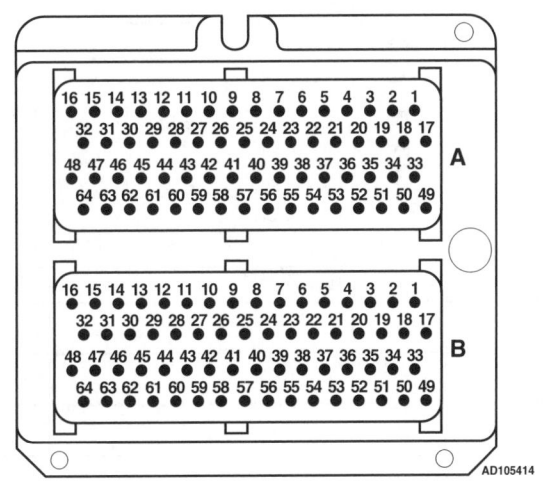

Component/circuit description	ECM pin	Signal	Condition	Typical value	Oscilloscope setting*	Wave form
AC compressor clutch relay – through multifunction control module 1	B51			1		
AC refrigerant pressure sensor – through multifunction control module 1	B7	←		1		
	B23	⇒	Ignition ON	5 V		
	B34	⅃−	Ignition ON	0 V		
Accelerator pedal position (APP) sensor – through multifunction control module 1	B8	←	Ignition ON – accelerator pedal released	1 V		
	B8	←	Ignition ON – accelerator pedal depressed	4,3 V		
	B24	←	Ignition ON – accelerator pedal released	0,5 V		
	B24	←	Ignition ON – accelerator pedal depressed	2,1 V		
	B39	⇒	Ignition ON	5 V		
	B40	⅃−	Ignition ON	0 V		
	B55	⇒	Ignition ON	5 V		
	B56	⅃−	Ignition ON	0 V		
Alternator	B26			1		

★ Suggested settings - Voltage/time per division

Component/circuit description	ECM pin	Signal	Condition	Typical value	Oscilloscope setting*	Wave form
Battery	B32	←	Ignition OFF	11-14 V		
Brake pedal position (BPP) switch – through multifunction control module 1	B28	←	Ignition ON – brake pedal released	0 V		
	B28	←	Ignition ON – brake pedal depressed	11-14 V		
	B42	←	Ignition ON – brake pedal released	11-14 V		
	B42	←	Ignition ON – brake pedal depressed	0 V		
Camshaft position (CMP) sensor	A1	⅃—	Ignition ON	0 V		
	A11	←	Ignition ON	0 V or 5 V		
	A11	←	Engine idling		2 V/100 ms	⩗⩗ 4
	A52	⇨	Ignition ON	5 V		
CAN data bus – low	B6	⬄		1		
CAN data bus – high	B38	⬄		1		
Clutch pedal position (CPP) switch (if fitted) – through multifunction control module 1	B10	←	Ignition ON – clutch pedal released	11-14 V		
	B10	←	Ignition ON – clutch pedal depressed	0 V		
Crankshaft position (CKP) sensor	A5	←	Engine idling	3 V ac	2 V/2 ms	Reversed ⩗⩗ 2
	A37	←	Engine idling	3 V ac	2 V/2 ms	⩗⩗ 2
Crankshaft position (CKP) sensor – shield wire	A33	⅃—	Ignition ON	0 V		
Engine control (EC) relay	A23	←	Ignition OFF	0 V		
	A23	←	Ignition ON	11-14 V		
	B31	←	Ignition OFF	0 V		
	B31	←	Ignition ON	11-14 V		
	B36	⅃⇨	Ignition OFF	11-14 V		
	B36	⅃⇨	Ignition ON	0-1 V		
	B47	←	Ignition OFF	0 V		
	B47	←	Ignition ON	11-14 V		
Engine coolant blower motor relay 1 – AT with AC	B46	⅃⇨		1		
Engine coolant blower motor relay 2 – AT with AC	B13	⅃⇨		1		
Engine coolant blower motor relay 3 – AT with AC	B29	⅃⇨		1		
Engine coolant blower motor relay 1 – MT with AC	B46	⅃⇨		1		
Engine coolant blower motor relay 2 – MT with AC	B29	⅃⇨		1		
Engine coolant blower motor relay 3 – MT with AC	B13	⅃⇨		1		
Engine coolant blower motor relay 2 – without AC	B29	⅃⇨		1		
Engine coolant blower motor relay 3 – without AC	B13	⅃⇨		1		
Engine coolant temperature (ECT) sensor	A1	⅃—	Ignition ON	0 V		
	A25	←	Ignition ON – coolant temp. 20°C	3,6 V		
	A25	←	Engine idling – engine hot	0,7 V		
Engine oil pressure switch	A60	←		1		
Engine oil level sensor	B59	←		1		
Evaporative emission (EVAP) canister purge valve	A34	⅃⇨	Ignition ON	11-14 V		
	A34	⅃⇨	Engine idling	1,4%	5 V/2 ms	Intermittent ⩗⩗ 68
Fuel pump (FP) relay	B19	⇨	Ignition ON	11-14 V briefly then 0 V		
	B19	⇨	Engine idling	11-14 V		

* Suggested settings - Voltage/time per division

Component/circuit description	ECM pin	Signal	Condition	Typical value	Oscilloscope setting*	Wave form
Heated oxygen sensor (HO2S) 1	A8	⊣—	Ignition ON	0 V		
	A19	⊣▷	Ignition ON	11-14 V		
	A19	⊣▷	Engine idling	0-1 V or 11-14 V switching	2 V/20 ms	65
	A35	⊣▷	Ignition ON	11-14 V		
	A35	⊣▷	Engine idling	0-1 V or 11-14 V switching	2 V/20 ms	65
	A57	←	Ignition ON	0,4 V		
	A57	←	Engine idling – engine hot	0,1-0,9 V fluctuating	0,2 V/1 sec.	21
Heated oxygen sensor (HO2S) 1 – shield wire	A33	⊣—	Ignition ON	0 V		
Heated oxygen sensor (HO2S) 2	A18	⊣▷	Ignition ON	11-14 V		
	A18	⊣▷	Engine idling	0-1 V or 11-14 V switching	2 V/20 ms	65
	A24	⊣—	Ignition ON	0 V		
	A40	←	Ignition ON	0,4 V		
	A40	←	Engine idling	0,6 V		
	A51	⊣▷	Ignition ON	11-14 V		
	A51	⊣▷	Engine idling	0-1 V or 11-14 V switching	2 V/20 ms	65
Heated oxygen sensor (HO2S) 2 – shield wire	A33	⊣—	Ignition ON	0 V		
Ignition coil	A15	⊣▷	Ignition ON	11-14 V		
	A15	⊣▷	Engine idling		5 V/1 ms	33
	A16	⊣▷	Ignition ON	11-14 V		
	A16	⊣▷	Engine idling		5 V/1 ms	33
	A31	⊣▷	Ignition ON	11-14 V		
	A31	⊣▷	Engine idling		5 V/1 ms	33
	A32	⊣▷	Ignition ON	11-14 V		
	A32	⊣▷	Engine idling		5 V/1 ms	33
	A47	⊣▷	Ignition ON	11-14 V		
	A47	⊣▷	Engine idling		5 V/1 ms	33
	A48	⊣▷	Ignition ON	11-14 V		
	A48	⊣▷	Engine idling		5 V/1 ms	33
	A63	⊣▷	Ignition ON	11-14 V		
	A63	⊣▷	Engine idling		5 V/1 ms	33
	A64	⊣▷	Ignition ON	11-14 V		
	A64	⊣▷	Engine idling		5 V/1 ms	33
Ignition main circuits relay 1	B64	←	Ignition OFF	0 V		
	B64	←	Ignition ON	11-14 V		
Injector 1	A29	⊣▷	Ignition ON	11-14 V briefly then 0-1 V		
	A29	⊣▷	Engine idling	3,2 ms	10 V/2 ms	35
Injector 2	A61	⊣▷	Ignition ON	11-14 V briefly then 0-1 V		
	A61	⊣▷	Engine idling	3,2 ms	10 V/2 ms	35
Injector 3	A44	⊣▷	Ignition ON	11-14 V briefly then 0-1 V		
	A44	⊣▷	Engine idling	3,2 ms	10 V/2 ms	35
Injector 4	A12	⊣▷	Ignition ON	11-14 V briefly then 0-1 V		
	A12	⊣▷	Engine idling	3,2 ms	10 V/2 ms	35

★ Suggested settings - Voltage/time per division

Component/circuit description	ECM pin	Signal	Condition	Typical value	Oscilloscope setting*	Wave form
Intake air temperature (IAT) sensor – in MAF sensor	A41	←	Ignition ON – air temp. 20°C	1,9 V		
Intake manifold air control solenoid	A2	⅂▷	Ignition ON	11-14 V		
	A2	⅂▷	Engine idling	11-14 V		
	A2	⅂▷	Engine idling – full throttle briefly	0-1 V briefly		
Knock sensor (KS)	A17	←	Ignition ON	2,4 V		
	A17	←	Engine idling – accelerate briefly		50 mV/1 ms	∿ 58
	A49	⅂─	Ignition ON	0 V		
Knock sensor (KS) – shield wire	A33	⅂─	Ignition ON	0 V		
Mass air flow (MAF) sensor	A27	⅂─	Ignition ON	0 V		
	A43	←	Ignition ON	0 V		
	A43	←	Engine idling	0,5 V		
	A43	←	Engine idling – accelerate briefly	4,8 V briefly		
Starter motor relay	B45	⅂▷	Engine cranking	0-1 V		
Steering column function control module – through multifunction control module 1	B63		Ignition ON	11-14 V		
Throttle motor	A13	⇨	Ignition ON	0 V		
	A13	⇨	Engine idling		2 V/2 ms	∿ 64
	A30	⇨	Ignition ON	0 V		
	A30	⇨	Engine idling	0 V		
	A45	⇨	Ignition ON	0 V		
	A45	⇨	Engine idling		2 V/2 ms	∿ 64
	A62	⇨	Ignition ON	0 V		
	A62	⇨	Engine idling	0 V		
Throttle motor position sensor	A3	⇨	Ignition ON	5 V		
	A10	←	Ignition ON	0,7 V		
	A10	←	Engine idling	0,5 V		
	A20	⇨	Ignition ON	5 V		
	A26	←	Ignition ON	4,2 V		
	A26	←	Engine idling	4,5 V		
	A42	⅂─	Ignition ON	0 V		
	A58	⅂─	Ignition ON	0 V		

*Suggested settings - Voltage/time per division

1 Connected pin - no test data available or random digital signal

Model:	Engine code:	Year:
Vectra-B 2,0 16V	20NEJ	1995-02
Omega-B 2,0	X20SE	1994-96
Sintra 2,2 16V	X22XE	1996-99
Frontera 2,0	X20SE	1995-98
Frontera 2,2 16V	X22XE	1995-98

ECM harness multi-plug

Terminal side

19 18 17 16 15 14 13 12 11 10 9 8 7 6 5 4 3 2 1
37 36 35 34 33 32 31 30 29 28 27 26 25 24 23 22 21 20
55 54 53 52 51 50 49 48 47 46 45 44 43 42 41 40 39 38

AD72618

Wire side

1 2 3 4 5 6 7 8 9 10 11 12 13 14 15 16 17 18 19
20 21 22 23 24 25 26 27 28 29 30 31 32 33 34 35 36 37
38 39 40 41 42 43 44 45 46 47 48 49 50 51 52 53 54 55

AD42077

Component/circuit description	ECM pin	Signal	Condition	Typical value	Oscilloscope setting*	Wave form
Air conditioning – if fitted	40	←	Engine idling – AC OFF	0 V		
	40	←	Engine idling – AC compressor ON	11-14 V		
	41	←	Engine idling – AC OFF	0 V		
	41	←	Engine idling – AC compressor ON	11-14 V		
AC compressor clutch relay	25	⊐▷	Engine idling – AC OFF	11-14 V		
	25	⊐▷	Engine idling – AC ON	0-1 V		
Battery	18	←	Ignition OFF	11-14 V		
Camshaft position (CMP) sensor – Sintra	8	←	Engine cranking		2 V/50 ms	12
Clutch pedal position (CPP) switch	52	←	Ignition ON – clutch pedal released	5 V		
	52	←	Ignition ON – clutch pedal depressed	0 V		
Crankshaft position (CKP) sensor	48	⊐⊢	Engine idling	0 V		
	49	←	Engine idling	3,7 V ac	2 V/2 ms	2
Data link connector (DLC)	13	←		1		
	55	◄▷		1		
Earth	2		Ignition ON	0 V		
	10		Ignition ON	0 V		
	14		Ignition ON	0 V		
	19		Ignition ON	0 V		
	24		Ignition ON	0 V		
Earth – MT	42		Ignition ON	0 V		
Engine control relay	37	←	Ignition ON	11-14 V		
	46	⊐▷	Ignition OFF	11-14 V		
	46	⊐▷	Ignition ON	0-1 V		
Engine control relay – Frontera	3	⊐▷	Ignition ON	0-1 V briefly then 11-14 V		
	3	⊐▷	Engine idling	0-1 V		
Engine coolant temperature (ECT) sensor	45	←	Ignition ON – engine cold	3,8 V		
	45	←	Engine idling – engine hot	0,8 V		
	30	⊐⊢	Ignition ON	0 V		

★ Suggested settings - Voltage/time per division

Component/circuit description	ECM pin	Signal	Condition	Typical value	Oscilloscope setting*	Wave form
Evaporative emission (EVAP) canister purge valve	5	⊐▷	Ignition ON	11-14 V		
	5	⊐▷	Engine running – accelerate briefly		10 V/20 ms	〰 20
Exhaust gas recirculation (EGR) solenoid – Omega	23	⊐▷	Ignition ON	11-14 V		
	23	⊐▷	Engine idling – valve not operating	11-14 V		
	23	⊐▷	Engine running – accelerate briefly – valve operating	1 V		
Exhaust gas recirculation (EGR) solenoid – Sintra	15	⊐▷	Ignition ON	11-14 V		
	15	⊐▷	Engine idling – valve not operating	11-14 V		
	15	⊐▷	Engine running – accelerate briefly – valve operating	1 V		
Exhaust gas recirculation (EGR) valve position sensor – Sintra	30	⊐–	Ignition ON	0 V		
	50	◀	Ignition ON	0,2-1,6 V		
	50	◀	Engine idling – engine hot	0,7-0,9 V		
	50	◀	Engine running – 2500 rpm min.	1 V min.		
Fuel pump relay – Omega/Sintra	3	⊐▷	Ignition ON	0-1 V briefly then 11-14 V		
	3	⊐▷	Engine idling	0-1 V		
Heated oxygen sensor (HO2S)	28	◀	Engine idling – engine hot	0,1-0,9 V fluctuating	0,2 V/1 sec.	〰 21
Idle air control (IAC) valve	4	⊐▷	Ignition ON	11-14 V		
	4	⊐▷	Engine idling – engine hot	44%	5 V/5 ms	〰 24
	26	⊐–	Ignition ON	0,2 V		
Ignition coil – cylinders 1 & 4	20	⊐▷	Ignition ON	11-14 V		
	20	⊐▷	Engine cranking		5 V/2 ms	〰 33
Ignition coil – cylinders 2 & 3	1	⊐▷	Ignition ON	11-14 V		
	1	⊐▷	Engine cranking		5 V/2 ms	〰 33
Ignition switch	27	◀	Ignition ON	11-14 V		
Immobilizer control module – Omega	9			1		
Immobilizer control module – Sintra/Frontera	9			1		
Injector 1	17	⊐▷	Ignition ON	11-14 V		
	17	⊐▷	Engine idling – engine hot	2,1 ms	10 V/2 ms	〰 35
Injector 2	34	⊐▷	Ignition ON	11-14 V		
	34	⊐▷	Engine idling – engine hot	2,1 ms	10 V/2 ms	〰 35
Injector 3	16	⊐▷	Ignition ON	11-14 V		
	16	⊐▷	Engine idling – engine hot	2,1 ms	10 V/2 ms	〰 35
Injector 4	35	⊐▷	Ignition ON	11-14 V		
	35	⊐▷	Engine idling – engine hot	2,1 ms	10 V/2 ms	〰 35
Instrument panel – Omega	32	⇨	Engine running		5 V/10 ms	〰 39
Intake air temperature (IAT) sensor	30	⊐–	Ignition ON	0 V		
	44	◀	Ignition ON – air temp. 0-10°C	4 V		
Knock sensor (KS)	11	◀	Engine running – accelerate briefly	1 V ac	0,2 V/1 ms	〰 38
	30	⊐–	Ignition ON	0 V		
Malfunction indicator lamp (MIL)	22	⊐▷	Ignition ON – MIL ON	0-1 V		
	22	⊐▷	Engine idling – MIL OFF	11-14 V		

* Suggested settings - Voltage/time per division

Component/circuit description	ECM pin	Signal	Condition	Typical value	Oscilloscope setting*	Wave form
Manifold absolute pressure (MAP) sensor – Sintra	7	⬅	Engine idling – engine hot	0,8-1,7 V		
	30	⅂⌐	Ignition ON	0 V		
Mass air flow (MAF) sensor – Omega/ Frontera	7	⬅	Engine idling – engine hot	0,9 V		
	7	⬅	Engine running – throttle fully open – briefly	3,9 V		
	30	⅂⌐	Ignition ON	0 V		
Secondary air injection (AIR) solenoid – Sintra	6	⅂⊳	Ignition ON	11-14 V		
	6	⅂⊳	Engine running – engine cold – throttle slightly open	0-1 V		
Tachometer – Omega/Sintra	43	⇒	Engine idling	29 Hz	2 V/10 ms	〜〜 39
	43	⇒	3000 rpm	100 Hz		
Throttle position (TP) sensor	12	⇒	Ignition ON	5 V		
	30	⅂⌐	Ignition ON	0 V		
	53	⬅	Ignition ON – throttle closed	0,5 V		
	53	⬅	Ignition ON – throttle fully open	4,5 V		
Transmission control module (TCM)	42	⬅	Ignition ON – AT in P or N	0 V		
	42	⬅	Ignition ON – AT not in P or N	9 V		
	51	⬅		1		
Transmission control module (TCM) – Omega	54	⬅		1		
Vehicle speed sensor (VSS) – Omega – without immobilizer	9	⬅	Ignition ON – vehicle moving	0-9,5 V fluctuating		

*Suggested settings - Voltage/time per division

1 Connected pin - no test data available or random digital signal

Model:	Engine code:	Year:
Vectra-B 2,0 DTi	X20DTH	1998-01
Omega-B 2,0 TD	X20DTH	1998-01

ECM harness multi-plug

Terminal side

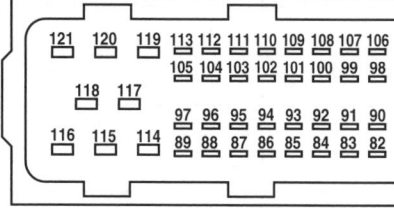

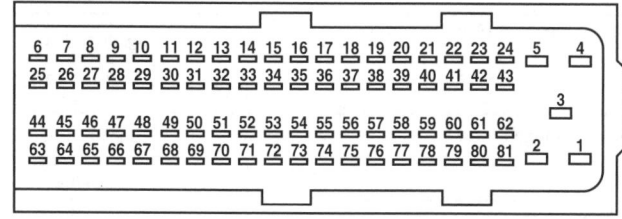

AD20712

Wire side

A

B

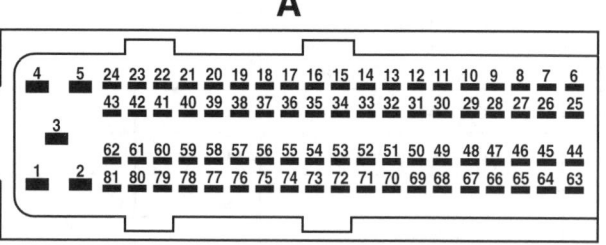

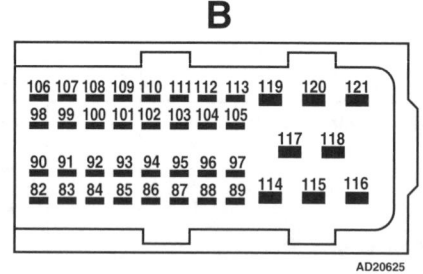

AD20625

Component/circuit description	ECM pin	Signal	Condition	Typical value
ABS control module – vehicle speed sensor (VSS) signal	68	←	Ignition ON – RH front wheel turned at 60 rpm	29 Hz
	68	←	Ignition ON – RH front wheel turned	5 V/10 ms per division ⏦ 4
AC compressor clutch relay	41	⇥▷	Ignition ON – AC compressor ON	0 V
	41	⇥▷	Ignition ON – AC compressor OFF	11-14 V
Accelerator pedal position (APP) sensor	38	←	Ignition ON – accelerator pedal in idle position	0,5 V
	38	←	Ignition ON – accelerator pedal in full load position	3,5 V
	49	⇥—	Ignition ON	0 V
	57	⇨	Ignition ON	5 V
	69	←	Ignition ON – accelerator pedal in idle position	3,7 V
	69	←	Ignition ON – accelerator pedal slightly depressed	0 V
Air conditioning	33	←		1
Brake pedal position (BPP) switch	30	←	Ignition ON – brake pedal released	0 V
	30	←	Ignition ON – brake pedal depressed	11-14 V
Brake pedal position (BPP) switch (cruise control)	65	←	Ignition ON – brake pedal released	11-14 V
	65	←	Ignition ON – brake pedal depressed	0 V
Clutch pedal position (CPP) switch (cruise control)	31	←	Ignition ON – clutch pedal released	0 V
	31	←	Ignition ON – clutch pedal depressed	11-14 V
Crankshaft position (CKP) sensor	90	←	Engine idling	60 Hz/900 rpm
	90	←	Engine idling	5 V/10 ms per division ⏦ 6
	98	⇥—	Ignition ON	0 V
Crankshaft position (CKP) sensor – screened lead	101	⇥—	Ignition ON	0 V
Cruise control master switch	45	←	Ignition ON – cruise control switch OFF	11-14 V
	63	←	Ignition ON – cruise control switch in 'RES' position	11-14 V
	64	←	Ignition ON – cruise control switch in 'SET' position	11-14 V

Component/circuit description	ECM pin	Signal	Condition	Typical value
Data link connector (DLC)	35	⬌	Ignition ON	11-14 V
Digital multifunction display	29	⇒		1
Earth	1		Ignition ON	0 V
	2		Ignition ON	0 V
Engine control relay	3	⇐	Ignition OFF	0 V
	3	⇐	Ignition ON	11-14 V
	58	⊐▷	Ignition OFF	11-14 V
	58	⊐▷	Ignition ON	0-1 V
Engine coolant temperature (ECT) sensor	89	⇐	Ignition ON – coolant temp. 20°C	3,5 V
	89	⇐	Ignition ON – coolant temp. 80°C	1 V
	93	⊐─	Ignition ON	0 V
Engine oil temperature sensor	86	⇐	Ignition ON – oil temp. 90°C	0,9 V
	93	⊐─	Ignition ON	0 V
Exhaust gas recirculation (EGR) solenoid	97	⊐▷	Ignition ON	140 Hz
	97	⊐▷	Engine running – accelerate briefly	5 V/5 ms per division 〰31
Fuel injection pump control module	91	⇒	Engine idling	60 Hz/900 rpm
	91	⇒	Engine idling	2 V/5 ms per division 〰15
	99	⬌	Ignition ON	2-3 V
	100	⬌	Ignition ON	2-3 V
Fuel injection pump control module – shut-off signal	105	⇒	Ignition OFF	10 V
	105	⇒	Engine idling	0,5 V
	105	⇒	Engine idling	38 Hz
	105	⇒	3000 rpm	150 Hz
	105	⇒	Engine idling	0,1 V/10 ms per division 〰17
Glow plug control module	87	⇐	Ignition ON – glow plugs OFF	11-14 V
	87	⇐	Ignition ON – glow plugs ON	0 V
	94	⇒	Ignition ON – glow plugs ON	0,2 V
Glow plug warning lamp	43	⊐▷	Engine idling – lamp OFF	11-14 V
	43	⊐▷	Ignition ON – lamp ON	0-1 V
Ignition switch	39	⇐	Ignition OFF	0 V
	39	⇐	Ignition ON	11-14 V
Intake air temperature (IAT) sensor	84	⇐	Ignition ON – air temp. 20°C	3,5 V
	92	⊐─	Ignition ON	0 V
Intake manifold air control solenoid	60	⊐▷	Ignition ON	140 Hz
	60	⊐▷	Engine running – accelerate briefly	5 V/2 ms per division 〰31
Malfunction indicator lamp (MIL)	42	⊐▷	Engine idling – MIL OFF	11-14 V
	42	⊐▷	Ignition ON – MIL ON	0-1 V
Manifold absolute pressure (MAP) sensor	82	⇒	Ignition ON	5 V
	85	⇐	Ignition ON	2 V
	85	⇐	Engine idling	1,5 V
	85	⇐	Engine idling – accelerate briefly	4,5 V
	93	⊐─	Ignition ON	0 V
Mass air flow (MAF) sensor	83	⇒	Ignition ON	5 V
	88	⇐	Engine idling	2 V
	88	⇐	Engine running – accelerate briefly	4,5 V
	88	⇐	Ignition ON	1 V
	92	⊐─	Ignition ON	0 V
Tachometer	27	⇒		1
Turbocharger (TC) wastegate regulating valve	96	⊐▷	Ignition ON	140 Hz
	96	⊐▷	Engine running – accelerate briefly	5 V/10 ms per division 〰29

1 Connected pin - no test data available

VAUXHALL-OPEL

Bosch Motronic M2.8.3

Model:	Engine code:	Year:
Vectra-B 2,5	X25XE	1995-00
Sintra 3,0	X30XE	1996-99

ECM harness multi-plug

Terminal side

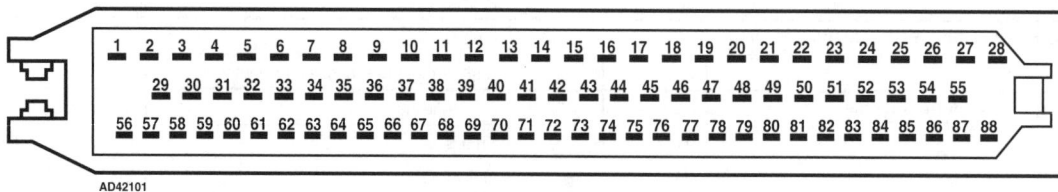

AD79776

Wire side

AD42101

Component/circuit description	ECM pin	Signal	Condition	Typical value	Oscilloscope setting*	Wave form
ABS control module	82	←		1		
Air conditioning	12	←	Engine idling – AC ON – AC compressor OFF	0 V		
	12	←	Engine idling – AC ON – AC compressor ON	11-14 V		
	36	⊐▷	Engine idling – AC OFF	11-14 V		
	36	⊐▷	Engine idling – AC ON	0 V		
	43	←		1		
	43	←		1		
Battery	26	←	Ignition OFF	11-14 V		
Camshaft position (CMP) sensor	38	←	Engine cranking	0-5 V fluctuating	2 V/20 ms	〰〰 12
Crankshaft position (CKP) sensor	20 (78)	←	Engine cranking		2 V/1 ms	〰〰 2
	78 (20)	←	Engine cranking		2 V/1 ms	Reversed 〰〰 2
Data link connector (DLC)	87	←	Ignition ON	11-14 V		
	88	◄▷	Ignition ON	3 V		
Earth	6		Ignition ON	0 V		
	28		Ignition ON	0 V		
	34		Ignition ON	0 V		
	46		Ignition ON	0 V		
	55		Ignition ON	0 V		
Earth – MT	69		Ignition ON	0 V		
Engine control relay	27	⊐▷	Ignition OFF	11-14 V		
	27	⊐▷	Ignition ON	0-1 V		
	54	←	Ignition OFF	0 V		
	54	←	Ignition ON	11-14 V		
Engine coolant temperature (ECT) sensor	71	⊐—	Engine running	0 V		
	74	←	Engine idling – coolant temp. 75-115°C	0,5-1,2 V		
Evaporative emission (EVAP) canister purge valve	61	⊐▷	Ignition ON	11-14 V		
	61	⊐▷	3000 rpm		10 V/20 ms	Intermittent 〰〰 20

* Suggested settings - Voltage/time per division

Component/circuit description	ECM pin	Signal	Condition	Typical value	Oscilloscope setting*	Wave form
Exhaust gas recirculation (EGR) solenoid	66	⊐⇥	Ignition ON	11-14 V		
	66	⊐⇥	Engine running – accelerate briefly		10 V/0,1 sec.	∿ 19
Exhaust gas recirculation (EGR) valve position sensor	15	⇐	Ignition ON	0,16-1,55 V		
	15	⇐	Engine idling – engine hot	0,7-0,9 V		
	53	⇨	Ignition ON	5 V		
	71	⊐⊢	Engine running	0 V		
Fuel pump relay	63	⊐⇥	Ignition ON	0-1 V briefly then 11-14 V		
	63	⊐⇥	Engine idling	0-1 V		
Heated oxygen sensor (HO2S) 1	19	⇐	Engine idling – engine hot	0,1-0,9 V fluctuating	0,2 V/1 sec.	∿ 21
Heated oxygen sensor (HO2S) 2	18	⇐	Engine idling – engine hot	0,1-0,9 V fluctuating	0,2 V/1 sec.	∿ 21
Idle air control (IAC) valve	2	⊐⇥	Engine idling – engine hot	8 V		
	2	⊐⇥	Engine idling – engine hot	60%	2 V/5 ms	∿ 24
	29	⊐⇥	Engine idling – engine hot	8 V		
	29	⊐⇥	Engine idling – engine hot	60%	2 V/5 ms	∿ 24
Ignition coil	49	⊐⇥	Ignition ON	11-14 V		
	49	⊐⇥	Engine cranking		5 V/2 ms	∿ 33
	50	⊐⇥	Ignition ON	11-14 V		
	50	⊐⇥	Engine cranking		5 V/2 ms	∿ 33
	51	⊐⇥	Ignition ON	11-14 V		
	51	⊐⇥	Engine cranking		5 V/2 ms	∿ 33
Ignition switch	56	⇐	Ignition ON	11-14 V		
Injector 1	3	⊐⇥	Ignition ON	11-14 V		
	3	⊐⇥	Engine idling – engine hot	3 ms	10 V/2 ms	∿ 35
Injector 2	31	⊐⇥	Ignition ON	11-14 V		
	31	⊐⇥	Engine idling – engine hot	3 ms	10 V/2 ms	∿ 35
Injector 3	4	⊐⇥	Ignition ON	11-14 V		
	4	⊐⇥	Engine idling – engine hot	3 ms	10 V/2 ms	∿ 35
Injector 4	32	⊐⇥	Ignition ON	11-14 V		
	32	⊐⇥	Engine idling – engine hot	3 ms	10 V/2 ms	∿ 35
Injector 5	5	⊐⇥	Ignition ON	11-14 V		
	5	⊐⇥	Engine idling – engine hot	3 ms	10 V/2 ms	∿ 35
Injector 6	33	⊐⇥	Ignition ON	11-14 V		
	33	⊐⇥	Engine idling – engine hot	3 ms	10 V/2 ms	∿ 35
Instrument panel	47	⇨	Engine idling	11-14 V		
Intake air temperature (IAT) sensor	16	⇐	Ignition ON – air temp. 10°C	4 V		
	16	⇐	Ignition ON – air temp. 80°C	1,3 V		
	71	⊐⊢	Engine running	0 V		
Intake manifold air control solenoid 1	35	⊐⇥	Ignition ON	11-14 V		
	35	⊐⇥	Engine idling – engine hot	11-14 V		
	35	⊐⇥	Engine running – accelerator pedal briefly fully depressed	0 V		
Intake manifold air control solenoid 2	7	⊐⇥	Ignition ON	11-14 V		
	7	⊐⇥	Engine idling – engine hot	11-14 V		
	7	⊐⇥	Engine running – accelerator pedal briefly fully depressed	0 V		
Knock sensor (KS) 1	70	⇐	Engine running – accelerate briefly	0,6 V ac	0,2 V/1 ms	∿ 38
	71	⊐⊢	Engine running	0 V		
Knock sensor (KS) 2	40	⇐	Engine running – accelerate briefly	0,6 V ac	0,2 V/1 ms	∿ 38
	71	⊐⊢	Engine running	0 V		
Malfunction indicator lamp (MIL)	8	⊐⇥	Ignition ON – MIL ON	0-1 V		
	8	⊐⇥	Engine idling – MIL OFF	11-14 V		

* Suggested settings - Voltage/time per division

Component/circuit description	ECM pin	Signal	Condition	Typical value	Oscilloscope setting*	Wave form
Mass air flow (MAF) sensor	17	←	Engine idling – engine hot	0,7 V		
	17	←	3000 rpm – engine hot	1,5 V		
	71	⌐—	Engine running	0 V		
Park/neutral position (PNP) switch – AT	69	←	Ignition ON – AT in P or N	0 V		
	69	←	Ignition ON – AT not in P or N	11-14 V		
Power steering pressure (PSP) sensor	53	⇒	Ignition ON	5 V		
	71	⌐—	Engine running	0 V		
Power steering pressure (PSP) sensor – except Sintra	73	←	Engine idling – steering – except full lock	0,6 V		
	73	←	Engine idling – steering – full lock	4 V		
Secondary air injection (AIR) solenoid relay	37	⌐⇒	Ignition ON	11-14 V		
	37	⌐⇒	Engine running – engine cold – throttle slightly open	0-1 V		
Tachometer	80	⇒	Engine idling	6,5 V/40 Hz		
	80	⇒	2500 rpm	6,5 V/125 Hz		
Tachometer/transmission control module (TCM)	80	⇒	Engine idling		2 V/10 ms	〜〜 39
Throttle position (TP) sensor	44	←	Ignition ON – throttle closed	0,6 V		
	44	←	Ignition ON – throttle fully open	4,6 V		
	53	⇒	Ignition ON	5 V		
	71	⌐—	Engine running	0 V		
Traction control module	82	←		[1]		
Transmission control module (TCM)	21	⇒	Engine idling	11-14 V		
	80	⇒	Engine idling	6,5 V/40 Hz		
	80	⇒	2500 rpm	6,5 V/125 Hz		
	82	←		[1]		
	48	←	Engine idling	11-14 V		
Vehicle speed sensor (VSS)	79	←	Ignition ON – vehicle moving	0-10 V fluctuating	5 V/1 sec.	〜〜 39

*Suggested settings - Voltage/time per division

[1] Connected pin - no test data available or random digital signal

Model:	Engine code:	Year:
Omega-B 2,5 V6	X25XE	1994-01
Omega-B 3,0 V6	X30XE	1995-00

ECM harness multi-plug

Terminal side

19 18 17 16 15 14 13 12 11 10 9 8 7 6 5 4 3 2 1
37 36 35 34 33 32 31 30 29 28 27 26 25 24 23 22 21 20
55 54 53 52 51 50 49 48 47 46 45 44 43 42 41 40 39 38

AD72618

Wire side

1 2 3 4 5 6 7 8 9 10 11 12 13 14 15 16 17 18 19
20 21 22 23 24 25 26 27 28 29 30 31 32 33 34 35 36 37
38 39 40 41 42 43 44 45 46 47 48 49 50 51 52 53 54 55

AD42077

Component/circuit description	ECM pin	Signal	Condition	Typical value	Oscilloscope setting*	Wave form
Air conditioning	25	⊐▷	Engine idling – AC ON	0 V		
	25	⊐▷	Engine idling – AC OFF	11-14 V		
	40	←	Ignition ON – AC OFF	0 V		
	40	←	Ignition ON – AC ON	0 V		
	40	←	Engine idling – AC ON	0 V		
	40	←	Engine running – full throttle briefly	11-14 V		
	41	←		[1]		
Battery	18	←	Ignition OFF	11-14 V		
Camshaft position (CMP) sensor	8	←	Engine turned	0-5 V fluctuating		
	8	←	Engine idling	4,5 V/7 Hz	2 V/20 ms	⩗⩗ 12
Crankshaft position (CKP) sensor	48 (49)	←	Engine cranking	2-5 V ac	2 V/1 ms	⩗⩗ 2
	48 (49)	←	Engine idling	7-10 V ac		
	48 (49)	←	2500 rpm	20 V ac		
	49 (48)	←	Engine cranking	2-5 V ac	2 V/1 ms	Reversed ⩗⩗ 2
	49 (48)	←	Engine idling	7-10 V ac		
	49 (48)	←	2500 rpm	20 V ac		
Data link connector (DLC)	13	←	Ignition ON	5 V		
	55	⬌		[1]		
Earth	2		Ignition ON	0 V		
	10		Ignition ON	0 V		
	14		Ignition ON	0 V		
	19		Ignition ON	0 V		
	24		Ignition ON	0 V		
Earth – MT	42	←	Ignition ON	0 V		
Engine control relay	37	←	Ignition ON	11-14 V		
	46	⊐▷	Ignition OFF	11-14 V		
	46	⊐▷	Ignition ON	0-1 V		
Engine coolant temperature (ECT) sensor	30	⊐—	Engine running	0 V		
	45	←	Engine idling – coolant temp. 75-115°C	0,5-1,2 V		
Evaporative emission (EVAP) canister purge valve	5	⊐▷	Ignition ON	11-14 V		
	5	⊐▷	Engine running – engine hot	15 Hz intermittent		
	5	⊐▷	Engine running – accelerate briefly		10 V/20 ms	Intermittent ⩗⩗ 20

* Suggested settings - Voltage/time per division

Component/circuit description	ECM pin	Signal	Condition	Typical value	Oscilloscope setting*	Wave form
Exhaust gas recirculation (EGR) solenoid	23	⸬▷	Ignition ON	11-14 V		
	23	⸬▷	Engine idling – valve not operating	11-14 V		
	23	⸬▷	Engine running – accelerate briefly – valve operating	1-12 V fluctuating		
Exhaust gas recirculation (EGR) valve position sensor	12	⇨	Ignition ON	5 V		
	30	⸬—	Engine running	0 V		
	50	⬅	Ignition ON	0,16-1,55 V		
	50	⬅	Engine idling – engine hot	0,7-0,9 V		
	50	⬅	Engine running – throttle operated – 2500 rpm min.	1 V min.		
Fuel pump relay	3	⸬▷	Ignition ON	0-1 V briefly then 11-14 V		
	3	⸬▷	Engine idling	0-1 V		
Heated oxygen sensor (HO2S) 1	28	⬅	Engine idling – engine hot	0,1-1 V fluctuating	0,2 V/1 sec.	MⱮ 21
Heated oxygen sensor (HO2S) 2	47	⬅	Engine idling – engine hot	0,1-1 V fluctuating	0,2 V/1 sec.	MⱮ 21
Idle air control (IAC) valve	4	⸬▷	Ignition ON	11-14 V		
	4	⸬▷	Engine idling – engine hot	5-7 V		
	4	⸬▷	Engine idling – engine hot	4-6 ms/ 100 Hz	2 V/5 ms	MⱮ 24
Ignition coil	1	⸬▷	Ignition ON	11-14 V min.		
	1	⸬▷	2000 rpm	0,2 V		
	1	⸬▷	Engine cranking		5 V/2 ms	MⱮ 33
	20	⇨	Ignition ON	11-14 V		
	20	⇨	2000 rpm	0,2 V		
	20	⇨	Engine cranking		5 V/2 ms	MⱮ 33
	21	⇨	Ignition ON	11-14 V		
	21	⇨	2000 rpm	0,2 V		
	21	⇨	Engine cranking		5 V/2 ms	MⱮ 33
Ignition switch	27	⬅	Ignition ON	11-14 V		
Injector 1	17	⸬▷	Ignition ON	11-14 V		
	17	⸬▷	Engine idling – engine hot	3 ms	10 V/2 ms	MⱮ 35
Injector 2	16	⸬▷	Ignition ON	11-14 V		
	16	⸬▷	Engine idling – engine hot	3 ms	10 V/2 ms	MⱮ 35
Injector 3	35	⸬▷	Ignition ON	11-14 V		
	35	⸬▷	Engine idling – engine hot	3 ms	10 V/2 ms	MⱮ 35
Injector 4	34	⸬▷	Ignition ON	11-14 V		
	34	⸬▷	Engine idling – engine hot	3 ms	10 V/2 ms	MⱮ 35
Injector 5	15	⸬▷	Ignition ON	11-14 V		
	15	⸬▷	Engine idling – engine hot	3 ms	10 V/2 ms	MⱮ 35
Injector 6	33	⸬▷	Ignition ON	11-14 V		
	33	⸬▷	Engine idling – engine hot	3 ms	10 V/2 ms	MⱮ 35
Intake air temperature (IAT) sensor	30	⸬—	Engine running	0 V		
	44	⬅	Ignition ON – air temp. 10°C	4 V		
	44	⬅	Ignition ON – air temp. 80°C	1,3 V		
Intake manifold air control solenoid 1	6	⸬▷	Ignition ON	11-14 V		
	6	⸬▷	Engine idling – engine hot	11-14 V		
	6	⸬▷	Engine running – accelerator pedal briefly fully depressed	0-1 V		
Intake manifold air control solenoid 2	31	⸬▷	Ignition ON	11-14 V		
	31	⸬▷	Engine idling – engine hot	11-14 V		
	31	⸬▷	Engine running – accelerator pedal briefly fully depressed	0 V		

* Suggested settings - Voltage/time per division

Component/circuit description	ECM pin	Signal	Condition	Typical value	Oscilloscope setting*	Wave form
Knock sensor (KS) 1	11	←	2000 rpm	0,02 V ac		
	11	←	Engine running – accelerate briefly		50 mV/1 ms	〰️ 38
	30	⊣⊢	Engine running	0 V		
Knock sensor (KS) 2	29	←	2000 rpm	0,02 V ac		
	29	←	Engine running – accelerate briefly		50 mV/1 ms	〰️ 38
	30	⊣⊢	Engine running	0 V		
Malfunction indicator lamp (MIL)	22	⊣▷	Ignition ON – MIL ON	0-1 V		
	22	⊣▷	Engine idling – MIL OFF	11-14 V		
Mass air flow (MAF) sensor	7	←	Engine idling – engine hot	0,8 V		
	7	←	2500 rpm – engine hot	1,2 V		
	7	←	Engine running – full load	3,5 V		
	30	⊣⊢	Engine running	0 V		
Park/neutral position (PNP) switch – AT	42	←	Ignition ON – AT in P or N	0 V		
	42	←	Ignition ON – AT not in P or N	11-14 V		
Secondary air injection (AIR) solenoid relay	26	⊣▷	Ignition ON	11-14 V		
	26	⊣▷	Engine running – engine cold – throttle slightly open	0-1 V		
Tachometer	43	⇒	Engine idling	40 Hz		
	43	⇒	2500 rpm	125 Hz		
Tachometer/transmission control module (TCM)/traction control module	43	⇒	Engine idling		2 V/10 ms	〰️ 39
Throttle position (TP) sensor	12	⇒	Ignition ON	5 V		
	30	⊣⊢	Engine running	0 V		
	53	←	Ignition ON – throttle closed	0,1-0,6 V		
	53	←	Ignition ON – throttle fully open	3,9-4,8 V		
Traction control module	38	←	Ignition ON – engine cold	0 V		
	38	←	Vehicle moving – wheels not slipping	0 V		
	38	←	Vehicle moving – wheels slipping	0 V or 11-14 V switching		
	43	⇒	Engine idling	40 Hz		
	43	⇒	2500 rpm	125 Hz		
Transmission control module (TCM)	43	⇒	Engine idling	40 Hz		
	43	⇒	2500 rpm	125 Hz		
	54	⇒	Engine idling – engine hot	9-16%		
	54	⇒	Engine running – accelerator pedal fully depressed	70-96%		
	51	←	Vehicle moving – constant speed	5 V		
	51	←	Vehicle moving – AT shifts	0 V briefly		
Vehicle speed sensor (VSS)	9	←	Ignition ON – vehicle moving	0-10 V fluctuating	5 V/1 sec.	〰️ 39

*Suggested settings - Voltage/time per division

1 Connected pin - no test data available or random digital signal

ECM harness multi-plug

Terminal side

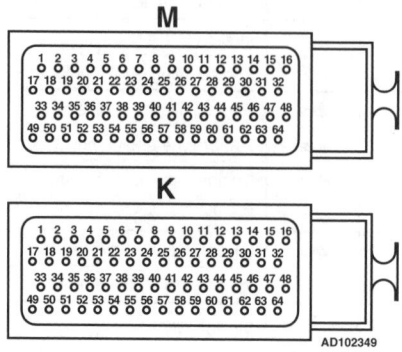

Wire side

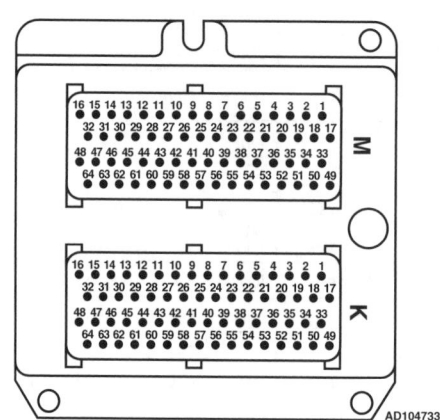

AD104733

Component/circuit description	ECM pin	Signal	Condition	Typical value	Oscilloscope setting*	Wave form
ABS control module – VSS signal	K41	←	Ignition ON – vehicle pushed	0 V or 11-14 V fluctuating		
AC compressor clutch relay – 2003→	K7	⊐▷	Engine idling – AC OFF	11-14 V		
	K7	⊐▷	Engine idling – AC ON – AC compressor OFF	11-14 V		
	K7	⊐▷	Engine idling – AC ON – AC compressor ON	0-1 V		
AC control module – ATC	K45	←	Ignition ON – AC OFF	0 V		
	K45	←	Ignition ON – AC ON	11-14 V		
AC master switch – MTC	K45	←	Ignition ON – AC OFF	0 V		
	K45	←	Ignition ON – AC ON	11-14 V		
AC refrigerant pressure sensor – 2003→	K3			1		
	K4			1		
	K49			1		

★ Suggested settings - Voltage/time per division

Component/circuit description	ECM pin	Signal	Condition	Typical value	Oscilloscope setting*	Wave form
Accelerator pedal position (APP) sensor	K20	⇨	Ignition ON	5 V		
	K33	⌐—	Ignition ON	0 V		
	K35	⇨	Ignition ON	5 V		
	K36	←	Ignition ON – accelerator pedal released	0,5 V		
	K36	←	Ignition ON – accelerator pedal depressed	2 V		
	K37	←	Ignition ON – accelerator pedal released	1 V		
	K37	←	Ignition ON – accelerator pedal depressed	4,1 V		
	K50	⌐—	Ignition ON	0 V		
Battery	K2	←	Ignition OFF	11-14 V		
	K19	←	Ignition OFF	11-14 V		
Brake pedal position (BPP) switch	K5	←	Ignition ON – brake pedal released	0 V		
	K5	←	Ignition ON – brake pedal depressed	11-14 V		
	K13	←	Ignition ON – brake pedal released	11-14 V		
	K13	←	Ignition ON – brake pedal depressed	0 V		
Camshaft position (CMP) sensor	M23	←	Ignition ON	0 or 5 V		
	M23	←	Engine idling		2 V/100 ms	⎍⎍⎍ 4
	M29	⌐—	Ignition ON	0 V		
	M30	⇨	Ignition ON	5 V		
CAN data bus – 2003→	K11	←⇨		1		
	K43	←⇨		1		
Clutch pedal position (CPP) switch – with cruise control	K61	←	Ignition ON – clutch pedal released	0 V		
	K61	←	Ignition ON – clutch pedal depressed	11-14 V		
Crankshaft position (CKP) sensor	M5	←	Engine idling	1,6 V ac	1 V/2 ms	Reversed ⎍⎍⎍ 2
	M22	←	Engine idling	2,4 V ac	1 V/2 ms	⎍⎍⎍ 2
Crankshaft position (CKP) sensor – shield wire	M37	⌐—	Ignition ON	0 V		
Cruise control master switch	K29			1		
	K44			1		
	K62			1		
Digital multifunction display	K47			1		
Engine control (EC) relay	K16	⌐⇨	Ignition OFF	11-14 V		
	K16	⌐⇨	Ignition ON	0-1 V		
	M47	←	Ignition OFF	0 V		
	M47	←	Ignition ON	11-14 V		
	M48	←	Ignition OFF	0 V		
	M48	←	Ignition ON	11-14 V		
	M64	←	Ignition OFF	0 V		
	M64	←	Ignition ON	11-14 V		
Engine coolant blower motor control module – →2002 with AC	K7			1		
	K55			1		
	K57			1		
Engine coolant blower motor control module – tachometer signal – →2002 with AC	K46	⇨	Engine idling	25 Hz		
	K46	⇨	3000 rpm	100 Hz		

* Suggested settings - Voltage/time per division

Component/circuit description	ECM pin	Signal	Condition	Typical value	Oscilloscope setting*	Wave form
Engine coolant blower motor relay 1 – 2003→, MT with AC	K39	⊐▷	Engine idling – coolant blower motor OFF	11-14 V		
	K39	⊐▷	Engine idling – coolant blower motor ON, 1st speed	0-1 V		
	K39	⊐▷	Engine idling – coolant blower motor ON, 2nd speed	11-14 V		
	K39	⊐▷	Engine idling – coolant blower motor ON, 3rd speed	11-14 V		
Engine coolant blower motor relay 1 – without AC	K39	⊐▷	Engine idling – coolant blower motor OFF	11-14 V		
	K39	⊐▷	Engine idling – coolant blower motor ON, 1st speed	0-1 V		
	K39	⊐▷	Engine idling – coolant blower motor ON, 2nd speed	11-14 V		
Engine coolant blower motor relay 1/2 – 2003→ AT with AC	K31	⊐▷		☐1		
Engine coolant blower motor relay 2 – 2003→, MT with AC	K31	⊐▷	Engine idling – coolant blower motor OFF	11-14 V		
	K31	⊐▷	Engine idling – coolant blower motor ON, 1st speed	11-14 V		
	K31	⊐▷	Engine idling – coolant blower motor ON, 2nd speed	0-1 V		
	K31	⊐▷	Engine idling – coolant blower motor ON, 3rd speed	11-14 V		
Engine coolant blower motor relay 2 – without AC	K31	⊐▷	Engine idling – coolant blower motor OFF	11-14 V		
	K31	⊐▷	Engine idling – coolant blower motor ON, 1st speed	11-14 V		
	K31	⊐▷	Engine idling – coolant blower motor ON, 2nd speed	0-1 V		
Engine coolant blower motor relay 3 – 2003→, AT with AC	K24	⊐▷		☐1		
Engine coolant blower motor relay 3 – 2003→, MT with AC	K24	⊐▷	Engine idling – coolant blower motor OFF	11-14 V		
	K24	⊐▷	Engine idling – coolant blower motor ON, 1st speed	11-14 V		
	K24	⊐▷	Engine idling – coolant blower motor ON, 2nd speed	11-14 V		
	K24	⊐▷	Engine idling – coolant blower motor ON, 3rd speed	0-1 V		
Engine coolant blower motor relay 4 – 2003→, AT with AC	K39	⊐▷		☐1		
Engine coolant temperature (ECT) sensor	M10	⬅	Ignition ON – coolant temp. 20°C	1,9 V		
	M10	⬅	Ignition ON – coolant temp. 80°C	2,3 V		
	M62	⊐⊢	Ignition ON	0 V		
Evaporative emission (EVAP) canister purge valve	M3	⊐▷	Ignition ON	11-14 V		
	M3	⊐▷	Engine idling		5 V/2 ms	Intermittent 〰 68
Exhaust gas recirculation (EGR) solenoid – →2003	M21	⊐▷	Ignition ON	11-14 V		
	M21	⊐▷	Engine idling – engine hot		5 V/2 ms	Intermittent 〰 68
Exhaust gas recirculation (EGR) valve position sensor – →2003	M28	⬅	Ignition ON	1,2 V		
	M28	⬅	Engine idling	1,2 V		
	M30	⇨	Ignition ON	5 V		
	M62	⊐⊢	Ignition ON	0 V		
Fuel gauge tank sensor signal	K53	⬅		☐1		
Fuel pump (FP) relay	K23	⊐▷	Ignition ON	0-1 V briefly then 11-14 V		
	K23	⊐▷	Engine idling	0-1 V		
Heated oxygen sensor (HO2S) 1	M44	⬅	Engine idling	0,1-0,9 V fluctuating	0,2 V/1 sec.	〰 21
	M52	⊐▷	Ignition ON	11-14 V		
	M52	⊐▷	Engine idling	0-1 V		
	M62	⊐⊢	Ignition ON	0 V		

★ Suggested settings - Voltage/time per division

Component/circuit description	ECM pin	Signal	Condition	Typical value	Oscilloscope setting*	Wave form
Heated oxygen sensor (HO2S) 2	M53	→▷	Ignition ON	11-14 V		
	M53	→▷	Engine idling	0-1 V		
	M61	←	Engine idling	0,6 V		
	M62	→—	Ignition ON	0 V		
Ignition coil	M1	→▷	Ignition ON	11-14 V		
	M1	→▷	Engine idling		5 V/2 ms	〰 33
	M2	→▷	Ignition ON	11-14 V		
	M2	→▷	Engine idling		5 V/2 ms	〰 33
	M17	→▷	Ignition ON	11-14 V		
	M17	→▷	Engine idling		5 V/2 ms	〰 33
	M18	→▷	Ignition ON	11-14 V		
	M18	→▷	Engine idling		5 V/2 ms	〰 33
	M33	→▷	Ignition ON	11-14 V		
	M33	→▷	Engine idling		5 V/2 ms	〰 33
	M34	→▷	Ignition ON	11-14 V		
	M34	→▷	Engine idling		5 V/2 ms	〰 33
	M49	→▷	Ignition ON	11-14 V		
	M49	→▷	Engine idling		5 V/2 ms	〰 33
	M50	→▷	Ignition ON	11-14 V		
	M50	→▷	Engine idling		5 V/2 ms	〰 33
Ignition switch	K52	←	Ignition OFF	0 V		
	K52	←	Ignition ON	11-14 V		
Immobilizer control module	K54	←▷		1		
Injector 1	M57	→▷	Ignition ON	11-14 V briefly then 0-1 V		
	M57	→▷	Engine idling	3,5 ms	10 V/2 ms	〰 35
Injector 2	M60	→▷	Ignition ON	11-14 V briefly then 0-1 V		
	M60	→▷	Engine idling	3,5 ms	10 V/2 ms	〰 35
Injector 3	M58	→▷	Ignition ON	11-14 V briefly then 0-1 V		
	M58	→▷	Engine idling	3,5 ms	10 V/2 ms	〰 35
Injector 4	M59	→▷	Ignition ON	11-14 V briefly then 0-1 V		
	M59	→▷	Engine idling	3,5 ms	10 V/2 ms	〰 35
Instrumentation control module	K55			1		
Instrumentation control module – tachometer signal	K46	▷	Engine idling	25 Hz		
	K46	▷	3000 rpm	100 Hz		
Intake air temperature (IAT) sensor	M29	→—	Ignition ON	0 V		
	M43	←	Ignition ON – air temp. 20°C	3,7 V		
Knock sensor (KS)	M39	←	Engine idling – accelerate briefly		50 mV/1 ms	〰 58
Knock sensor (KS) – shield wire	M62	→—	Ignition ON	0 V		
Malfunction indicator lamp (MIL) 1	K64	→▷	Ignition ON – MIL ON	0-1 V		
	K64	→▷	Engine running – MIL OFF	11-14 V		
Malfunction indicator lamp (MIL) 2	K32	→▷	Ignition ON – MIL ON	0-1 V		
	K32	→▷	Engine running – MIL OFF	11-14 V		
Manifold absolute pressure (MAP) sensor	M26	←	Ignition ON	4,9 V		
	M26	←	Engine idling	1,3 V		
	M26	←	Engine running – full throttle briefly	4,9 V		
	M45	→—	Ignition ON	0 V		
	M63	▷	Ignition ON	5 V		

* Suggested settings - Voltage/time per division

Component/circuit description	ECM pin	Signal	Condition	Typical value	Oscilloscope setting*	Wave form
Power steering control module	K15	←		[1]		
Throttle motor	M15	⇨	Ignition ON	11-14 V		
	M15	⇨	Engine idling		5 V/0,2 ms	∿∿ 68
	M16	⇨	Ignition ON		5 V/0,2 ms	(intermittent for 10 seconds only) ∿∿ 68
	M16	⇨	Engine idling	11-14 V		
	M31	⇨	Ignition ON	11-14 V		
	M31	⇨	Engine idling		5 V/0,2 ms	∿∿ 68
	M32	⇨	Ignition ON		5 V/0,2 ms	(intermittent for 10 seconds only) ∿∿ 68
	M32	⇨	Engine idling	11-14 V		
Throttle motor position sensor	M9	←	Ignition ON – accelerator pedal released	1 V		
	M9	←	Ignition ON – accelerator pedal depressed	4,4 V		
	M12	←	Ignition ON – accelerator pedal released	4,1 V		
	M12	←	Ignition ON – accelerator pedal depressed	0,7 V		
	M13	⌐	Ignition ON	0 V		
	M14	⇨	Ignition ON	5 V		
	M29	⌐	Ignition ON	0 V		
	M46	⇨	Ignition ON	5 V		
Vehicle speed sensor (VSS) signal amplifier – without ABS	K41	←	Ignition ON – vehicle pushed	0 V or 11-14 V fluctuating		

*Suggested settings - Voltage/time per division

[1] Connected pin - no test data available or random digital signal

Model:	Engine code:	Year:
Lupo 1,0	AER/ALL	1998-05
Polo 1,0	AER/ALL	1996-02
Polo/Classic/Estate/Caddy 1,4	AEX/AKV/APQ/ANX	1995-02
Golf/Vento 1,4	AEX/APQ	1995-98

VOLKSWAGEN

Bosch Motronic MP9.0

ECM harness multi-plug

Terminal side

AD81645

Wire side

AD42108

Component/circuit description	ECM pin	Signal	Condition	Typical value	Oscilloscope setting*	Wave form
Air conditioning	33			1		
	35			1		
Automatic transmission	12			1		
Battery	21	←	Ignition OFF	11-14 V		
Closed throttle position (CTP) switch	10	←	Ignition ON – throttle closed	0 V		
	10	←	Ignition ON – throttle slightly open	9 V min.		
	17	⊣⌐	Ignition ON	0 V		
Crankshaft position (CKP) sensor	8	⇨	Ignition ON	9 V min.		
	13	←	Ignition ON – engine turned	0 V or 9-14 V switching		
	13	←	Engine idling	30 Hz	5 V/20 ms	⎍⎍ 4
	13	←	3000 rpm	100 Hz		
	17	⊣⌐	Ignition ON	0 V		
Earth	1		Ignition ON	0 V		
Earth – some models	12		Ignition ON	0 V		
Engine coolant temperature (ECT) sensor	17	⊣⌐	Ignition ON	0 V		
	42	←	Ignition ON – coolant temp. 10°C	4,2 V		
	42	←	Ignition ON – coolant temp. 80°C	1,7 V		
Evaporative emission (EVAP) canister purge valve	3	⊣⇨	Ignition ON	11-14 V		
	3	⊣⇨	Engine hot – valve operating		10 V/20 ms	⎍⎍ 20
Exhaust gas recirculation (EGR) solenoid – if fitted	5	⊣⇨	Engine hot – valve operating		10 V/50 ms	⎍⎍ 20
Fuel pump relay	25	⊣⇨	Ignition ON	0-1 V briefly then 11-14 V		
	25	⊣⇨	Engine cranking	0-1 V		
Heated oxygen sensor (HO2S)	15	⊣⌐	Engine idling	0 V		
	38	←	Engine idling – engine hot	0,1-1 V fluctuating	0,2 V/1 sec.	⎍⎍ 21
Heated rear window switch – AER 05/97→	33	←	Ignition ON – heated rear window OFF	0 V		
	33	←	Ignition ON – heated rear window ON	11-14 V		
Idle speed control (ISC) actuator	2	⇨	Engine idling – engine hot	16-24%	5 V/2 ms	⎍⎍ 28
	26	⊣⌐	Engine idling	0 V		

★ Suggested settings - Voltage/time per division

Component/circuit description	ECM pin	Signal	Condition	Typical value	Oscilloscope setting*	Wave form
Idle speed control (ISC) actuator position sensor	14	⟹	Ignition ON	4,5 V min.		
	16	⟸	Engine idling – engine hot	3 V		
	17	⌐	Ignition ON	0 V		
Ignition amplifier	24	⟹	Engine idling	30 Hz	1 V/10 ms	⌁⌁ 32
	24	⟹	3000 rpm	100 Hz		
Ignition switch	23	⟸	Ignition OFF	0 V		
	23	⟸	Ignition ON	11-14 V		
Immobilizer control module	29	⟺	Ignition ON	11-14 V		
Injector 1	7	⌐⟹	Ignition ON	11-14 V briefly then 0 V		
	7	⌐⟹	Engine idling – engine hot	4,8 ms	10 V/2 ms	⌁⌁ 35
Injector 2	6	⌐⟹	Ignition ON	11-14 V briefly then 0 V		
	6	⌐⟹	Engine idling – engine hot	4,8 ms	10 V/2 ms	⌁⌁ 35
Injector 3	28	⌐⟹	Ignition ON	11-14 V briefly then 0 V		
	28	⌐⟹	Engine idling – engine hot	4,8 ms	10 V/2 ms	⌁⌁ 35
Injector 4	4	⌐⟹	Ignition ON	11-14 V briefly then 0 V		
	4	⌐⟹	Engine idling – engine hot	4,8 ms	10 V/2 ms	⌁⌁ 35
Instrument panel	9		Engine idling – engine hot	30 Hz		
	9		3000 rpm	100 Hz		
	36			1		
Instrument panel – some models	27			1		
Intake air temperature (IAT) sensor	17	⌐	Ignition ON	0 V		
	43	⟸	Ignition ON – air temp. 10°C	3,7 V		
Knock sensor (KS)	19	⌐	Engine idling	0 V		
	39	⟸	Engine idling – accelerate briefly		50 mV/1 ms	⌁⌁ 38
Knock sensor (KS) – shield wire – Polo/Caddy	45	⌐	Engine idling	0 V		
Manifold absolute pressure (MAP) sensor	18	⟸	Ignition ON	4 V		
	18	⟸	Engine idling – engine hot	1 V		
	18	⟸	3000 rpm	0,5 V		
	37	⟹	Ignition ON	5 V		
Power steering pressure (PSP) switch – AER/ALL	11			1		
	17	⌐	Ignition ON	0 V		
Throttle position (TP) sensor	14	⟹	Ignition ON	4,5 V min.		
	17	⌐	Ignition ON	0 V		
	41	⟸	Ignition ON – throttle closed	4,2 V		
	41	⟸	Ignition ON – throttle fully open	0,7 V		
Transmission control module (TCM), engine RPM signal	9	⟹	Engine idling – engine hot	30 Hz		
	9	⟹	3000 rpm	100 Hz		
Transmission control module (TCM)	30			1		
	34			1		

*Suggested settings - Voltage/time per division

1 Connected pin - no test data available or random digital signal

Model:	Engine code:	Year:
Lupo 1,0	ALD	1998-05
Polo 1,0	ALD	1999-02
Polo 1,4	AKK	1998-02
Polo Classic/Estate 1,4	AKK	1999-02

VOLKSWAGEN
Bosch Motronic
ME7.5.10

ECM harness multi-plug

Terminal side

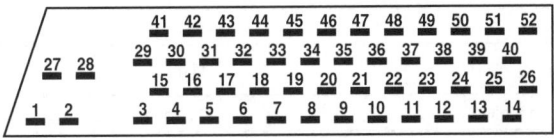

AD42344

Wire side

AD42345

Component/circuit description	ECM pin	Signal	Condition	Typical value	Oscilloscope setting*	Wave form
Accelerator pedal position (APP) sensor	6	⇨	Ignition ON	5 V		
	7	⌐	Ignition ON	0 V		
	8	⇨	Ignition ON	5 V		
	19	⌐	Ignition ON	0 V		
	33	⬅	Ignition ON – accelerator pedal released	0,8 V		
	33	⬅	Ignition ON – accelerator pedal depressed	3,8 V		
	45	⬅	Ignition ON – accelerator pedal released	0,4 V		
	45	⬅	Ignition ON – accelerator pedal depressed	1,8 V		
Air conditioning/engine coolant blower motor control module	17			1		
	42			1		
Alternator	11	⇨	Engine idling		2 V/10 ms	〜 89
Battery	15	⬅	Ignition OFF	11-14 V		
Brake pedal position (BPP) switch 1	23	⬅	Ignition ON – brake pedal released	0 V		
	23	⬅	Ignition ON – brake pedal depressed	11-14 V		
Brake pedal position (BPP) switch 2	51	⬅	Ignition ON – brake pedal released	11-14 V		
	51	⬅	Ignition ON – brake pedal depressed	0 V		
Camshaft position (CMP) sensor	62	⇨	Ignition ON	5 V		
	54	⌐	Ignition ON	0 V		
	60	⬅	Ignition ON	0 or 11-14 V		
	60	⬅	Engine idling		2 V/20 ms	〜 14
CAN data bus – high	31	⬌		1		
CAN data bus – low	32	⬌		1		
Crankshaft position (CKP) sensor	53	⬅	Ignition ON	0 V		
	53	⬅	Engine idling		2 V/2 ms	〜 73
	62	⇨	Ignition ON	5 V		
	67	⌐	Ignition ON	0 V		
Earth	2		Ignition ON	0 V		
	28		Ignition ON	0 V		
Engine coolant 'low' sensor – Lupo	54	⌐	Ignition ON	0 V		
Engine coolant temperature (ECT) sensor	54	⌐	Ignition ON	0 V		
	74	⬅	Ignition ON – coolant temp. 20°C	1,9 V		
	74	⬅	Ignition ON – coolant temp. 80°C	0,5 V		
Evaporative emission (EVAP) canister purge valve	14	⌐⟶	Engine running – engine hot – valve operating		10 V/5 ms	〜 35

★ Suggested settings - Voltage/time per division

Component/circuit description	ECM pin	Signal	Condition	Typical value	Oscilloscope setting*	Wave form
Fuel pump (FP) relay	26	⇥⇥	Ignition ON	0-1 V briefly then 11-14 V		
	26	⇥⇥	Engine idling	0-1 V		
Heated oxygen sensor (HO2S)	21	⇥—	Ignition ON	0 V		
	47	⇐	Engine idling – engine hot		0,2 V/1 sec.	〰️ 21
Heated oxygen sensor (HO2S) – heater control	13	⇥⇥	Engine idling – engine hot		5 V/50 ms	〰️ 18
Ignition amplifier	57	⇒	Ignition ON	0 V		
	57	⇒	Engine idling		1 V/20 ms	〰️ 32
	71	⇒	Ignition ON	0 V		
	71	⇒	Engine idling		1 V/20 ms	〰️ 32
Ignition switch	27	⇐	Ignition OFF	0 V		
	27	⇐	Ignition ON	11-14 V		
Immobilizer control module – diagnosis signal – Polo	29		Engine idling	11-14 V		
Injector 1	79	⇥⇥	Engine idling	4,2 ms	10 V/2 ms	〰️ 35
Injector 2	59	⇥⇥	Engine idling	4,2 ms	10 V/2 ms	〰️ 35
Injector 3	73	⇥⇥	Engine idling	4,2 ms	10 V/2 ms	〰️ 35
Injector 4	65	⇥⇥	Engine idling	4,2 ms	10 V/2 ms	〰️ 35
Instrumentation control module – Classic/Estate	30			1		
Instrumentation control module – diagnosis signal – Lupo	29			1		
Instrumentation control module – engine RPM signal	41	⇒	Engine idling	28 Hz		
Instrumentation control module – some models	12			1		
	16			1		
Instrumentation control module – vehicle speed signal	5	⇐	Ignition ON – vehicle pushed	0 V or 11-14 V switching		
Intake air temperature (IAT) sensor	54	⇥—	Ignition ON	0 V		
	56	⇐	Ignition ON – air temp. 15°C	2,2 V		
Knock sensor (KS)	63	⇐	Engine idling – accelerate briefly		50 mV/1 ms	〰️ 38
	77	⇐	Engine idling – accelerate briefly		50 mV/1 ms	〰️ 38
Manifold absolute pressure (MAP) sensor	54	⇥—	Ignition ON	0 V		
	62	⇒	Ignition ON	5 V		
	70	⇐	Ignition ON	4,1 V		
	70	⇐	Engine idling	0,9 V		
	70	⇐	Engine running – full throttle briefly	4,1 V		
Power steering pressure (PSP) switch – some models	21	⇥—	Ignition ON	0 V		
	49	⇐		1		
Spare cable – Lupo	3			1		
Throttle motor	66	⇒	Ignition ON	11-14 V		
	66	⇒	Engine idling	11-14 V		
	80	⇒	Ignition ON	11-14 V for 30 seconds then 3 V		
	80	⇒	Ignition ON – accelerator pedal released		2 V/0,5 ms	(30 seconds only) 〰️ 64
	80	⇒	Ignition ON – accelerator pedal depressed		2 V/0,5 ms	〰️ 71
Throttle motor position sensor	55	⇒	Ignition ON	5 V		
	61	⇥—	Ignition ON	0 V		
	68	⇐	Ignition ON – accelerator pedal released	0,6 V		
	68	⇐	Ignition ON – accelerator pedal depressed	4,4 V		
	75	⇐	Ignition ON – accelerator pedal released	4,5 V		
	75	⇐	Ignition ON – accelerator pedal depressed	0,7 V		

*Suggested settings - Voltage/time per division

1 Connected pin - no test data available or random digital signal

Model:	Engine code:	Year:
Lupo 1,0	ANV/AUC	1998-05
Lupo 1,4	AUD	2000-05
Polo 1,0	AUC	1999-02
Polo 1,4	AKP/ANW/AUD	1999-02
Polo Classic/Estate 1,4	ANW/AUD	1999-02
Golf/Bora 1,4	APE	1999-03
Golf/Bora 1,4	AXP	2000-03

ECM harness multi-plug

Terminal side

```
80 79 78 77 76 75 74        52 51 50 49 48 47 46 45 44 43 42 41
 73 72 71 70 69 68 67         40 39 38 37 36 35 34 33 32 31 30 29      28 27
66 65 64 63 62 61 60        26 25 24 23 22 21 20 19 18 17 16 15
 59 58 57 56 55 54 53         14 13 12 11 10 9 8 7 6 5 4 3        2 1
AD42344
```

Wire side

```
                  41 42 43 44 45 46 47 48 49 50 51 52        74 75 76 77 78 79 80
              29 30 31 32 33 34 35 36 37 38 39 40        67 68 69 70 71 72 73
 27 28          15 16 17 18 19 20 21 22 23 24 25 26        60 61 62 63 64 65 66
 1  2         3 4 5 6 7 8 9 10 11 12 13 14                53 54 55 56 57 58 59
AD42345
```

Component/circuit description	ECM pin	Signal	Condition	Typical value	Oscilloscope setting★	Wave form
Accelerator pedal position (APP) sensor	6	⇨	Ignition ON	5 V		
	7	⌐	Ignition ON	0 V		
	8	⇨	Ignition ON	5 V		
	19	⌐	Ignition ON	0 V		
	33	⟵	Ignition ON – accelerator pedal released	0,8 V		
	33	⟵	Ignition ON – accelerator pedal depressed	3,8 V		
	45	⟵	Ignition ON – accelerator pedal released	0,4 V		
	45	⟵	Ignition ON – accelerator pedal depressed	1,8 V		
Air conditioning/engine coolant blower motor control module	17			1		
	42			1		
Alternator	11	⇨	Engine idling		2 V/10 ms	89
Battery	15	⟵	Ignition OFF	11-14 V		
Brake pedal position (BPP) switch I	23	⟵	Ignition ON – brake pedal released	0 V		
	23	⟵	Ignition ON – brake pedal depressed	11-14 V		
Brake pedal position (BPP) switch II	51	⟵	Ignition ON – brake pedal released	11-14 V		
	51	⟵	Ignition ON – brake pedal depressed	0 V		
Camshaft position (CMP) sensor	62	⇨	Ignition ON	5 V		
	54	⌐	Ignition ON	0 V		
	60	⟵	Ignition ON	0 or 11-14 V		
	60	⟵	Engine idling		2 V/20 ms	14
CAN data bus – high	31	⟷		1		
CAN data bus – low	32	⟷		1		
Clutch pedal position (CPP) switch – Golf/Bora	38	⟵	Ignition ON – clutch pedal released	11-14 V		
	38	⟵	Ignition ON – clutch pedal depressed	0 V		
Crankshaft position (CKP) sensor	53	⟵	Ignition ON	0 V		
	53	⟵	Engine idling		2 V/2 ms	73
	62	⇨	Ignition ON	5 V		
	67	⌐	Ignition ON	0 V		

★ Suggested settings - Voltage/time per division

Component/circuit description	ECM pin	Signal	Condition	Typical value	Oscilloscope setting*	Wave form
Cruise control – Golf/Bora – if fitted	24			1		
	25			1		
	39			1		
	50			1		
Earth	2		Ignition ON	0 V		
	28		Ignition ON	0 V		
Engine coolant 'low' sensor – Lupo	54	⊣—	Ignition ON	0 V		
Engine coolant temperature (ECT) sensor	54	⊣—	Ignition ON	0 V		
	74	⟵	Ignition ON – coolant temp. 20°C	1,9 V		
	74	⟵	Ignition ON – coolant temp. 80°C	0,5 V		
Evaporative emission (EVAP) canister purge valve	14	⊐▷	Engine running – engine hot – valve operating		10 V/5 ms	35
Exhaust gas recirculation (EGR) valve actuator – some models	78	⊐▷	Ignition ON	11-14 V		
	78	⊐▷	Engine idling		5 V/1 ms – intermittent	53
Exhaust gas recirculation (EGR) valve position sensor – some models	54	⊣—	Ignition ON	0 V		
	62	⟹	Ignition ON	5 V		
	69	⟵	Ignition ON	0,92 V		
	69	⟵	Engine idling	0,95 V		
Fuel pump (FP) relay	26	⊐▷	Ignition ON	0-1 V briefly then 11-14 V		
	26	⊐▷	Engine idling	0-1 V		
Heated oxygen sensor (HO2S) 1	20	⟵	Engine idling	2,55 V		
	20 (46)	⟵	Engine idling	0,45 V		
	34	⟵▷	Engine idling	2,33-2,55 V		
	35	⟵▷	Engine idling	2,33-2,55 V		
	46	⟵	Engine idling	3 V		
	46 (20)	⟵	Engine idling	0,45 V		
Heated oxygen sensor (HO2S) 1 – heater control	1	⊐▷	Engine idling – engine hot	58%	2 V/0,2 secs.	55
Heated oxygen sensor (HO2S) 2	21	⊣—	Ignition ON	0 V		
	47	⟵	Engine idling – engine hot	0,6 V		
Heated oxygen sensor (HO2S) 2 – heater control	13	⊐▷	Ignition ON	11-14 V briefly then 0-1 V		
	13	⊐▷	Engine idling	0-1 V		
Ignition amplifier	57	⟹	Ignition ON	0 V		
	57	⟹	Engine idling		1 V/20 ms	32
	71	⟹	Ignition ON	0 V		
	71	⟹	Engine idling		1 V/20 ms	32
Ignition switch	27	⟵	Ignition OFF	0 V		
	27	⟵	Ignition ON	11-14 V		
Immobilizer control module – diagnosis signal – Polo	29			1		
Injector 1	79	⊐▷	Engine idling	4,2 ms	10 V/2 ms	35
Injector 2	59	⊐▷	Engine idling	4,2 ms	10 V/2 ms	35
Injector 3	73	⊐▷	Engine idling	4,2 ms	10 V/2 ms	35
Injector 4	65	⊐▷	Engine idling	4,2 ms	10 V/2 ms	35
Instrumentation control module – diagnosis signal – Lupo/Golf/Bora	29			1		
Instrumentation control module – engine RPM signal	41	⟹	Engine idling	26 Hz		

* Suggested settings - Voltage/time per division

Component/circuit description	ECM pin	Signal	Condition	Typical value	Oscilloscope setting*	Wave form
Instrumentation control module – Lupo/Polo – some models	12			☐1		
	16			☐1		
	30			☐1		
Instrumentation control module – vehicle speed signal	5	←	Ignition ON – vehicle pushed	0 V or 11-14 V (switching)		
Intake air temperature (IAT) sensor	54	⊐−	Ignition ON	0 V		
	56	←	Ignition ON – air temp. 15°C	2,2 V		
Knock sensor (KS)	63	←	Engine idling – accelerate briefly		50 mV/1 ms	∿∿ 38
	77	←	Engine idling – accelerate briefly		50 mV/1 ms	∿∿ 38
Manifold absolute pressure (MAP) sensor	54	⊐−	Ignition ON	0 V		
	62	⇒	Ignition ON	5 V		
	70	←	Ignition ON	4,1 V		
	70	←	Engine idling	0,9 V		
	70	←	Engine running – full throttle briefly	4,1 V		
Power steering pressure (PSP) switch – some models	21	⊐−	Ignition ON	0 V		
	49	←		☐1		
Spare cable – Golf/Bora	12			☐1		
	16			☐1		
	30			☐1		
Spare cable – Lupo/Golf/Bora	3			☐1		
Throttle motor	66	⇒	Ignition ON	11-14 V		
	66	⇒	Engine idling	11-14 V		
	80	⇒	Ignition ON	11-14 V for 30 seconds then 3 V		
	80	⇒	Ignition ON – accelerator pedal released		2 V/0,5 ms	(30 seconds only) ∿∿ 64
	80	⇒	Ignition ON – accelerator pedal depressed		2 V/0,5 ms	∿∿ 71
Throttle motor position sensor	55	⇒	Ignition ON	5 V		
	61	⊐−	Ignition ON	0 V		
	68	←	Ignition ON – accelerator pedal released	0,6 V		
	68	←	Ignition ON – accelerator pedal depressed	4,4 V		
	75	←	Ignition ON – accelerator pedal released	4,5 V		
	75	←	Ignition ON – accelerator pedal depressed	0,7 V		

*Suggested settings - Voltage/time per division

☐1 Connected pin - no test data available or random digital signal

VOLKSWAGEN

Siemens Simos 2P

Model:	Engine code:	Year:
Lupo 1,0	AHT	1998-05

ECM harness multi-plug

Terminal side

```
80 79 78 77 76 75 74
   73 72 71 70 69 68 67
66 65 64 63 62 61 60
   59 58 57 56 55 54 53
```

```
52 51 50 49 48 47 46 45 44 43 42 41
  40 39 38 37 36 35 34 33 32 31 30 29        28 27
26 25 24 23 22 21 20 19 18 17 16 15
  14 13 12 11 10 9 8 7 6 5 4 3          2 1
```

AD42344

Wire side

```
         41 42 43 44 45 46 47 48 49 50 51 52
       29 30 31 32 33 34 35 36 37 38 39 40
27 28     15 16 17 18 19 20 21 22 23 24 25 26
 1  2    3 4 5 6 7 8 9 10 11 12 13 14
```

```
74 75 76 77 78 79 80
67 68 69 70 71 72 73
  60 61 62 63 64 65 66
53 54 55 56 57 58 59
```

AD42345

Component/circuit description	ECM pin	Signal	Condition	Typical value	Oscilloscope setting*	Wave form
Battery	3	←	Ignition OFF	11-14 V		
Closed throttle position (CTP) switch	69	←	Ignition ON – throttle closed	V		
	69	←	Ignition ON – throttle open	9 V min.		
	70	⌐	Engine idling	0 V		
Crankshaft position (CKP) sensor	62	⇨	Ignition ON	5 V		
	70	⌐	Engine idling	0 V		
	76	←	Engine idling		2 V/1 ms	〜 5
Earth	2		Ignition ON	0 V		
Engine coolant temperature (ECT) sensor	53	←	Ignition ON – coolant temp. 15°C	2,1 V		
	53	←	Ignition ON – coolant temp. 80°C	0,4 V		
	70	⌐	Engine idling	0 V		
Evaporative emission (EVAP) canister purge valve	15	⇥▷	Ignition ON	11-14 V briefly then 0 V		
	15	⇥▷	Engine hot – valve operating		10 V/20 ms	〜 59
Fuel pump relay – without airbag	4	⇥▷	Ignition ON	0-1 V briefly then 11-14 V		
	4	⇥▷	Engine idling	0-1 V		
Fuel pump relay, through fuel pump shut-off control module – with airbag	4	⇥▷	Ignition ON	0-1 V briefly then 11-14 V		
	4	⇥▷	Engine idling	0-1 V		
Heated oxygen sensor (HO2S)	25	⌐	Engine idling	0 V		
	26	←	Engine idling – engine hot	0,1-1 V fluctuating	0,2 V/1 sec.	〜 21
	27	⇥▷	Ignition ON	11-14 V briefly then 0 V		
	27	⇥▷	Engine idling	0-1 V		
Idle speed control (ISC) actuator	59	⇨	Ignition ON	11-14 V		
	66	⇨	Ignition ON	11-14 V		
	66	⇨	Engine idling	10-20%	2 V/2 ms	〜 71
Idle speed control (ISC) actuator position sensor	62	⇨	Ignition ON	5 V		
	70	⌐	Engine idling	0 V		
	74	←	Ignition ON	3,8 V		
	74	←	Engine idling	3,8 V		

* Suggested settings - Voltage/time per division

Component/circuit description	ECM pin	Signal	Condition	Typical value	Oscilloscope setting*	Wave form
Ignition amplifier	71	⇒	Engine idling		2 V/10 ms	32
	78	⇒	Engine idling		2 V/10 ms	32
Ignition switch	1	⇐	Ignition OFF	0 V		
	1	⇐	Ignition ON	11-14 V		
Ignition switch, start signal	22	⇐	Engine cranking	8 V min.		
Immobilizer control module, immobilization/diagnosis signal	19	⇔		[1]		
Injectors 1 & 4	73	⇥⇥	Ignition ON	11-14 V briefly then 0 V		
	73	⇥⇥	Engine idling – engine hot	1-3 ms	10 V/2 ms	35
Injectors 2 & 3	80	⇥⇥	Ignition ON	11-14 V briefly then 0 V		
	80	⇥⇥	Engine idling – engine hot	1-3 ms	10 V/2 ms	35
Instrumentation control module, engine RPM signal	6	⇒	Engine idling	30 Hz		
	6	⇒	3000 rpm	100 Hz		
Instrumentation control module, vehicle speed signal	20	⇐	Ignition ON – vehicle pushed	0 V or 11-14 V switching		
Intake air temperature (IAT) sensor, in MAP sensor	54	⇐	Ignition ON – air temp. 15°C	1,5 V		
	70	⇥	Engine idling	0 V		
Knock sensor (KS)	67	⇥	Engine idling	0 V		
	68	⇐	Engine idling – full throttle briefly		50 mV/1 ms	58
Knock sensor (KS) – shield wire	67	⇥	Engine idling	0 V		
Manifold absolute pressure (MAP) sensor	13	⇐	Ignition ON	4 V		
	13	⇐	Engine idling	1 V		
	13	⇐	Engine idling – full throttle briefly	4,2 V		
	62	⇒	Ignition ON	5 V		
	70	⇥	Engine idling	0 V		
Power steering pressure (PSP) switch	24	⇐		[1]		
Throttle position (TP) sensor	62	⇒	Ignition ON	5 V		
	70	⇥	Engine idling	0 V		
	75	⇐	Ignition ON – throttle closed	4,3 V		
	75	⇐	Ignition ON – throttle fully open	0,6 V		

*Suggested settings - Voltage/time per division

[1] Connected pin - no test data available or random digital signal

VOLKSWAGEN

Magneti Marelli 4AV/4CV

Model:	Engine code:	Year:
Lupo 1,4	AHW/AKQ	1998-05
Golf/Bora 1,4	AHW/AKQ	1997-05

ECM harness multi-plug

Terminal side

80 79 78 77 76 75 74
73 72 71 70 69 68 67
66 65 64 63 62 61 60
59 58 57 56 55 54 53

52 51 50 49 48 47 46 45 44 43 42 41
40 39 38 37 36 35 34 33 32 31 30 29
26 25 24 23 22 21 20 19 18 17 16 15   28 27
14 13 12 11 10 9 8 7 6 5 4 3   2 1

AD42344

Wire side

41 42 43 44 45 46 47 48 49 50 51 52
29 30 31 32 33 34 35 36 37 38 39 40
27 28
15 16 17 18 19 20 21 22 23 24 25 26
1 2
3 4 5 6 7 8 9 10 11 12 13 14

74 75 76 77 78 79 80
67 68 69 70 71 72 73
60 61 62 63 64 65 66
53 54 55 56 57 58 59

AD42345

Component/circuit description	ECM pin	Signal	Condition	Typical value	Oscilloscope setting*	Wave form
Air conditioning	8			1		
	10			1		
Battery	1	←	Ignition OFF	11-14 V		
Camshaft position (CMP) sensor	64	⇒	Ignition ON	5 V		
	67	⌐	Ignition ON	0 V		
	76	←	Ignition ON – engine turned	0 V or 4,2 V switching		
	76	←	Engine idling		2 V/50 ms	69
CAN data bus – Lupo 10/98→	29	⟷		1		
	41	⟷		1		
CAN data bus – Golf/Bora 05/98→	29	⟷		1		
	41	⟷		1		
Closed throttle position (CTP) switch	67	⌐	Ignition ON	0 V		
	69	←	Ignition ON – throttle closed	0 V		
	69	←	Ignition ON – throttle slightly open	10,5 V		
Crankshaft position (CKP) sensor	56	⇒	Ignition ON	5 V		
	63	←	Engine idling		2 V/2 ms	6
	67	⌐	Ignition ON	0 V		
Crankshaft position (CKP) sensor, shield wire	67	⌐	Ignition ON	0 V		
Earth	2		Ignition ON	0 V		
Engine coolant blower control module – with AC	13			1		
Engine coolant temperature (ECT) sensor	53	←	Ignition ON – coolant temp. 20°C	2,2 V		
	53	←	Engine idling – engine hot	0,5 V		
	67	⌐	Ignition ON	0 V		
Evaporative emission (EVAP) canister purge valve	15	⌐▷	Ignition ON	11-14 V briefly then 0 V		
	15	⌐▷	Engine idling	11-14 V		
	15	⌐▷	Engine hot – valve operating		10 V/20 ms	20
Exhaust gas recirculation (EGR) solenoid	72	⌐▷	Ignition ON	11-14 V briefly then 0 V		
	72	⌐▷	Engine hot – valve operating		10 V/20 ms	59

* Suggested settings - Voltage/time per division

Component/circuit description	ECM pin	Signal	Condition	Typical value	Oscilloscope setting*	Wave form
Fuel pump relay	4	⊐▷	Ignition ON	0 V briefly then 11-14 V		
	4	⊐▷	Engine idling	0 V		
Heated oxygen sensor (HO2S)	25	⊐–	Ignition ON	0 V		
	26	⬅	Engine idling	0,1-0,9 V fluctuating	0,2 V/1 sec.	∿ 21
Idle speed control (ISC) actuator	59	⇨	Engine idling		2 V/2 ms	∿ 64
	66	⬅	Ignition ON	11-14 V		
	66	⬅	Engine idling		2 V/2 ms	∿ 64
Idle speed control (ISC) actuator position sensor	64	⇨	Ignition ON	5 V		
	67	⊐–	Ignition ON	0 V		
	74	⬅	Ignition ON	2,9 V then 3,4 V after 5 seconds		
Ignition amplifier	71	⇨	Ignition ON	0 V		
	71	⇨	Engine idling		1 V/20 ms	∿ 32
	78	⇨	Ignition ON	0 V		
	78	⇨	Engine idling		1 V/20 ms	∿ 32
Ignition switch	3	⬅	Ignition ON	11-14 V		
Injector 1	73	⊐▷	Ignition ON	11-14 V		
	73	⊐▷	Engine idling	3,5 ms	10 V/2 ms	∿ 35
Injector 2	80	⊐▷	Ignition ON	11-14 V		
	80	⊐▷	Engine idling	3,5 ms	10 V/2 ms	∿ 35
Injector 3	58	⊐▷	Ignition ON	11-14 V		
	58	⊐▷	Engine idling	3,5 ms	10 V/2 ms	∿ 35
Injector 4	65	⊐▷	Ignition ON	11-14 V		
	65	⊐▷	Engine idling	3,5 ms	10 V/2 ms	∿ 35
Immobilizer control module, immobilization/diagnosis signal – Lupo	19			▣1		
Instrumentation control module, fuel consumption signal – with digital multifunction display	18			▣1		
Instrumentation control module, immobilization/diagnosis signal – Golf/Bora	19			▣1		
Instrumentation control module, engine RPM signal	6	⇨	Engine idling	30 Hz	5 V/20 ms	∿ 43
Instrumentation control module, vehicle speed signal	20	⬅	Ignition ON – vehicle pushed	0 V or 11-14 V switching		
Intake air temperature (IAT) sensor	54	⬅	Ignition ON – air temp. 15°C	2,5 V		
	67	⊐–	Ignition ON	0 V		
Knock sensor (KS)	60	⬅	Ignition ON	0 V		
	60	⬅	Engine idling – full throttle briefly		50 mV/1 ms	∿ 58
	68	⬅	Ignition ON	2,5 V		
	68	⬅	Engine idling – full throttle briefly		50 mV/1 ms	∿ 58
Manifold absolute pressure (MAP) sensor	61	⇨	Ignition ON	5 V		
	62	⬅	Ignition ON	5 V		
	62	⬅	Engine idling	0,9 V		
	62	⬅	Engine idling – full throttle briefly	4 V		
	67	⊐–	Ignition ON	0 V		
Throttle position (TP) sensor	64	⇨	Ignition ON	5 V		
	67	⊐–	Ignition ON	0 V		
	75	⬅	Ignition ON – throttle closed	4,2 V		
	75	⬅	Ignition ON – throttle fully open	0,8 V		

*Suggested settings - Voltage/time per division

▣1 Connected pin - no test data available or random digital signal

Model:	Engine code:	Year:
Polo 1,2	AWY	2002-06

ECM harness multi-plug

Terminal side

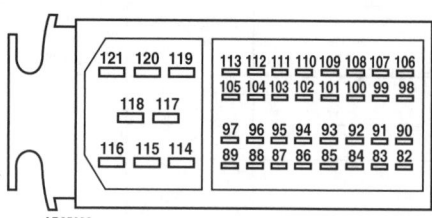
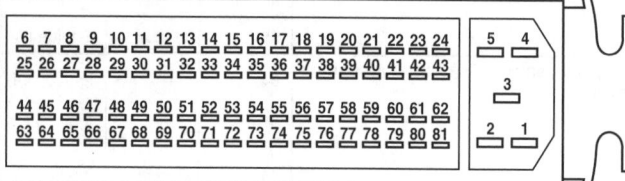

AD25036

Wire side

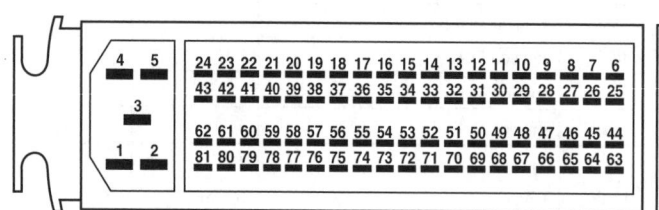
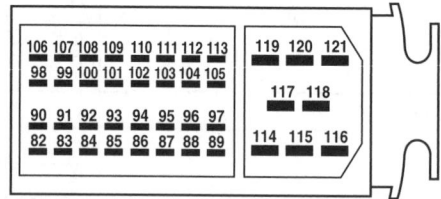

AD25035

Component/circuit description	ECM pin	Signal	Condition	Typical value	Oscilloscope setting★	Wave form
Accelerator pedal position (APP) sensor	18	⇨	Ignition ON	5 V		
	19	⇨	Ignition ON	5 V		
	45	⌐	Ignition ON	0 V		
	50	⌐	Ignition ON	0 V		
	51	⬅	Ignition ON – accelerator pedal released	0,7 V		
	51	⬅	Ignition ON – accelerator pedal fully depressed	4,1 V		
	64	⬅	Ignition ON – accelerator pedal released	0,4 V		
	64	⬅	Ignition ON – accelerator pedal fully depressed	2 V		
Alternator	13	⇨		1		
Brake pedal position (BPP) switch	53	⬅	Ignition ON – brake pedal released	0 V		
	53	⬅	Ignition ON – brake pedal depressed	11-14 V		
	63	⬅	Ignition ON – brake pedal released	11-14 V		
	63	⬅	Ignition ON – brake pedal depressed	0 V		
Camshaft position (CMP) sensor	89	⇨	Ignition ON	5 V		
	105	⬅	Ignition ON	0 or 5 V		
	105	⬅	Engine idling		2 V/0,1 sec.	⬳⬳ 4
	111	⌐	Ignition ON	0 V		
CAN data bus – high	20	⬅⇨		1		
CAN data bus – low	21	⬅⇨		1		
Clutch pedal position (CPP) switch	65	⬅	Ignition ON – clutch pedal released	11-14 V		
	65	⬅	Ignition ON – clutch pedal depressed	0 V		

★ Suggested settings - Voltage/time per division

Component/circuit description	ECM pin	Signal	Condition	Typical value	Oscilloscope setting*	Wave form
Crankshaft position (CKP) sensor	89	⇨	Ignition ON	5 V		
	99	⊣⊢	Ignition ON	0 V		
	106	⬅	Engine idling		2 V/2 ms	〰104
Cruise control master switch	69			[1]		
Cruise control selector switch	69			[1]		
Data link connector (DLC) – diagnosis signal	17	⬌		[1]		
Diagnostic module – diagnosis signal	17	⬌		[1]		
Earth	1		Ignition ON	0 V		
	2		Ignition ON	0 V		
Engine control (EC) relay	3	⬅	Ignition OFF	0 V		
	3	⬅	Ignition ON	11-14 V		
Engine coolant temperature (ECT) sensor	83	⊣⊢	Ignition ON	0 V		
	104	⬅	Ignition ON – coolant temp. 20°C	2,2 V		
	104	⬅	Ignition ON – coolant temp. 80°C	0,5 V		
Evaporative emission (EVAP) canister purge valve	61	⊣▷	Ignition ON	11-14 V briefly then 0 V		
	61	⊣▷	Engine running – engine hot – valve operating		10 V/20 ms	Intermittent 〰 20
Fuel pump (FP) relay	80	⊣▷	Ignition ON	0-1 V briefly then 11-14 V		
	80	⊣▷	Engine idling	0-1 V		
Heated oxygen sensor (HO2S) 1	14	⬅	Engine idling – engine hot	0,1-1 V fluctuating	0,2 V/2 ms	〰 21
	31	⊣⊢	Engine idling	0 V		
Heated oxygen sensor (HO2S) 1 – heater control	4	⊣▷	Ignition ON	11-14 V briefly then 0 V		
	4	⊣▷	Engine idling – engine hot	0-1 V		
Heated oxygen sensor (HO2S) 2	16	⬅	Engine idling – engine hot	0,6 V		
	35	⊣⊢	Ignition ON	0 V		
Heated oxygen sensor (HO2S) 2 – heater control	5	⊣▷	Ignition ON	11-14 V briefly then 0 V		
	5	⊣▷	Engine idling – engine hot	0-1 V		
Ignition amplifier	100	⇨	Ignition ON	0 V		
	100	⇨	Engine idling		2 V/5 ms	〰 62
	112	⇨	Ignition ON	0 V		
	112	⇨	Engine idling		2 V/5 ms	〰 62
	113	⇨	Ignition ON	0 V		
	113	⇨	Engine idling		2 V/5 ms	〰 62
	120	⊣⊢	Ignition ON	0 V		
Ignition switch	62	⬅	Ignition OFF	0 V		
	62	⬅	Ignition ON	11-14 V		
Ignition switch – through engine control (EC) relay	23	⬅	Ignition OFF	0 V		
	23	⬅	Ignition ON	11-14 V		
Injector 1	88	⊣▷	Ignition ON	11-14 V briefly then 0 V		
	88	⊣▷	Engine idling	3,2 ms	10 V/2 ms	〰 35

* Suggested settings - Voltage/time per division

Component/circuit description	ECM pin	Signal	Condition	Typical value	Oscilloscope setting*	Wave form
Injector 2	87	⊐▷	Ignition ON	11-14 V briefly then 0 V		
	87	⊐▷	Engine idling	3,2 ms	10 V/2 ms	∿∿ 35
Injector 3	85	⊐▷	Ignition ON	11-14 V briefly then 0 V		
	85	⊐▷	Engine idling	3,2 ms	10 V/2 ms	∿∿ 35
Instrumentation control module – vehicle speed signal	9	←	Ignition ON – vehicle pushed	0 V or 10 V switching		
Intake air temperature (IAT) sensor	93	←	Ignition ON – air temp. 20°C	2 V		
	107	⊐–	Ignition ON	0 V		
Knock sensor (KS)	101	⊐–	Engine idling	0 V		
	109	←	Engine idling – accelerate briefly		50 mV/1 ms	∿∿ 38
Knock sensor (KS) – screened lead	102	⊐–	Engine idling	0 V		
Manifold absolute pressure (MAP) sensor	95	←	Ignition ON	4 V		
	95	←	Engine idling	1 V		
	95	←	Engine running – full throttle briefly	4,1 V briefly		
	96	⇨	Ignition ON	5 V		
	107	⊐–	Ignition ON	0 V		
Throttle motor	119	⇨	Ignition ON – accelerator pedal released		2 V/2 ms	(30 seconds only) ∿∿ 64
	121	⇨	Ignition ON – accelerator pedal released		2 V/2 ms	(30 seconds only) ∿∿ 64
Throttle motor position sensor	90	←	Ignition ON – accelerator pedal released	0,9 V		
	90	←	Ignition ON – accelerator pedal fully depressed	4,4 V		
	91	⊐–	Ignition ON	0 V		
	92	←	Ignition ON – accelerator pedal released	4,1 V		
	92	←	Ignition ON – accelerator pedal fully depressed	0,7 V		
	97	⇨	Ignition ON	5 V		

*Suggested settings - Voltage/time per division

1 Connected pin - no test data available or random digital signal

ECM harness multi-plug

Terminal side

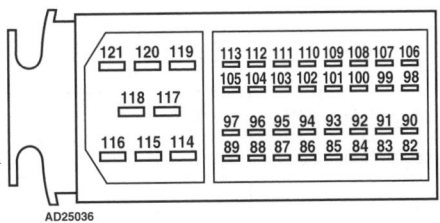

AD25036

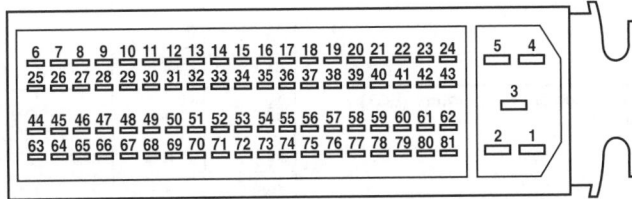

Wire side

AD25035

Component/circuit description	ECM pin	Signal	Condition	Typical value	Oscilloscope setting★	Wave form
AC control module – ATC	40			☐1		
	41			☐1		
AC refrigerant pressure sensor – MTC	61			☐1		
Accelerator pedal position (APP) sensor	33	‾ʃ‾	Ignition ON	0 V		
	34	←	Ignition ON – accelerator pedal released	0,4 V		
	34	←	Ignition ON – accelerator pedal depressed	2 V		
	35	←	Ignition ON – accelerator pedal released	0,8 V		
	35	←	Ignition ON – accelerator pedal depressed	4,1 V		
	36	‾ʃ‾	Ignition ON	0 V		
	72	⇒	Ignition ON	5 V		
	73	⇒	Ignition ON	5 V		
Alternator	28	⇒	Engine idling		1 V/10 ms	∿ 89
Battery	3	←	Ignition OFF	11-14 V		
Brake pedal position (BPP) switch	55	←	Ignition ON – brake pedal released	11-14 V		
	55	←	Ignition ON – brake pedal depressed	0 V		
	56	←	Ignition ON – brake pedal released	0 V		
	56	←	Ignition ON – brake pedal depressed	11-14 V		
Camshaft position (CMP) sensor	86	←	Ignition ON	0 or 5 V		
	86	←	Engine idling		2 V/50 ms	∿ 69
	98	⇒	Ignition ON	5 V		
	108	‾ʃ‾	Ignition ON	0 V		
CAN data bus – high	60	←⇒		☐1		
CAN data bus – low	58	←⇒		☐1		

★ Suggested settings - Voltage/time per division

Component/circuit description	ECM pin	Signal	Condition	Typical value	Oscilloscope setting*	Wave form
Crankshaft position (CKP) sensor	82	←	Engine idling		2 V/1 ms	ᴡ 73
	87	⇒	Ignition ON	5 V		
	108	ꟼ−	Ignition ON	0 V		
Earth	1		Ignition ON	0 V		
	2		Ignition ON	0 V		
Engine coolant blower motor control module – MTC	40			[1]		
	41			[1]		
	61			[1]		
Engine coolant temperature (ECT) sensor	93	←	Ignition ON – coolant temp. 20°C	2,2 V		
	93	←	Ignition ON – coolant temp. 80°C	0,5 V		
	108	ꟼ−	Ignition ON	0 V		
Evaporative emission (EVAP) canister purge valve	64	ꟼ▷	Ignition ON	11-14 V		
	64	ꟼ▷	Engine running – engine hot – valve operating		10 V/20 ms	ᴡ 20
Exhaust gas recirculation (EGR) valve actuator	114	ꟼ▷	Ignition ON	11-14 V		
	114	ꟼ▷	Engine idling		5 V/1 ms	Intermittent ᴡ 53
Exhaust gas recirculation (EGR) valve position sensor	98	⇒	Ignition ON	5 V		
	100	←	Ignition ON	0,92 V		
	100	←	Engine idling	0,95 V		
	108	ꟼ−	Ignition ON	0 V		
Fuel pump (FP) relay	65	ꟼ▷	Ignition ON	0-1 V briefly then 11-14 V		
	65	ꟼ▷	Engine idling	0-1 V		
Heated oxygen sensor (HO2S) 1	51	←	Engine idling	3,79 V		
	51 (70)	←	Engine idling	0,46 V		
	52	◄⇒	Engine idling	3,94 V		
	70	←	Engine idling	4,25 V		
	70 (51)	←	Engine idling	0,46 V		
	71	◄⇒	Engine idling	8,24 V		
Heated oxygen sensor (HO2S) 1 – heater control	5	ꟼ▷	Engine idling – engine hot		2 V/10 ms	ᴡ 65
Heated oxygen sensor (HO2S) 2	68	ꟼ−	Ignition ON	0 V		
	69	←	Engine idling – engine hot	0,6 V		
Heated oxygen sensor (HO2S) 2 – heater control	63	ꟼ▷	Ignition ON	11-14 V briefly then 0-1 V		
	63	ꟼ▷	Engine idling – engine hot		2 V/5 ms	ᴡ 65
Ignition amplifier	102	⇒	Engine idling		1 V/20 ms	ᴡ 32
	103	⇒	Engine idling		1 V/20 ms	ᴡ 32
Ignition switch	4	←	Ignition OFF	0 V		
	4	←	Ignition ON	11-14 V		
Immobilizer control module	43	◄⇒		[1]		
Injector 1	96	ꟼ▷	Ignition ON	11-14 V briefly then 0-1 V		
	96	ꟼ▷	Engine idling	2,5 ms	10 V/2 ms	ᴡ 35
Injector 2	97	ꟼ▷	Ignition ON	11-14 V briefly then 0-1 V		
	97	ꟼ▷	Engine idling	2,5 ms	10 V/2 ms	ᴡ 35
Injector 3	88	ꟼ▷	Ignition ON	11-14 V briefly then 0-1 V		
	88	ꟼ▷	Engine idling	2,5 ms	10 V/2 ms	ᴡ 35

* Suggested settings - Voltage/time per division

Component/circuit description	ECM pin	Signal	Condition	Typical value	Oscilloscope setting*	Wave form
Injector 4	89	⇥▷	Ignition ON	11-14 V briefly then 0-1 V		
	89	⇥▷	Engine idling	2,5 ms	10 V/2 ms	〰 35
Instrumentation control module	37			1		
Instrumentation control module – vehicle speed signal	54	⬅		1		
Intake air temperature (IAT) sensor	85	⬅	Ignition ON – air temp. 20°C	2,4 V		
	108	⊣⊢	Ignition ON	0 V		
Knock sensor (KS)	99	⊣⊢	Engine idling	0 V		
	106	⬅	Engine idling – accelerate briefly		50 mV/1 ms	〰 38
Manifold absolute pressure (MAP) sensor	98	⇨	Ignition ON	5 V		
	108	⊣⊢	Ignition ON	0 V		
	109	⬅	Ignition ON	4 V		
	109	⬅	Engine idling	1,1 V		
	109	⬅	Engine running – full throttle briefly	4,1 V		
Spare cable	81			1		
Throttle motor	117	⇨	Ignition ON	11-14 V for 30 seconds then 3 V		
	117	⇨	Ignition ON – accelerator pedal released		2 V/2 ms	(30 seconds only) 〰 64
	118	⇨	Ignition ON	11-14 V for 30 seconds then 3 V		
	118	⇨	Ignition ON – accelerator pedal released		2 V/2 ms	(30 seconds only) 〰 64
Throttle motor position sensor	83	⇨	Ignition ON	5 V		
	84	⬅	Ignition ON – accelerator pedal released	4,3 V		
	84	⬅	Ignition ON – accelerator pedal depressed	0,7 V		
	91	⊣⊢	Ignition ON	0 V		
	92	⬅	Ignition ON – accelerator pedal released	0,7 V		
	92	⬅	Ignition ON – accelerator pedal depressed	4,4 V		
Transmission control module (TCM) – APE/AUA	41			1		

*Suggested settings - Voltage/time per division

1 Connected pin - no test data available or random digital signal

VOLKSWAGEN
Magneti Marelli 4MV

Model:	Engine code:	Year:
Polo 1,4	BBY	2002-06
Polo 1,4	BBZ	2002-06

ECM harness multi-plug

Terminal side

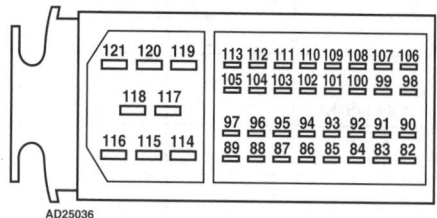
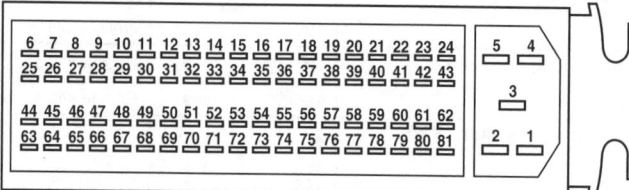

AD25036

Wire side

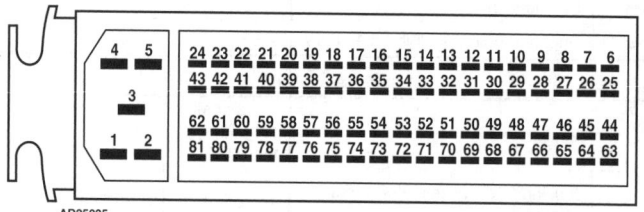
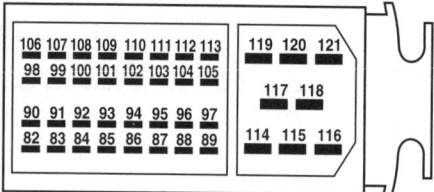

AD25035

Component/circuit description	ECM pin	Signal	Condition	Typical value	Oscilloscope setting*	Wave form
Accelerator pedal position (APP) sensor	33	⌐	Ignition ON	0 V		
	34	←	Ignition ON – accelerator pedal depressed	2 V		
	34	←	Ignition ON – accelerator pedal released	0,4 V		
	35	←	Ignition ON – accelerator pedal depressed	4,1 V		
	35	←	Ignition ON – accelerator pedal released	0,8 V		
	36	⌐	Ignition ON	0 V		
	72	⇒	Ignition ON	5 V		
	73	⇒	Ignition ON	5 V		
Alternator	28	⇒	Engine idling		1 V/10 ms	〰 89
Battery	3	←	Ignition OFF	11-14 V		
Brake pedal position (BPP) switch	55	←	Ignition ON – brake pedal depressed	0 V		
	55	←	Ignition ON – brake pedal released	11-14 V		
	56	←	Ignition ON – brake pedal depressed	11-14 V		
	56	←	Ignition ON – brake pedal released	0 V		
Camshaft position (CMP) sensor	108	⌐	Ignition ON	0 V		
	86	←	Engine idling		2 V/50 ms	〰 69
	86	←	Ignition ON	0 or 5 V		
	98	⇒	Ignition ON	5 V		
CAN data bus – high	60	↔		1		
CAN data bus – low	58	↔		1		
Clutch pedal position (CPP) switch	39	←	Ignition ON – clutch pedal depressed	0 V		
	39	←	Ignition ON – clutch pedal released	11-14 V		

★ Suggested settings - Voltage/time per division

Component/circuit description	ECM pin	Signal	Condition	Typical value	Oscilloscope setting*	Wave form
Crankshaft position (CKP) sensor	108	⌐—	Ignition ON	0 V		
	82	←	Engine idling		2 V/1 ms	73
	87	⇒	Ignition ON	5 V		
Cruise control master switch	38			1		
Data link connector (DLC)	43			1		
Earth	1		Ignition ON	0 V		
	2		Ignition ON	0 V		
Engine coolant temperature (ECT) sensor	108	⌐—	Ignition ON	0 V		
	93	←	Ignition ON – coolant temp. 20°C	2,2 V		
	93	←	Ignition ON – coolant temp. 80°C	0,5 V		
Evaporative emission (EVAP) canister purge valve	64	⌐⇒	Engine running – engine hot – valve operating		10 V/20 ms	20
	64	⌐⇒	Ignition ON	11-14 V briefly then 0-1 V		
Exhaust gas recirculation (EGR) valve actuator	114	⌐⇒	Engine idling		5 V/1 ms	Intermittent 53
	114	⌐⇒	Ignition ON	11-14 V		
Exhaust gas recirculation (EGR) valve position sensor	100	←	Engine idling	0,95 V		
	100	←	Ignition ON	0,92 V		
	108	⌐—	Ignition ON	0 V		
	98	⇒	Ignition ON	5 V		
Fuel pump (FP) relay	65	⌐⇒	Engine idling	0-1 V		
	65	⌐⇒	Ignition ON	0-1 V briefly then 11-14 V		
Heated oxygen sensor (HO2S) 1	51 (70)	←	Engine idling	0,46 V		
	70 (51)	←	Engine idling	0,46 V		
	51	←	Engine idling	3,8 V		
	52	←⇒	Engine idling	3,94 V		
	70	←	Engine idling	4,25 V		
	71	←⇒	Engine idling	8,24 V		
Heated oxygen sensor (HO2S) 1 – heater control	5	⌐⇒	Engine idling – engine hot		2 V/10 ms	65
Heated oxygen sensor (HO2S) 2	68	⌐—	Ignition ON	0 V		
	69	←	Engine idling – engine hot	0,6 V		
Heated oxygen sensor (HO2S) 2 – heater control	63	⌐⇒	Engine idling – engine hot		2 V/10 ms	65
	63	⌐⇒	Ignition ON	11-14 V briefly then 0-1 V		
Ignition coil 1	102	⇒	Engine idling		2 V/20 ms	62
	102	⇒	Ignition ON	0 V		
Ignition coil 2	103	⇒	Engine idling		2 V/20 ms	62
	103	⇒	Ignition ON	0 V		
Ignition coil 3	94	⇒	Engine idling		2 V/20 ms	62
	94	⇒	Ignition ON	0 V		
Ignition coil 4	95	⇒	Engine idling		2 V/20 ms	62
	95	⇒	Ignition ON	0 V		

* Suggested settings - Voltage/time per division

Component/circuit description	ECM pin	Signal	Condition	Typical value	Oscilloscope setting*	Wave form
Ignition switch	4	←	Ignition OFF	0 V		
	4	←	Ignition ON	11-14 V		
Injector 1	96	⇥▷	Engine idling	2,5 ms	10 V/2 ms	⎍⎍ 35
	96	⇥▷	Ignition ON	11-14 V briefly then 0-1 V		
Injector 2	97	⇥▷	Engine idling	2,5 ms	10 V/2 ms	⎍⎍ 35
	97	⇥▷	Ignition ON	11-14 V briefly then 0-1 V		
Injector 3	88	⇥▷	Engine idling	2,5 ms	10 V/2 ms	⎍⎍ 35
	88	⇥▷	Ignition ON	11-14 V briefly then 0-1 V		
Injector 4	89	⇥▷	Engine idling	2,5 ms	10 V/2 ms	⎍⎍ 35
	89	⇥▷	Ignition ON	11-14 V briefly then 0-1 V		
Instrument panel – vehicle speed signal	54	←		[1]		
Intake air temperature (IAT) sensor	108	⊣−	Ignition ON	0 V		
	85	←	Ignition ON – air temp. 20°C	2,4 V		
Knock sensor (KS)	106	←	Engine idling – accelerate briefly		50 mV/1 ms	⎍⎍ 38
	99	⊣−	Engine idling	0 V		
Manifold absolute pressure (MAP) sensor	108	⊣−	Ignition ON	0 V		
	109	←	Engine idling	0,9 V		
	109	←	Engine running – full throttle briefly	4,3 V		
	109	←	Ignition ON	4 V		
	98	⇒	Ignition ON	5 V		
Throttle motor	117	⇒	Ignition ON	11-14 V for 30 seconds then 3 V		
	117	⇒	Ignition ON – accelerator pedal released		2 V/2 ms	(30 seconds only) ⎍⎍ 64
	118	⇒	Ignition ON	11-14 V for 30 seconds then 3 V		
	118	⇒	Ignition ON – accelerator pedal released		2 V/2 ms	(30 seconds only) ⎍⎍ 64
Throttle motor position sensor	83	⇒	Ignition ON	5 V		
	84	←	Ignition ON – accelerator pedal depressed	0,7 V		
	84	←	Ignition ON – accelerator pedal released	4,3 V		
	91	⊣−	Ignition ON	0 V		
	92	←	Ignition ON – accelerator pedal depressed	4,4 V		
	92	←	Ignition ON – accelerator pedal released	0,7 V		

*Suggested settings - Voltage/time per division

[1] Connected pin - no test data available or random digital signal

Model:	Engine code:	Year:
Polo Classic/Estate 1,6	AFT/AKS	1995-00
Golf/Vento/Cabrio 1,6/2,0	AFT/AKS/ADY/AGG/AKR	1995-02
Passat/Syncro 1,6/2,0	ADY/AFT/AGG/AKR/AKS	1995-97
Corrado 2,0	ADY	1994-95
Caddy 1,6	AFT	1995-00
Transporter 2,5	AET	1996-98

VOLKSWAGEN

Siemens Simos

ECM harness multi-plug

Terminal side

AD81718

Wire side

AD42119

Component/circuit description	ECM pin	Signal	Condition	Typical value	Oscilloscope setting*	Wave form
Air conditioning	13			1		
	39			1		
Automatic transmission	5			1		
	15			1		
Camshaft position (CMP) sensor	35	⌐—	Ignition ON	0 V		
	44	←	Ignition ON – engine turned	0 V or 10-14 V switching		
	44	←	Engine idling	8 Hz	5 V/20 ms	12
	44	←	3000 rpm	25 Hz		
	45	⇒	Ignition ON	10 V min.		
Closed throttle position (CTP) switch	18	←	Ignition ON – throttle closed	0 V		
	18	←	Ignition ON – throttle slightly open	9 V min.		
	35	⌐—	Ignition ON	0 V		
Crankshaft position (CKP) sensor	16	⌐—	Engine idling	0 V		
	67	←	Engine idling		2 V/1 ms	5
	68	⇒	Ignition ON	11-14 V		
Earth	1		Ignition ON	0 V		
Engine control relay	23	←	Ignition OFF	0 V		
	23	←	Ignition ON	11-14 V		
Engine coolant temperature (ECT) sensor	12	←	Ignition ON – coolant temp. 10°C	2,8 V		
	12	←	Ignition ON – coolant temp. 80°C	0,4 V		
	35	⌐—	Ignition ON	0 V		
Evaporative emission (EVAP) canister purge valve	33	⌐—▷	Ignition ON	11-14 V		
	33	⌐—▷	Engine hot – valve operating		10 V/20 ms	20
Fuel pump relay	31	⌐—▷	Engine cranking	0-1 V		
Heated oxygen sensor (HO2S)	17	←	Ignition ON	1,3-1,4 V		
	20	⌐—▷	Engine idling	0 V		
	42	⌐—	Engine idling	0 V		
Heated oxygen sensor (HO2S) – 1,6	17	←	Engine idling – engine hot	0,2-1 V fluctuating	0,2 V/1 sec.	21
Heated oxygen sensor (HO2S) – 2,0/2,5	17	←	Engine idling – engine hot	0,1-1,1 V fluctuating	0,2 V/1 sec.	21

* Suggested settings - Voltage/time per division

Component/circuit description	ECM pin	Signal	Condition	Typical value	Oscilloscope setting*	Wave form
Heated oxygen sensor (HO2S) – shield wire	21	⌐	Engine idling	0 V		
Idle speed control (ISC) actuator	25 (30)	⇨	Engine idling		5 V/2 ms	Intermittent 〰 27
	30 (25)	⇨	Engine idling		5 V/2 ms	Intermittent 〰 27
Idle speed control (ISC) actuator position sensor	28	⬅	Engine idling – engine hot	3,7 V		
	35	⌐	Ignition ON	0 V		
	41	⇨	Ignition ON	4-6 V		
Ignition amplifier	7	⇨	Engine idling		2 V/10 ms	〰 32
Ignition switch	38	⬅	Ignition OFF	0 V		
	38	⬅	Ignition ON	11-14 V		
Ignition switch, start signal – some models	32	⬅	Engine cranking	9 V min.		
Ignition switch – through engine control relay	8	⇨	Ignition OFF	0 V		
	8	⇨	Ignition ON	11-14 V		
Immobilizer control module	43	⬅	Ignition ON	11-14 V		
Injector 1	2	⌐⇨	Engine idling – engine hot	3,8 ms	10 V/2 ms	〰 35
Injector 2	46	⌐⇨	Engine idling – engine hot	3,8 ms	10 V/2 ms	〰 35
Injector 3	47	⌐⇨	Engine idling – engine hot	3,8 ms	10 V/2 ms	〰 35
Injector 4	48	⌐⇨	Engine idling – engine hot	3,8 ms	10 V/2 ms	〰 35
Injector 5 – 2,5	49	⌐⇨	Engine idling – engine hot	3,8 ms	10 V/2 ms	〰 35
Instrument panel – vehicle speed signal	11	⬅	Ignition ON – vehicle pushed	0 V or 11-14 V switching		
	11	⬅	Vehicle moving		5 V/50 ms	〰 43
	19			[1]		
Instrument panel – except 2,5	10			[1]		
Intake air temperature (IAT) sensor	37	⬅	Ignition ON – air temp. 10°C	2 V		
Intake air temperature (IAT) sensor – 1,6	35	⌐	Ignition ON	0 V		
Intake air temperature (IAT) sensor – 2,0/2,5	29	⌐	Ignition ON	0 V		
Intake manifold air control solenoid – 1,6	22	⌐⇨	Engine idling	11-14 V		
	22	⌐⇨	Above 4000 rpm	0-1 V		
Knock sensor (KS) 1	34	⬅	Engine idling – accelerate briefly		50 mV/1 ms	〰 38
	36	⌐	Engine idling	0 V		
Knock sensor (KS) 1 – shield wire	9	⌐	Engine idling	0 V		
Knock sensor (KS) 2 – Transporter	56	⬅	Engine idling – accelerate briefly		50 mV/1 ms	〰 38
	57	⌐	Engine idling	0 V		
Knock sensor (KS) 2 – shield wire – Transporter	55	⌐	Engine idling	0 V		
Mass air flow (MAF) sensor	14	⬅	Engine idling – engine hot	1,2 V		
	14	⬅	3000 rpm	1,7 V		
	26	⌐	Ignition ON	0 V		
Mass air flow (MAF) sensor – 2,5	35	⌐	Ignition ON	0 V		
Throttle position (TP) sensor	35	⌐	Ignition ON	0 V		
	40	⬅	Ignition ON – throttle closed	4,3 V		
	40	⬅	Ignition ON – throttle fully open	0,7 V		
	41	⇨	Ignition ON	4-6 V		

*Suggested settings - Voltage/time per division

[1] Connected pin - no test data available or random digital signal

Model:	Engine code:	Year:
Polo Classic/Estate 1,6	AEH/AKL	1999-02
Golf/Bora 1,6	AEH/AKL	1997-02
Passat 1,6	AHL/ARM	1996-00

ECM harness multi-plug

Terminal side

AD42344

Wire side

AD42345

Component/circuit description	ECM pin	Signal	Condition	Typical value	Oscilloscope setting*	Wave form
Air conditioning – Golf/Bora 05/99→	11			1		
Air conditioning, AC ON signal	10	←		1		
Air conditioning, compressor ON/shut-off signal – except Passat →07/97	8	←→		1		
Battery	3	←	Ignition OFF	11-14 V		
Camshaft position (CMP) sensor	62	→	Ignition ON	5 V		
	76	←	Ignition ON – engine turned	0 V or 5 V switching		
	76	←	Engine idling		2 V/50 ms	⌁ 45
Camshaft position (CMP) sensor – Passat	67	⌐	Engine idling	0 V		
Camshaft position (CMP) sensor – Polo/Golf/Bora	70	⌐	Engine idling	0 V		
CAN data bus – except Passat →07/97	29	←→		1		
	31	←→		1		
Closed throttle position (CTP) switch	69	←	Ignition ON – throttle closed	0 V		
	69	←	Ignition ON – throttle open	9 V min.		
Closed throttle position (CTP) switch – Passat	67	⌐	Engine idling	0 V		
Closed throttle position (CTP) switch – Polo/Golf/Bora	70	⌐	Engine idling	0 V		
Clutch pedal position (CPP) switch – Polo, if fitted	21	←	Ignition ON – clutch pedal released	11-14 V		
	21	←	Ignition ON – clutch pedal depressed	0 V		
Crankshaft position (CKP) sensor	56	←	Engine idling	13,7 V ac	10 V/1 ms	⌁ 2
	63	⌐	Engine idling	0 V		
Crankshaft position (CKP) sensor – Polo	70	⌐	Engine idling	0 V		
Crankshaft position (CKP) sensor, shield wire – Polo/Golf/Bora	70	⌐	Engine idling	0 V		
Earth	2		Ignition ON	0 V		
Engine control module (ECM), pin 22 – Golf/Bora, MT	70	⌐	Ignition ON	0 V		
Engine control module (ECM), pin 70 – Golf/Bora, MT →04/99	22	←	Ignition ON	0 V		
Engine coolant temperature (ECT) sensor	53	←	Ignition ON – coolant temp. 15°C	2,1 V		
	53	←	Ignition ON – coolant temp. 80°C	0,4 V		

* Suggested settings - Voltage/time per division

Component/circuit description	ECM pin	Signal	Condition	Typical value	Oscilloscope setting*	Wave form
Engine coolant temperature (ECT) sensor – Passat	67	⊣⊢	Engine idling	0 V		
Engine coolant temperature (ECT) sensor – Polo/Golf/Bora	70	⊣⊢	Engine idling	0 V		
Evaporative emission (EVAP) canister purge valve	15	⊣⊳	Ignition ON	11-14 V briefly then 0 V		
	15	⊣⊳	Engine idling – engine hot	10%	10 V/20 ms	〰 59
Exhaust gas recirculation (EGR) valve – Passat →07/97	72	⊣⊳	Ignition ON	11-14 V		
	72	⊣⊳	Engine hot – valve operating		10 V/50 ms	〰 59
Fuel pump relay	4	⊣⊳	Ignition ON	0-1 V briefly then 11-14 V		
	4	⊣⊳	Engine idling	0-1 V		
Heated oxygen sensor (HO2S)	25	⊣⊢	Engine idling	0 V		
	26	⟵	Engine idling – engine hot	0,1-1 V fluctuating	0,2 V/1 sec.	〰 21
	27	⊣⊳	Ignition ON	11-14 V briefly then 0 V		
	27	⊣⊳	Engine idling	0-1 V		
Idle speed control (ISC) actuator	59	⟹	Ignition ON	11-14 V		
	66	⟹	Ignition ON	11-14 V		
	66	⟹	Engine idling	10-20%	2 V/2 ms	〰 71
Idle speed control (ISC) actuator position sensor	62	⟹	Ignition ON	5 V		
	74	⟵	Ignition ON	3,8 V		
	74	⟵	Engine idling	3,8 V		
Idle speed control (ISC) actuator position sensor – Passat	67	⊣⊢	Engine idling	0 V		
Idle speed control (ISC) actuator position sensor – Polo/Golf/Bora	70	⊣⊢	Engine idling	0 V		
Ignition amplifier	71	⟹	Engine idling		2 V/10 ms	〰 32
	78	⟹	Engine idling		2 V/10 ms	〰 32
Ignition switch	1	⟵	Ignition OFF	0 V		
	1	⟵	Ignition ON	11-14 V		
Ignition switch, start signal – Golf/Bora, MT 05/99→	22	⟵	Engine cranking	8 V min.		
Ignition switch, start signal – Polo	22	⟵	Engine cranking	8 V min.		
Immobilizer control module, immobilization/diagnosis signal – Polo	19	⟷		1		
Injector 1	73	⊣⊳	Ignition ON	11-14 V briefly then 0 V		
Injector 1 – Golf/Bora	73	⊣⊳	Engine idling – engine hot	2-4,1 ms	10 V/2 ms	〰 35
Injector 1 – Polo/Passat	73	⊣⊳	Engine idling – engine hot	2-5 ms	10 V/2 ms	〰 35
Injector 2	80	⊣⊳	Ignition ON	11-14 V briefly then 0 V		
Injector 2 – Golf/Bora	80	⊣⊳	Engine idling – engine hot	2-4,1 ms	10 V/2 ms	〰 35
Injector 2 – Polo/Passat	80	⊣⊳	Engine idling – engine hot	2-5 ms	10 V/2 ms	〰 35
Injector 3	58	⊣⊳	Ignition ON	11-14 V briefly then 0 V		
Injector 3 – Golf/Bora	58	⊣⊳	Engine idling – engine hot	2-4,1 ms	10 V/2 ms	〰 35
Injector 3 – Polo/Passat	58	⊣⊳	Engine idling – engine hot	2-5 ms	10 V/2 ms	〰 35
Injector 4	65	⊣⊳	Ignition ON	11-14 V briefly then 0 V		
Injector 4 – Golf/Bora	65	⊣⊳	Engine idling – engine hot	2-4,1 ms	10 V/2 ms	〰 35
Injector 4 – Polo/Passat	65	⊣⊳	Engine idling – engine hot	2-5 ms	10 V/2 ms	〰 35
Instrumentation control module, engine RPM signal – except Passat 05/99→	6	⟹	Engine idling	30 Hz		
	6	⟹	3000 rpm	100 Hz		

* Suggested settings - Voltage/time per division

Component/circuit description	ECM pin	Signal	Condition	Typical value	Oscilloscope setting*	Wave form
Instrumentation control module, fuel consumption signal – some models	18	⟹		1		
Instrumentation control module, immobilization/diagnosis signal – Golf/Bora/Passat	19	⟺		1		
Instrumentation control module, vehicle speed signal	20	⟸	Ignition ON – vehicle pushed	0 V or 11-14 V switching		
Intake air temperature (IAT) sensor – Passat →07/97	54	⟸	Ignition ON – air temp. 15°C	1,5 V		
	67	⌐⊢	Engine idling	0 V		
Intake manifold air control solenoid – except Passat →07/98	64	⌐⊢▷	Ignition ON	11-14 V briefly then 0 V		
	64	⌐⊢▷	Engine idling	11-14 V		
	64	⌐⊢▷	Engine idling – full throttle briefly	0-1 V briefly then 11-14 V		
Knock sensor (KS)	67	⌐⊢	Engine idling	0 V		
	68	⟸	Engine idling – full throttle briefly		50 mV/1 ms	〰〰 58
Knock sensor (KS), shield wire	67	⌐⊢	Engine idling	0 V		
Mass air flow (MAF) sensor	12	⌐⊢	Engine idling	0 V		
	13	⟸	Engine idling	1 V		
	13	⟸	Engine idling – full throttle briefly	4,2 V		
Mass air flow (MAF) sensor, IAT signal – except Passat →07/97	9	⟸	Ignition ON – air temp. 15°C	1,5 V		
Mass air flow (MAF) sensor, IAT signal – Passat 08/98→	54	⟸	Ignition ON – air temp. 15°C	1,5 V		
Power steering pressure (PSP) switch – Polo/Golf/Bora	14	⟸		1		
	24	⟸		1		
Spare cable – Passat 05/99→	6			1		
	18			1		
Starter motor relay/reversing lamp/s relay – Golf/Bora/Passat, AT	22	⟸		1		
Throttle position (TP) sensor	62	⟹	Ignition ON	5 V		
	75	⟸	Ignition ON – throttle closed	4,3 V		
	75	⟸	Ignition ON – throttle fully open	0,6 V		
Throttle position (TP) sensor – Passat	67	⌐⊢	Engine idling	0 V		
Throttle position (TP) sensor – Polo/Golf/Bora	70	⌐⊢	Engine idling	0 V		
Transmission control module (TCM), torque reduction signal – Polo/Passat	23	⟸		1		
Transmission control module (TCM), TP signal – Passat	7	⟹		1		
Transmission control module (TCM), engine RPM signal – some models	6	⟹	Engine idling	30 Hz		
	6	⟹	3000 rpm	100 Hz		

*Suggested settings - Voltage/time per division

1 Connected pin - no test data available or random digital signal

VOLKSWAGEN

Bosch EDC 15V

Model:	Engine code:	Year:
Polo 1,7/1,9 SDI	AGD/AHG/AKU	1997-09/99
Polo Classic/Estate 1,7/1,9 SDI	AEY/AKW	12/97-01
Caddy 1,7/1,9 SDI	AEY/AKW	12/97-01

ECM harness multi-plug

Terminal side

80 79 78 77 76 75 74
73 72 71 70 69 68 67
66 65 64 63 62 61 60
59 58 57 56 55 54 53

AD42344

52 51 50 49 48 47 46 45 44 43 42 41
40 39 38 37 36 35 34 33 32 31 30 29   28 27
26 25 24 23 22 21 20 19 18 17 16 15
14 13 12 11 10 9 8 7 6 5 4 3   2 1

Wire side

27 28
41 42 43 44 45 46 47 48 49 50 51 52
29 30 31 32 33 34 35 36 37 38 39 40
15 16 17 18 19 20 21 22 23 24 25 26
1 2   3 4 5 6 7 8 9 10 11 12 13 14

AD42345

74 75 76 77 78 79 80
67 68 69 70 71 72 73
60 61 62 63 64 65 66
53 54 55 56 57 58 59

Component/circuit description	ECM pin	Signal	Condition	Typical value
Accelerator pedal position (APP) sensor	11	⇨	Ignition ON	5 V
	23	⅂	Ignition ON	0 V
	24	⬅	Ignition ON – accelerator pedal released	0,4 V
	24	⬅	Ignition ON – accelerator pedal depressed	4,4 V
Accelerator pedal position (APP) switch	12	⬅	Ignition ON – accelerator pedal released	0,1 V
	12	⬅	Ignition ON – accelerator pedal depressed	2,8 V
	25	⅂	Ignition ON	0 V
Alternator – with engine coolant heater	22	⬅	Engine idling	0 V
Brake pedal position (BPP) switch I	20	⬅	Ignition OFF – brake pedal released	0 V
	20	⬅	Ignition OFF – brake pedal depressed	11-14 V
Brake pedal position (BPP) switch II	9	⬅	Ignition ON – brake pedal released	11-14 V
	9	⬅	Ignition ON – brake pedal depressed	0 V
Clutch pedal position (CPP) switch	46	⬅	Ignition ON – clutch pedal released	11-14 V
	46	⬅	Ignition ON – clutch pedal depressed	0 V
Crankshaft position (CKP) sensor	67	⬅	Engine idling	3,8 V ac
	67	⬅	Engine idling	5 V/5 ms per division 〰〰 6
	69	⅂	Engine idling	0 V
Earth	1		Ignition ON	0 V
	27		Ignition ON	0 V
	71		Ignition ON	0 V
Earth – without engine coolant heater	22	⬅	Engine idling	0 V
Engine control relay	2	⬅	Ignition OFF	0 V
	2	⬅	Ignition ON	11-14 V
	28	⬅	Ignition OFF	0 V
	28	⬅	Ignition ON	11-14 V
	33	⅂⇨	Ignition OFF	11-14 V
	33	⅂⇨	Ignition ON	0-1 V
Engine coolant heater relay I	17	⅂⇨	Engine idling – relay contacts open	11-14 V
	17	⅂⇨	Engine idling – relay contacts closed	0-1 V
Engine coolant heater relay II	34	⅂⇨	Engine idling – relay contacts open	11-14 V
	34	⅂⇨	Engine idling – relay contacts closed	0-1 V

Component/circuit description	ECM pin	Signal	Condition	Typical value
Engine coolant temperature (ECT) sensor	54	←	Ignition ON – coolant temp. 20°C	3,5 V
	54	←	Ignition ON – coolant temp. 80°C	1,4 V
	70	⌐	Ignition ON	0 V
Exhaust gas recirculation (EGR) solenoid	29	⊐▷	Ignition ON	11-14 V
	29	⊐▷	Engine idling	5 V/5 ms per division ⌁ 4
Exhaust gas recirculation (EGR) throttle control valve	15	⊐▷	Ignition ON	11-14 V
	15	⊐▷	Engine idling – throttle valve closed	0-1 V
	15	⊐▷	Above 2200 rpm – throttle valve open	11-14 V
Fuel injection timing solenoid	79	⊐▷	Ignition ON	11-14 V
	79	⊐▷	Engine idling	2 V/10 ms per division ⌁ 10
Fuel quantity adjuster	59	⊐▷	Engine idling	11,3 V
	59	⊐▷	Engine idling	2 V/2 ms per division ⌁ 5
	66	⊐▷	Engine idling	11,3 V
	66	⊐▷	Engine idling	2 V/2 ms per division ⌁ 5
	80	⊐▷	Engine idling	11,3 V
	80	⊐▷	Engine idling	2 V/2 ms per division ⌁ 5
Fuel quantity adjuster position sensor	56	←	Ignition ON	2,5 V
	56	←	Engine idling	0,5 V/0,1 ms per division ⌁ 8
	57	⇒	Ignition ON	2,5 V
	64	←	Ignition ON	2,5 V
	64	←	Engine idling	0,5 V/0,1 ms per division ⌁ 8
Fuel shut-off solenoid	77	⇒	Ignition OFF	0 V
	77	⇒	Ignition ON	11-14 V
Fuel temperature sensor	53	←	Ignition ON – fuel temp. 20°C	3,5 V
	76	⌐	Ignition ON	0 V
Glow plug relay	42	⊐▷	Ignition ON – glow plugs ON	0-1 V
	42	⊐▷	Ignition ON – glow plugs OFF	11-14 V
Glow plug warning lamp	41	⊐▷	Ignition ON – lamp ON	0 V
	41	⊐▷	Ignition ON – lamp OFF	10,5 V
Ignition switch	47	←	Ignition OFF	0 V
	47	←	Ignition ON	11-14 V
Injector needle lift sensor	55	⌐	Engine idling	0 V
	62	←	Engine idling	0,02 V ac
	62	←	Engine idling	0,2 V/1 ms per division ⌁ 7
Immobilizer control module	45	⟷	Ignition ON	11-14 V
	45	⟷	Engine idling	11-14 V
Instrumentation control module – engine speed signal	6	⇒	Engine idling	30 Hz
	6	⇒	Engine idling	5 V/10 ms per division ⌁ 2
Instrumentation control module – fuel consumption signal	18	⇒		1
Instrumentation control module – vehicle speed signal	51	←	Ignition ON – vehicle pushed	0 V or 11-14 V (switching)
Intake air temperature (IAT) sensor	13	←	Ignition ON – air temp. 20°C	3,75 V
	25	⌐	Ignition ON	0 V
Transmission kick-down switch	8	←		1
	25	⌐	Ignition ON	0 V

1 Connected pin - no test data available

VOLKSWAGEN

Bosch EDC 15P

Model:	Engine code:	Year:
Polo 1,9 TDI PD	ATD/AXR	2002-06
Polo 1,9 TDI PD	ASZ	2003-06

ECM harness multi-plug

Terminal side

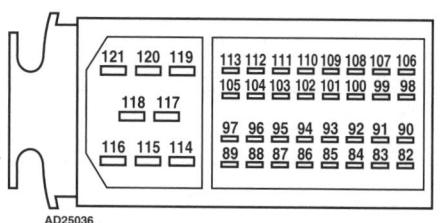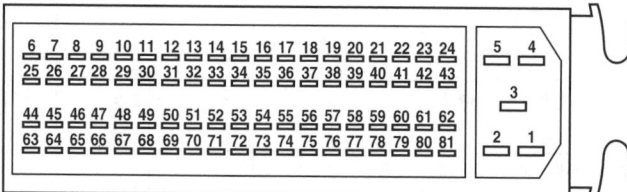

AD25036

Wire side

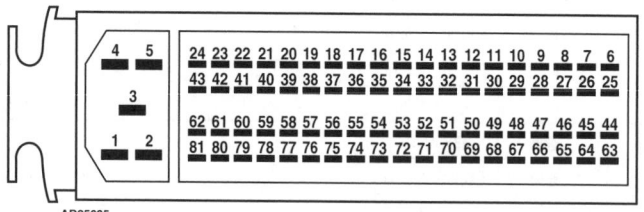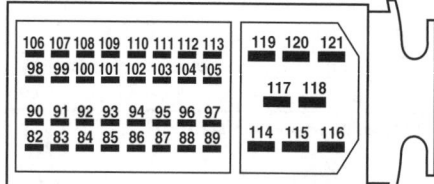

AD25035

Component/circuit description	ECM pin	Signal	Condition	Typical value	Oscilloscope setting*	Wave form
Accelerator pedal position (APP) sensor	12	⇒	Ignition ON	5 V		
	50	⊐⌐	Ignition ON	0 V		
	69	⬅	Ignition ON – accelerator pedal released	0,4 V		
	69	⬅	Ignition ON – accelerator pedal fully depressed	4,4 V		
Accelerator pedal position (APP) switch	51	⊐⌐	Ignition ON	0 V		
	70	⬅	Ignition ON – accelerator pedal released	0,2 V		
	70	⬅	Ignition ON – accelerator pedal depressed	5 V		
Alternator, charging signal	38	⇒	Ignition ON		2 V/20 ms	〰43
Auxiliary heater switch – if fitted	15			1		
Brake pedal position (BPP) switch	32	⬅	Ignition OFF – brake pedal released	0 V		
	32	⬅	Ignition OFF – brake pedal depressed	11-14 V		
	65	⬅	Ignition ON – brake pedal released	11-14 V		
	65	⬅	Ignition ON – brake pedal depressed	0 V		
Camshaft position (CMP) sensor	101	⊐⌐	Ignition ON	0 V		
	109	⬅	Engine idling		2 V/0,5 ms	〰58
CAN data bus – high	7	⬅⇒		1		
CAN data bus – low	6	⬅⇒		1		
Clutch pedal position (CPP) switch	66	⬅	Ignition ON – clutch pedal released	11-14 V		
	66	⬅	Ignition ON – clutch pedal depressed	0 V		
Crankshaft position (CKP) sensor	102	⬅	Ignition ON	2,5 V		
	102	⬅	Engine idling	1,9 V ac		
	102	⬅	Engine idling		2 V/1 ms	〰25
	110	⬅	Ignition ON	2,5 V		
	110	⬅	Engine idling	1,9 V ac		
	110	⬅	Engine idling		2 V/1 ms	Reversed 〰25
Cruise control master switch	14	⬅	Ignition ON – selector switch set to 'OFF'	0 V		
	14	⬅	Ignition ON – selector switch set to 'ON'	11-14 V		

* Suggested settings - Voltage/time per division

| //Autodata

Component/circuit description	ECM pin	Signal	Condition	Typical value	Oscilloscope setting*	Wave form
Cruise control selector switch	14	⬅	Ignition ON – selector switch set to 'OFF'	0 V		
	14	⬅	Ignition ON – selector switch set to 'ON'	11-14 V		
Data link connector (DLC)	16	⬅➡		1		
Earth	4		Ignition ON	0 V		
	5		Ignition ON	0 V		
Engine control (EC) relay	1	⬅	Ignition OFF	0 V		
	1	⬅	Ignition ON	11-14 V		
	2	⬅	Ignition OFF	0 V		
	2	⬅	Ignition ON	11-14 V		
	18	⊐➡	Ignition OFF	11-14 V		
	18	⊐➡	Ignition ON	0-1 V		
Engine coolant blower motor relay – ASZ without AC	11	⊐➡		1		
Engine coolant heater relay 1, low output – if fitted	21	⊐➡		1		
Engine coolant heater relay 2, high output – if fitted	22	⊐➡		1		
Engine coolant temperature (ECT) sensor	104	⊐–	Ignition ON	0 V		
	112	⬅	Ignition ON – coolant temp. 10°C	4 V		
	112	⬅	Ignition ON – coolant temp. 80°C	1,2 V		
Exhaust gas recirculation (EGR) solenoid	61	⊐➡	Ignition ON	11-14 V		
	61	⊐➡	Engine idling		5 V/1 ms	〰 2
Fuel lift pump relay	80	⊐➡	Ignition ON	0-1 V briefly then 11-14 V		
	80	⊐➡	Engine idling	0-1 V		
Fuel temperature sensor	103	⊐–	Ignition ON	0 V		
	111	⬅	Ignition ON – fuel temp. 5°C	4,6 V		
Glow plug relay	42	⊐➡	Ignition ON – glow plugs ON	0-1 V		
	42	⊐➡	Ignition ON – glow plugs OFF	11-14 V		
Ignition switch	37	⬅	Ignition OFF	0 V		
	37	⬅	Ignition ON	11-14 V		
	37	⬅	Engine cranking	11-14 V		
	37	⬅	Engine idling	11-14 V		
Ignition switch – ATD/ASZ	88	⬅	Ignition OFF	0 V		
	88	⬅	Ignition ON	11-14 V		
	88	⬅	Engine cranking	0 V		
	88	⬅	Engine idling	11-14 V		
Injector 1	114	➡	Ignition ON	0,3 V		
	116	➡	Ignition ON	0,3 V		
	116 (114)	➡	Engine idling	2,2 ms		
	116 (114)	➡	Engine idling		10 V/0,5 ms	〰 57
Injector 2	114	➡	Ignition ON	0,3 V		
	117	➡	Ignition ON	0,3 V		
	117 (114)	➡	Engine idling	2,2 ms		
	117 (114)	➡	Engine idling		10 V/0,5 ms	〰 57
Injector 3	114	➡	Ignition ON	0,3 V		
	118	➡	Ignition ON	0,3 V		
	118 (114)	➡	Engine idling	2,2 ms		
	118 (114)	➡	Engine idling		10 V/0,5 ms	〰 57

★ Suggested settings - Voltage/time per division

Component/circuit description	ECM pin	Signal	Condition	Typical value	Oscilloscope setting*	Wave form
Injector 4	114	⇨	Ignition ON	0,3 V		
	121	⇨	Ignition ON	0,3 V		
	121 (114)	⇨	Engine idling	2,2 ms		
	121 (114)	⇨	Engine idling		10 V/0,5 ms	〰 57
Instrumentation control module – vehicle speed signal	20	⟵	Ignition ON – vehicle pushed	0 V or 10 V min. (switching)		
Intake air temperature (IAT) sensor	52	⌐—	Ignition ON	0 V		
	73	⟵	Ignition ON – air temp. 10°C	3 V		
Intake manifold air control actuator – AXR	75			1		
	81			1		
Intake manifold air control solenoid – ASZ/ATD	81	⌐⊳	Ignition ON	11-14 V		
	81	⌐⊳	Engine idling	11-14 V		
	81	⌐⊳	Engine idling – switch ignition OFF	0-1 V for 2,5 secs., 11-14 V for 0,5 sec., then 0-1 V		
Mass air flow (MAF) sensor	30	⇨	Ignition ON	5 V		
	49	⌐—	Ignition ON	0 V		
	68	⟵	Ignition ON	1 V		
	68	⟵	Engine idling	1,5-2,1 V		
	68	⟵	3000 rpm	3,2 V		
Transmission kick-down switch	51	⌐—	Ignition ON	0 V		
	63	⟵	Ignition ON – accelerator pedal released	5 V		
	63	⟵	Ignition ON – accelerator pedal fully depressed	0 V		
Turbocharger (TC) boost pressure sensor	31	⇨	Ignition ON	5 V		
	52	⌐—	Ignition ON	0 V		
	71	⟵	Ignition ON	1,6 V		
	71	⟵	Engine idling	1,7 V		
Turbocharger (TC) wastegate regulating valve	62	⌐⊳	Ignition ON	11-14 V		
	62	⌐⊳	Engine idling	11-14 V		
	62	⌐⊳	Engine idling – accelerator pedal briefly fully depressed	0-1 V briefly		
	62	⌐⊳	Engine running – valve not operating	11-14 V		
	62	⌐⊳	Engine running – valve operating	0-1 V		

*Suggested settings - Voltage/time per division

1 Connected pin - no test data available or random digital signal

Model:	Engine code:	Year:
Beetle 1,9 TDI	ALH	05/99-04

ECM harness multi-plug

Terminal side

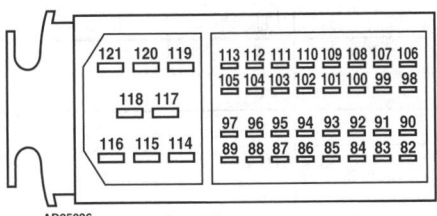

AD25036

Wire side

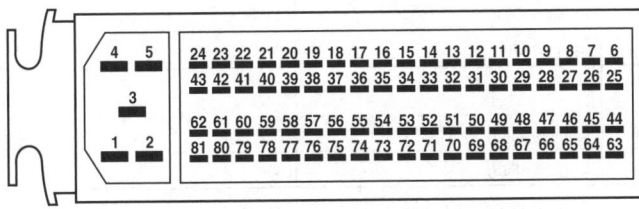

AD25035

Component/circuit description	ECM pin	Signal	Condition	Typical value	Oscilloscope setting★	Wave form
Accelerator pedal position (APP) sensor	12	⟹	Ignition ON	5 V		
	50	⅂	Ignition ON	0 V		
Accelerator pedal position (APP) sensor – →12/01	63	⟵	Ignition ON – accelerator pedal released	0,4 V		
	63	⟵	Ignition ON – accelerator pedal fully depressed	4,4 V		
Accelerator pedal position (APP) sensor – 01/02→	69	⟵	Ignition ON – accelerator pedal released	0,4 V		
	69	⟵	Ignition ON – accelerator pedal fully depressed	4,4 V		
Accelerator pedal position (APP) switch	51	⅂	Ignition ON	0 V		
Accelerator pedal position (APP) switch – →12/01	69	⟵	Ignition ON – accelerator pedal released	0 V		
	69	⟵	Ignition ON – accelerator pedal depressed	2,8 V		
Accelerator pedal position (APP) switch – 01/02→	70	⟵	Ignition ON – accelerator pedal released	0 V		
	70	⟵	Ignition ON – accelerator pedal depressed	2,8 V		
Alternator	38	⟵		1		
Brake pedal position (BPP) switch	32	⟵	Ignition OFF – brake pedal released	0 V		
	32	⟵	Ignition OFF – brake pedal depressed	11-14 V		
	65	⟵	Ignition OFF – brake pedal released	11-14 V		
	65	⟵	Ignition OFF – brake pedal depressed	0 V		
CAN data bus – high	6	⟷		1		
CAN data bus – low	7	⟷		1		
Clutch pedal position (CPP) switch	66	⟵	Ignition ON – clutch pedal released	11-14 V		
	66	⟵	Ignition ON – clutch pedal depressed	0 V		
Crankshaft position (CKP) sensor	86	⅂	Engine idling	0 V		
	102	⅂	Engine idling	0 V		
	110	⟵	Engine idling	3,8 V ac		
	110	⟵	Engine idling		5 V/5 ms	〰 6

★ Suggested settings - Voltage/time per division

Component/circuit description	ECM pin	Signal	Condition	Typical value	Oscilloscope setting*	Wave form
Crankshaft position (CKP) sensor – screened lead	86	⊣—	Engine idling	0 V		
Cruise control master switch	14			1		
	45			1		
	46			1		
Cruise control selector switch	14			1		
	44			1		
Earth	4		Ignition ON	0 V		
	5		Ignition ON	0 V		
Engine control (EC) relay	1	←	Ignition OFF	0 V		
	1	←	Ignition ON	11-14 V		
	2	←	Ignition OFF	0 V		
	2	←	Ignition ON	11-14 V		
	18	⊣▷	Ignition OFF	11-14 V		
	18	⊣▷	Ignition ON	0-1 V		
Engine coolant blower motor control module/AC compressor control module	29	⇒		1		
	34	←	Engine idling – AC OFF	0 V		
	34	←	Engine idling – AC ON	11-14 V		
Engine coolant heater relay 1, low output – if fitted	21	⊣▷	Engine idling – relay contacts open	11-14 V		
	21	⊣▷	Engine idling – relay contacts closed	0-1 V		
Engine coolant heater relay 2, high output – if fitted	22	⊣▷	Engine idling – relay contacts open	11-14 V		
	22	⊣▷	Engine idling – relay contacts closed	0-1 V		
Engine coolant temperature (ECT) sensor	104	⊣—	Ignition ON	0 V		
	112	←	Ignition ON – coolant temp. 20°C	3,5 V		
	112	←	Ignition ON – coolant temp. 80°C	1,4 V		
Exhaust gas recirculation (EGR) solenoid	61	⊣▷	Ignition ON	11-14 V		
	61	⊣▷	Engine running – valve operating		5 V/5 ms	∿ 4
Fuel injection timing solenoid	114	⊣▷	Ignition ON	11-14 V		
	114	⊣▷	Engine idling		2 V/10 ms	∿ 10
Fuel quantity adjuster	116	⊣▷	Ignition ON	11,3 V then 11-14 V		
	116	⊣▷	Engine idling		2 V/2 ms	∿ 5
	121	⊣▷	Ignition ON	11,3 V then 11-14 V		
	121	⊣▷	Engine idling		2 V/2 ms	∿ 5
Fuel quantity adjuster position sensor	99	←	Ignition ON	2,5 V		
	99	←	Engine idling		0,5 V/0,1 ms	∿ 8
	106	⇒	Ignition ON	2,5 V		
	108	←	Ignition ON	2,5 V		
	108	←	Engine idling		0,5 V/0,1 ms	∿ 8
Fuel shut-off solenoid	120	⇒	Engine idling	11-14 V		
	120	⇒	Ignition ON	11-14 V then 0 V		
Fuel temperature sensor	103	⊣—	Ignition ON	0 V		
	111	←	Ignition ON – fuel temp. 20°C	3,5 V		
Glow plug relay – →12/01	28			1		
	33			1		
Glow plug relay – 01/02→	42	⊣▷	Ignition ON – glow plugs ON	0-1 V		
	42	⊣▷	Ignition ON – glow plugs OFF	11-14 V		

* Suggested settings - Voltage/time per division

Component/circuit description	ECM pin	Signal	Condition	Typical value	Oscilloscope setting*	Wave form
Glow plug warning lamp – →12/01	40	⊐⊢▷	Ignition ON – lamp ON	0-1 V		
	40	⊐⊢▷	Ignition ON – lamp OFF	11-14 V		
Ignition switch	37	⟵	Ignition OFF	0 V		
	37	⟵	Ignition ON	11-14 V		
Ignition switch – 01/02→	88	⟵	Ignition OFF	0 V		
	88	⟵	Ignition ON	11-14 V		
	88	⟵	Engine cranking	0 V		
	88	⟵	Engine idling	11-14 V		
Injector needle lift sensor	101	⊐⊢	Engine idling	0 V		
	109	⟵	Engine idling	0,02 V ac		
	109	⟵	Engine idling		0,2 V/1 ms	∿∿ 7
Injector needle lift sensor – screened lead	86	⊐⊢	Engine idling	0 V		
Instrumentation control module – immobilization/diagnosis signal	16	⟵▷	Ignition ON	11-14 V		
	16	⟵▷	Engine idling	11-14 V		
Instrumentation control module – vehicle speed signal	20	⟵	Ignition ON – vehicle pushed	0 V or 10 V min. (switching)		
Intake air temperature (IAT) sensor	52	⊐⊢	Ignition ON	0 V		
	73	⟵	Ignition ON – air temp. 20°C	3,75 V		
Intake manifold air control solenoid	81	⊐⊢▷	Ignition ON	11-14 V		
	81	⊐⊢▷	Engine idling	11-14 V		
	81	⊐⊢▷	Engine idling – switch ignition OFF	0-1 V for 2,5 secs., 11-14 V for 0,5 sec., then 0-1 V		
Mass air flow (MAF) sensor	30	▷	Ignition ON	5 V		
	49	⊐⊢	Ignition ON	0 V		
	68	⟵	Ignition ON	0,28 V		
	68	⟵	Engine idling	1 V		
	68	⟵	Engine running – accelerator pedal briefly fully depressed	4,35 V (briefly)		
Spare cable	27			1		
	47			1		
Spare cable – →12/01	24			1		
	42			1		
Spare cable – 01/02→	33			1		
Transmission control module (TCM) – kick-down signal	9	▷		1		
Transmission kick-down switch	51	⊐⊢	Ignition ON	0 V		
Transmission kick-down switch – →12/01	70	⟵		1		
Transmission kick-down switch – 01/02→	63	⟵		1		
Turbocharger (TC) boost pressure sensor	31	▷	Ignition ON	5 V		
	52	⊐⊢	Ignition ON	0 V		
	71	⟵	Ignition ON	1,9 V		
	71	⟵	Engine idling	1,85 V		
	71	⟵	Engine running – accelerator pedal briefly fully depressed	3,65 V (briefly)		
Turbocharger (TC) wastegate regulating valve	62	⊐⊢▷	Ignition ON	11-14 V		
	62	⊐⊢▷	Engine running – valve not operating	11-14 V		
	62	⊐⊢▷	Engine running – valve operating	0-1 V		

*Suggested settings - Voltage/time per division

1 Connected pin - no test data available or random digital signal

VOLKSWAGEN

Bosch EDC 15P

Model:	Engine code:	Year:
Beetle 1,9 TDI PD	ATD	2000-06
Beetle Convertible 1,9 TDI PD	AXR	2003-06

ECM harness multi-plug

Terminal side

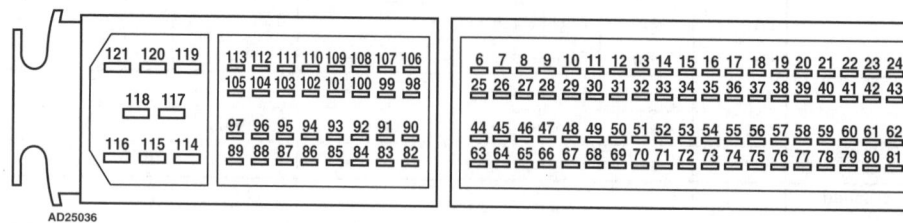

AD25036

Wire side

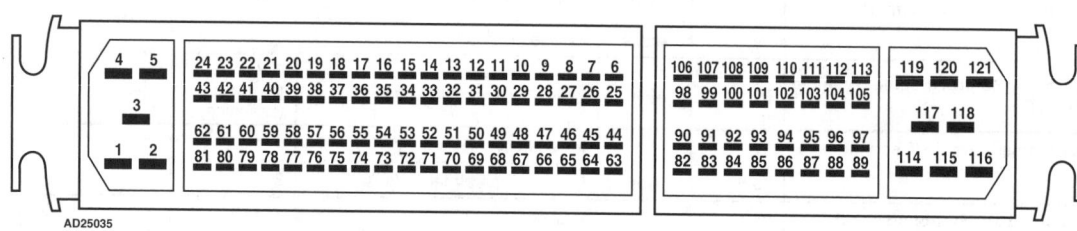

AD25035

Component/circuit description	ECM pin	Signal	Condition	Typical value	Oscilloscope setting*	Wave form
AC compressor control module/engine coolant blower motor control module	11			①		
	29			①		
	34			①		
AC/heater function control panel	34			①		
Accelerator pedal position (APP) sensor	12	⇨	Ignition ON	5 V		
	50	⅂	Ignition ON	0 V		
	69	⬅	Ignition ON – accelerator pedal released	0,4 V		
	69	⬅	Ignition ON – accelerator pedal fully depressed	4,4 V		
Accelerator pedal position (APP) switch	51	⅂	Ignition ON	0 V		
	70	⬅	Ignition ON – accelerator pedal released	0,2 V		
	70	⬅	Ignition ON – accelerator pedal depressed	5 V		
Alternator, charging signal	38	⇨	Ignition ON		2 V/20 ms	〰 43
Brake pedal position (BPP) switch	32	⬅	Ignition OFF – brake pedal released	0 V		
	32	⬅	Ignition OFF – brake pedal depressed	11-14 V		
	65	⬅	Ignition ON – brake pedal released	11-14 V		
	65	⬅	Ignition ON – brake pedal depressed	0 V		
Camshaft position (CMP) sensor	101	⅂	Ignition ON	0 V		
	109	⬅	Engine idling		2 V/0,5 ms	〰 58
CAN data bus – high	7	⬅⇨		①		
CAN data bus – low	6	⬅⇨		①		
Clutch pedal position (CPP) switch	66	⬅	Ignition ON – clutch pedal released	11-14 V		
	66	⬅	Ignition ON – clutch pedal depressed	0 V		

* Suggested settings - Voltage/time per division

/Autodata

Component/circuit description	ECM pin	Signal	Condition	Typical value	Oscilloscope setting*	Wave form
Crankshaft position (CKP) sensor	102	←	Ignition ON	2,5 V		
	102	←	Engine idling	1,9 V ac		
	102	←	Engine idling		2 V/1 ms	⟋⟍ 25
	110	←	Ignition ON	2,5 V		
	110	←	Engine idling	1,9 V ac		
	110	←	Engine idling		2 V/1 ms	Reversed ⟋⟍ 25
Cruise control master switch	14	←	Ignition ON – selector switch set to 'OFF'	0 V		
	14	←	Ignition ON – selector switch set to 'ON'	11-14 V		
	44	←	Ignition ON – master switch released	0 V		
	44	←	Ignition ON – master switch depressed	11-14 V		
Cruise control selector switch	14	←	Ignition ON – selector switch set to 'OFF'	0 V		
	14	←	Ignition ON – selector switch set to 'ON'	11-14 V		
	45	←	Ignition ON – selector switch set to 'ON'	0 V		
	45	←	Ignition ON – selector switch set to 'RES'	11-14 V		
	46	←	Ignition ON – selector switch set to 'OFF'	0 V		
	46	←	Ignition ON – selector switch set to 'ON'	11-14 V		
Earth	4		Ignition ON	0 V		
	5		Ignition ON	0 V		
Engine control (EC) relay	1	←	Ignition OFF	0 V		
	1	←	Ignition ON	11-14 V		
	2	←	Ignition OFF	0 V		
	2	←	Ignition ON	11-14 V		
	18	⊐▷	Ignition OFF	11-14 V		
	18	⊐▷	Ignition ON	0-1 V		
Engine coolant blower motor relay – without AC	11	⊐▷		①		
Engine coolant heater relay 1, low output – if fitted	21	⊐▷		①		
Engine coolant heater relay 2, high output – if fitted	22	⊐▷		①		
Engine coolant temperature (ECT) sensor	104	⊐—	Ignition ON	0 V		
	112	←	Ignition ON – coolant temp. 10°C	4 V		
	112	←	Ignition ON – coolant temp. 80°C	1,2 V		
Exhaust gas recirculation (EGR) solenoid 1	61	⊐▷	Ignition ON	11-14 V		
	61	⊐▷	Engine idling		5 V/1 ms	⟋⟍ 2
Exhaust gas recirculation (EGR) solenoid 2 – AXR	59	⊐▷	Ignition ON	11-14 V		
	59	⊐▷	Engine running – valve not operating	11-14 V		
	59	⊐▷	Engine running – valve operating	0-1 V		
Fuel lift pump relay	80	⊐▷	Ignition ON	0-1 V briefly then 11-14 V		
	80	⊐▷	Engine idling	0-1 V		
Fuel temperature sensor	103	⊐—	Ignition ON	0 V		
	111	←	Ignition ON – fuel temp. 5°C	4,6 V		

* Suggested settings - Voltage/time per division

VOLKSWAGEN

Component/circuit description	ECM pin	Signal	Condition	Typical value	Oscilloscope setting*	Wave form
Glow plug relay	42	⊐▷	Ignition ON – glow plugs ON	0-1 V		
	42	⊐▷	Ignition ON – glow plugs OFF	11-14 V		
Ignition switch	37	⬅	Ignition OFF	0 V		
	37	⬅	Ignition ON	11-14 V		
	37	⬅	Engine cranking	11-14 V		
	37	⬅	Engine idling	11-14 V		
	88	⬅	Ignition OFF	0 V		
	88	⬅	Ignition ON	11-14 V		
	88	⬅	Engine cranking	0 V		
	88	⬅	Engine idling	11-14 V		
Injector 1	114	⇨	Ignition ON	0,3 V		
	116	⇨	Ignition ON	0,3 V		
	116 (114)	⇨	Engine idling	2,2 ms		
	116 (114)	⇨	Engine idling		10 V/0,5 ms	〰 57
Injector 2	114	⇨	Ignition ON	0,3 V		
	117	⇨	Ignition ON	0,3 V		
	117 (114)	⇨	Engine idling	2,2 ms		
	117 (114)	⇨	Engine idling		10 V/0,5 ms	〰 57
Injector 3	114	⇨	Ignition ON	0,3 V		
	118	⇨	Ignition ON	0,3 V		
	118 (114)	⇨	Engine idling	2,2 ms		
	118 (114)	⇨	Engine idling		10 V/0,5 ms	〰 57
Injector 4	114	⇨	Ignition ON	0,3 V		
	121	⇨	Ignition ON	0,3 V		
	121 (114)	⇨	Engine idling	2,2 ms		
	121 (114)	⇨	Engine idling		10 V/0,5 ms	〰 57
Instrument panel, immobilization/ diagnosis signal	16	⬅⇨		1		
Instrumentation control module – vehicle speed signal	20	⬅	Ignition ON – vehicle pushed	0 V or 10 V min. (switching)		
Intake air temperature (IAT) sensor	52	⊐—	Ignition ON	0 V		
	73	⬅	Ignition ON – air temp. 10°C	3 V		
Intake manifold air control actuator – AXR	75			1		
	81			1		
Intake manifold air control solenoid – ATD	81	⊐▷	Ignition ON	11-14 V		
	81	⊐▷	Engine idling	11-14 V		
	81	⊐▷	Engine idling – switch ignition OFF	0-1 V for 2,5 secs., 11-14 V for 0,5 sec., then 0-1 V		

* Suggested settings - Voltage/time per division

Component/circuit description	ECM pin	Signal	Condition	Typical value	Oscilloscope setting*	Wave form
Mass air flow (MAF) sensor	30	⇨	Ignition ON	5 V		
	49	⊐—	Ignition ON	0 V		
	68	⬅	Ignition ON	1 V		
	68	⬅	Engine idling	1,5-2,1 V		
	68	⬅	3000 rpm	3,2 V		
Spare cable	27			1		
	47			1		
Transmission kick-down switch	51	⊐—	Ignition ON	0 V		
	63	⬅	Ignition ON – accelerator pedal released	5 V		
	63	⬅	Ignition ON – accelerator pedal fully depressed	0 V		
Turbocharger (TC) boost pressure sensor	31	⇨	Ignition ON	5 V		
	52	⊐—	Ignition ON	0 V		
	71	⬅	Ignition ON	1,6 V		
	71	⬅	Engine idling	1,7 V		
Turbocharger (TC) wastegate regulating valve	62	⊐⇨	Ignition ON	11-14 V		
	62	⊐⇨	Engine idling	11-14 V		
	62	⊐⇨	Engine idling – accelerator pedal briefly fully depressed	0-1 V briefly		
	62	⊐⇨	Engine running – valve not operating	11-14 V		
	62	⊐⇨	Engine running – valve operating	0-1 V		

*Suggested settings - Voltage/time per division

1 Connected pin - no test data available or random digital signal

VOLKSWAGEN
Bosch Motronic
MED9.5.10

Model:	Engine code:	Year:
Golf 1,4 FSI	BKG	2003-06
Golf 1,6 FSI	BAG	2003-06

ECM harness multi-plug

Terminal side

Wire side

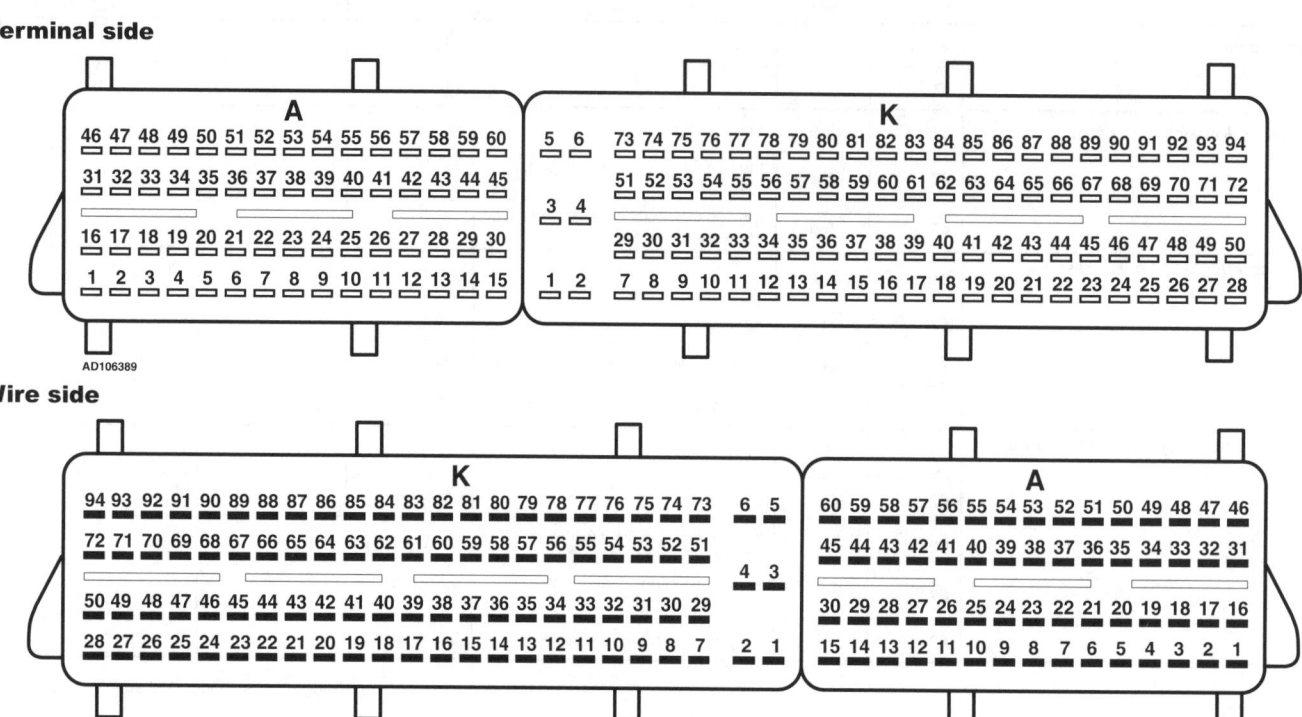

AD106389

AD106390

Component/circuit description	ECM pin	Signal	Condition	Typical value	Oscilloscope setting*	Wave form
Accelerator pedal position (APP) sensor	K11	⌐⌐	Ignition ON	0 V		
	K12	←	Ignition ON – accelerator pedal released	0,3 V		
	K12	←	Ignition ON – accelerator pedal fully depressed	2 V		
	K13	⇒	Ignition ON	5 V		
	K33	⌐⌐	Ignition ON	0 V		
	K34	←	Ignition ON – accelerator pedal released	0,7 V		
	K34	←	Ignition ON – accelerator pedal fully depressed	4 V		
	K35	⇒	Ignition ON	5 V		
Alternator	K64	⇒	Ignition ON	9,8 V	5 V/10 ms	〜〜 68
	K64	⇒	Engine idling		5 V/10 ms	〜〜 39
Battery	K92	←	Ignition OFF	11-14 V		
Brake pedal position (BPP) switch	K24	←	Ignition ON – brake pedal released	11-14 V		
	K24	←	Ignition ON – brake pedal depressed	0 V		
	K46	←	Ignition OFF – brake pedal released	0 V		
	K46	←	Ignition OFF – brake pedal depressed	11-14 V		
Brake system vacuum sensor	K31	⌐⌐	Ignition ON	0 V		
	K37	⇒	Ignition ON	5 V		
	K83	←	Ignition ON – brake servo evacuated	4 V		
	K83	←	Engine idling	0,8 V		

* Suggested settings - Voltage/time per division

Component/circuit description	ECM pin	Signal	Condition	Typical value	Oscilloscope setting*	Wave form
Clutch position potentiometer	K18	←	Ignition ON – clutch pedal released	11,7 V		
	K18	←	Ignition ON – clutch pedal depressed	0 V		
Camshaft position (CMP) sensor	A10	⇒	Ignition ON	5 V		
	A23	←	Engine idling		2 V/50 ms	∿ 14
	A42	⊣	Ignition ON	0 V		
Camshaft position (CMP) actuator – 1,6	A5	⊣▷	Ignition ON	11-14 V		
	A5	⊣▷	Engine idling		5 V/0,5 ms	∿ 4
CAN data bus – high	K68	◄►		1		
CAN data bus – low	K67	◄►		1		
Crankshaft position (CKP) sensor	A36	⊣	Ignition ON	0 V		
	A41	⇒	Ignition ON	5 V		
	A51	←	Engine idling		2 V/2 ms	∿ 73
Data link connector (DLC)	K86	◄►	Ignition ON	10 V		
	K86	◄►	Engine idling	12,2 V		
Earth	K1		Ignition ON	0 V		
	K2		Ignition ON	0 V		
	K4		Ignition ON	0 V		
Engine coolant blower motor control module	K71	⇒	Ignition ON	89%	5 V/10 ms	∿ 99
	K71	⇒	Engine idling	81%	5 V/20 ms	∿ 45
Engine coolant temperature (ECT) sensor 1	A27	←	Ignition ON – coolant temp. 10°C	2,7 V		
	A42	⊣	Ignition ON	0 V		
Engine coolant temperature (ECT) sensor 2	K57	←	Ignition ON – coolant temp. 10°C	2,7 V		
	K57	←	Engine idling – engine hot	0,85 V		
	K31	⊣	Ignition ON	0 V		
Evaporative emission (EVAP) canister purge valve	A35	⊣▷	Ignition ON	11-14 V		
	A35	⊣▷	Engine running – engine hot – valve operating	1-99%	10 V/20 ms	∿ 20
Exhaust gas recirculation (EGR) valve actuator	A1	⇒	Engine idling – valve operating		2 V/1 ms	∿ 71
	A2	⇒	Engine idling	11-14 V		
Exhaust gas recirculation (EGR) valve position sensor	A10	⇒	Ignition ON	5 V		
	A42	⊣	Ignition ON	0 V		
	A59	←	Ignition ON	0,86 V		
	A59	←	Engine idling	0,93 V		
Exhaust gas temperature sensor	K31	⊣	Ignition ON	0 V		
	K79	←	Ignition ON – engine cold	0,87 V		
	K79	←	Engine idling – engine hot	1,55 V		
Fuel lift pump control module	K48	⇒	Engine idling		5 V/50 ms	∿ 39
Fuel pressure regulator control solenoid	A19	⊣▷	Ignition ON	11-14 V		
	A19	⊣▷	Engine idling		10 V/50 ms	∿ 20
Fuel rail pressure (FRP) sensor	A10	⇒	Ignition ON	5 V		
	A42	⊣	Ignition ON	0 V		
	A43	←	Ignition ON	1,96 V		
	A43	←	Engine idling	2 V		
	A43	←	Engine running – 3000 rpm	3,2 V		
Fuel system pressure sensor – low pressure	A10	⇒	Ignition ON	5 V		
	A42	⊣	Ignition ON	0 V		
	A55	←	Ignition ON	0,62 V		
	A55	←	Engine idling	2,1 V		

* Suggested settings - Voltage/time per division

Component/circuit description	ECM pin	Signal	Condition	Typical value	Oscilloscope setting*	Wave form
Heated oxygen sensor (HO2S)	K55	←	Engine idling	2,9 V		
	K56	⇨	Engine idling	3 V		
	K77	←	Engine idling	2,19 V		
	K78	←	Engine idling	2,54 V		
Heated oxygen sensor (HO2S) – heater control	K7	⇥⇨	Ignition ON	11-14 V		
	K7	⇥⇨	Engine idling		2 V/0,2 sec.	〜〜 55
Heater function control module	K30			1		
Ignition amplifier 1	A7	⇨	Ignition ON	0 V		
	A7	⇨	Engine idling		2 V/20 ms	〜〜 106
Ignition amplifier 2	A21	⇨	Ignition ON	0 V		
	A21	⇨	Engine idling		2 V/20 ms	〜〜 106
Ignition amplifier 3	A22	⇨	Ignition ON	0 V		
	A22	⇨	Engine idling		2 V/20 ms	〜〜 106
Ignition amplifier 4	A6	⇨	Ignition ON	0 V		
	A6	⇨	Engine idling		2 V/20 ms	〜〜 106
Ignition main circuits relay 1	K3	←	Ignition OFF	0 V		
	K3	←	Ignition ON	11-14 V		
	K5	←	Ignition OFF	0 V		
	K5	←	Ignition ON	11-14 V		
	K6	←	Ignition OFF	0 V		
	K6	←	Ignition ON	11-14 V		
	K69	⇥⇨	Ignition OFF	11-14 V		
	K69	⇥⇨	Ignition ON	0-1 V		
Ignition main circuits relay 2	K87	←	Ignition OFF	0 V		
	K87	←	Ignition ON	11-14 V		
Injector 1	A32	⇨	Ignition ON	0 V		
	A32	⇨	Engine idling – hot	1,8 ms	20 V/1 ms	〜〜 111
	A33	⇨	Ignition ON	0 V		
	A33	⇨	Engine idling – hot	1,8 ms	20 V/1 ms	〜〜 111
Injector 2	A31	⇨	Ignition ON	0 V		
	A31	⇨	Engine idling – hot	1,8 ms	20 V/1 ms	〜〜 111
	A48	⇨	Ignition ON	0 V		
	A48	⇨	Engine idling – hot	1,8 ms	20 V/1 ms	〜〜 111
Injector 3	A46	⇨	Ignition ON	0 V		
	A46	⇨	Engine idling – hot	1,8 ms	20 V/1 ms	〜〜 111
	A49	⇨	Ignition ON	0 V		
	A49	⇨	Engine idling – hot	1,8 ms	20 V/1 ms	〜〜 111
Injector 4	A34	⇨	Ignition ON	0 V		
	A34	⇨	Engine idling – hot	1,8 ms	20 V/1 ms	〜〜 111
	A47	⇨	Ignition ON	0 V		
	A47	⇨	Engine idling – hot	1,8 ms	20 V/1 ms	〜〜 111
Intake air temperature (IAT) sensor 1	A42	⊣	Ignition ON	0 V		
	A44	←	Ignition ON – air temp. 10°C	2,7 V		
Intake air temperature (IAT) sensor 2	A28	←	Ignition ON – air temp. 10°C	2,7 V		
	A42	⊣	Ignition ON	0 V		
Intake manifold air control actuator position sensor	A10	⇨	Ignition ON	5 V		
	A42	⊣	Ignition ON	0 V		
	A57	←	Ignition ON	1,44 V		
	A57	←	Engine idling	3,2 V		

* Suggested settings - Voltage/time per division

Component/circuit description	ECM pin	Signal	Condition	Typical value	Oscilloscope setting*	Wave form
Intake manifold air control solenoid	A45	→▷	Ignition ON	11-14 V		
	A45	→▷	Engine idling	0-1 V		
	A45	→▷	Engine running – full throttle briefly	11-14 V briefly		
Knock sensor (KS)	A8	⌐—	Ignition ON	0 V		
	A39	←	Ignition ON	2,2 V		
	A39	←	Engine idling – accelerate briefly		50 mV/1 ms	38
	A54	←	Ignition ON	2,2 V		
	A54	←	Engine idling – accelerate briefly		50 mV/1 ms	38
Manifold absolute pressure (MAP) sensor	A10	⇒	Ignition ON	5 V		
	A42	⌐—	Ignition ON	0 V		
	A58	←	Ignition ON	4 V		
	A58	←	Engine idling	1,2 V		
	A58	←	Engine running – full throttle briefly	3,8 V briefly		
Nitrogen oxide (NOx) sensor control module	K29	→▷	Ignition ON	11-14 V		
	K29	→▷	Engine idling		5 V/20 ms	68
	K53	←	Ignition ON	4,78 V		
	K53	←	Engine idling	4,81 V		
	K54	←	Ignition ON	2,4 V		
	K54	←	Engine idling	2,52 V		
	K76	←	Ignition ON	0,65 V		
	K76	←	Engine idling	0,8 V		
	K80	←	Ignition ON	2,48 V		
	K80	←	Engine idling	3,54 V		
	K81	←	Ignition ON	4,75 V		
	K81	←	Engine idling	2,19 V		
Steering column function control module	K25			[1]		
Throttle motor	A16	⇒	Ignition ON	3,19 V (after 3 seconds)		
	A16	⇒	Engine idling		2 V/10 ms	Intermittent 88
	A17	⇒	Ignition ON	3,19 V (after 3 seconds)		
	A17	⇒	Engine idling		2 V/1 ms	71
Throttle motor position sensor	A11	←	Ignition ON – accelerator pedal released	4,16 V briefly		
	A11	←	Ignition ON – accelerator pedal fully depressed	0,67 V briefly		
	A11	←	Engine idling	4,38 V		
	A12	⌐—	Ignition ON	0 V		
	A25	⇒	Ignition ON	5 V		
	A26	←	Ignition ON – accelerator pedal released	0,8 V		
	A26	←	Ignition ON – accelerator pedal fully depressed	4,3 V briefly		
	A26	←	Engine idling	0,76 V		

*Suggested settings - Voltage/time per division

[1] Connected pin - no test data available or random digital signal

VOLKSWAGEN
Bosch Mono-Motronic MA1.2.2/1.2.3/1.3 (45-pin)

Model:	Engine code:	Year:
Golf/Vento 1,4	ABD	1991-95
Golf/Vento 1,6	ABU/AEA	1992-95
Golf/Vento/Cabrio 1,8	AAM	1991-00
Golf/Vento/Cabrio 1,8	ABS/ADZ	1991-00
Golf/Vento/Cabrio 1,8	ANN/ANP	1998-00

ECM harness multi-plug

Terminal side

AD81645

Wire side

AD42108

Component/circuit description	ECM pin	Signal	Condition	Typical value	Oscilloscope setting*	Wave form
Air conditioning – 1,6/1,8	33			1		
	35			1		
Automatic transmission – 1,8	34		Ignition ON	11-14 V		
Battery	21	←	Ignition OFF	11-14 V		
Closed throttle position (CTP) switch	10	←	Ignition ON – throttle closed	0 V		
	10	←	Ignition ON – throttle open	11-14 V		
Crankshaft position (CKP) sensor	8	⇒	Ignition OFF	0 V		
	8	⇒	Ignition ON	10 V min.		
	13	←	Ignition ON – engine turned	0 V or 11-14 V switching		
	13	←	Engine idling	30 Hz	5 V/20 ms	⟋⟍ 4
	13	←	3000 rpm	100 Hz		
Data link connector (DLC) – 1991-94	29	⇔	Ignition ON	5 V		
Data link connector (DLC) – some models	11	←	Ignition ON	8 V		
Earth	1		Ignition ON	0 V		
	20		Ignition ON	0 V		
Earth – 1,8 1991-94	15		Ignition ON	0 V		
Earth – 1997→	32		Ignition ON	0 V		
Earth – some models	12		Ignition ON	0 V		
Engine coolant temperature (ECT) sensor	17	⊐	Ignition ON	0 V		
	42	←	Ignition ON – coolant temp. 20°C	2 V		
	42	←	Ignition ON – coolant temp. 80°C	0,2 V		
Evaporative emission (EVAP) canister purge valve	3	⊐▷	Ignition OFF	11-14 V		
	3	⊐▷	Engine hot – valve operating		10 V/20 ms	⟋⟍ 20
Fuel pump relay	25	⊐▷	Ignition ON	0-1 V briefly then 11-14 V		
	25	⊐▷	Engine cranking	0-1 V		

* Suggested settings - Voltage/time per division

Autodata

Component/circuit description	ECM pin	Signal	Condition	Typical value	Oscilloscope setting*	Wave form
Heated oxygen sensor (HO2S)	38	←	Engine idling – engine hot	0,1-1 V fluctuating	0,2 V/1 sec.	∿ 21
Heated oxygen sensor (HO2S) – except 1,8 1991-94	15	⊣⊢	Engine idling	0 V		
Heated oxygen sensor (HO2S) – shield wire – ABD/ABU	44	⊣⊢	Engine idling	0 V		
Idle speed control (ISC) actuator	2 (26)	⇒	Engine idling		5 V/2 ms	Intermittent ∿ 27
	26 (2)	⇒	Engine idling		5 V/2 ms	Intermittent ∿ 27
Idle speed control (ISC) actuator position sensor – if fitted	16	←	Engine idling – engine hot	3 V or 11-14 V – intermittent	10 V/50 ms	Intermittent ∿ 31
Ignition amplifier	24	⇒	Engine idling	30 Hz	1 V/10 ms	∿ 32
	24	⇒	3000 rpm	100 Hz		
Ignition switch	23	←	Ignition OFF	0 V		
	23	←	Ignition ON	11-14 V		
Ignition switch – AT 1,8 1994-98	40	←	Ignition OFF	0 V		
	40	←	Ignition ON	11-14 V		
Immobilizer control module – 10/94-98	29		Ignition ON	11-14 V		
Injector	7	⊣▷	Ignition ON	11-14 V briefly then 0 V		
	7	⊣▷	Engine idling – engine hot	2 ms	10 V/2 ms	∿ 35
Instrument panel	9	⇒		1		
Instrument panel – 1,8	27			1		
Instrument panel, vehicle speed signal – except ABD	36	←	Ignition ON – vehicle pushed	0 V or 11-14 V switching		
Intake air temperature (IAT) sensor	17	⊣⊢	Ignition ON	0 V		
	43	←	Ignition ON – air temp. 20°C	2,3 V		
Intake manifold heater relay	28	⊣▷	Ignition ON – engine cold	0-1 V		
	28	⊣▷	Ignition ON – engine hot	11-14 V		
Throttle position (TP) sensor	14	←	Ignition ON	5 V		
	17	⊣⊢	Ignition ON	0 V		
	18	←	Ignition ON – throttle closed	0,1 V		
	18	←	Ignition ON – throttle fully open	4,5 V		
	41	←	Ignition ON – throttle closed	1,9 V		
	41	←	Ignition ON – throttle fully open	4,9 V		

*Suggested settings - Voltage/time per division

1 Connected pin - no test data available or random digital signal

VOLKSWAGEN

Magneti Marelli 4LV

Model:	Engine code:	Year:
Golf/Bora 1,6	ATN	1999-02
Golf/Bora 1,6	AUS	2000-02

ECM harness multi-plug

Terminal side

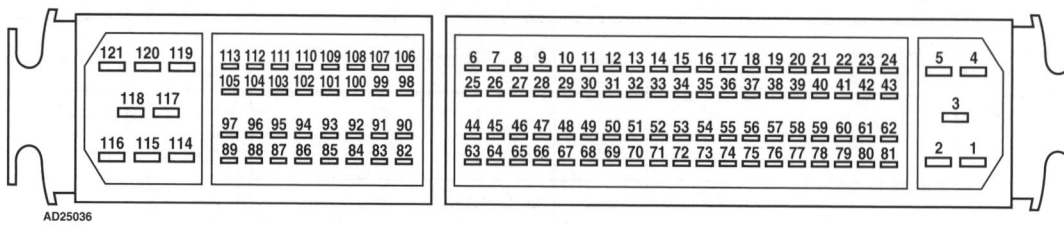

AD25036

Wire side

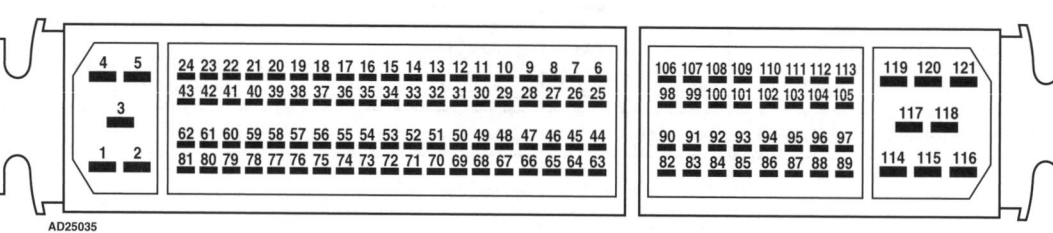

AD25035

Component/circuit description	ECM pin	Signal	Condition	Typical value	Oscilloscope setting★	Wave form
AC control module – ATC	40			1		
	41			1		
AC refrigerant pressure sensor	61			1		
AC/heater function control panel – MTC	40			1		
Accelerator pedal position (APP) sensor	33	⌐	Ignition ON	0 V		
	34	←	Ignition ON – accelerator pedal released	0,4 V		
	34	←	Ignition ON – accelerator pedal depressed	2 V		
	35	←	Ignition ON – accelerator pedal released	0,8 V		
	35	←	Ignition ON – accelerator pedal depressed	4,1 V		
	36	⌐	Ignition ON	0 V		
	72	⇒	Ignition ON	5 V		
	73	⇒	Ignition ON	5 V		
Alternator	28	⇒	Engine idling		1 V/10 ms	89
Battery	3	←	Ignition OFF	11-14 V		
Brake pedal position (BPP) switch	55	←	Ignition ON – brake pedal released	11-14 V		
	55	←	Ignition ON – brake pedal depressed	0 V		
	56	←	Ignition ON – brake pedal released	0 V		
	56	←	Ignition ON – brake pedal depressed	11-14 V		
Camshaft position (CMP) sensor	86	←	Ignition ON	0 or 5 V		
	86	←	Engine idling		2 V/50 ms	69
	98	⇒	Ignition ON	5 V		
	108	⌐	Ignition ON	0 V		
CAN data bus – high	60	←⇒		1		
CAN data bus – low	58	←⇒		1		

★ Suggested settings - Voltage/time per division

/Autodata

Component/circuit description	ECM pin	Signal	Condition	Typical value	Oscilloscope setting*	Wave form
Clutch pedal position (CPP) switch	39	←	Ignition ON – clutch pedal released	11-14 V		
	39	←	Ignition ON – clutch pedal depressed	0 V		
Crankshaft position (CKP) sensor	82	←	Engine idling		5 V/1 ms	[5]
	87	⇒	Ignition ON	5 V		
	108	⌐	Ignition ON	0 V		
Cruise control master switch	38			[1]		
	57			[1]		
Cruise control selector switch	38			[1]		
	75			[1]		
	76			[1]		
Earth	1		Ignition ON	0 V		
	2		Ignition ON	0 V		
Engine coolant blower motor control module	61			[1]		
Engine coolant blower motor control module – MTC	40			[1]		
	41			[1]		
Engine coolant temperature (ECT) sensor	93	←	Ignition ON – coolant temp. 20°C	2,2 V		
	93	←	Ignition ON – coolant temp. 80°C	0,5 V		
	108	⌐	Ignition ON	0 V		
Evaporative emission (EVAP) canister purge valve	64	⌐▷	Ignition ON	11-14 V briefly then 0-1 V		
	64	⌐▷	Engine idling	11-14 V		
	64	⌐▷	Engine running – engine hot – valve operating		10 V/20 ms	[20]
Exhaust gas recirculation (EGR) valve actuator	114	⌐▷	Ignition ON	11-14 V		
	114	⌐▷	Engine idling		5 V/1 ms	Intermittent [53]
Exhaust gas recirculation (EGR) valve position sensor	98	⇒	Ignition ON	5 V		
	100	←	Ignition ON	0,92 V		
	100	←	Engine idling	0,95 V		
	108	⌐	Ignition ON	0 V		
Fuel pump (FP) relay	65	⌐▷	Ignition ON	0-1 V briefly then 11-14 V		
	65	⌐▷	Engine idling	0-1 V		
Heated oxygen sensor (HO2S) 1	51	←	Engine idling	3,79 V		
	51 (70)	←	Engine idling	0,46 V		
	52	◄►	Engine idling	3,94 V		
	70	←	Engine idling	4,25 V		
	70 (51)	←	Engine idling	0,46 V		
	71	◄►	Engine idling	8,24 V		
Heated oxygen sensor (HO2S) 1 – heater control	5	⌐▷	Engine idling – engine hot		2 V/10 ms	[65]
Heated oxygen sensor (HO2S) 2	68	⌐	Ignition ON	0 V		
	69	←	Engine idling – engine hot	0,6 V		
Heated oxygen sensor (HO2S) 2 – heater control	63	⌐▷	Ignition ON	11-14 V briefly then 0-1 V		
	63	⌐▷	Engine idling – engine hot		2 V/5 ms	[65]
Ignition amplifier	102	⇒	Engine idling		1 V/20 ms	[32]
	103	⇒	Engine idling		1 V/20 ms	[32]
Ignition switch	4	←	Ignition OFF	0 V		
	4	←	Ignition ON	11-14 V		

* Suggested settings - Voltage/time per division

Component/circuit description	ECM pin	Signal	Condition	Typical value	Oscilloscope setting*	Wave form
Injector 1	96	⊐▷	Ignition ON	11-14 V briefly then 0-1 V		
	96	⊐▷	Engine idling	2,8 ms	10 V/2 ms	〰〰 35
Injector 2	97	⊐▷	Ignition ON	11-14 V briefly then 0-1 V		
	97	⊐▷	Engine idling	2,8 ms	10 V/2 ms	〰〰 35
Injector 3	88	⊐▷	Ignition ON	11-14 V briefly then 0-1 V		
	88	⊐▷	Engine idling	2,8 ms	10 V/2 ms	〰〰 35
Injector 4	89	⊐▷	Ignition ON	11-14 V briefly then 0-1 V		
	89	⊐▷	Engine idling	2,8 ms	10 V/2 ms	〰〰 35
Instrumentation control module – diagnosis signal	43			☐1		
Instrumentation control module – engine RPM signal	37	⇨	Engine idling	28 Hz		
Instrumentation control module – vehicle speed signal	54	⬅		☐1		
Intake air temperature (IAT) sensor	85	⬅	Ignition ON – air temp. 20°C	2,4 V		
	108	⊐⊢	Ignition ON	0 V		
Knock sensor (KS)	99	⊐⊢	Engine idling	0 V		
	106	⬅	Engine idling – accelerate briefly		50 mV/1 ms	〰〰 38
Manifold absolute pressure (MAP) sensor	98	⇨	Ignition ON	5 V		
	108	⊐⊢	Ignition ON	0 V		
	109	⬅	Ignition ON	4 V		
	109	⬅	Engine idling	0,8 V		
	109	⬅	Engine running – full throttle briefly	4,3 V		
Spare cable	66			☐1		
Throttle motor	117	⇨	Ignition ON	11-14 V for 30 seconds then 3 V		
	117	⇨	Ignition ON – accelerator pedal released		2 V/2 ms	(30 seconds only) 〰〰 64
	118	⇨	Ignition ON	11-14 V for 30 seconds then 3 V		
	118	⇨	Ignition ON – accelerator pedal released		2 V/2 ms	(30 seconds only) 〰〰 64
Throttle motor position sensor	83	⇨	Ignition ON	5 V		
	84	⬅	Ignition ON – accelerator pedal released	4,3 V		
	91	⊐⊢	Ignition ON	0 V		
	92	⬅	Ignition ON – accelerator pedal released	0,7 V		

*Suggested settings - Voltage/time per division

☐1 Connected pin - no test data available or random digital signal

Model:	Engine code:	Year:
Golf/Bora 1,6	AZD	2000-04
Golf/Bora 1,6	BCB	2002-05

ECM harness multi-plug

Terminal side

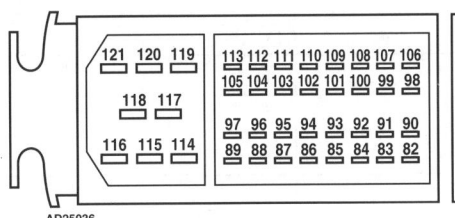

AD25036

Wire side

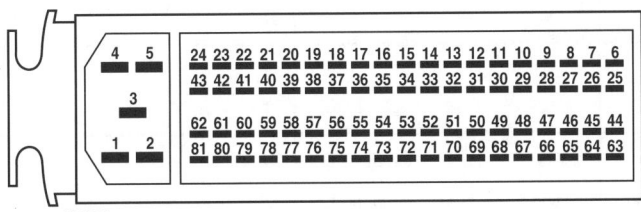

AD25035

Component/circuit description	ECM pin	Signal	Condition	Typical value	Oscilloscope setting*	Wave form
Accelerator pedal position (APP) sensor	33	⌐⌐	Ignition ON	0 V		
	34	←	Ignition ON – accelerator pedal released	0,4 V		
	34	←	Ignition ON – accelerator pedal depressed	2 V		
	35	←	Ignition ON – accelerator pedal released	0,8 V		
	35	←	Ignition ON – accelerator pedal depressed	4,1 V		
	36	⌐⌐	Ignition ON	0 V		
	72	⇒	Ignition ON	5 V		
	73	⇒	Ignition ON	5 V		
AC control module, engine RPM signal – ATC	37	⇒	Engine idling	28 Hz		
AC control module – ATC	40			☐1		
	41			☐1		
AC refrigerant pressure sensor	61			☐1		
AC/heater function control panel – MTC	40			☐1		
Alternator	28	⇒	Engine idling		1 V/10 ms	⎍⎍ 89
Battery	3	←	Ignition OFF	11-14 V		
Brake pedal position (BPP) switch	55	←	Ignition ON – brake pedal released	11-14 V		
	55	←	Ignition ON – brake pedal depressed	0 V		
	56	←	Ignition ON – brake pedal released	0 V		
	56	←	Ignition ON – brake pedal depressed	11-14 V		
Camshaft position (CMP) sensor	86	←	Ignition ON	0 or 5 V		
	86	←	Engine idling		2 V/50 ms	⎍⎍ 69
	98	⇒	Ignition ON	5 V		
	108	⌐⌐	Ignition ON	0 V		
CAN data bus – high	60	←⇒		☐1		
CAN data bus – low	58	←⇒		☐1		

* Suggested settings - Voltage/time per division

Component/circuit description	ECM pin	Signal	Condition	Typical value	Oscilloscope setting*	Wave form
Clutch pedal position (CPP) switch	39	←	Ignition ON – clutch pedal released	11-14 V		
	39	←	Ignition ON – clutch pedal depressed	0 V		
Crankshaft position (CKP) sensor	82	←	Engine idling		5 V/1 ms	⎍ 5
	87	⇒	Ignition ON	5 V		
	108	⌐	Ignition ON	0 V		
Cruise control master switch	38			1		
	57			1		
Cruise control selector switch	38			1		
	75			1		
	76			1		
Earth	1		Ignition ON	0 V		
	2		Ignition ON	0 V		
Engine coolant blower motor control module	61			1		
Engine coolant blower motor control module – MTC	40			1		
	41			1		
Engine coolant temperature (ECT) sensor	93	←	Ignition ON – coolant temp. 20°C	2,2 V		
	93	←	Ignition ON – coolant temp. 80°C	0,5 V		
	108	⌐	Ignition ON	0 V		
Evaporative emission (EVAP) canister purge valve	64	⌐⇒	Ignition ON	11-14 V briefly then 0 V		
	64	⌐⇒	Engine running – engine hot – valve operating		10 V/20 ms	⎍ 20
Exhaust gas recirculation (EGR) valve actuator	114	⌐⇒	Ignition ON	11-14 V		
	114	⌐⇒	Engine idling		5 V/1 ms	Intermittent ⎍ 53
Exhaust gas recirculation (EGR) valve position sensor	98	⇒	Ignition ON	5 V		
	100	←	Ignition ON	0,92 V		
	100	←	Engine idling	0,95 V		
	108	⌐	Ignition ON	0 V		
Fuel pump (FP) relay	65	⌐⇒	Ignition ON	0-1 V briefly then 11-14 V		
	65	⌐⇒	Engine idling	0-1 V		
Heated oxygen sensor (HO2S) 1	51	←	Engine idling	3,79 V		
	51 (70)	←	Engine idling	0,46 V		
	52	⇔	Engine idling	3,94 V		
	70	←	Engine idling	4,25 V		
	70 (51)	←	Engine idling	0,46 V		
	71	⇔	Engine idling	8,24 V		
Heated oxygen sensor (HO2S) 1, heater control	5	⌐⇒	Engine idling – engine hot		2 V/10 ms	⎍ 65
Heated oxygen sensor (HO2S) 2	68	⌐	Ignition ON	0 V		
	69	←	Engine idling – engine hot	0,6 V		
Heated oxygen sensor (HO2S) 2, heater control	63	⌐⇒	Ignition ON	11-14 V briefly then 0 V		
	63	⌐⇒	Engine idling – engine hot		2 V/5 ms	⎍ 65
Ignition coil 1	102	⇒	Ignition ON	0 V		
	102	⇒	Engine idling		2 V/20 ms	⎍ 62
Ignition coil 2	103	⇒	Ignition ON	0 V		
	103	⇒	Engine idling		2 V/20 ms	⎍ 62
Ignition coil 3	94	⇒	Ignition ON	0 V		
	94	⇒	Engine idling		2 V/20 ms	⎍ 62

* Suggested settings - Voltage/time per division

Component/circuit description	ECM pin	Signal	Condition	Typical value	Oscilloscope setting*	Wave form
Ignition coil 4	95	⇨	Ignition ON	0 V		
	95	⇨	Engine idling		2 V/20 ms	〰 62
Ignition switch	4	⇦	Ignition OFF	0 V		
	4	⇦	Ignition ON	11-14 V		
Injector 1	96	⊣▷	Ignition ON	11-14 V briefly then 0 V		
	96	⊣▷	Engine idling	2,5 ms	10 V/2 ms	〰 35
Injector 2	97	⊣▷	Ignition ON	11-14 V briefly then 0 V		
	97	⊣▷	Engine idling	2,5 ms	10 V/2 ms	〰 35
Injector 3	88	⊣▷	Ignition ON	11-14 V briefly then 0 V		
	88	⊣▷	Engine idling	2,5 ms	10 V/2 ms	〰 35
Injector 4	89	⊣▷	Ignition ON	11-14 V briefly then 0 V		
	89	⊣▷	Engine idling	2,5 ms	10 V/2 ms	〰 35
Instrumentation control module, diagnosis signal	43			1		
Instrumentation control module, engine RPM signal – →04/02	37	⇨	Engine idling	28 Hz		
Instrumentation control module, vehicle speed signal	54	⇦		1		
Intake air temperature (IAT) sensor	85	⇦	Ignition ON – air temp. 20°C	2,4 V		
	108	⊣—	Ignition ON	0 V		
Knock sensor (KS)	99	⊣—	Engine idling	0 V		
	106	⇦	Engine idling – accelerate briefly		50 mV/1 ms	〰 38
Manifold absolute pressure (MAP) sensor	98	⇨	Ignition ON	5 V		
	108	⊣—	Ignition ON	0 V		
	109	⇦	Ignition ON	4 V		
	109	⇦	Engine idling	0,8 V		
	109	⇦	Engine running – full throttle briefly	4,3 V		
Spare cable	66			1		
Throttle motor	117	⇨	Ignition ON	11-14 V for 30 seconds then 3 V		
	117	⇨	Ignition ON – accelerator pedal released		2 V/2 ms	(30 seconds only) 〰 64
	118	⇨	Ignition ON	11-14 V for 30 seconds then 3 V		
	118	⇨	Ignition ON – accelerator pedal released		2 V/2 ms	(30 seconds only) 〰 64
Throttle motor position sensor	83	⇨	Ignition ON	5 V		
	84	⇦	Ignition ON – accelerator pedal released	4,3 V		
	91	⊣—	Ignition ON	0 V		
	92	⇦	Ignition ON – accelerator pedal released	0,7 V		
Transmission control module (TCM)	41			1		

*Suggested settings - Voltage/time per division

1 Connected pin - no test data available or random digital signal

VOLKSWAGEN

Bosch Motronic M3.8.3/5

Model:	Engine code:	Year:
Golf/Bora 1,8	AGN	1997-03
Golf/Bora 1,8 Turbo	AGU	1997-04
Sharan 1,8 Turbo	AJH	1997-01

ECM harness multi-plug

Terminal side

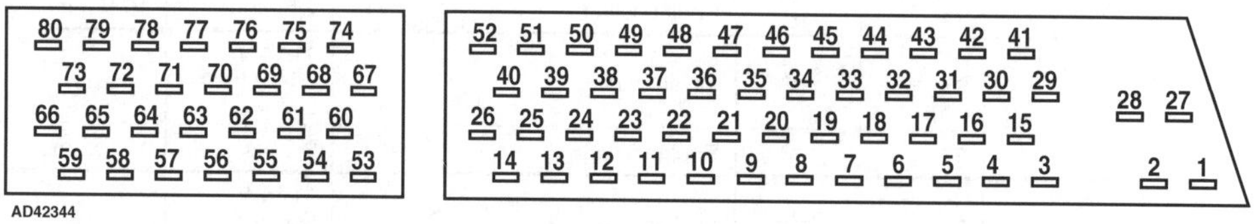

AD42344

Wire side

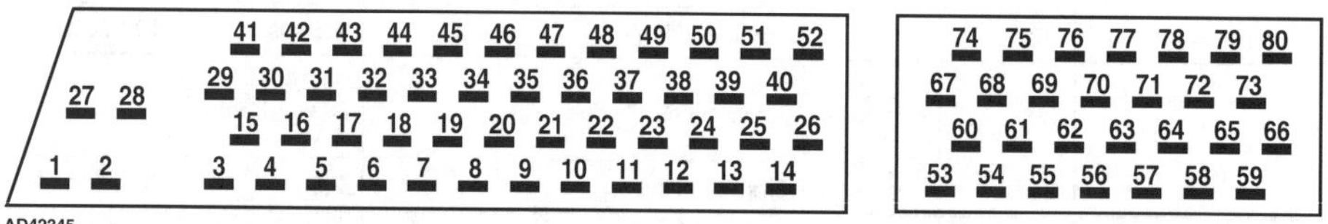

AD42345

Component/circuit description	ECM pin	Signal	Condition	Typical value	Oscilloscope setting*	Wave form
Air conditioning, compressor clutch signal	8	←	Engine idling – AC OFF	0 V		
	8	←	Engine idling – AC ON, AC compressor OFF	0 V		
	8	←	Engine idling – AC ON, AC compressor ON	11-14 V		
Air conditioning, load signal	10	←	Engine idling – AC OFF	0 V		
	10	←	Engine idling – AC ON	11-14 V		
Barometric pressure (BARO) sensor – Golf/Bora Turbo	61	←	Ignition ON – at sea level	4 V		
	61	←	Ignition ON – 1000 m above sea level	3 V		
	61	←	Ignition ON – 2000 m above sea level	2,1 V		
	62	⇨	Ignition ON	5 V		
	67	⏚	Ignition ON	0 V		
Barometric pressure (BARO) sensor – Sharan	50	←	Ignition ON – at sea level	4 V		
	50	←	Ignition ON – 1000 m above sea level	3 V		
	50	←	Ignition ON – 2000 m above sea level	2,1 V		
	11	⇨	Ignition ON	5 V		
	14	⏚	Ignition ON	0 V		
Battery	3	←	Ignition ON	11-14 V		
Camshaft position (CMP) actuator – non-Turbo	55	⏚⇨	Ignition ON	11-14 V briefly then 0 V		
	55	⏚⇨	Engine idling	11-14 V		
	55	⏚⇨	Engine idling – accelerate briefly	0,4 V briefly		
Camshaft position (CMP) sensor	67	⏚	Ignition ON	0 V		
Camshaft position (CMP) sensor – Golf/Bora	62	⇨	Ignition ON	5 V		
Camshaft position (CMP) sensor – Motronic M3.8.3	76	←	Engine idling		5 V/20 ms	12
Camshaft position (CMP) sensor – Motronic M3.8.5	76	←	Engine idling		5 V/20 ms	14
CAN data bus – Golf/Bora	29	⇦⇨	Ignition ON	1		
	41	⇦⇨	Ignition ON	1		

* Suggested settings - Voltage/time per division

Component/circuit description	ECM pin	Signal	Condition	Typical value	Oscilloscope setting*	Wave form
Closed throttle position (CTP) switch	67	⊣—	Ignition ON	0 V		
	69	⟵	Ignition ON – throttle closed	0 V		
	69	⟵	Ignition ON – throttle slightly open	11-14 V		
Crankshaft position (CKP) sensor	56	⟵	Ignition ON	1,53 V		
	56	⟵	Engine idling	3 V ac		
	56	⟵	Engine idling		2 V/2 ms	⎍⎍ 2
	63	⟵	Ignition ON	1,53 V		
	63	⟵	Engine idling	3 V ac		
	63	⟵	Engine idling		2 V/2 ms	Reversed ⎍⎍ 2
	67	⊣—	Ignition ON	0 V		
Crankshaft position (CKP) sensor, shield wire – Golf/Bora	67	⊣—	Ignition ON	0 V		
Clutch pedal position (CPP) switch – Golf/Bora Turbo	9	⟵	Ignition ON – clutch pedal released	11-14 V briefly then 0 V		
	9	⟵	Engine idling – clutch pedal released	11-14 V		
	9	⟵	Engine idling – clutch pedal depressed	0 V		
Data link connector (DLC), pin 13	43			☐1		
Earth	2	⊣—	Ignition ON	0 V		
Earth – Sharan, MT	22	⊣—	Ignition ON	0 V		
Engine coolant temperature (ECT) sensor	53	⟵	Ignition ON – coolant temp. 12°C approx.	2,25 V		
	53	⟵	Ignition ON – coolant temp. 85°C approx.	0,5 V		
	67	⊣—	Ignition ON	0 V		
Evaporative emission (EVAP) canister purge valve	15	⊣▷	Ignition ON	11-14 V briefly then 0 V		
	15	⊣▷	Engine idling	11-14 V		
	15	⊣▷	Engine hot – valve operating		10 V/20 ms	⎍⎍ 20
Fuel pump relay – except Sharan 05/98→	4	⊣▷	Ignition ON	0,6 V briefly then 11-14 V		
	4	⊣▷	Engine cranking	0,6 V		
	4	⊣▷	Engine idling	0,6 V		
Fuel pump relay, through fuel pump shut-off control module – Sharan 05/98-10/98	4	⊣▷	Ignition ON	0,6 V briefly then 11-14 V		
	4	⊣▷	Engine cranking	0,6 V		
	4	⊣▷	Engine idling	0,6 V		
Fuel pump relay, incorporates fuel pump shut-off control module function – Sharan 11/98→	4	⊣▷	Ignition ON	0,6 V briefly then 11-14 V		
	4	⊣▷	Engine cranking	0,6 V		
	4	⊣▷	Engine idling	0,6 V		
Heated oxygen sensor (HO2S)	25	⊣—	Ignition ON	0 V		
	26	⟵	Ignition ON	0,68 V		
	26	⟵	Engine running	0,1-0,9 V fluctuating	0,2 V/1 sec.	⎍⎍ 21
	27	⊣▷	Ignition ON	11-14 V briefly then 0 V		
	27	⊣▷	Engine idling	0,3 V		
Idle speed control (ISC) actuator	59	⟹	Ignition ON	8,4 V		
	59	⟹	Engine idling	60%		
	59	⟹	Engine idling		2 V/2 ms	⎍⎍ 64
	66	⟵	Ignition ON	11-14 V		
	66	⟵	Engine idling	0,1 V		

* Suggested settings - Voltage/time per division

Component/circuit description	ECM pin	Signal	Condition	Typical value	Oscilloscope setting★	Wave form
Idle speed control (ISC) actuator position sensor	62	⇨	Ignition ON	5 V		
	67	⊰–	Ignition ON	0 V		
	74	⬅	Ignition ON	3,2 V		
	74	⬅	Engine idling	3,7 V		
Ignition amplifier	71	⇨	Ignition ON	0 V		
	71	⇨	Engine idling		1 V/20 ms	〰 56
	78	⇨	Ignition ON	0 V		
	78	⇨	Engine idling		1 V/20 ms	〰 56
Ignition amplifier – Turbo	70	⇨	Ignition ON	0 V		
	70	⇨	Engine idling		1 V/20 ms	〰 56
	77	⇨	Ignition ON	0 V		
	77	⇨	Engine idling		1 V/20 ms	〰 56
Ignition switch	1	⬅	Ignition OFF	0 V		
	1	⬅	Ignition ON	11-14 V		
Immobilizer control module, immobilization/diagnosis signal – Sharan	19			1		
Injector 1	73	⊰⊳	Ignition ON	11-14 V briefly then 0 V		
	73	⊰⊳	Engine idling	3,5 ms	10 V/2 ms	〰 35
Injector 2	80	⊰⊳	Ignition ON	11-14 V briefly then 0 V		
	80	⊰⊳	Engine idling	3,5 ms	10 V/2 ms	〰 35
Injector 3	58	⊰⊳	Ignition ON	11-14 V briefly then 0 V		
	58	⊰⊳	Engine idling	3,5 ms	10 V/2 ms	〰 35
Injector 4	65	⊰⊳	Ignition ON	11-14 V briefly then 0 V		
	65	⊰⊳	Engine idling	3,5 ms	10 V/2 ms	〰 35
Instrumentation control module, immobilization/diagnosis signal – Golf/Bora	19			1		
Instrumentation control module, fuel consumption signal – with digital multifunction display	18		Ignition ON	0,15 V		
Instrumentation control module, engine RPM signal	6	⇨	Ignition ON	0,26 V		
	6	⇨	Engine idling	41 Hz	4 V/10 ms	〰 24
	6	⇨	3000 rpm	100 Hz		
Instrumentation control module, vehicle speed signal	20		Ignition ON – vehicle pushed	0 V or 11-14 V switching		
Intake air temperature (IAT) sensor – Turbo	54	⬅	Ignition ON – air temp. 10°C	2 V		
	67	⊰–	Ignition ON	0 V		
Intake manifold air control solenoid – non-Turbo	64	⊰⊳	Ignition ON	11-14 V briefly then 0 V		
	64	⊰⊳	Engine idling	11-14 V		
	64	⊰⊳	Engine idling – accelerate briefly	0,2 V briefly		
Knock sensor (KS) 1	67	⊰⊳	Ignition ON	0 V		
Knock sensor (KS) 1, shield wire	67	⊰⊳	Ignition ON	0 V		
Knock sensor (KS) 1 – Golf/Bora Turbo 04/98→	60	⬅	Ignition ON	0 V		
	60	⬅	Engine idling – accelerate briefly		50 mV/1 ms	〰 58
Knock sensor (KS) 1 – except Golf/Bora Turbo 04/98→	68	⬅	Ignition ON	0 V		
	68	⬅	Engine idling – accelerate briefly		50 mV/1 ms	〰 58
Knock sensor (KS) 2	67	⊰⊳	Ignition ON	0 V		

★ Suggested settings - Voltage/time per division

Component/circuit description	ECM pin	Signal	Condition	Typical value	Oscilloscope setting*	Wave form
Knock sensor (KS) 2, shield wire	67	⌐⊃	Ignition ON	0 V		
Knock sensor (KS) 2 – except Golf/Bora Turbo 04/98→	60	←	Ignition ON	0 V		
	60	←	Engine idling – accelerate briefly		50 mV/1 ms	⎍⎍ 58
Knock sensor (KS) 2 – Golf/Bora Turbo 04/98→	68	←	Ignition ON	0 V		
	68	←	Engine idling – accelerate briefly		50 mV/1 ms	⎍⎍ 58
Mass air flow (MAF) sensor	12	⌐⊢	Ignition ON	0 V		
	13	←	Engine idling	1,5 V		
	13	←	Engine idling – full throttle briefly	3,6 V		
Mass air flow (MAF) sensor – non-Turbo	11	⇨	Ignition ON	5 V		
Mass air flow (MAF) sensor, IAT signal – non-Turbo	40	←	Ignition ON – air temp. 10°C approx.	2,4 V		
Power steering pressure (PSP) switch – Golf/Bora	14	⌐⊢	Ignition ON	0 V		
	49	←	Engine idling – steering wheel not turned	11-14 V		
	49	←	Engine idling – steering wheel turned	0 V		
Starter motor inhibitor switch relay – Sharan, AT	22			1		
Secondary air injection (AIR) pump relay – Sharan	30	⌐⊃	Ignition ON	11-14 V briefly then 0 V		
	30	⌐⊃	Cold start – AIR pump running	0-1 V		
	30	⌐⊃	Hot start – AIR pump not running	11-14 V		
Secondary air injection (AIR) solenoid – Sharan	33	⌐⊃	Ignition ON	11-14 V briefly then 0 V		
	33	⌐⊃	Cold start – valve operating	0-1 V		
	33	⌐⊃	Hot start – valve not operating	11-14 V		
Throttle position (TP) sensor	62	⇨	Ignition ON	5 V		
	67	⌐⊢	Ignition ON	0 V		
	75	←	Ignition ON – throttle closed	4,16 V		
	75	←	Ignition ON – throttle fully open	0,65 V		
Transmission control module (TCM) – Sharan	29	⟷	Ignition ON	1		
	41	⟷	Ignition ON	1		
Turbocharger (TC) wastegate regulating valve	64	⌐⊃	Ignition ON	11-14 V briefly then 0 V		
	64	⌐⊃	Engine idling	11-14 V		
	64	⌐⊃	Vehicle moving – accelerate, full load	1-99%		

*Suggested settings - Voltage/time per division

1 Connected pin - no test data available or random digital signal

VOLKSWAGEN

Bosch Motronic ME7.5

Model:	Engine code:	Year:
Golf/Bora 1,8 Turbo	AQA/ARZ	1998-03

ECM harness multi-plug

Terminal side

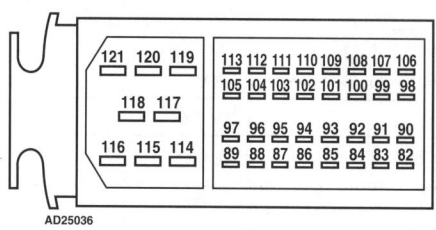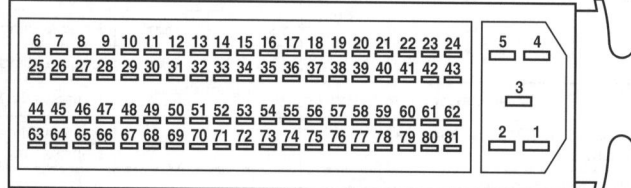

AD25036

Wire side

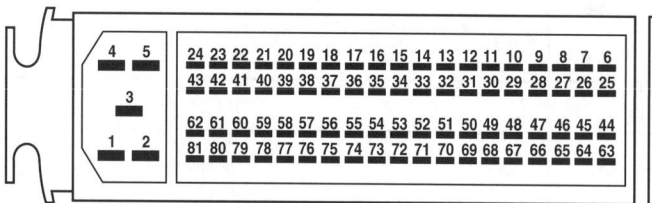

AD25035

Component/circuit description	ECM pin	Signal	Condition	Typical value	Oscilloscope setting*	Wave form
Accelerator pedal position (APP) sensor	33	⌐	Ignition ON	0 V		
	34	←	Ignition ON – accelerator pedal released	0,4 V		
	34	←	Ignition ON – accelerator pedal depressed	2 V		
	35	←	Ignition ON – accelerator pedal released	0,7 V		
	35	←	Ignition ON – accelerator pedal depressed	4,1 V		
	36	⌐	Ignition ON	0 V		
	72	⇒	Ignition ON	5 V		
	73	⇒	Ignition ON	5 V		
Air conditioning	40			1		
	41			1		
Air conditioning – ARZ	61			1		
Airbag control module – AQA	67			1		
Alternator	28	⇒	Engine idling		5 V/50 ms	94
Battery	62	←	Ignition OFF	11-14 V		
Brake pedal position (BPP) switch 1	56	←	Ignition ON – brake pedal released	0 V		
	56	←	Ignition ON – brake pedal depressed	11-14 V		
Brake pedal position (BPP) switch 2	55	←	Ignition ON – brake pedal released	11-14 V		
	55	←	Ignition ON – brake pedal depressed	0 V		
Camshaft position (CMP) sensor	86	←	Ignition ON	0 or 11-14 V		
	86	←	Engine idling		2 V/20 ms	14
	98	⇒	Ignition ON	5 V		
	108	⌐	Ignition ON	0 V		
CAN data bus – high	60	←⇒		1		
CAN data bus – low	58	←⇒		1		

* Suggested settings - Voltage/time per division

Component/circuit description	ECM pin	Signal	Condition	Typical value	Oscilloscope setting*	Wave form
Clutch pedal position (CPP) switch	39	←	Ignition ON – clutch pedal released	11-14 V		
	39	←	Ignition ON – clutch pedal depressed	0 V		
Crankshaft position (CKP) sensor	82	←	Engine idling	3,1 V ac		
	82	←	Engine idling		2 V/2 ms	2
	90	←	Engine idling	3,1 V ac		
	90	←	Engine idling		2 V/2 ms	Reversed 2
	108	⊐—	Ignition ON	0 V		
Cruise control master switch	38			1		
	57			1		
Cruise control selector switch	38			1		
	75			1		
	76			1		
Earth	1		Ignition ON	0 V		
	2		Ignition ON	0 V		
Engine control (EC) relay – ARZ	21	⊐▷	Ignition ON	0-1 V		
	21	⊐▷	Engine idling	0-1 V		
	121	←	Ignition ON	11-14 V		
Engine coolant temperature (ECT) sensor	93	←	Ignition ON – coolant temp. 20°C	2,2 V		
	93	←	Ignition ON – coolant temp. 80°C	0,4 V		
	108	⊐—	Ignition ON	0 V		
Evaporative emission (EVAP) canister purge valve	64	⊐▷	Ignition ON	11-14 V briefly then 0-1 V		
	64	⊐▷	Engine running – engine hot – valve operating		10 V/5 ms	35
Fuel pump (FP) relay	65	⊐▷	Ignition ON	0-1 V briefly then 11-14 V		
	65	⊐▷	Engine idling	0-1 V		
Heated oxygen sensor (HO2S) 1	51	⊐—	Ignition ON	0 V		
	70	←	Engine idling – engine hot		0,2 V/1 sec.	21
Heated oxygen sensor (HO2S) 1 – heater control	5	⊐▷	Engine idling – engine hot		5 V/50 ms	18
Heated oxygen sensor (HO2S) 2 – ARZ	68	⊐—	Ignition ON	0 V		
	69	←	Engine idling – engine hot	0,6 V		
Heated oxygen sensor (HO2S) 2 – ARZ – heater control	63	⊐▷	Ignition ON	11-14 V briefly then 0-1 V		
	63	⊐▷	Engine idling	0-1 V		
Ignition coil 1	102	⇨	Ignition ON	0 V		
	102	⇨	Engine idling		2 V/20 ms	62
Ignition coil 2	95	⇨	Ignition ON	0 V		
	95	⇨	Engine idling		2 V/20 ms	62
Ignition coil 3	103	⇨	Ignition ON	0 V		
	103	⇨	Engine idling		2 V/20 ms	62
Ignition coil 4	94	⇨	Ignition ON	0 V		
	94	⇨	Engine idling		2 V/20 ms	62
Ignition switch	3	←	Ignition OFF	0 V		
	3	←	Ignition ON	11-14 V		
Injector 1	96	⊐▷	Ignition ON	11-14 V briefly then 0-1 V		
	96	⊐▷	Engine idling	2,5 ms	10 V/2 ms	35
Injector 2	89	⊐▷	Ignition ON	11-14 V briefly then 0-1 V		
	89	⊐▷	Engine idling	2,5 ms	10 V/2 ms	35

* Suggested settings - Voltage/time per division

Component/circuit description	ECM pin	Signal	Condition	Typical value	Oscilloscope setting*	Wave form
Injector 3	97	⫣▷	Ignition ON	11-14 V briefly then 0-1 V		
	97	⫣▷	Engine idling	2,5 ms	10 V/2 ms	∿∿ 35
Injector 4	88	⫣▷	Ignition ON	11-14 V briefly then 0-1 V		
	88	⫣▷	Engine idling	2,5 ms	10 V/2 ms	∿∿ 35
Instrumentation control module – diagnosis signal	43			1		
Instrumentation control module – engine RPM signal	37	⇨	Engine idling	28 Hz		
Instrumentation control module – fuel consumption signal – AQA	81	⇨		1		
Instrumentation control module – vehicle speed signal	54	⬅		1		
Intake air temperature (IAT) sensor	85	⬅	Ignition ON – air temp. 20°C	2,1 V		
	108	⊣	Ignition ON	0 V		
Knock sensor (KS) 1	99	⊣	Engine idling	0 V		
	106	⬅	Engine idling – accelerate briefly		50 mV/1 ms	∿∿ 38
	108	⊣	Ignition ON	0 V		
Knock sensor (KS) 2	99	⊣	Engine idling	0 V		
	107	⬅	Engine idling – accelerate briefly		50 mV/1 ms	∿∿ 38
	108	⊣	Ignition ON	0 V		
Mass air flow (MAF) sensor	27	⊣	Ignition ON	0 V		
	29	⬅	Engine idling	1,4 V		
	53	⇨	Ignition ON	5 V		
Power steering pressure (PSP) switch	49	⬅	Engine idling – steering wheel not turned	11-14 V		
	49	⬅	Engine idling – steering wheel turned	0 V		
	50	⊣	Ignition ON	0 V		
Secondary air injection (AIR) pump relay – ARZ	66	⫣▷	Ignition ON	11-14 V briefly then 0-1 V		
	66	⫣▷	Engine running – pump OFF	11-14 V		
	66	⫣▷	Engine running – pump ON	0-1 V		
Secondary air injection (AIR) solenoid – ARZ	9	⫣▷	Ignition ON	11-14 V briefly then 0-1 V		
	9	⫣▷	Engine running – solenoid OFF	11-14 V		
	9	⫣▷	Engine running – solenoid ON	0-1 V		
Spare cable	25			1		
	30			1		
	80			1		
Spare cable – AQA	61			1		
	116			1		
Spare cable – ARZ	48			1		
	67			1		
	81			1		
Throttle control system warning lamp – AQA	48	⫣▷		1		

✱ Suggested settings - Voltage/time per division

Component/circuit description	ECM pin	Signal	Condition	Typical value	Oscilloscope setting*	Wave form
Throttle motor	**117**	⇨	Ignition ON	11-14 V for 30 seconds then 3 V		
	117	⇨	Ignition ON – accelerator pedal released		2 V/0,5 ms	(30 seconds only) 64
	117	⇨	Ignition ON – accelerator pedal depressed		2 V/0,5 ms	71
	118	⇨	Ignition ON	11-14 V		
	118	⇨	Engine idling	11-14 V		
Throttle motor position sensor	**83**	⇨	Ignition ON	5 V		
	84	⬅	Ignition ON – accelerator pedal released	4,3 V		
	84	⬅	Ignition ON – accelerator pedal depressed	0,7 V		
	91	⏚	Ignition ON	0 V		
	92	⬅	Ignition ON – accelerator pedal released	0,7 V		
	92	⬅	Ignition ON – accelerator pedal depressed	4,3 V		
Turbocharger (TC) bypass valve	**105**	⏚▷	Ignition ON	11-14 V briefly then 0-1 V		
	105	⏚▷	Engine idling	11-14 V		
Turbocharger (TC) wastegate pressure sensor	**98**	⇨	Ignition ON	5 V		
	101	⬅	Ignition ON	1,9 V		
	101	⬅	Engine idling	1,9 V		
	104	⏚▷	Ignition ON	11-14 V briefly then 0-1 V		
	104	⏚▷	Engine idling	11-14 V		
	108	⏚	Ignition ON	0 V		

*Suggested settings - Voltage/time per division

[1] Connected pin - no test data available or random digital signal

VOLKSWAGEN

Bosch Motronic ME7.5

Model:	Engine code:	Year:
Golf/Bora 1,8 Turbo	AUM/AUQ	2000-04

ECM harness multi-plug

Terminal side

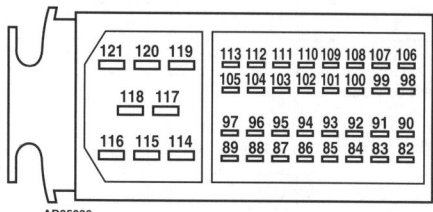
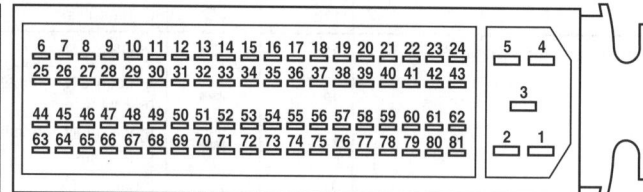

AD25036

Wire side

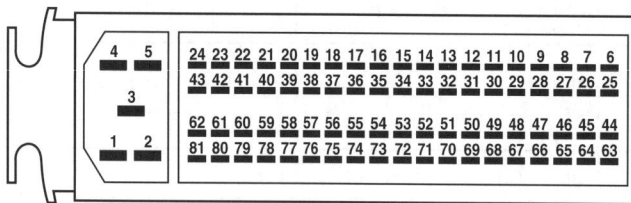

AD25035

Component/circuit description	ECM pin	Signal	Condition	Typical value	Oscilloscope setting★	Wave form
Accelerator pedal position (APP) sensor	33	⌐	Ignition ON	0 V		
	34	←	Ignition ON – accelerator pedal released	0,4 V		
	34	←	Ignition ON – accelerator pedal depressed	2 V		
	35	←	Ignition ON – accelerator pedal released	0,7 V		
	35	←	Ignition ON – accelerator pedal depressed	4,1 V		
	36	⌐	Ignition ON	0 V		
	72	⇒	Ignition ON	5 V		
	73	⇒	Ignition ON	5 V		
Air conditioning	40			1		
	41			1		
Air conditioning – some models	61			1		
Alternator	28	⇒	Engine idling		5 V/50 ms	⟋⟍⟋ 94
Battery	62	←	Ignition OFF	11-14 V		
Brake pedal position (BPP) switch 1	56	←	Ignition ON – brake pedal released	0 V		
	56	←	Ignition ON – brake pedal depressed	11-14 V		
Brake pedal position (BPP) switch 2	55	←	Ignition ON – brake pedal released	11-14 V		
	55	←	Ignition ON – brake pedal depressed	0 V		
Brake servo control module – AT	22			1		
Camshaft position (CMP) actuator	115	⌐⇒	Ignition ON	11-14 V briefly then 0-1 V		
	115	⌐⇒	Engine idling	11-14 V		

★ Suggested settings - Voltage/time per division

Component/circuit description	ECM pin	Signal	Condition	Typical value	Oscilloscope setting*	Wave form
Camshaft position (CMP) sensor	86	←	Ignition ON	0 or 11-14 V		
	86	←	Engine idling		5 V/20 ms	⎍⋀⋀ 14
	98	⇒	Ignition ON	5 V		
	108	⅃—	Ignition ON	0 V		
CAN data bus – high	60	⇐⇒		1		
CAN data bus – low	58	⇐⇒		1		
Clutch pedal position (CPP) switch	39	←	Ignition ON – clutch pedal released	11-14 V		
	39	←	Ignition ON – clutch pedal depressed	0 V		
Crankshaft position (CKP) sensor	82	←	Engine idling	3,1 V ac		
	82	←	Engine idling		2 V/2 ms	⎍⋀⋀ 2
	90	←	Engine idling	3,1 V ac		
	90	←	Engine idling		2 V/2 ms	Reversed ⎍⋀⋀ 2
	108	⅃—	Ignition ON	0 V		
Cruise control master switch	38			1		
	57			1		
Cruise control selector switch	38			1		
	75			1		
	76			1		
Earth	1		Ignition ON	0 V		
	2		Ignition ON	0 V		
Engine control (EC) relay	21	⅃⇒	Ignition ON	0-1 V		
	21	⅃⇒	Engine idling	0-1 V		
	121	←	Ignition ON	11-14 V		
Engine coolant temperature (ECT) sensor	93	←	Ignition ON – coolant temp. 20°C	2,2 V		
	93	←	Ignition ON – coolant temp. 80°C	0,4 V		
	108	⅃—	Ignition ON	0 V		
Evaporative emission (EVAP) canister purge valve	64	⅃⇒	Ignition ON	11-14 V briefly then 0-1 V		
	64	⅃⇒	Engine running – engine hot – valve operating		10 V/5 ms	⎍⋀⋀ 35
Fuel pump (FP) relay	65	⅃⇒	Ignition ON	0-1 V briefly then 11-14 V		
	65	⅃⇒	Engine idling	0-1 V		
Heated oxygen sensor (HO2S) 1	51	←	Engine idling	2,5 V		
	51 (70)	←	Engine idling	0,45 V		
	52	⇐⇒	Engine idling	2,34-2,55 V		
	70	←	Engine idling	2,9 V		
	70 (51)	←	Engine idling	0,45 V		
	71	⇐⇒	Engine idling	2,34-2,55 V		
Heated oxygen sensor (HO2S) 1 – heater control	5	⅃⇒			2 V/0,2 sec.	⎍⋀⋀ 55
Heated oxygen sensor (HO2S) 2	68	⅃⇒	Ignition ON	0 V		
	69	←	Engine idling – engine hot	0,6 V		

* Suggested settings - Voltage/time per division

Component/circuit description	ECM pin	Signal	Condition	Typical value	Oscilloscope setting*	Wave form
Heated oxygen sensor (HO2S) 2 – heater control	63	⊐⇒	Ignition ON	11-14 V briefly then 0-1 V		
	63	⊐⇒	Engine idling	0-1 V		
Ignition coil 1	102	⇒	Ignition ON	0 V		
	102	⇒	Engine idling		2 V/20 ms	〜 62
Ignition coil 2	95	⇒	Ignition ON	0 V		
	95	⇒	Engine idling		2 V/20 ms	〜 62
Ignition coil 3	103	⇒	Ignition ON	0 V		
	103	⇒	Engine idling		2 V/20 ms	〜 62
Ignition coil 4	94	⇒	Ignition ON	0 V		
	94	⇒	Engine idling		2 V/20 ms	〜 62
Ignition switch	3	⟵	Ignition OFF	0 V		
	3	⟵	Ignition ON	11-14 V		
Injector 1	96	⊐⇒	Ignition ON	11-14 V briefly then 0-1 V		
	96	⊐⇒	Engine idling	2,5 ms	10 V/2 ms	〜 35
Injector 2	89	⊐⇒	Ignition ON	11-14 V briefly then 0-1 V		
	89	⊐⇒	Engine idling	2,5 ms	10 V/2 ms	〜 35
Injector 3	97	⊐⇒	Ignition ON	11-14 V briefly then 0-1 V		
	97	⊐⇒	Engine idling	2,5 ms	10 V/2 ms	〜 35
Injector 4	88	⊐⇒	Ignition ON	11-14 V briefly then 0-1 V		
	88	⊐⇒	Engine idling	2,5 ms	10 V/2 ms	〜 35
Instrumentation control module – diagnosis signal	43			[1]		
Instrumentation control module – engine RPM signal	37	⇒	Engine idling	28 Hz		
Instrumentation control module – vehicle speed signal	54	⟵		[1]		
Intake air temperature (IAT) sensor	85	⟵	Ignition ON – air temp. 20°C	2,1 V		
	108	⊐—	Ignition ON	0 V		
Knock sensor (KS) 1	99	⊐—	Engine idling	0 V		
	106	⟵	Engine idling – accelerate briefly		50 mV/1 ms	〜 38
	108	⊐—	Ignition ON	0 V		
Knock sensor (KS) 2	99	⊐—	Engine idling	0 V		
	107	⟵	Engine idling – accelerate briefly		50 mV/1 ms	〜 38
	108	⊐—	Ignition ON	0 V		
Mass air flow (MAF) sensor	27	⊐—	Ignition ON	0 V		
	29	⟵	Engine idling	1,4 V		
	53	⇒	Ignition ON	5 V		
Power steering pressure (PSP) switch	49	⟵	Engine idling – steering wheel not turned	11-14 V		
	49	⟵	Engine idling – steering wheel turned	0 V		
	50	⊐—	Ignition ON	0 V		

* Suggested settings - Voltage/time per division

Component/circuit description	ECM pin	Signal	Condition	Typical value	Oscilloscope setting*	Wave form
Secondary air injection (AIR) pump relay	66	⊐▷	Ignition ON	11-14 V briefly then 0-1 V		
	66	⊐▷	Engine running – pump OFF	11-14 V		
	66	⊐▷	Engine running – pump ON	0-1 V		
Secondary air injection (AIR) solenoid	9	⊐▷	Ignition ON	11-14 V briefly then 0-1 V		
	9	⊐▷	Engine running – solenoid OFF	11-14 V		
	9	⊐▷	Engine running – solenoid ON	0-1 V		
Spare cable	30			1		
	47			1		
	48			1		
	67			1		
	81			1		
Throttle motor	117	⇒	Ignition ON	11-14 V for 30 seconds then 3 V		
	117	⇒	Ignition ON – accelerator pedal released		2 V/0,5 ms	⩗⩘ 64
	117	⇒	Ignition ON – accelerator pedal depressed		2 V/0,5 ms	⩗⩘ 71
	118	⇒	Ignition ON	11-14 V		
	118	⇒	Engine idling	11-14 V		
Throttle motor position sensor	83	⇒	Ignition ON	5 V		
	84	←	Ignition ON – accelerator pedal released	4,3 V		
	84	←	Ignition ON – accelerator pedal depressed	0,7 V		
	91	⊐—	Ignition ON	0 V		
	92	←	Ignition ON – accelerator pedal released	0,7 V		
	92	←	Ignition ON – accelerator pedal depressed	4,3 V		
Turbocharger (TC) bypass valve	105	⊐▷	Ignition ON	11-14 V briefly then 0-1 V		
	105	⊐▷	Engine idling	11-14 V		
Turbocharger (TC) wastegate pressure sensor	98	⇒	Ignition ON	5 V		
	101	←	Ignition ON	1,9 V		
	101	←	Engine idling	1,9 V		
	108	⊐—	Ignition ON	0 V		
Turbocharger (TC) wastegate regulating valve	104	⊐▷	Ignition ON	11-14 V briefly then 0-1 V		
	104	⊐▷	Engine idling	11-14 V		

*Suggested settings - Voltage/time per division

1 Connected pin - no test data available or random digital signal

VOLKSWAGEN

Bosch EDC 15V

Model:	Engine code:	Year:
Golf/Bora 1,9 TDI	AGR/AHF/ALH	1997-04/99

ECM harness multi-plug

Terminal side

AD42344

Wire side

AD42345

Component/circuit description	ECM pin	Signal	Condition	Typical value
AC master switch	48	←	Engine idling – AC OFF	0 V
	48	←	Engine idling – AC ON	11-14 V
Accelerator pedal position (APP) sensor	11	⇨	Ignition ON	5 V
	23	⌐	Ignition ON	0 V
	24	←	Ignition ON – accelerator pedal released	0,4 V
	24	←	Ignition ON – accelerator pedal depressed	4,4 V
Accelerator pedal position (APP) switch	12	←	Ignition ON – accelerator pedal released	0,1 V
	12	←	Ignition ON – accelerator pedal depressed	2,8 V
	25	⌐	Ignition ON	0 V
Alternator – MT	22	←	Engine idling	0 V
Brake pedal position (BPP) switch I	20	←	Ignition OFF – brake pedal released	0 V
	20	←	Ignition OFF – brake pedal depressed	11-14 V
Brake pedal position (BPP) switch II	9	←	Ignition ON – brake pedal released	11-14 V
	9	←	Ignition ON – brake pedal depressed	0 V
CAN data bus	68	↔		1
	75	↔		1
Clutch pedal position (CPP) switch	46	←	Ignition ON – clutch pedal released	11-14 V
	46	←	Ignition ON – clutch pedal depressed	0 V
Crankshaft position (CKP) sensor	67	←	Engine idling	3,8 V ac
	67	←	Engine idling	5 V/5 ms per division 〰 6
	69	⌐	Engine idling	0 V
	71	⌐	Engine idling	0 V
Crankshaft position (CKP) sensor – screened lead	71	⌐	Engine idling	0 V
Cruise control master switch	19			1
	21			1
	35			1

Component/circuit description	ECM pin	Signal	Condition	Typical value
Cruise control selector switch	10			1️⃣
	19			1️⃣
Earth	1		Ignition ON	0 V
	27		Ignition ON	0 V
Earth – AT	22	←	Engine idling	0 V
Engine control relay	2	←	Ignition OFF	0 V
	2	←	Ignition ON	11-14 V
	28	←	Ignition OFF	0 V
	28	←	Ignition ON	11-14 V
	33	⊐▷	Ignition OFF	11-14 V
	33	⊐▷	Ignition ON	0-1 V
Engine coolant blower motor control module/ AC compressor control module	16	⇒		1️⃣
Engine coolant blower motor relay	31	⊐▷		1️⃣
Engine coolant heater relay I	17	⊐▷	Engine idling – relay contacts open	11-14 V
	17	⊐▷	Engine idling – relay contacts closed	0-1 V
Engine coolant heater relay II	34	⊐▷	Engine idling – relay contacts open	11-14 V
	34	⊐▷	Engine idling – relay contacts closed	0-1 V
Engine coolant temperature (ECT) sensor	54	←	Ignition ON – coolant temp. 20°C	3,5 V
	54	←	Ignition ON – coolant temp. 80°C	1,4 V
	70	⊐—	Ignition ON	0 V
Exhaust gas recirculation (EGR) solenoid	29	⊐▷	Ignition ON	11-14 V
	29	⊐▷	Engine idling	5 V/5 ms per division ⟋⟍ww 4
Fuel injection timing solenoid	79	⊐▷	Engine idling	2 V/10 ms per division ⟋⟍ww 10
	79	⊐▷	Ignition ON	11-14 V
Fuel quantity adjuster	59	⊐▷	Engine idling	11,3 V
	59	⊐▷	Engine idling	2 V/2 ms per division ⟋⟍ww 5
	66	⊐▷	Engine idling	11,3 V
	66	⊐▷	Engine idling	2 V/2 ms per division ⟋⟍ww 5
	80	⊐▷	Engine idling	11,3 V
	80	⊐▷	Engine idling	2 V/2 ms per division ⟋⟍ww 5
Fuel quantity adjuster position sensor	56	←	Ignition ON	2,5 V
	56	←	Engine idling	0,5 V/0,1 ms per division ⟋⟍ww 8
	57	⇒	Ignition ON	2,5 V
	64	←	Ignition ON	2,5 V
	64	←	Engine idling	0,5 V/0,1 ms per division ⟋⟍ww 8
Fuel shut-off solenoid	77	⇒	Ignition OFF	0 V
	77	⇒	Ignition ON	11-14 V
Fuel temperature sensor	53	←	Ignition ON – fuel temp. 20°C	3,5 V
	76	⊐—	Ignition ON	0 V
Glow plug relay	42	⊐▷	Ignition ON – glow plugs ON	0-1 V
	42	⊐▷	Ignition ON – glow plugs OFF	11-14 V

Component/circuit description	ECM pin	Signal	Condition	Typical value
Glow plug warning lamp	41	⊣⊳	Ignition ON – lamp ON	0 V
	41	⊣⊳	Ignition ON – lamp OFF	10,5 V
Ignition switch	47	⟵	Ignition OFF	0 V
	47	⟵	Ignition ON	11-14 V
Injector needle lift sensor	55	⊣—	Engine idling	0 V
	62	⟵	Engine idling	0,02 V ac
	62	⟵	Engine idling	0,2 V/1 ms per division ⎍⎍ 7
Injector needle lift sensor – screened lead	71	⊣—	Engine idling	0 V
Instrument panel – immobilization/diagnosis signal	45	⟵⟳	Ignition ON	11-14 V
	45	⟵⟳	Engine idling	11-14 V
Instrumentation control module – fuel consumption signal	18	⟹		1
Instrumentation control module – tachometer signal	6	⟹	Engine idling	30 Hz
	6	⟹	Engine idling	5 V/10 ms per division ⎍⎍ 2
Instrumentation control module – vehicle speed signal	51	⟵	Ignition ON – vehicle pushed	0 V or 11-14 V (switching)
Intake air temperature (IAT) sensor	13	⟵	Ignition ON – air temp. 20°C	3,75 V
	25	⊣—	Ignition ON	0 V
Intake manifold air control solenoid	3	⊣⊳	Ignition ON	11-14 V
	3	⊣⊳	Engine idling	11-14 V
	3	⊣⊳	Engine idling – switch ignition OFF	0-1 V for 3 seconds
Manifold absolute pressure (MAP) sensor	25	⊣—	Engine idling	0 V
	39	⟹	Ignition ON	5 V
	40	⟵	Ignition ON	1,9 V
	40	⟵	Engine idling	1,85 V
	40	⟵	Engine running – accelerator pedal briefly fully depressed	3,65 V (briefly)
Mass air flow (MAF) sensor – ALH 05/98→	4	⊣—	Engine idling	0 V
	50	⟹	Ignition ON	5 V
	52	⟵	Ignition ON	0,28 V
	52	⟵	Engine idling	1 V
	52	⟵	Engine running – accelerator pedal briefly fully depressed	4,35 V (briefly)
Mass air flow (MAF) sensor – except ALH 05/98→	25	⊣—	Engine idling	0 V
Transmission control module (TCM) – kick-down signal	44	⟹		1
Transmission kick-down switch	25	⊣—	Ignition ON	0 V
	8	⟵		1
Turbocharger (TC) wastegate regulating valve	15	⊣⊳	Ignition ON	11-14 V
	15	⊣⊳	Engine running – valve not operating	11-14 V
	15	⊣⊳	Engine running – valve operating	0-1 V

1 Connected pin - no test data available

Model:	Engine code:	Year:
Golf/Bora 1,9 TDI PD	AJM/ARL/ASZ/ATD/AUY	1999-05
Passat 1,9 TDI PD	AJM/ATJ/AVB/AVF/AWX	1998-05
Sharan 1,9 TDI PD	ANU/AUY	1999-06

VOLKSWAGEN

Bosch EDC 15P/16

ECM harness multi-plug

Terminal side

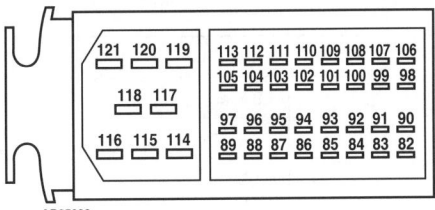

AD25036

Wire side

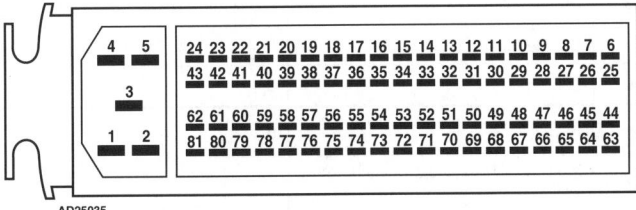

AD25035

Component/circuit description	ECM pin	Signal	Condition	Typical value	Oscilloscope setting*	Wave form
AC connection, AC ON signal	34	←	Engine idling – AC OFF	0 V		
	34	←	Engine idling – AC ON	11-14 V		
AC connection, compressor shut-off signal	29	⇨	Engine idling – AC OFF	0 V		
	29	⇨	Engine idling – AC ON – compressor ON	11-14 V		
AC control module, engine RPM signal – Golf/Bora/Passat, with ATC	27	⇨	Engine idling	30 Hz		
	27	⇨	Engine idling		5 V/10 ms	ᴡᴡ 2
	27	⇨	3000 rpm	100 Hz		
Accelerator pedal position (APP) sensor	12	⇨	Ignition ON	5 V		
	50	⌐	Ignition ON	0 V		
	69	←	Ignition ON – accelerator pedal released	0,4 V		
	69	←	Ignition ON – accelerator pedal fully depressed	4,4 V		
Accelerator pedal position (APP) switch	51	⌐	Ignition ON	0 V		
	70	←	Ignition ON – accelerator pedal released	0,2 V		
	70	←	Ignition ON – accelerator pedal depressed	5 V		
Alternator, charging signal – except Sharan →04/99	38	⇨	Ignition ON		2 V/20 ms	ᴡᴡ 43
Auxiliary circuits relay – Sharan 09/00→ & Passat, ATJ	88	←	Ignition OFF	0 V		
	88	←	Ignition ON	11-14 V		
	88	←	Engine cranking	0 V		
	88	←	Engine idling	11-14 V		
Brake pedal position (BPP) switch 1	32	←	Ignition OFF – brake pedal released	0 V		
	32	←	Ignition OFF – brake pedal depressed	11-14 V		
Brake pedal position (BPP) switch 2	65	←	Ignition ON – brake pedal released	11-14 V		
	65	←	Ignition ON – brake pedal depressed	0 V		

★ Suggested settings - Voltage/time per division

Component/circuit description	ECM pin	Signal	Condition	Typical value	Oscilloscope setting*	Wave form
Camshaft position (CMP) sensor	101	⌐—	Ignition ON	0 V		
	109	⬅	Engine idling		2 V/5 ms	∿ 58
CAN data bus – except Sharan →04/00	6	⬌		[1]		
	7	⬌		[1]		
Clutch pedal position (CPP) switch	66	⬅	Ignition ON – clutch pedal released	11-14 V		
	66	⬅	Ignition ON – clutch pedal depressed	0 V		
Crankshaft position (CKP) sensor	102	⬅	Ignition ON	2,5 V		
	102	⬅	Engine idling	1,9 V ac		
	102	⬅	Engine idling		2 V/1 ms	∿ 25
	102	⬅	3000 rpm	3,1 V		
	110	⬅	Ignition ON	2,5 V		
	110	⬅	Engine idling	1,9 V ac		
	110	⬅	Engine idling		2 V/1 ms	Reversed ∿ 25
	110	⬅	3000 rpm	3,1 V		
Cruise control master switch	14	⬅	Ignition ON – selector switch set to 'OFF'	0 V		
	14	⬅	Ignition ON – selector switch set to 'ON'	11-14 V		
	44	⬅	Ignition ON – master switch released	0 V		
	44	⬅	Ignition ON – master switch depressed	11-14 V		
Cruise control selector switch	14	⬅	Ignition ON – selector switch set to 'OFF'	0 V		
	14	⬅	Ignition ON – selector switch set to 'ON'	11-14 V		
	45	⬅	Ignition ON – selector switch set to 'ON'	0 V		
	45	⬅	Ignition ON – selector switch set to 'RES'	11-14 V		
	46	⬅	Ignition ON – selector switch set to 'OFF'	0 V		
	46	⬅	Ignition ON – selector switch set to 'ON'	11-14 V		
Data link connector (DLC)	6			[1]		
	7			[1]		
Earth	4		Ignition ON	0 V		
	5		Ignition ON	0 V		
Engine control (EC) relay	1	⬅	Ignition OFF	0 V		
	1	⬅	Ignition ON	11-14 V		
	2	⬅	Ignition OFF	0 V		
	2	⬅	Ignition ON	11-14 V		
	18	⌐▷	Ignition OFF	11-14 V		
	18	⌐▷	Ignition ON	0-1 V		
Engine coolant blower motor control module – Golf/Bora/Sharan, if fitted	11			[1]		
Engine coolant blower motor run-on relay – if fitted	11			[1]		
Engine coolant heater relay 1, low output – if fitted	21	⌐▷		[1]		
Engine coolant heater relay 2, high output – if fitted	22	⌐▷		[1]		
Engine coolant temperature (ECT) sensor	104	⌐—	Ignition ON	0 V		
	112	⬅	Ignition ON – coolant temp. 10°C	4 V		
	112	⬅	Ignition ON – coolant temp. 80°C	1,2 V		

* Suggested settings - Voltage/time per division

Component/circuit description	ECM pin	Signal	Condition	Typical value	Oscilloscope setting*	Wave form
Exhaust gas recirculation (EGR) solenoid	61	⊐⊳	Ignition ON	11-14 V		
	61	⊐⊳	Engine idling		5 V/1 ms	ᴡᴧᴡ 2
Fuel cooling pump motor relay – Passat	43	⊐⊳	Ignition ON – pump motor OFF	11-14 V		
	43	⊐⊳	Engine idling – pump motor ON	0-1 V		
Fuel lift pump relay – some models	80	⊐⊳	Ignition ON	0-1 V briefly then 11-14 V		
	80	⊐⊳	Engine idling	0-1 V		
Fuel temperature sensor	103	⊐—	Ignition ON	0 V		
	111	⟵	Ignition ON – fuel temp. 5°C	4,6 V		
Glow plug relay	42	⊐⊳	Ignition ON – glow plugs ON	0-1 V		
	42	⊐⊳	Ignition ON – glow plugs OFF	11-14 V		
Glow plug warning lamp – Passat →04/99 & Sharan →04/00	40	⊐⊳	Ignition ON – warning lamp ON	0-1 V		
	40	⊐⊳	Ignition ON – warning lamp OFF	11-14 V		
Heated rear window switch – Passat	34	⟵	Engine idling – heated rear window OFF	0 V		
	34	⟵	Engine idling – heated rear window ON	11-14 V		
Ignition switch	37	⟵	Ignition OFF	0 V		
	37	⟵	Ignition ON	11-14 V		
	37	⟵	Engine cranking	11-14 V		
	37	⟵	Engine idling	11-14 V		
Ignition switch – Sharan 5/00-8/00 & Golf/Bora	88	⟵	Ignition OFF	0 V		
	88	⟵	Ignition ON	11-14 V		
	88	⟵	Engine cranking	0 V		
	88	⟵	Engine idling	11-14 V		
Immobilizer control module, immobilization/diagnosis signal – Sharan	16	⟷		1		
Injector 1	114	⟹	Ignition ON	0,3 V		
	116	⟹	Ignition ON	0,3 V		
	116 (114)	⟹	Engine idling	2,2 ms		
	116 (114)	⟹	Engine idling		10 V/0,5 ms	ᴡᴧᴡ 57
Injector 2	114	⟹	Ignition ON	0,3 V		
	117	⟹	Ignition ON	0,3 V		
	117 (114)	⟹	Engine idling	2,2 ms		
	117 (114)	⟹	Engine idling		10 V/0,5 ms	ᴡᴧᴡ 57
Injector 3	114	⟹	Ignition ON	0,3 V		
	118	⟹	Ignition ON	0,3 V		
	118 (114)	⟹	Engine idling	2,2 ms		
	118 (114)	⟹	Engine idling		10 V/0,5 ms	ᴡᴧᴡ 57
Injector 4	114	⟹	Ignition ON	0,3 V		
	121	⟹	Ignition ON	0,3 V		
	121 (114)	⟹	Engine idling	2,2 ms		
	121 (114)	⟹	Engine idling		10 V/0,5 ms	ᴡᴧᴡ 57
Instrument panel, immobilization/ diagnosis signal – Golf/Bora/Passat	16	⟷		1		

* Suggested settings - Voltage/time per division

Component/circuit description	ECM pin	Signal	Condition	Typical value	Oscilloscope setting*	Wave form
Instrumentation control module – vehicle speed signal	20	←	Ignition ON – vehicle pushed	0 V or 10 V min. (switching)		
Instrumentation control module, engine RPM signal – some models	27	⇒	Engine idling	30 Hz		
	27	⇒	Engine idling		5 V/10 ms	∿∿ 2
	27	⇒	3000 rpm	100 Hz		
Instrumentation control module, fuel consumption signal – some models	28	⇒		1		
Intake air temperature (IAT) sensor	52	⅂	Ignition ON	0 V		
	73	←	Ignition ON – air temp. 10°C	3 V		
Intake manifold air control solenoid	81	⅂⇒	Ignition ON	11-14 V		
	81	⅂⇒	Engine idling	11-14 V		
	81	⅂⇒	Engine idling – switch ignition OFF	0-1 V for 2,5 secs., 11-14 V for 0,5 sec then 0 V		
Manifold absolute pressure (MAP) sensor, TC system	31	⇒	Ignition ON	5 V		
	52	⅂	Ignition ON	0 V		
	71	←	Ignition ON	1,6 V		
	71	←	Engine idling	1,7 V		
Mass air flow (MAF) sensor	30	⇒	Ignition ON	5 V		
	49	⅂	Ignition ON	0 V		
	68	←	Ignition ON	1 V		
	68	←	Engine idling	1,5-2,1 V		
	68	←	3000 rpm	3,2 V		
Spare cable, engine rear bulkhead – Passat 10/00→	15			1		
Spare cable, engine rear bulkhead – Golf/Bora	33			1		
Spare cable, engine rear bulkhead – Passat 05/99→ & Golf/Bora	40			1		
Spare cable, engine rear bulkhead – some models	28			1		
	47			1		
Transmission control module (TCM) – some models	19			1		
Transmission kick-down switch	51	⅂	Ignition ON	0 V		
	63	←	Ignition ON – accelerator pedal released	5 V		
	63	←	Ignition ON – accelerator pedal fully depressed	0 V		
Turbocharger (TC) wastegate regulating valve	62	⅂⇒	Ignition ON	11-14 V		
	62	⅂⇒	Engine idling	11-14 V		
	62	⅂⇒	Engine idling – accelerator pedal fully depressed, briefly	0-1 V briefly		
	62	⅂⇒	Engine running – valve not operating	11-14 V		
	62	⅂⇒	Engine running – valve operating	0-1 V		

*Suggested settings - Voltage/time per division

1 Connected pin - no test data available

Model:	Engine code:	Year:
Golf/Bora 2,0	AQY	1998-02
Golf/Bora 2,0	APK	1998-02
Golf Cabrio 2,0	ATU/AWF/AWG	1999-02

VOLKSWAGEN

Bosch Motronic M5.9.2

ECM harness multi-plug

Terminal side

```
80 79 78 77 76 75 74
   73 72 71 70 69 68 67
66 65 64 63 62 61 60
   59 58 57 56 55 54 53
AD42344
```

```
52 51 50 49 48 47 46 45 44 43 42 41
   40 39 38 37 36 35 34 33 32 31 30 29        28 27
26 25 24 23 22 21 20 19 18 17 16 15
   14 13 12 11 10  9  8  7  6  5  4  3     2  1
```

Wire side

```
          41 42 43 44 45 46 47 48 49 50 51 52
          29 30 31 32 33 34 35 36 37 38 39 40
27 28      15 16 17 18 19 20 21 22 23 24 25 26
 1  2     3  4  5  6  7  8  9 10 11 12 13 14
AD42345
```

```
74 75 76 77 78 79 80
67 68 69 70 71 72 73
60 61 62 63 64 65 66
53 54 55 56 57 58 59
```

Component/circuit description	ECM pin	Signal	Condition	Typical value	Oscilloscope setting*	Wave form
Air conditioning	8	←	Engine idling – AC OFF	0 V		
	8	←	Engine idling – AC ON – AC compressor ON	11-14 V		
	10	⇒	Engine idling – AC OFF	0 V		
	10	⇒	Engine idling – AC ON – AC compressor ON	11-14 V		
Battery	3	←	Ignition OFF	11-14 V		
Camshaft position (CMP) sensor	67	⊣⎯	Ignition ON	0 V		
	76	←	Engine idling		5 V/20 ms	∿ 14
CAN data bus – some models	29	⬌		[1]		
	41	⬌		[1]		
Closed throttle position (CTP) switch	67	⊣⎯	Ignition ON	0 V		
	69	←	Ignition ON – throttle closed	0 V		
	69	←	Ignition ON – throttle open	11-14 V		
Crankshaft position (CKP) sensor	56	←	Engine idling	1,6 V ac	5 V/1 ms	∿ 2
	63	←	Engine idling	1,6 V ac	5 V/1 ms	Reversed ∿ 2
Crankshaft position (CKP) sensor – shield wire	67	⊣⎯	Ignition ON	0 V		
Data link connector (DLC) – ATU	43	⬌		[1]		
Earth	2		Ignition ON	0 V		
Engine coolant temperature (ECT) sensor	53	←	Ignition ON – coolant temp. 20°C	2,2 V		
	53	←	Ignition ON – coolant temp. 90°C	0,36 V		
	67	⊣⎯	Ignition ON	0 V		
Evaporative emission (EVAP) canister purge valve	15	⊣⎯▷	Engine running – engine hot – valve operating		10 V/20 ms	∿ 20
Fuel pump relay	4	⊣⎯▷	Ignition ON	0 V briefly then 11-14 V		
	4	⊣⎯▷	Engine idling	0-1 V		

* Suggested settings - Voltage/time per division

Component/circuit description	ECM pin	Signal	Condition	Typical value	Oscilloscope setting*	Wave form
Heated oxygen sensor (HO2S) 1	25	⌐—	Engine idling	0 V		
	26	←	Engine idling – engine hot	0,1-1 V fluctuating	0,2 V/2 ms	〜21
	27	⌐▷	Engine idling	0,2 V		
Heated oxygen sensor (HO2S) 2	28	⌐▷	Engine idling	0,2 V		
	51	⌐—	Engine idling	0 V		
	52	←	3000 rpm – engine hot	0,6 V		
Heated oxygen sensor (HO2S) – shield wire – ATU/AWF/AWG	24	⌐—	Ignition ON	0 V		
Idle speed control (ISC) actuator	59	⇨	Engine idling		5 V/2 ms	〜28
	66	⇨	Engine idling	0,1 V		
Idle speed control (ISC) actuator position sensor	62	⇨	Ignition ON	5 V		
	67	⌐—	Ignition ON	0 V		
	74	←	Engine idling	3,6-3,9 V		
Ignition amplifier – ATU	71	⇨	Ignition ON	0,15 V		
	71	⇨	Engine idling		1 V/20 ms	〜32
Ignition amplifier – AQY/APK	71	⇨	Ignition ON	0,15 V		
	71	⇨	Engine idling		1 V/20 ms	〜32
	78	⇨	Ignition ON	0,15 V		
	78	⇨	Engine idling		1 V/20 ms	〜32
Ignition switch	1	←	Ignition OFF	0 V		
	1	←	Ignition ON	11-14 V		
Injector 1	73	⌐▷	Engine idling	3,6 ms	10 V/2 ms	〜35
Injector 2	80	⌐▷	Engine idling	3,6 ms	10 V/2 ms	〜35
Injector 3	58	⌐▷	Engine idling	3,6 ms	10 V/2 ms	〜35
Injector 4	65	⌐▷	Engine idling	3,6 ms	10 V/2 ms	〜35
Instrumentation control module – engine RPM signal	6	⇨	Engine idling	26 Hz		
Immobilizer control module	19		Engine idling	11-14 V		
Instrumentation control module – vehicle speed signal	20	←	Ignition ON	10,5 V		
Instrumentation control module – ATU/AWF/AWG	18			[1]		
Intake air temperature (IAT) sensor – ATU/AWF/AWG	54	←	Ignition ON – air temp. 20°C	2 V		
	67	⌐—	Engine idling	0 V		
Knock sensor (KS) – ATU/AWF/AWG	67	⌐—	Ignition ON	0 V		
	68	←	Engine idling – accelerate briefly		50 mV/1 ms	〜38
Knock sensor (KS) 1 – AQY/APK	60	←	Engine idling – accelerate briefly		50 mV/1 ms	〜38
	67	⌐—	Ignition ON	0 V		
Knock sensor (KS) 2 – AQY/APK	67	⌐—	Ignition ON	0 V		
	68	←	Engine idling – accelerate briefly		50 mV/1 ms	〜38
Knock sensor (KS) 1 – shield wire – AQY/APK	67	⌐—	Ignition ON	0 V		
Knock sensor (KS) 2 – shield wire – AQY/APK	67	⌐—	Ignition ON	0 V		
Malfunction indicator lamp (MIL) – ATU/AWF/AWG	17	⌐▷	Ignition ON – MIL ON	0-1 V		
	17	⌐▷	Engine running – MIL OFF	11-14 V		

* Suggested settings - Voltage/time per division

Component/circuit description	ECM pin	Signal	Condition	Typical value	Oscilloscope setting*	Wave form
Mass air flow (MAF) sensor	11	⇨	Ignition ON	5 V		
	12	⊣	Engine idling	0 V		
	13	⬅	Engine idling	1,4 V		
	13	⬅	Engine idling – full throttle briefly	4 V briefly		
Mass air flow (MAF) sensor – AQY/APK – IAT signal	40	⬅	Ignition ON – air temp. 20°C	2 V		
Secondary air injection (AIR) pump relay – AQY/ATU	30	⊐▷	Ignition ON	11-14 V briefly then 0 V		
	30	⊐▷	Engine running – pump OFF	11-14 V		
	30	⊐▷	Engine running – pump ON	0 V		
Secondary air injection (AIR) solenoid – AQY/ATU – if fitted	33	⊐▷	Ignition ON	11-14 V briefly then 0 V		
	33	⊐▷	Engine running – solenoid OFF	11-14 V		
	33	⊐▷	Engine running – solenoid ON	0 V		
Spare cable	21			1		
Spare cable – AQY/APK	17			1		
	18			1		
	43			1		
Throttle position (TP) sensor	62	⇨	Ignition ON	5 V		
	67	⊣	Ignition ON	0 V		
	75	⬅	Ignition ON – throttle closed	4 V		
	75	⬅	Ignition ON – throttle fully open	0,6 V		
Transmission control module (TCM)	8	⬅	Engine idling – AC ON – AC compressor ON	11-14 V		
	22			1		
	32			1		

*Suggested settings - Voltage/time per division

1 Connected pin - no test data available or random digital signal

VOLKSWAGEN

Bosch Motronic M3.2

Model:	Engine code:	Year:
Passat 1,6	ADP	1996-00

ECM harness multi-plug

Terminal side

E A B C D

AD42347

Wire side

D C B A E

AD42348

Component/circuit description	ECM pin	Signal	Condition	Typical value	Oscilloscope setting★	Wave form
Air conditioning	C14			1		
Automatic transmission	B1			1		
	B9			1		
	B11			1		
Battery	D9	←	Ignition OFF	11-14 V		
Camshaft position (CMP) sensor	A3	⇨	Ignition ON	5 V		
	A15	⌐	Ignition ON	0 V		
	B2	←	Ignition ON – engine turned	0 V or 11-14 V switching		
	B2	←	Engine idling		5 V/20 ms	12
Closed throttle position (CTP) switch	A15	⌐	Ignition ON	0 V		
	B4	←	Ignition ON – throttle closed	0 V		
	B4	←	Ignition ON – throttle open	11-14 V		
Crankshaft position (CKP) sensor	B15	⌐	Engine idling	0 V		
	B16	←	Engine idling		2 V/1 ms	2
Earth	D11		Ignition ON	0 V		
	D12		Ignition ON	0 V		
	E11		Ignition ON	0 V		
	E12		Ignition ON	0 V		
Engine coolant temperature (ECT) sensor	A5	←	Ignition ON – coolant temp. 10°C	2 V		
	A5	←	Ignition ON – coolant temp. 80°C	0,4 V		
	A15	⌐	Ignition ON	0 V		
Evaporative emission (EVAP) canister purge valve	D4	⇨	Engine hot – valve operating		10 V/20 ms	20
Fuel pump relay	D6	⇨	Engine cranking	0-1 V		

★ Suggested settings - Voltage/time per division

Component/circuit description	ECM pin	Signal	Condition	Typical value	Oscilloscope setting*	Wave form
Heated oxygen sensor (HO2S)	A10	⌐—	Engine idling	0 V		
	A11	←	Engine idling – engine hot	0,1-1 V fluctuating	0,2 V/1 sec.	ᴡᴡ 21
Idle speed control (ISC) actuator	D1 (D5)	⇨	Engine idling		5 V/2 ms	ᴡᴡ 28
	D5 (D1)	⇨	Engine idling		5 V/2 ms	ᴡᴡ 28
Idle speed control (ISC) actuator position sensor	A3	⇨	Ignition ON	5 V		
	A13	←	Engine idling – engine hot	3,6 V		
	A15	⌐—	Ignition ON	0 V		
Ignition amplifier	B5	⇨	Engine idling		1 V/10 ms	ᴡᴡ 32
Ignition switch	D10	←	Ignition OFF	0 V		
	D10	←	Ignition ON	11-14 V		
Injector 1	E1	⌐⇨	Engine idling – engine hot	2-3,5 ms	10 V/2 ms	ᴡᴡ 35
Injector 2	E6	⌐⇨	Engine idling – engine hot	2-3,5 ms	10 V/2 ms	ᴡᴡ 35
Injector 3	E5	⌐⇨	Engine idling – engine hot	2-3,5 ms	10 V/2 ms	ᴡᴡ 35
Injector 4	E2	⌐⇨	Engine idling – engine hot	2-3,5 ms	10 V/2 ms	ᴡᴡ 35
Instrumentation control module	A7	⇨	Ignition ON	11-14 V		
	C12			1		
Instrumentation control module – engine RPM signal	C10	⇨	Engine idling	30 Hz		
	C10	⇨	3000 rpm	100 Hz		
Instrumentation control module – vehicle speed signal	C13	←	Ignition ON – vehicle pushed	0 V or 11-14 V switching		
Knock sensor (KS)	A8	←	Engine idling – accelerate briefly		50 mV/1 ms	ᴡᴡ 38
	A15	⌐—	Engine idling	0 V		
Mass air flow (MAF) sensor	A1	←	Engine idling	1,2 V		
	A1	←	2000 rpm	1,6 V		
	A1	←	4000 rpm	2,2 V		
	A9	⌐—	Engine idling	0 V		
Throttle position (TP) sensor	A3	⇨	Ignition ON	5 V		
	A14	←	Ignition ON – throttle closed	4 V		
	A14	←	Ignition ON – throttle fully open	0,6 V		
	A15	⌐—	Ignition ON	0 V		

*Suggested settings - Voltage/time per division

1 Connected pin - no test data available or random digital signal

VOLKSWAGEN

Bosch Motronic M3.8.2

Model:	Engine code:	Year:
Passat 1,8	ADR	1996-00
Passat 1,8 Turbo	AEB	1996-00

ECM harness multi-plug

Terminal side

```
80 79 78 77 76 75 74        52 51 50 49 48 47 46 45 44 43 42 41
   73 72 71 70 69 68 67       40 39 38 37 36 35 34 33 32 31 30 29        28 27
66 65 64 63 62 61 60        26 25 24 23 22 21 20 19 18 17 16 15
   59 58 57 56 55 54 53       14 13 12 11 10  9  8  7  6  5  4  3           2  1
```
AD42344

Wire side

```
              41 42 43 44 45 46 47 48 49 50 51 52      74 75 76 77 78 79 80
            29 30 31 32 33 34 35 36 37 38 39 40      67 68 69 70 71 72 73
  27 28     15 16 17 18 19 20 21 22 23 24 25 26      60 61 62 63 64 65 66
   1  2      3  4  5  6  7  8  9 10 11 12 13 14      53 54 55 56 57 58 59
```
AD42345

Component/circuit description	ECM pin	Signal	Condition	Typical value	Oscilloscope setting*	Wave form
ABS control module – AT – Turbo	5			①		
Air conditioning	8		Engine idling – AC OFF	0 V		
	8		Engine idling – AC ON – AC compressor ON	11-14 V		
Air conditioning – except Turbo 1997-99	10			①		
Automatic transmission	7			①		
	22			①		
	23			①		
Automatic transmission – Turbo	49			①		
Barometric pressure (BARO) sensor – Turbo	61	←	Ignition ON – at sea level	4 V		
	61	←	Ignition ON – 1000 m above sea level	3 V		
	61	←	Ignition ON – 2000 m above sea level	2,1 V		
	62	⇒	Ignition ON	5 V		
	67	⌐	Ignition ON	0 V		
Battery	3	←	Ignition OFF	11-14 V		
Camshaft position (CMP) actuator – non-Turbo	55	⌐⇒	Engine idling	11-14 V		
	55	⌐⇒	Accelerate in first gear, MT – accelerate in second gear, AT – 1800-3200 rpm	0-1 V briefly		
Camshaft position (CMP) sensor	67	⌐	Ignition ON	0 V		
	76	←	Engine idling		5 V/20 ms	〜 12
Camshaft position (CMP) sensor – non-Turbo	62	⇒	Ignition ON	5 V		
Camshaft position (CMP) sensor – Turbo	11	⇒	Ignition ON	5 V		
Closed throttle position (CTP) switch	67	⌐	Ignition ON	0 V		
	69	←	Ignition ON – throttle closed	0 V		
	69	←	Ignition ON – throttle open	11-14 V		
Crankshaft position (CKP) sensor	56	←	Engine idling		2 V/1 ms	〜 2
	63	←	Engine idling		2 V/1 ms	〜 2
Earth	2		Ignition ON	0 V		
Engine coolant temperature (ECT) sensor	53	←	Ignition ON – coolant temp. 10°C	2 V		
	53	←	Ignition ON – coolant temp. 80°C	0,4 V		
	67	⌐	Ignition ON	0 V		
Evaporative emission (EVAP) canister purge valve	15	⌐⇒	Engine hot – valve operating		10 V/20 ms	〜 20
Fuel pump relay	4	⌐⇒	Ignition ON	0 V briefly then 11-14 V		
	4	⌐⇒	Engine idling	0-1 V		

* Suggested settings - Voltage/time per division

Autodata

Component/circuit description	ECM pin	Signal	Condition	Typical value	Oscilloscope setting*	Wave form
Heated oxygen sensor (HO2S)	25	⊣—	Engine idling	0 V		
	26	←	Engine idling – engine hot	0,1-1 V fluctuating	0,2 V/2 ms	〰 21
	27	⊣▷	Engine idling	0-1 V		
Idle speed control (ISC) actuator	59 (66)	⇒	Engine idling		2 V/2 ms	〰 28
	66 (59)	⇒	Engine idling		2 V/2 ms	〰 28
Idle speed control (ISC) actuator position sensor	67	⊣—	Ignition ON	0 V		
	74	←	Engine idling – engine hot	3,6-3,9 V		
Idle speed control (ISC) actuator position sensor – non-Turbo	62	⇒	Ignition ON	5 V		
Idle speed control (ISC) actuator position sensor – Turbo	11	⇒	Ignition ON	5 V		
Ignition amplifier	71	⇒	Engine idling		1 V/10 ms	〰 32
	78	⇒	Engine idling		1 V/10 ms	〰 32
Ignition amplifier – Turbo	70	⇒	Engine idling		1 V/10 ms	〰 32
	77	⇒	Engine idling		1 V/10 ms	〰 32
Ignition switch	1	←	Ignition OFF	0 V		
	1	←	Ignition ON	11-14 V		
Injector 1 – non-Turbo	73	⊣▷	Engine idling – engine hot	2-5 ms	10 V/2 ms	〰 35
Injector 1 – Turbo	73	⊣▷	Engine idling – engine hot	1-3 ms	10 V/2 ms	〰 35
Injector 2 – non-Turbo	80	⊣▷	Engine idling – engine hot	2-5 ms	10 V/2 ms	〰 35
Injector 2 – Turbo	80	⊣▷	Engine idling – engine hot	1-3 ms	10 V/2 ms	〰 35
Injector 3 – non-Turbo	58	⊣▷	Engine idling – engine hot	2-5 ms	10 V/2 ms	〰 35
Injector 3 – Turbo	58	⊣▷	Engine idling – engine hot	1-3 ms	10 V/2 ms	〰 35
Injector 4 – non-Turbo	65	⊣▷	Engine idling – engine hot	2-5 ms	10 V/2 ms	〰 35
Injector 4 – Turbo	65	⊣▷	Engine idling – engine hot	1-3 ms	10 V/2 ms	〰 35
Instrumentation control module	18			1		
Instrumentation control module – engine RPM signal	6	⇒	Engine idling	30 Hz		
Instrumentation control module – immobilization/diagnosis signal	19		Engine idling	11-14 V		
Instrumentation control module – vehicle speed signal	20	←	Ignition ON – vehicle pushed	0 V or 11-14 V switching		
Intake air temperature (IAT) sensor	54	←	Ignition ON – air temp. 10°C	2 V		
	67	⊣—	Ignition ON	0 V		
Intake manifold air control solenoid – non-Turbo	64	⊣▷	Engine idling	11-14 V		
	64	⊣▷	Engine idling – throttle fully open briefly	0-1 V briefly		
Knock sensor (KS) 1	60	←	Engine idling – accelerate briefly		50 mV/1 ms	〰 38
	67	⊣—	Engine idling	0 V		
Knock sensor (KS) 2	67	⊣—	Engine idling	0 V		
	68	←	Engine idling – accelerate briefly		50 mV/1 ms	〰 38
Mass air flow (MAF) sensor	12	⊣—	Engine idling	0 V		
	13	←	Engine idling – engine hot	0,8-1,1 V		
	13	←	3000 rpm	1,7-2 V		
Throttle position (TP) sensor	67	⊣—	Ignition ON	0 V		
	75	←	Ignition ON – throttle closed	4,3 V after 20 seconds		
	75	←	Ignition ON – throttle fully open	0,6 V		
Throttle position (TP) sensor – non-Turbo	62	⇒	Ignition ON	5 V		
Throttle position (TP) sensor – Turbo	11	⇒	Ignition ON	5 V		
Turbocharger (TC) wastegate regulating valve	64	⊣▷	Engine idling	11-14 V		
	64	⊣▷	Vehicle moving – accelerate – full load	1-99%		

*Suggested settings - Voltage/time per division

1 Connected pin - no test data available or random digital signal

VOLKSWAGEN

Bosch EDC 15V

Model:	Engine code:	Year:
Passat 1,9 TDI	AFN/AHH/AHU/AVG	08/97-01

ECM harness multi-plug

Terminal side

```
80 79 78 77 76 75 74        52 51 50 49 48 47 46 45 44 43 42 41
   73 72 71 70 69 68 67         40 39 38 37 36 35 34 33 32 31 30 29      28 27
66 65 64 63 62 61 60         26 25 24 23 22 21 20 19 18 17 16 15
   59 58 57 56 55 54 53         14 13 12 11 10 9  8  7  6  5  4  3      2  1
```
AD42344

Wire side

```
                    41 42 43 44 45 46 47 48 49 50 51 52        74 75 76 77 78 79 80
                 29 30 31 32 33 34 35 36 37 38 39 40        67 68 69 70 71 72 73
   27 28            15 16 17 18 19 20 21 22 23 24 25 26        60 61 62 63 64 65 66
   1  2          3  4  5  6  7  8  9  10 11 12 13 14        53 54 55 56 57 58 59
```
AD42345

Component/circuit description	ECM pin	Signal	Condition	Typical value
AC compressor control module – MTC	16			☐1
AC control module – ATC – AT	48	←		☐1
	16			☐1
AC control module – tachometer signal	6	⇒	Engine idling	30 Hz
	6	⇒	Engine idling	5 V/10 ms per division 〰〰 2
AC diode – MTC – AT	48	←		☐1
Accelerator pedal position (APP) sensor	11	⇒	Ignition ON	5 V
	23	⊣⊢	Ignition ON	0 V
	24	←	Ignition ON – accelerator pedal released	0,4 V
	24	←	Ignition ON – accelerator pedal fully depressed	3,5 V
Accelerator pedal position (APP) switch	12	←	Ignition ON – accelerator pedal released	0,1 V
	12	←	Ignition ON – accelerator pedal depressed	2,8 V
Accelerator pedal position (APP) switch – 05/99→	25	⊣⊢	Ignition ON	0 V
Alternator – MT	22	←	Engine idling	0 V
Brake pedal position (BPP) switch I	20	←	Ignition OFF – brake pedal released	0 V
	20	←	Ignition OFF – brake pedal depressed	11-14 V
Brake pedal position (BPP) switch II	9	←	Ignition ON – brake pedal released	11-14 V
	9	←	Ignition ON – brake pedal depressed	0 V
CAN data bus – 05/99→	68	⬄		☐1
	75	⬄		☐1
Clutch pedal position (CPP) switch	46	←	Ignition ON – clutch pedal released	11-14 V
	46	←	Ignition ON – clutch pedal depressed	0 V
Crankshaft position (CKP) sensor	67	←	Engine idling	3,8 V ac
	67	←	Engine idling	5 V/5 ms per division 〰〰 6
	69	⊣⊢	Engine idling	0 V
Cruise control master switch	10			☐1
	19			☐1

Component/circuit description	ECM pin	Signal	Condition	Typical value
Cruise control selector switch	19			[1]
	21			[1]
	35			[1]
Earth	1		Ignition ON	0 V
	27		Ignition ON	0 V
Earth – AT	22		Ignition ON	0 V
Earth – →04/99	25		Ignition ON	0 V
Engine control relay	2	←	Ignition OFF	0 V
	2	←	Ignition ON	11-14 V
	28	←	Ignition OFF	0 V
	28	←	Ignition ON	11-14 V
	33	⫤▷	Ignition OFF	11-14 V
	33	⫤▷	Ignition ON	0-1 V
Engine coolant blower motor run-on relay – AFN/AVG	31	⫤▷		[1]
Engine coolant heater relay I – MT	17	⫤▷	Engine idling – relay contacts open	11-14 V
	17	⫤▷	Engine idling – relay contacts closed	0-1 V
Engine coolant heater relay II – MT	34	⫤▷	Engine idling – relay contacts open	11-14 V
	34	⫤▷	Engine idling – relay contacts closed	0-1 V
Engine coolant temperature (ECT) sensor	54	←	Ignition ON – coolant temp. 20°C	3,5 V
	54	←	Ignition ON – coolant temp. 80°C	1,4 V
	70	⫤—	Ignition ON	0 V
Exhaust gas recirculation (EGR) solenoid	29	⫤▷	Ignition ON	11-14 V
	29	⫤▷	Engine idling	5 V/5 ms per division [4]
Fuel injection timing solenoid	79	⫤▷	Engine idling	2 V/10 ms per division [10]
	79	⫤▷	Ignition ON	11-14 V
Fuel quantity adjuster	59	⫤▷	Engine idling	11,3 V
	59	⫤▷	Engine idling	2 V/2 ms per division [5]
	66	⫤▷	Engine idling	11,3 V
	66	⫤▷	Engine idling	2 V/2 ms per division [5]
	80	⫤▷	Engine idling	11,3 V
	80	⫤▷	Engine idling	2 V/2 ms per division [5]
Fuel quantity adjuster position sensor	56	←	Ignition ON	2,5 V
	56	←	Engine idling	0,5 V/0,1 ms per division [8]
	57	⇨	Ignition ON	2,5 V
	64	←	Ignition ON	2,5 V
	64	←	Engine idling	0,5 V/0,1 ms per division [8]
Fuel shut-off solenoid	77	⇨	Ignition OFF	0 V
	77	⇨	Ignition ON	11-14 V
Fuel temperature sensor	53	←	Ignition ON – fuel temp. 20°C	3,5 V
	76	⫤—	Ignition ON	0 V
Glow plug relay	42	⫤▷	Ignition ON – glow plugs ON	0-1 V
	42	⫤▷	Ignition ON – glow plugs OFF	11-14 V

Component/circuit description	ECM pin	Signal	Condition	Typical value
Glow plug warning lamp	41	⊣→	Ignition ON – lamp ON	0 V
	41	⊣→	Ignition ON – lamp OFF	10,5 V
Heated rear window switch – AT – 05/98→	48	←		1
Ignition switch	47	←	Ignition OFF	0 V
	47	←	Ignition ON	11-14 V
Injector needle lift sensor	55	⊣⊢	Engine idling	0 V
	62	←	Engine idling	0,02 V ac
	62	←	Engine idling	0,2 V/1 ms per division 〰7
Instrument panel – immobilization/diagnosis signal	45	←⇒	Ignition ON	11-14 V
	45	←⇒	Engine idling	11-14 V
Instrumentation control module – fuel consumption signal – →04/99	18	⇒		1
Instrumentation control module – tachometer signal – →04/99	6	⇒	Engine idling	30 Hz
	6	⇒	Engine idling	5 V/10 ms per division 〰2
Instrumentation control module – vehicle speed signal	51	←	Ignition ON – vehicle pushed	0 V or 11-14 V (switching)
Intake air temperature (IAT) sensor	13	←	Ignition ON – air temp. 20°C	3,7 V
Intake air temperature (IAT) sensor – 05/99→	25	⊣⊢	Ignition ON	0 V
Manifold absolute pressure (MAP) sensor	39	⇒	Ignition ON	5 V
	40	←	Ignition ON	1,9 V
	40	←	Engine idling	1,85 V
	40	←	Engine running – accelerator pedal briefly fully depressed	3,65 V (briefly)
Manifold absolute pressure (MAP) sensor – 05/99→	25	⊣⊢	Ignition ON	0 V
Mass air flow (MAF) sensor	4	⊣⊢	Engine idling	0 V
	50	⇒	Ignition ON	5 V
	52	←	Engine idling	1 V
	52	←	Engine running – accelerator pedal briefly fully depressed	4,35 V (briefly)
	52	←	Ignition ON	0,28 V
Spare cable, engine compartment rear – AT 05/99→	18			
	44			
Spare cable, engine compartment rear – 05/99→	7			
	36			
Transmission control module (TCM) – →04/99	7			1
	36			1
	44			1
Transmission kick-down switch	8	←		1
Transmission kick-down switch – 05/99→	25	⊣⊢	Ignition ON	0 V
Turbocharger (TC) wastegate regulating valve	15	⊣→	Ignition ON	11-14 V
	15	⊣→	Engine running – valve not operating	11-14 V
	15	⊣→	Engine running – valve operating	0-1 V

1 Connected pin - no test data available

Model:		Engine code:		Year:
Sharan 2,0		ADY		1995-01

VOLKSWAGEN
Siemens Simos

ECM harness multi-plug

Terminal side

AD81718

Wire side

AD42119

Component/circuit description	ECM pin	Signal	Condition	Typical value	Oscilloscope setting*	Wave form
Air conditioning	13			1		
	39			1		
Automatic transmission	5			1		
	13			1		
	15			1		
Camshaft position (CMP) sensor	35		Ignition ON	0 V		
	44	←	Ignition ON – engine turned	0 V or 10-14 V switching		
	44	←	Engine idling	8 Hz	5 V/20 ms	12
	44	←	3000 rpm	25 Hz		
	45	⇒	Ignition ON	10 V min.		
Closed throttle position (CTP) switch	18	←	Ignition ON – throttle closed	0 V		
	18	←	Ignition ON – throttle slightly open	9 V min.		
	35		Ignition ON	0 V		
Crankshaft position (CKP) sensor	16		Engine idling	0 V		
	67	←	Engine idling		2 V/1 ms	5
	68	⇒	Ignition ON	11-14 V		
Earth	1		Ignition ON	0 V		
Engine control relay	23	←	Ignition OFF	0 V		
	23	←	Ignition ON	11-14 V		
Engine coolant temperature (ECT) sensor	12	←	Ignition ON – coolant temp. 10°C	2,8 V		
	12	←	Ignition ON – coolant temp. 80°C	0,4 V		
	35		Ignition ON	0 V		
Evaporative emission (EVAP) canister purge valve	33		Ignition ON	11-14 V		
	33		Engine hot – valve operating		10 V/20 ms	20
Exhaust gas recirculation (EGR) solenoid	22		Ignition ON	11-14 V		
	22		Engine hot – valve operating		10 V/50 ms	20
Fuel pump relay – 1995-04/98	31		Engine cranking	0-1 V		
Fuel pump relay, through fuel pump shut-off control module – 05/98-10/98	31		Engine cranking	0-1 V		
Fuel pump relay, incorporates fuel pump shut-off control module function – 11/98→	31		Engine cranking	0-1 V		

* Suggested settings - Voltage/time per division

Component/circuit description	ECM pin	Signal	Condition	Typical value	Oscilloscope setting*	Wave form
Heated oxygen sensor (HO2S)	17	←	Engine idling – engine hot	0,1-1,1 V fluctuating	0,2 V/1 sec.	⎍⎍ 21
	20	⌐▷	Engine idling	0 V		
	42	⌐—	Engine idling	0 V		
Heated oxygen sensor (HO2S) – shield wire	21	⌐—	Engine idling	0 V		
Idle speed control (ISC) actuator	25 (30)	⇒	Engine idling		5 V/2 ms	Intermittent ⎍⎍ 27
	30 (25)	⇒	Engine idling		5 V/2 ms	Intermittent ⎍⎍ 27
Idle speed control (ISC) actuator position sensor	28	←	Engine idling – engine hot	3,7 V		
	35	⌐—	Ignition ON	0 V		
	41	⇒	Ignition ON	4-6 V		
Ignition amplifier	7	⇒	Engine idling		2 V/10 ms	⎍⎍ 32
Ignition switch	32	←	Engine cranking	9 V min.		
	38	←	Ignition OFF	0 V		
	38	←	Ignition ON	11-14 V		
Ignition switch – through engine control relay	8	⇒	Ignition OFF	0 V		
	8	⇒	Ignition ON	11-14 V		
Immobilizer control module	43	←		1		
Injector 1	2	⌐▷	Engine idling – engine hot	3,8 ms	10 V/2 ms	⎍⎍ 35
Injector 2	46	⌐▷	Engine idling – engine hot	3,8 ms	10 V/2 ms	⎍⎍ 35
Injector 3	47	⌐▷	Engine idling – engine hot	3,8 ms	10 V/2 ms	⎍⎍ 35
Injector 4	48	⌐▷	Engine idling – engine hot	3,8 ms	10 V/2 ms	⎍⎍ 35
Instrument panel	10			1		
	11	←		1		
	19			1		
Intake air temperature (IAT) sensor	37	←	Ignition ON – air temp. 10°C	2 V		
	29	⌐—	Ignition ON	0 V		
Knock sensor (KS)	34	←	Engine idling – accelerate briefly		50 mV/1 ms	⎍⎍ 38
	36	⌐—	Engine idling	0 V		
Knock sensor (KS) – shield wire	9	⌐—	Engine idling	0 V		
Mass air flow (MAF) sensor	14	←	Engine idling – engine hot	1,2 V		
	14	←	3000 rpm	1,7 V		
	26	⌐—	Ignition ON	0 V		
Throttle position (TP) sensor	35	⌐—	Ignition ON	0 V		
	40	←	Ignition ON – throttle closed	4,3 V		
	40	←	Ignition ON – throttle fully open	0,7 V		
	41	⇒	Ignition ON	4-6 V		

*Suggested settings - Voltage/time per division

1 Connected pin - no test data available or random digital signal

Model:	Engine code:	Year:
S40/V40 1,6i	B4164S	1997-00
S40/V40 1,8i	B4184S	1996-00
S40/V40 2,0i	B4204S	1996-01

ECM harness multi-plug

Terminal side

27 26 25 24 23 22 21 20 19 18 17 16 15 14 13 12 11 10 9 8 7 6 5 4 3 2 1

55 54 53 52 51 50 49 48 47 46 45 44 43 42 41 40 39 38 37 36 35 34 33 32 31 30 29 28

AD81647

Wire side

1 2 3 4 5 6 7 8 9 10 11 12 13 14 15 16 17 18 19 20 21 22 23 24 25 26 27

28 29 30 31 32 33 34 35 36 37 38 39 40 41 42 43 44 45 46 47 48 49 50 51 52 53 54 55

AD42110

Component/circuit description	ECM pin	Signal	Condition	Typical value	Oscilloscope setting*	Wave form
AC compressor clutch relay	51	→▷	Ignition ON	10 V		
	51	→▷	Engine idling – AC compressor OFF	10 V		
	51	→▷	Engine idling – AC compressor ON	0-1 V		
AC refrigerant pressure switch	10	←	Ignition ON	0 V		
	10	←	Engine idling – AC OFF	0 V		
	10	←	Engine idling – AC ON	10 V		
Battery	32	←	Ignition OFF	11-14 V		
Camshaft position (CMP) sensor	6	←	Ignition ON	0 V or 5 V		
	6	←	Engine idling	6,3 Hz	2 V/20 ms	∿∿ 12
	45	▷	Ignition ON	5 V		
	46	⊣	Ignition ON	0 V		
Crankshaft position (CKP) sensor	33 (34)	←	Ignition ON	0 V		
	33 (34)	←	Engine idling	1,8 V ac	1 V/1 ms	∿∿ 2
	34 (33)	←	Ignition ON	0 V		
	34 (33)	←	Engine idling	1,8 V ac	1 V/1 ms	∿∿ 2
Data link connector (DLC)	11	←▷	Ignition ON	0 V		
	38	←▷	Ignition ON	0 V		
Earth	2		Ignition ON	0 V		
	3		Ignition ON	0 V		
Engine control relay	48	→▷	Ignition ON	11-14 V		
	48	→▷	Engine idling	0-1 V		
	52	←	Ignition ON	11-14 V briefly then 0 V		
	52	←	Engine idling	11-14 V		
Engine coolant blower motor relay	23	→▷	Coolant blower motor OFF	11-14 V		
	23	→▷	Coolant blower motor ON	0-1 V		

* Suggested settings - Voltage/time per division

Component/circuit description	ECM pin	Signal	Condition	Typical value	Oscilloscope setting*	Wave form
Engine coolant temperature (ECT) sensor	15	←	Ignition ON – coolant temp. 20°C	2 V		
	15	←	Ignition ON – coolant temp. 80°C	0,5 V		
	15	←	Ignition ON – coolant temp. 100°C	0,23 V		
	44	⊣⎼	Ignition ON	0 V		
Evaporative emission (EVAP) canister purge valve	50	⊣▷	Ignition ON	11-14 V briefly then 0 V		
	50	⊣▷	Engine hot – valve operating		10 V/50 ms	20
Heated oxygen sensor (HO2S)	17 (18)	←	Ignition ON	0,4 V		
	17 (18)	←	Engine idling	0,1-0,9 V fluctuating	0,2 V/1 sec.	21
	18	⊣⎼	Ignition ON	0 V		
Idle air control (IAC) valve	54	⊣▷	Ignition ON	1,2 V		
	54	⊣▷	Engine idling	10 V		
	54	⊣▷	Engine idling	28%	5 V/5 ms	24
Ignition coil – cylinders 1 & 4	28	⊣▷	Ignition ON	11-14 V briefly then 0 V		
	28	⊣▷	Engine idling	11-14 V	5 V/2 ms	33
Ignition coil – cylinders 2 & 3	29	⊣▷	Ignition ON	11-14 V briefly then 0 V		
	29	⊣▷	Engine idling	11-14 V	5 V/2 ms	33
Ignition switch	24	←	Ignition ON	11-14 V		
Immobilizer control module	35	←	Ignition ON	2-4 V fluctuating		
Injector 1	53	⊣▷	Ignition ON	11-14 V briefly then 0 V		
	53	⊣▷	Engine idling	3,5-5,0 ms	10 V/2 ms	35
Injector 2	25	⊣▷	Ignition ON	11-14 V briefly then 0 V		
	25	⊣▷	Engine idling	3,5-5,0 ms	10 V/2 ms	35
Injector 3	4	⊣▷	Ignition ON	11-14 V briefly then 0 V		
	4	⊣▷	Engine idling	3,5-5,0 ms	10 V/2 ms	35
Injector 4	30	⊣▷	Ignition ON	11-14 V briefly then 0 V		
	30	⊣▷	Engine idling	3,5-5,0 ms	10 V/2 ms	35
Intake air temperature (IAT) sensor	20	←	Ignition ON – air temp. 20°C	2 V		
	46	⊣⎼	Ignition ON	0 V		
Knock sensor (KS)	8	⇨	Ignition ON	5 V		
	8	←	Engine idling – accelerate briefly		50 mV/1 ms	38
	44	⊣⎼	Ignition ON	0 V		
Malfunction indicator lamp (MIL)	26	⊣▷	Ignition ON – MIL ON	0-1 V		
	26	⊣▷	Engine idling – MIL OFF	11-14 V		

★ Suggested settings - Voltage/time per division

Component/circuit description	ECM pin	Signal	Condition	Typical value	Oscilloscope setting*	Wave form
Manifold absolute pressure (MAP) sensor	16	←	Ignition ON	5 V		
	16	←	Engine idling	0,9-1,5 V		
	16	←	Engine idling – full throttle briefly	4,8 V		
	44	⌐−	Ignition ON	0 V		
	45	⇒	Ignition ON	5 V		
Manual transmission	7	←	Ignition ON	5 V		
Secondary air injection (AIR) pump relay	27	⌐⇒	Engine idling – air pump OFF	11-14 V		
	27	⌐⇒	Engine idling – air pump ON	0-1 V		
Speedometer	12	←	Ignition ON	0 V		
Tachometer	43	⇒	Ignition ON	0 V		
	43	⇒	Engine idling	25 Hz		
Throttle position (TP) sensor	19	←	Ignition ON – throttle closed	0,7 V		
	19	←	Ignition ON – accelerator pedal fully depressed	4,7 V		
	45	⇒	Ignition ON	5 V		
	46	⌐−	Ignition ON	0 V		
Traction control module	31	⌐−	Ignition ON	0 V		
	37	⇒	Ignition ON	2 Hz		
	37	⇒	Engine idling	25 Hz		
	41	⇒	Ignition ON	50 Hz		
	41	⇒	Ignition ON – throttle closed	3 ms		
	41	⇒	Ignition ON – throttle fully open	15 ms		
	42	←	Ignition ON	5 V after 3 seconds		
	42	←	Engine idling	2 V		
Transmission control module (TCM)	7	←	Ignition ON – AT in P or N	5 V		
	7	←	Ignition ON – AT not in P or N	0,5 V		
	37	⇒	Ignition ON	2 Hz		
	37	⇒	Engine idling	25 Hz		
	41	⇒	Ignition ON	50 Hz		
	41	⇒	Ignition ON – throttle closed	3 ms		
	41	⇒	Ignition ON – throttle fully open	15 ms		
Trip computer – some models	13	←	Ignition ON	5 V		

*Suggested settings - Voltage/time per division

1 Connected pin - no test data available or random digital signal

VOLVO

Siemens EMS 2000

Model:	Engine code:	Year:
S40/V40 1,6	B4164S2	2000-04
S40/V40 1,8	B4184S2, B4184S3	2000-04
S40/V40 1,9 Turbo	B4194T, B4194T2	1998-00
S40/V40 2,0	B4204S2	2000-04
S40/V40 2,0 Turbo	B4204T, B4204T2	1998-00

ECM harness multi-plug

Terminal side

61 62 63 64 65 66 67 68 69 70 71 72 73 74 75   76 77 78 79 80 81 82 83 84 85 86 87 88 89 90

31 32 33 34 35 36 37 38 39 40 41 42 43 44 45   46 47 48 49 50 51 52 53 54 55 56 57 58 59 60

1 2 3 4 5 6 7 8 9 10 11 12 13 14 15   16 17 18 19 20 21 22 23 24 25 26 27 28 29 30

AD23453

Wire side

90 89 88 87 86 85 84 83 82 81 80 79 78 77 76   75 74 73 72 71 70 69 68 67 66 65 64 63 62 61

60 59 58 57 56 55 54 53 52 51 50 49 48 47 46   45 44 43 42 41 40 39 38 37 36 35 34 33 32 31

30 29 28 27 26 25 24 23 22 21 20 19 18 17 16   15 14 13 12 11 10 9 8 7 6 5 4 3 2 1

AD23452

Component/circuit description	ECM pin	Signal	Condition	Typical value	Oscilloscope setting*	Wave form
ABS control module – vehicle speed signal	52	←	Engine idling – vehicle pushed	0-1 V or 11-14 V fluctuating		
AC compressor clutch relay	68	⊣▷	Engine idling – AC OFF	11-14 V		
	68	⊣▷	Engine idling – AC ON	0-1 V		
AC condenser blower motor relay	69	⊣▷	Engine idling – condenser blower motor OFF	11-14 V		
	69	⊣▷	Engine idling – condenser blower motor ON	0-1 V		
AC control module/AC compressor control module	88	←	Engine idling – AC OFF	0 V		
	88	←	Engine idling – AC ON	11-14 V		
AC refrigerant pressure sensor	14	←	Engine idling – AC OFF	0,9 V		
	14	←	Engine idling – AC ON	1,4-1,8 V		
	74	⇨	Ignition ON	5 V		
	77	⊣−	Ignition ON	0 V		
Barometric pressure (BARO) sensor – if fitted	18	←		1		
	77	⊣−	Ignition ON	0 V		
	78	⇨	Ignition ON	5 V		
Battery	30	←	Ignition OFF	11-14 V		
Camshaft position (CMP) actuator – if fitted	62	⊣▷	Ignition ON	11-14 V briefly then 0 V		
	62	⊣▷	Engine idling	250 Hz		
Camshaft position (CMP) sensor	58	←	Ignition ON	0 or 5 V		
	58	←	Engine idling		2 V/20 ms	∿∿ 14
	79	⊣−	Ignition ON	0 V		
	83	⇨	Ignition ON	5 V		
CAN data bus, transmission control module (TCM)	27	◄⇨		1		
	57	◄⇨		1		

* Suggested settings - Voltage/time per division

Component/circuit description	ECM pin	Signal	Condition	Typical value	Oscilloscope setting*	Wave form
Crankshaft position (CKP) sensor	24	←	Ignition ON	1,8 V		
	24	←	Engine idling	0,7 ac	0,5 V/1 ms	⋀⋀ 2
	54	←	Ignition ON	1,8 V		
	54	←	Engine idling	0,7 V ac	0,5 V/1 ms	Reversed ⋀⋀ 2
Earth	3		Ignition ON	0 V		
	28		Ignition ON	0 V		
	33		Ignition ON	0 V		
	67		Ignition ON	0 V		
Engine control relay	10	⊣▷	Ignition ON	0 V briefly then 11-14 V		
	10	⊣▷	Engine idling	0-1 V		
	66	←	Ignition ON	11-14 V briefly then 0 V		
Engine coolant blower motor relay – high speed	8	⊣▷	Engine idling – coolant blower motor OFF	11-14 V		
	8	⊣▷	Engine idling – coolant blower motor ON	0-1 V		
Engine coolant blower motor relay – low speed	38	⊣▷	Engine idling – coolant blower motor OFF	11-14 V		
	38	⊣▷	Engine idling – coolant blower motor ON	0-1 V		
Engine coolant temperature (ECT) sensor	13	←	Ignition ON – coolant temp. 25°C	2,6 V		
	13	←	Ignition ON – coolant temp. 100°C	0,6 V		
	73	⊣—	Ignition ON	0 V		
Engine coolant temperature gauge	11	▷	Engine idling – coolant temp. 25°C	45 Hz		
	11	▷	Engine idling – coolant temp. 100°C	20 Hz		
Evaporative emission (EVAP) canister purge valve	4	⊣▷	Ignition ON	11-14 V briefly then 0 V		
Heated oxygen sensor (HO2S) 1	45	←	Ignition ON	5 V		
	45	←	Engine idling – engine hot	0-5 V fluctuating		
	75	⊣—	Ignition ON	0 V		
Heated oxygen sensor (HO2S) 1 – heater control	63	⊣▷	Ignition ON	11-14 V briefly then 0 V		
	63	⊣▷	Engine idling – engine hot		2 V/5 ms	⋀⋀ 65
Heated oxygen sensor (HO2S) 2	44	←	Ignition ON	5 V		
	44	←	Engine idling – engine hot	0,2-4,8 V fluctuating		
	75	⊣—	Ignition ON	0 V		
Heated oxygen sensor (HO2S) 2 – heater control	65	⊣▷	Ignition ON	11-14 V briefly then 0 V		
	65	⊣▷	Engine idling – engine hot		2 V/5 ms	⋀⋀ 65
Idle air control (IAC) valve	64	⊣▷	Engine idling	160 Hz	2 V/2 ms	⋀⋀ 72
Ignition coil – cylinders 1 & 4	32	⊣▷	Ignition ON	11-14 V briefly then 0 V		
	32	⊣▷	Engine idling	13 Hz	10 V/2 ms	⋀⋀ 33
Ignition coil – cylinders 2 & 3	1	⊣▷	Ignition ON	11-14 V briefly then 0 V		
	1	⊣▷	Engine idling	13 Hz	5 V/2 ms	⋀⋀ 33
Ignition switch	29	←	Ignition ON	11-14 V		
Immobilizer control module – immobilization/diagnosis signal	56	←▷		1		
Injector 1	59	⊣▷	Ignition ON	11-14 V briefly then 0 V		
	59	⊣▷	Engine idling	2 ms	10 V/2 ms	⋀⋀ 35

* Suggested settings - Voltage/time per division

Component/circuit description	ECM pin	Signal	Condition	Typical value	Oscilloscope setting*	Wave form
Injector 2	90	⊐⊳	Ignition ON	11-14 V briefly then 0 V		
	90	⊐⊳	Engine idling	2 ms	10 V/2 ms	∿∿ 35
Injector 3	60	⊐⊳	Ignition ON	11-14 V briefly then 0 V		
	60	⊐⊳	Engine idling	2 ms	10 V/2 ms	∿∿ 35
Injector 4	89	⊐⊳	Ignition ON	11-14 V briefly then 0 V		
	89	⊐⊳	Engine idling	2 ms	10 V/2 ms	∿∿ 35
Instrument panel	40	⇨		1		
Instrument panel – engine speed signal	70	⇨	Engine idling	25 Hz	5 V/20 ms	∿∿ 4
	70	⇨	3000 rpm	100 Hz		
Intake air temperature (IAT) sensor	48	⬅	Ignition ON – air temp. 25°C	2 V		
	48	⬅	Ignition ON – air temp. 100°C	0,25 V		
	79	⊐⊢	Ignition ON	0 V		
Knock sensor (KS)	51	⬅	Engine idling – accelerate briefly		0,1 mV/1 ms	∿∿ 38
	76	⊐⊢	Ignition ON	0 V		
Knock sensor (KS) – shield wire	19	⊐⊢	Ignition ON	0 V		
Malfunction indicator lamp (MIL)	34	⊐⊳	Ignition ON – MIL ON	0-1 V		
	34	⊐⊳	Ignition ON – MIL OFF	11-14 V		
Mass air flow (MAF) sensor	15	⊐⊢	Ignition ON	0 V		
	16	⬅	Engine idling	0,6-0,75 V		
	16	⬅	Engine idling – accelerate briefly	4,3 V briefly		
Secondary air injection (AIR) solenoid – if fitted	6	⊐⊳	Ignition ON	11-14 V briefly then 0 V		
Throttle position (TP) sensor	43	⬅	Ignition ON – throttle closed	0,6 V		
	43	⬅	Ignition ON – throttle fully open	4,6 V		
Throttle position (TP) sensor – →2000	73	⊐⊢	Ignition ON	0 V		
	74	⇨	Ignition ON	5 V		
Throttle position (TP) sensor – 2001→	77	⊐⊢	Ignition ON	0 V		
	78	⇨	Ignition ON	5 V		
Traction control module – if fitted	20	⬅	Ignition ON	5 V		
	20	⬅	Engine idling – traction control OFF	5 V		
	20	⬅	Engine idling – traction control ON	2 V		
	36	⇨		1		
	71	⇨		1		
Turbocharger (TC) wastegate regulating valve	5	⊐⊳	Ignition ON	11-14 V briefly then 0 V		
	5	⊐⊳	Engine idling – accelerate briefly		10 V/20 ms	∿∿ 25

*Suggested settings - Voltage/time per division

1 Connected pin - no test data available or random digital signal

ECM harness multi-plug

Terminal side

D   C   B   A

```
D                          C              B                    A
 1  2  3  4  5  6  7  8  9 10 11   1  2  3  4  5  6    1  2  3  4  5  6  7  8    1  2  3  4  5  6  7  8  9 10 11 12 13
12 13 14 15 16 17 18 19 20 21 22   7  8  9 10 11 12    9 10 11 12 13 14 15 16   14 15 16 17 18 19 20 21 22 23 24 25 26
```
AD23533

Wire side

A   B   C   D

```
A                              B                  C                D
13 12 11 10  9  8  7  6  5  4  3  2  1    8  7  6  5  4  3  2  1    6  5  4  3  2  1    11 10  9  8  7  6  5  4  3  2  1
26 25 24 23 22 21 20 19 18 17 16 15 14   16 15 14 13 12 11 10  9   12 11 10  9  8  7   22 21 20 19 18 17 16 15 14 13 12
```
AD23534

Component/circuit description	ECM pin	Signal	Condition	Typical value	Oscilloscope setting*	Wave form
AC compressor clutch relay	A6	⊐⊳	Engine idling – AC OFF	0 V		
	A6	⊐⊳	Engine idling – AC ON	6-12 V briefly then 0 V		
AC condenser blower motor	A19	⊐⊳	Engine idling – condenser blower motor OFF	11-14 V		
	A19	⊐⊳	Engine idling – condenser blower motor ON	0 V		
AC refrigerant pressure switch	B10	⟵	Engine idling – AC OFF	0-1 V		
	B10	⟵	Engine idling – AC ON	11-14 V		
Alternator	B6	⟵	Engine idling – electrical load OFF	25 Hz		
	B6	⟵	Engine idling – electrical load ON	6,5-7,5 V		
	B14	⟵	Engine idling – electrical load OFF	2-3 V		
	B14	⟵	Engine idling – electrical load ON	1-2 V		
Auxiliary air valve 1	A11	⊐⊳	Engine idling – engine cold, air valve operating	0 V		
	A11	⊐⊳	Engine idling – engine hot	11-14 V		
Auxiliary air valve 2	A24	⊐⊳	Engine idling – air valve operating	203 Hz		
Barometric pressure (BARO) sensor	D19	⟵	Ignition ON – at sea level	3,9-4,1 V		
	D19	⟵	Ignition ON – 1200 m above sea level	3,3-3,6 V		
Battery	D2	⟵	Ignition OFF	11-14 V		
Brake booster vacuum sensor	B13	⟵	Ignition ON – brake booster discharged	4 V		
	B13	⟵	Engine idling	0,8 V		
	D1	⟹	Ignition ON	5 V		
	D12	⊐⊢	Ignition ON	0 V		
Brake pedal position (BPP) switch	B4	⟵	Ignition ON – brake pedal released	0-1 V		
	B4	⟵	Ignition ON – brake pedal depressed	11-14 V		
Camshaft position (CMP) sensor	D16	⟵	Ignition ON – engine turned	0 or 5 V switching		
	D16	⟵	Engine idling		1 V/0,1 sec.	〰89
Closed throttle position (CTP) switch	D17	⟵	Ignition ON – throttle closed	0 V		
	D17	⟵	Ignition ON – throttle slightly open	4,6 V		
Crankshaft position (CKP) sensor	D15	⟵	Ignition ON – engine turned	0 or 5 V switching		
	D15	⟵	Engine idling		2 V/20 ms	〰4
Data link connector (DLC)	C1	⟺		1		

* Suggested settings - Voltage/time per division

Component/circuit description	ECM pin	Signal	Condition	Typical value	Oscilloscope setting*	Wave form
Earth	A1		Ignition ON	0 V		
	A14		Ignition ON	0 V		
	D13		Ignition ON	0 V		
Engine control relay	A2	←	Ignition OFF	0 V		
	A2	←	Ignition ON	11-14 V		
	A15	←	Ignition OFF	0 V		
	A15	←	Ignition ON	11-14 V		
	B1	⊐▷	Ignition OFF	11-14 V		
	B1	⊐▷	Ignition ON	0 V		
Engine coolant blower motor relay	C3	←	Ignition ON – coolant temp. below 90°C	11-14 V		
	C3	←	Ignition ON – coolant temp. above 105°C	0-1 V		
	C3	⊐▷	Engine idling – coolant blower motor OFF	11-14 V		
	C3	⊐▷	Engine idling – coolant blower motor ON	0-1 V		
Engine coolant temperature (ECT) sensor	D12	⊐⊢	Ignition ON	0 V		
	D21	←	Ignition ON – coolant temp. 0°C	3,2-3,8 V		
	D21	←	Ignition ON – coolant temp. 20°C	2,3-2,9 V		
	D21	←	Ignition ON – coolant temp. 50°C	1-1,6 V		
	D21	←	Ignition ON – coolant temp. 80°C	0,3-0,9 V		
Evaporative emission (EVAP) canister purge valve	C12	⊐▷	Ignition ON	11-14 V		
	C12	⊐▷	Engine idling – engine hot	9%	10 V/20 ms	〰 20
Exhaust gas recirculation (EGR) solenoid	B7	⊐▷	Ignition ON	0 V		
	B7	⊐▷	Engine idling	0 V		
	B8	⊐▷	Ignition ON	11-14 V		
	B8	⊐▷	Engine idling	11-14 V		
	B15	⊐▷	Ignition ON	0 V		
	B15	⊐▷	Engine idling	0 V		
	B16	⊐▷	Ignition ON	11-14 V		
	B16	⊐▷	Engine idling	11-14 V		
Fuel pump relay	A18	⊐▷	Ignition ON	0 V briefly then 11-14 V		
	A18	⊐▷	Engine idling	0 V		
Fuel rail pressure (FRP) sensor	D5	⇨	Ignition ON	5 V		
	D8	←	Ignition ON	0-0,5 V		
	D8	←	Engine idling	2,85 V		
	D12	⊐⊢	Ignition ON	0 V		
Headlamp switch	C5	←	Engine idling – headlamp switch OFF	0-1 V		
	C5	←	Engine idling – headlamp switch ON	11-14 V		
Heated oxygen sensor (HO2S)	C9	←	Ignition ON	11-14 V		
	C9	←	Engine idling	0-1 V		
	D6	←	Engine running – 2000 rpm	0,1-0,9 V fluctuating	0,2 V/1 sec.	〰 21
	D12	⊐⊢	Ignition ON	0 V		
Idle air control (IAC) valve	A9	⇨	Engine idling		5 V/50 ms	Intermittent 〰 86
	A10	⇨	Engine idling		5 V/50 ms	Intermittent 〰 87
	A22	⊐▷	Engine idling		5 V/50 ms	Intermittent 〰 86
	A23	⊐▷	Engine idling		5 V/50 ms	Intermittent 〰 87
Ignition coil 1	A4	⇨	Ignition ON	0 V		
	A4	⇨	Engine idling		1 V/10 ms	〰 32

* Suggested settings - Voltage/time per division

Component/circuit description	ECM pin	Signal	Condition	Typical value	Oscilloscope setting*	Wave form
Ignition coil 2	A3	⇒	Ignition ON	0 V		
	A3	⇒	Engine idling		1 V/10 ms	〰 32
Ignition coil 3	A17	⇒	Ignition ON	0 V		
	A17	⇒	Engine idling		1 V/50 ms	〰 32
Ignition coil 4	A16	⇒	Ignition ON	0 V		
	A16	⇒	Engine idling		1 V/50 ms	〰 32
Ignition coil relay	A20	⊐▷	Ignition OFF	0 V		
	A20	⊐▷	Ignition ON	11-14 V		
Ignition switch	D22	⇐	Ignition OFF	0 V		
	D22	⇐	Ignition ON	11-14 V		
Immobilizer control module – diagnostic signal	C7	⇔		1		
Injector control module – diagnostic signal	C6	⇔		1		
Injector control module – injector 1	A13	⊐▷	Engine idling – engine hot		2 V/10 ms	〰 88
Injector control module – injector 2	A26	⊐▷	Engine idling – engine hot		2 V/10 ms	〰 88
Injector control module – injector 3	A12	⊐▷	Engine idling – engine hot		2 V/10 ms	〰 88
Injector control module – injector 4	A25	⊐▷	Engine idling – engine hot		2 V/10 ms	〰 88
Injector relay	A20	⊐▷	Ignition OFF	0 V		
	A20	⊐▷	Ignition ON	11-14 V		
Instrument panel	B12	⇒		1		
Instrument panel – tachometer signal	C11	⇒	Engine idling	26 Hz		
	C11	⇒	3000 rpm	100 Hz		
Intake air temperature (IAT) sensor	D10	⇐	Ignition ON – air temp. 0°C	3,2-3,8 V		
	D10	⇐	Ignition ON – air temp. 20°C	2,3-2,9 V		
	D10	⇐	Ignition ON – air temp. 40°C	1,5-2 V		
	D12	⊐⊢	Ignition ON	0 V		
Knock sensor (KS)	D4	⇐	Engine idling – accelerate briefly		50 mV/1 ms	〰 38
Malfunction indicator lamp (MIL)	B3	⊐▷	Ignition ON – MIL ON	0-1 V		
	B3	⊐▷	Ignition ON – MIL OFF	11-14 V		
Power steering pressure (PSP) switch	B2	⇐	Engine idling – steering wheel not turned	11-14 V		
	B2	⇐	Engine idling – steering wheel turned	0-1 V		
Spare cable	D3					
Starter motor	D11	⇐	Engine cranking	9-12 V		
Throttle position (TP) sensor	D1	⇒	Ignition ON	5 V		
	D12	⊐⊢	Ignition ON	0 V		
	D20	⇐	Ignition ON – throttle closed	0,6 V		
	D20	⇐	Ignition ON – throttle fully open	4,8 V		
Transmission fluid temperature sensor	D7	⇐	Ignition ON – fluid temp. 25°C	2,4-2,7 V		
	D7	⇐	Ignition ON – fluid temp. 80°C	0,5-0,8 V		
	D12	⊐⊢	Ignition ON	0 V		
Vehicle speed sensor (VSS)	D18	⇐	Ignition ON – vehicle pushed	0 V or 5 V switching		
Volume air flow (VAF) sensor	A21	⇐	Ignition ON	7,5 V		
	A21	⇐	Engine idling	0-1 V		
	A21	⇐	Engine running – above idle speed	7,5 V		
	D1	⇒	Ignition ON	5 V		
	D12	⊐⊢	Ignition ON	0 V		
	D14	⇐	Engine idling	2,2-3,2 V	2 V/20 ms	〰 39

*Suggested settings - Voltage/time per division

1 Connected pin - no test data available or random digital signal

Model:	Engine code:	Year:
S40/V40 1,8 GDI	B4184SM	1998-02

Injector control module harness multi-plug

Terminal side

26 25 24 23 22 21 20 19 18
17 16 15 14 13 12 11 10
9 8 7 6 5 4 3 2 1

AD23546

Wire side

18 19 20 21 22 23 24 25 26
10 11 12 13 14 15 16 17
1 2 3 4 5 6 7 8 9

AD23547

Component/circuit description	ECM pin	Signal	Condition	Typical value	Oscilloscope setting*	Wave form
Earth	14		Ignition ON	0 V		
	22		Ignition ON	0 V		
ECM pin A12	16	←	Engine idling		2 V/10 ms	88
ECM pin A13	24	←	Engine idling		2 V/10 ms	88
ECM pin A25	17	←	Engine idling		2 V/10 ms	88
ECM pin A26	25	←	Engine idling		2 V/10 ms	88
ECM pin C6	9	⇔	Engine idling	0 or 5 V		
Ignition relay	15	←	Ignition ON	11-14 V		
	23	←	Ignition ON	11-14 V		
Injector 1	10	⊣▷	Engine idling	0,5 ms	10 V/2 ms	35
	18	⇨	Ignition ON	100 V		
Injector 2	11	⊣▷	Engine idling	0,5 ms	10 V/2 ms	35
	19	⇨	Ignition ON	100 V		
Injector 3	12	⊣▷	Engine idling	0,5 ms	10 V/2 ms	35
	20	⇨	Ignition ON	100 V		
Injector 4	13	⊣▷	Engine idling	0,5 ms	10 V/2 ms	35
	21	⇨	Ignition ON	100 V		

*Suggested settings - Voltage/time per division

1 Connected pin - no test data available or random digital signal

ECM harness multi-plug

Terminal side

AD23453

Wire side

AD23452

Component/circuit description	ECM pin	Signal	Condition	Typical value	Oscilloscope setting*	Wave form
ABS control module – vehicle speed signal	52	←	Engine idling – vehicle pushed	0-1 V or 11-14 V fluctuating		
AC compressor clutch relay	68	⅂▷	Engine idling – AC OFF	11-14 V		
	68	⅂▷	Engine idling – AC ON	0-1 V		
AC condenser blower motor relay	69	⅂▷	Engine idling – condenser blower motor OFF	11-14 V		
	69	⅂▷	Engine idling – condenser blower motor ON	0-1 V		
AC control module	88	←	Engine idling – AC OFF	0 V		
	88	←	Engine idling – AC ON	11-14 V		
AC refrigerant pressure sensor	14	←	Engine idling – AC OFF	0,9 V		
	14	←	Engine idling – AC ON	1,4-1,8 V		
	74	⇨	Ignition ON	5 V		
	77	⅂	Ignition ON	0 V		
Battery	30	←	Ignition OFF	11-14 V		
Camshaft position (CMP) actuator	62	⅂▷	Ignition ON	11-14 V briefly then 0 V		
	62	⅂▷	Engine idling	250 Hz		
Camshaft position (CMP) sensor	58	←	Ignition ON	0 or 5 V		
	58	←	Engine idling		2 V/20 ms	ᚃᚃ 14
	79	⅂	Ignition ON	0 V		
	83	⇨	Ignition ON	5 V		
CAN data bus, transmission control module (TCM)	27	⬄		①		
	57	⬄		①		
Crankshaft position (CKP) sensor	24	←	Ignition ON	1,8 V		
	24	←	Engine idling	0,7 V ac	0,5 V/1 ms	ᚃᚃ 2
	54	←	Ignition ON	1,8 V		
	54	←	Engine idling	0,7 V ac	0,5 V/1 ms	Reversed ᚃᚃ 2

★ Suggested settings - Voltage/time per division

Component/circuit description	ECM pin	Signal	Condition	Typical value	Oscilloscope setting*	Wave form
Earth	3		Ignition ON	0 V		
	28		Ignition ON	0 V		
	33		Ignition ON	0 V		
	67		Ignition ON	0 V		
Engine control relay	10	⊐⊳	Ignition ON	0 V briefly then 11-14 V		
	10	⊐⊳	Engine idling	0-1 V		
	66	⟵	Ignition ON	11-14 V briefly then 0 V		
Engine coolant blower motor relay – high speed	8	⊐⊳	Engine idling – coolant blower motor OFF	11-14 V		
	8	⊐⊳	Engine idling – coolant blower motor ON	0-1 V		
Engine coolant blower motor relay – low speed	38	⊐⊳	Engine idling – coolant blower motor OFF	11-14 V		
	38	⊐⊳	Engine idling – coolant blower motor ON	0-1 V		
Engine coolant temperature (ECT) sensor	47	⟵	Ignition ON – coolant temp. 25°C	2,6 V		
	47	⟵	Ignition ON – coolant temp. 100°C	0,6 V		
	73	⊐—	Ignition ON	0 V		
Engine coolant temperature gauge	11	⟹	Engine idling – coolant temp. 25°C	45 Hz		
	11	⟹	Engine idling – coolant temp. 100°C	20 Hz		
Evaporative emission (EVAP) canister purge valve	4	⊐⊳	Ignition ON	11-14 V briefly then 0 V		
Heated oxygen sensor (HO2S) 1	45	⟵	Ignition ON	0,5 V		
	45	⟵	Engine idling – engine hot	0-1 V fluctuating		
	75	⊐—	Ignition ON	0 V		
Heated oxygen sensor (HO2S) 1 – heater control	63	⊐⊳	Ignition ON	11-14 V briefly then 0 V		
	63	⊐⊳	Engine idling – engine hot		2 V/5 ms	〰 65
Heated oxygen sensor (HO2S) 2	44	⟵	Ignition ON	0,5 V		
	44	⟵	Engine idling – engine hot	0,6-0,8 V		
	75	⊐—	Ignition ON	0 V		
Heated oxygen sensor (HO2S) 2 – heater control	65	⊐⊳	Ignition ON	11-14 V briefly then 0 V		
	65	⊐⊳	Engine idling – engine hot		2 V/5 ms	〰 65
Idle air control (IAC) valve	64	⊐⊳	Engine idling	450 Hz	2 V/2 ms	〰 72
Ignition coil – cylinders 1 & 4	32	⊐⊳	Ignition ON	11-14 V briefly then 0 V		
	32	⊐⊳	Engine idling	13 Hz	5 V/2 ms	〰 33
Ignition coil – cylinders 2 & 3	1	⊐⊳	Ignition ON	11-14 V briefly then 0 V		
	1	⊐⊳	Engine idling	13 Hz	5 V/2 ms	〰 33
Ignition switch	29	⟵	Ignition ON	11-14 V		
Immobilizer control module – immobilization/diagnosis signal	56	⟷		1		
Injector 1	59	⊐⊳	Ignition ON	11-14 V briefly then 0 V		
	59	⊐⊳	Engine idling	2 ms	10 V/2 ms	〰 35
Injector 2	90	⊐⊳	Ignition ON	11-14 V briefly then 0 V		
	90	⊐⊳	Engine idling	2 ms	10 V/2 ms	〰 35

* Suggested settings - Voltage/time per division

Component/circuit description	ECM pin	Signal	Condition	Typical value	Oscilloscope setting*	Wave form
Injector 3	60	⅂▷	Ignition ON	11-14 V briefly then 0 V		
	60	⅂▷	Engine idling	2 ms	10 V/2 ms	∿∿ 35
Injector 4	89	⅂▷	Ignition ON	11-14 V briefly then 0 V		
	89	⅂▷	Engine idling	2 ms	10 V/2 ms	∿∿ 35
Instrument panel	40	⇨		1		
Instrument panel – engine speed signal	70	⇨	Engine idling	25 Hz	5 V/20 ms	∿∿ 4
	70	⇨	3000 rpm	100 Hz		
Intake air temperature (IAT) sensor	48	⬅	Ignition ON – air temp. 25°C	2 V		
	48	⬅	Ignition ON – air temp. 100°C	0,25 V		
	79	⅂	Ignition ON	0 V		
Knock sensor (KS)	51	⬅	Engine idling – accelerate briefly		0,1 mV/1 ms	∿∿ 38
	76	⅂	Ignition ON	0 V		
Knock sensor (KS) – shield wire	19	⅂	Ignition ON	0 V		
Malfunction indicator lamp (MIL)	34	⅂▷	Ignition ON – MIL ON	0-1 V		
	34	⅂▷	Ignition ON – MIL OFF	11-14 V		
Manifold absolute pressure (MAP) sensor	72	⬅	Ignition ON	1,8 V		
	72	⬅	Engine idling	1,8 V		
	74	⇨	Ignition ON	5 V		
	79	⅂	Ignition ON	0 V		
Mass air flow (MAF) sensor	15	⅂	Ignition ON	0 V		
	16	⬅	Engine idling	0,6-0,75 V		
	16	⬅	Engine idling – accelerate briefly	4,3 V briefly		
Throttle position (TP) sensor	43	⬅	Ignition ON – throttle closed	0,6 V		
	43	⬅	Ignition ON – throttle fully open	4,6 V		
	77	⅂	Ignition ON	0 V		
	78	⇨	Ignition ON	5 V		
Traction control module – if fitted	20	⬅	Ignition ON	5 V		
	20	⬅	Engine idling – traction control OFF	5 V		
	20	⬅	Engine idling – traction control ON	2 V		
	36	⇨		1		
	71	⇨		1		
Turbocharger (TC) boost pressure sensor	13	⬅	Ignition ON	1,8 V		
	13	⬅	Engine idling	0,7 V		
	73	⅂	Ignition ON	0 V		
	74	⇨	Ignition ON	5 V		
Turbocharger (TC) wastegate regulating valve	5	⅂▷	Ignition ON	11-14 V briefly then 0 V		
	5	⅂▷	Engine idling – accelerate briefly		10 V/20 ms	∿∿ 25

*Suggested settings - Voltage/time per division

1 Connected pin - no test data available or random digital signal

VOLVO

Denso

Model:	Engine code:	Year:
S60 2,4	B5244S, B5244S2	2000-06
S70/V70 2,3	B5234FS	1999
S70/V70/C70 2,4	B5244S, B5244S2	2000-06
S70/V70/C70 2,5	B5254S	1999
S80 2,4	B5244S, B5244S2	1998-06

ECM harness multi-plug

Terminal side

AD23531

Wire side

AD23530

Component/circuit description	ECM pin	Signal	Condition	Typical value	Oscilloscope setting*	Wave form
AC compressor clutch relay	B44	⅂▷	Engine idling – AC OFF	11-14 V		
	B44	⅂▷	Engine idling – AC ON	0 V		
AC control module – some models	B27	⇨		1		
AC refrigerant pressure sensor	A21	⬅	Ignition ON	0,9 V		
	A21	⬅	Engine idling – AC OFF	1,3 V		
	A21	⬅	Engine idling – AC ON	2,3 V		
	A58	⇨	Ignition ON	5 V		
	A61	⅂—	Ignition ON	0 V		
AC refrigerant pressure sensor – some models	B32	⬅		1		
Accelerator pedal position (APP) sensor	B5	⅂—	Ignition ON	0 V		
	B9	⇨	Ignition ON	5 V		
	B17	⬅	Ignition ON – accelerator pedal released	0,4 V		
	B17	⬅	Ignition ON – accelerator pedal fully depressed	4,4 V		
	B25	⬅	Ignition ON – accelerator pedal released	87%	5 V/5 ms	〜 18
	B25	⬅	Ignition ON – accelerator pedal fully depressed	6,9%	5 V/2 ms	〜 68
Auxiliary air valve – if fitted	A52	⇨	Ignition ON	11-14 V		
Battery	B11	⬅	Ignition OFF	11-14 V		
Brake pedal position (BPP) sensor	B4	⅂—	Ignition ON	0 V		
Brake pedal position (BPP) sensor – type 1	B16	⬅	Ignition ON – brake pedal released	4,4 V		
	B16	⬅	Brake pedal depressed 25 mm	3,9 V		
Brake pedal position (BPP) sensor – type 2	B16	⬅	Ignition ON – brake pedal released	3,1 V		
	B16	⬅	Brake pedal depressed 25 mm	2,6 V		
Brake pedal position (BPP) switch	B26	⬅	Ignition ON – brake pedal released	0 V		
	B26	⬅	Ignition ON – brake pedal depressed	11-14 V		

* Suggested settings - Voltage/time per division

Component/circuit description	ECM pin	Signal	Condition	Typical value	Oscilloscope setting*	Wave form
Camshaft position (CMP) actuator – if fitted	A12	⊐▷	Ignition ON	14%	5 V/1 ms	〰 67
	A12	⊐▷	Engine idling	50%		
Camshaft position (CMP) sensor	A47	←	Ignition ON	0 or 5 V		
	A47	←	Engine idling		2 V/20 ms	〰 14
	A57	⇒	Ignition ON	5 V		
	A65	⊐—	Ignition ON	0 V		
CAN data bus, "high" signal line	B13	⇔		1		
CAN data bus, "low" signal line	B1	⇔		1		
Clutch pedal position (CPP) sensor – if fitted	B4	⊐—	Ignition ON	0 V		
	B15	←	Ignition ON – clutch pedal released	3,3 V		
	B15	←	Ignition ON – clutch pedal depressed 100 mm	2,2 V		
Crankshaft position (CKP) sensor	A48	←	Ignition ON	2,5 V		
	A48	←	Engine idling	3,7 V	2 V/1 ms	〰 2
	A66	⊐—	Ignition ON	0 V		
Cruise control selector switch – some models	B19	←		1		
	B20	←		1		
	B33	←		1		
	B34	←		1		
	B47	⇒		1		
Data link connector (DLC)	B22	⇔	Ignition ON	10,6 V		
Earth	A36		Ignition ON	0 V		
	A53		Ignition ON	0 V		
	A54		Ignition ON	0 V		
	A62		Ignition ON	0 V		
Engine control relay	A69	←	Ignition OFF	0 V		
	A69	←	Ignition ON	11-14 V		
	A70	←	Ignition OFF	0 V		
	A70	←	Ignition ON	11-14 V		
	B38	⊐▷	Ignition OFF	11-14 V		
	B38	⊐▷	Ignition ON	0 V		
Engine coolant blower motor control module – some models	A7	⇒	Ignition OFF	11-14 V		
	A7	⇒	Ignition ON	10-90%		
	A7	⇒	Engine idling	100 Hz		
Engine coolant blower motor relay, high speed – some models	A5	⊐▷	Engine idling – coolant blower motor OFF	11-14 V		
	A5	⊐▷	Engine idling – coolant blower motor ON	0 V		
Engine coolant blower motor relay, low speed – some models	A6	⊐▷	Engine idling – coolant blower motor OFF	11-14 V		
	A6	⊐▷	Engine idling – coolant blower motor ON	0 V		
Engine coolant 'low' sensor	B8	←	Ignition ON	0 V		
Engine coolant temperature (ECT) sensor	A40	←	Ignition ON – coolant temp. 20°C	3,1 V		
	A40	←	Ignition ON – coolant temp. 30°C	2,6 V		
	A40	←	Ignition ON – coolant temp. 80°C	0,9 V		
	A40	←	Ignition ON – coolant temp. 100°C	0,5 V		
	A61	⊐—	Ignition ON	0 V		
Engine oil pressure switch	A39	←	Ignition ON	0 V		
	A39	←	Engine idling	11-14 V		

* Suggested settings - Voltage/time per division

Component/circuit description	ECM pin	Signal	Condition	Typical value	Oscilloscope setting*	Wave form
Evaporative emission (EVAP) canister purge valve 1	A2	⊐⊳	Ignition ON	11-14 V		
	A2	⊐⊳	Engine hot – valve operating		10 V/50 ms	∿∿ 20
Evaporative emission (EVAP) canister purge valve 2	B40	⊐⊳		1		
Fuel pump relay	B45			1		
Fuel tank pressure sensor	B4	⊐—	Ignition ON	0 V		
	B10	⇨	Ignition ON	5 V		
	B31	⬅	Ignition ON	2,5-4,1 V		
Heated oxygen sensor (HO2S) 1	A41	⬅	Engine idling	3,45 V		
	A41	⬅	Ignition ON	3,77 V		
	A42	⬅	Ignition ON	3,77 V		
	A42	⬅	Engine idling	3,78 V		
Heated oxygen sensor (HO2S) 1 – heater control	A18	⊐⊳	Ignition ON	11-14 V		
	A18	⊐⊳	Engine idling – engine hot	7,9 Hz		
Heated oxygen sensor (HO2S) 2	A24	⬅	Engine idling	0,8 V		
	A61	⊐—	Ignition ON	0 V		
Heated oxygen sensor (HO2S) 2 – heater control	A11	⊐⊳	Ignition ON	11-14 V		
	A11	⊐⊳	Engine idling – engine hot	3,9 Hz		
Ignition coil 1	A28	⬅	Ignition ON	4,98 V		
	A28	⬅	Engine idling		2 V/10 ms	∿∿ 68
	A31	⊐⊳	Engine idling		0,5 V/20 ms	∿∿ 65
Ignition coil 2	A28	⬅	Ignition ON	4,98 V		
	A28	⬅	Engine idling		2 V/10 ms	∿∿ 68
	A30	⊐⊳	Engine idling		0,5 V/20 ms	∿∿ 65
Ignition coil 3	A28	⬅	Ignition ON	4,98 V		
	A28	⬅	Engine idling		2 V/10 ms	∿∿ 68
	A29	⊐⊳	Engine idling		0,5 V/20 ms	∿∿ 65
Ignition coil 4	A28	⬅	Ignition ON	4,98 V		
	A28	⬅	Engine idling		2 V/10 ms	∿∿ 68
	A51	⊐⊳	Engine idling		0,5 V/20 ms	∿∿ 65
Ignition coil 5	A28	⬅	Ignition ON	4,98 V		
	A28	⬅	Engine idling		2 V/10 ms	∿∿ 68
	A50	⊐⊳	Engine idling		0,5 V/20 ms	∿∿ 65
Ignition switch	B37	⬅	Ignition ON	11-14 V		
Ignition switch – starter signal	B23	⬅	Engine cranking	9 V min.		
Immobilizer control module – some models	B22	⬄	Ignition ON	10,6 V		
Injector 1	A16	⊐⊳	Ignition ON	11-14 V		
	A16	⊐⊳	Engine idling	2-3 ms	10 V/2 ms	∿∿ 35
Injector 2	A34	⊐⊳	Ignition ON	11-14 V		
	A34	⊐⊳	Engine idling	2-3 ms	10 V/2 ms	∿∿ 35
Injector 3	A15	⊐⊳	Ignition ON	11-14 V		
	A15	⊐⊳	Engine idling	2-3 ms	10 V/2 ms	∿∿ 35
Injector 4	A33	⊐⊳	Ignition ON	11-14 V		
	A33	⊐⊳	Engine idling	2-3 ms	10 V/2 ms	∿∿ 35
Injector 5	A14	⊐⊳	Ignition ON	11-14 V		
	A14	⊐⊳	Engine idling	2-3 ms	10 V/2 ms	∿∿ 35
Instrument panel	B41			1		
Instrument panel – some models	B27	⇨		1		

* Suggested settings - Voltage/time per division

Component/circuit description	ECM pin	Signal	Condition	Typical value	Oscilloscope setting*	Wave form
Intake air temperature (IAT) sensor, in MAF sensor	A4	⬅	Ignition ON – air temp. 10°C	2 V		
	A4	⬅	Ignition ON – air temp. 20°C	2,6 V		
	A4	⬅	Ignition ON – air temp. 30°C	3,2 V		
	A61	⊣—	Ignition ON	0 V		
Knock sensor (KS) 1	A46	⬅	Engine idling – accelerate briefly		50 mV/1 ms	∿∿ 38
	A64	⬅	Ignition ON	0 V		
Knock sensor (KS) 2 – if fitted	A45	⬅	Engine idling – accelerate briefly		50 mV/1 ms	∿∿ 38
	A64	⬅	Ignition ON	0 V		
Malfunction indicator lamp (MIL)	B46	⊣▷	Ignition ON – MIL ON	0 V		
	B46	⊣▷	Ignition ON – MIL OFF	11-14 V		
Manifold absolute pressure (MAP) sensor	A23	⬅	Ignition ON	3,6 V		
	A23	⬅	Engine idling	1,6 V		
	A23	⬅	Engine idling – accelerate briefly	3,85 V briefly		
	A58	▷	Ignition ON	5 V		
	A61	⊣—	Ignition ON	0 V		
Mass air flow (MAF) sensor	A22	⬅	Ignition ON	0,6 V		
	A22	⬅	Engine idling	1,3 V		
	A22	⬅	Engine idling – accelerate briefly	3,75 V briefly		
	A60	⊣—	Ignition ON	0 V		
Multifunction control module – some models	B22	◄▷	Ignition ON	10,6 V		
Multifunction control module, fuel pump relay control – some models	B45	▷	Engine idling	50 Hz		
Outside air temperature sensor	B4	⊣—	Ignition ON	0 V		
Outside air temperature sensor – type 1	B29	⬅	Ignition ON – air temp. 0°C	4 V		
	B29	⬅	Ignition ON – air temp. 10°C	3,5 V		
	B29	⬅	Ignition ON – air temp. 20°C	3 V		
	B29	⬅	Ignition ON – air temp. 30°C	2,5 V		
Outside air temperature sensor – type 2	B29	⬅	Ignition ON – air temp. 0°C	2,3 V		
	B29	⬅	Ignition ON – air temp. 10°C	1,8 V		
	B29	⬅	Ignition ON – air temp. 20°C	1,4 V		
	B29	⬅	Ignition ON – air temp. 25°C	1,2 V		
	B29	⬅	Ignition ON – air temp. 30°C	1 V		
Throttle control unit	A38	▷	Ignition ON	0 V		
	A56	▷	Ignition ON – accelerator pedal released	87%	5 V/5 ms	∿∿ 18
	A56	▷	Ignition ON – accelerator pedal fully depressed	6,9%	5 V/2 ms	∿∿ 68
Throttle control unit – CAN data bus	A37	◄▷		1		
	A55	◄▷		1		
Transmission control module (TCM)	B22	◄▷	Ignition ON	10,6 V		

*Suggested settings - Voltage/time per division

1 Connected pin - no test data available or random digital signal

Model:	Engine code:	Year:
S60 2,4D D5	D5244T/T2	2001-06
S80 2,4D D5	D5244T/T2	2000-06
V70 2,4D D5	D5244T/T2	2001-06

ECM harness multi-plug

Terminal side

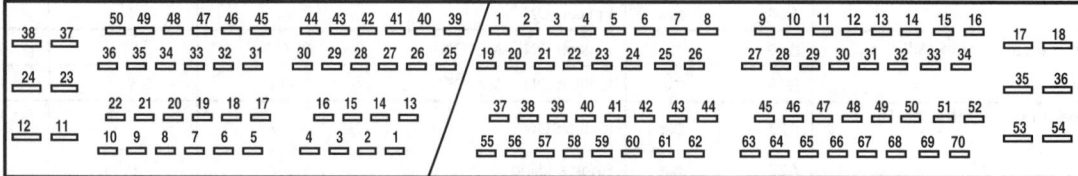

AD23531

Wire side

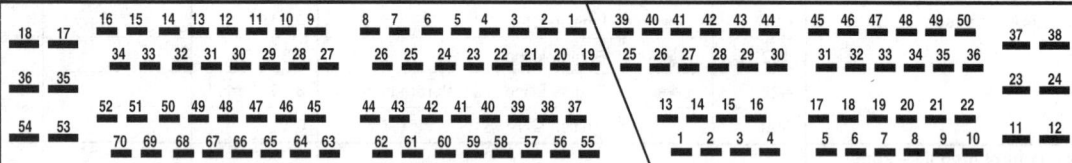

AD23530

Component/circuit description	ECM pin	Signal	Condition	Typical value	Oscilloscope setting*	Wave form
AC compressor clutch relay	B44	⬅➡		1		
AC refrigerant pressure sensor	A25	⬅➡		1		
	A43	⬅➡		1		
	A61	⬅➡		1		
Accelerator pedal position (APP) sensor	B5		Ignition ON	0 V		
	B9	➡	Ignition ON	5 V		
	B17	⬅	Ignition ON – throttle closed	0,4 V		
	B17	⬅	Ignition ON – throttle fully open	4,4 V		
	B25	⬅		1		
Brake pedal position (BPP) switch	B26	⬅	Pedal released	0 V		
	B26	⬅	Pedal depressed	11-14 V		
Brake servo diaphragm position sensor	B4		Ignition ON	0 V		
	B16	⬅	Ignition ON – pedal released	3,0 V		
	B16	⬅	Ignition ON – pedal depressed	0,9 V		
Camshaft position (CMP) sensor	A20	⬅	Ignition ON	11-14 V		
	A20	⬅	Engine idling	0 V or 11-14 V (switching)		
	A38	➡	Ignition ON	5 V		
	A38	➡	Engine idling	5 V		
	A56		Ignition ON	0 V		
Clutch position potentiometer	B4		Ignition ON	0 V		
	B15	⬅	Ignition ON – pedal released	3,2 V		
	B15	⬅	Ignition ON – pedal depressed	0,9 V		

* Suggested settings - Voltage/time per division

Autodata

Component/circuit description	ECM pin	Signal	Condition	Typical value	Oscilloscope setting*	Wave form
Crankshaft position (CKP) sensor	A47 (A65)	←	Engine idling		2 V/1 ms	6
	A65 (A47)	←	Engine idling		2 V/1 ms	Reversed 6
Data link connector (DLC)	B22	◄⟶		1		
Earth	A36		Ignition ON	0 V		
	A53		Ignition ON	0 V		
	A54		Ignition ON	0 V		
Engine control (EC) relay	A17	←	Ignition OFF	0 V		
	A17	←	Ignition ON	11-14 V		
	A17	←	Engine idling	11-14 V		
	A18	←	Ignition OFF	0 V		
	A18	←	Ignition ON	11-14 V		
	A18	←	Engine idling	11-14 V		
	A35	←	Ignition OFF	0 V		
	A35	←	Ignition ON	11-14 V		
	A35	←	Engine idling	11-14 V		
	B38	⊣▷	Ignition OFF	11-14 V		
	B38	⊣▷	Ignition ON	0-1 V		
Engine coolant blower motor control module	A8	◄⟶		1		
Engine coolant temperature (ECT) sensor	A27	←	Ignition ON – coolant temp. 20°C	3,8 V		
	A27	←	Ignition ON – coolant temp. 80°C	1,5 V		
	A63	⊣—	Ignition ON	0 V		
Engine mounting control solenoid	A7	⊣▷	Ignition ON	0-1 V		
	A7	⊣▷	Engine running – over 1500 rpm	11-14 V		
Engine oil pressure sensor	A67	⊣▷	Ignition ON	0-1 V		
	A67	⊣▷	Engine idling	11-14 V		
Exhaust gas recirculation (EGR) solenoid	A2	⊣▷	Ignition ON	11-14 V		
	A2	⊣▷	Engine idling – valve operating		5 V/2 ms	31
Fuel pressure control solenoid	A37	←		1		
	A55	←		1		
Fuel rail pressure (FRP) sensor	A22	←	Ignition ON	0,5 V		
	A22	←	Engine idling	1,3 V		
	A40	⇒	Ignition ON	5 V		
	A40	⇒	Engine idling	5 V		
	A58	⊣—	Ignition ON	0 V		
Glow plug relay	B50	⊣▷	Ignition ON	11-14 V		
Ignition switch	B37	←	Ignition ON	11-14 V		
Ignition switch – start signal	B23	←	Ignition ON	0 V		
	B23	←	Engine cranking	11-14 V		

* Suggested settings - Voltage/time per division

Component/circuit description	ECM pin	Signal	Condition	Typical value	Oscilloscope setting*	Wave form
Injector 1	A51 (A52)	⇨	Engine idling – engine hot	0,3 ms	10 V/0,1 ms	⩗ 61
	A51 (A70)	⇨	Engine idling – engine hot	0,3 ms	10 V/0,1 ms	⩗ 61
	A52 (A51)	⇨	Engine idling – engine hot	0,3 ms	10 V/0,1 ms	⩗ 61
	A52 (A69)	⇨	Engine idling – engine hot	0,3 ms	10 V/0,1 ms	⩗ 61
	A69 (A52)	⇨	Engine idling – engine hot	0,3 ms	10 V/0,1 ms	⩗ 61
	A69 (A70)	⇨	Engine idling – engine hot	0,3 ms	10 V/0,1 ms	⩗ 61
	A70 (A51)	⇨	Engine idling – engine hot	0,3 ms	10 V/0,1 ms	⩗ 61
	A70 (A69)	⇨	Engine idling – engine hot	0,3 ms	10 V/0,1 ms	⩗ 61
Injector 2	A14 (A15)	⇨	Engine idling – engine hot	0,3 ms	10 V/0,1 ms	⩗ 61
	A14 (A33)	⇨	Engine idling – engine hot	0,3 ms	10 V/0,1 ms	⩗ 61
	A15 (A14)	⇨	Engine idling – engine hot	0,3 ms	10 V/0,1 ms	⩗ 61
	A15 (A33)	⇨	Engine idling – engine hot	0,3 ms	10 V/0,1 ms	⩗ 61
	A32 (A15)	⇨	Engine idling – engine hot	0,3 ms	10 V/0,1 ms	⩗ 61
	A32 (A33)	⇨	Engine idling – engine hot	0,3 ms	10 V/0,1 ms	⩗ 61
	A33 (A14)	⇨	Engine idling – engine hot	0,3 ms	10 V/0,1 ms	⩗ 61
	A33 (A32)	⇨	Engine idling – engine hot	0,3 ms	10 V/0,1 ms	⩗ 61
Injector 3	A16 (A52)	⇨	Engine idling – engine hot	0,3 ms	10 V/0,1 ms	⩗ 61
	A16 (A70)	⇨	Engine idling – engine hot	0,3 ms	10 V/0,1 ms	⩗ 61
	A34 (A52)	⇨	Engine idling – engine hot	0,3 ms	10 V/0,1 ms	⩗ 61
	A34 (A70)	⇨	Engine idling – engine hot	0,3 ms	10 V/0,1 ms	⩗ 61
	A52 (A16)	⇨	Engine idling – engine hot	0,3 ms	10 V/0,1 ms	⩗ 61
	A52 (A34)	⇨	Engine idling – engine hot	0,3 ms	10 V/0,1 ms	⩗ 61
	A70 (A16)	⇨	Engine idling – engine hot	0,3 ms	10 V/0,1 ms	⩗ 61
	A70 (A34)	⇨	Engine idling – engine hot	0,3 ms	10 V/0,1 ms	⩗ 61
Injector 4	A50 (A52)	⇨	Engine idling – engine hot	0,3 ms	10 V/0,1 ms	⩗ 61
	A50 (A70)	⇨	Engine idling – engine hot	0,3 ms	10 V/0,1 ms	⩗ 61
	A52 (A50)	⇨	Engine idling – engine hot	0,3 ms	10 V/0,1 ms	⩗ 61
	A52 (A68)	⇨	Engine idling – engine hot	0,3 ms	10 V/0,1 ms	⩗ 61
	A68 (A52)	⇨	Engine idling – engine hot	0,3 ms	10 V/0,1 ms	⩗ 61
	A68 (A70)	⇨	Engine idling – engine hot	0,3 ms	10 V/0,1 ms	⩗ 61
	A70 (A50)	⇨	Engine idling – engine hot	0,3 ms	10 V/0,1 ms	⩗ 61
	A70 (A68)	⇨	Engine idling – engine hot	0,3 ms	10 V/0,1 ms	⩗ 61

* Suggested settings - Voltage/time per division

Component/circuit description	ECM pin	Signal	Condition	Typical value	Oscilloscope setting*	Wave form
Injector 5	A13 (A15)	⇒	Engine idling – engine hot	0,3 ms	10 V/0,1 ms	61
	A13 (A33)	⇒	Engine idling – engine hot	0,3 ms	10 V/0,1 ms	61
	A15 (A13)	⇒	Engine idling – engine hot	0,3 ms	10 V/0,1 ms	61
	A15 (A31)	⇒	Engine idling – engine hot	0,3 ms	10 V/0,1 ms	61
	A31 (A15)	⇒	Engine idling – engine hot	0,3 ms	10 V/0,1 ms	61
	A31 (A33)	⇒	Engine idling – engine hot	0,3 ms	10 V/0,1 ms	61
	A33 (A13)	⇒	Engine idling – engine hot	0,3 ms	10 V/0,1 ms	61
	A33 (A31)	⇒	Engine idling – engine hot	0,3 ms	10 V/0,1 ms	61
Intake air temperature (IAT) sensor	A45	⇐		1		
Mass air flow (MAF) sensor	A21	⇐	Ignition ON	1 V		
	A21	⇐	Engine idling	1,6 V		
	A39	⇒	Ignition ON	5 V		
	A39	⇒	Engine idling	5 V		
	A57	⌐	Ignition ON	0 V		
Multifunction control module	B1	⇔		1		
	B13	⇔		1		
Turbocharger (TC) boost pressure sensor	A23	⇐	Ignition ON	2,2 V		
	A23	⇐	Engine idling	2,3 V		
	A41	⇒	Ignition ON	5 V		
	A41	⇒	Engine idling	5 V		
	A59	⌐	Ignition ON	0 V		
Turbocharger (TC) wastegate regulating valve	A4	⌐⊳	Ignition ON	11-14 V		
	A4	⌐⊳	Engine idling – valve operating	0 V or 11-14 V (switching)		

*Suggested settings - Voltage/time per division

1 Connected pin - no test data available or random digital signal

Model:	Engine code:	Year:
850 2,0/2,3 Turbo	B5204T/T2/T3/B5234T	1993-97
850 2,3 R/T-5R	B5234T4/T5	1994-97
850 2,5/Turbo	B5254S/T	1996-97
S70/V70/C70 2,0 Turbo	B5204T/T2/T3	1997-99
S70/V70/C70 2,3/Turbo	B5234T/T3/T4/T6/T7/FS	1997-01
S70/V70/C70 2,5 20V/Turbo	B5254S/T	1997-00

ECM harness multi-plug

Terminal side

```
14 13 12 11 10 9 8 7 6 5 4 3 2 1       30 31 32 33 34 35 36 37 38 39 40 41 42 43
29 28 27 26 25 24 23 22 21 20 19 18 17 16 15    15 16 17 18 19 20 21 22 23 24 25 26 27 28 29
43 42 41 40 39 38 37 36 35 34 33 32 31 30       1 2 3 4 5 6 7 8 9 10 11 12 13 14
AD84097
```
A   **B**

Wire side

```
43 42 41 40 39 38 37 36 35 34 33 32 31 30       1 2 3 4 5 6 7 8 9 10 11 12 13 14
29 28 27 26 25 24 23 22 21 20 19 18 17 16 15    15 16 17 18 19 20 21 22 23 24 25 26 27 28 29
14 13 12 11 10 9 8 7 6 5 4 3 2 1       30 31 32 33 34 35 36 37 38 39 40 41 42 43
AD42139
```
B   **A**

Component/circuit description	ECM pin	Signal	Condition	Typical value	Oscilloscope setting*	Wave form
AC refrigerant pressure sensor	B9	←	Ignition ON	0,9 V		
	B9	←	Engine idling – AC OFF	0,9 V		
	B9	←	Engine idling – AC ON	0,9 V increases with AC pressure		
	B28	⌐	Ignition ON	0 V		
	B29	⇒	Ignition ON	5 V		
AC refrigerant pressure switch	B6	←	Ignition ON	0 V		
	B6	←	Engine idling – AC compressor OFF	0 V		
	B6	←	Ignition ON – AC compressor ON	10-13 V		
AC refrigerant pressure switch – some models	B25	←		1		
AC relay	B25	←	Ignition ON	0 V		
	B40	⌐⇒	Ignition ON	9 V		
	B40	⌐⇒	Engine idling – AC ON	0 V		
	B40	⌐⇒	Engine idling – AC OFF	11 V		
AC relay – M4.3	B25	←	Engine idling – relay ON	0 V		
	B25	←	Engine idling – relay OFF	11-14 V		
AC relay – M4.4	B25	←	Engine idling – relay ON	11-14 V		
	B25	←	Engine idling – relay OFF	0 V		
Barometric pressure (BARO) sensor – if fitted	B22	←		1		
	B28	⌐	Ignition ON	0 V		
	B29	⇒	Ignition ON	5 V		
Battery	A26	←	Ignition OFF	11-14 V		
Camshaft position (CMP) sensor – type 1	A18	⌐	Ignition ON	0 V		
	A21	←	Ignition ON	0 V or 5 V		
	A21	←	Engine idling	7 Hz	2 V/20 ms	〰〰 12
	A36	⇒	Ignition ON	10-13 V		

* Suggested settings - Voltage/time per division

Component/circuit description	ECM pin	Signal	Condition	Typical value	Oscilloscope setting*	Wave form
Camshaft position (CMP) sensor – type 2	A18	⊣⊢	Ignition ON	0 V		
	A21	←	Ignition ON	0 V or 11-14 V		
	A21	←	Engine idling	7 Hz	5 V/20 ms	12
	A36	⇨	Ignition ON	10-13 V		
Crankshaft position (CKP) sensor	A6 (A20)	←	Ignition ON	0 V		
	A6 (A20)	←	Engine cranking	0,3 V ac		
	A6 (A20)	←	Engine idling	1,5 V ac	1 V/1 ms	2
	A20 (A6)	←	Ignition ON	0 V		
	A20 (A6)	←	Engine cranking	0,3 V ac		
	A20 (A6)	←	Engine idling	1,5 V ac	1 V/1 ms	2
Data link connector (DLC)	B5	⇔	Ignition ON	10-13 V		
	B36	⇔	Ignition ON	9-12 V		
Earth	A13		Ignition ON	0 V		
	A28		Ignition ON	0 V		
	A42		Ignition ON	0 V		
Engine control relay	A27	←	Ignition ON	11-14 V		
	A41	⊣⇨	Ignition OFF	11-14 V		
	A41	⊣⇨	Ignition ON	0-1 V		
Engine coolant blower motor relay	A7	⊣⇨	Coolant blower motor OFF – low speed	11-14 V		
	A7	⊣⇨	Coolant blower motor ON – low speed	0-1 V		
	A22	⊣⇨	Coolant blower motor OFF – high speed	11-14 V		
	A22	⊣⇨	Coolant blower motor ON – high speed	0-1 V		
Engine coolant temperature gauge	B23	⇨	Ignition ON – coolant temp. 20°C	40 Hz		
	B23	⇨	Ignition ON – coolant temp. 100°C	21 Hz		
Engine coolant temperature (ECT) sensor	A18	⊣⊢	Ignition ON	0 V		
	A31	←	Engine idling – coolant temp. 20°C	1,8 V		
	A31	←	Engine idling – coolant temp. 100°C	0,5 V		
Evaporative emission (EVAP) cut-off valve – if fitted	B19	⊣⇨	Ignition ON	11-14 V		
	B19	⊣⇨	Engine idling – valve not operating	11-14 V		
	B19	⊣⇨	Engine idling – valve operating	0-1 V		
Evaporative emission (EVAP) canister purge valve	A39	⊣⇨	Ignition ON	11-14 V		
	A39	⊣⇨	Engine hot – valve operating		10 V/50 ms	20
Exhaust gas recirculation (EGR) solenoid – if fitted	A40	⊣⇨	Ignition ON	11-14 V		
	A40	⊣⇨	Engine hot – valve operating		5 V/5 ms	43
Exhaust gas recirculation temperature (EGRT) sensor – if fitted – M4.3	A35	←	Ignition ON – sensor temp. 20°C min.	4,0 V		
	A35	←	Ignition ON – sensor temp. 100°C min.	1,2 V		
	A18	⊣⊢	Ignition ON	0 V		
Fuel pump relay	B27	⇨	Engine idling	40 Hz		

★ Suggested settings - Voltage/time per division

Component/circuit description	ECM pin	Signal	Condition	Typical value	Oscilloscope setting*	Wave form
Fuel tank pressure sensor – if fitted	B15	⇨	Ignition ON	5 V		
	B28	⊐─	Ignition ON	0 V		
	B31	⟵	Ignition ON		0,6 V min./4,7 V max.	
Heated oxygen sensor (HO2S) – front	A14	⊐▷	Ignition ON	11-14 V		
	A14	⊐▷	Engine idling – heater OFF	11-14 V		
	A14	⊐▷	Engine idling – heater ON	0-1 V		
	A32 (A42)	⟵	Ignition ON	1,2 V		
	A32 (A33)	⟵	Engine idling	0,1-0,9 V fluctuating	0,2 V/1 sec.	⎍⎍ 21
	A33		Ignition ON	0,7 V		
Heated oxygen sensor (HO2S) – rear – if fitted	A19	⊐─	Ignition ON	0,7 V		
	A29	⊐▷	Ignition ON	11-14 V		
	A29	⊐▷	Engine idling – heater OFF	11-14 V		
	A29	⊐▷	Engine idling – heater ON	0-1 V		
	A34 (A42)	⟵	Ignition ON	0 V		
	A34 (A19)	⟵	Engine running	0,1-0,9 V slowly fluctuating		
Idle air control (IAC) valve	A11	⊐▷	Ignition ON	25%		
	A11	⊐▷	Engine idling	21-32%	5 V/5 ms	⎍⎍ 25
	A25	⊐▷	Ignition ON	75%		
	A25	⊐▷	Engine idling	66-74%	5 V/5 ms	⎍⎍ 25
Ignition amplifier	B11	⇨	Ignition ON	0,1 V		
Ignition amplifier – M4.3	B11	⇨	Engine idling	71 Hz		
Ignition amplifier – M4.4	B11	⇨	Engine idling	35 Hz		
Ignition switch	A12	⟵	Ignition ON	11-14 V		
Injector 1	A10	⊐▷	Ignition ON	11-14 V		
	A10	⊐▷	Engine idling	2,2-3,6 ms	10 V/2 ms	⎍⎍ 35
Injector 2	A38	⊐▷	Ignition ON	11-14 V		
	A38	⊐▷	Engine idling	2,2-3,6 ms	10 V/2 ms	⎍⎍ 35
Injector 3	A24	⊐▷	Ignition ON	11-14 V		
	A24	⊐▷	Engine idling	2,2-3,6 ms	10 V/2 ms	⎍⎍ 35
Injector 4	A23	⊐▷	Ignition ON	11-14 V		
	A23	⊐▷	Engine idling	2,2-3,6 ms	10 V/2 ms	⎍⎍ 35
Injector 5	A9	⊐▷	Ignition ON	11-14 V		
	A9	⊐▷	Engine idling	2,2-3,6 ms	10 V/2 ms	⎍⎍ 35
Knock sensor (KS) – front	A2 (A17)	⟵	Engine idling – accelerate briefly		50 mV/1 ms	⎍⎍ 38
	A17	⊐─	Ignition ON	0 V		
Knock sensor (KS) – rear	A17	⊐─	Ignition ON	0 V		
	A30 (A17)	⟵	Engine idling – accelerate briefly		50 mV/1 ms	⎍⎍ 38
Malfunction indicator lamp (MIL)	B7	⊐▷	Ignition ON – MIL ON	0,8 V		
	B7	⊐▷	Engine idling – MIL OFF	11-14 V		
Manual transmission	B24	⟵	Ignition ON	9 V		

* Suggested settings - Voltage/time per division

Component/circuit description	ECM pin	Signal	Condition	Typical value	Oscilloscope setting*	Wave form
Mass air flow (MAF) sensor	A3	⊣—	Ignition ON	0 V		
	A4 (A5)	⬅	Ignition ON	0,1-0,2 V		
	A4 (A5)	⬅	Engine idling	1,0 V		
	A5	⊣—	Ignition ON	0 V		
Outside air temperature sensor – if fitted – M4.4	A35	⬅	Ignition ON – 10°C	4 V		
Secondary air injection (AIR) pump relay – if fitted	B38	⊣▷	Ignition ON	11-14 V		
	B38	⊣▷	Engine idling – air pump ON	0 V		
	B38	⊣▷	Engine idling – air pump OFF	11-14 V		
Secondary air injection (AIR) solenoid – if fitted	A37	⊣▷	Ignition ON	11-14 V		
	A37	⊣▷	Engine idling – solenoid ON	0-1 V		
Suspension G-force sensor	B1	⇨	Ignition ON	5 V		
	B28	⊣—	Ignition ON	0 V		
	B32	⬅	Ignition ON	2,5 V		
Tachometer	B21	⇨	Ignition ON	11-14 V		
	B21	⇨	Engine idling	28 Hz		
Throttle position (TP) sensor	A15	⇨	Ignition ON	5 V		
	A16	⬅	Ignition ON – throttle closed	0,5 V		
	A16	⬅	Ignition ON – throttle fully open	4,2 V		
	A18	⊣—	Ignition ON	0 V		
Transmission control module (TCM)	B2	⬅	Ignition ON	9-12 V		
	B3	⬅	Ignition ON	9-12 V		
	B4	⇨	Ignition ON	9-12 V		
	B12	⇨	Ignition ON	0,8 V		
	B12	⇨	Engine idling	35 Hz		
	B20	⇨	Engine idling	0,5 V		
	B20	⇨	Throttle fully open	4,2 V		
	B24	⬅	Ignition ON – AT in P or N	10-13 V		
	B24	⬅	Ignition ON – AT not in P or N	0 V		
	B26	⬅	Ignition ON	0-1 V		
	B26	⬅	Engine idling	10-13 V		
	B42	⬅	Ignition ON	9-12 V		
	B42	⬅	Engine idling	0,3 V		
Trip computer – if fitted	B39	⇨	Engine idling	14-25 Hz		
Turbocharger (TC) wastegate regulating valve – if fitted	B41	⊣▷	Ignition ON	11-14 V		
Vehicle speed sensor (VSS)	B18	⬅	Ignition ON – vehicle pushed	0 V or 11-14 V		

*Suggested settings - Voltage/time per division

1 Connected pin - no test data available or random digital signal

Autodata

Diagnostic Trouble Codes
Fault locations and probable causes
with Flash, MIL and EOBD codes for Engines, Transmissions and Immobilizers

In response to questions from workshops and technicians, Autodata has produced the definitive manual for interpreting trouble codes. The answers to these and other questions can be found in the Diagnostic Trouble Codes manual

? *Which systems on this vehicle have trouble codes, and do I need a scan tool to read them*

? *How can I tell if the immobilizer causes the 'no-start' on a particular vehicle and if so - why*

? *I've checked a particular component and found no fault, yet the trouble code for it resets. What else should I check*

? *My scan tool can list the trouble code and the fault location, but what is the most probable cause*

? *Where is the data link connector located*

2006 Autodata **2006**

Diagnostic Trouble Codes

Fault locations and probable causes

- Flash, MIL and EOBD codes
- Engine management systems
- Transmissions
- Immobilizers
- Data link connector locations

Now includes P2 and U0 codes

Petrol and Diesel Cars, MPVs, 4x4s and LCVs 1994-2006

This new manual features:
- General test procedures and circuit testing
- Abbreviations and terminology
- Tools and equipment
- Comprehensive EOBD section listing the industry standard P0, P2 and U0 trouble codes with their probable causes

Manufacturer and system specific chapters containing:
- Retrieval and erasure methods - many needing a scan tool
- Data link connector locations
- Trouble code tables include manufacturer specific 'P' codes
- Fault locations listed with comprehensively researched probable causes that save time by eliminating guesswork

---

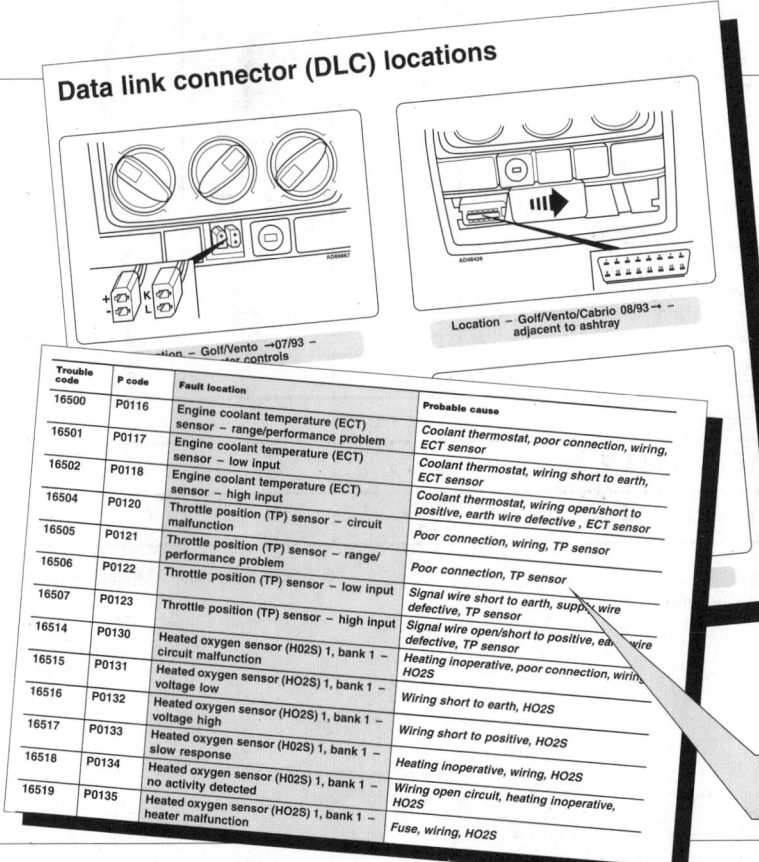

Data link connector (DLC) locations

Location – Golf/Vento →07/93 – ...er controls

Location – Golf/Vento/Cabrio 08/93 → adjacent to ashtray

Trouble code	P code	Fault location	Probable cause
16500	P0116	Engine coolant temperature (ECT) sensor – range/performance problem	Coolant thermostat, poor connection, wiring, ECT sensor
16501	P0117	Engine coolant temperature (ECT) sensor – low input	Coolant thermostat, wiring short to earth, ECT sensor
16502	P0118	Engine coolant temperature (ECT) sensor – high input	Coolant thermostat, wiring open/short to positive, earth wire defective , ECT sensor
16504	P0120	Throttle position (TP) sensor – circuit malfunction	Poor connection, wiring, TP sensor
16505	P0121	Throttle position (TP) sensor – range/performance problem	Poor connection, TP sensor
16506	P0122	Throttle position (TP) sensor – low input	Signal wire short to earth, supply wire defective, TP sensor
16507	P0123	Throttle position (TP) sensor – high input	Signal wire open/short to positive, earth wire defective, TP sensor
16514	P0130	Heated oxygen sensor (HO2S) 1, bank 1 – circuit malfunction	Heating inoperative, poor connection, wiring, HO2S
16515	P0131	Heated oxygen sensor (HO2S) 1, bank 1 – voltage low	Wiring short to earth, HO2S
16516	P0132	Heated oxygen sensor (HO2S) 1, bank 1 – voltage high	Wiring short to positive, HO2S
16517	P0133	Heated oxygen sensor (HO2S) 1, bank 1 – slow response	Heating inoperative, wiring, HO2S
16518	P0134	Heated oxygen sensor (HO2S) 1, bank 1 – no activity detected	Wiring open circuit, heating inoperative, HO2S
16519	P0135	Heated oxygen sensor (HO2S) 1, bank 1 – heater malfunction	Fuse, wiring, HO2S

Includes 'Probable causes'